$y = e^x$

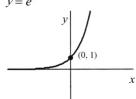

$y = \ln x$

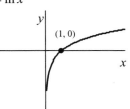

$y = \sin x$

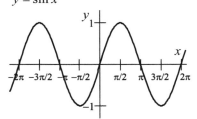

$y = \cos x$

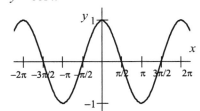

$y = \tan x$

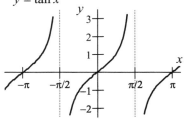

$y = \arcsin x$

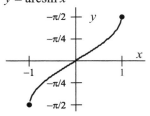

$y = \arccos x$

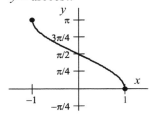

$y = \arctan x$

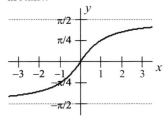

A FUNCTION APPROACH TO
College Algebra
Trigonometry
&
Precalculus

Second Edition

A FUNCTION APPROACH TO
College Algebra
Trigonometry
&
Precalculus

Second Edition

Customized for

BROOKDALE COMMUNITY COLLEGE

MATH 152 and MATH 153

Developed from:

Connally, Hughes-Hallett, Gleason, et al. / Functions Modelling Change, 2e

Connally, Hughes-Hallett, Gleason, et al. / Functions Modelling Change, 1e

Barnett, Ziegler, Byleen. / Analytic Trigonometry with Applications, 8e

And from materials developed by members of the Brookdale Community College Mathematics Department:

Virginia Lee   Brian McKeon   Ellen Musen   Glenn Noé

Oly Malpica-Proctor   Ana Vamadeva   Fran Ventola

John Wiley & Sons, Inc.

To order books or for customer service, please call 1(800)-CALL-WILEY (225-5945).

Printed in the United States of America.

Printed and bound by Integrated Book Technology, Inc.

ISBN-13   978-0-470-40902-2

10 9 8 7 6 5 4 3 2 1

PREFACE

In the spring of 2002, motivated by a desire for consistency in vision and approach, the Mathematics Department of Brookdale Community College met and collaboratively sketched out an outline of a comprehensive revision to the four-course sequence leading to calculus. That collaboration led to the current sequence of courses MATH 025, MATH 151, MATH 152, and MATH 153 and this textbook is intended for the last two courses.

The Vision

Common to the four courses, students should be able to:
- Develop the skills needed to rewrite and simplify expressions and solve equations.
- Identify the various function types and their properties.
- Use graphical and numerical tools as an aid to understanding and problem solving.
- Analyze and solve application problems.
- Write clear and correct explanations of thought processes and interpretations of solutions.

The Approaches

The guidelines for each course recommend some consistent approaches, such as:
- The nearly daily use of the graphing calculator as an aid to computation as well as a tool for developing visual and numerical thought processes.
- Development of a high level of proficiency with the appropriate algebraic skills needed to simplify expressions and solve equations.
- Motivating topics through applications and treating applications throughout the course.
- Using a multiple-perspective approach to all topics; algebraic, numerical, graphical, and verbal.
- Connecting concepts to those previously learned.
- Development of the students' ability to communicate mathematics.
- Frequent group work, both in and out of the classroom.

This textbook is intended for two courses: MATH 152, College Algebra and Trigonometry, and MATH 153, Precalculus. Much of the material is from *Functions Modeling Change: A Preparation for Calculus* by Connally et al, a text we have used successfully for several years. Of the rest of the material, much has been written and edited by the curriculum group responsible for these two courses and the remainder of the material is from *Analytic Trigonometry with Applications* by Barnett et al. The committee has worked very hard to ensure a seamless text that integrates the trigonometric topics throughout the two courses and we hope that the text will enable students to learn and use mathematics with enthusiasm.

Ananda Vamadeva
Brian McKeon
Ellen Musen
Frances Ventola

Glenn Noé
Olga Malpica Proctor
Virginia Lee

TABLE OF CONTENTS

7 EXPONENTIAL FUNCTIONS   389

8 LOGARITHMIC FUNCTIONS   439

9 MODELING, PARAMETRIC EQUATIONS, AND CONIC SECTIONS   479

10 CURVE FITTING   545

APPENDICES   559

ANSWER TO ODD-NUMBERED PROBLEMS   641

INDEX   673

Chapter One

FUNCTIONS, LINES, AND CHANGE

A function describes how the value of one quantity depends on the value of another. A function can be represented by words, a graph, a formula, or a table of numbers. Section 1.1 gives examples of all four representations and introduces the notation used to represent a function. Section 1.2 introduces the idea of a rate of change.

Sections 1.3–1.5 investigate linear functions, whose rate of change is constant. Section 1.4 gives the equations for a line, and Section 1.5 focuses on parallel and perpendicular lines.

1.1   FUNCTIONS AND FUNCTION NOTATION

In everyday language, the word *function* expresses the notion of dependence. For example, a person might say that election results are a function of the economy, meaning that the winner of an election is determined by how the economy is doing. Someone else might claim that car sales are a function of the weather, meaning that the number of cars sold on a given day is affected by the weather.

In mathematics, the meaning of the word *function* is more precise, but the basic idea is the same. A function is a relationship between two quantities. If the value of the first quantity determines exactly one value of the second quantity, we say the second quantity is a function of the first. We make the following definition:

> A **function** is a rule which takes certain numbers as inputs and assigns to each input number exactly one output number. The output is a function of the input.

The inputs and outputs are also called *variables*.

Representing Functions: Words, Tables, Graphs, and Formulas

A function can be described using words, data in a table, points on a graph, or a formula.

Example 1   It is a surprising biological fact that most crickets chirp at a rate that increases as the temperature increases. For the snowy tree cricket (*Oecanthus fultoni*), the relationship between temperature and chirp rate is so reliable that this type of cricket is called the thermometer cricket. We can estimate the temperature (in degrees Fahrenheit) by counting the number of times a snowy tree cricket chirps in 15 seconds and adding 40. For instance, if we count 20 chirps in 15 seconds, then a good estimate of the temperature is $20 + 40 = 60°$F.

The rule used to find the temperature T (in °F) from the chirp rate R (in chirps per minute) is an example of a function. The input is chirp rate and the output is temperature. Describe this function using words, a table, a graph, and a formula.

Solution
- **Words**: To estimate the temperature, we count the number of chirps in fifteen seconds and add forty. Alternatively, we can count R chirps per minute, divide R by four and add forty. This is because there are one-fourth as many chirps in fifteen seconds as there are in sixty seconds. For instance, 80 chirps per minute works out to $\frac{1}{4} \cdot 80 = 20$ chirps every 15 seconds, giving an estimated temperature of $20 + 40 = 60°$F.
- **Table**: Table 1.1 gives the estimated temperature, T, as a function of R, the number of chirps per minute. Notice the pattern in Table 1.1: each time the chirp rate, R, goes up by 20 chirps per minute, the temperature, T, goes up by 5°F.
- **Graph**: The data from Table 1.1 are plotted in Figure 1.1. For instance, the pair of values $R = 80$, $T = 60$ are plotted as the point P, which is 80 units along the horizontal axis and 60 units up the vertical axis. Data represented in this way are said to be plotted on the *Cartesian plane*. The precise position of P is shown by its coordinates, written $P = (80, 60)$.

Table 1.1 *Chirp rate and temperature*

R, chirp rate (chirps/minute)	T, predicted temperature (°F)
20	45
40	50
60	55
80	60
100	65
120	70
140	75
160	80

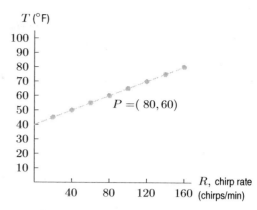

Figure 1.1: Chirp rate and temperature

- **Formula**: A formula is an equation giving T in terms of R. Dividing the chirp rate by four and adding forty gives the estimated temperature, so:

$$\underbrace{\text{Estimated temperature (in °F)}}_{T} = \frac{1}{4} \cdot \underbrace{\text{Chirp rate (in chirps/min)}}_{R} + 40.$$

Rewriting this using the variables T and R gives the formula:

$$T = \frac{1}{4}R + 40.$$

Let's check the formula. Substituting $R = 80$, we have

$$T = \frac{1}{4} \cdot 80 + 40 = 60$$

which agrees with point $P = (80, 60)$ in Figure 1.1. The formula $T = \frac{1}{4}R + 40$ also tells us that if $R = 0$, then $T = 40$. Thus, the dashed line in Figure 1.1 crosses (or intersects) the T-axis at $T = 40$; we say the T-intercept is 40.

All the descriptions given in Example 1 provide the same information, but each description has a different emphasis. A relationship between variables is often given in words, as at the beginning of Example 1. Table 1.1 is useful because it shows the predicted temperature for various chirp rates. Figure 1.1 is more suggestive of a trend than the table, although it is harder to read exact values of the function. For example, you might have noticed that every point in Figure 1.1 falls on a straight line that slopes up from left to right. In general, a graph can reveal a pattern that might otherwise go unnoticed. Finally, the formula has the advantage of being both compact and precise. However, this compactness can also be a disadvantage since it may be harder to gain as much insight from a formula as from a table or a graph.

Mathematical Models

When we use a function to describe an actual situation, the function is referred to as a **mathematical model**. The formula $T = \frac{1}{4}R + 40$ is a mathematical model of the relationship between the temperature and the cricket's chirp rate. Such models can be powerful tools for understanding phenomena and making predictions. For example, this model predicts that when the chirp rate is 80 chirps per minute, the temperature is 60°F. In addition, since $T = 40$ when $R = 0$, the model predicts that the chirp rate is 0 at 40°F. Whether the model's predictions are accurate for chirp rates down to 0 and temperatures as low as 40°F is a question that mathematics alone cannot answer; an understanding of the biology of crickets is needed. However, we can safely say that the model does not apply for temperatures below 40°F, because the chirp rate would then be negative. For the range of chirp rates and temperatures in Table 1.1, the model is remarkably accurate.

In everyday language, saying that T is a function of R suggests that making the cricket chirp faster would somehow make the temperature change. Clearly, the cricket's chirping doesn't cause the temperature to be what it is. In mathematics, saying that the temperature "depends" on the chirp rate means only that knowing the chirp rate is sufficient to tell us the temperature.

Function Notation

To indicate that a quantity Q is a function of a quantity t, we abbreviate

$$Q \text{ is a function of } t \quad \text{to} \quad Q \text{ equals "} f \text{ of } t\text{"}$$

and, using function notation, to

$$Q = f(t).$$

Thus, applying the rule f to the input value, t, gives the output value, $f(t)$. In other words, $f(t)$ represents a value of Q. Here Q is called the *dependent variable* and t is called the *independent variable*. Symbolically,

$$\text{Output} = f(\text{Input})$$

or

$$\text{Dependent} = f(\text{Independent}).$$

We could have used any letter, not just f, to represent the rule.

Example 2   The number of gallons of paint needed to paint a house depends on the size of the house. A gallon of paint typically covers 250 square feet. Thus, the number of gallons of paint, n, is a function of the area to be painted, A ft². We write $n = f(A)$.

(a) Find a formula for f.
(b) Explain in words what the statement $f(10,000) = 40$ tells us about painting houses.

Solution   (a) If $A = 5000$ ft², then $n = 5000/250 = 20$ gallons of paint. In general, n and A are related by the formula

$$n = \frac{A}{250}.$$

(b) The input of the function $n = f(A)$ is an area and the output is an amount of paint. The statement $f(10,000) = 40$ tells us that an area of $A = 10,000$ ft² requires $n = 40$ gallons of paint.

The expressions "Q depends on t" or "Q is a function of t" do *not* imply a cause-and-effect relationship, as the snowy tree cricket example illustrates.

Example 3   Example 1 gives the following formula for estimating air temperature based on the chirp rate of the snowy tree cricket:

$$T = \frac{1}{4}R + 40.$$

In this formula, T depends on R. Writing $T = f(R)$ indicates that the relationship is a function.

Functions Don't Have to Be Defined by Formulas

People sometimes think that functions are always represented by formulas. However, the next example shows a function which is not given by a formula.

Example 4   The average monthly rainfall, R, at Chicago's O'Hare airport is given in Table 1.2, where time, t, is in months and $t = 1$ is January, $t = 2$ is February, and so on. The rainfall is a function of the month, so we write $R = f(t)$. However there is no equation that gives R when t is known. Evaluate $f(1)$ and $f(11)$. Explain what your answers mean.

Table 1.2   *Average monthly rainfall at Chicago's O'Hare airport*

Month, t	1	2	3	4	5	6	7	8	9	10	11	12
Rainfall, R (inches)	1.8	1.8	2.7	3.1	3.5	3.7	3.5	3.4	3.2	2.5	2.4	2.1

Solution   The value of $f(1)$ is the average rainfall in inches at Chicago's O'Hare airport in a typical January. From the table, $f(1) = 1.8$. Similarly, $f(11) = 2.4$ means that in a typical November, there are 2.4 inches of rain at O'Hare.

When Is a Relationship Not a Function?

It is possible for two quantities to be related and yet for neither quantity to be a function of the other.

Example 5   A national park contains foxes that prey on rabbits. Table 1.3 gives the two populations, F and R, over a 12-month period, where $t = 0$ means January 1, $t = 1$ means February 1, and so on.

Table 1.3   *Number of foxes and rabbits in a national park, by month*

t, month	0	1	2	3	4	5	6	7	8	9	10	11
R, rabbits	1000	750	567	500	567	750	1000	1250	1433	1500	1433	1250
F, foxes	150	143	125	100	75	57	50	57	75	100	125	143

(a) Is F a function of t? Is R a function of t?
(b) Is F a function of R? Is R a function of F?

Solution   (a) Both F and R are functions of t. For each value of t, there is exactly one value of F and exactly one value of R. For example, Table 1.3 shows that if $t = 5$, then $R = 750$ and $F = 57$. This means that on June 1 there are 750 rabbits and 57 foxes in the park. If we write $R = f(t)$ and $F = g(t)$, then $f(5) = 750$ and $g(5) = 57$.

(b) No, F is not a function of R. For example, suppose $R = 750$, meaning there are 750 rabbits. This happens both at $t = 1$ (February 1) and at $t = 5$ (June 1). In the first instance, there are 143 foxes; in the second instance, there are 57 foxes. Since there are R-values which correspond to more than one F-value, F is not a function of R.

Similarly, R is not a function of F. At time $t = 5$, we have $R = 750$ when $F = 57$, while at time $t = 7$, we have $R = 1250$ when $F = 57$ again. Thus, the value of F does not uniquely determine the value of R.

How to Tell if a Graph Represents a Function: Vertical Line Test

What does it mean graphically for y to be a function of x? Look at the graph of y against x. For a function, each x-value corresponds to exactly one y-value. This means that the graph intersects any vertical line at most once. If a vertical line cuts the graph twice, the graph would contain two points with different y-values but the same x-value; this would violate the definition of a function. Thus, we have the following criterion:

> **Vertical Line Test**: If there is a vertical line which intersects a graph in more than one point, then the graph does not represent a function.

Example 6   In which of the graphs in Figures 1.2 and 1.3 could y be a function of x?

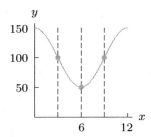

Figure 1.2: ince no vertical line intersects this curve at more than one point, y could be a function of x

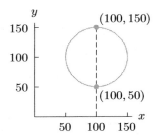

Figure 1.3: Since one vertical line intersects this curve at more than one point, y is not a function of x

Solution   The graph in Figure 1.2 could represent y as a function of x because no vertical line intersects this curve in more than one point. The graph in Figure 1.3 does not represent a function because the vertical line shown intersects the curve at two points.

A graph fails the vertical line test if at least one vertical line cuts the graph more than once, as in Figure 1.3. However, if a graph represents a function, then *every* vertical line must intersect the graph at no more than one point.

Exercises and Problems for Section 1.1

Exercises

In Exercises 1–2, write the relationship using function notation (i.e. y is a function of x is written $y = f(x)$).

1. Weight, w, is a function of caloric intake, c.

2. Number of molecules, m, in a gas, is a function of the volume of the gas, v.

3. (a) Which of the graphs in Figure 1.4 represent y as a function of x? (Note that an open circle indicates a point that is not included in the graph; a solid dot indicates a point that is included in the graph.)

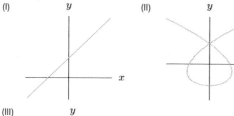

(I)   y   (II)   y

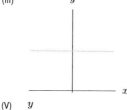

(III)   y

(IV)   y

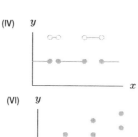

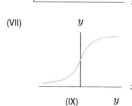

(V)   y   (VI)   y

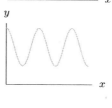

(VII)   y   (VIII)   y

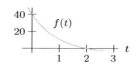

(IX)   y

Figure 1.4

(b) Which of the graphs in Figure 1.4 could represent the following situations? Give reasons.

   (i) SAT Math score versus SAT Verbal score for a small number of students.

   (ii) Total number of daylight hours as a function of the day of the year, shown over a period of several years.

(c) Among graphs (I)–(IX) in Figure 1.4, find two which could give the cost of train fare as a function of the time of day. Explain the relationship between cost and time for both choices.

4. Using Table 1.4, graph $n = f(A)$, the number of gallons of paint needed to cover a house of area A. Identify the independent and dependent variables.

Table 1.4

A	0	250	500	750	1000	1250	1500
n	0	1	2	3	4	5	6

5. Use Table 1.5 to fill in the missing values. (There may be more than one answer.)

(a) $f(0) =?$ **(b)** $f(?) = 0$
(c) $f(1) =?$ **(d)** $f(?) = 1$

Table 1.5

x	0	1	2	3	4
$f(x)$	4	2	1	0	1

6. Use Figure 1.5 to fill in the missing values:
(a) $f(0) =?$ (b) $f(?) = 0$

Figure 1.5

7. (a) You are going to graph $p = f(w)$. Which variable goes on the horizontal axis?

(b) If $10 = f(-4)$, give the coordinates of a point on the graph of f.

(c) If 6 is a solution of the equation $f(w) = 1$, give a point on the graph of f.

In Exercises 8–11, label the axes for a sketch to illustrate the given statement.

8. "Over the past century we have seen changes in the population, P (in millions), of the city..."

9. "Sketch a graph of the cost of manufacturing q items..."

10. "Graph the pressure, p, of a gas as a function of its volume, v, where p is in pounds per square inch and v is in cubic inches."

11. "Graph D in terms of y..."

Problems

12. You are looking at the graph of y, a function of x.

(a) What is the maximum number of times that the graph can intersect the y-axis? Explain.

(b) Can the graph intersect the x-axis an infinite number of times? Explain.

13. Let $f(t)$ be the number of people, in millions, who own cell phones t years after 1990. Explain the meaning of the following statements.

(a) $f(10) = 100.3$ (b) $f(a) = 20$
(c) $f(20) = b$ (d) $n = f(t)$

14. According to the Social Security Administration (SSA), the most popular name for male babies in 2001 was Jacob. However, this popularity is a recent phenomenon. Table 1.6 gives the popularity ranking r of the name Jacob for baby boys born t years after 1990 (so $t = 0$ is 1990). A ranking of 1 means most popular, a ranking of 2 means second most popular, and so forth.[1]

(a) In what year did Jacob first become the most popular name?
(b) In what year did Jacob first enter the top ten most popular names?
(c) In what year(s) was Jacob among the top five most popular names?

Table 1.6

t	0	1	2	3	4	5	6	7	8	9	10	11
r	20	16	15	11	7	5	3	2	2	1	1	1

15. Let $r = f(t)$ be the function given by Table 1.6. Explain what your answers to the following questions tell you about the popularity ranking of the name Jacob.

(a) Evaluate $f(3)$
(b) Solve $f(t) = 3$.
(c) Evaluate $f(5) - f(4)$.
(d) Evaluate $f(11) - f(10)$.

16. Table 1.7 shows the daily low temperature for a one-week period in New York City during July.

(a) What was the low temperature on July 19?
(b) When was the low temperature 73°F?
(c) Is the daily low temperature a function of the date?
(d) Is the date a function of the daily low temperature?

Table 1.7

Date	17	18	19	20	21	22	23
Low temp (°F)	73	77	69	73	75	75	70

17. Use the data from Table 1.3.

(a) Plot R on the vertical axis and t on the horizontal axis. Use this graph to explain why you believe that R is a function of t.

(b) Plot F on the vertical axis and t on the horizontal axis. Use this graph to explain why you believe that F is a function of t.
(c) Plot F on the vertical axis and R on the horizontal axis. From this graph show that F is not a function of R.
(d) Plot R on the vertical axis and F on the horizontal axis. From this graph show that R is not a function of F.

18. Since Roger Bannister broke the 4-minute mile on May 6, 1954, the record has been lowered by over sixteen seconds. Table 1.8 shows the year and times (as min:sec) of new world records for the one-mile run.[2]

(a) Is the time a function of the year? Explain.
(b) Is the year a function of the time? Explain.
(c) Let $y(r)$ be the year in which the world record, r, was set. Explain what is meant by the statement $y(3\!:\!47.33) = 1981$.
(d) Evaluate and interpret $y(3\!:\!51.1)$.

Table 1.8

Year	Time	Year	Time	Year	Time
1954	3:59.4	1966	3:51.3	1981	3:48.53
1954	3:58.0	1967	3:51.1	1981	3:48.40
1957	3:57.2	1975	3:51.0	1981	3:47.33
1958	3:54.5	1975	3:49.4	1985	3:46.32
1962	3:54.4	1979	3:49.0	1993	3:44.39
1964	3:54.1	1980	3:48.8	1999	3:43.13
1965	3:53.6				

19. Rebecca Latimer Felton of Georgia was the first woman to serve in the US Senate.[3] She took the oath of office on November 22, 1922 and served for just two days. The first woman actually elected to the Senate was Hattie Wyatt Caraway of Arkansas. She was appointed to fill the vacancy caused by the death of her husband, then won election in 1932, was reelected in 1938, and served until 1945. Table 1.9 shows the number of female senators at the beginning of the first session of each Congress.[4]

(a) Is the number of female senators a function of the Congress's number, c? Explain.
(b) Is the Congress's number a function of the number of female senators? Explain.
(c) Let $S(c)$ represent the number of female senators Senators serving in the cth Congress. What does the statement $S(104) = 8$ mean?
(d) Evaluate and interpret $S(107)$.

---

[1] Data from the SSA website at http://www.ssa.gov.
[2] The World Almanac and Book of Facts, 2002, p. 910
[3] http://www.senate.gov/learning/stat_14.html
[4] U.S. Census Bureau, Statistical Abstract of the United States: 2000 (120th edition) Washington, DC, 2000, Table 463

Table 1.9

Congress, c	96	98	100	102	104	106	107
Female senators	1	2	2	2	8	9	13

20. Match each story about a bike ride to one of the graphs (i)–(v), where d represents distance from home and t is time in hours since the start of the ride. (A graph may be used more than once.)

   (a) Starts 5 miles from home and rides 5 miles per hour away from home.

   (b) Starts 5 miles from home and rides 10 miles per hour away from home.

   (c) Starts 10 miles from home and arrives home one hour later.

   (d) Starts 10 miles from home and is halfway home after one hour.

   (e) Starts 5 miles from home and is 10 miles from home after one hour.

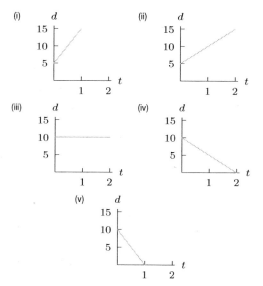

21. A bug starts out ten feet from a light, flies closer to the light, then farther away, then closer than before, then farther away. Finally the bug hits the bulb and flies off. Sketch the distance of the bug from the light as a function of time.

22. A light is turned off for several hours. It is then turned on. After a few hours it is turned off again. Sketch the light bulb's temperature as a function of time.

23. The sales tax on an item is 6%. Express the total cost, C, in terms of the price of the item, P.

24. A cylindrical can is closed at both ends and its height is twice its radius. Express its surface area, S, as a function of its radius, r. [Hint: The surface of a can consists of a rectangle plus two circular disks.]

25. According to Charles Osgood, CBS news commentator, it takes about one minute to read 15 double-spaced type-written lines on the air.[5]

   (a) Construct a table showing the time Charles Osgood is reading on the air in seconds as a function of the number of double-spaced lines read for $0, 1, 2, \ldots, 10$ lines. From your table, how long does it take Charles Osgood to read 9 lines?

   (b) Plot this data on a graph with the number of lines on the horizontal axis.

   (c) From your graph, estimate how long it takes Charles Osgood to read 9 lines. Estimate how many lines Charles Osgood can read in 30 seconds.

   (d) Construct a formula which relates the time T to n, the number of lines read.

26. A chemical company spends $2 million to buy machinery before it starts producing chemicals. Then it spends $0.5 million on raw materials for each million liters of chemical produced.

   (a) The number of liters produced ranges from 0 to 5 million. Make a table showing the relationship between the number of million liters produced, l, and the total cost, C, in millions of dollars, to produce that number of million liters.

   (b) Find a formula that expresses C as a function of l.

27. The distance between Cambridge and Wellesley is 10 miles. A person walks part of the way at 5 miles per hour, then jogs the rest of the way at 8 mph. Find a formula that expresses the total amount of time for the trip, $T(d)$, as a function of d, the distance walked.

28. A person leaves home and walks due west for a time and then walks due north.

   (a) The person walks 10 miles in total. If w represents the (variable) distance west she walks, and D represents her (variable) distance from home at the end of her walk, is D a function of w? Why or why not?

   (b) Suppose now that x is the distance that she walks in total. Is D a function of x? Why or why not?

[5] T. Parker, *Rules of Thumb*, (Boston: Houghton Mifflin, 1983).

1.2 RATE OF CHANGE

Sales of compact discs (CDs) have been increasing since they were introduced in the early 1980s. To measure how fast sales were increasing, we calculate a *rate of change* of the form

$$\frac{\text{Change in sales}}{\text{Change in time}}.$$

At the same time, sales of vinyl long playing records (LPs) have been decreasing. See Table 1.10.

Let us calculate the rate of change of CD and LP sales between 1982 and 1994. Table 1.10 gives

$$\begin{array}{c}\text{Average rate of change of CD sales}\\ \text{from 1982 to 1994}\end{array} = \frac{\text{Change in CD sales}}{\text{Change in time}} = \frac{662 - 0}{1994 - 1982} \approx 55.2 \begin{array}{c}\text{million}\\ \text{discs/year.}\end{array}$$

Thus, CD sales increased on average by 55.2 million discs per year between 1982 and 1994. See Figure 1.6.

Similarly, Table 1.10 gives

$$\begin{array}{c}\text{Average rate of change of LP sales}\\ \text{from 1982 to 1994}\end{array} = \frac{\text{Change in LP sales}}{\text{Change in time}} = \frac{1.9 - 244}{1994 - 1982} \approx -20.2 \begin{array}{c}\text{million}\\ \text{records/year.}\end{array}$$

Thus, LP sales decreased on average by 20.2 million records per year between 1982 and 1994. See Figure 1.7.

Table 1.10 *Annual sales of CDs and LPs in millions*

Year	1982	1984	1986	1988	1990	1992	1994
CD sales (millions)	0	5.8	53	150	287	408	662
LP sales (millions)	244	205	125	72	12	2.3	1.9

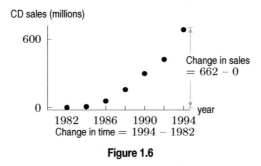

Figure 1.6

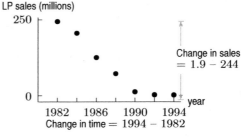

Figure 1.7

Rate of Change of a Function

The rate of change of sales is an example of the rate of change of a function. In general, if $Q = f(t)$, we write ΔQ for a change in Q and Δt for a change in t. We define:[6]

> The **average rate of change**, or **rate of change**, of Q with respect to t over an interval is
>
> $$\begin{array}{c}\text{Average rate of change}\\ \text{over an interval}\end{array} = \frac{\text{Change in } Q}{\text{Change in } t} = \frac{\Delta Q}{\Delta t}.$$

[6]The Greek letter Δ, delta, is often used in mathematics to represent change. In this book, we use rate of change to mean average rate of change across an interval. In calculus, rate of change means something called instantaneous rate of change.

The average rate of change of the function $Q = f(t)$ over an interval tells us how much Q changes, on average, for each unit change in t within that interval. On some parts of the interval, Q may be changing rapidly, while on other parts Q may be changing slowly. The average rate of change evens out these variations.

Increasing and Decreasing Functions

In the previous example, the average rate of change of CD sales is positive on the interval from 1982 to 1994 since sales of CDs increased over this interval. Similarly, the average rate of change of LP sales is negative on the same interval since sales of LPs decreased over this interval. The annual sales of CDs is an example of an *increasing function* and the annual sales of LPs is an example of a *decreasing function*. In general we say the following:

If $Q = f(t)$ for t in the interval $a \le t \le b$,

- f is an **increasing function** if the values of f increase as t increases in this interval.
- f is a **decreasing function** if the values of f decrease as t increases in this interval.

Looking at CD sales, we see that an increasing function has a positive rate of change. From the LP sales, we see that a decreasing function has a negative rate of change. In general:

If $Q = f(t)$,

- If f is an increasing function, then the average rate of change of Q with respect to t is positive on every interval.
- If f is a decreasing function, then the average rate of change of Q with respect to t is negative on every interval.

Example 1   The function $A = q(r) = \pi r^2$ gives the area, A, of a circle as a function of its radius, r. Graph q. Explain how the fact that q is an increasing function can be seen on the graph.

Solution   The area increases as the radius increases, so $A = q(r)$ is an increasing function. We can see this in Figure 1.8 because the graph climbs as we move from left to right and the average rate of change, $\Delta A / \Delta r$, is positive on every interval.

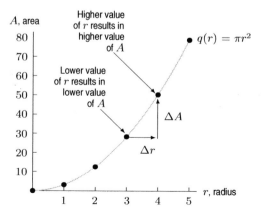

Figure 1.8: The graph of an increasing function, $A = q(r)$, rises when read from left to right

Example 2   Carbon-14 is a radioactive element that exists naturally in the atmosphere and is absorbed by living organisms. When an organism dies, the carbon-14 present at death begins to decay. Let $L = g(t)$ represent the quantity of carbon-14 (in micrograms, μg) in a tree t years after its death. See Table 1.11. Explain why we expect g to be a decreasing function of t. How is this represented on a graph?

Table 1.11   *Quantity of carbon-14 as a function of time*

t, time (years)	0	1000	2000	3000	4000	5000
L, quantity of carbon-14 (μg)	200	177	157	139	123	109

Solution   Since the amount of carbon-14 is decaying over time, g is a decreasing function. In Figure 1.9, the graph falls as we move from left to right and the average rate of change in the level of carbon-14 with respect to time, $\Delta L / \Delta t$, is negative on every interval.

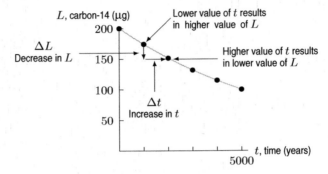

Figure 1.9: The graph of a decreasing function, $L = g(t)$, falls when read from left to right

In general, we can identify an increasing or decreasing function from its graph as follows:

- The graph of an increasing function rises when read from left to right.
- The graph of a decreasing function falls when read from left to right.

Many functions have some intervals on which they are increasing and other intervals on which they are decreasing. These intervals can often be identified from the graph.

Example 3   On what intervals is the function graphed in Figure 1.10 increasing? Decreasing?

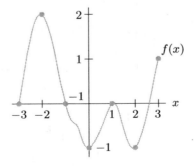

Figure 1.10: Graph of a function which is increasing on some intervals and decreasing on others

Solution   The function appears to be increasing for values of x between -3 and -2, for x between 0 and 1, and for x between 2 and 3. The function appears to be decreasing for x between -2 and 0 and for x between 1 and 2. Using inequalities, we say that f is increasing for $-3 < x < -2$, for $0 < x < 1$, and for $2 < x < 3$. Similarly, f is decreasing for $-2 < x < 0$ and $1 < x < 2$.

Function Notation for the Average Rate of Change

Suppose we want to find the average rate of change of a function $Q = f(t)$ over the interval $a \leq t \leq b$. On this interval, the change in t is given by

$$\Delta t = b - a.$$

At $t = a$, the value of Q is $f(a)$, and at $t = b$, the value of Q is $f(b)$. Therefore, the change in Q is given by

$$\Delta Q = f(b) - f(a).$$

Using function notation, we express the average rate of change as follows:

$$\begin{array}{c} \text{Average rate of change of } Q = f(t) \\ \text{over the interval } a \leq t \leq b \end{array} = \frac{\text{Change in } Q}{\text{Change in } t} = \frac{\Delta Q}{\Delta t} = \frac{f(b) - f(a)}{b - a}.$$

In Figure 1.11, notice that the average rate of change is given by the ratio of the rise, $f(b) - f(a)$, to the run, $b - a$. This ratio is also called the *slope* of the dashed line segment.[7]

In the future, we may drop the word "average" and talk about the rate of change over an interval.

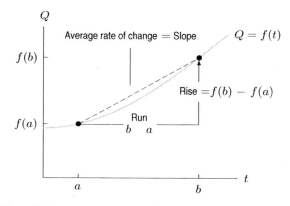

Figure 1.11: The average rate of change is the ratio Rise/Run

In previous examples we calculated the average rate of change from data. We now calculate average rates of change for functions given by formulas.

---

[7]See Section 1.3 for further discussion of slope.

Example 4   Calculate the average rates of change of the function $f(x) = x^2$ between $x = 1$ and $x = 3$ and between $x = -2$ and $x = 1$. Show your results on a graph.

Solution   Between $x = 1$ and $x = 3$, we have

$$\begin{aligned}\text{Average rate of change of } f(x) \\ \text{over the interval } 1 \le x \le 3\end{aligned} = \frac{\text{Change in } f(x)}{\text{Change in } x} = \frac{f(3) - f(1)}{3 - 1}$$

$$= \frac{3^2 - 1^2}{3 - 1} = \frac{9 - 1}{2} = 4.$$

Between $x = -2$ and $x = 1$, we have

$$\begin{aligned}\text{Average rate of change of } f(x) \\ \text{over the interval } -2 \le x \le 1\end{aligned} = \frac{\text{Change in } f(x)}{\text{Change in } x} = \frac{f(1) - f(-2)}{1 - (-2)}$$

$$= \frac{1^2 - (-2)^2}{1 - (-2)} = \frac{1 - 4}{3} = -1.$$

The average rate of change between $x = 1$ and $x = 3$ is positive because $f(x)$ is increasing on this interval. See Figure 1.12. However, on the interval from $x = -2$ and $x = 1$, the function is partly decreasing and partly increasing. The average rate of change on this interval is negative because the decrease on the interval is larger than the increase.

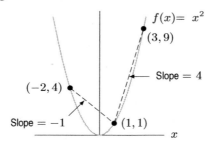

Figure 1.12: Average rate of change of $f(x)$ on an interval is slope of dashed line on that interval

Exercises and Problems for Section 1.2

Exercises

1. Table 1.10 gives the annual sales (in millions) of compact discs and vinyl long playing records. What was the average rate of change of annual sales of each of them between

    (a) 1982 and 1984?   **(b)** 1986 and 1988?
    (c) Interpret these results in terms of sales.

2. Table 1.10 shows that CD sales are a function of LP sales. Is it an increasing or decreasing function?

3. Figure 1.13 shows distance traveled as a function of time.

    (a) Find ΔD and Δt between:
       (i) $t = 2$ and $t = 5$ (ii) $t = 0.5$ and $t = 2.5$
       (iii) $t = 1.5$ and $t = 3$

    (b) Compute the rate of change, $\Delta D / \Delta t$, and interpret its meaning.

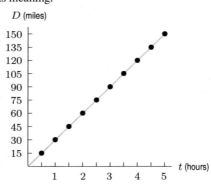

Figure 1.13

4. Table 1.12 shows data for two populations (in hundreds) for five different years. Find the average rate of change of each population over the following intervals.

(a) 1980 to 1990   (b) 1985 to 1997

(c) 1980 to 1997

Table 1.12

Year	1980	1982	1985	1990	1997
P_1	53	63	73	83	93
P_2	85	80	75	70	65

5. Table 1.13 gives the populations of two cities (in thousands) over a 17-year period.

(a) Find the average rate of change of each population on the following intervals:

(i) 1980 to 1990   (ii) 1980 to 1997

(iii) 1985 to 1997

(b) What do you notice about the average rate of change of each population? Explain what the average rate of change tells you about each population.

Table 1.13

Year	1980	1982	1985	1990	1997
P_1	42	46	52	62	76
P_2	82	80	77	72	65

Problems

6. Because scientists know how much carbon-14 a living organism should have in its tissues, they can measure the amount of carbon-14 present in the tissue of a fossil and then calculate how long it took for the original amount to decay to the current level, thus determining the time of the organism's death. A tree fossil is found to contain 130 μg of carbon-14, and scientists determine from the size of the tree that it would have contained 200 μg of carbon-14 at the time of its death. Using Table 1.11 approximately how long ago did the tree die?

7. Table 1.14 shows the number of calories used per minute as a function of body weight for three sports.[8]

(a) Determine the number of calories that a 200-lb person uses in one half-hour of walking.

(b) Who uses more calories, a 120-lb person swimming for one hour or a 220-lb person bicycling for a half-hour?

(c) Does the number of calories used by a person walking increase or decrease as weight increases?

Table 1.14

Activity	100 lb	120 lb	150 lb	170 lb	200 lb	220 lb
Walking	2.7	3.2	4.0	4.6	5.4	5.9
Bicycling	5.4	6.5	8.1	9.2	10.8	11.9
Swimming	5.8	6.9	8.7	9.8	11.6	12.7

8. (a) What is the average rate of change of $g(x) = 2x - 3$ between the points $(-2, -7)$ and $(3, 3)$?

(b) Based on your answer to part (a), is g increasing or decreasing on the given interval? Explain.

(c) Graph the function and determine over what intervals g is increasing and over what intervals g is decreasing.

[8]From *1993 World Almanac.*

9. (a) Let $f(x) = 16 - x^2$. Compute each of the following expressions, and interpret each as an average rate of change.

(i) $\dfrac{f(2) - f(0)}{2 - 0}$ (ii) $\dfrac{f(4) - f(2)}{4 - 2}$

(iii) $\dfrac{f(4) - f(0)}{4 - 0}$

(b) Graph $f(x)$. Illustrate each ratio in part (a) by sketching the line segment with the given slope. Over which interval is the average rate of decrease the greatest?

10. Figure 1.14 shows the graph of the function $g(x)$.

(a) Estimate $\dfrac{g(4) - g(0)}{4 - 0}$.

(b) The ratio in part (a) is the slope of a line segment joining two points on the graph. Sketch this line segment on the graph.

(c) Estimate $\dfrac{g(b) - g(a)}{b - a}$ for $a = -9$ and $b = -1$.

(d) On the graph, sketch the line segment whose slope is given by the ratio in part (c).

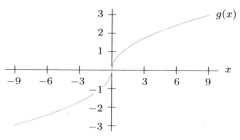

Figure 1.14

For the functions in Problems 11–13:

(a) Find the average rate of change between the points

  (i) $(-1, f(-1))$ and $(3, f(3))$
  (ii) $(a, f(a))$ and $(b, f(b))$
  (iii) $(x, f(x))$ and $(x + h, f(x + h))$

(b) What pattern do you see in the average rate of change between the three pairs of points?

11. $f(x) = 5x - 4$ **12.** $f(x) = \frac{1}{2}x + \frac{5}{2}$

13. $f(x) = x^2 + 1$

14. The surface of the sun has dark areas known as sunspots, which are cooler than the rest of the sun's surface. The number of sunspots fluctuates with time, as shown in Figure 1.15.

(a) Explain how you know the number of sunspots, s, in year t is a function of t.
(b) Approximate the time intervals on which s is an increasing function of t.

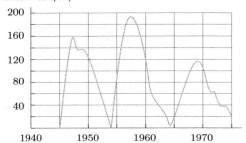

s (number of sunspots)

Figure 1.15

15. Table 1.15 gives the amount of garbage, G, in millions of tons, produced[9] in the US in year t.

(a) What is the value of Δt for consecutive entries in this table?
(b) Calculate the value of ΔG for each pair of consecutive entries in this table.
(c) Are all the values of ΔG you found in part (b) the same? What does this tell you?

Table 1.15

t	1960	1965	1970	1975	1980	1985	1990
G	90	105	120	130	150	165	180

16. Table 1.16 shows the times, t, in sec, achieved every 10 meters by Carl Lewis in the 100 meter final of the World Championship in Rome in 1987.[10] Distance, d, is in meters.

(a) For each successive time interval, calculate the average rate of change of distance. What is a common name for the average rate of change of distance?
(b) Where did Carl Lewis attain his maximum speed during this race? Some runners are running their fastest as they cross the finish line. Does that seem to be true in this case?

Table 1.16

t	0.00	1.94	2.96	3.91	4.78	5.64
d	0	10	20	30	40	50
t	6.50	7.36	8.22	9.07	9.93	
d	60	70	80	90	100	

1.3 LINEAR FUNCTIONS

Constant Rate of Change

In the previous section, we introduced the average rate of change of a function on an interval. For many functions, the average rate of change is different on different intervals. For the remainder of this chapter, we consider functions which have the same average rate of change on every interval. Such a function has a graph which is a line and is called *linear*.

Population Growth

Mathematical models of population growth are used by city planners to project the growth of towns and states. Biologists model the growth of animal populations and physicians model the spread of

[9]Adapted from *Characterization of Solid Waste in the United States.* 1992, EPA.
[10] W. G. Pritchard, "Mathematical Models of Running", *SIAM Review.* 35, 1993, p. 359–379.

an infection in the bloodstream. One possible model, a linear model, assumes that the population changes at the same average rate on every time interval.

Example 1   A town of 30,000 people grows by 2000 people every year. Since the population, P, is growing at the constant rate of 2000 people per year, P is a linear function of time, t, in years.

(a) What is the average rate of change of P over every time interval?
(b) Make a table that gives the town's population every five years over a 20-year period. Graph the population.
(c) Find a formula for P as a function of t.

Solution   (a) The average rate of change of population with respect to time is 2000 people per year.
(b) The initial population in year $t = 0$ is $P = 30,000$ people. Since the town grows by 2000 people every year, after five years it has grown by

$$\frac{2000 \text{ people}}{\text{year}} \cdot 5 \text{ years} = 10,000 \text{ people}.$$

Thus, in year $t = 5$ the population is given by

$$P = \text{Initial population} + \text{New population} = 30,000 + 10,000 = 40,000.$$

In year $t = 10$ the population is given by

$$P = 30,000 + \underbrace{2000 \text{ people/year} \cdot 10 \text{ years}}_{20,000 \text{ new people}} = 50,000.$$

Similar calculations for year $t = 15$ and year $t = 20$ give the values in Table 1.17. See Figure 1.16; the dashed line shows the trend in the data.

Table 1.17   *Population over 20 years*

t, years	P, population
0	30,000
5	40,000
10	50,000
15	60,000
20	70,000

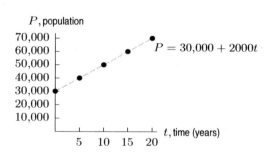

Figure 1.16: Town's population over 20 years

(c) From part (b), we see that the size of the population is given by

$$P = \text{Initial population} + \text{Number of new people}$$
$$= 30,000 + 2000 \text{ people/year} \cdot \text{Number of years},$$

so a formula for P in terms of t is

$$P = 30,000 + 2000t.$$

The graph of the population data in Figure 1.16 is a straight line. The average rate of change of the population over every interval is the same, namely 2000 people per year. Any linear function has the same average rate of change over every interval. Thus, we talk about *the* rate of change of a linear function. In general:

- A **linear function** has a constant rate of change.
- The graph of any linear function is a straight line.

Financial Models

Economists and accountants use linear functions for *straight-line depreciation*. For tax purposes, the value of certain equipment is considered to decrease, or depreciate, over time. For example, computer equipment may be state-of-the-art today, but after several years it is outdated. Straight-line depreciation assumes that the rate of change of value with respect to time is constant.

Example 2   A small business spends $20,000 on new computer equipment and, for tax purposes, chooses to depreciate it to $0 at a constant rate over a five-year period.

(a) Make a table and a graph showing the value of the equipment over the five-year period.
(b) Give a formula for value as a function of time.

Solution   (a) After five years, the equipment is valued at $0. If V is the value in dollars and t is the number of years, we see that

$$\text{Rate of change of value from } t = 0 \text{ to } t = 5 = \frac{\text{Change in value}}{\text{Change in time}} = \frac{\Delta V}{\Delta t} = \frac{-\$20,000}{5 \text{ years}} = -\$4000 \text{ per year.}$$

Thus, the value drops at the constant rate of $4000 per year. (Notice that ΔV is negative because the value of the equipment decreases.) See Table 1.18 and Figure 1.17. Since V changes at a constant rate, $V = f(t)$ is a linear function and its graph is a straight line. The rate of change, −$4000 per year, is negative because the function is decreasing and the graph slopes down.

Table 1.18   *Value of equipment depreciated over a 5-year period*

t, years	V, value ($)
0	20,000
1	16,000
2	12,000
3	8,000
4	4,000
5	0

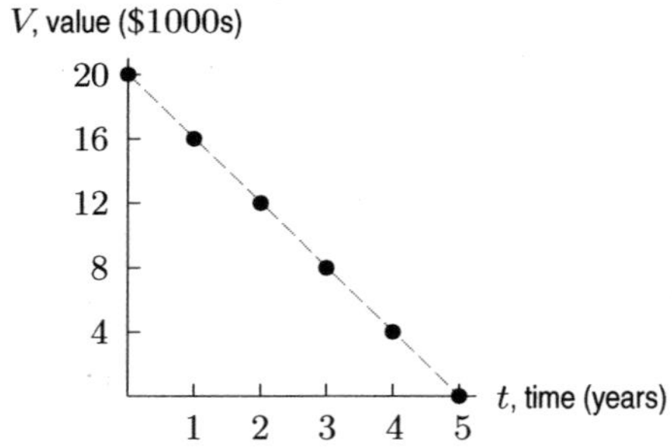

Figure 1.17: Value of equipment depreciated over a 5-year period

(b) After t years have elapsed,

$$\text{Decrease in value of equipment} = \$4000 \cdot \text{Number of years} = \$4000t.$$

The initial value of the equipment is $20,000, so at time t,

$$V = 20,000 - 4000t.$$

The total cost of production is another application of linear functions in economics.

A General Formula for the Family of Linear Functions

Example 1 involved a town whose population is growing at a constant rate with formula

$$\underset{\text{population}}{\text{Current}} = \underset{\substack{\text{population} \\ \underbrace{}_{\text{30,000 people}}}}{\text{Initial}} + \underset{\substack{\text{rate} \\ \underbrace{}_{\text{2000 people per year}}}}{\text{Growth}} \times \underset{\substack{\text{years} \\ \underbrace{}_{t}}}{\text{Number of}}$$

so

$$P = 30,000 + 2000t.$$

In Example 2, the value, V, as a function of t is given by

$$\underset{\text{cost}}{\text{Total}} = \underset{\substack{\text{value} \\ \underbrace{}_{\$20,000}}}{\text{Initial}} + \underset{\substack{\text{year} \\ \underbrace{}_{-\$4000 \text{ per year}}}}{\text{Change per}} \times \underset{\substack{\text{years} \\ \underbrace{}_{t}}}{\text{Number of}}$$

so

$$V = 20,000 + (-4000)t.$$

Using the symbols x, y, b, m, we see formulas for both of these linear functions follow the same pattern:

$$\underset{y}{\underbrace{\text{Output}}} = \underset{b}{\underbrace{\text{Initial value}}} + \underset{m}{\underbrace{\text{Rate of change}}} \times \underset{x}{\underbrace{\text{Input}}}.$$

Summarizing, we get the following results:

If $y = f(x)$ is a linear function, then for some constants b and m:

$$y = b + mx.$$

- m is called the **slope**, and gives the rate of change of y with respect to x. Thus,

$$m = \frac{\Delta y}{\Delta x}.$$

If (x_0, y_0) and (x_1, y_1) are any two distinct points on the graph of f, then

$$m = \frac{\Delta y}{\Delta x} = \frac{y_1 - y_0}{x_1 - x_0}.$$

- b is called the **vertical intercept**, or **y-intercept**, and gives the value of y for $x = 0$. In mathematical models, b typically represents an initial, or starting, value of the output.

Every linear function can be written in the form $y = b + mx$. Different linear functions have different values for m and b. These constants are known as *parameters*.

Example 3   In Example 1, the population function, $P = 30{,}000 + 2000t$, has slope $m = 2000$ and vertical intercept $b = 30{,}000$. In Example 2, the value of the computer equipment, $V = 20{,}000 - 4000t$, has slope $m = -4000$ and vertical intercept $b = 20{,}000$.

Tables for Linear Functions

A table of values could represent a linear function if the rate of change is constant, for all pairs of points in the table; that is,

$$\text{Rate of change of linear function} = \frac{\text{Change in output}}{\text{Change in input}} = \text{Constant.}$$

Thus, if the value of x goes up by equal steps in a table for a linear function, then the value of y goes up (or down) by equal steps as well. We say that changes in the value of y are *proportional* to changes in the value of x.

Example 4   Table 1.19 gives values of two functions, p and q. Could either of these functions be linear?

Table 1.19   *Values of two functions p and q*

x	50	55	60	65	70
$p(x)$	0.10	0.11	0.12	0.13	0.14
$q(x)$	0.01	0.03	0.06	0.14	0.15

Solution   The value of x goes up by equal steps of $\Delta x = 5$. The value of $p(x)$ also goes up by equal steps of $\Delta p = 0.01$, so $\Delta p / \Delta x$ is a constant. See Table 1.20. Thus, p could be a linear function.

Table 1.20   *Values of $\Delta p / \Delta x$*

x	$p(x)$	Δp	$\Delta p/\Delta x$
50	0.10		
		0.01	0.002
55	0.11		
		0.01	0.002
60	0.12		
		0.01	0.002
65	0.13		
		0.01	0.002
70	0.14		

Table 1.21   *Values of $\Delta q / \Delta x$*

x	$q(x)$	Δq	$\Delta q/\Delta x$
50	0.01		
		0.02	0.004
55	0.03		
		0.03	0.006
60	0.06		
		0.08	0.016
65	0.14		
		0.01	0.002
70	0.15		

In contrast, the value of $q(x)$ does not go up by equal steps. The value climbs by 0.02, then by 0.03, and so on. See Table 1.21. This means that $\Delta q / \Delta x$ is not constant. Thus, q could not be a linear function.

It is possible to have data from a linear function in which neither the x-values nor the y-values go up by equal steps. However the rate of change must be constant, as in the following example.

Example 5   The former Republic of Yugoslavia began exporting cars called Yugos in 1985. Table 1.22 gives the quantity of Yugos sold, Q, and the price, p, for each year from 1985 to 1988.

(a) Using Table 1.22, explain why Q could be a linear function of p.

(b) What does the rate of change of this function tell you about Yugos?

Table 1.22 *Price and sales of Yugos*

Year	Price in $, p	Number sold, Q
1985	3990	49,000
1986	4110	43,000
1987	4200	38,500
1988	4330	32,000

Solution   (a) We are interested in Q as a function of p, so we plot Q on the vertical axis and p on the horizontal axis. The data points in Figure 1.18 appear to lie on a straight line, suggesting a linear function.

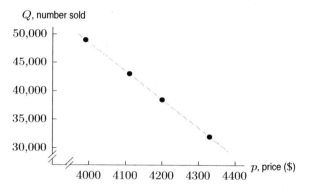

Figure 1.18: Since the data from Table 1.22 falls on a straight line, the table could represent a linear function

To provide further evidence that Q is a linear function, we check that the rate of change of Q with respect to p is constant for the points given. When the price of a Yugo rose from $3990 to $4110, sales fell from 49,000 to 43,000. Thus,

$$\Delta p = 4110 - 3990 = 120,$$
$$\Delta Q = 43,000 - 49,000 = -6000.$$

Since the number of Yugos sold decreased, ΔQ is negative. Thus, as the price increased from $3990 to $4110,

$$\text{Rate of change of quantity as price increases} = \frac{\Delta Q}{\Delta p} = \frac{-6000}{120} = -50 \text{ cars per dollar.}$$

Next, we calculate the rate of change as the price increased from $4110 to $4200 to see if the rate remains constant:

$$\text{Rate of change} = \frac{\Delta Q}{\Delta p} = \frac{38,500 - 43,000}{4200 - 4110} = \frac{-4500}{90} = -50 \text{ cars per dollar,}$$

and as the price increased from \$4200 to \$4330:

$$\text{Rate of change} = \frac{\Delta Q}{\Delta p} = \frac{32{,}000 - 38{,}500}{4330 - 4200} = \frac{-6500}{130} = -50 \text{ cars per dollar.}$$

Since the rate of change, -50, is constant, Q could be a linear function of p. Given additional data, $\Delta Q / \Delta p$ might not remain constant. However, based on the table, it appears that the function is linear.

(b) Since ΔQ is the change in the number of cars sold and Δp is the change in price, the rate of change is -50 cars per dollar. Thus the number of Yugos sold decreased by 50 each time the price increased by \$1.

Warning: Not All Graphs That Look Like Lines Represent Linear Functions

The graph of any linear function is a line. However, a function's graph can look like a line without actually being one. Consider the following example.

Example 6 The function $P = 67.38(1.026)^t$ models the population of Mexico in the early 1980s. Here P is the population (in millions) and t is the number of years since 1980. Table 1.23 and Figure 1.19 show values of P over a six-year period. Is P a linear function of t?

Table 1.23 *Population of Mexico t years after 1980*

t (years)	P (millions)
0	67.38
1	69.13
2	70.93
3	72.77
4	74.67
5	76.61
6	78.60

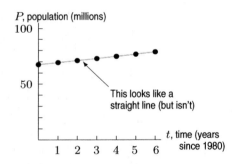

Figure 1.19: Graph of $P = 67.38(1.026)^t$ over 6-year period: Looks linear (but isn't)

Solution The formula $P = 67.38(1.026)^t$ is not of the form $P = b + mt$, so P is not a linear function of t. However, the graph of P in Figure 1.19 appears to be a straight line. We check P's rate of change in Table 1.23. When $t = 0$, $P = 67.38$ and when $t = 1$, $P = 69.13$. Thus, between 1980 and 1981,

$$\text{Rate of change of population} = \frac{\Delta P}{\Delta t} = \frac{69.13 - 67.38}{1 - 0} = 1.75.$$

For the interval from 1981 to 1982, we have

$$\text{Rate of change} = \frac{\Delta P}{\Delta t} = \frac{70.93 - 69.13}{2 - 1} = 1.80,$$

and for the interval from 1985 to 1986, we have

$$\text{Rate of change} = \frac{\Delta P}{\Delta t} = \frac{78.60 - 76.61}{6 - 5} = 1.99.$$

Thus, P's rate of change is not constant. In fact, P appears to be increasing at a faster and faster rate. Table 1.24 and Figure 1.20 show values of P over a longer (60-year) period. On this scale, these points do not fall on a straight line. However, the graph of P curves upward so gradually at first that over the short interval shown in Figure 1.19, it barely curves at all. The graphs of many nonlinear functions, when viewed on a small scale, appear to be linear.

Table 1.24 *Population over 60 years*

t (years since 1980)	P (millions)
0	67.38
10	87.10
20	112.58
30	145.53
40	188.12
50	243.16
60	314.32

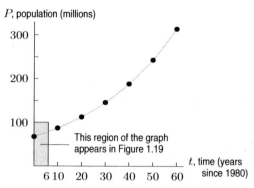

Figure 1.20: Graph of $P = 67.38(1.026)^t$ over 60 years: Not linear

Exercises and Problems for Section 1.3

Exercises

Which of the tables in Exercises 1–6 could represent a linear function?

1.

t	1	2	3	4	5
$g(t)$	5	4	5	4	5

2.

x	0	5	10	15
$f(x)$	10	20	30	40

3.

x	0	100	300	600
$g(x)$	50	100	150	200

4.

x	0	10	20	30
$h(x)$	20	40	50	55

5.

x	−3	−1	0	3
$j(x)$	5	1	−1	−7

6.

γ	9	8	7	6	5
$p(\gamma)$	42	52	62	72	82

In Exercises 7–10, identify the vertical intercept and the slope, and explain their meanings in practical terms.

7. A phone company charges according to the formula: $C(n) = 29.99 + 0.05n$, where n is the number of minutes, and $C(n)$ is the monthly phone charge, in dollars.

8. A stalactite grows according to the formula $L(t) = 17.75 + \frac{1}{250}t$, where $L(t)$ represents the length of the stalactite, in inches, and t represents the time, in years, since the stalactite was first measured.

9. The population of a town can be represented by the formula $P(t) = 54.25 - \frac{2}{7}t$, where $P(t)$ represents the population, in thousands, and t represents the time, in years, since 1970.

10. The profit in dollars, of selling n items is given by $P(n) = 0.98n - 3000$.

Problems

11. The population, $P(t)$, in millions, of a country in year t, is given by the formula $P(t) = 22 + 0.3t$.

(a) Construct a table of values for $t = 0, 10, 20, \ldots, 50$.
(b) Plot the points you found in part (a).
(c) What is the country's initial population?
(d) What is the average rate of change of the population, in millions of people/year?

12. In 2002, the population of a town was 18,310 and growing by 58 people per year. Find a formula for P, the town's population, in terms of t, the number of years since 2002.

13. Table 1.25 shows the cost C, in dollars, of selling x cups of coffee per day from a cart.

(a) Using the table, show that the relationship appears to be linear.
(b) Plot the data in the table.
(c) Find the slope of the line. Explain what this means in the context of the given situation.
(d) Why should it cost $50 to serve zero cups of coffee?

Table 1.25

x	0	5	10	50	100	200
C	50.00	51.25	52.50	62.50	75.00	100.00

14. A woodworker sells rocking horses. His start-up costs, including tools, plans, and advertising, total $5000. Labor and materials for each horse cost $350.

(a) Calculate the woodworker's total cost, C, to make 1, 2, 5, 10, and 20 rocking horses. Graph C against n, the number of rocking horses that he carves.
(b) Find a formula for C in terms of n.
(c) What is the rate of change of the function C? What does the rate of change tell us about the woodworker's expenses?

15. In each case, graph a linear function with the given rate of change. Label and put scales on the axes.

(a) Increasing at 2.1 inches/day
(b) Decreasing at 1.3 gallons/mile

16. Table 1.26 gives the area and perimeter of a square as a function of the length of its side.

(a) From the table, decide if either area or perimeter could be a linear function of side length.
(b) From the data make two graphs, one showing area as a function of side length, the other showing perimeter as a function of side length. Connect the points.

(c) If you find a linear relationship, give its corresponding rate of change and interpret its significance.

Table 1.26

Length of side	0	1	2	3	4	5	6
Area of square	0	1	4	9	16	25	36
Perimeter of square	0	4	8	12	16	20	24

17. Make two tables, one comparing the radius of a circle to its area, the other comparing the radius of a circle to its circumference. Repeat parts (a), (b), and (c) from Problem 16, this time comparing radius with circumference, and radius with area.

18. A new Toyota RAV4 costs $21,000. The car's value depreciates linearly to $10,500 in three years time. Write a formula which expresses its value, V, in terms of its age, t, in years.

19. Sri Lanka is an island which experienced approximately linear population growth from 1970 to 1990. On the other hand, Afghanistan was torn by warfare in the 1980s and did not experience linear nor near-linear growth.

(a) Table 1.27 gives the population of these two countries, in millions. Which of these two countries is A and which is B? Explain.
(b) What is the approximate rate of change of the linear function? What does the rate of change represent in practical terms?
(c) Estimate the population of Sri Lanka in 1988.

Table 1.27

Year	1970	1975	1980	1985	1990
Population of country A	13.5	15.5	16	14	16
Population of country B	12.2	13.5	14.7	15.8	17

20. Tuition cost T (in dollars) for part-time students at Stonewall College is given by $T = 300 + 200C$, where C represents the number of credits taken.

(a) Find the tuition cost for eight credits.
(b) How many credits were taken if the tuition was $1700?
(c) Make a table showing costs for taking from one to twelve credits. For each value of C, give both the tuition cost, T, and the cost per credit, T/C. Round to the nearest dollar.
(d) Which of these values of C has the smallest cost per credit?
(e) What does the 300 represent in the formula for T?
(f) What does the 200 represent in the formula for T?

21. Outside the US, temperature readings are usually given in degrees Celsius; inside the US, they are often given in degrees Fahrenheit. The exact conversion from Celsius, C, to Fahrenheit, F, uses the formula

$$F = \frac{9}{5}C + 32.$$

An approximate conversion is obtained by doubling the temperature in Celsius and adding $30°$ to get the equivalent Fahrenheit temperature.

   (a) Write a formula using C and F to express the approximate conversion.
   (b) How far off is the approximation if the Celsius temperature is $-5°, 0°, 15°, 30°$?
   (c) For what temperature (in Celsius) does the approximation agree with the actual formula?

22. A company finds that there is a linear relationship between the amount of money that it spends on advertising and the number of units it sells. If it spends no money on advertising, it sells 300 units. For each additional $5000 spent, an additional 20 units are sold.

   (a) If x is the amount of money that the company spends on advertising, find a formula for y, the number of units sold as a function of x.
   (b) How many units does the firm sell if it spends $25,000 on advertising? $50,000?
   (c) How much advertising money must be spent to sell 700 units?
   (d) What is the slope of the line you found in part (a)? Give an interpretation of the slope that relates units sold and advertising costs.

23. Graph the following function in the window $-10 \le x \le 10, -10 \le y \le 10$. Is this graph a line? Explain.

$$y = -x\left(\frac{x - 1000}{900}\right)$$

24. Graph $y = 2x + 400$ using the window $-10 \le x \le 10, -10 \le y \le 10$. Describe what happens, and how you can fix it by using a better window.

25. Figure 1.21 shows the graph of $y = x^2/1000 + 5$ in the window $-10 \le x \le 10, -10 \le y \le 10$. Discuss whether this is a linear function.

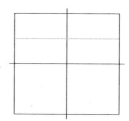

Figure 1.21

26. Graph $y = 200x + 4$ using the window $-10 \le x \le 10, -10 \le y \le 10$. Describe what happens and how you can fix it by using a better window.

27. The cost of a cab ride is given by the function $C = 1.50 + 2d$, where d is the number of miles traveled and C is in dollars. Choose an appropriate window and graph the cost of a ride for a cab that travels no farther than a 10 mile radius from the center of the city.

28. Let $f(x) = 0.003 - (1.246x + 0.37)$.

   (a) Calculate the following average rates of change:
   (i) $\dfrac{f(2) - f(1)}{2 - 1}$ (ii) $\dfrac{f(1) - f(2)}{1 - 2}$
   (iii) $\dfrac{f(3) - f(4)}{3 - 4}$
   (c) Rewrite $f(x)$ in the form $f(x) = b + mx$.

29. The graph of a linear function $y = f(x)$ passes through the two points $(a, f(a))$ and $(b, f(b))$, where $a < b$ and $f(a) < f(b)$.

   (a) Graph the function labeling the two points.
   (b) Find the slope of the line in terms of f, a, and b.

1.4   FORMULAS FOR LINEAR FUNCTIONS

To find a formula for a linear function we find values for the slope, m, and the vertical intercept, b in the formula $y = b + mx$.

Finding a Formula for a Linear Function from a Table of Data

If a table of data represents a linear function, we first calculate m and then determine b.

Example 1 A grapefruit is thrown into the air. Its velocity, v, is a linear function of t, the time since it was thrown. A positive velocity indicates the grapefruit is rising and a negative velocity indicates it is falling. Check that the data in Table 1.28 corresponds to a linear function. Find a formula for v in terms of t.

Table 1.28 *Velocity of a grapefruit t seconds after being thrown into the air*

t, time (sec)	1	2	3	4
v, velocity (ft/sec)	48	16	−16	−48

Solution Figure 1.22 shows the data in Table 1.28. The points appear to fall on a line. To check that the velocity function is linear, calculate the rates of change of v and see that they are constant. From time $t = 1$ to $t = 2$, we have

$$\text{Rate of change of velocity with time} = \frac{\Delta v}{\Delta t} = \frac{16 - 48}{2 - 1} = -32.$$

For the next second, from $t = 2$ to $t = 3$, we have

$$\text{Rate of change} = \frac{\Delta v}{\Delta t} = \frac{-16 - 16}{3 - 2} = -32.$$

You can check that the rate of change from $t = 3$ to $t = 4$ is also −32.

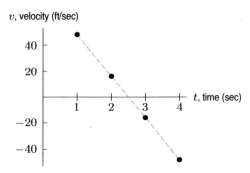

Figure 1.22: Velocity of a grapefruit is a linear function of time

A formula for v is of the form $v = b + mt$. Since m is the rate of change, we have $m = -32$ so $v = b - 32t$. The initial velocity (at $t = 0$) is represented by b. We are not given the value of v when $t = 0$, but we can use any data point to calculate b. For example, $v = 48$ when $t = 1$, so

$$48 = b - 32 \cdot 1,$$

which gives

$$b = 80.$$

Thus, a formula for the velocity is $v = 80 - 32t$.

What does the rate of change, m, in Example 1 tell us about the grapefruit? Think about the units:

$$m = \frac{\Delta v}{\Delta t} = \frac{\text{Change in velocity}}{\text{Change in time}} = \frac{-32 \text{ ft/sec}}{1 \text{ sec}} = -32 \text{ ft/sec per second.}$$

The value of m, -32 ft/sec per second, tells us that the grapefruit's velocity is decreasing by 32 ft/sec for every second that goes by. We say the grapefruit is accelerating at -32 ft/sec per second. (The units ft/sec per second are often written ft/sec^2. Negative acceleration is also called deceleration.)[11]

Finding a Formula for a Linear Function from a Graph

We can calculate the slope, m, of a linear function using two points on its graph. Having found m we can use either of the points to calculate b, the vertical intercept.

Example 2   Figure 1.23 shows oxygen consumption as a function of heart rate for two people.

(a) Assuming linearity, find formulas for these two functions.
(b) Interpret the slope of each graph in terms of oxygen consumption.

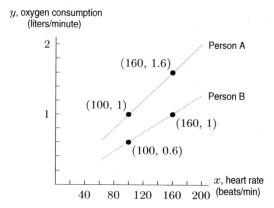

Figure 1.23: Oxygen consumption of two people running on treadmills

Solution   (a) Let x be heart rate and let y be oxygen consumption. Since we are assuming linearity, $y = b + mx$. The two points on person A's line, $(100, 1)$ and $(160, 1.6)$, give

$$\text{Slope of } A\text{'s line} = m = \frac{\Delta y}{\Delta x} = \frac{1.6 - 1}{160 - 100} = 0.01.$$

Thus $y = b + 0.01x$. To find b, use the fact that $y = 1$ when $x = 100$:

$$1 = b + 0.01(100)$$
$$1 = b + 1$$
$$b = 0.$$

Alternatively, b can be found using the fact that $x = 160$ if $y = 1.6$. Either way leads to the formula $y = 0.01x$.

---

[11]The notation ft/sec^2 is shorthand for ft/sec per second; it does not mean a "square second" in the same way that areas are measured square feet or square meters.

For person B, we again begin with the formula $y = b + mx$. In Figure 1.23, two points on B's line are $(100, 0.6)$ and $(160, 1)$, so

$$\text{Slope of } B\text{'s line } = m = \frac{\Delta y}{\Delta x} = \frac{1 - 0.6}{160 - 100} = \frac{0.4}{60} \approx 0.0067.$$

To find b, use the fact that $y = 1$ when $x = 160$:

$$1 = b + (0.4/60) \cdot 160$$
$$1 = b + 1.067$$
$$b = -0.067.$$

Thus, for person B, we have $y = -0.067 + 0.0067x$.

(b) The slope for person A is $m = 0.01$, so

$$m = \frac{\text{Change in oxygen consumption}}{\text{Change in heart rate}} = \frac{\text{Change in liters/min}}{\text{Change in beats/min}} = 0.01 \frac{\text{liters}}{\text{heart beat}}.$$

Every additional heart beat (per minute) for person A translates to an additional 0.01 liters (per minute) of oxygen consumed.

The slope for person B is $m = 0.0067$. Thus, for every additional beat (per minute), person B consumes an additional 0.0067 liter of oxygen (per minute). Since the slope for person B is smaller than for person A, person B consumes less additional oxygen than person A for the same increase in pulse.

What do the y-intercepts of the functions in Example 2 say about oxygen consumption? Often the y-intercept of a function is a starting value. In this case, the y-intercept would be the oxygen consumption of a person whose pulse is zero (i.e. $x = 0$). Since a person running on a treadmill must have a pulse, in this case it makes no sense to interpret the y-intercept this way. The formula for oxygen consumption is useful only for realistic values of the pulse.

Finding a Formula for a Linear Function from a Verbal Description

Sometimes the verbal description of a linear function is less straightforward than those we saw in Section 1.3. Consider the following example.

Example 3   We have \$24 to spend on soda and chips for a party. A six-pack of soda costs \$3 and a bag of chips costs \$2. The number of six-packs we can afford, y, is a function of the number of bags of chips we decide to buy, x.

(a) Find an equation relating x and y.
(b) Graph the equation. Interpret the intercepts and the slope in the context of the party.

Solution   (a) If we spend all \$24 on soda and chips, then we have the following equation:

$$\text{Amount spent on chips } + \text{ Amount spent on soda } = \$24.$$

If we buy x bags of chips at \$2 per bag, then the amount spent on chips is \$$2x$. Similarly, if we buy y six-packs of soda at \$3 per six-pack, then the amount spent on soda is \$$3y$. Thus,

$$2x + 3y = 24.$$

We can solve for y, giving

$$3y = 24 - 2x$$
$$y = 8 - \frac{2}{3}x.$$

This is a linear function with slope $m = -2/3$ and y-intercept $b = 8$.

(b) The graph of this function is a discrete set of points, since the number of bags of chips and the number of six-packs of soda must be (nonnegative) integers.

To find the y-intercept, we set $x = 0$, giving

$$2 \cdot 0 + 3y = 24.$$

So $3y = 24$, giving $y = 8$.
Substituting $y = 0$ gives the x-intercept,

$$2x + 3 \cdot 0 = 24.$$

So $2x = 24$, giving $x = 12$. Thus the points $(0, 8)$ and $(12, 0)$ are on the graph.

The point $(0, 8)$ indicates that we can buy 8 six-packs of soda if we buy no chips. The point $(12, 0)$ indicates that we can buy 12 bags of chips if we buy no soda. The other points on the line describe affordable options between these two extremes. For example, the point $(6, 4)$ is on the line, because

$$2 \cdot 6 + 3 \cdot 4 = 24.$$

This means that if we buy 6 bags of chips, we can afford 4 six-packs of soda.

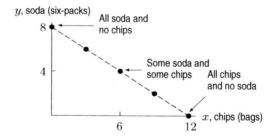

Figure 1.24: Relation between the number of six-packs, y, and the number of bags of chips, x

The points marked in Figure 1.24 represent affordable options. All affordable options lie on or below the line $2x + 3y = 24$. Not all points on the line are affordable options. For example, suppose we purchase one six-pack of soda for $3.00. That leaves $21.00 to spend on chips, meaning we would have to buy 10.5 bags of chips, which is not possible. Therefore, the point $(10.5, 1)$ is not an option, although it is a point on the line $2x + 3y = 24$.

To interpret the slope, notice that

$$m = \frac{\Delta y}{\Delta x} = \frac{\text{Change in number of six-packs}}{\text{Change in number of bags of chips}},$$

so the units of m are six-packs of soda per bags of chips. The fact that $m = -2/3$ means that for each additional 3 bags of chips purchased, we can purchase 2 fewer six-packs of soda. This occurs because 2 six-packs cost $6, the same as 3 bags of chips. Thus, $m = -2/3$ is the rate at which the amount of soda we can buy decreases as we buy more chips.

Alternative Forms for the Equation of a Line

In Example 3, the equation $2x + 3y = 24$ represents a linear relationship between x and y even though the equation is not in the form $y = b + mx$. The following equations represent lines.

- The *slope-intercept form* is
  $$y = b + mx \qquad \text{where } m \text{ is the slope and } b \text{ is the } y\text{-intercept.}$$
- The *point-slope form* is
  $$y - y_0 = m(x - x_0) \quad \text{where } m \text{ is the slope and } (x_0, y_0) \text{ is a point on the line.}$$
- The *standard form* is
  $$Ax + By + C = 0 \qquad \text{where } A, B, \text{ and } C \text{ are constants.}$$

If we know the slope of a line and the coordinates of a point on the line, it is often convenient to use the point-slope form of the equation.

Example 4   Use the point-slope form to find the equation of the line for the oxygen consumption of Person A in Example 2.

Solution   In Example 2, we found the slope of person A's line to be $m = 0.01$. Since the point $(100, 1)$ lies on the line, the point-slope form gives the equation

$$y - 1 = 0.01(x - 100).$$

To check that this gives the same equation we got in Example 2, we multiply out and simplify:

$$y - 1 = 0.01x - 1$$
$$y = 0.01x.$$

Alternatively, we could have used the point $(160, 1.6)$ instead of $(100, 1)$, giving

$$y - 1.6 = 0.01(x - 160).$$

Multiplying out again gives $y = 0.01x$.

Exercises and Problems for Section 1.4

Exercises

If possible, rewrite the equations in Exercises 1–9 in slope-intercept form, $y = b + mx$.

1. $3x + 5y = 20$

2. $0.1y + x = 18$

3. $y - 0.7 = 5(x - 0.2)$

4. $5(x + y) = 4$

5. $5x - 3y + 2 = 0$

6. $3x + 2y + 40 = x - y$

7. $x = 4$

8. $y = 5$

9. $\dfrac{x + y}{7} = 3$

Find formulas for the linear functions in Exercises 10–15.

10. Slope 3 and y-intercept 8

11. Passes through the points $(-1, 5)$ and $(2, -1)$

12. Slope -4 and x-intercept 7

13. Has x-intercept 3 and y-intercept -5

14. Slope 2/3 and passes through the point $(5, 7)$

15. Slope 0.1, passes through $(-0.1, 0.02)$

Exercises 16–22 give data from a linear function. Find a formula for the function.

16.

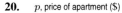

Year, t	0	1	2
Value of computer, $\$V = f(t)$	2000	1500	1000

17.

Price per bottle, p ($)		0.50	0.75	1.00
Number of bottles sold, $q = f(p)$		1500	1000	500

18.

Temperature, $y = f(x)$ (°C)	0	5	20
Temperature, x (°F)	32	41	68

19.

Temperature, $y = f(x)$, (°R)	459.7	469.7	489.7
Temperature, x (°F)	0	10	30

20.

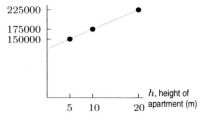

21.

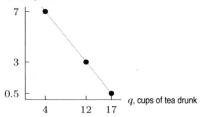

22.

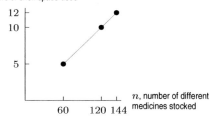

Problems

23. If $y = f(x)$ is a linear function and if $f(-2) = 7$ and $f(3) = -3$, find a formula for f.

24. Describe a linear (or nearly linear) relationship that you have encountered outside the classroom. Determine the rate of change and interpret it in practical terms.

25. John wants to buy a dozen rolls. The local bakery sells sesame and poppy seed rolls for the same price.

(a) Make a table of all the possible combinations of rolls if he buys a dozen, where s is the number of sesame seed rolls and p is the number of poppy seed rolls.
(b) Find a formula for p as a function of s.
(c) Graph this function.

26. In a college meal plan you pay a membership fee; then all your meals are at a fixed price per meal.

(a) If 30 meals cost $152.50 and 60 meals cost $250, find the membership fee and the price per meal.
(b) Write a formula for the cost of a meal plan, C, in terms of the number of meals, n.
(c) Find the cost for 50 meals.
(d) Find n in terms of C.
(e) Use part (d) to determine the maximum number of meals you can buy on a budget of $300.

27. A theater manager graphed weekly profits as a function of the number of patrons and found that the relationship was linear. One week the profit was $11,328 when 1324 patrons attended. Another week 1529 patrons produced a profit of $13,275.50.

(a) Find a formula for weekly profit, y, as a function of the number of patrons, x.
(b) Interpret the slope and the y-intercept.
(c) What is the break-even point (the number of patrons for which there is zero profit)?
(d) Find a formula for the number of patrons as a function of profit.
(e) If the weekly profit was $17,759.50, how many patrons attended the theater?

28. An empty champagne bottle is tossed from a hot-air balloon. Its upward velocity is measured every second and recorded in Table 1.29.

(a) Describe the motion of the bottle in words. What do negative values of v represent?
(b) Find a formula for v in terms of t.
(c) Explain the physical significance of the slope of your formula.
(d) Explain the physical significance of the t-axis and v-axis intercepts.

Table 1.29

t (sec)	0	1	2	3	4	5
v (ft/sec)	40	8	-24	-56	-88	-120

29. A bullet is shot straight up into the air from ground level. After t seconds, the velocity of the bullet, in meters per second, is approximated by the formula

$$v = f(t) = 1000 - 9.8t.$$

(a) Evaluate the following: $f(0)$, $f(1)$, $f(2)$, $f(3)$, $f(4)$. Compile your results in a table.

(b) Describe in words what is happening to the speed of the bullet. Discuss why you think this is happening.

(c) Evaluate and interpret the slope and both intercepts of $f(t)$.

(d) The gravitational field near the surface of Jupiter is stronger than that near the surface of the earth, which, in turn, is stronger than the field near the surface of the moon. How is the formula for $f(t)$ different for a bullet shot from Jupiter's surface? From the moon?

30. Find the equation of the line l, shown in Figure 1.25, if its slope is $m = 4$.

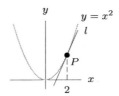

Figure 1.25

31. Find the equation of the line l in Figure 1.26. The shapes under the line are squares.

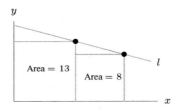

Figure 1.26

32. Find the equation of line l in Figure 1.27.

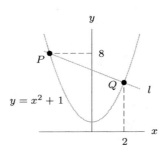

Figure 1.27

33. Find an equation for the line l in Figure 1.28 in terms of the constant A and values of the function f.

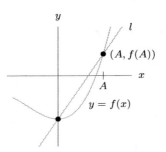

Figure 1.28

34. The demand for gasoline can be modeled as a linear function of price. If the price of gasoline is $p = \$1.10$ per gallon, the quantity demanded in a fixed period is $q = 65$ gallons. If the price rises to $\$1.50$ per gallon, the quantity demanded falls to 45 gallons in that period.

(a) Find a formula for q in terms of p.

(b) Explain the economic significance of the slope of your formula.

(c) Explain the economic significance of the q-axis and p-axis intercepts.

35. A business consultant works 10 hours a day, 6 days a week. She divides her time between meetings with clients and meetings with co-workers. A client meeting requires 3 hours while a co-worker meeting requires 2 hours. Let x be the number of co-worker meetings the consultant holds during a given week. If y is the number of client meetings for which she has time remaining, then y is a function of x. Assume this relationship is linear and that meetings can be split up and continued on different days.

(a) Graph the relationship between y and x. [Hint: Consider the maximum number of client and co-worker meetings that can be held.]

(b) Find a formula for y as a function of x.

(c) Explain what the slope and the x- and y-intercepts represent in the context of the consultant's meeting schedule.

(d) A change is made so that co-worker meetings take 90 minutes instead of 2 hours. Graph this situation. Describe those features of this graph that have changed from the one sketched in part (a) and those that have remained the same.

36. The development time, t, of an organism is the number of days required for the organism to mature, and the development rate is defined as $r = 1/t$. In cold-blooded organisms such as insects, the development rate depends on temperature: the colder it is, the longer the organism takes to develop. For such organisms, the degree-day model[12] assumes that the development rate r is a linear function of temperature H (in °C):

$$r = b + kH.$$

(a) According to the degree-day model, there is a minimum temperature H_{min} below which an organism never matures. Find a formula for H_{min} in terms of the constants b and k.

(b) Define S as $S = (H - H_{min})t$, where S is the number of degree-days. That is, S is the number of days t times the number of degrees between H and H_{min}. Use the formula for r to show that S is a constant. In other words, find a formula for S that does not involve H. Your formula will involve k.

(c) A certain organism requires $t = 25$ days to develop at a constant temperature of $H = 20$°C and has $H_{min} = 15$°C. Using the fact that S is a constant, how many days does it take for this organism to develop at a temperature of 25°C?

(d) In part (c) we assumed that the temperature H is constant throughout development. If the temperature varies from day to day, the number of degree-days can be accumulated until they total S, at which point the organism completes development. For instance,

suppose on the first day the temperature is $H = 20$°C and that on the next day it is $H = 22$°C. Then for these first two days

Total number of degree days
$$= (20 - 15) \cdot 1 + (22 - 15) \cdot 1 = 12.$$

Based on Table 1.30, on what day does the organism reach maturity?

Table 1.30

Day	1	2	3	4	5	6	7	8	9	10	11	12
H (°C)	20	22	27	28	27	31	29	30	28	25	24	26

37. (Continuation of Problem 36.) Table 1.31 gives the development time t (in days) for an insect as a function of temperature H (in °C).

(a) Find a linear formula for r, the development rate, in terms of H.

(b) Find the value of S, the number of degree-days required for the organism to mature.

Table 1.31

H, °C	20	22	24	26	28	30
t, days	14.3	12.5	11.1	10.0	9.1	8.3

1.5 GEOMETRIC PROPERTIES OF LINEAR FUNCTIONS

Interpreting the Parameters of a Linear Function

The slope-intercept form for a linear function is $y = b + mx$, where b is the y-intercept and m is the slope. The parameters b and m can be used to compare linear functions.

Example 1   With time, t, in years, the populations of four towns, P_A, P_B, P_C and P_D, are given by the following formulas:

$$P_A = 20{,}000 + 1600t, \quad P_B = 50{,}000 - 300t, \quad P_C = 650t + 45{,}000, \quad P_D = 15{,}000(1.07)^t.$$

(a) Which populations are represented by linear functions?

(b) Describe in words what each linear model tells you about that town's population. Which town starts out with the most people? Which town is growing fastest?

Solution   (a) The populations of towns A, B, and C are represented by linear functions because they are written in the form $P = b + mt$. Town D's population does not grow linearly since its formula, $P_D = 15{,}000(1.07)^t$, cannot be expressed in the form $P_D = b + mt$.

[12]Information drawn from a web site created by Dr. Alexei A. Sharov at the Virginia Polytechnic Institute, http://www.ento.vt.edu/ sharov/PopEcol/popecol.html.

(b) For town A, we have

$$P_A = \underbrace{20{,}000}_{b} + \underbrace{1600}_{m} \cdot t,$$

so $b = 20{,}000$ and $m = 1600$. This means that in year $t = 0$, town A has $20{,}000$ people. It grows by 1600 people per year.

For town B, we have

$$P_B = \underbrace{50{,}000}_{b} + \underbrace{(-300)}_{m} \cdot t,$$

so $b = 50{,}000$ and $m = -300$. This means that town B starts with $50{,}000$ people. The negative slope indicates that the population is decreasing at the rate of 300 people per year.

For town C, we have

$$P_C = \underbrace{45{,}000}_{b} + \underbrace{650}_{m} \cdot t,$$

so $b = 45{,}000$ and $m = 650$. This means that town C begins with $45{,}000$ people and grows by 650 people per year.

Town B starts out with the most people, $50{,}000$, but town A, with a rate of change of 1600 people per year, grows the fastest of the three towns that grow linearly.

The Effect of the Parameters on the Graph of a Linear Function

The graph of a linear function is a line. Changing the values of b and m gives different members of the family of linear functions. In summary:

Let $y = b + mx$. Then the graph of y against x is a line.

- The y-intercept, b, tells us where the line crosses the y-axis.
- If the slope, m, is positive, the line climbs from left to right. If the slope, m, is negative, the line falls from left to right.
- The slope, m, tells us how fast the line is climbing or falling.
- The larger the magnitude of m (either positive or negative), the steeper the graph of f.

Example 2   (a) Graph the three linear functions P_A, P_B, P_C from Example 1 and show how to identify the values of b and m from the graph.

(b) Graph P_D from Example 1 and explain how the graph shows P_D is not a linear function.

Solution   (a) Figure 1.29 gives graphs of the three functions:

$$P_A = 20{,}000 + 1600t, \qquad P_B = 50{,}000 - 300t, \quad \text{and} \quad P_C = 45{,}000 + 650t.$$

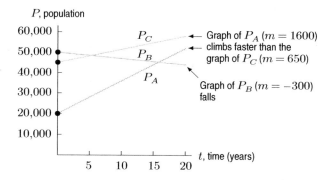

Figure 1.29: Graphs of three linear functions, P_A, P_B, and P_C, showing starting values and rates of climb

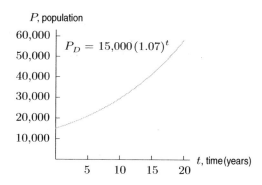

Figure 1.30: Graph of $P_D = 15,000(1.07)^t$ is not a line

The values of b identified in Example 1 tell us the vertical intercepts. Figure 1.29 shows that the graph of P_A crosses the P-axis at $P = 20,000$, the graph of P_B crosses at $P = 50,000$, and the graph of P_C crosses at $P = 45,000$.

Notice that the graphs of P_A and P_C are both climbing and that P_A climbs faster than P_C. This corresponds to the fact that the slopes of these two functions are positive ($m = 1600$ for P_A and $m = 650$ for P_C) and the slope of P_A is larger than the slope of P_C.

The graph of P_B falls when read from left to right, indicating that population decreases over time. This corresponds to the fact that the slope of P_C is negative ($m = -300$).

(b) Figure 1.30 gives a graph of P_D. Since it is not a line, P_D is not a linear function.

Intersection of Two Lines

To find the point at which two lines intersect, notice that the (x, y)-coordinates of such a point must satisfy the equations for both lines. Thus, in order to find the point of intersection algebraically, solve the equations simultaneously.

If linear functions are modeling real quantities, their points of intersection often have practical significance. Consider the next example.

Example 3
The cost in dollars of renting a car for a day from three different rental agencies and driving it d miles is given by the following functions:

$$C_1 = 50 + 0.10d, \qquad C_2 = 30 + 0.20d, \qquad C_3 = 0.50d.$$

(a) Describe in words the daily rental arrangements made by each of these three agencies.
(b) Which agency is cheapest?

Solution
(a) Agency 1 charges $50 plus $0.10 per mile driven. Agency 2 charges $30 plus $0.20 per mile. Agency 3 charges $0.50 per mile driven.
(b) The answer depends on how far we want to drive. If we aren't driving far, agency 3 may be cheapest because it only charges for miles driven and has no other fees. If we want to drive a long way, agency 1 may be cheapest (even though it charges $50 up front) because it has the lowest per-mile rate.

The three functions are graphed in Figure 1.31. The graph shows that for d up to 100 miles, the value of C_3 is less than C_1 and C_2 because its graph is below the other two. For d between

100 and 200 miles, the value of C_2 is less than C_1 and C_3. For d more than 200 miles, the value of C_1 is less than C_2 and C_3.

By graphing these three functions on a calculator, we can estimate the coordinates of the points of intersection by tracing. To find the exact coordinates, we solve simultaneous equations. Starting with the intersection of lines C_1 and C_2, we set the costs equal, $C_1 = C_2$, and solve for d:

$$50 + 0.10d = 30 + 0.20d$$
$$20 = 0.10d$$
$$d = 200.$$

Thus, the cost of driving 200 miles is the same for agencies 1 and 2. Solving $C_2 = C_3$ gives

$$30 + 0.20d = 0.50d$$
$$0.30d = 30$$
$$d = 100,$$

which means the cost of driving 100 miles is the same for agencies 2 and 3.

Thus, agency 3 is cheapest up to 100 miles. Agency 1 is cheapest for more than 200 miles. Agency 2 is cheapest between 100 and 200 miles. See Figure 1.31. Notice that the point of intersection of C_1 and C_3, $(125, 62.5)$, does not influence our decision as to which agency is the cheapest.

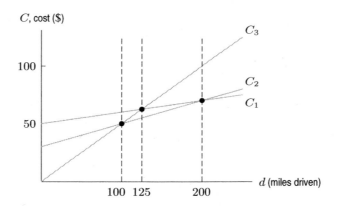

Figure 1.31: Cost of driving a car d miles when renting from three different agencies. Cheapest agency corresponds to the lowest graph for a given d value

Equations of Horizontal and Vertical Lines

An increasing linear function has positive slope and a decreasing linear function has negative slope. What about a line with slope $m = 0$? If the rate of change of a quantity is zero, then the quantity does not change. Thus, if the slope of a line is zero, the value of y must be constant. Such a line is horizontal.

Example 4   Explain why the equation $y = 4$ represents a horizontal line and the equation $x = 4$ represents a vertical line.

Solution   The equation $y = 4$ represents a linear function with slope $m = 0$. To see this, notice that this equation can be rewritten as $y = 4 + 0 \cdot x$. Thus, the value of y is 4 no matter what the value of x is. See Figure 1.32. Similarly, the equation $x = 4$ means that x is 4 no matter what the value of y is. Every point on the line in Figure 1.33 has x equal to 4, so this line is the graph of $x = 4$.

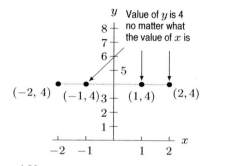

Figure 1.32: The horizontal line $y = 4$ has slope 0

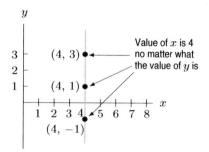

Figure 1.33: The vertical line $x = 4$ has an undefined slope

What is the slope of a vertical line? Figure 1.33 shows three points, $(4, -1)$, $(4, 1)$, and $(4, 3)$ on a vertical line. Calculating the slope, gives

$$m = \frac{\Delta y}{\Delta x} = \frac{3 - 1}{4 - 4} = \frac{2}{0}.$$

The slope is undefined because the denominator, Δx, is 0. The slope of every vertical line is undefined for the same reason. All the x-values on such a line are equal, so Δx is 0, and the denominator of the expression for the slope is 0. A vertical line is not the graph of a function, since it fails the vertical line test. It does not have an equation of the form $y = b + mx$.

In summary,

For any constant k:

- The graph of the equation $y = k$ is a horizontal line and its slope is zero.
- The graph of the equation $x = k$ is a vertical line and its slope is undefined.

Slopes of Parallel and Perpendicular Lines

Figure 1.34 shows two parallel lines. These lines are parallel because they have equal slopes.

Figure 1.34: Parallel lines: l_1 and l_2 have equal slopes

Figure 1.35: Perpendicular lines: l_1 has a positive slope and l_2 has a negative slope

What about perpendicular lines? Two perpendicular lines are graphed in Figure 1.35. We can see that if one line has a positive slope, then any perpendicular line must have a negative slope. Perpendicular lines have slopes with opposite signs.

We show that if l_1 and l_2 are two perpendicular lines with slopes, m_1 and m_2, then m_1 is the negative reciprocal of m_2. If m_1 and m_2 are not zero, we have the following result:

Let l_1 and l_2 be two lines having slopes m_1 and m_2, respectively. Then:

- These lines are parallel if and only if $m_1 = m_2$.

- These lines are perpendicular if and only if $m_1 = -\dfrac{1}{m_2}$.

In addition, any two horizontal lines are parallel and $m_1 = m_2 = 0$. Any two vertical lines are parallel and m_1 and m_2 are undefined. A horizontal line is perpendicular to a vertical line. See Figures 1.36–1.38.

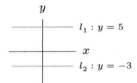

Figure 1.36: Any two horizontal lines are parallel

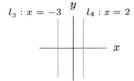

Figure 1.37: Any two vertical lines are parallel

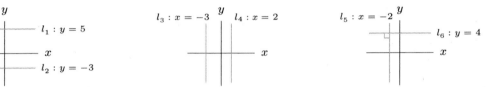

Figure 1.38: A horizontal line and a vertical line are perpendicular

Justification of Formula for Slopes of Perpendicular Lines

Figure 1.39 shows l_1 and l_2, two perpendicular lines with slope m_1 and m_2. Neither line is horizontal or vertical, so m_1 and m_2 are both defined and nonzero. We will show that

$$m_1 = -\frac{1}{m_2},$$

We use the two triangles, $\triangle PQR$ and $\triangle SPR$. We show that $\triangle PQR$ and $\triangle SPR$ are similar by showing that corresponding angles have equal measure. The line PR is horizontal, so $\angle QRP = \angle SRP$ since both are right angles. Since $\triangle QPS$ is a right triangle, $\angle S$ is complementary to $\angle Q$ (that is, $\angle S$ and $\angle Q$ add to $90°$). Since $\triangle QRP$ is a right triangle, $\angle QPR$ is complementary to $\angle Q$. Therefore $\angle S = \angle QPR$. Since two pairs of angles in $\triangle PQR$ and $\triangle SPR$ have equal measure, the third must be equal also; the triangles are similar.

Corresponding sides of similar triangles are proportional. (See Figure 1.40.) Therefore,

$$\frac{||RS||}{||RP||} = \frac{||RP||}{||RQ||},$$

where $||RS||$ means the length of side RS.

Next, we calculate m_1 using points S and P, and we calculate m_2 using points Q and P. In Figure 1.39, we see that

$$\Delta x = ||RP||, \quad \Delta y_1 = ||RS||, \quad \text{and} \quad \Delta y_2 = -||RQ||,$$

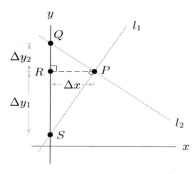

Figure 1.39

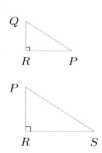

Figure 1.40

where Δy_2 is negative because y-values of points on l_2 decrease as x increases. Thus,

$$m_1 = \frac{\Delta y_1}{\Delta x} = \frac{||RS||}{||RP||} \quad \text{and} \quad m_2 = \frac{\Delta y_2}{\Delta x} = -\frac{||RQ||}{||RP||}.$$

Therefore, using the result obtained from the similar triangles, we have

$$m_1 = \frac{||RS||}{||RP||} = \frac{||RP||}{||RQ||} = -\frac{1}{m_2}.$$

Thus, $m_1 = -1/m_2$.

Exercises and Problems for Section 1.5

Exercises

In Exercises 1–3, which line has the greater

(a) Slope?   **(b)** y-intercept?

1. $y = -1 + 2x, \quad y = -2 + 3x$

2. $y = 3 + 4x, \quad y = 5 - 2x$

3. $y = \frac{1}{4}x, \quad y = 1 - 6x$

4. Without a calculator, match the functions (a)–(c) to the graphs (i)–(iii).

  (a) $f(x) = 3x + 1$ **(b)** $g(x) = -2x + 1$
  (c) $h(x) = 1$

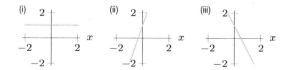

5. Without a calculator, match the equations (a)–(g) to the graphs (I)–(VII).

  (a) $y = x - 5$ **(b)** $-3x + 4 = y$
  (c) $5 = y$ **(d)** $y = -4x - 5$
  (e) $y = x + 6$ **(f)** $y = x/2$

(g) $5 = x$

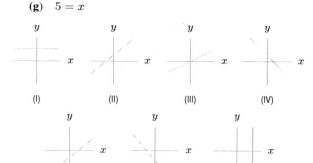

6. Figure 1.41 gives lines, A, B, C, D, and E. Without a calculator, match each line to f, g, h, u or v:

$$f(x) = 20 + 2x$$
$$g(x) = 20 + 4x$$
$$h(x) = 2x - 30$$
$$u(x) = 60 - x$$
$$v(x) = 60 - 2x$$

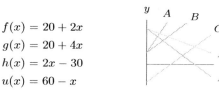

Figure 1.41

7. Without a calculator, match the following functions to the lines in Figure 1.42:

$$f(x) = 5 + 2x$$
$$g(x) = -5 + 2x$$
$$h(x) = 5 + 3x$$
$$j(x) = 5 - 2x$$
$$k(x) = 5 - 3x$$

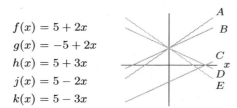

Figure 1.42

8. (a) By hand, graph $y = 3$ and $x = 3$.

(b) Can the equations in part (a) be written in slope-intercept form?

Are the lines in Exercises 9–14 perpendicular? Parallel? Neither?

9. $y = 5x - 7$; $y = 5x + 8$

10. $y = 4x + 3$; $y = 13 - \frac{1}{4}x$

11. $y = 2x + 3$ $y = 2x - 7$

12. $y = 4x + 7$ $y = \frac{1}{4}x - 2$

13. $f(q) = 12q + 7$; $g(q) = \frac{1}{12}q + 96$

14. $2y = 16 - x$; $4y = -8 - 2x$

Problems

15. Line l is given by $y = 3 - \frac{2}{3}x$ and point P has coordinates $(6, 5)$.

    (a) Find the equation of the line containing P and parallel to l.
    (b) Find the equation of the line containing P and perpendicular to l.
    (c) Graph the equations in parts (a) and (b).

16. Using the window $-10 \le x \le 10$, $-10 \le y \le 10$, graph $y = x$, $y = 10x$, $y = 100x$, and $y = 1000x$.

    (a) Explain what happens to the graphs of the lines as the slopes become large.
    (b) Write an equation of a line that passes through the origin and is horizontal.

17. Graph $y = x + 1$, $y = x + 10$, and $y = x + 100$ in the window $-10 \le x \le 10$, $-10 \le y \le 10$.

    (a) Explain what happens to the graph of a line, $y = b + mx$, as b becomes large.
    (b) Write a linear equation whose graph cannot be seen in the window $-10 \le x \le 10$, $-10 \le y \le 10$ because all its y-values are less than the y-values shown.

18. The graphical interpretation of the slope is that it shows steepness. Using a calculator or a computer, graph the function $y = 2x - 3$ in the following windows:

    (a) $-10 \le x \le 10$ by $-10 \le y \le 10$
    (b) $-10 \le x \le 10$ by $-100 \le y \le 100$
    (c) $-10 \le x \le 10$ by $-1000 \le y \le 1000$
    (d) Write a sentence about how steepness is related to the window being used.

19. Find the coordinates of point P in Figure 1.43.

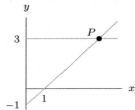

Figure 1.43

20. Estimate the slope of the line in Figure 1.44 and find an approximate equation for the line.

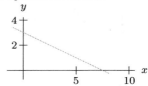

Figure 1.44

21. Line l in Figure 1.45 is parallel to the line $y = 2x + 1$. Find the coordinates of the point P.

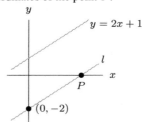

Figure 1.45

22. Find the equation of the line l_2 in Figure 1.46.

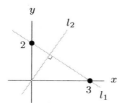

Figure 1.46

23. Fill in the missing coordinates for the points in the following figures.

  (a) The triangle in Figure 1.47.
  (b) The parallelogram in Figure 1.48.

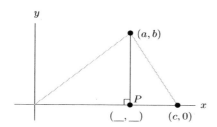

Figure 1.47

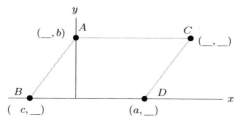

Figure 1.48

24. The cost of a Frigbox refrigerator is $950, and it depreciates $50 each year. The cost of an Arctic Air refrigerator is $1200, and it depreciates $100 per year.

  (a) If a Frigbox and an Arctic Air are bought at the same time, when do the two refrigerators have equal value?
  (b) If both refrigerators continue to depreciate at the same rates, what happens to the values of the refrigerators in 20 years time? What does this mean?

25. You need to rent a car and compare the charges of three different companies. Company A charges 20 cents per mile plus $20 per day. Company B charges 10 cents per mile plus $35 per day. Company C charges $70 per day with no mileage charge.

  (a) Find formulas for the cost of driving cars rented from companies A, B, and C, in terms of x, the distance driven in miles in one day.
  (b) Graph the costs for each company for $0 \le x \le 500$. Put all three graphs on the same set of axes.
  (c) What do the slope and the vertical intercept tell you in this situation?
  (d) Use the graph in part (b) to find under what circumstances company A is the cheapest? What about Company B? Company C? Explain why your results make sense.

26. You want to choose one long-distance telephone company from the following options.

  • Company A charges $0.37 per minute.

  • Company B charges $13.95 per month plus $0.22 per minute.

  • Company C charges a fixed rate of $50 per month.

  Let Y_A, Y_B, Y_C represent the monthly charges using Company A, B, and C, respectively. Let x be the number of minutes per month spent on long distance calls.

  (a) Find formulas for Y_A, Y_B, Y_C as functions of x.
  (b) Figure 1.49 gives the graphs of the functions in part (a). Which function corresponds to which graph?
  (c) Find the x-values for which Company B is cheapest.

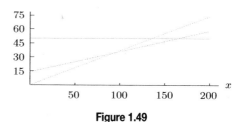

Figure 1.49

27. The solid waste generated each year in the cities of the US is increasing.[13] The solid waste generated, in millions of tons, was 82.3 in 1960 and 139.1 in 1980. The trend appears linear during this time.

  (a) Construct a formula for the amount of municipal solid waste generated in the US by finding the equation of the line through these two points.
  (b) Use this formula to predict the amount of municipal solid waste generated in the US, in millions of tons, in the year 2020.

[13]*Statistical Abstracts of the US*, 1988, p. 193, Table 333.

28. Fill in the missing coordinates in Figure 1.50. Write an equation for the line connecting the two points. Check your answer by solving the system of two equations.

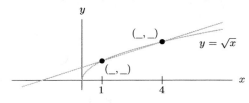

Figure 1.50

29. Two lines are given by $y = b_1 + m_1 x$ and $y = b_2 + m_2 x$, where $b_1, b_2, m_1,$ and m_2 are constants.

(a) What conditions are imposed on $b_1, b_2, m_1,$ and m_2 if the two lines have no points in common?
(b) What conditions are imposed on $b_1, b_2, m_1,$ and m_2 if the two lines have all points in common?
(c) What conditions are imposed on $b_1, b_2, m_1,$ and m_2 if the two lines have exactly one point in common?
(d) What conditions are imposed on $b_1, b_2, m_1,$ and m_2 if the two lines have exactly two points in common?

CHAPTER SUMMARY

- **Functions**
  Definition: a rule which takes certain numbers as inputs and assigns to each input exactly one output number.
  Function notation, $y = f(x)$.
  Use of vertical line test.

- **Average rate of change**
  Average rate of change of $Q = f(t)$ on $[a, b]$ is

$$\frac{\Delta Q}{\Delta t} = \frac{f(b) - f(a)}{b - a}.$$

  Increasing, decreasing functions; identifying from average rate of change.

- **Linear Functions**
  Value of y changes at constant rate.

- **Formulas for Linear Functions**
  Slope-intercept form: $y = b + mx$.
  Point-slope form: $y - y_0 = m(x - x_0)$.
  Standard form: $Ax + By + C = 0$.

- **Properties of Linear Functions**
  Interpretation of slope, vertical and horizontal intercepts.
  Intersection of lines: Solution of equations.
  Parallel lines: $m_1 = m_2$.
  Perpendicular lines: $m_1 = -\dfrac{1}{m_2}$.

REVIEW EXERCISES AND PROBLEMS FOR CHAPTER ONE

Exercises

In Exercises 1-5 a relationship is given between two quantities. Are both quantities functions of the other one, or is one or neither a function of the other? Explain.

1.

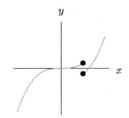

Figure 1.51

2. $y = x^4 - 1$ **3.** $7w^2 + 5 = z^2$ **4.** $m = \sqrt{t}$

5. The number of gallons of gas, g, at \$2 per gallon and the number of pounds of coffee, c, at \$10 per pound that can be bought for a total of \$100.

6. In 2005, you have 40 CDs in your collection. In 2008, you have 120 CDs. In 2012, you have 40. What is the average rate of change in the size of your CD collection between

(a) 2005 and 2008?   (b) 2008 and 2012?
(c) 2005 and 2012?

7. Find the average rate of change of $f(x) = 3x^2 + 1$ between the points

(a) $(1, 4)$ and $(2, 13)$ (b) (j, k) and (m, n)
(c) $(x, f(x))$ and $(x + h, f(x + h))$

In Exercises 8–9, could the table represent a linear function?

8.

t	3	6	9	12	15
$a(t)$	2	4	6	8	10

9.

λ	1	2	3	4	5
$q(\lambda)$	2	4	8	16	32

Problems 10–12 give data from a linear function. Find a formula for the function.

10.

t	1.2	1.3	1.4	1.5
$f(t)$	0.736	0.614	0.492	0.37

11.

x	200	230	300	320	400
$g(x)$	70	68.5	65	64	60

12.

t	1.2	1.3	1.4	1.5
$f(t)$	0.736	0.614	0.492	0.37

In Exercises 13–14, which line has the greater

(a) Slope?   **(b)** y-intercept?

13. $y = 5 - 2x, \quad y = 7 - 3x$

14. $y = 7 + 2x, \quad y = 8 - 15x$

Are the lines in Exercises 15–18 perpendicular? Parallel? Neither?

15. $y = 3x + 3 \quad y = -\frac{1}{3}x + 3$

16. $y = 5x + 2 \quad y = 2x + 5$

17. $y = 14x - 2 \quad y = -\frac{1}{14}x + 2$

18. $7y = 8 + 21x; \, 9y = 77 - 3x$

19. Find the equation of the line parallel to $3x + 5y = 6$ and passing through the point $(0, 6)$.

20. Find the equation of the line passing through the point $(2, 1)$ and perpendicular to the line $y = 5x - 3$.

21. Find the equations of the lines parallel to and perpendicular to the line $y + 4x = 7$, and through the point $(1, 5)$.

Problems

22. You have zero dollars now and the average rate of change in your net worth is $5000 per year. How much money will you have in forty years?

23. A flight costs $10,000 to operate, regardless of the number of passengers. Each ticket costs $127. Express profit, π, as a linear function of the number of passengers, n, on the flight.

24. Table 1.32 gives the ranking r for three different names—Hannah, Alexis, and Madison—for girls born between 1990 (year $t = 0$) and 2001 (year $t = 11$).[14] The rankings are denoted by r_h, r_a, and r_m respectively. Of the three names, which was most popular and which was least popular in

(a) 1990?   **(b)** 2001?

Table 1.32 *Ranking of names—Hannah (r_h), Alexis (r_a), and Madison (r_m)—for girls born t years after 1990*

t	0	1	2	3	4	5	6	7	8	9	10	11
r_h	31	29	26	20	16	7	7	5	2	2	2	3
r_a	67	47	41	29	18	14	8	8	6	3	6	5
r_m	216	133	112	78	53	29	15	10	9	7	3	2

25. Table 1.32 gives information about the popularity of the names Hannah, Madison, and Alexis. Describe in words

what your answers to parts (a)–(c) tell you about these names.

(a) Evaluate $r_m(0) - r_h(0)$.
(b) Evaluate $r_m(11) - r_h(11)$.
(c) Solve $r_m(t) < r_a(t)$.

26. Figure 1.52 gives the depth of the water at Montauk Point, New York, for a day in November.

(a) How many high tides took place on this day?
(b) How many low tides took place on this day?
(c) How much time elapsed in between high tides?

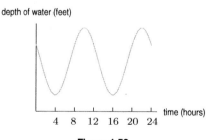

depth of water (feet)

time (hours)

4   8   12   16   20   24

Figure 1.52

27. (a) Is the area, A, of a square a function of the length of one of its sides, s?

[14]Data from the SSA website at http://www.ssa.gov.

(b) Is the area, A, of a rectangle a function of the length of one of its sides, s?

28. A person's blood sugar level at a particular time of the day is partially determined by the time of the most recent meal. After a meal, blood sugar level increases rapidly, then slowly comes back down to a normal level. Sketch a person's blood sugar level as a function of time over the course of a day. Label the axes to indicate normal blood sugar level and the time of each meal.

29. Many people think that hair growth is stimulated by haircuts. In fact, there is no difference in the rate hair grows after a haircut, but there *is* a difference in the rate at which hair's ends break off. A haircut eliminates dead and split ends, thereby slowing the rate at which hair breaks. However, even with regular haircuts, hair will not grow to an indefinite length. The average life cycle of human scalp hair is 3–5 years, after which the hair is shed.[15]

Judy trims her hair once a year, when its growth is slowed by split ends. She cuts off just enough to eliminate dead and split ends, and then lets it grow another year. After 5 years, she realizes her hair won't grow any longer. Graph the length of her hair as a function of time. Indicate when she receives her haircuts.

30. At the end of a semester, students' math grades are listed in a table which gives each student's ID number in the left column and the student's grade in the right column. Let N represent the ID number and the G represent the grade. Which quantity, N or G, must necessarily be a function of the other?

31. A price increases 5% due to inflation and is then reduced 10% for a sale. Express the final price as a function of the original price, P.

32. An 8-foot tall cylindrical water tank has a base of diameter 6 feet.

(a) How much water can the tank hold?
(b) How much water is in the tank if the water is 5 feet deep?
(c) Write a formula for the volume of water as a function of its depth in the tank.

33. Figure 1.53 shows the fuel consumption (in miles per gallon, mpg) of a car traveling at various speeds.

(a) How much gas is used on a 300 mile trip at 40 mph?
(b) How much gas is saved by traveling 60 mph instead of 70 mph on a 200 mile trip?
(c) According to this graph, what is the most fuel-efficient speed to travel? Explain.

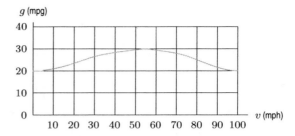

Figure 1.53

34. Academics have suggested that loss of worker productivity can result from sleep deprivation. An article in the Sunday, September 26, 1993, *New York Times* quotes David Poltrack, the senior vice president for planning and research at CBS, as saying that seven million Americans are staying up an hour later than usual to watch talk show host David Letterman. The article goes on to quote Timothy Monk, a professor at the University of Pittsburgh School of Medicine, as saying "... my hunch is that the effect [on productivity due to sleep deprivation among this group] would be in the area of a 10 percent decrement." The article next quotes Robert Solow, a Nobel prize-winning professor of economics at MIT, who suggests the following procedure to estimate the impact that this loss in productivity will have on the US economy—an impact he dubbed "the Letterman loss." First, Solow says, we find the percentage of the work force who watch the program. Next, we determine this group's contribution to the gross domestic product (GDP). Then we reduce the group's contribution by 10% to account for the loss in productivity due to sleep deprivation. The amount of this reduction is "the Letterman loss."

(a) The article estimated that the GDP is $6.325 trillion, and that 7 million Americans watch the show. Assume that the nation's work force is 118 million people and that 75% of David Letterman's audience belongs to this group. What percentage of the work force is in Dave's audience?
(b) What percent of the GDP would be expected to come from David Letterman's audience? How much money would they have contributed if they hadn't watched the show?
(c) How big is "the Letterman Loss"?

35. Sketch a family of functions $y = -2 - ax$ for five different values of x with $a < 0$.

---

[15]*Britannica Micropedia* vol. 5. (Chicago: Encyclopaedia Britannica, Inc., 1989).

36. Assume A, B, C are constants with $A \neq 0$, $B \neq 0$. Consider the equation

$$Ax + By = C.$$

(a) Show that $y = f(x)$ is linear. State the slope and the x- and y-intercepts of $f(x)$.

(b) Graph $y = f(x)$, labeling the x- and y-intercepts in terms of A, B, and C, assuming

    (i) $A > 0$, $B > 0$, $C > 0$
    (ii) $A > 0$, $B > 0$, $C < 0$
    (iii) $A > 0$, $B < 0$, $C > 0$

37. There are x male job-applicants at a certain company and y female applicants. Suppose that 15% of the men are accepted and 18% of the women are accepted. Write an expression in terms of x and y representing each of the following quantities:

(a) The total number of applicants to the company.

(b) The total number of applicants accepted.

(c) The percentage of all applicants accepted.

38. You start 60 miles east of Pittsburgh and drive east at a constant speed of 50 miles per hour. (Assume that the road is straight and permits you to do this.) Find a formula for d, your distance from Pittsburgh as a function of t, the number of hours of travel.

39. A small café sells coffee for $0.95 per cup. On average, it costs the café $0.25 to make a cup of coffee (for grounds, hot water, filters). The café also has a fixed daily cost of $200 (for rent, wages, utilities).

(a) Let R, C, and P be the café's daily revenue, costs, and profit, respectively, for selling x cups of coffee in a day. Find formulas for R, C, and P as a function of x. [Hint: The revenue, R, is the total amount of money that the café brings in. The cost, C, includes the fixed daily cost as well as the cost for all x cups of coffee sold. P is the café's profit after costs have been accounted for.]

(b) Plot P against x. For what x-values is the graph of P below the x-axis? Above the x-axis? Interpret your results.

(c) Interpret the slope and both intercepts of your graph in practical terms.

40. Owners of an inactive quarry in Australia have decided to resume production. They estimate that it will cost them $1000 per month to maintain and insure their equipment and that monthly salaries will be $3000. It costs $80 to mine a ton of rocks. Write a formula that expresses the total cost each month, c, as a function of r, the number of tons of rock mined per month.

Table 1.33 gives the cost, $C(n)$, of producing a certain good as a linear function of n, the number of units produced. Use the table to answer Problems 41–43.

Table 1.33

n (units)	100	125	150	175
$C(n)$ (dollars)	11000	11125	11250	11375

41. Evaluate the following expressions. Give economic interpretations for each.

(a) $C(175)$ (b) $C(175) - C(150)$

(c) $\dfrac{C(175) - C(150)}{175 - 150}$

42. Estimate $C(0)$. What is the economic significance of this value?

43. The *fixed cost* of production is the cost incurred before any goods are produced. The *unit cost* is the cost of producing an additional unit. Find a formula for $C(n)$ in terms of n, given that

Total cost = Fixed cost + Unit cost · Number of units

44. A rock is thrown into the air. The rock's velocity in feet per second after t seconds is given by $v = 80 - 32t$

(a) Construct a table of values of v for $t = 0$, 0.5, 1, 1.5, 2, 2.5, 3, 3.5, 4.

(b) Describe the motion of the rock. How can you interpret negative values of v?

(c) At what time t is the rock highest above the ground?

(d) Interpret the slope and both intercepts of the graph of v against t.

(e) How would the slope of the graph of v be different on the moon, whose gravitational pull is less than the earth's? How would the slope be different on Jupiter, which has a greater gravitational pull than the earth?

45. A dose-response function can be used to describe the increase in risk associated with the increase in exposure to various hazards. For example, the risk of contracting lung cancer depends, among other things, on the number of cigarettes a person smokes per day. This risk can be described by a linear dose-response function. For example, it is known that smoking 10 cigarettes per day increases a person's probability of contracting lung cancer by a factor of 25, while smoking 20 cigarettes a day increases the probability by a factor of 50.

(a) Find a formula for $i(x)$, the increase in the probability of contracting lung cancer for a person who smokes x cigarettes per day as compared to a non-smoker.

(b) Evaluate $i(0)$.

(c) Interpret the slope of the function i.

46. In economics, the *demand* for a product is the amount of that product that consumers are willing to buy at a given price. The quantity demanded of a product usually decreases if the price of that product increases. Suppose that a company believes there is a linear relationship between the demand for its product and its price. The company knows that when the price of its product was $3 per unit, the quantity demanded weekly was 500 units, and that when the unit price was raised to $4, the quantity demanded weekly dropped to 300 units. Let D represent the quantity demanded weekly at a unit price of p dollars.

(a) Calculate D when $p = 5$. Interpret your result.
(b) Find a formula for D in terms of p.
(c) The company raises the price of the good and that the new quantity demanded weekly is 50 units. What is the new price?
(d) Give an economic interpretation of the slope of the function you found in part (b).
(e) Find D when $p = 0$. Find p when $D = 0$. Give economic interpretations of both these results.

47. In economics, the *supply* of a product is the quantity of that product suppliers are willing to provide at a given price. In theory, the quantity supplied of a product increases if the price of that product increases. Suppose that there is a linear relationship between the quantity supplied, S, of the product described in Problem 46 and its price, p. The quantity supplied weekly is 100 when the price is $2 and the quantity supplied rises by 50 units when the price rises by $0.50.

(a) Find a formula for S in terms of p.
(b) Interpret the slope of your formula in economic terms.
(c) Is there a price below which suppliers will not provide this product?
(d) The *market clearing price* is the price at which supply equals demand. According to theory, the free-market price of a product is its market clearing price. Using the demand function from Problem 46, find the market clearing price for this product.

48. When economists graph demand or supply equations, they place quantity on the horizontal axis and price on the vertical axis.

(a) On the same set of axes, graph the demand and supply equations you found in Problems 46 and 47, with price on the vertical axis.
(b) Indicate how you could estimate the market clearing price from your graph.

49. A student exercised for 30 minutes and then measured her ten-second pulse count at one minute intervals as she rested. The data are shown in Table 1.34, where time is in minutes after exercise.

(a) Make a scatter plot of this data.
(b) Because the pulse values are the same after 4 and 5 minutes, these data are clearly not linear. Are there values of t for which a regression line is a good model for these data? If so, what values?

(c) Discuss the correlation between minutes after exercising and pulse rate.

Table 1.34

Time (min)	0	1	2	3	4	5
Pulse	22	18	15	12	10	10

50. Repeat Problem 49 after collecting your own data in a table like Table 1.34.

51. Record the height and shoe size of at least five females or five males in your class and make a data table.

(a) Make a scatter plot of these data, with height on the y-axis and shoe size on the x-axis.
(b) By eye, draw a line that fits this data and find its equation.
(c) Use a graphing calculator or computer to find the equation of the least-squares line.
(d) Discuss interpolation and extrapolation using specific examples in relation to this regression line. Check the interpolation with a student in the class whose shoe size is close to the one you have chosen.
(e) Find and interpret r, the correlation coefficient.

52. You spend c dollars on x apples and y bananas. In Figure 1.54, line l gives y as a function of x.

(a) If apples cost p dollars each and bananas cost q each, label the x- and y-intercepts of l. [Note: Your labels will involve the constants p, q or c.]
(b) What is the slope of l?

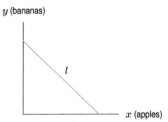

Figure 1.54: Axes not necessarily to scale

53. The apples in Problem 52 cost more than bananas, so $p > q$. Which of the two lines, l_1 or l_2, in Figure 1.55 could represent $y = f(x)$?

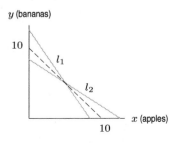

Figure 1.55

54. Figure 1.56 shows line l from Problem 52 and three other lines, l_1, l_2, l_3. If possible, match the following stories to lines l_1, l_2, l_3.

    (a) Your total budget, c, has increased, but the prices of apples and bananas have not changed.

    (b) Your total budget and the cost of bananas do not change, but the cost of apples increases.

    (c) Your budget increases, as does the price of apples, but the price of bananas stays fixed.

    (d) Your budget increases, but the price of apples goes down, and the price of bananas stays fixed.

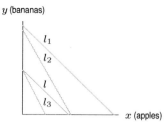

Figure 1.56: Axes not necessarily to scale

CHECK YOUR UNDERSTANDING

Are the statements in Problems 1–54 true or false? Give an explanation for your answer.

1. $Q = f(t)$ means Q is equal to f times t.

2. A function must be defined by a formula.

3. If $P = f(x)$ then P is called the dependent variable.

4. Independent variables are always denoted by the letter x or t.

5. It is possible for two quantities to be related and yet neither be a function of the other.

6. A function is a rule that takes certain values as inputs and assigns to each input value exactly one output value.

7. It is possible for a table of values to represent a function.

8. If Q is a function of P, then P is a function of Q.

9. The graph of a circle is not the graph of a function.

10. If $n = f(A)$ is the number of angels that can dance on the head of a pin whose area is A square millimeters, then $f(10) = 100$ tells us that 10 angels can dance on the head of a pin whose area is 100 square millimeters.

11. Average speed can be computed by dividing the distance traveled by the time elapsed.

12. The average rate of change of a function Q with respect to t over an interval can be symbolically represented as $\dfrac{\Delta t}{\Delta Q}$.

13. If $y = f(x)$ and as x increases, y increases, then f is an increasing function.

14. If f is a decreasing function, then the average rate of change of f on any interval is negative.

15. The average rate of change of a function over an interval is the slope of a line connecting two points of the graph of the function.

16. The average rate of change of $y = 3x - 4$ between $x = 2$ and $x = 6$ is 7.

17. The average rate of change of $f(x) = 10 - x^2$ between $x = 1$ and $x = 2$ is the ratio $\dfrac{10 - 2^2 - 10 - 1^2}{2 - 1}$.

18. If $y = x^2$ then the slope of the line connecting the point $(2, 4)$ to the point $(3, 9)$ is the same as the slope of the line connecting the point $(-2, 4)$ to the point $(-3, 9)$.

19. A linear function can have different rates of change over different intervals.

20. The graph of a linear function is a straight line.

21. If a line has the equation $3x + 2y = 7$, then the slope of the line is 3.

22. A table of values represents a linear function if $\dfrac{\text{Change in output}}{\text{Change in input}} = \text{constant}$.

23. If a linear function is decreasing, then its slope is negative.

24. If $y = f(x)$ is linear and its slope is negative, then in the expression $\dfrac{\Delta y}{\Delta x}$ either Δx or Δy is negative, but not both.

25. A linear function can have a slope that is zero.

26. If a line has slope 2 and y-intercept -3, then its equation may be written $y = -3x + 2$.

27. The line $3x + 5y = 7$ has slope $3/5$.

28. A line that goes through the point $(-2, 3)$ and whose slope is 4 has the equation $y = 4x + 5$.

29. The line $4x + 3y = 52$ intersects the x-axis at $x = 13$.

30. If $f(x) = -2x + 7$ then $f(2) = 3$.

31. The line that passes through the points $(1, 2)$ and $(4, -10)$ has slope 4.

32. The linear equation $y - 5 = 4(x + 1)$ is equivalent to the equation $y = 4x + 6$.

33. The line $y - 4 = -2(x + 3)$ goes through the point $(4, -3)$.

34. The line whose equation is $y = 3 - 7x$ has slope -7.

35. The line $y = -5x + 8$ intersects the y-axis at $y = 8$.

36. The equation $y = -2 - \frac{2}{3}x$ represents a linear function.

37. The lines $y = 8 - 3x$ and $-2x + 16y = 8$ both cross the y-axis at $y = 8$.

38. The graph of $f(x) = 6$ is a line whose slope is six.

39. The lines $y = -\frac{4}{5}x + 7$ and $4x - 5y = 8$ are parallel.

40. The lines $y = 7 + 9x$ and $y - 4 = -\frac{1}{9}(x + 5)$ are perpendicular.

41. The lines $y = -2x + 5$ and $y = 6x - 3$ intersect at the point $(1, 3)$.

42. If two lines never intersect then their slopes are equal.

43. The equation of a line parallel to the y-axis could be $y = -\frac{3}{4}$.

44. A line parallel to the x-axis has slope zero.

45. The slope of a vertical line is undefined.

46. Fitting the best line to a set of data is called linear regression.

47. The process of estimating a value within the range for which we have data is called interpolation.

48. Extrapolation tends to be more reliable than interpolation.

49. If two quantities have a high correlation then one quantity causes the other.

50. If the correlation coefficient is zero, there is not a relationship between the two quantities.

51. A correlation coefficient can have a value of $-\frac{3}{7}$.

52. A value of a correlation coefficient is always between negative and positive one.

53. A correlation coefficient of one indicates that all the data points lie on a straight line.

54. A regression line is also referred to as a least squares line.

Chapter Two

FUNCTIONS, FUNCTION LIBRARY, AND TRANSFORMATIONS

In this chapter, we investigate properties and notation common to all functions. The concepts of domain, range, increasing and decreasing functions, and concavity are defined and explored. A library of basic functions is introduced and used in the development of piecewise-defined functions. We then introduce some tools that allow us to transform functions by shifting and reflecting their graphs, always considering the relationship between changes made to the formula of a function and changes made to its graph.

2.1 INPUT AND OUTPUT

Finding Output Values: Evaluating a Function

Evaluating a function means calculating the value of a function's output from a particular value of the input.

In the housepainting example in Section1.1, the notation $n = f(A)$ indicates that n is a function of A. The expression $f(A)$ represents the output of the function—specifically, the amount of paint required to cover an area of A ft^2. For example $f(20,000)$ represents the number of gallons of paint required to cover a house of 20,000 ft^2.

Example 1   Using the fact that 1 gallon of paint covers 250 ft^2, evaluate the expression $f(20,000)$.

Solution   To evaluate $f(20,000)$, calculate the number of gallons required to cover 20,000 ft^2:

$$f(20,000) = \frac{20,000 \text{ ft}^2}{250 \text{ ft}^2/\text{gallon}} = 80 \text{ gallons of paint.}$$

Evaluating a Function Using a Formula

If we have a formula for a function, we evaluate it by substituting the input value into the formula.

Example 2   The formula for the area of a circle of radius r is $A = q(r) = \pi r^2$. Use the formula to evaluate $q(10)$ and $q(20)$. What do your results tell you about circles?

Solution   In the expression $q(10)$, the value of r is 10, so

$$q(10) = \pi \cdot 10^2 = 100\pi \approx 314.$$

Similarly, substituting $r = 20$, we have

$$q(20) = \pi \cdot 20^2 = 400\pi \approx 1257.$$

The statements $q(10) \approx 314$ and $q(20) \approx 1257$ tell us that a circle of radius 10 cm has an area of approximately 314 cm^2 and a circle of radius 20 cm has an area of approximately 1257 cm^2.

Example 3   Let $g(x) = \dfrac{x^2 + 1}{5 + x}$. Evaluate the following expressions.

(a) $g(3)$ (b) $g(-1)$ (c) $g(a)$

Solution   (a) To evaluate $g(3)$, replace every x in the formula with 3:

$$g(3) = \frac{3^2 + 1}{5 + 3} = \frac{10}{8} = 1.25.$$

(b) To evaluate $g(-1)$, replace every x in the formula with (-1):

$$g(-1) = \frac{(-1)^2 + 1}{5 + (-1)} = \frac{2}{4} = 0.5.$$

(c) To evaluate $g(a)$, replace every x in the formula with a:

$$g(a) = \frac{a^2 + 1}{5 + a}.$$

Evaluating a function may involve algebraic simplification, as the following example shows.

Example 4   Let $h(x) = x^2 - 3x + 5$. Evaluate and simplify the following expressions.

(a) $h(2)$ (b) $h(a - 2)$ (c) $h(a) - 2$ (d) $h(a) - h(2)$

Solution   Notice that x is the input and $h(x)$ is the output. It is helpful to rewrite the formula as

$$\text{Output} = h(\text{Input}) = (\text{Input})^2 - 3 \cdot (\text{Input}) + 5.$$

(a) For $h(2)$, we have Input $= 2$, so

$$h(2) = (2)^2 - 3 \cdot (2) + 5 = 3.$$

(b) In this case, Input $= a - 2$. We substitute and multiply out

$$\begin{aligned}
h(a - 2) &= (a - 2)^2 - 3(a - 2) + 5 \\
&= a^2 - 4a + 4 - 3a + 6 + 5 \\
&= a^2 - 7a + 15.
\end{aligned}$$

(c) First input a, then subtract 2:

$$\begin{aligned}
h(a) - 2 &= a^2 - 3a + 5 - 2 \\
&= a^2 - 3a + 3.
\end{aligned}$$

(d) Since we found $h(2) = 3$ in part (a), we subtract from $h(a)$:

$$\begin{aligned}
h(a) - h(2) &= a^2 - 3a + 5 - 3 \\
&= a^2 - 3a + 2.
\end{aligned}$$

Finding Input Values: Solving Equations

Given an input, we evaluate the function to find the output. Sometimes the situation is reversed; we know the output and we want to find the corresponding input. If the function is given by a formula, the input values are solutions to an equation.

Example 5   Use the cricket function $T = \frac{1}{4}R + 40$, introduced in Chapter 1 to find the rate, R, at which the snowy tree cricket chirps when the temperature, T, is $76°F$.

Solution   We want to find R when $T = 76$. Substitute $T = 76$ into the formula and solve the equation

$$76 = \frac{1}{4}R + 40$$
$$36 = \frac{1}{4}R \qquad \text{subtract 40 from both sides}$$
$$144 = R. \qquad \text{multiply both sides by 4}$$

The cricket chirps at a rate of 144 chirps per minute when the temperature is $76°F$.

Example 6   Suppose $f(x) = \dfrac{1}{\sqrt{x-4}}$.

(a) Find an x-value that results in $f(x) = 2$.

(b) Is there an x-value that results in $f(x) = -2$?

Solution   (a) To find an x-value that results in $f(x) = 2$, solve the equation

$$2 = \frac{1}{\sqrt{x-4}}.$$

Square both sides

$$4 = \frac{1}{x-4}.$$

Now multiply by $(x-4)$

$$4(x-4) = 1$$
$$4x - 16 = 1$$
$$x = \frac{17}{4} = 4.25.$$

The x-value is 4.25. (Note that the simplification $(x-4)/(x-4) = 1$ in the second step was valid because $x - 4 \neq 0$.)

(b) Since $\sqrt{x-4}$ is nonnegative if it is defined, its reciprocal, $f(x) = \dfrac{1}{\sqrt{x-4}}$ is also nonnegative if it is defined. Thus, $f(x)$ is not negative for any x input, so there is no x-value that results in $f(x) = -2$.

In the next example, we solve an equation for a quantity that is being used to model a physical quantity; we must choose the solutions that make sense in the context of the model.

Example 7   Let $A = q(r)$ be the area of a circle of radius r, where r is in cm. What is the radius of a circle whose area is 100 cm^2?

Solution   The output $q(r)$ is an area. Solving the equation $q(r) = 100$ for r gives the radius of a circle whose area is 100 cm^2. Since the formula for the area of a circle is $q(r) = \pi r^2$, we solve

$$q(r) = \pi r^2 = 100$$
$$r^2 = \frac{100}{\pi}$$
$$r = \pm\sqrt{\frac{100}{\pi}} = \pm 5.642.$$

We have two solutions for r, one positive and one negative. Since a circle cannot have a negative radius, we take $r = 5.642$ cm. A circle of area 100 cm^2 has a radius of 5.642 cm.

Finding Output and Input Values From Tables and Graphs

The following two examples use function notation with a table and a graph respectively.

Example 8   Table 2.1 shows the revenue, $R = f(t)$, received or expected, by the National Football League,[1] NFL, from network TV as a function of the year, t, since 1975.

(a) Evaluate and interpret $f(25)$.   (b) Solve and interpret $f(t) = 1159$.

Table 2.1

Year, t (since 1975)	0	5	10	15	20	25	30
Revenue, R (million $)	201	364	651	1075	1159	2200	2200

Solution   (a) The table shows $f(25) = 2200$. Since $t = 25$ in the year 2000, we know that NFL's projected revenue from TV was $2200 million in the year 2000.

(b) Solving $f(t) = 1159$ means finding the year in which TV revenues were $1159 million; it is $t = 20$. In 1995, NFL's TV revenues were $1159 million.

Example 9   A man drives from his home to a store and back. The entire trip takes 30 minutes. Figure 2.1 gives his velocity $v(t)$ (in mph) as a function of the time t (in minutes) since he left home. A negative velocity indicates that he is traveling away from the store back to his home.

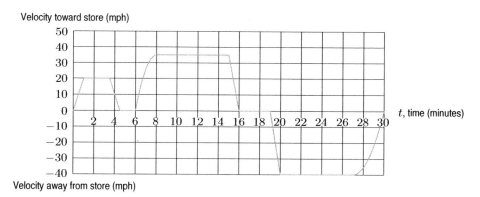

Figure 2.1: Velocity of a man on a trip to the store and back

Evaluate and interpret:

(a) $v(5)$ (b) $v(24)$ (c) $v(8) - v(6)$ (d) $v(-3)$

Solve for t and interpret:

(e) $v(t) = 15$ (f) $v(t) = -20$ (g) $v(t) = v(7)$

Solution   (a) To evaluate $v(5)$, look on the graph where $t = 5$ minutes. Five minutes after he left home, his velocity is 0 mph. Thus, $v(5) = 0$. Perhaps he had to stop at a light.

(b) The graph shows that $v(24) = -40$ mph. After 24 minutes, he is traveling at 40 mph away from the store.

[1]*Newsweek*, January 26, 1998.

(c) From the graph, $v(8) = 35$ mph and $v(6) = 0$ mph. Thus, $v(8) - v(6) = 35 - 0 = 35$. This shows that the man's speed increased by 35 mph in the interval between $t = 6$ minutes and $t = 8$ minutes.

(d) The quantity $v(-3)$ is not defined since the graph only gives velocities for nonnegative times.

(e) To solve for t when $v(t) = 15$, look on the graph where the velocity is 15 mph. This occurs at $t \approx 0.75$ minute, 3.75 minutes, 6.5 minutes, and 15.5 minutes. At each of these four times the man's velocity was 15 mph.

(f) To solve $v(t) = -20$ for t, we see that the velocity is -20 mph at $t \approx 19.5$ and $t \approx 29$ minutes.

(g) First we evaluate $v(7) \approx 27$. To solve $v(t) = 27$, we look for the values of t making the velocity 27 mph. One such t is of course $t = 7$; the other t is $t \approx 15$ minutes.

Exercises and Problems for Section 2.1

Exercises

In Exercises 1–2, evaluate the function for $x = -7$.

1. $f(x) = x/2 - 1$

2. $f(x) = x^2 - 3$

In Exercises 3–6, solve $f(x) = 8$ for x.

3. $f(x) = 5x + 3$

4. $f(x) = x - 7$

5. $f(x) = x^2 - 8$

6. $f(x) = \sqrt{x} + 1$

7. If $f(x) = 2x + 1$,
(a) Find $f(0)$ (b) Solve $f(x) = 0$.

8. If $f(t) = t^2 - 4$,
(a) Find $f(0)$ (b) Solve $f(t) = 0$.

9. If $g(x) = x^2 - 5x + 6$,
(a) Find $g(0)$ (b) Solve $g(x) = 0$.

10. If $g(t) = \dfrac{1}{t+2} - 1$,
(a) Find $g(0)$ (b) Solve $g(t) = 0$.

11. Let $F = g(t)$ be the number of foxes in a park as a function of t, the number of months since January 1. Evaluate $g(9)$ using Table 1.3 in chapter 1. What does this tell us about the fox population?

12. Let $F = g(t)$ be the number of foxes in month t in the national park described in Example 5 in chapter 1. Solve the equation $g(t) = 75$. What does your solution tell you about the fox population?

Problems

13. Chicago's average monthly rainfall, $R = f(t)$ inches, is given as a function of month, t, in Table 2.2. (January is $t = 1$.) Solve and interpret:

(a) $f(t) = 3.7$ (b) $f(t) = f(2)$

Table 2.2

t	1	2	3	4	5	6	7	8
R	1.8	1.8	2.7	3.1	3.5	3.7	3.5	3.4

14. Let $g(x) = x^2 + x$. Find formulas for the following functions. Simplify your answers.

(a) $g(-3x)$ (b) $g(1-x)$ (c) $g(x+\pi)$
(d) $g(\sqrt{x})$ (e) $g(1/(x+1))$ (f) $g(x^2)$

15. Let $f(x) = \dfrac{x}{x-1}$.

(a) Find and simplify

(i) $f\left(\dfrac{1}{t}\right)$ (ii) $f\left(\dfrac{1}{t+1}\right)$

(b) Solve $f(x) = 3$.

16. (a) Find a point on the graph of $h(x) = \sqrt{x+4}$ whose x-coordinate is 5.
(b) Find a point on the graph whose y-coordinate is 5.
(c) Graph $h(x)$ and mark the points in parts (a) and (b).
(d) Let $p = 2$. Calculate $h(p+1) - h(p)$.

17. Use the graph of $f(x)$ in Figure 2.2 to estimate:
(a) $f(0)$ (b) $f(1)$ (c) $f(b)$ (d) $f(c)$ (e) $f(d)$

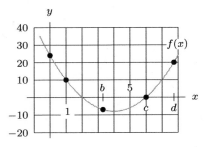

Figure 2.2

18. **(a)** Using Figure 2.3, fill in Table 2.3:

Table 2.3

x	-2	-1	0	1	2	3
$h(x)$						

(b) Evaluate $h(3) - h(1)$ **(c)** Evaluate $h(2) - h(0)$
(d) Evaluate $2h(0)$ **(e)** Evaluate $h(1) + 3$

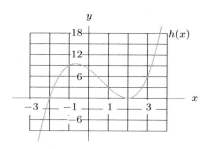

Figure 2.3

19. Let $f(x) = \sqrt{x^2 + 16} - 5$.

   (a) Find $f(0)$
   (b) For what values of x is $f(x)$ zero?
   (c) Find $f(3)$
   (d) What is the vertical intercept of the graph of $f(x)$?
   (e) Where does the graph cross the x-axis?

20. Use the letters a, b, c, d, e, h in Figure 2.4 to answer the following questions.

   (a) What are the coordinates of the points P and Q?
   (b) Evaluate $f(b)$.
   (c) Solve $f(x) = e$ for x.
   (d) Suppose $c = f(z)$ and $z = f(x)$. What is x?
   (e) Suppose $f(b) = -f(d)$. What additional information does this give you?

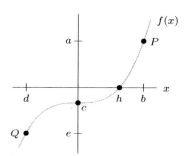

Figure 2.4

21. **(a)** Complete Table 2.4 using

   $$f(x) = 2x(x - 3) - x(x - 5) \quad \text{and} \quad g(x) = x^2 - x.$$

   What do you notice? Graph these two functions. Are the two functions the same? Explain.
   (b) Complete Table 2.5 using

   $$h(x) = x^5 - 5x^3 + 6x + 1 \quad \text{and} \quad j(x) = 2x + 1.$$

   What do you notice? Graph these two functions. Are the two functions the same? Explain.

Table 2.4

x	-2	-1	0	1	2
$f(x)$					
$g(x)$					

Table 2.5

x	-2	-1	0	1	2
$h(x)$					
$j(x)$					

22. A ball is thrown up from the ground with initial velocity 64 ft/sec. Its height at time t is

   $$h(t) = -16t^2 + 64t.$$

   (a) Evaluate $h(1)$ and $h(3)$. What does this tell us about the height of the ball?
   (b) Sketch this function. Using a graph, determine when the ball hits the ground and the maximum height of the ball.

23. Let $v(t) = t^2 - 2t$ be the velocity, in ft/sec, of an object at time t, in seconds.

   (a) What is the initial velocity, $v(0)$?
   (b) When does the object have a velocity of zero?
   (c) What is the meaning of the quantity $v(3)$? What are its units?

24. Let $s(t) = 11t^2 + t + 100$ be the position, in miles, of a car driving on a straight road at time t, in hours. The car's velocity at any time t is given by $v(t) = 22t + 1$.

   (a) Use function notation to express the car's position after 2 hours. Where is the car then?
   (b) Use function notation to express the question, "When is the car going 65 mph?"
   (c) Where is the car when it is going 67 mph?

25. New York state income tax is based on taxable income, which is part of a person's total income. The tax owed to the state is calculated using the taxable income (not

total income). For a single person with a taxable income between $65,000 and $100,000, the tax owed is $4056 plus 6.85% of the taxable income over $65,000.

(a) Compute the tax owed by a lawyer whose taxable income is $68,000.

(b) Consider a lawyer whose taxable income is 80% of her total income, x, where x is between $85,000 and $120,000. Write a formula for $T(x)$, the taxable income.

(c) Write a formula for $L(x)$, the amount of tax owed by the lawyer in part (b).

(d) Use $L(x)$ to evaluate the tax liability for $x = 85,000$ and compare your results to part (a).

26. (a) The Fibonacci sequence is a sequence of numbers that begins 1, 1, 2, 3, 5, ... Each term in the sequence is the sum of the two preceding terms. For example,

$$2 = 1 + 1, \quad 3 = 2 + 1, \quad 5 = 2 + 3, \ldots.$$

Based on this observation, complete the following table of values for $f(n)$, the nth term in the Fibonacci sequence.

n	1	2	3	4	5	6	7	8	9	10	11	12
$f(n)$	1	1	2	3	5							

(b) The table of values in part (a) can be completed even though we don't have a formula for $f(n)$. Does the fact that we don't have a formula mean that $f(n)$ is not a function?

(c) Are you able to evaluate the following expressions using parts (a) and (b)? If so, do so; if not, explain why not.

$$f(0), \quad f(-1), \quad f(-2), \quad f(0.5).$$

27. In bowling, ten pins are arranged in a triangular fashion as shown in Figure 2.5. If a fifth row were added, the total number of pins would be fifteen. Let $s(n)$ be the sum of the pins in rows 1 to n inclusive. For example, $s(3) = 1 + 2 + 3 = 6$.

(a) Complete Table 2.6.

(b) Using Table 2.6, check that the following formula holds for $1 \leq n \leq 5$:

$$s(n) = \frac{n(n + 1)}{2}.$$

(c) Assuming the formula for $s(n)$ holds for all n, calculate how many pins are used in 100 rows.

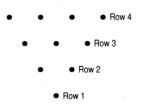

Figure 2.5

Table 2.6

n	1	2	3	4	5
$s(n)$					

2.2 DOMAIN AND RANGE

In Section 1.1, we defined R to be the average monthly rainfall at Chicago's O'Hare airport in month t. Although R is a function of t, the value of R is not defined for every possible value of t. For instance, it makes no sense to consider the value of R for $t = -3$, or $t = 8.21$, or $t = 13$ (since a year has 12 months). Thus, although R is a function of t, this function is defined only for certain values of t. Notice also that R, the output value of this function, takes only the values {1.8, 2.1, 2.4, 2.5, 2.7, 3.1, 3.2, 3.4, 3.5, 3.7}.

A function is often defined only for certain values of the independent variable. Also, the dependent variable often takes on only certain values. This leads to the following definitions:

If $Q = f(t)$, then

- the **domain** of f is the set of input values, t, which yield an output value.
- the **range** of f is the corresponding set of output values, Q.

Thus, the domain of a function is the set of input values, and the range is the set of output values.

If the domain of a function is not specified, we usually assume that it is as large as possible—that is, all numbers that make sense as inputs for the function. For example, if there are no restrictions, the domain of the function $f(x) = x^2$ is the set of all real numbers, because we can substitute any real number into the formula $f(x) = x^2$. Sometimes, however, we may restrict the domain to suit a particular application. If the function $f(x) = x^2$ is used to represent the area of a square of side x, we restrict the domain to positive numbers.

If a function is being used to model a real-world situation, the domain and range of the function are often determined by the constraints of the situation being modeled, as in the next example.

Example 1   The house painting function $n = f(A)$ in Section 1.1 has domain $A > 0$ because all houses have some positive area. There is a practical upper limit to A because houses cannot be infinitely large, but in principle, A can be as large or as small as we like, as long as it is positive. Therefore we take the domain of f to be $A > 0$.

The range of this function is $n \geq 0$, because we cannot use a negative amount of paint.

Choosing Realistic Domains and Ranges

When a function is used to model a real situation, it may be necessary to modify the domain and range.

Example 2   Algebraically speaking, the formula

$$T = \frac{1}{4}R + 40$$

can be used for all values of R. If we know nothing more about this function than its formula, its domain is all real numbers. The formula for $T = \frac{1}{4}R + 40$ can return any value of T when we choose an appropriate R-value (See Figure 2.6.) Thus, the range of the function is also all real numbers. However, if we use this formula to represent the temperature, T, as a function of a cricket's chirp rate, R, as we did in Example 1 in Section 1.1, some values of R cannot be used. For example, it doesn't make sense to talk about a negative chirp rate. Also, there is some maximum chirp rate R_{max} that no cricket can physically exceed. Thus, to use this formula to express T as a function of R, we must restrict R to the interval $0 \leq R \leq R_{max}$ shown in Figure 2.7.

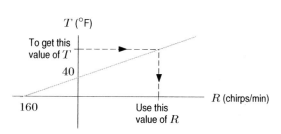

Figure 2.6: Graph showing that any T value can be obtained from some R value

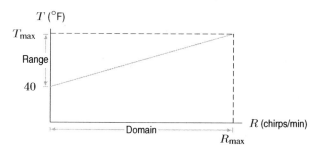

Figure 2.7: Graph showing that if $0 \leq R \leq R_{max}$, then $40 \leq T \leq T_{max}$

The range of the cricket function is also restricted. Since the chirp rate is nonnegative, the smallest value of T occurs when $R = 0$. This happens at $T = 40$. On the other hand, if the temperature gets too hot, the cricket won't be able to keep chirping faster. If the temperature T_{max} corresponds to the chirp rate R_{max}, then the values of T are restricted to the interval $40 \leq T \leq T_{max}$.

Using a Graph to Find the Domain and Range of a Function

A good way to estimate the domain and range of a function is to examine its graph. The domain is the set of input values on the horizontal axis which give rise to a point on the graph; the range is the corresponding set of output values on the vertical axis.

Example 3   A sunflower plant is measured every day t, for $t \geq 0$. The height, $h(t)$ centimeters, of the plant[2] can be modeled by using the *logistic function*

$$h(t) = \frac{260}{1 + 24(0.9)^t}.$$

(a) Using a graphing calculator or computer, graph the height over 80 days.
(b) What is the domain of this function? What is the range? What does this tell you about the height of the sunflower?

Solution   (a) The logistic function is graphed in Figure 2.8.

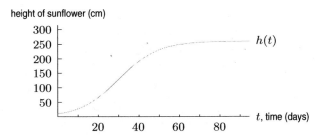

Figure 2.8: Height of sunflower as a function of time

(b) The domain of this function is $t \geq 0$. If we consider the fact that the sunflower dies at some point, then there is an upper bound on the domain, $0 \leq t \leq T$, where T is the day on which the sunflower dies.

To find the range, notice that the smallest value of h occurs at $t = 0$. Evaluating gives $h(0) = 10.4$ cm. This means that the plant was 10.4 cm high when it was first measured on day $t = 0$. Tracing along the graph, $h(t)$ increases. As t-values get large, $h(t)$-values approach, but never reach, 260. This suggests that the range is $10.4 \leq h(t) < 260$. This information tells us that sunflowers typically grow to a height of about 260 cm.

[2]Adapted from H.S. Reed and R.H. Holland, "Growth of an Annual Plant Helianthus" *Proc. Nat. Acad. Sci.*, 5, 1919.

Using a Formula to Find the Domain and Range of a Function

When a function is defined by a formula, its domain and range can often be determined by examining the formula algebraically.

Example 4 State the domain and range of g, where

$$g(x) = \frac{1}{x}.$$

Solution The domain is all real numbers except those which do not yield an output value. The expression $1/x$ is defined for any real number x except 0 (division by 0 is undefined). Therefore,

Domain: all real x, $\quad x \neq 0$.

The range is all real numbers that the formula can return as output values. It is not possible for $g(x)$ to equal zero, since 1 divided by a real number is never zero. All real numbers except 0 are possible output values, since all nonzero real numbers have reciprocals. Thus

Range: all real values, $\quad g(x) \neq 0$.

The graph in Figure 2.9 indicates agreement with these values for the domain and range.

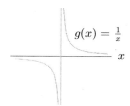

Figure 2.9: Domain and range of $g(x) = 1/x$

Example 5 Find the domain of the function $f(x) = \dfrac{1}{\sqrt{x-4}}$ by examining its formula.

Solution The domain is all real numbers except those for which the function is undefined. The square root of a negative number is undefined (if we restrict ourselves to real numbers), and so is division by zero. Therefore we need

$$x - 4 > 0.$$

Thus, the domain is all real numbers greater than 4.

Domain: $\quad x > 4$.

In Example 6 in Section 2.1, we saw that for $f(x) = 1/\sqrt{x-4}$, the output, $f(x)$, cannot be negative. Note that $f(x)$ cannot be zero either. (Why?) The range of $f(x) = 1/\sqrt{x-4}$ is $f(x) > 0$. See Problem 16.

Exercises and Problems for Section 2.2

Exercises

In Exercises 1–4, use a graph to find the range of the function on the given domain.

1. $f(x) = \dfrac{1}{x^2}, \quad -1 \le x \le 1$

2. $f(x) = \dfrac{1}{x}, \quad -2 \le x \le 2$

3. $f(x) = x^2 - 4, \quad -2 \le x \le 3$

4. $f(x) = \sqrt{9 - x^2}, \quad -3 \le x \le 1$

Graph and give the domain and range of the functions in Exercises 5–12.

5. $f(x) = \sqrt{x - 3}$

6. $f(x) = \sqrt{8 - x}$

7. $f(x) = \dfrac{1}{x^2}$

8. $f(x) = \dfrac{-1}{(x + 1)^2}$

9. $f(x) = x^2 - 4$

10. $f(x) = 9 - x^2$

11. $f(x) = x^3 + 2$

12. $f(x) = (x - 4)^3$

Find the domain and range of functions in Exercises 13–16 algebraically.

13. $m(x) = 9 - x$

14. $n(x) = 9 - x^4$

15. $q(x) = \sqrt{x^2 - 9}$

16. $f(x) = \dfrac{1}{\sqrt{x - 4}}$

In Exercises 17–22, find the domain and range.

17. $f(x) = \sqrt[3]{x + 77}$

18. $f(x) = x - 3$

19. $f(x) = x^2 + 2$

20. $f(x) = -x^2 + 7$

21. $f(x) = (x - 3)^2 + 2$

22. $f(x) = 1/(x + 1) + 3$

23. A restaurantn is open from 2 pm to 2 am each day, and a maximum of 200 clients can fit inside. If $f(t)$ is the number of clients in the restaurant t hours after 2 pm each day, what are a reasonable domain and range for $f(t)$?

In Exercises 24–25, estimate the domain and range of the function. Assume the entire graph is shown.

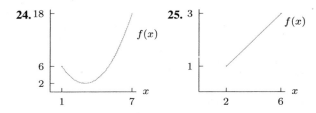

Problems

26. What is the domain of the function f giving average monthly rainfall at Chicago's O'Hare airport? (See Table 1.2 in Section 1.1)

27. A movie theater seats 200 people. For any particular show, the amount of money the theater makes is a function of the number of people, n, in attendance. If a ticket costs \$4.00, find the domain and range of this function. Sketch its graph.

28. A car gets the best mileage at intermediate speeds. Graph the gas mileage as a function of speed. Determine a reasonable domain and range for the function and justify your reasoning.

29. **(a)** Use Table 2.7 to determine the number of calories that a person weighing 200 lb uses in a half–hour of walking.[3]
   (b) Table 2.7 illustrates a relationship between the number of calories used per minute walking and a person's weight in pounds. Describe in words what is

true about this relationship. Identify the dependent and independent variables. Specify whether it is an increasing or decreasing function.

(c) (i) Graph the linear function for walking, as described in part (b), and estimate its equation.
   (ii) Interpret the meaning of the vertical intercept of the graph of the function.
   (iii) Specify a meaningful domain and range for your function.
   (iv) Use your function to determine how many calories per minute a person who weighs 135 lb uses per minute of walking.

Table 2.7 *Calories per minute as a function of weight*

Activity	100 lb	120 lb	150 lb	170 lb	200 lb	220 lb
Walking	2.7	3.2	4.0	4.6	5.4	5.9
Bicycling	5.4	6.5	8.1	9.2	10.8	11.9
Swimming	5.8	6.9	8.7	9.8	11.6	12.7

[3]Source: 1993 World Almanac. Speeds assumed are 3 mph for walking, 10 mph for bicycling, and 2 mph for swimming.

In Exercises 30–31, find the domain and range.

30. $g(x) = a + 1/x$, where a is a constant

31. $q(r) = (x - b)^{1/2} + 6$, where b is a constant

32. The last digit, d, of a phone number is a function of n, its position in the phone book. Table 2.8 gives d for the first 10 listings in the 1998 Boston telephone directory. The table shows that the last digit of the first listing is 3, the last digit of the second listing is 8, and so on. In principle we could use a phone book to figure out other values of d. For instance, if $n = 300$, we could count down to the 300th listing in order to determine d. So we write $d = f(n)$.

(a) What is the value of $f(6)$?
(b) Explain how you could use the phone book to find the domain of f.
(c) What is the range of f?

Table 2.8

n	1	2	3	4	5	6	7	8	9	10
d	3	8	4	0	1	8	0	4	3	5

33. In month $t = 0$, a small group of rabbits escapes from a ship onto an island where there are no rabbits. The island rabbit population, $p(t)$, in month t is given by

$$p(t) = \frac{1000}{1 + 19(0.9)^t}, \quad t \geq 0.$$

(a) Evaluate $p(0)$, $p(10)$, $p(50)$, and explain their meaning in terms of rabbits.
(b) Graph $p(t)$ for $0 \leq t \leq 100$. Describe the graph in words. Does it suggest the growth in population you would expect among rabbits on an island?
(c) Estimate the range of $p(t)$. What does this tell you about the rabbit population?
(d) Explain how you can find the range of $p(t)$ from its formula.

34. Bronze is an alloy or mixture of the metals copper and tin. The properties of bronze depend on the percentage of copper in the mix. A chemist decides to study the properties of a given alloy of bronze as the proportion of copper is varied. She starts with 9 kg of bronze that contain 3 kg of copper and 6 kg of tin and either adds or removes copper. Let $f(x)$ be the percentage of copper in the mix if x kg of copper are added ($x > 0$) or removed ($x < 0$).

(a) State the domain and range of f. What does your answer mean in the context of bronze?
(b) Find a formula in terms of x for $f(x)$.
(c) If the formula you found in part (b) was not intended to represent the percentage of copper in an alloy of bronze, but instead simply defined an abstract mathematical function, what would be the domain and range of this function?

2.3 PIECEWISE DEFINED FUNCTIONS

A function may employ different formulas on different parts of its domain. Such a function is said to be *piecewise defined*. For example, the function graphed in Figure 2.10 has the following formulas:

$$\begin{array}{ll} y = x^2 & \text{for} \quad x \leq 2 \\ y = 6 - x & \text{for} \quad x > 2 \end{array} \quad \text{or more compactly} \quad y = \begin{cases} x^2 & \text{for} \quad x \leq 2 \\ 6 - x & \text{for} \quad x > 2. \end{cases}$$

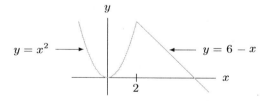

Figure 2.10: Piecewise defined function

Example 1   Graph the function $y = g(x)$ given by the following formulas:

$$g(x) = x + 1 \quad \text{for} \quad x \leq 2 \qquad \text{and} \qquad g(x) = 1 \quad \text{for} \quad x > 2.$$

Using bracket notation, this function is written:

$$g(x) = \begin{cases} x + 1 & \text{for } x \leq 2 \\ 1 & \text{for } x > 2. \end{cases}$$

Solution   For $x \leq 2$, graph the line $y = x + 1$. The solid dot at the point $(2, 3)$ shows that it is included in the graph. For $x > 2$, graph the horizontal line $y = 1$. See Figure 2.11. The open circle at the point $(2, 1)$ shows that it is not included in the graph. (Note that $g(2) = 3$, and $g(2)$ cannot have more than one value.)

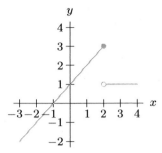

Figure 2.11: Graph of the piecewise defined function g

Example 2   A long-distance calling plan charges 99 cents for any call up to 20 minutes in length and 7 cents for each additional minute or part of a minute.

(a) Use bracket notation to write a formula for the cost, C, of a call as a function of its length t in minutes.

(b) Graph the function.

(c) State the domain and range of the function

Solution   (a) For $0 < t \leq 20$, the value of C is 99 cents. If $t > 20$, we subtract 20 to find the additional minutes and multiply by the rate 7 cents per minute.[4] The cost function in cents is thus

$$C = f(t) = \begin{cases} 99 & \text{for } 0 < t \leq 20 \\ 99 + 7(t - 20) & \text{for } t > 20, \end{cases}$$

or, after simplifying,

$$C = f(t) = \begin{cases} 99 & \text{for } 0 < t \leq 20 \\ 7t - 41 & \text{for } t > 20. \end{cases}$$

(b) See Figure 2.12.

(c) Because negative and zero call lengths do not make sense, the domain is $t > 0$. From the graph, we see that the range is $C \geq 99$.

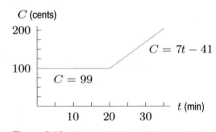

Figure 2.12: Cost of a long-distance phone call

Example 3   The Ironman Triathlon is a race that consists of three parts: a 2.4 mile swim followed by a 112 mile bike race and then a 26.2 mile marathon. A participant swims steadily at 2 mph, cycles steadily at 20 mph, and then runs steadily at 9 mph.[5] Assuming that no time is lost during the transition from

---

[4]In actuality, most calling plans round the call length to whole minutes or specified fractions of a minute.

[5]Data supplied by Susan Reid, Athletics Department, University of Arizona.

one stage to the next, find a formula for the distance d, covered in miles, as a function of the elapsed time t in hours, from the beginning of the race. Graph the function.

Solution   For each leg of the race, we use the formula Distance = Rate · Time. First, we calculate how long it took for the participant to cover each of the three parts of the race. The first leg took $2.4/2 = 1.2$ hours, the second leg took $112/20 = 5.6$ hours, and the final leg took $26.2/9 \approx 2.91$ hours. Thus, the participant finished the race in $1.2 + 5.6 + 2.91 = 9.71$ hours.

During the first leg, $t \leq 1.2$ and the speed is 2 mph, so

$$d = 2t \qquad \text{for} \qquad 0 \leq t \leq 1.2.$$

During the second leg, $1.2 < t \leq 1.2 + 5.6 = 6.8$ and the speed is 20 mph. The length of time spent in the second leg is $(t - 1.2)$ hours. Thus, by time t,

$$\text{Distance covered in the second leg} = 20(t - 1.2) \quad \text{for } 1.2 < t \leq 6.8.$$

When the participant is in the second leg, the total distance covered is the sum of the distance covered in the first leg (2.4 miles) plus the part of the second leg that has been covered by time t.

$$d = 2.4 + 20(t - 1.2)$$
$$= 20t - 21.6 \qquad \text{for } 1.2 < t \leq 6.8.$$

In the third leg, $6.8 < t \leq 9.71$ and the speed is 9 mph. Since 6.8 hours were spent on the first two parts of the race, the length of time spent on the third leg is $(t - 6.8)$ hours. Thus, by time t,

$$\text{Distance covered in the third leg} = 9(t - 6.8) \quad \text{for } 6.8 < t \leq 9.71.$$

When the participant is in the third leg, the total distance covered is the sum of the distances covered in the first leg (2.4 miles) and the second leg (112 miles), plus the part of the third leg that has been covered by time t:

$$d = 2.4 + 112 + 9(t - 6.8)$$
$$= 9t + 53.2 \qquad \text{for } 6.8 < t \leq 9.71.$$

The formula for d is different on different intervals of t:

$$d = \begin{cases} 2t & \text{for} & 0 \leq t \leq 1.2 \\ 20t - 21.6 & \text{for} & 1.2 < t \leq 6.8 \\ 9t + 53.2 & \text{for} & 6.8 < t \leq 9.71 \end{cases}$$

Figure 2.13 gives a graph of the distance covered, d, as a function of time, t. Notice the three pieces.

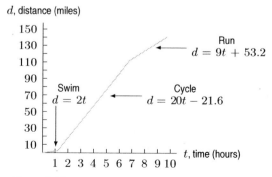

Figure 2.13: Ironman Triathlon: d as a function of t

The Absolute Value Function

The absolute value of a x, written $|x|$, is defined piecewise

$$\text{For positive } x, \quad |x| = x.$$
$$\text{For negative } x, \quad |x| = -x.$$

(Remember that $-x$ is a positive number if x is a negative number.) For example, if $x = -3$, then

$$|-3| = -(-3) = 3.$$

For $x = 0$, we have $|0| = 0$. This leads to the following two-part definition:

> The **Absolute Value Function** is defined by
>
> $$f(x) = |x| = \begin{cases} x & \text{for} \quad x \geq 0 \\ -x & \text{for} \quad x < 0 \end{cases}.$$

Table 2.9 gives values of $f(x) = |x|$ and Figure 2.14 shows a graph of $f(x)$.

Table 2.9 *Absolute value function*

x	$|x|$
-3	3
-2	2
-1	1
0	0
1	1
2	2
3	3

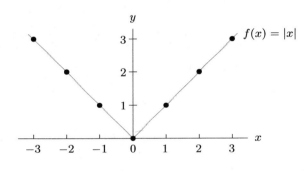

Figure 2.14: Graph of absolute value function

Exercises and Problems for Section 2.3

Exercises

Graph the piecewise defined functions in Exercises 1–4. Use an open circle to represent a point which is not included and a solid dot to indicate a point which is on the graph.

1. $f(x) = \begin{cases} -1, & -1 \leq x < 0 \\ 0, & 0 \leq x < 1 \\ 1, & 1 \leq x < 2 \end{cases}$

2. $f(x) = \begin{cases} x + 4, & x \leq -2 \\ 2, & -2 < x < 2 \\ 4 - x, & x \geq 2 \end{cases}$

3. $f(x) = \begin{cases} x^2, & x \leq 0 \\ \sqrt{x}, & 0 < x < 4 \\ x/2, & x \geq 4 \end{cases}$

4. $f(x) = \begin{cases} x + 1, & -2 \leq x < 0 \\ x - 1, & 0 \leq x < 2 \\ x - 3, & 2 \leq x < 4 \end{cases}$

In Exercises 5–8, write formulas for the functions.

5.
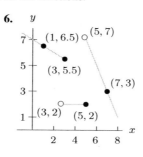

6.

7.
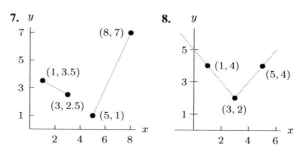

8.

Problems

9. Consider the graph in Figure 2.15. An open circle represents a point which is not included.

    (a) Is y a function of x? Explain.

    (b) Is x a function of y? Explain.

    (c) The domain of $y = f(x)$ is $0 \leq x < 4$. What is the range of $y = f(x)$?

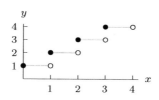

Figure 2.15

10. Many people believe that $\sqrt{x^2} = x$. We will investigate this claim graphically and numerically.

    (a) Graph the two functions x and $\sqrt{x^2}$ in the window $-5 \leq x \leq 5$, $-5 \leq y \leq 5$. Based on what you see, do you believe that $\sqrt{x^2} = x$? What function does the graph of $\sqrt{x^2}$ remind you of?

    (b) Complete Table 2.10. Based on this table, do you believe that $\sqrt{x^2} = x$? What function does the table for $\sqrt{x^2}$ remind you of? Is this the same function you found in part (a)?

Table 2.10

x	-5	-4	-3	-2	-1	0	1	2	3	4	5
$\sqrt{x^2}$											

    (c) Explain how you know that $\sqrt{x^2}$ is the same as the function $|x|$.

    (d) Graph the function $\sqrt{x^2} - |x|$ in the window $-5 \leq x \leq 5$, $-5 \leq y \leq 5$. Explain what you see.

11. (a) Graph $u(x) = |x|/x$ in the window $-5 \leq x \leq 5$, $-5 \leq y \leq 5$. Explain what you see.

(b) Complete Table 2.11. Does this table agree with what you found in part (a)?

Table 2.11

x	-5	-4	-3	-2	-1	0	1	2	3	4	5
$|x|/x$											

    (c) Identify the domain and range of $u(x)$.

    (d) Comment on the claim that $u(x)$ can be written as

$$u(x) = \begin{cases} -1 & \text{if } x < 0, \\ 0 & \text{if } x = 0, \\ 1 & \text{if } x > 0. \end{cases}$$

12. The charge for a taxi ride is \$1.50 for the first $1/8$ of a mile, and \$0.25 for each additional $1/8$ of a mile (rounded up to the nearest $1/8$ mile).

    (a) Make a table showing the cost of a trip as a function of its length. Your table should start at zero and go up to one mile in $1/8$-mile intervals.

    (b) What is the cost for a $5/8$-mile ride?

    (c) How far can you go for \$3.00?

    (d) Graph the cost function in part (a).

13. A contractor purchases gravel one cubic yard at a time.

    (a) A gravel driveway L yards long and 6 yards wide is to be poured to a depth of 1 foot. Find a formula for $n(L)$, the number of cubic yards of gravel the contractor buys, assuming that he buys 10 more cubic yards of gravel than are needed (to be sure he'll have enough).

    (b) Assuming no driveway is less than 5 yards long, state the domain and range of $n(L)$. Graph $n(L)$ showing the domain and range.

    (c) If the function $n(L)$ did not represent an amount of gravel, but was a mathematical relationship defined by the formula in part (a), what is its domain and range?

14. A floor-refinishing company charges \$1.83 per square foot to strip and refinish a tile floor for up to 1000 square feet. There is an additional charge of $350 for toxic waste disposal for any job which includes more than 150 square feet of tile.

(a) Express the cost, y, of refinishing a floor as a function of the number of square feet, x, to be refinished.

(b) Graph the function. Give the domain and range.

15. A museum charges $40 for a group of 10 or fewer people. A group of more than 10 people must, in addition to the $40, pay $2 per person for the number of people above 10. For example, a group of 12 pays $44 and a group of 15 pays $50. The maximum group size is 50.

(a) Draw a graph that represents this situation.

(b) What are the domain and range of the cost function?

16. At a supermarket checkout, a scanner records the prices of the foods you buy. In order to protect consumers, the state of Michigan passed a "scanning law" that says something similar to the following:

> If there is a discrepancy between the price marked on the item and the price recorded by the scanner, the consumer is entitled to receive 10 times the difference between those prices; this amount given must be at least $1 and at most $5. Also, the consumer will be given the difference between the prices, in addition to the amount calculated above.

For example: If the difference is 5¢, you should receive $1 (since 10 times the difference is only 50¢ and you are to receive at least $1), plus the difference of 5¢. Thus, the total you should receive is $1.00 + $0.05 = $1.05, If the difference is 25¢, you should receive 10 times the difference in addition to the difference, giving $(10)(0.25) + 0.25 = \$2.75$.
If the difference is 95¢, you should receive $5 (because $10(.95) = \$9.50$ is more than $5, the maximum penalty), plus 95¢, giving $5 + 0.95 = \$5.95$.

(a) What is the lowest possible refund?

(b) Suppose x is the difference between the price scanned and the price marked on the item, and y is the amount refunded to the customer. Write a formula for y in terms of x. (Hints: Look at the sample calculations.)

(c) What would the difference between the price scanned and the price marked have to be in order to obtain a $9.00 refund?

(d) Graph y as a function of x.

17. Many printing presses are designed with large plates that print a fixed number of pages as a unit. Each unit is called a signature. A particular press prints signatures of 16 pages each. Suppose $C(p)$ is the cost of printing a book of p pages, assuming each signature printed costs $0.14.

(a) What is the cost of printing a book of 128 pages? 129 pages? p pages?

(b) What are the domain and range of C?

(c) Graph $C(p)$ for $0 \leq p \leq 128$.

18. Gore Mountain is a ski resort in the Adirondack mountains in upstate New York. Table 2.12 shows the cost of a weekday ski-lift ticket for various ages and dates.

(a) Graph cost as a function of age for each time period given. (One graph will serve for times when rates are identical).

(b) For which age group does the date affect cost?

(c) Graph cost as a function of date for the age group mentioned in part (b).

(d) Why does the cost fluctuate as a function of date?

Table 2.12 *Ski-lift ticket prices at Gore Mountain, 1998–1999*[6]

Age	Opening-Dec 12	Dec 13-Dec 24	Dec 25-Jan 3	Jan 4-Jan 15	Jan 16-Jan 18
Up to 6	Free	Free	Free	Free	Free
7–12	$19	$19	$19	$19	$19
13–69	$29	$34	$39	$34	$39
70+	Free	Free	Free	Free	Free

Age	Jan 19-Feb 12	Feb 13-Feb 21	Feb 22-Mar 28	Mar 29-Closing
Up to 6	Free	Free	Free	Free
7–12	$19	$19	$19	$19
13–69	$34	$39	$34	$29
70+	Free	Free	Free	Free

19. Sometimes a relationship is defined by two independent variables. The wind chill index is one such function. The wind chill, denoted W, is a measure of how cold it *feels*; it takes into account both the temperature, T, and the wind velocity, V. The function can be called $W(T, V)$ to show that W depends on both T and V. One model for wind chill is the piecewise function shown below.

$$W(T, V) =$$
$$\begin{cases} T & \text{for } 0 \leq V \leq 4 \\ 0.0817(5.81 + 3.71\sqrt{V} - 0.25V)(T - 91.4) + 91.4 & \\ & \text{for } 4 < V \leq 45 \\ 1.60T - 55 & \text{for } V > 45. \end{cases}$$

(a) Two of the three rules of the piecewise function are linear. Which are they?

(b) For which velocities does the wind have no further effect on the perceived temperature?

(c) How hard must the wind blow so that a temperature of 40°F feels like 9°F?

---

[6] The Olympic Regional Development Authority.

2.4 CONCAVITY

Concavity and Rates of Change

The graph of a linear function is a straight line because the average rate of change is a constant. However, not all graphs are straight lines; they may bend up or down. Consider the salary function $S(t)$ shown in Table 2.13 and Figure 2.16 where t is time in years since being hired. Since the rate of change increases with time, the slope of the graph increases as t increases, so the graph bends upward. We say such graphs are *concave up*.

Table 2.13 *Salary: Increasing rate of change*

t (years)	S ($1000s)	Rate of change $\Delta S/\Delta t$
0	40	
		3.2
10	72	
		5.6
20	128	
		10.2
30	230	
		18.1
40	411	

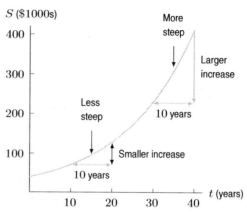

Figure 2.16: Graph of salary function is concave up because rate of change increases

The next example shows that a decreasing function can also be concave up.

Example 1   Table 2.14 shows Q, the quantity of carbon-14 (in μg) in a 200 μg sample remaining after t thousand years. We see from Figure 2.17 that Q is a decreasing function of t, so its rate of change is always negative. What can we say about the concavity of the graph, and what does this mean about the rate of change of the function?

Table 2.14 *Carbon-14: Increasing rate of change*

t (thousand years)	Q (μg)	Rate of change $\Delta Q/\Delta t$
0	200	
		-18.2
5	109	
		-9.8
10	60	
		-5.4
15	33	

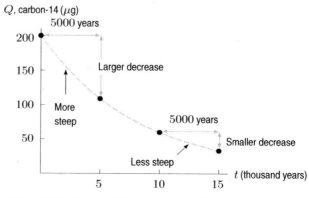

Figure 2.17: Graph of the quantity of carbon-14 is concave up

Solution The graph bends upward, so it is concave up. Table 2.14 shows that the rate of change of the function is increasing, because the rate is becoming less negative. Figure 2.17 shows how the increasing rate of change can be visualized on the graph: the slope is negative and increasing.

Graphs can bend downward; we call such graphs *concave down*.

Example 2 Table 2.15 gives the distance traveled by a cyclist, Karim, as a function of time. What is the concavity of the graph? Was Karim's speed (that is, the rate of change of distance with respect to time) increasing, decreasing, or constant?

Solution Table 2.15 shows Karim's speed was decreasing throughout the trip. Figure 2.18 shows how the decreasing speed leads to a decreasing slope and a graph which bends downward; thus the graph is concave down.

Table 2.15 *Karim's distance as a function of time, with the average speed for each hour*

t, time (hours)	d, distance (miles)	Average speed, $\Delta d / \Delta t$ (mph)
0	0	
		20 mph
1	20	
		15 mph
2	35	
		10 mph
3	45	
		7 mph
4	52	
		5 mph
5	57	

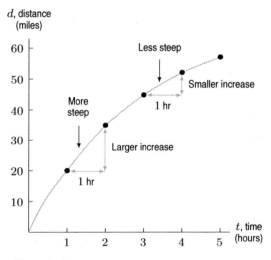

Figure 2.18: Karim's distance as a function of time

Summary: Increasing and Decreasing Functions; Concavity

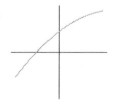

Figure 2.19: Increasing and concave down

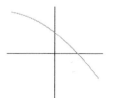

Figure 2.20: Decreasing and concave down

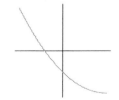

Figure 2.21: Decreasing and concave up

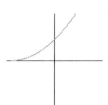

Figure 2.22: Increasing and concave up

Figures 2.19–2.22 reflect the following relationships between concavity and rate of change:

- If f is a function whose rate of change increases (gets less negative or more positive as we move from left to right[7]), then the graph of f is **concave up**. That is, the graph bends upward.
- If f is a function whose rate of change decreases (gets less positive or more negative as we move from left to right), then the graph of f is **concave down**. That is, the graph bends downward.

If a function has a constant rate of change, its graph is a line and it is neither concave up nor concave down.

Exercises and Problems for Section 2.4

Exercises

1. Calculate successive rates of change for the function, $p(t)$, in Table 2.16 to decide whether you expect the graph of $p(t)$ to be concave up or concave down.

Table 2.16

t	0.2	0.4	0.6	0.8
$p(t)$	−3.19	−2.32	−1.50	−0.74

2. Calculate successive rates of change for the function, $H(x)$, in Table 2.17 to decide whether you expect the graph of $H(x)$ to be concave up or concave down.

Table 2.17

x	12	15	18	21
$H(x)$	21.40	21.53	21.75	22.02

Do the graphs of the functions in Exercises 3–10 appear to be concave up, concave down, or neither?

3.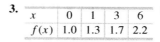

x	0	1	3	6
$f(x)$	1.0	1.3	1.7	2.2

4.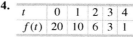

t	0	1	2	3	4
$f(t)$	20	10	6	3	1

5.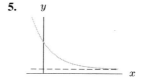

6.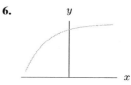

7. $y = x^2$

8. $y = -x^2$

9. $y = x^3, x > 0$

10. $y = x^3, x < 0$

Problems

Are the functions in Problems 11–15 increasing or decreasing? What does the scenario tell you about the concavity of the graph modeling it?

11. When money is deposited in the bank, the amount of money increases slowly at first. As the size of the account increases, the amount of money increases more rapidly, since the account is earning interest on the new interest, as well as on the original amount.

12. After a cup of hot chocolate is poured, the temperature cools off very rapidly at first, and then cools off more slowly, until the temperature of the hot chocolate eventually reaches room temperature.

13. When a rumor begins, the number of people who have heard the rumor increases slowly at first. As the rumor spreads, the rate of increase gets greater (as more people continue to tell their friends the rumor), and then slows down again (when almost everyone has heard the rumor).

14. When a drug is injected into a person's bloodstream, the amount of the drug present in the body increases rapidly at first. If the person receives daily injections, the body metabolizes the drug so that the amount of the drug present in the body continues to increase, but at a decreasing rate. Eventually, the quantity levels off at a saturation level.

---

[7]In fact, we need to take the average rate of change over an arbitrarily small interval.

15. When a new product is introduced, the number of people who use the product increases slowly at first, and then the rate of increase is faster (as more and more people learn about the product). Eventually, the rate of increase slows down again (when most people who are interested in the product are already using it).

16. Match each story with the table and graph which best represent it.

  (a) When you study a foreign language, the number of new verbs you learn increases rapidly at first, but slows almost to a halt as you approach your saturation level.

  (b) You board an airplane in Philadelphia heading west. Your distance from the Atlantic Ocean, in kilometers per minute, increases at a constant rate.

  (c) The interest on your savings plan is compounded annually. At first your balance grows slowly, but its rate of growth continues to increase.

(E)

x	0	5	10	15	20	25
y	20	275	360	390	395	399

(F)

x	0	5	10	15	20	25
y	20	36	66	120	220	400

(G)

x	0	5	10	15	20	25
y	20	95	170	245	320	395

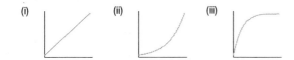

(i)   (ii)   (iii)

17. Match each of the following descriptions with an appropriate graph and table of values.

  (a) The weight of your jumbo box of Fruity Flakes decreases by an equal amount every week.

  (b) The machinery depreciated rapidly at first, but its value declined more slowly as time went on.

  (c) In free fall, your distance from the ground decreases at an increasing rate.

  (d) For a while it looked like the decline in profits was slowing down, but then they began declining ever more rapidly.

(E)

x	0	1	2	3	4	5
y	400	384	336	256	144	0

(F)

x	0	1	2	3	4	5
y	400	320	240	160	80	0

(G)

x	0	1	2	3	4	5
y	400	184	98	63	49	43

(H)

x	0	1	2	3	4	5
y	412	265	226	224	185	38

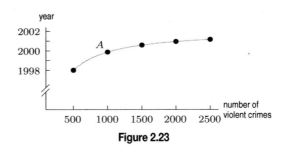

(i)   (ii)

(iii)   (iv)

18. An incumbent politician running for reelection declared that the number of violent crimes is no longer rising and is presently under control. Does the graph shown in Figure 2.23 support this claim? Why or why not?

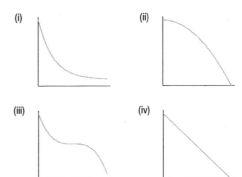

Figure 2.23

19. The rate at which water is entering a reservoir is given for time $t > 0$ by the graph in Figure 2.24. A negative rate means that water is leaving the reservoir. For each of the following statements, give the largest interval on which:

  (a) The volume of water is increasing.

  (b) The volume of water is constant.

  (c) The volume of water is increasing fastest.

  (d) The volume of water is decreasing.

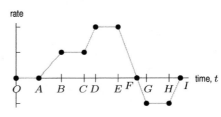

Figure 2.24

20. The relationship between the swimming speed U (in cm/sec) of a salmon to the length l of the salmon (in cm) is given by the function[8]

$$U = 19.5\sqrt{l}.$$

(a) If one salmon is 4 times the length of another salmon, how are their swimming speeds related?

(b) Graph the function $U = 19.5\sqrt{l}$. Describe the graph using words such as increasing, decreasing, concave up, concave down.

(c) Using a property that you described in part (b), answer the question "Do larger salmon swim faster than smaller ones?"

(d) Using a property that you described in part (b), answer the question "Imagine four salmon—two small and two large. The smaller salmon differ in length by 1 cm, as do the two larger. Is the difference in speed between the two smaller fish, greater than, equal to, or smaller than the difference in speed between the two larger fish?"

2.5 VERTICAL AND HORIZONTAL SHIFTS

Suppose we shift the graph of some function vertically or horizontally, giving the graph of a new function. In this section we investigate the relationship between the formulas for the original function and the new function.

Vertical and Horizontal Shift: The Heating Schedule For an Office Building

We start with an example of a vertical shift in the context of the heating schedule for a building.

Example 1 To save money, an office building is kept warm only during business hours. Figure 2.25 shows the temperature, H, in °F, as a function of time, t, in hours after midnight. At midnight ($t = 0$), the building's temperature is 50°F. This temperature is maintained until 4 am. Then the building begins to warm up so that by 8 am the temperature is 70°F. At 4 pm the building begins to cool. By 8 pm, the temperature is again 50°F.

Suppose that the building's superintendent decides to keep the building 5°F warmer than before. Sketch a graph of the resulting function.

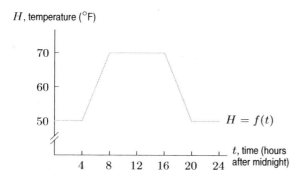

Figure 2.25: The heating schedule at an office building

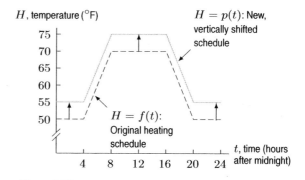

Figure 2.26: Graph of new heating schedule, $H = p(t)$, obtained by shifting original graph, $H = f(t)$, upward by 5 units

Solution The graph of f, the heating schedule function of Figure 2.25, is shifted upward by 5 units. The new heating schedule, $H = p(t)$, is graphed in Figure 2.26. The building's overnight temperature is

---

[8]From K. Schmidt-Nielsen, *Scaling–Why is animal size so important?* (London: Cambridge University Press, 1984).

now 55°F instead of 50°F and its daytime temperature is 75°F instead of 70°F. The 5°F increase in temperature corresponds to the 5-unit vertical shift in the graph.

The next example involves shifting a graph horizontally.

Example 2   The superintendent then changes the original heating schedule to start two hours earlier. The building now begins to warm at 2 am instead of 4 am, reaches 70°F at 6 am instead of 8 am, begins cooling off at 2 pm instead of 4 pm, and returns to 50°F at 6 pm instead of 8 pm. How are these changes reflected in the graph of the heating schedule?

Solution   Figure 2.27 gives a graph of $H = q(t)$, the new heating schedule, which is obtained by shifting the graph of the original heating schedule, $H = f(t)$, two units to the left.

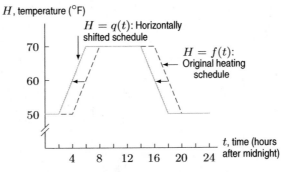

Figure 2.27: Graph of new heating schedule, $H = q(t)$, found by shifting, f, the original graph 2 units to the left

Notice that the upward shift in Example 1 results in a warmer temperature, whereas the leftward shift in Example 2 results in an earlier schedule.

Formulas for a Vertical or Horizontal Shift

How does a horizontal or vertical shift of a function's graph affect its formula?

Example 3   In Example 1, the graph of the original heating schedule, $H = f(t)$, was shifted upward by 5 units; the result was the warmer schedule $H = p(t)$. How are the formulas for $f(t)$ and $p(t)$ related?

Solution   The temperature under the new schedule, $p(t)$, is always 5°F warmer than the temperature under the old schedule, $f(t)$. Thus,

$$\text{New temperature at time } t = \text{Old temperature at time } t + 5.$$

Writing this algebraically:

$$\underbrace{p(t)}_{\substack{\text{New temperature} \\ \text{at time } t}} = \underbrace{f(t)}_{\substack{\text{Old temperature} \\ \text{at time } t}} + 5.$$

The relationship between the formulas for p and f is given by the equation $p(t) = f(t) + 5$.

We can get information from the relationship $p(t) = f(t) + 5$, although we do not have an explicit formula for f or p.

Suppose we need to know the temperature at 6 am under the schedule $p(t)$. The graph of $f(t)$ shows that under the old schedule $f(6) = 60$. Substituting $t = 6$ into the equation relating f and p gives $p(6)$:

$$p(6) = f(6) + 5 = 60 + 5 = 65.$$

Thus, at 6 am the temperature under the new schedule is 65°F.

Example 4   In Example 2 the heating schedule was changed to 2 hours earlier, shifting the graph horizontally 2 units to the left. Find a formula for q, this new schedule, in terms of f, the original schedule.

Solution   The old schedule always reaches a given temperature 2 hours after the new schedule. For example, at 4 am the temperature under the new schedule reaches 60°. The temperature under the old schedule reaches 60° at 6 am, 2 hours later. The temperature reaches 65° at 5 am under the new schedule, but not until 7 am, under the old schedule. In general, we see that

$$\begin{array}{c} \text{Temperature under new schedule} \\ \text{at time } t \end{array} = \begin{array}{c} \text{Temperature under old schedule} \\ \text{at time } (t+2) \text{, two hours later.} \end{array}$$

Algebraically, we have

$$q(t) = f(t + 2).$$

This is a formula for q in terms of f.

Let's check the formula from Example 4 by using it to calculate $q(14)$, the temperature under the new schedule at 2 pm. The formula gives

$$q(14) = f(14 + 2) = f(16).$$

Figure 2.25 shows that $f(16) = 70$. Thus, $q(14) = 70$. This agrees with Figure 2.27.

Translations of a Function and Its Graph

In the heating schedule example, the function representing a warmer schedule,

$$p(t) = f(t) + 5,$$

has a graph which is a vertically shifted version of the graph of f. On the other hand, the earlier schedule is represented by

$$q(t) = f(t + 2)$$

and its graph is a horizontally shifted version of the graph of f. Adding 5 to the temperature, or output value, $f(t)$, shifted its graph *up* five units. Adding 2 to the time, or input value, t, shifted its graph to the *left* two units. Generalizing these observations to any function g:

If $y = g(x)$ is a function and k is a constant, then the graph of

- $y = g(x) + k$ is the graph of $y = g(x)$ shifted vertically $|k|$ units. If k is positive, the shift is up; if k is negative, the shift is down.
- $y = g(x + k)$ is the graph of $y = g(x)$ shifted horizontally $|k|$ units. If k is positive, the shift is to the left; if k is negative, the shift is to the right.

A vertical or horizontal shift of the graph of a function is called a *translation* because it does not change the shape of the graph, but simply translates it to another position in the plane. Shifts or translations are the simplest examples of *transformations* of a function. We will see others in later sections of Chapter 2.

Inside and Outside Changes

Since $y = g(x + k)$ involves a change to the input value, x, it is called an *inside change* to g. Similarly, since $y = g(x) + k$ involves a change to the output value, $g(x)$, it is called an *outside change*. In general, an inside change in a function results in a horizontal change in its graph, whereas an outside change results in a vertical change.

In this section, we consider changes to the input and output of a function. For the function

$$Q = f(t),$$

a change inside the function's parentheses can be called an "inside change" and a change outside the function's parentheses can be called an "outside change."

Example 5   If $n = f(A)$ gives the number of gallons of paint needed to cover a house of area A ft^2, explain the meaning of the expressions $f(A + 10)$ and $f(A) + 10$ in the context of painting.

Solution   These two expressions are similar in that they both involve adding 10. However, for $f(A + 10)$, the 10 is added on the inside, so 10 is added to the area, A. Thus,

$$n = f(\underbrace{A + 10}_{\text{Area}}) = \begin{array}{c} \text{Amount of paint needed} \\ \text{to cover an area of } (A + 10) \text{ ft}^2 \end{array} = \begin{array}{c} \text{Amount of paint needed to cover} \\ \text{an area } 10 \text{ ft}^2 \text{ larger than } A. \end{array}$$

The expression $f(A) + 10$ represents an outside change. We are adding 10 to $f(A)$, which represents an amount of paint, not an area. We have

$$n = \underbrace{f(A)}_{\substack{\text{Amount} \\ \text{of paint}}} + 10 = \begin{array}{c} \text{Amount of paint needed} \\ \text{to cover region of area } A \end{array} + 10 \text{ gals} = \begin{array}{c} 10 \text{ gallons more paint than} \\ \text{amount needed to cover area } A. \end{array}$$

In $f(A + 10)$, we added 10 square feet on the inside of the function, which means that the area to be painted is now 10 ft^2 larger. In $f(A) + 10$, we added 10 gallons to the outside, which means that we have 10 more gallons of paint than we need.

Example 6   Let $s(t)$ be the average weight (in pounds) of a baby at age t months. The weight, V, of a particular baby named Jonah is related to the average weight function $s(t)$ by the equation

$$V = s(t) + 2.$$

Find Jonah's weight at ages $t = 3$ and $t = 6$ months. What can you say about Jonah's weight in general?

Solution   At $t = 3$ months, Jonah's weight is

$$V = s(3) + 2.$$

Since $s(3)$ is the average weight of a 3-month old boy, we see that at 3 months, Jonah weighs 2 pounds more than average. Similarly, at $t = 6$ months we have

$$V = s(6) + 2,$$

which means that, at 6 months, Jonah weighs 2 pounds more than average. In general, Jonah weighs 2 pounds more than average for babies of his age.

Example 7   The weight, W, of another baby named Ben is related to $s(t)$ by the equation

$$W = s(t + 4).$$

What can you say about Ben's weight at age $t = 3$ months? At $t = 6$ months? Assuming that babies increase in weight over the first year of life, decide if Ben is of average weight for his age, above average, or below average.

Solution   Since $W = s(t + 4)$, at age $t = 3$ months Ben's weight is given by

$$W = s(3 + 4) = s(7).$$

We defined $s(7)$ to be the average weight of a 7-month old baby. At age 3 months, Ben's weight is the same as the average weight of 7-month old babies. Since, on average, a baby's weight increases as the baby grows, this means that Ben is heavier than the average for a 3-month old. Similarly, at age $t = 6$, Ben's weight is given by

$$W = s(6 + 4) = s(10).$$

Thus, at 6 months, Ben's weight is the same as the average weight of 10-month old babies. In both cases, we see that Ben is above average in weight.

Notice that in Example 7, the equation

$$W = s(t + 4)$$

involves an inside change, or a change in months. This equation tells us that Ben weighs as much as babies who are 4 months older than he is. However in Example 6, the equation

$$V = s(t) + 2$$

involves an outside change, or a change in weight. This equation tells us that Jonah is 2 pounds heavier than the average weight of babies his age. Although both equations tell us that the babies are heavier than average for their age, they vary from the average in different ways.

Combining Horizontal and Vertical Shifts

We have seen what happens when we shift a function's graph either horizontally or vertically. What happens if we shift it both horizontally and vertically?

Example 8   Let r be the transformation of the heating schedule function, $H = f(t)$, defined by the equation

$$r(t) = f(t - 2) - 5.$$

(a) Sketch the graph of $H = r(t)$.
(b) Describe in words the heating schedule determined by r.

Solution   (a) To graph r, we break this transformation into two steps. First, we sketch a graph of $H = f(t - 2)$. This is an inside change to the function f and it results in the graph of f being shifted 2 units to the right. Next, we sketch a graph of $H = f(t - 2) - 5$. This graph can be found by shifting our sketch of $H = f(t - 2)$ down 5 units. The resulting graph is shown in Figure 2.28. The graph of r is the graph of f shifted 2 units to the right and 5 units down.

(b) The function r represents a schedule that is both 2 hours later and 5 degrees cooler than the original schedule.

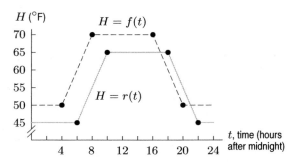

Figure 2.28: Graph of $r(t) = f(t - 2) - 5$ is graph of $H = f(t)$ shifted right by 2 and down by 5

We can use transformations to understand an unfamiliar function by relating it to a function we already know.

Example 9   A graph of $f(x) = x^2$ is in Figure 2.29. Define g by shifting the graph of f to the right 2 units and down 1 unit; see Figure 2.30. Find a formula for g in terms of f. Find a formula for g in terms of x.

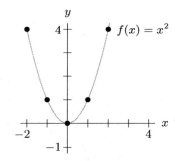

Figure 2.29: The graph of $f(x) = x^2$

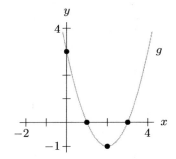

Figure 2.30: The graph of g, a transformation of f

Solution   The graph of g is the graph of f shifted to the right 2 units and down 1 unit, so a formula for g is $g(x) = f(x - 2) - 1$. Since $f(x) = x^2$, we have $f(x - 2) = (x - 2)^2$. Therefore,

$$g(x) = (x - 2)^2 - 1.$$

It is a good idea to check by graphing $g(x) = (x - 2)^2 - 1$ and comparing the graph with Figure 2.30.

Exercises and Problems for Section 2.5

Exercises

1. Using Table 2.18, complete the tables for g, h, k, m, where:

(a) $g(x) = f(x-1)$ (b) $h(x) = f(x+1)$
(c) $k(x) = f(x) + 3$ (d) $m(x) = f(x-1) + 3$

Explain how the graph of each function relates to the graph of $f(x)$.

Table 2.18

x	-2	-1	0	1	2
$f(x)$	-3	0	2	1	-1

x	-1	0	1	2	3
$g(x)$					

x	-3	-2	-1	0	1
$h(x)$					

x	-2	-1	0	1	2
$k(x)$					

x	-1	0	1	2	3
$m(x)$					

2. Complete the following tables using $f(p) = p^2 + 2p - 3$, and $g(p) = f(p+2)$, and $h(p) = f(p-2)$. Graph the three functions. Explain how the graphs of g and h are related to the graph of f.

p	-3	-2	-1	0	1	2	3
$f(p)$							

p	-3	-2	-1	0	1	2	3
$g(p)$							

p	-3	-2	-1	0	1	2	3
$h(p)$							

Write a formula and graph the transformations of $m(n) = \frac{1}{2}n^2$ in Exercises 3–10.

3. $y = m(n) + 1$ **4.** $y = m(n+1)$

5. $y = m(n) - 3.7$ **6.** $y = m(n - 3.7)$

7. $y = m(n) + \sqrt{13}$ **8.** $y = m(n + 2\sqrt{2})$

9. $y = m(n+3) + 7$ **10.** $y = m(n - 17) - 159$

Write a formula and graph the transformations of $k(w) = 3^w$ in Exercises 11–16.

11. $y = k(w) - 3$ **12.** $y = k(w - 3)$

13. $y = k(w) + 1.8$ **14.** $y = k(w + \sqrt{5})$

15. $y = k(w + 2.1) - 1.3$ **16.** $y = k(w - 1.5) - 0.9$

17. Match the graphs in (a)–(f) with the formulas in (i)–(vi).

(i) $y = |x|$ (ii) $y = |x| - 1.2$
(iii) $y = |x - 1.2|$ (iv) $y = |x| + 2.5$
(v) $y = |x + .3.4|$ (vi) $y = |x - 3| + 2.7$

(a)
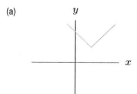

(b)
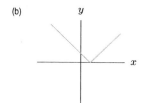

(c)
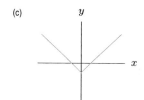

(d)
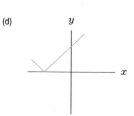

(e)
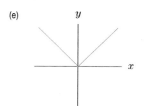

(f)
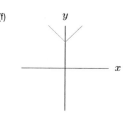

18. Let $f(x) = 4^x$, $g(x) = 4^x + 2$, and $h(x) = 4^x - 3$. What is the relationship between the graph of $f(x)$ and the graphs of $h(x)$ and $g(x)$?

19. Let $f(x) = \left(\frac{1}{3}\right)^x$, $g(x) = \left(\frac{1}{3}\right)^{x+4}$, and $h(x) = \left(\frac{1}{3}\right)^{x-2}$. How do the graphs of $g(x)$ and $h(x)$ compare to the graph of $f(x)$?

Explain in words the effects of the transformations in Exercises 20–26 on the graph of $q(z)$. Assume a, b are positive constants.

20. $q(z) + 3$

21. $q(z) - a$

22. $q(z + 4)$

23. $q(z - a)$

24. $q(z + b) - a$

25. $q(z - 2b) + ab$

26. Graph $f(x) = \ln(|x - 3|)$ and $g(x) = \ln(|x|)$. Find the vertical asymptotes of both functions.

Problems

27. (a) Using Table 2.19, evaluate

  (i) $f(x)$ for $x = 6$.
  (ii) $f(5) - 3$.
  (iii) $f(5 - 3)$.
  (iv) $g(x) + 6$ for $x = 2$.
  (v) $g(x + 6)$ for $x = 2$.
  (vi) $3g(x)$ for $x = 0$.
  (vii) $f(3x)$ for $x = 2$.
  (viii) $f(x) - f(2)$ for $x = 8$.
  (ix) $g(x + 1) - g(x)$ for $x = 1$.

(b) Solve

  (i) $g(x) = 6$.
  (ii) $f(x) = 574$.
  (iii) $g(x) = 281$.

(c) The values in the table were obtained using the formulas $f(x) = x^3 + x^2 + x - 10$ and $g(x) = 7x^2 - 8x - 6$. Use the table to find two solutions to the equation $x^3 + x^2 + x - 10 = 7x^2 - 8x - 6$.

Table 2.19

x	0	1	2	3	4	5	6	7	8	9
$f(x)$	−10	−7	4	29	74	145	248	389	574	809
$g(x)$	−6	−7	6	33	74	129	198	281	378	489

28. Using the graph of $v(t)$ in Figure 2.1 Section 2.1, solve the equation $v(t + 2) = -10$ and interpret your result.

29. (a) Let $f(x) = \left(\dfrac{x}{2}\right)^3 + 2$. Calculate $f(-6)$.

(b) Solve $f(x) = -6$.

(c) Find points that correspond to parts (a) and (b) on the graph of $f(x)$ in Figure 2.31.

(d) Calculate $f(4) - f(2)$. Draw a vertical line segment on the y-axis that illustrates this calculation.

(e) If $a = -2$, compute $f(a + 4)$ and $f(a) + 4$.

(f) In part (e), what x-value corresponds to $f(a + 4)$? To $f(a) + 4$?

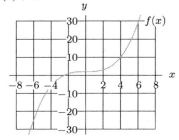

Figure 2.31

30. (a) Let $g(x) = \dfrac{1}{x + 1}$. Calculate $g(-2)$.

(b) Solve $g(x) = -2$.

(c) Find points that correspond to parts (a) and (b) on the graph of $g(x)$ in Figure 2.32.

(d) Calculate $g(0) - g(2)$. Draw a vertical line segment on the y-axis that illustrates this calculation.

(e) If $a = -3$, compute $g(a - 1)$ and $g(a) - 1$.

(f) In part (e), what x-value corresponds to $g(a - 1)$? To $g(a) - 1$?

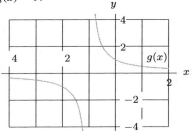

Figure 2.32

31. Suppose $S(d)$ gives the height of high tide in Seattle on a specific day, d, of the year. Use shifts of the function $S(d)$ to find formulas for each of the following functions:

(a) $T(d)$, the height of high tide in Tacoma on day d, given that high tide in Tacoma is always one foot higher than high tide in Seattle.

(b) $P(d)$, the height of high tide in Portland on day d, given that high tide in Portland is the same height as the previous day's high tide in Seattle.

32. Using Figure 2.33, graph the transformations of c.

(a) $s = c(t) + 3$

(b) $s = c(t + 3)$

(c) $s = c(t) - 1.5$

(d) $s = c(t - 1.5)$

(e) $s = c(t - 2) + 2$

(f) $s = c(t + 0.5) - 3$

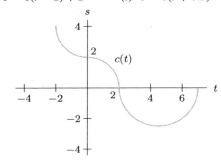

Figure 2.33

33. Table 2.20 contains values of $f(x)$. Each function in parts (a)–(c) is a translation of $f(x)$. Find a possible formula for each of these functions in terms of f. For example, given the data in Table 2.21, you could say that $k(x) = f(x) + 1$.

Table 2.20

x	0	1	2	3	4	5	6	7
$f(x)$	0	0.5	2	4.5	8	12.5	18	24.5

Table 2.21

x	0	1	2	3	4	5	6	7
$k(x)$	1	1.5	3	5.5	9	13.5	19	25.5

(a)

x	0	1	2	3	4	5	6	7
$h(x)$	-2	-1.5	0	2.5	6	10.5	16	22.5

(b)

x	0	1	2	3	4	5	6	7
$g(x)$	0.5	2	4.5	8	12.5	18	24.5	32

(c)

x	0	1	2	3	4	5	6	7
$i(x)$	-1.5	0	2.5	6	10.5	16	22.5	30

34. Table 2.22 contains values of $g(t)$. Each function in parts (a)–(e) is a translation of $g(t)$. Find a possible formula for each of these functions in terms of g.

Table 2.22

t	-1	-0.5	0	0.5	1
$g(t)$	0.5	0.8	1.0	0.9	0.6

(a)

t	-1	-0.5	0	0.5	1
$a(t)$	1.0	1.3	1.50	1.4	1.1

(b)

t	-1	-0.5	0	0.5	1
$b(t)$	1.0	0.9	0.6	0.1	-0.4

(c)

t	-1	-0.5	0	0.5	1
$c(t)$	0.7	0.6	0.3	-0.2	-0.7

(d)

t	-1	-0.5	0	.5	1
$d(t)$	0	0.5	0.8	1.0	0.9

(e)

t	-1	-0.5	0	0.5	1
$e(t)$	1.2	1.7	2.0	2.2	2.1

35. Graph $y = \log x$, $y = \log(10x)$, and $y = \log(100x)$. How do the graphs compare? Use a property of logs to show that the graphs are vertical shifts of one another.

36. For $t \geq 0$, let $H(t) = 68 + 93(0.91)^t$ give the temperature of a cup of coffee in degrees Fahrenheit t minutes after it is brought to class.

(a) Find formulas for $H(t + 15)$ and $H(t) + 15$.
(b) Graph $H(t)$, $H(t + 15)$, and $H(t) + 15$.
(c) Describe in practical terms a situation modeled by the function $H(t + 15)$. What about $H(t) + 15$?
(d) Which function, $H(t + 15)$ or $H(t) + 15$, approaches the same final temperature as the function $H(t)$? What is that temperature?

37. Suppose $T(d)$ gives the average temperature in your hometown on the dth day of last year (where $d = 1$ is January 1st, and so on).

(a) Graph $T(d)$ for $1 \leq d \leq 365$.
(b) Give a possible value for each of the following: $T(6)$; $T(100)$; $T(215)$; $T(371)$.
(c) What is the relationship between $T(d)$ and $T(d + 365)$? Explain.
(d) If you were to graph $w(d) = T(d + 365)$ on the same axes as $T(d)$, how would the two graphs compare?
(e) Do you think the function $T(d) + 365$ has any practical significance? Explain.

38. A carpenter remodeling your kitchen quotes you a price based on the cost of labor and materials. Materials are subject to a sales tax of 8.2%. Labor is not taxed.

(a) One option is based on a fixed labor cost of $800 and the variable cost of materials. The total cost is given by $C(x) = 800 + x + 0.082x$ where x is the cost of materials in dollars. Later the carpenter says the job will actually cost $C(x) - 50$. Find a formula for $C(x) - 50$ and describe in practical terms what might have changed.
(b) Under another option, you pay a fixed amount of $1000 for the materials (including tax) plus an hourly labor rate. This time, the total cost is given by $D(x) = 1000 + 15x$ where x is the number of hours to complete the job. Find a formula for $D(x) + 250$ and explain what this might mean in terms of the job.
(c) Using the option from part (b), find a formula for $D(x - 8)$. Explain what this suggests about the job.

39. At a jazz club, the cost of an evening is based on a cover charge of $5 plus a beverage charge of $3 per drink.

(a) Find a formula for $t(x)$, the total cost for an evening in which x drinks are consumed.
(b) If the price of the cover charge is raised by $1, express the new total cost function, $n(x)$, as a transformation of $t(x)$.
(c) The management increases the cover charge to $10, leave the price of a drink at $3, but include the first two drinks for free. For $x \geq 2$, express $p(x)$, the new total cost, as a transformation of $t(x)$.

40. A hot brick is removed from a kiln and set on the floor to cool. Let t be time in minutes after the brick was removed. The difference, $D(t)$, between the brick's temperature, initially 350°F, and room temperature, 70°F, decays ex-ponentially over time at a rate of 3% per minute. The brick's temperature, $H(t)$, is a transformation of $D(t)$. Find a formula for $H(t)$. Compare the graphs of $D(t)$ and $H(t)$, paying attention to the asymptotes.

2.6 REFLECTIONS AND SYMMETRY

In Section 2.5 we saw that a horizontal shift of the graph of a function results from a change to the input of the function. (Specifically, adding or subtracting a constant inside the function's parentheses.) A vertical shift corresponds to an outside change.

In this section we consider the effect of reflecting a function's graph across the x or y-axis. A reflection across the x-axis corresponds to an outside change to the function's formula; a reflection across the y-axis and corresponds to an inside change.

A Formula for a Reflection

Figure 2.34 shows the graph of a function $y = f(x)$ and Table 2.23 gives a corresponding table of values. Note that we do not need an explicit formula for f.

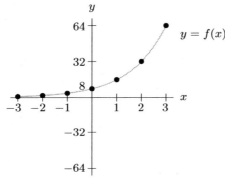

Figure 2.34: A graph of the function $y = f(x)$

Table 2.23 *Values of the function $y = f(x)$*

x	y
-3	1
-2	2
-1	4
0	8
1	16
2	32
3	64

Figure 2.35 shows a graph of a function $y = g(x)$, resulting from a vertical reflection of the graph of f across the x-axis. Figure 2.36 is a graph of a function $y = h(x)$, resulting from a horizontal reflection of the graph of f across the y-axis. Figure 2.37 is a graph of a function $y = k(x)$, resulting from a horizontal reflection of the graph of f across the y-axis followed by a vertical reflection across the x-axis.

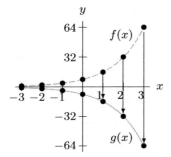

Figure 2.35: Graph reflected across x-axis

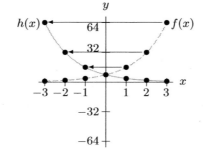

Figure 2.36: Graph reflected across y-axis

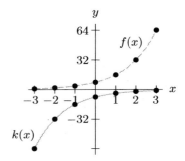

Figure 2.37: Graph reflected across y- and x-axes

Example 1   Find a formula in terms of f for   (a) $y = g(x)$ (b) $y = h(x)$ (c) $y = k(x)$

Solution   (a) The graph of $y = g(x)$ is obtained by reflecting the graph of f vertically across the x-axis. For example, the point $(3, 64)$ on the graph of f reflects to become the point $(3, -64)$ on the graph of g. The point $(2, 32)$ on the graph of f becomes $(2, -32)$ on the graph of g. See Table 2.24.

Table 2.24   *Values of the functions $g(x)$ and $f(x)$ graphed in Figure 2.35*

x	-3	-2	-1	0	1	2	3
$g(x)$	-1	-2	-4	-8	-16	-32	-64
$f(x)$	1	2	4	8	16	32	64

Notice that when a point is reflected vertically across the x-axis, the x-value stays fixed, while the y-value changes sign. That is, for a given x-value,

y-value of g is the negative of y-value of f.

Algebraically, this means

$$g(x) = -f(x).$$

(b) The graph of $y = h(x)$ is obtained by reflecting the graph of $y = f(x)$ horizontally across the y-axis. In part (a), a vertical reflection corresponded to an outside change in the formula, specifically, multiplying by -1. Thus, you might guess that a horizontal reflection of the graph corresponds to an inside change in the formula. This is correct. To see why, consider Table 2.25.

Table 2.25   *Values of the functions $h(x)$ and $f(x)$ graphed in Figure 2.36*

x	-3	-2	-1	0	1	2	3
$h(x)$	64	32	16	8	4	2	1
$f(x)$	1	2	4	8	16	32	64

Notice that when a point is reflected horizontally across the y-axis, the y-value remains fixed, while the x-value changes sign. For example, since $f(-3) = 1$ and $h(3) = 1$, we have $h(3) = f(-3)$. Since $f(-1) = 4$ and $h(1) = 4$, we have $h(1) = f(-1)$. In general,

$$h(x) = f(-x).$$

(c) The graph of the function $y = k(x)$ results from a horizontal reflection of the graph of f across the y-axis, followed by a vertical reflection across the x-axis. Since a horizontal reflection corresponds to multiplying the inputs by -1 and a vertical reflection corresponds to multiplying the outputs by -1, we have

Vertical reflection across the x-axis
$$\downarrow$$
$$h(x) = \ -f(-x).$$
$$\uparrow$$
Horizontal reflection across the y-axis

Let's check a point. If $x = 1$, then the formula $k(x) = -f(-x)$ gives:

$$k(1) = -f(-1) = -4 \qquad \text{since } f(-1) = 4.$$

This result is consistent with the graph, since $(1, -4)$ is on the graph of $k(x)$.

For a function f:

- The graph of $y = -f(x)$ is a reflection of the graph of $y = f(x)$ across the x-axis.
- The graph of $y = f(-x)$ is a reflection of the graph of $y = f(x)$ across the y-axis.

Symmetry About the y-Axis

The graph of $p(x) = x^2$ in Figure 2.38 is *symmetric* about the y-axis. In other words, the part of the graph to the left of the y-axis is the mirror image of the part to the right of the y-axis. Reflecting the graph of $p(x)$ across the y-axis gives the graph of $p(x)$ again.

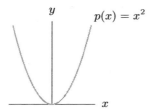

Figure 2.38: Reflecting the graph of $p(x) = x^2$ across the y-axis does not change its appearance

Symmetry about the y-axis is called *even symmetry*, because power functions with even exponents, such as $y = x^2$, $y = x^4$, $y = x^6$, ... have this property. Since $y = p(-x)$ is a reflection of the graph of p across the y-axis and $p(x)$ has even symmetry, we have

$$p(-x) = p(x).$$

To check this relationship, let $x = 2$. Then $p(2) = 2^2 = 4$, and $p(-2) = (-2)^2 = 4$, so $p(-2) = p(2)$. This means that the point $(2, 4)$ and its reflection across the y-axis, $(-2, 4)$, are both on the graph of $p(x)$.

Example 2   For the function $p(x) = x^2$, check algebraically that $p(-x) = p(x)$ for all x.

Solution   Substitute $-x$ into the formula for $p(x)$ giving

$$p(-x) = (-x)^2 = (-x) \cdot (-x)$$
$$= x^2$$
$$= p(x).$$

Thus, $p(-x) = p(x)$.

In general,

If f is a function, then f is called an **even function** if, for all values of x in the domain of f,
$$f(-x) = f(x).$$
The graph of f is symmetric about the y-axis.

Symmetry About the Origin

Figures 2.39 and 2.40 show the graph of $q(x) = x^3$. Reflecting the graph of q first across the y-axis and then across the x-axis (or vice-versa) gives the graph of q again. This kind of symmetry is called symmetry about the origin, or *odd symmetry*.

In Example 1, we saw that $y = -f(-x)$ is a reflection of the graph of $y = f(x)$ across both the y-axis and the x-axis. Since $q(x) = x^3$ is symmetric about the origin, q is the same function as this double reflection. That is,

$$q(x) = -q(-x) \quad \text{which means that} \quad q(-x) = -q(x).$$

To check this relationship, let $x = 2$. Then $q(2) = 2^3 = 8$, and $q(-2) = (-2)^3 = -8$, so $q(-2) = -q(2)$. This means the point $(2, 8)$ and its reflection across the origin, $(-2, -8)$, are both on the graph of q.

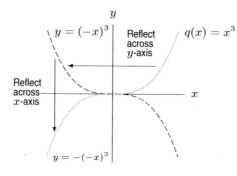

Figure 2.39: If the graph is reflected across the y-axis and then across the x-axis, it does not change

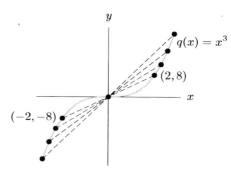

Figure 2.40: If every point on this graph is reflected about the origin, the graph is unchanged

Example 3   For the function $q(x) = x^3$, check algebraically that $q(-x) = -q(x)$ for all x.

Solution   We evaluate $q(-x)$ giving

$$\begin{aligned} q(-x) &= (-x)^3 = (-x) \cdot (-x) \cdot (-x) \\ &= -x^3 \\ &= -q(x). \end{aligned}$$

Thus, $q(-x) = -q(x)$.

In general,

If f is a function, then f is called an **odd function** if, for all values of x in the domain of f,
$$f(-x) = -f(x).$$
The graph of f is symmetric about the origin.

Example 4   Determine whether the following functions are symmetric about the *y*-axis, the origin, or neither.

(a) $f(x) = |x|$ (b) $g(x) = 1/x$ (c) $h(x) = -x^3 - 3x^2 + 2$

Solution   The graphs of the functions in Figures 2.41, 2.42, and 2.43 can be helpful in identifying symmetry.

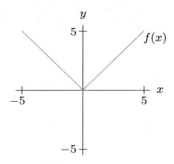

Figure 2.41: The graph of $f(x) = |x|$ appears to be symmetric about the *y*-axis

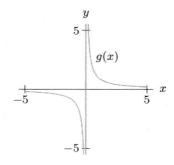

Figure 2.42: The graph of $g(x) = 1/x$ appears to be symmetric about the origin

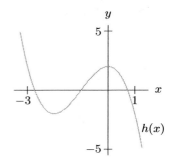

Figure 2.43: The graph of $h(x) = -x^3 - 3x^2 + 2$ is symmetric neither about the *y*-axis nor about the origin

From the graphs it appears that f is symmetric about the *y*-axis (even symmetry), g is symmetric about the origin (odd symmetry), and h has neither type of symmetry. However, how can we be sure that $f(x)$ and $g(x)$ are really symmetric? We check algebraically.

If $f(-x) = f(x)$, then f has even symmetry. We check by substituting $-x$ in for x:

$$f(-x) = |-x|$$
$$= |x|$$
$$= f(x).$$

Thus, f does have even symmetry.

If $g(-x) = -g(x)$, then g is symmetric about the origin. We check by substituting $-x$ for x:

$$g(-x) = \frac{1}{-x}$$
$$= -\frac{1}{x}$$
$$= -g(x).$$

Thus, g is symmetric about the origin.

The graph of h does not exhibit odd or even symmetry. To confirm, look at an example, say $x = 1$:

$$h(1) = -1^3 - 3 \cdot 1^2 + 2 = -2.$$

Now substitute $x = -1$, giving

$$h(-1) = -(-1)^3 - 3 \cdot (-1)^2 + 2 = 0.$$

Thus $h(1) \neq h(-1)$, so the function is not symmetric about the *y*-axis. Also, $h(-1) \neq -h(1)$, so the function is not symmetric about the origin.

Combining Shifts and Reflections

We can combine the horizontal and vertical shifts from Section 2.5 with the horizontal and vertical reflections of this section to make more complex transformations of functions.

Example 5   A cold yam is placed in a hot oven. Newton's Law of Heating tells us that the difference between the oven's temperature and the yam's temperature decays exponentially with time. The yam's temperature is initially $0°F$, the oven's temperature is $300°F$, and the temperature difference decreases by 3% per minute. Find a formula for $Y(t)$, the yam's temperature at time t.

Solution   Let $D(t)$ be the difference between the oven's temperature and the yam's temperature, which is given by an exponential function $D(t) = ab^t$. The initial temperature difference is $300°F - 0°F = 300°F$, so $a = 300$. The temperature difference decreases by 3% per minute, so $b = 1 - 0.03 = 0.97$. Thus,

$$D(t) = 300(0.97)^t.$$

If the yam's temperature is represented by $Y(t)$, then the temperature difference is given by

$$D(t) = 300 - Y(t),$$

so, solving for $Y(t)$, we have

$$Y(t) = 300 - D(t),$$

giving

$$Y(t) = 300 - 300(0.97)^t.$$

Writing $Y(t)$ in the form

$$Y(t) = \underbrace{-D(t)}_{\text{Reflect}} + \underbrace{300}_{\text{Shift}}$$

shows that the graph of Y is obtained by reflecting the graph of D across the t-axis and then shifting it vertically up 300 units. Notice that the horizontal asymptote of D, which is on the t-axis, is also shifted upward, resulting in a horizontal asymptote at $300°F$ for Y.

Figures 2.44 and 2.45 give the graphs of D and Y. Figure 2.45 shows that the yam heats up rapidly at first and then its temperature levels off toward $300°F$, the oven temperature.

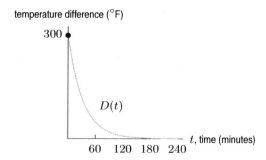
Figure 2.44: Graph of $D(t) = 300(0.97)^t$, the temperature difference between the yam and the oven

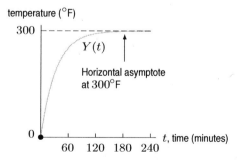
Figure 2.45: The transformation $Y(t) = -D(t) + 300$, where $D(t) = 300(0.97)^t$

Note that the temperature difference, D, is a decreasing function, so its average rate of change is negative. However, Y, the yam's temperature, is an increasing function, so its average rate of change is positive. Reflecting the graph of D over the t-axis to obtain the graph of Y changed the sign of the average rate of change.

Exercises and Problems for Section 2.6

Exercises

1. Complete the following tables using $f(p) = p^2 + 2p - 3$, and $g(p) = f(-p)$, and $h(p) = -f(p)$. Graph the three functions. Explain how the graphs of g and h are related to the graph of f.

p	-3	-2	-1	0	1	2	3
$f(p)$							

p	-3	-2	-1	0	1	2	3
$g(p)$							

p	-3	-2	-1	0	1	2	3
$h(p)$							

2. Graph $y = f(x) = 4^x$ and $y = f(-x)$ on the same set of axes. How are these graphs related? Give an explicit formula for $y = f(-x)$.

3. Graph $y = g(x) = \left(\frac{1}{3}\right)^x$ and $y = -g(x)$ on the same set of axes. How are these graphs related? Give an explicit formula for $y = -g(x)$.

Give a formula and graph for each of the transformations of $m(n) = n^2 - 4n + 5$ in Exercises 4–10.

4. $y = m(-n)$

5. $y = -m(n)$

6. $y = -m(-n)$

7. $y = -m(n + 2)$

8. $y = m(-n) - 4$

9. $y = -m(-n) + 3$

10. $y = 1 - m(n)$

Give a formula and graph for each of the transformations of $k(w) = 3^w$ in Exercises 11–17.

11. $y = k(-w)$

12. $y = -k(w)$

13. $y = -k(-w)$

14. $y = -k(w - 2)$

15. $y = k(-w) + 4$

16. $y = -k(-w) - 1$

17. $y = -3 - k(w)$

In Exercises 18–21, show that the function is even, odd, or neither.

18. $f(x) = 7x^2 - 2x + 1$

19. $f(x) = 4x^7 - 3x^5$

20. $f(x) = 8x^6 + 12x^2$

21. $f(x) = x^5 + 3x^3 - 2$

Problems

22. (a) Graph the function obtained from $f(x) = x^3$ by first reflecting across the x-axis, then translating up two units. Write a formula for the resulting function.
(b) Graph the function obtained from f by first translating up two units, then reflecting across the x-axis. Write a formula for the resulting function.
(c) Are the functions in parts (a) and (b) the same?

23. (a) Graph the function obtained from $g(x) = 2^x$ by first reflecting across the y-axis, then translating down three units. Write a formula for the resulting function.
(b) Graph the function obtained from g by first translating down three units, then reflecting across the y-axis. Write a formula for the resulting function.
(c) Are the functions in parts (a) and (b) the same?

24. If the graph of a line $y = b + mx$ is reflected across the y-axis, what are the slope and intercepts of the resulting line?

25. Graph $y = \log(1/x)$ and $y = \log x$ on the same axes.

How are the two graphs related? Use the properties of logarithms to explain the relationship algebraically.

26. The function $d(t)$ graphed in Figure 2.46 gives the winter temperature in °F at a high school, t hours after midnight.

(a) Describe in words the heating schedule for this building during the winter months.
(b) Graph $c(t) = 142 - d(t)$.
(c) Explain why c might describe the cooling schedule for summer months.

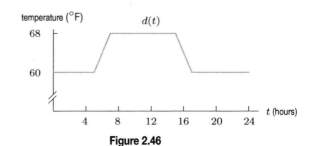

Figure 2.46

27. Using Figure 2.47, match the formulas (i)–(vi) with a graph from (a)–(f).

(i) $y = f(-x)$ (ii) $y = -f(x)$
(iii) $y = f(-x) + 3$ (iv) $y = -f(x - 1)$
(v) $y = -f(-x)$ (vi) $y = -2 - f(x)$

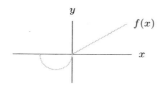

Figure 2.47

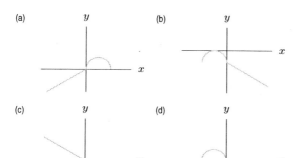

28. In Table 2.26, fill in as many y-values as you can if you know that f is

(a) An even function   (b) An odd function.

Table 2.26

x	-3	-2	-1	0	1	2	3
y	5		-4			-8	

29. Figure 2.48 shows the graph of a function f in the second quadrant. In each of the following cases, sketch $y = f(x)$, given that f is symmetric about

(a) The y-axis. (b) The origin. (c) The line $y = x$.

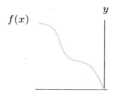

Figure 2.48

30. For each table, decide whether the function could be symmetric about the y-axis, about the origin, or neither.

(a)

x	-3	-2	-1	0	1	2	3
$f(x)$	6	1	-2	-3	-2	1	6

(b)

x	-3	-2	-1	0	1	2	3
$g(x)$	-8.1	-2.4	-0.3	0	0.3	2.4	8.1

(c)

x	-3	-2	-1	0	1	2	3
$f(x) + g(x)$	-2.1	-1.4	-2.3	-3	-1.7	3.4	14.1

(d)

x	-3	-2	-1	0	1	2	3
$f(x + 1)$	1	-2	-3	-2	1	6	13

31. A function is called symmetric about the line $y = x$ if interchanging x and y gives the same graph. The simplest example is the function $y = x$. Graph another straight line that is symmetric about the line $y = x$ and give its equation.

32. Show that the graph of the function h is symmetric about the origin, given that

$$h(x) = \frac{1 + x^2}{x - x^3}.$$

33. Comment on the following justification that the function $f(x) = x^3 - x^2 + 1$ is an even function: Because $f(0) = 1 \neq -f(0)$, we know that $f(x)$ is not odd. If a function is not odd, it must be even.

34. Is it possible for an odd function whose domain is all real numbers to be strictly concave up?

35. If f is an odd function and defined at $x = 0$, what is the value of $f(0)$? Explain how you can use this result to show that $c(x) = x + 1$ and $d(x) = 2^x$ are not odd.

36. In the first quadrant an even function is increasing and concave down. What can you say about the function's behavior in the second quadrant?

37. Show that the power function $f(x) = x^{1/3}$ is odd. Give a counterexample to the statement that all power functions of the form $f(x) = x^p$ are odd.

38. Graph $s(x) = 2^x + (\frac{1}{2})^x$, $c(x) = 2^x - (\frac{1}{2})^x$, and $n(x) = 2^x - (\frac{1}{2})^{x-1}$. State whether you think these functions are even, odd or neither. Show that your statements are true using algebra. That is, prove or disprove statements such as $s(-x) = s(x)$.

39. There are functions which are *neither* even nor odd. Is there a function that is *both* even and odd?

40. Some functions are symmetric about the y-axis. Is it possible for a function to be symmetric about the x-axis?

CHAPTER SUMMARY

- **Input and Output**
  Evaluating functions: finding $f(a)$ for given a.
  Solving equations: finding x if $f(x) = b$ for given b.

- **Domain and Range**
  Domain: set of input values.
  Range: set of output values
  Piecewise functions: different formulas on different intervals.

- **Concavity**
  Concave up: increasing rate of change.
  Concave down: decreasing rate of change.

- **Vertical and Horizontal Shifts**
  Vertical: $y = g(x) + k$.
    Upward if $k > 0$; downward if $k < 0$.
  Horizontal: $y = g(x + k)$.
    Left if $k > 0$; right if $k < 0$.

- **Reflections**

Across x-axis: $y = -f(x)$.
Across y-axis: $y = f(-x)$.

- **Symmetry**
  About y-axis: $f(-x) = f(x)$; even function.
  About the origin: $f(-x) = -f(x)$; odd function.

- **Stretches and Compressions**
  Vertical: $y = kf(x)$. Stretch if $k > 0$; compress if $0 < k < 1$; reflect across x-axis if $k < 0$.
  Horizontal: $y = f(kx)$. Compress if $k > 0$; stretch if $0 < k < 1$; reflect across y-axis if $k < 0$.

- **Quadratic Functions**
  Standard form: $y = ax^2 + bx + c$.
  Vertex form: $y = a(x - h)^2 + k$.
    Opening upward if $a > 0$; downward if $a < 0$.
  Vertex (h, k), axis of symmetry $x = h$, maximum, minimum.
    Completing the square.

REVIEW EXERCISES AND PROBLEMS FOR CHAPTER TWO

Exercises

If $p(r) = r^2 + 5$, evaluate the expressions in Exercises 1–2.

1. $p(7)$ **2.** $p(x) + p(8)$

3. Find the zeros of $s(l) = 7l - l^2$.

4. If $g(x) = x\sqrt{x} + 100x$, evaluate without a calculator
  (a) $g(100)$ **(b)** $g(4/25)$ **(c)** $g(1.21 \cdot 10^4)$

5. Let $h(x) = x^2 + bx + c$. Evaluate and simplify:
  (a) $h(1)$ **(b)** $h(b + 1)$

In Exercises 6–11:

(a) Complete the table of values. (If the function is undefined for a given x-value, say so.)

x	-5	-4	-3	-2	-1	$-\frac{3}{4}$	$-\frac{1}{2}$	$-\frac{1}{4}$
y								

x	0	$\frac{1}{4}$	$\frac{1}{2}$	$\frac{3}{4}$	1	2	3	4	5
y									

(b) Graph the function for $-5 \le x \le 5$. What is the range for the y-values you calculated for the table from part (a)?

(c) Give the complete domain and range of the function.
(d) For what values of x is the function increasing? Decreasing?

6. $y = x^2$ **7.** $y = x^3$ **8.** $y = \dfrac{1}{x}$

9. $y = \dfrac{1}{x^2}$ **10.** $y = \sqrt{x}$ **11.** $y = \sqrt[3]{x}$

12. (a) How can you tell from the graph of a function that a given x-value is not in the domain? Sketch an example.
  (b) How can you tell from the formula for a function that a given x-value is not in the domain? Give an example.

In Exercises 13–16, state the domain and range.

13. $f(x) = \sqrt{x - 4}$ **14.** $h(x) = x^2 + 8x$

15. $g(x) = \dfrac{4}{4 + x^2}$ **16.** $r(x) = \sqrt{4 - \sqrt{x - 4}}$

17. Let $g(x) = x^2 + x$. Evaluate and simplify the following.
  (a) $-3g(x)$ **(b)** $g(1) - x$ **(c)** $g(x) + \pi$
  (d) $\sqrt{g(x)}$ **(e)** $g(1)/(x + 1)$ **(f)** $(g(x))^2$

18. Let $f(x) = 1 - x$. Evaluate and simplify the following.
  (a) $2f(x)$ **(b)** $f(x) + 1$ **(c)** $f(1 - x)$
  (d) $(f(x))^2$ **(e)** $f(1)/x$ **(f)** $\sqrt{f(x)}$

19. Suppose $x = 2$. Determine the value of the input of the function f in each of the following expressions:

    (a) $f(2x)$ **(b)** $f(\frac{1}{2}x)$ **(c)** $f(x + 3)$ **(d)** $f(-x)$

20. Determine the value of x in each of the following expressions which leads to an input of 2 to the function f:

    (a) $f(2x)$ **(b)** $f(\frac{1}{2}x)$ **(c)** $f(x + 3)$ **(d)** $f(-x)$

21. The point $(2, 5)$ is on the graph of $y = f(x)$. Give the coordinates of one point on the graph of each of the following functions.

    (a) $y = f(x - 4)$ **(b)** $y = f(x) - 4$
    (c) $y = f(4x)$ **(d)** $y = 4f(x)$

22. The point $(-3, 4)$ is on the graph of $y = g(x)$. Give the coordinates of one point on the graph of each of the following functions.

    (a) $y = g(\frac{1}{3}x)$ **(b)** $y = \frac{1}{3}g(x)$
    (c) $y = g(-3x)$ **(d)** $y = -g(3x)$

Are the functions in Exercises 23–29 even, odd, or neither?

23. $m(x) = \dfrac{1}{x^2}$ **24.** $a(x) = \dfrac{1}{x}$

25. $b(x) = |x|$ **26.** $e(x) = x + 3$

27. $p(x) = x^2 + 2x$ **28.** $q(x) = 2^{x+1}$

29. $f(x) = \dfrac{-1}{(x-2)^2} + 1$

30. Let $f(x) = 1 - x$. Evaluate and simplify:

    (a) $f(2x)$ **(b)** $f(x + 1)$ **(c)** $f(1 - x)$
    (d) $f(x^2)$ **(e)** $f(1/x)$ **(f)** $f(\sqrt{x})$

In Exercises 31–34, find a formula for the parabola.

31.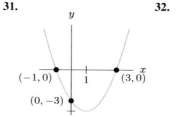

32.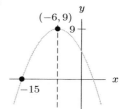

33.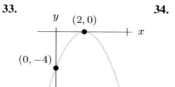

34.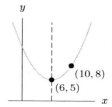

Problems

In Problems 35–37, if $f(x) = \dfrac{ax}{a + x}$, find and simplify

35. $f(a)$ **36.** $f(1 - a)$ **37.** $f\left(\dfrac{1}{1-a}\right)$

In Figure 2.49, show the coordinates of the point(s) representing the statements in Problems 38–41.

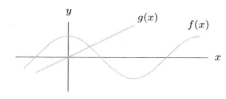

Figure 2.49

38. $f(0) = 2$ **39.** $f(-3) = f(3) = f(9) = 0$

40. $f(2) = g(2)$ **41.** $g(x) > f(x)$ for $x > 2$

42. An epidemic of influenza spreads through a city. Figure 2.50 is the graph of $I = f(w)$, where I is the number of individuals (in thousands) infected w weeks after the epidemic begins.

    (a) Evaluate $f(2)$ and explain its meaning in terms of the epidemic.
    (b) Approximately how many people were infected at the height of the epidemic? When did that occur? Write your answer in the form $f(a) = b$.
    (c) Solve $f(w) = 4.5$ and explain what the solutions mean in terms of the epidemic.
    (d) The graph was obtained using the formula $f(w) = 6w(1.3)^{-w}$. Use the graph to estimate the solution of the inequality $6w(1.3)^{-w} \geq 6$. Explain what the solution means in terms of the epidemic.

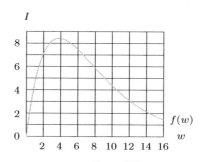

Figure 2.50

43. Let t be time in seconds and let $r(t)$ be the rate, in gallons/second, that water enters a reservoir:

$$r(t) = 800 - 40t.$$

(a) Evaluate the expressions $r(0)$, $r(15)$, $r(25)$, and explain their physical significance.
(b) Graph $y = r(t)$ for $0 \le t \le 30$, labeling the intercepts. What is the physical significance of the slope and the intercepts?
(c) For $0 \le t \le 30$, when does the reservoir have the most water? When does it have the least water?
(d) What are the domain and range of $r(t)$?

44. Suppose that $f(x)$ is invertible and that both f and f^{-1} are defined for all values of x. Let $f(2) = 3$ and $f^{-1}(5) = 4$. Evaluate the following expressions, or, if the given information is insufficient, write unknown.
(a) $f^{-1}(3)$ (b) $f^{-1}(4)$ (c) $f(4)$

45. Suppose that $j(x) = h^{-1}(x)$ and that both j and h are defined for all values of x. Let $h(4) = 2$ and $j(5) = -3$. Evaluate if possible:
(a) $j(h(4))$ (b) $j(4)$ (c) $h(j(4))$
(d) $j(2)$ (e) $h^{-1}(-3)$ (f) $j^{-1}(-3)$
(g) $h(5)$ (h) $(h(-3))^{-1}$ (i) $(h(2))^{-1}$

46. Values of f and g are given in Table 2.27.
(a) Evaluate $f(1)$ and $g(3)$.
(b) Describe in full sentences the patterns you see in the values for each function.
(c) Assuming that the patterns you observed in part (b) hold true for all values of x, calculate $f(5)$, $f(-2)$, $g(5)$, and $g(-2)$.
(d) Find possible formulas for $f(x)$ and $g(x)$.

Table 2.27

x	-1	0	1	2	3	4
$f(x)$	-4	-1	2	5	8	11
$g(x)$	4	1	0	1	4	9

47. Let $k(x) = 6 - x^2$.
(a) Find a point on the graph of $k(x)$ whose x-coordinate is -2.
(b) Find two points on the graph whose y-coordinates are -2.
(c) Graph $k(x)$ and locate the points in parts (a) and (b).
(d) Let $p = 2$. Calculate $k(p) - k(p - 1)$.

48. Let $f(a)$ be the cost in dollars of a kilograms of apples. What do the following statements tell you? What are the units of each of the numbers?
(a) $f(2) = 1.50$ (b) $f(0.1) = 0.75$
(c) $f^{-1}(3) = 4$ (d) $f^{-1}(1.5) = 2$

49. Let $t(x)$ be the time required, in seconds, to melt 1 gram of a compound at $x°C$.
(a) Express the following statement as an equation using $t(x)$: It takes 272 seconds to melt 1 gram of the compound at $400°C$.
(b) Explain the following equations in words:
     (i) $t(800) = 136$ (ii) $t^{-1}(68) = 1600$
(c) Above a certain temperature, doubling the temperature, x, halves the melting time. Express this fact with an equation involving $t(x)$.

50. Table 2.28 shows $N(s)$, the number of sections of Economics 101, as a function of s, the number of students in the course. If s is between two numbers listed in the table, then $N(s)$ is the higher number of sections.

Table 2.28

s	50	75	100	125	150	175	200
$N(s)$	4	4	5	5	6	6	7

(a) Evaluate and interpret:
     (i) $N(150)$ (ii) $N(80)$ (iii) $N(55.5)$
(b) Solve for s and interpret:
     (i) $N(s) = 4$ (ii) $N(s) = N(125)$

51. The surface area of a cylindrical aluminum can is a measure of how much aluminum the can requires. If the can has radius r and height h, its surface area A and its volume V are given by the equations:

$$A = 2\pi r^2 + 2\pi rh \quad \text{and} \quad V = \pi r^2 h.$$

(a) The volume, V, of a 12 oz cola can is 355 cm^3. A cola can is approximately cylindrical. Express its surface area A as a function of its radius r, where r is measured in centimeters. [Hint: First solve for h in terms of r.]
(b) Graph $A = s(r)$, the surface area of a cola can whose volume is 355 cm^3, for $0 \le r \le 10$.
(c) What is the domain of $s(r)$? Based on your graph, what, approximately, is the range of $s(r)$?
(d) The manufacturers wish to use the least amount of aluminum (in cm^2) necessary to make a 12 oz cola can. Use your answer in (c) to find the minimum amount of aluminum needed. State the values of r and h that minimize the amount of aluminum used.
(e) The radius of a real 12 oz cola can is about 3.25 cm. Show that real cola cans use more aluminum than necessary to hold 12 oz of cola. Why do you think real cola cans are made to this way?

52. Table 2.29 shows the population, P, in millions, of Ireland[9] at various times between 1780 and 1910, with t in years since 1780.

  (a) When was the population increasing? Decreasing?
  (b) For each successive time interval, construct a table showing the average rate of change of the population.
  (c) From the table you constructed in part (b), when is the graph of the population concave up? Concave down?
  (d) When was the average rate of change of the population the greatest? The least? How is this related to part (c)? What does this mean in human terms?
  (e) Graph the data in Table 2.29 and join the points by a curve to show the trend in the data. From this graph identify where the curve is increasing, decreasing, concave up and concave down. Compare your answers to those you got in parts (a) and (c). Identify the region you found in part (d).
  (f) Something catastrophic happened in Ireland between 1780 and 1910. When? What happened in Ireland at that time to cause this catastrophe?

Table 2.29 *The population of Ireland from 1780 to 1910, where $t = 0$ corresponds to 1780*

t	0	20	40	60	70	90	110	130
P	4.0	5.2	6.7	8.3	6.9	5.4	4.7	4.4

53. Let $D(p)$ be the number of iced cappuccinos sold each week by a coffeehouse when the price is p cents.

  (a) What does the expression $D(225)$ represent?
  (b) Do you think that $D(p)$ is an increasing function or a decreasing function? Why?
  (c) What does the following equation tell you about p?
   $D(p) = 180$
  (d) The coffeehouse sells n iced cappuccinos when they charge the average price in their area, t cents. Thus, $D(t) = n$. What is the meaning of the following expressions: $D(1.5t)$, $1.5D(t)$, $D(t + 50)$, $D(t) + 50$?

54. Suppose $w = j(x)$ is the average daily quantity of water (in gallons) required by an oak tree of height x feet.

  (a) What does the expression $j(25)$ represent? What about $j^{-1}(25)$?
  (b) What does the following equation tell you about v: $j(v) = 50$. Rewrite this statement in terms of j^{-1}.
  (c) Oak trees are on average z feet high and a tree of average height requires p gallons of water. Represent this fact in terms of j and then in terms of j^{-1}.
  (d) Using the definitions of z and p from part (c), what do the following expressions represent?

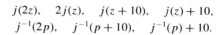

$$j(2z), \quad 2j(z), \quad j(z + 10), \quad j(z) + 10,$$
$$j^{-1}(2p), \quad j^{-1}(p + 10), \quad j^{-1}(p) + 10.$$

55. Without a calculator, match each of the functions (a)–(f) with one of the graphs (I) – (VI).

  (a) $y = e^x$ **(b)** $y = e^{5x}$ **(c)** $y = 5e^x$
  (d) $y = e^{x+5}$ **(e)** $y = e^{-x}$ **(f)** $y = e^x + 5$

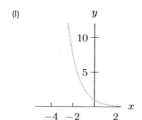
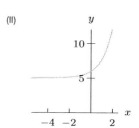
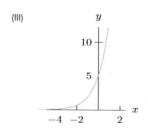
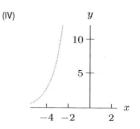
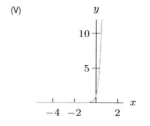
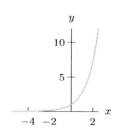

The functions graphed in Problems 56–57 are transformations of some basic function. Give a possible formula for each one.

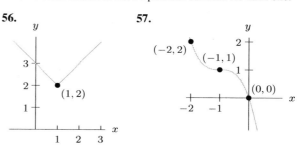

56.

57.

[9] Adapted from D. N. Burghes and A. D. Wood, Ellis Horwood, *Mathematical Models in the Social, Management and Life Science,* p. 104 (Ellis Horwood, 1980).

Using Figure 2.51, graph the functions in Problems 58–62 without a calculator.

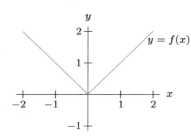

Figure 2.51

58. $y = -f(x)$ **59.** $y = f(x + 3)$

60. $y = f(x) - 4$ **61.** $y = 5f(x)$

62. $y = f(\frac{1}{4}x)$

Using Figure 2.52, graph the functions in Problems 63–67 on the same axes as $g(x)$:

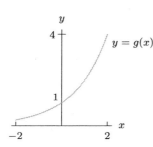

Figure 2.52

63. $y = -g(x)$ **64.** $y = g(-x)$

65. $y = -g(-x)$ **66.** $y = g(x) + 3$

67. $y = 5 - g(x)$

68. In Figure 2.53, the value of d is labeled on the x-axis. Locate the following quantities on the y-axis:

    (a) $g(d)$ **(b)** $g(-d)$ **(c)** $-g(-d)$

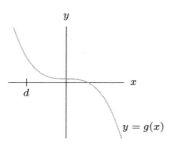

Figure 2.53

69. In Figure 2.54, the values c and d are labeled on the x-axis. On the y-axis, locate the following quantities:

    (a) $h(c)$ **(b)** $h(d)$

    (c) $h(c + d)$ **(d)** $h(c) + h(d)$

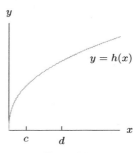

Figure 2.54

70. Graph $f(x) = 3^x$, $g(x) = 2(3^x)$, and $h(x) = 3^{2x}$. Describe the relationships between the three functions.

71. Without a calculator, match the formulas (a)–(e) to one of the graphs (i)–(v).

    (a) $y = \log(x - a), a > 0$ **(b)** $y = \log(x/a), a > 1$

    (c) $y = \dfrac{1}{\log x}$ **(d)** $y = \log(x + a), a > 0$

    (e) $y = a \log x, a > 0$

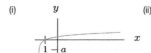

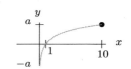

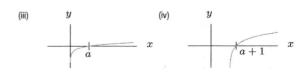

In Problems 72–74, use Figure 2.55 to find a formula for the graphs in terms of h.

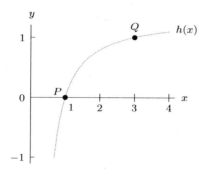

Figure 2.55

72.   **73.**

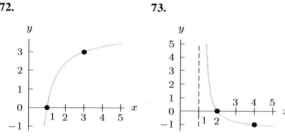

74.

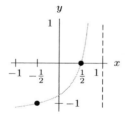

Problems 75–79 use Table 2.30 which gives the total cost, $C = f(n)$, for a carpenter to build n wooden chairs.

Table 2.30

n	0	10	20	30	40	50
$f(n)$	5000	6000	6800	7450	8000	8500

75. Evaluate the following expressions. Explain in everyday terms what they mean.

(a) $f(10)$ (b) $f(x)$ if $x = 30$
(c) z if $f(z) = 8000$ (d) $f(0)$

76. Find approximate values for p and q if $f(p) = 6400$ and $q = f(26)$.

77. Let $d_1 = f(30) - f(20)$, $d_2 = f(40) - f(30)$, and $d_3 = f(50) - f(40)$.

(a) Evaluate d_1, d_2 and d_3.
(b) What do these numbers tell you about the carpenter's cost of building chairs?

78. Graph $f(n)$. Label the quantities you found in Problems 75–77 on your graph.

79. The carpenter currently builds k chairs per week.

(a) What do the following expressions represent?

(i) $f(k + 10)$ (ii) $f(k) + 10$
(iii) $f(2k)$ (iv) $2f(k)$

(b) If the carpenter sells his chairs at 80% above cost, plus an additional 5% sales tax, write an expression for his gross income (including sales tax) each week.

80. The graph in Figure 2.56 gives the number of hours of daylight in Charlotte, North Carolina on day d of the year, where $d = 0$ is January 1. Graph the number of hours of daylight in Buenos Aires, Argentina, which is as far south of the equator as Charlotte is north. [Hint: When it is summer in the Northern Hemisphere, it is winter in the Southern Hemisphere.]

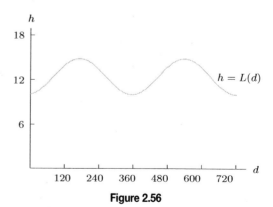

Figure 2.56

CHECK YOUR UNDERSTANDING

Are the statements in Problems 1–77 true or false? Give an explanation for your answer.

1. If $f(t) = 3t^2 - 4$ then $f(2) = 0$.

2. If $f(x) = x^2 - 9x + 10$ then $f(b) = b^2 - 9b + 10$.

3. If $f(x) = x^2$ then $f(x + h) = x^2 + h^2$.

4. If $q = \dfrac{1}{\sqrt{z^2 + 5}}$ then the values of z that make $q = \frac{1}{3}$ are $z = \pm 2$.

5. If $W = \dfrac{t + 4}{t - 4}$ then when $t = 8$, $W = 1$.

6. If $f(t) = t^2 + 64$ then $f(0) = 64$.

7. If $f(x) = 0$ then $x = 0$.

8. If $f(x) = x^2 + 2x + 7$ then $f(-x) = f(x)$.

9. If $g(x) = \dfrac{3}{\sqrt{x^2 + 4}}$ then $g(x)$ can never be zero.

10. If $h(p) = -6p + 9$ then $h(3) + h(4) = h(7)$.

11. The domain of a function is the set of input values.

12. If a function is being used to model a real world situation, the domain and range are often determined by the constraints of the situation being modeled.

13. The domain of $f(x) = \dfrac{4}{x - 3}$ consists of all real numbers x, $x \neq 0$.

14. If $f(x) = \sqrt{2 - x}$, the domain of f consists of all real numbers $x \geq 2$.

15. The range of $f(x) = \dfrac{1}{x}$ is all real numbers.

16. The range of $y = 4 - \dfrac{1}{x}$ is $0 < y < 4$.

17. If $f(x) = \frac{2}{5}x + 6$ and its domain is $15 \leq x \leq 20$ then the range of f is $12 \leq 4 \leq 14$.

18. The domain of $f(x) = \dfrac{x}{\sqrt{x^2 + 1}}$ is all real numbers.

19. The graph of the absolute value function $y = |x|$ has a V shape.

20. The domain of $f(x) = |x|$ is all real numbers.

21. If $f(x) = |x|$ and $g(x) = |-x|$ then for all x, $f(x) = g(x)$.

22. If $f(x) = |x|$ and $g(x) = -|x|$ then for all x, $f(x) = g(x)$.

23. If $y = \dfrac{x}{|x|}$ then $y = 1$ for $x \neq 0$.

24. If $f(x) = \begin{cases} 3 & \text{if } x < 0 \\ x^2 & \text{if } 0 \leq x \leq 4 \\ 7 & \text{if } x > 4 \end{cases}$, then $f(3) = 0$.

25. Let $f(x) = \begin{cases} x & \text{if } x < 0 \\ x^2 & \text{if } 0 \leq x \leq 4 \\ -x & \text{if } x > 4 \end{cases}$ If $f(x) = 4$ then $x = 2$.

26. If $f(3) = 5$ and f is invertible, then $f^{-1}(3) = 1/5$.

27. If $g(3) = g(5)$, then g is not invertible.

28. If $h(7) = 4$ and h is invertible, then $h^{-1}(4) = 7$.

29. If $f(x) = \frac{3}{4}x - 6$ then $f^{-1}(8) = 0$.

30. If $R = f(S) = \frac{2}{3}S + 8$ then $S = f^{-1}(R) = \frac{3}{2}(R - 8)$.

31. In general $f^{-1}(x) = (f(x))^{-1}$.

32. If $f(x) = \dfrac{x}{x + 1}$ then $f(t^{-1}) = \dfrac{1/t}{1/t + 1}$.

33. The units of the output of a function are the same as the units of output of its inverse.

34. If the graph of a function is concave up, then the average rate of change of a function over an interval of length 1 increases as the interval moves from left to right.

35. The function f in the table could be concave up.

x	−2	0	2	4
$f(x)$	5	6	8	12

36. The function g in the table could be concave down.

t	−1	1	3	5
$g(t)$	9	8	6	3

37. A straight line is concave up.

38. A function can be both decreasing and concave down.

39. If a function is concave up, it must be increasing.

40. The quadratic function $f(x) = x(x + 2)$ is in factored form.

41. If $f(x) = (x + 1)(x + 2)$, then the zeros of f are 1 and 2.

42. A quadratic function whose graph is concave up has a maximum.

43. All quadratic equations have the form $f(x) = ax^2$.

44. If the height above the ground of an object at time t is given by $s(t) = at^2 + bt + c$, then $s(0)$ tells us when the object hits the ground.

45. To find the zeros of $f(x) = ax^2 + bx + c$, solve the equation $ax^2 + bx + c = 0$ for x.

46. Every quadratic equation has two real solutions.

47. There is only one quadratic function with zeros at $x = -2$ and $x = 2$.

48. A quadratic function has exactly two zeros.

49. If $g(x) = f(x) + 3$ then the graph of $g(x)$ is a vertical shift of the graph of f.

50. If $g(t) = f(t - 2)$ then the graph of $g(t)$ can be obtained by shifting the graph of f two units to the left.

51. If $g(x) = f(x) + k$ and k is negative, the graph of $g(x)$ is the same as the graph of f, but shifted down.

52. Vertical and horizontal shifts are called translations.

53. The reflection of $y = x^2$ across the x-axis is $y = -x^2$.

54. If $f(x)$ is an odd function, then $f(x) = f(-x)$.

55. The graphs of odd functions are symmetric about the y-axis.

56. The graph of $y = -f(x)$ is the reflection of the graph of $y = f(x)$ across the x-axis.

57. The graph of $y = f(-x)$ is the reflection of the graph of $y = f(x)$ across the y-axis.

58. If the graph of a function f is symmetric about the y-axis then $f(x) = f(-x)$.

59. Figure 2.57 suggests that $g(x) = f(x + 2) + 1$.

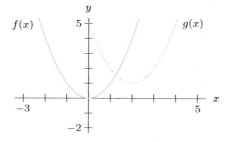

Figure 2.57

60. If $g(x) = x^2 + 4$ then $g(x - 2) = x^2$.

61. For any function f, we have $f(x + k) = f(x) + k$.

62. Figure 2.58 could be the graph of $f(x) = |x - 1| - 2$.

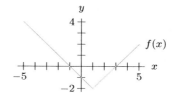

Figure 2.58

63. Let $f(x) = 3^x$. If the graph of $f(x)$ is reflected across the x-axis and then shifted up four units, the new graph has the equation $y = -3^x + 4$.

64. If $q(p) = p^2 + 2p + 4$ then $-q(-p) = p^2 - 2p + 4$.

65. Multiplying a function by a constant k, with $k > 1$, vertically stretches its graph.

66. If $g(x) = kf(x)$, then on any interval the average rate of change of g is k times the average rate of change of f.

67. Figure 2.59 suggests that $g(x) = -2f(x + 1) + 3$.

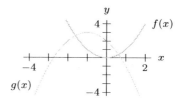

Figure 2.59

68. Using Table 2.31, we can conclude that if $g(x) = -\frac{1}{2}f(x + 1) - 3$, then $g(-2) = -10$.

Table 2.31

x	-3	-2	-1	0	1	2	3
$f(x)$	10	6	4	1	-2	-4	-10

69. Shifting the graph of a function up by one unit and then compressing it vertically by a factor of $\frac{1}{2}$ produces the same result as first compressing the graph by a factor of $\frac{1}{2}$ and then shifting it up by one unit.

70. Figure 2.60 suggests that $g(x) = 3f(\frac{1}{2}x)$.

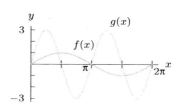

Figure 2.60

71. For the function given in Table 2.32, for $x = -2$, we have $3f(2x) + 1 = -2f(\frac{1}{2}x)$.

Table 2.32

x	-4	-3	-2	-1	0	1	2
$f(x)$	1	4	0	-2	0	0	-2

72. The graph of every quadratic equation is a parabola.

73. The maximum or minimum point of a parabola is called its vertex.

74. If a parabola is concave up its vertex is a maximum point.

75. If the equation of a parabola is written as $y = a(x - h)^2 + k$, then the vertex is located at the point $(-h, k)$.

76. If the equation of a parabola is written as $y = a(x - h)^2 + k$, then the axis of symmetry is found at $x = h$.

77. If the equation of a parabola is $y = ax^2 + bx + c$ and $a < 0$, then the parabola opens downward.

Chapter Three

TRIGONOMETRIC FUNCTIONS AND THEIR PROPERTIES

Having studied function properties and notation, the library of basic functions, and some transformations of functions, we turn our attention to the trigonometric functions. We begin with a brief review of right triangle trigonometry and then examine how the trigonometric functions can be used to model periodic phenomena, such as blood pressure in the heart, an alternating electric current, the phases of the moon, and the hours of daylight during the year.

3.0   REVIEW OF RIGHT TRIANGLE TRIG

Angles, Degrees, and Arcs

An **angle** is formed by rotating a half-line, called a **ray,** around its end point. See Figure 3.1: One ray k, called the **initial side** of the angle, remains fixed; a second ray l, called the **terminal side** of the angle, starts in the initial side position and is rotated around the common end point P in a plane until it reaches its terminal position. The common end point is called the **vertex.** An angle is **positive** if the terminal side is rotated counterclockwise and **negative** if the terminal side is rotated clockwise. Different angles with the same initial and terminal sides are called **coterminal.** An angle of **1 degree** is $\frac{1}{360}$ of a complete revolution in a counterclockwise direction. Names for special angles are noted in Figure 3.2.

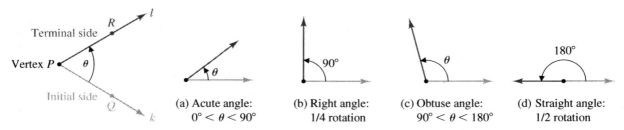

Figure 3.1

(a) Acute angle: $0° < \theta < 90°$

(b) Right angle: 1/4 rotation

(c) Obtuse angle: $90° < \theta < 180°$

(d) Straight angle: 1/2 rotation

Figure 3.2

Two positive angles are **complementary** if the sum of their measures is 90°; they are **supplementary** if the sum of their measures is 180°.

Angles can be represented in terms of **decimal degrees,** or in terms of **minutes** ($\frac{1}{60}$ of a degree) and **seconds** ($\frac{1}{60}$ of a minute). Calculators can be used to convert from decimal degrees (DD) to degrees-minutes-seconds (DMS), and vice versa. The **arc length** s of an arc **subtended** by a **central angle** θ in a circle of radius r (Fig. 3.3) satisfies

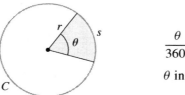

$$\frac{\theta}{360°} = \frac{s}{C} \qquad C = 2\pi r = \pi d$$

θ in decimal degrees; s and C in same units

Figure 3.3

Similar Triangles

The properties of similar triangles stated in **Euclid's theorem** are central to the development of trigonometry: If two triangles are similar, their corresponding sides are proportional. See Figure 3.4.

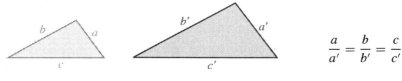

$$\frac{a}{a'} = \frac{b}{b'} = \frac{c}{c'}$$

Similar triangles

Figure 3.4

Trigonometric Ratios and Right Triangles

The six **trigonometric ratios** for the angle θ in a right triangle (see Fig. 3.5) with **opposite side** b, **adjacent side** a, and **hypotenuse** c are:

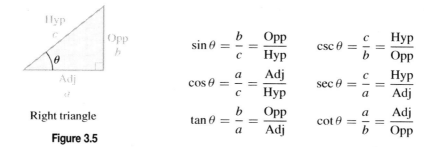

Right triangle

Figure 3.5

$$\sin \theta = \frac{b}{c} = \frac{\text{Opp}}{\text{Hyp}} \qquad \csc \theta = \frac{c}{b} = \frac{\text{Hyp}}{\text{Opp}}$$

$$\cos \theta = \frac{a}{c} = \frac{\text{Adj}}{\text{Hyp}} \qquad \sec \theta = \frac{c}{a} = \frac{\text{Hyp}}{\text{Adj}}$$

$$\tan \theta = \frac{b}{a} = \frac{\text{Opp}}{\text{Adj}} \qquad \cot \theta = \frac{a}{b} = \frac{\text{Adj}}{\text{Opp}}$$

The complementary relationships shown below illustrate why cosine, cotangent, and cosecant are called the **cofunctions** of sine, tangent, and secant, respectively. See Figure 3.6.

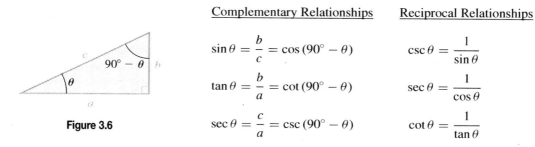

Figure 3.6

Complementary Relationships

$$\sin \theta = \frac{b}{c} = \cos (90° - \theta)$$

$$\tan \theta = \frac{b}{a} = \cot (90° - \theta)$$

$$\sec \theta = \frac{c}{a} = \csc (90° - \theta)$$

Reciprocal Relationships

$$\csc \theta = \frac{1}{\sin \theta}$$

$$\sec \theta = \frac{1}{\cos \theta}$$

$$\cot \theta = \frac{1}{\tan \theta}$$

Solving a right triangle involves finding the measures of the remaining sides and acute angles when given the measure of two sides or the measure of one side and one acute angle. Accuracy of these computations is governed by the following table:

Angle to nearest	Significant digits for side measure
1°	2
10' or 0.1°	3
1' or 0.01°	4
10'' or 0.001°	5

Right Triangle Applications

An angle measured upward from the horizontal is called an **angle of elevation** and one measured downward from the horizontal is called an **angle of depression.**

Exercises for Section 3.0

Work through all the problems and check answers in the back of the book.

1. $2°9'5''4 = ?''$

2. An arc of $\frac{1}{8}$ the circumference of a circle subtends a central angle of how many degrees?

3. Given two similar triangles, as shown in the figure, find a if $c = 20,000$, $a' = 4$, and $c' = 5$.

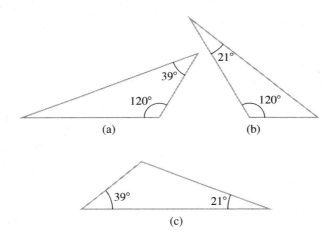

4. Change $36°20'$ to decimal degrees (to two decimal places).

5. Write a definition of an angle of degree measure 1.

6. Which of the following triangles are similar? Explain why.

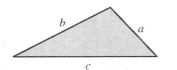

(a)   (b)

(c)

7. Is it possible in two triangles that are similar to have one with an obtuse angle and the other with no obtuse angle? Explain.

8. Explain why a triangle cannot have more than one obtuse angle.

9. If an office building casts a shadow of 40 ft at the same time a vertical yardstick (36 in.) casts a shadow of 2.0 in., how tall is the building?

10. For the triangle shown here, identify each ratio:

(a) $\sin\theta$ (b) $\sec\theta$ (c) $\tan\theta$
(d) $\csc\theta$ (e) $\cos\theta$ (f) $\cot\theta$

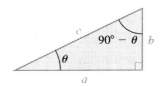

11. Solve the right triangle in Problem 10, given $c = 20.2$ cm and $\theta = 35.2°$.

12. Find the degree measure of a central angle subtended by an arc of 8.00 cm in a circle with circumference 20.0 cm.

13. If the minute hand of a clock is 2.00 in. long, how far does the tip of the hand travel in exactly 20 min?

14. One angle has a measure of $27°14'$ and another angle has a measure of $27.25°$. Which is larger? Explain how you obtained your answer.

15. Use a calculator to:

   (a) Convert $67°42'31''$ to decimal degree form.
   (b) Convert $129.317°$ to degree-minute-second form.

16. Perform the following calculations on a calculator and write the results in DMS form:

   (a) $82°14'37'' - 16°32'45''$
   (b) $3(13°47'18'' + 95°28'51'')$

17. For the triangles in Problem 3, find b to two significant digits if $a = 4.1 \times 10^{-6}$ mm, $a' = 1.5 \times 10^{-4}$ mm, and $b' = 2.6 \times 10^{-4}$ mm.

18. For the triangle in Problem 10, identify by name each of the following ratios relative to angle θ:

   (a) a/c (b) b/a (c) b/c
   (d) c/a (e) c/b (f) a/b

19. For a given value θ, explain why $\sin\theta$ is independent of the size of a right triangle having θ as an acute angle.

20. Solve the right triangle in Problem 10, given $\theta = 62°20'$ and $a = 4.00 \times 10^{-8}$ m.

21. Find each θ to the accuracy indicated.

   (a) $\tan\theta = 2.497$ (to two decimal places)
   (b) $\theta = \arccos 0.3721$ (to the nearest 10')
   (c) $\theta = \sin^{-1} 0.0559$ (to the nearest second)

22. Which of the following window displays from a graphing calculator is the result of the calculator being set in degree

mode and which is the result of the calculator being set in radian mode?

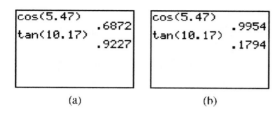

|cos(5.47)| |
|tan(10.17)| .6872|
| | .9227|

(a)

|cos(5.47)| |
|tan(10.17)| .9954|
| | .1794|

(b)

23. Solve the right triangle in Problem 10, given $b = 13.3$ mm and $a = 15.7$ mm. (Find angles to the nearest $0.1°$.)

24. Find the angles in Problem 23 to the nearest $10'$.

25. If an equilateral triangle has a side of 10 ft, what is its altitude (to two significant digits)?

26. A curve of a railroad track follows an arc of a circle of radius 1,500 ft. If the arc subtends a central angle of $36°$ how far will a train travel on this arc?

27. Find the area of a sector with central angle $36.5°$ in a circle with radius 18.3 ft. Compute your answer to the nearest unit.

28. Solve the triangle in Problem 10, given $90° - \theta = 23°43'$ and $c = 232.6$ km.

29. Solve the triangle in Problem 10, given $a = 2,421$ m and $c = 4,883$ m. (Find angles to the nearest $0.01°$.)

30. Use a calculator to find csc $67.1357°$ to four decimal places.

31. **Precalculus: Shadow Problem** A person is standing 20 ft away from a lamppost. If the lamp is 18 ft above the ground and the person is 5 ft 6 in. tall, how long is the person's shadow?

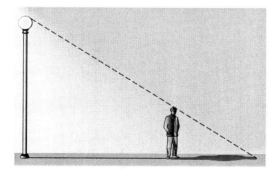

32. **Construction** The front porch of a house is 4.25 ft high. The angle of elevation of a ramp from the ground to the

porch is $10.0°$. (See the figure.) How long is the ramp? How far is the end of the ramp from the porch?

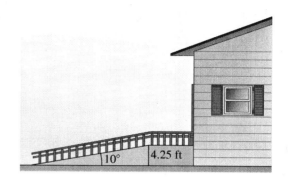

33. **Medicine: Stress Test** Cardiologists give stress tests by having patients walk on a treadmill at various speeds and inclinations. The amount of inclination may be given as an angle or as a percentage (see the figure). Find the angle of inclination if the treadmill is set at a 4% incline. Find the percentage of inclination if the angle of inclination is $4°$.

Angle of inclination: θ

Percentage of inclination: $\dfrac{a}{b}$

34. **Geography/Navigation** Find the distance (to the nearest mile) between Green Bay, WI, with latitude $44°31'$N and Mobile, AL, with latitude $30°42'$N. (Both cities have approximately the same longitude.) Use $r = 3,960$ mi for the earth's radius.

*35. **Precalculus: Balloon Flight** The angle of elevation from the ground to a hot air balloon at an altitude of 2,800 ft is $64°$. What will be the new angle of elevation if the balloon descends straight down 1,400 ft?

*36. **Surveying** Use the information in the figure to find the length x of the island.

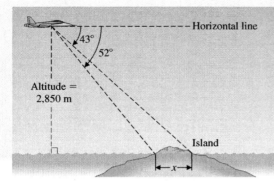

39. Solar Energy A truncated conical solar collector is aimed directly at the sun as shown in part (a) of the figure. An analysis of the amount of solar energy absorbed by the collecting disk requires certain equations relating the quantities shown in part (b) of the figure. Find an equation that expresses

(a) β in terms of α
(b) r in terms of α and h
(c) $H - h$ in terms of r, R, and α

(Based on the article, "The Solar Concentrating Properties of a Conical Reflector," by Don Leake in *The UMAP Journal,* Vol. 8, No. 4, 1987.)

*37. Precalculus: Balloon Flight Two tracking stations 525 m apart measure angles of elevation of a weather balloon to be 73.5° and 54.2°, as indicated in the figure. How high is the balloon at the time of the measurements?

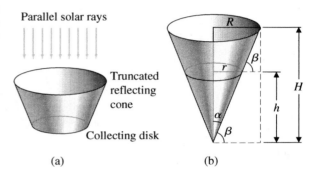

(a)   (b)

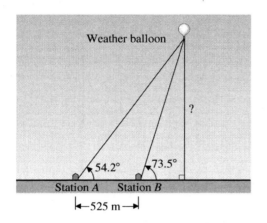

40. Precalculus: Optimization A 5 ft fence is 4 ft away from a building. A ladder is to go from the ground, across the top of the fence to the building. (See the figure.) We want to find the length of the shortest ladder that can accomplish this.

*38. Navigation: Chasing the Sun Your flight is westward from Buffalo, NY, and you notice the sun just above the horizon. How fast would the plane have to fly to keep the sun in the same position? (The latitude of Buffalo is 42°50′N, the radius of the earth is 3,960 mi, and the earth makes a complete rotation about its axis in 24 hr.)

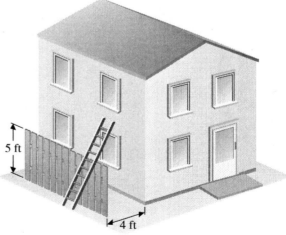

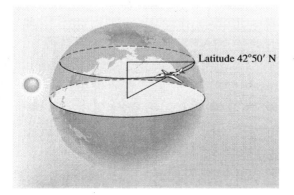

(a) How is the required length of the ladder affected as the foot of the ladder moves away from the fence? How is the length affected as the foot moves closer to the fence?

(b) Express the length of the ladder in terms of the distance from the fence to the building, the height of the fence, and θ, the angle of elevation that the ladder makes with the level ground.

(c) Complete the table, giving values of L to two decimal places:

θ	25°	35°	45°	55°	65°	75°	85°
L	16.25						

(d) Explain what happens to L as θ moves from 25° to 85°. What value of θ produces the minimum value of L in the table? What is the minimum value?

(e) Describe how you can continue the process to get a better estimate of the minimum ladder length.

3.1 DEGREES AND RADIANS

- Degree and Radian Measure of Angles
- Angle in Standard Position
- Arc Length and Sector Area

The trigonometric ratios we studied in Section 3.0 provide a powerful tool for indirect measurement. It was for this purpose only that trigonometry was used for nearly 2,000 years. Astronomy, surveying, map-making, navigation, construction, and military uses catalyzed the extensive development of trigonometry as a tool for indirect measurement.

A turning point in trigonometry occurred after the development of the rectangular coordinate system (credited mainly to the French philosopher–mathematician René Descartes, 1596–1650). The trigonometric ratios, through the use of this system, were generalized into trigonometric functions. This generalization increased their usefulness far beyond the dreams of those originally responsible for this development. The Swiss mathematician Leonhard Euler (1707–1783), probably the greatest mathematician of his century, made substantial contributions in this area. (In fact, there were very few areas in mathematics in which Euler did not make significant contributions.)

Through the demands of modern science, the *periodic* nature of these new functions soon become apparent, and they were quickly put to use in the study of various types of periodic phenomena. The trigonometric functions began to be used on problems that had nothing whatsoever to do with angles and triangles.

In this chapter we will generalize the concept of trigonometric ratios along the lines just suggested. Before we undertake this task, however, we will introduce another form of angle measure called the *radian*.

Degree and Radian Measure of Angles

In Section 3.0 we defined an angle and its degree measure. Recall that a central angle in a circle has angle measure 1° if it subtends an arc $\frac{1}{360}$ of the circumference of the circle. Another angle measure that is of considerable use is *radian measure*. A central angle subtended by an arc of length equal to the radius of the circle is defined to be an angle of **radian measure 1** (see Fig. 3.7). Thus, when we write $\theta = 2°$, we are referring to an angle of degree measure 2. When we write $\theta = 2$ rad, we are referring to an angle of radian measure 2.

Figure 3.7: Degree and radian measure

Explore/
Discuss 1

Discuss why the radian measure and degree measure of an angle are independent of the size of the circle having the angle as a central angle.

It follows from the definition that the radian measure of a central angle θ subtended by an arc of length s is found by determining how many times the length of the radius r, used as a unit length, is contained in the arc length s. In terms of a formula, we have the following:

RADIAN MEASURE OF CENTRAL ANGLES

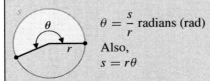

$\theta = \dfrac{s}{r}$ radians (rad)

Also,

$s = r\theta$

[*Note:* s and r must be in the same unit.]

Because of their importance, the formulas in the above box should be understood before proceeding further.

What is the radian measure of a central angle subtended by an arc of 32 cm in a circle of radius 8 cm?

$$\theta = \frac{32 \text{ cm}}{8 \text{ cm}} = 4 \text{ rad}$$

Remark

Radian measure is a unitless number. The units in which the arc length and radius are measured cancel; hence, we are left with a "unitless," or pure, number. For this reason, the word *radian* is often omitted when we are dealing with the radian measure of angles unless a special emphasis is desired.

What is the radian measure of an angle of 180°? A central angle of 180° is subtended by an arc $\frac{1}{2}$ of the circumference of the circle. Thus, if C is the circumference of a circle, then $\frac{1}{2}$ of the circumference is given by

$$s = \frac{C}{2} = \frac{2\pi r}{2} = \pi r \quad \text{and} \quad \theta = \frac{s}{r} = \frac{\pi r}{r} = \pi \text{ rad}$$

Hence, 180° corresponds to π rad. This is important to remember, since the radian measures of many special angles can be obtained from this correspondence. For example, 90° is 180°/2; therefore, 90° corresponds to $\pi/2$ rad. Since 360° is twice 180°, 360° corresponds to 2π rad. Similarly, 60° corresponds to $\pi/3$ rad, 45° to $\pi/4$ rad, and 30° to $\pi/6$ rad. These special angles and their degree and radian measures will be referred to frequently throughout this book. Table 3.1 summarizes these special correspondences for ease of reference.

Table 3.1

Radians	$\pi/6$	$\pi/4$	$\pi/3$	$\pi/2$	π	2π
Degrees	30	45	60	90	180	360

In general, the following proportion can be used to convert degree measure to radian measure and vice versa.

RADIAN–DEGREE CONVERSION FORMULAS

$$\frac{\theta_d}{180°} = \frac{\theta_r}{\pi \text{ rad}}$$ **or**

$$\theta_d = \frac{180°}{\pi \text{ rad}} \theta_r \quad \textbf{Radians to degrees}$$

$$\theta_r = \frac{\pi \text{ rad}}{180°} \theta_d \quad \textbf{Degrees to radians}$$

[*Note:*   The proportion is usually easier to remember. Also, we will omit units in calculations until the final answer.]

Radian–Degree Conversion

Example 1
(a) Find the degree measure of -1.5 rad in exact form and in decimal form to four decimal places.
(b) Find the radian measure of $44°$ in exact form and in decimal form to four decimal places.
(c) Use a calculator with automatic conversion capability to perform the conversions in parts (a) and (b).

Solution
(a) $\theta_d = \dfrac{180°}{\pi \text{ rad}} \theta_r$

$\quad = \dfrac{180}{\pi} (-1.5)$

$\quad = -\dfrac{270°}{\pi}$ Exact form

$\quad = -85.9437°$ To four decimal places

(b) $\theta_r = \dfrac{\pi \text{ rad}}{180°} \theta_d$

$\quad = \dfrac{\pi}{180} (44)$

$\quad = \dfrac{11\pi}{45}$ rad   Exact form

$\quad = 0.7679$ rad   To four decimal places

(c) Check the user's manual for your calculator to find out how to convert parts (a) and (b) with an automatic routine. The following window display is from a graphing calculator with an automatic conversion routine:

```
(-1.5)ʳ
          -85.9437
44°
            .7679
```

Matched Problem 1
(a) Find the degree measure of 1 rad in exact form and in decimal form to four decimal places.
(b) Find the radian measure of $-120°$ in exact form and in decimal form to four decimal places.

(c) Use a calculator with automatic conversion capability to perform the conversions in parts (a) and (b).

Angle in Standard Position

To generalize the concept of trigonometric ratios, we first locate an angle in **standard position** in a rectangular coordinate system. To do this, we place the vertex at the origin and the initial side along the positive x axis. Recall that when the rotation is counterclockwise, the angle is positive and when the rotation is clockwise, the angle is negative. Figure 3.8 illustrates several angles in standard position.

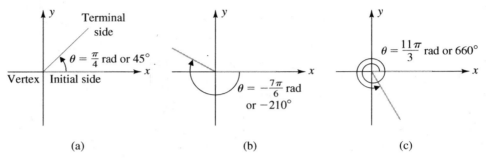

(a)   (b)   (c)

Figure 3.8: Angles in standard position

Sketching Angles in Standard Position

Example 2   Sketch the following angles in their standard positions:

(a) $-60°$ (b) $3\pi/2$ rad   (c) -3π rad   (d) $405°$

Solution   (a)

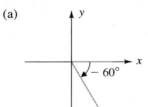

(b)

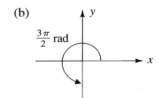

(c)

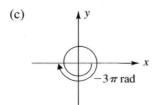

(d)

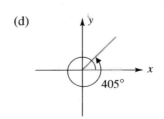

Matched Problem 2   Sketch the following angles in their standard positions:

(a) $120°$ (b) $-\pi/6$ rad   (c) $7\pi/2$ rad   (d) $-495°$

Two angles are said to be **coterminal** if their terminal sides coincide when both angles are placed in their standard positions in the same rectangular coordinate system. Figure 3.9 shows two pairs of coterminal angles.

Remarks
1. The degree measures of two coterminal angles differ by an integer[*] multiple of 360°.
2. The radian measures of two coterminal angles differ by an integer multiple of 2π.

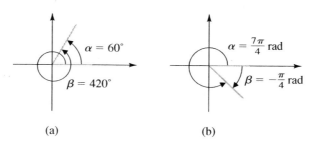

(a)   (b)

Figure 3.9: Coterminal angles

Recognizing Coterminal Angles

Example 3   Which of the following pairs of angles are coterminal?

(a) $\alpha = -135°$
     $\beta = 225°$

(b) $\alpha = 120°$
     $\beta = -420°$

(c) $\alpha = -\pi/3$ rad
     $\beta = -2\pi/3$ rad

(d) $\alpha = \pi/3$ rad
     $\beta = 7\pi/3$ rad

Solution   (a)   The angles are coterminal if $\alpha - \beta$ is an integer multiple of 360°.

$$\alpha - \beta = (-135°) - 225° = -360° = -1\,(360°)$$

Thus, α and β are coterminal.

(b)
$$\alpha - \beta = 120° - (-420°) = 540°$$

The angles are not coterminal, since 540° is not an integer multiple of 360°.

(c) The angles are coterminal if $\alpha - \beta$ is an integer multiple of 2π.

$$\alpha - \beta = \left(-\frac{\pi}{3}\right) - \frac{2\pi}{3} = -\frac{3\pi}{3} = -\pi$$

The angles are not coterminal, since $-\pi$ is not an integer multiple of 2π.

(d)
$$\alpha - \beta = \frac{\pi}{3} - \frac{7\pi}{3} = -\frac{6\pi}{3} = -2\pi = (-1)(2\pi)$$

Thus, α and β are coterminal.

Matched Problem 3   Which of the following pairs of angles are coterminal?

(a) $\alpha = 90°$
     $\beta = -90°$

(b) $\alpha = 750°$
     $\beta = 30°$

(c) $\alpha = -\pi/6$ rad
     $\beta = -25\pi/6$ rad

(d) $\alpha = 3\pi/4$ rad
     $\beta = 7\pi/4$ rad

[*]An integer is a positive or negative whole number or 0; that is, the set of interger is (....−4, −3, −2, −1, 0, 1, 2, 3, 4,.....).

Explore/
Discuss 2

(a) List all angles that are coterminal with $\theta = \pi/3$ rad, $-5\pi \le \theta \le 5\pi$. Explain how you arrived at your answer.

(b) List all angles that are coterminal with $\theta = -45°$, $-900° \le \theta \le 900°$. Explain how you arrived at your answer.

Arc Length and Sector Area

At first it may appear that radian measure of angles is more complicated and less useful than degree measure. However, just the opposite is true. The computation of arc length and the area of a circular sector, which we now discuss, should begin to convince you of some of the advantages of radian measure over degree measure. Refer to Figure 3.10 in the following discussion.

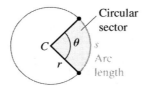

Figure 3.10: Circular sector

From the definition of radian measure of an angle.

$$\theta = \frac{s}{r} \text{ rad}$$

Solving for s, we obtain a **formula for arc length:**

$$s = r\theta \qquad \theta \text{ in radian measure} \tag{1}$$

If θ is in degree measure, we must multiply by $p/180$ first (to convert to radians); then formula (1) becomes

$$s = \frac{\pi}{180}r\theta \qquad \theta \text{ in degree measure} \tag{2}$$

We see that the formula for arc length is much simpler when θ is in radian measure.

Arc Length

Example 4

In a circle of radius 4.00 cm, find the arc length subtended by a central angle of:

(a) 3.40 rad   (b) 10.0°

Solution

(a) $s = r\theta$
   $= 4.00(3.40) = 13.6$ cm

(b) $s = \frac{\pi}{180}r\theta$

   $= \frac{\pi}{180}(4.00)(10.0) = 0.698$ cm

Matched
Problem 4

In a circle of radius 6.00 ft, find the arc length subtended by a central angle of:

(a) 1.70 rad   (b) 40.0°

**Explore/
Discuss 3**

When you look at a full moon, the image appears on the retina of your eye as shown in Figure 3.11.

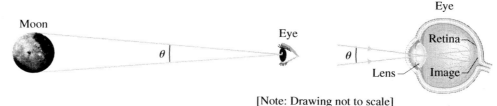

[Note: Drawing not to scale]

Figure 3.11: Vision

(a) Discuss how you would estimate the diameter of the moon's image d' on the retina, given the moon's diameter d, the distance u from the moon to the eye lens, and the distance v from the image to the eye lens. [For small central angles in circles with very large radii, the intercepted arc and its chord are approximately the same length.]

(b) The moon's image on the retina is smaller than a period on this page! To verify this, find the diameter of the moon's image d' on the retina to two decimal places, given:

Moon diameter $= d = 2{,}160$ mi
Moon distance from the eye $= u = 239{,}000$ mi
Distance from eye lens to retina $= v = 17.4$ mm

The formula for the **area A of a circular sector** in a circle with radius r and central angle θ in radian measure (see Fig. 3.10) can be found by starting with the following proportion:

$$\frac{A}{\pi r^2} = \frac{\theta}{2\pi}$$

$$A = \frac{1}{2}r^2\theta \qquad \theta \text{ in radian measure} \tag{3}$$

If θ is in degree measure, we must multiply by $\pi/180$ first (to convert to radians); then formula (3) becomes

$$A = \frac{\pi}{360}r^2\theta \qquad \theta \text{ in degree measure} \tag{4}$$

Again we see that the formula for sector area is much simpler when θ is in radian measure.

Area of a Sector

Example 5

In a circle of radius 3 m, find the area (to three significant digits) of the circular sector with central angle:

(a) 0.4732 rad   (b) 25°

Solution

(a) $A = \dfrac{1}{2}r^2\theta$

$\quad = \dfrac{1}{2}(3)^2(0.4732) = 2.13 \text{ m}^2$

(b) $A = \dfrac{\pi}{360}r^2\theta$

$\quad = \dfrac{\pi}{360}(3)^2(25) = 1.96 \text{ m}^2$

Matched Problem 5   In a circle of radius 7 in., find the area (to four significant digits) of the circular sector with central angle:

(a) 0.1332 rad   (b) 110°

Angular velocity is another significant application of radian measure in engineering and physics problems. A detailed discussion of angular velocity is presented in the next section.

It is important to gain experience in the use of radian measure, since the concept will be used extensively in many developments that follow. By the time you finish this book you should feel as comfortable with radian measure as you now do with degree measure.

Answers to Matched Problems

1. (a) $180°/\pi$; 57.2958°
   (b) $-2\pi/3$ rad; -2.0944 rad   (c)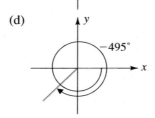

2. (a) 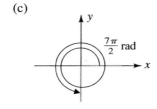   (b)

   (c)   (d)

3. (a) Not coterminal   (b) Cotermina   (c) Coterminal   (d) Not coterminal
4. (a) 10.2 ft   (b) 4.19 ft   5. (a) 3.263 in.^{2} (b) 47.04 in.^{2}

Exercises for Section 3.1

1. Explain the meaning of an angle of radian measure 1.

2. Explain the meaning of an angle of degree measure 1.

3. Mentally convert the following to exact radian measure by starting with 30° and taking multiples (remember that 180° corresponds to π radians):

$$30°, 60°, 90°, 120°, 150°, 180°, 210°, 240°,$$
$$270°, 300°, 330°, 360°$$

4. Mentally convert the following to exact radian measure by starting with 45° and taking multiples (remember that 180° corresponds to π radians):

$$45°, 90°, 135°, 180°, 225°, 270°, 315°, 360°$$

5. Which is larger: an angle of degree measure 50 or an angle of radian measure 1? Explain.

6. Which is smaller: an angle of degree measure 20 or an angle of radian measure $\frac{1}{2}$? Explain.

In Problems 7–10, sketch each angle in its standard position and find the degree measure of the two nearest angles (one negative and one positive) that are coterminal to the given angle.

7. $60°$ **8.** $45°$ **9.** $-30°$ **10.** $-45°$

In Problems 11–14, find the radian measure for each angle. Express the answer in exact form and in approximate form to four significant digits.

11. $18°$ **12.** $9°$ **13.** $130°$ **14.** $140°$

In Problems 15–18, find the degree measure for each angle. Express the answer in exact form and in approximate form with decimal degrees to four significant digits.

15. 1.6 rad   **16.** 0.5 rad

17. $\pi/60$ rad   **18.** $\pi/180$ rad

In Problems 19–24, sketch each angle in its standard position.

19. $-\pi/6$ rad   **20.** $-\pi/3$ rad   **21.** $300°$

22. $390°$ **23.** $-7\pi/3$ rad   **24.** $-11\pi/4$ rad

In Problems 25–28, use a calculator with an automatic radian–degree conversion routine.

25. Find the degree measure of:
    (a) 0.50 rad   **(b)** 1.4 rad
    (c) 6.20 rad   **(d)** −4.59 rad

26. Find the degree measure of:
    (a) 0.750 rad   **(b)** 1.5 rad
    (c) 3.80 rad   **(d)** −7.21 rad

27. Find the radian measure of:
    (a) $25°$ **(b)** $164°$
    (c) $648°$ **(d)** $-221.7°$

28. Find the radian measure of:
    (a) $35°$ **(b)** $187°$
    (c) $437°$ **(d)** $-175.3°$

29. If the radius of a circle is 5.0 m, find the radian measure and the degree measure of an angle subtended by an arc of length:
    (a) 2 m   **(b)** 6 m
    (c) 12.5 m   **(d)** 20 m

30. If the radius of a circle is 40.0 cm, find the radian measure and the degree measure of an angle subtended by an arc of length:
    (a) 15 cm   **(b)** 65 cm
    (c) 123.5 cm   **(d)** 210 cm

31. In a circle of radius 7 m, find the length of the arc subtended by a central angle of:
    (a) 1.35 rad   **(b)** $42.0°$
    (c) 0.653 rad   **(d)** $125°$

32. In a circle of radius 5 in., find the length of the arc subtended by a central angle of:
    (a) 0.228 rad   **(b)** $37.0°$
    (c) 1.537 rad   **(d)** $175.0°$

33. If the radian measure of an angle is doubled, is the degree measure of the same angle also doubled? Explain.

34. If the degree measure of an angle is cut in half, is the radian measure of the same angle also cut in half? Explain.

35. An arc length s on a circle is held constant while the radius of the circle r is doubled. Explain what happens to the central angle subtended by the arc.

36. The radius of a circle r is held constant while an arc length s on the circle is doubled. Explain what happens to the central angle subtended by the arc.

37. In a circle of radius 12.0 cm, find the area of the circular sector with central angle:
    (a) 2.00 rad   **(b)** $25.0°$
    (c) 0.650 rad   **(d)** $105°$

38. In a circle of radius 10.5 ft, find the area of the circular sector with central angle:
    (a) 0.150 rad   **(b)** $15.0°$
    (c) 1.74 rad   **(d)** $105°$

39. Explain why an angle in standard position and of radian measure m intercepts an arc of length m on a unit circle with center at the origin.

40. An angle in standard position intercepts an arc of length s on a unit circle with center at the origin. Explain why the radian measure of the angle is also s.

In Problems 41–50, indicate the quadrant* in which the terminal side of each angle lies.

41. $495°$ **42.** $9\pi/4$ rad

43. $-17\pi/6$ rad   **44.** $696°$

45. $-937°$ **46.** $-11\pi/3$ rad

47. $29\pi/4$ rad   **48.** $-672°$

49. 10 rad   **50.** −20 rad

*Recall that a rectangular coordinate system divides a plane into four parts called quadrants. These quadrants are numbered in a counterclockwise direction starting in the upper right-hand corner.

II	I
III	IV

In Problems 51–58, find each value to four decimal places. Convert radians to decimal degrees.

51. $56.1225° = ?$ rad

52. $116.9853° = ?$ rad

53. 0.4638 rad $= ?°$

54. 2.562 rad $= ?°$

55. $87°39'42'' = ?$ rad

56. $261°15'45'' = ?$ rad

57. $19\pi/7$ rad $= ?°$

58. $43\pi/11 = ?°$

59. Radian Measure   What is the radian measure of the smaller angle made by the hands of a clock at 2:30 (see the figure)? Express the answer in terms of π and as a decimal fraction to two decimal places.

60. Radian Measure   Repeat Problem 59 for 4:30.

61. Pendulum   A clock has a pendulum 22 cm long. If it swings through an angle of $32°$, how far does the bottom of the bob travel in one swing?

62. Pendulum   If the bob on the bottom of the 22 cm pendulum in Problem 61 traces a 9.5 cm arc on each swing, through what angle (in degrees) does the pendulum rotate on each swing?

63. Engineering   Oil is pumped from some wells using a donkey pump as shown in the figure. Through how many degrees must an arm with a 72 in. radius rotate to produce a 24 in. vertical stroke at the pump down in the ground?

Note that a point at the end of the arm must travel through a 24 in. arc to produce a 24 in. vertical stroke at the pump.

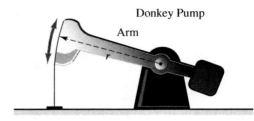

Donkey Pump

Arm

64. Engineering   In Problem 63, find the arm length r that would produce an 18 in. vertical stroke while rotating through $21°$.

65. Bioengineering   A particular woman, when standing erect and facing forward, can swing an arm in a plane perpendicular to her shoulders through an angle of $3\pi/2$ rad (see the figure). Find the length of the arc (to the nearest centimeter) her fingertips trace out for one complete swing of her arm. The length of her arm from the pivot point in her shoulder to the end of her longest finger is 54.3 cm while it is kept straight and her fingers are extended with palm facing in.

66. Bioengineering   A particular man, when standing erect and facing forward, can swing a leg through an angle of $2\pi/3$ rad (see the figure). Find the length of the arc (to the nearest centimeter) his heel traces out for one complete swing of the leg. The length of his leg from the pivot point in his hip to the bottom of his heel is 102 cm while his leg is kept straight and his foot is kept at right angles to his leg.

67. Astronomy The sun is about 1.5×10^8 km from the earth. If the angle subtended by the diameter of the sun on the surface of the earth is 9.3×10^{-3} rad, approximately what is the diameter of the sun? [*Hint:* Use the intercepted arc to approximate the diameter.]

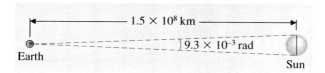

*68. Surveying If a natural gas tank 5.000 km away subtends an angle of 2.44°, approximate its height to the nearest meter. (See Problem 67.)

69. Photography The angle of view for a 300 mm telephoto lens is 8°. At 1,250 ft, what is the approximate width of the field of view? Use an arc length to approximate the chord length to the nearest foot.

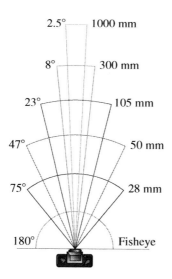

70. Photography The angle of view for a 1,000 mm telephoto lens is 2.5°. At 865 ft, what is the approximate width of the field of view? Use an arc length to approximate the chord length to the nearest foot.

*71. Spy Satellites Some spy satellites have cameras that can distinguish objects that subtend angles of as little as 5×10^{-7} rad. If such a satellite passes over a particular country at an altitude of 250 mi, how small an object can the camera distinguish? Give the answer in meters to one decimal place and also in inches to one decimal place. (1 mi = 1,609 m; 1 m = 39.37 in.)

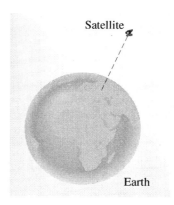

72. Spy Satellites Repeat Problem 71 if the satellite passes over the country at an altitude of 155 mi. Give the answers to three decimal places.

73. Astronomy Assume that the earth's orbit is circular. A line from the earth to the sun sweeps out an angle of how many radians in 1 week? Express the answer in terms of π and as a decimal fraction to two decimal places. (Assume exactly 52 weeks in a year.)

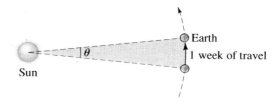

74. Astronomy Repeat Problem 73 for 13 weeks.

*75. Astronomy When measuring time, an error of 1 sec per day may not seem like a lot. But suppose a clock is in error by at most 1 sec per day. Then in 1 year the accumulated error could be as much as 365 sec. If we assume the earth's orbit about the sun is circular, with a radius of 9.3×10^7 mi, what would be the maximum error (in miles) in computing the distance the earth travels in its orbit after 1 year?

*76. Astronomy Using the clock described in Problem 75, what would be the maximum error (in miles) in computing the distance that Venus travels in a "Venus year"? Assume Venus's orbit around the sun is circular, with a radius of 6.7×10^7 mi, and that Venus completes one orbit (a "Venus year") in 224 earth days.

*77. Geometry A circular sector has an area of 52.39 ft² and a radius of 10.5 ft. Calculate the perimeter of the sector to the nearest foot.

*78. Geometry   A circular sector has an area of 145.7 cm^2 and a radius of 8.4 cm. Calculate the perimeter of the sector to the nearest centimeter.

*79. Revolutions and Radians

(a) Describe how you would find the number of radians generated by the spoke in a bicycle wheel that turns through n revolutions.

(b) Does your answer to part (a) depend on the size of the bicycle wheel? Explain.

(c) Find the number of radians generated for a wheel turning through 5 revolutions. Through 3.6 revolutions.

*80. Revolutions and Radians

(a) Describe how you would find the number of radians through which a 10 cm diameter pulley turns if u meters of rope are pulled through without slippage.

(b) Does your answer to part (a) depend on the diameter of the pulley? Explain.

(c) Through how many radians does the pulley in part (a) turn when 5.75 m of rope are pulled through without slippage?

*81. Engineering   Rotation of a drive wheel causes a shaft to rotate (see the figure). If the drive wheel completes 3 revolutions, how many revolutions will the shaft complete? Through how many radians will the shaft turn? Compute answers to one decimal place.

*82. Engineering   In Problem 81, find the radius (to the nearest millimeter) of the drive wheel required for the 12 mm shaft to make 7 revolutions when the drive wheel makes 3 revolutions.

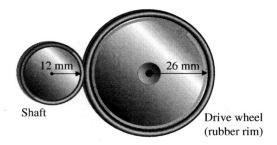

Shaft   Drive wheel (rubber rim)

83. Radians and Arc Length   A bicycle wheel of diameter 32 in. travels a distance of 20 ft. Find the angle (to the nearest degree) swept out by one of the spokes.

84. Radians and Arc Length   A bicycle has a front wheel with a diameter of 24 cm and a back wheel with a diameter of 60 cm. Through what angle (in radians) does the front wheel turn if the back wheel turns through 12 rad?

3.2   TRIGONOMETRIC FUNCTIONS OF ANY ANGLE

- Trigonometric Functions with Angle Domains
- Trigonometric Functions with Real Number Domains
- Calculator Evaluation
- Application
- Summary of Sign Properties

In Section 3.0 we introduced the concept of trigonometric ratios and tied this idea to right triangles. We were able to use these ratios to define six trigonometric functions with angle domains restricted to 0°–90°. In this section we introduce more general definitions that will apply to angle domains of arbitrary size, positive, negative, or zero, in degree or radian measure. We then move one (giant) step further and define these functions for arbitrary real numbers. With these new functions we will be able to do everything we did with the trigonometric ratios in the first chapter, plus a great deal more. In Section 3.5 we will approach the subject from a more modern point of view, where angles are not a necessary part of the definition. Each approach has its advantages for certain applications and uses.

Trigonometric Functions with Angle Domains

We start with an arbitrary angle θ located in a rectangular coordinate system in a standard position. We then choose an arbitrary point $P(a, b)$ on the terminal side of θ, but away from the origin. If r is the distance of $P(a, b)$ from the origin, we can form six ratios involving r and the coordinates of P. We will use these six ratios to define six trigonometric functions, which are direct generalizations of the six trigonometric ratios given in Section 3.0. It is important to understand the definitions of the six trigonometric functions—a great deal depends on them.

Definition 1

TRIGONOMETRIC FUNCTIONS WITH ANGLE DOMAINS

For an arbitray angle θ:

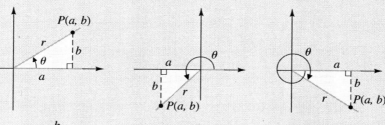

$$\sin \theta = \frac{b}{r}$$

$$\csc \theta = \frac{r}{b} \quad b \neq 0$$

$$r = \sqrt{a^2 + b^2} > 0$$

$$\cos \theta = \frac{a}{r}$$

$$\sec \theta = \frac{r}{a} \quad a \neq 0$$

$P(a, b)$ is an arbitrary point on the terminal side of θ,

$$\tan \theta = \frac{b}{a} \quad a \neq 0$$

$$\cot \theta = \frac{a}{b} \quad b \neq 0$$

$(a, b) \neq (0, 0)$

Domains: Sets of all possible angles for which the ratios are defined
Ranges: Subsets of the set of real numbers

[*Note:* A trigonometric function has the some value at coterminal angles. Also, more precise statements about domains and ranges will be given in later in this section.]

Remarks

1. Definition 1 of the six trigonometric functions is stated in terms of an a, b coordinate system instead of an x, y coordinate system because when we generalize the definition of trigonometric functions still further (later in this section), we want to reserve x for an independent variable and y for a dependent variable.

2. In Definition 1 the right triangle formed by dropping a perpendicular from $P(a, b)$ to the horizontal axis is called the **reference triangle** associated with the angle θ. (A more complete discussion of reference triangles is given in Section 3.3.) We label the legs of the reference triangle with the coordinates of P, which means that one or both legs are labeled with negative numbers if P is in quadrant II, III, or IV.

Explore/ Discuss 1

(a) Discuss why, for a given θ, the ratios in Definition 1 are independent of the choice of $P(a, b)$ on the terminal side of θ, as long as $(a, b) \neq (0, 0)$.

(b) Explain how Definition 1 includes, as a special case, the trigonometric functions of acute angles discussed in Section 3.0.

(c) For a given angle θ, discuss the relationship between the sign of a ratio in Definition 1 and the quadrant in which the terminal side of θ lies.

Evaluating Trigonometric Functions, Given a Point on the Terminal Side of θ

Example 1   Find the exact value of each of the six trigonometric functions for the angle θ with terminal side containing $P(-4, -3)$. (See Fig. 3.12. Note that the legs of the reference triangle are labeled with negative numbers—see Remark 2 above.)

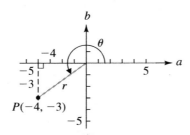

Figure 3.12

Solution

$$(a, b) = (-4, -3)$$

$$r = \sqrt{a^2 + b^2} = \sqrt{(-4)^2 + (-3)^2} = \sqrt{25} = 5$$

$$\sin \theta = \frac{b}{r} = \frac{-3}{5} = -\frac{3}{5} \qquad \csc \theta = \frac{r}{b} = \frac{5}{-3} = -\frac{5}{3}$$

$$\cos \theta = \frac{a}{r} = \frac{-4}{5} = -\frac{4}{5} \qquad \sec \theta = \frac{r}{a} = \frac{5}{-4} = -\frac{5}{4}$$

$$\tan \theta = \frac{b}{a} = \frac{-3}{-4} = \frac{3}{4} \qquad \cot \theta = \frac{a}{b} = \frac{-4}{-3} = \frac{4}{3}$$

Matched Problem 1   Find the exact value of each of the six trigonometric functions if the terminal side of θ contains the point $(-8, -6)$. [*Note:*   This point lies on the terminal side of the same angle as in Example 1.]

Using Given Information to Evaluate Trigonometric Functions

Example 2   Find the exact value of each of the other five trigonometric functions for the given angle θ—without finding θ—given that the terminal side of θ is in quadrant III and

$$\cos \theta = \frac{-3}{5}$$

Solution   The information given is sufficient for us to locate a reference triangle in quadrant III for θ even though we do not know θ (see Fig. 3.13). We sketch the reference triangle, label what we know, and then complete the problem as indicated.

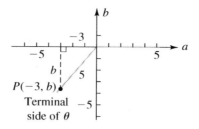

Figure 3.13

Since

$$\cos \theta = \frac{a}{r} = \frac{-3}{5}$$

we know that $a = -3$ and $r = 5$ (r is never negative). If we can find b, we can determine the values of the other five functions using their definitions.

We use the Pythagorean theorem to find b:

$$(-3)^2 + b^2 = 5^2$$
$$b^2 = 25 - 9 = 16 \qquad \text{b is negative since $P(a, b)$ is in quadrant III.}$$
$$b = -4$$

Thus,

$$(a, b) = (-3, -4) \quad \text{and} \quad r = 5$$

We can now find the other five functions using their definitions.

$$\sin \theta = \frac{b}{r} = \frac{-4}{5} = -\frac{4}{5} \qquad \csc \theta = \frac{r}{b} = \frac{5}{-4} = -\frac{5}{4}$$

$$\tan \theta = \frac{b}{a} = \frac{-4}{-3} = \frac{4}{3} \qquad \cot \theta = \frac{a}{b} = \frac{-3}{-4} = \frac{3}{4}$$

$$\sec \theta = \frac{r}{a} = \frac{5}{-3} = -\frac{5}{3}$$

Matched Problem 2   Repeat Example 2 for $\tan \theta = -\frac{3}{4}$ and the terminal side of θ in quadrant II.

Trigonometric Functions with Real Number Domains

We now turn to the problem of defining trigonometric functions for real number domains. First note that to each real number x there corresponds an angle of x radians, and to each angle of x radians there corresponds the real number x. We define trigonometric functions with real number domains in terms of trigonometric functions with angle domains.

Definition 2

TRIGONOMETRIC FUNCTIONS WITH REAL NUMBER DOMAINS

For x any real number:

$$\sin x = \sin (x \text{ rad}) \qquad \csc x = \csc (x \text{ rad})$$
$$\cos x = \cos (x \text{ rad}) \qquad \sec x = \sec (x \text{ rad})$$
$$\tan x = \tan (x \text{ rad}) \qquad \cot x = \cot (x \text{ rad})$$

Domains: Subsets of the set of real numbers
Ranges: Subsets of the set of real numbers

Thus, for example, $\sin 3 = \sin(3 \text{ rad})$, $\cos 1.23 = \cos (1.23 \text{ rad})$, $\tan (-9) = \tan (-9 \text{ rad})$, and so on.

Remark   Because of Definition 2, we will often omit "rad" after x and interpret x as a real number or an angle with radian measure x, whichever fits the context in which x appears.

At first glance, the definition of trigonometric functions with real number domains (Definition 2) appears artificial, but we will see that it frees the trigonometric functions from angles and opens them up to a large variety of significant applications not directly connected to angles.

Calculator Evaluation

We used a calculator in Section 3.0 to approximate trigonometric ratios for acute angles in degree measure. These same calculators are internally programmed to approximate (to eight or ten significant digits) trigonometric functions for *any* angle (however large or small, positive or negative) in degree or radian measure, or for *any* real number. (Remember, most graphing calculators use different sequences of steps than scientific calculators. Consult the owner's manual for your calculator.) In Section 3.3 we will show how to obtain exact values for certain special angles (integer multiples of $30°$ and $45°$ or integer multiples of $\pi/6$ and $\pi/4$) without the use of a calculator.

Caution   1. Set your calculator in **degree mode** when evaluating trigonometric functions of angles in degree measure.
2. Set your calculator in **radian mode** when evaluating trigonometric functions of angles in radian measure or trigonometric functions of real numbers.

We generalize the reciprocal relationships stated in Section 3.0 to evaluate secant, cosecant, and cotangent.

RECIPROCAL RELATIONSHIPS

For x any real number or angle in degree or radian measure,

$$\csc x = \frac{1}{\sin x} \qquad \sin x \neq 0$$

$$\sec x = \frac{1}{\cos x} \qquad \cos x \neq 0$$

$$\cot x = \frac{1}{\tan x} \qquad \tan x \neq 0$$

Calculator Evaluation of Trigonometric Functions

Example 3   With a calculator, evaluate each to four significant digits. [*Note:*   When evaluating trigonometric functions with angle domains in degree measure, some calculators require decimal degrees (DD) and others can use either DD or DMS. Check your user's manual.]

(a) $\sin 286.38°$ (b) $\tan (3.472 \text{ rad})$ (c) $\cot 5.063$

(d) $\cos (-107°35')$ (e) $\sec (-4.799)$ (f) $\csc 192°47'22''$

Solution   (a) $\sin 286.38° = -0.9594$ Degree mode

(b) $\tan (3.472 \text{ rad}) = 0.3430$ Radian mode

(c) $\cot 5.063 \boxed{= \dfrac{1}{\tan 5.063}}$

$= -0.3657$ Radian mode

(d) $\cos (107°35') \boxed{= \cos (-107.5833 \ldots)}$

$= -0.3021$ Degree mode

(e) $\sec (-4.799) \boxed{= \dfrac{1}{\cos (-4.799)}}$

$= 11.56$ Radian mode

(f) $\csc 192°47'22'' \boxed{= \dfrac{1}{\sin 192.7894 \ldots}}$

$= -4.517$ Degree mode

Matched Problem 3   With a calculator, evaluate to four significant digits:

(a) $\cos 303.73°$ (b) $\sec (-2.805)$ (c) $\tan (-83°29')$

(d) $\sin (12 \text{ rad})$ (e) $\csc 100°52'43''$ (f) $\cot 9$

Application

An application of trigonometric functions that does not involve any angles will now be considered. More will be said about alternating current in subsequent sections.

Wind Generators

Example 4   The Department of Energy reports that wind-produced electricity will jump to close to 1% of the nation's total electrical output by the year 2010, about ten times that produced today. "Wind farms" are springing up in many parts of the United States (see Fig. 3.14). A particular wind generator can generate alternating current given by the equation

$$I = 50 \cos (120\pi t + 45\pi)$$

where t is time in seconds and I is current in amperes. What is the current I (to two decimal places) when $t = 1.09$ sec? (More will be said about alternating current in subsequent sections.)

Figure 3.14: Wind generators

Solution   Set the calculator in radian mode; then evaluate the equation for $t = 1.09$:

$$I = 50 \cos\left[120\pi\,(1.09) + 45\pi\right] = 40.45 \text{ amperes}$$

Matched Problem 4   Repeat Example 4 for $t = 2.17$ sec .

Summary of Sign Properties

We close this important section by having you summarize the sign properties of the six trigonometric functions in Table 3.2 in Explore–Discuss 2. Note that Table 3.2 does not need to be committed to memory, because particular cases are readily determined from the definitions of the functions involved (see Fig. 3.15).

Explore/ Discuss 2   Using Figure 3.15 as an aid, complete Table 3.2 by determining the sign of each of the six trigonometric functions in each quadrant. In Table 3.2, x is associated with an angle that terminates in the respective quadrant, (a, b) is a point on the terminal side of the angle, and $r = \sqrt{a^2 + b^2} > 0$.

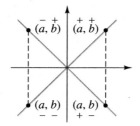

Figure 3.15

Table 3.2

	Quadrant I			Quadrant II			Quadrant III			Quadrant IV		
	a	b	r	a	b	r	a	b	r	a	b	r
	+	+	+	−	+	+	−	−	+	+	−	+
$\sin x = b/r$ $\csc x = r/b$										−		
$\cos x = a/r$ $\sec x = r/a$												
$\tan x = b/a$ $\cot x = a/b$	+											

Answers to Matched Problems

1. $\sin\theta = -\frac{3}{5}$, $\cos\theta = -\frac{4}{5}$, $\tan\theta = \frac{3}{4}$, $\csc\theta = -\frac{5}{3}$, $\sec\theta = -\frac{5}{4}$, $\cot\theta = \frac{4}{3}$

[What do you think the values of the six trigonometric functions would be if we "picked another point, say $(-12, -9)$, on the terminal side of the same angle θ as in Example 1? *Answer:* The same. (Why?)]

2. $\sin\theta = \frac{3}{5}$, $\csc\theta = \frac{5}{3}$, $\cot\theta = -\frac{4}{3}$, $\cos\theta = -\frac{4}{5}$, $\sec\theta = -\frac{5}{4}$

3. (a) 0.5553   (b) -1.059 (c) -8.754 (d) -0.5366
   (e) 1.018   (f) -2.211

4. $I = -15.45$ amperes

Exercises for Section 3.2

Find the exact value of each of the six trigonometric functions if the terminal side of θ contains the point $P(a, b)$. Do the same for $Q(a, b)$.

1. $P(3, 4)$; $Q(6, 8)$

2. $P(-3, -4)$; $Q(-9, -12)$

3. $P(4, -3)$; $Q(12, -9)$

4. $P(-3, 4)$; $Q(-6, 8)$

In Problems 5–10, find the exact value of each of the other five trigonometric functions for the angle θ (without finding θ), given the indicated information. It would be helpful to sketch a reference triangle.

5. $\cos\theta = \frac{3}{5}$
θ is a quadrant I angle

6. $\sin\theta = \frac{3}{5}$
θ is a quadrant I angle

7. $\cos\theta = \frac{3}{5}$
θ is a quadrant IV angle

8. $\sin\theta = \frac{3}{5}$
θ is a quadrant II angle

9. $\csc\theta = -\frac{5}{4}$
θ is a quadrant III angle

10. $\tan\theta = -\frac{4}{3}$
θ is a quadrant II angle

11. Is it possible to find a real number x such that $\cos x$ is positive and $\sec x$ is negative? Explain.

12. Is it possible to find an angle θ such that $\tan\theta$ is negative and $\cot x$ is positive? Explain.

Use a calculator to find the answers to Problems 13–30 to four significant digits. Make sure the calculator is in the correct mode (degree or radian) for each problem.

13. $\sin 62°$

14. $\cos (7 \text{ rad})$

15. $\tan (6 \text{ rad})$

16. $\cot 5$

17. $\sec 4$

18. $\csc 129°$

19. $\cos 208°$

20. $\sin 198°$

21. $\cot 312°$

22. $\tan 483°$

23. $\csc 2$

24. $\sec 39\pi/5$

25. $\sin 11\pi/7$

26. $\csc(-9)$

27. $\sec (-1)$

28. $\cos (-55°)$

29. $\cot(-22°)$

30. $\tan(-138°)$

In Problems 31–34, find the exact value of each of the six trigonometric functions for an angle θ that has a terminal side containing the indicated point.

31. $(\sqrt{3}, 1)$

32. $(1, 1)$

33. $(1, -\sqrt{3})$

34. $(-1, \sqrt{3})$

In which quadrants must the terminal side of an angle θ lie in order for each of the following to be true?

35. $\cos\theta > 0$

36. $\sin\theta > 0$

37. $\tan\theta > 0$

38. $\cot\theta > 0$

39. $\sec\theta > 0$

40. $\csc\theta > 0$

41. $\sin\theta < 0$

42. $\cos\theta < 0$

43. $\cot\theta < 0$

44. $\tan\theta < 0$

45. $\csc\theta < 0$

46. $\sec\theta < 0$

In Problems 47–50, find the exact value of each of the other five trigonometric functions for an angle θ (without finding θ), given the indicated information. It would be helpful to sketch a reference triangle.

47. $\sin\theta = -\frac{2}{3}$; $\cot\theta > 0$

48. $\cos\theta = -\frac{3}{5}$; $\tan\theta < 0$

49. $\sec\theta = \sqrt{3}$; $\sin\theta < 0$

50. $\tan\theta = -2$; $\csc\theta > 0$

51. If angles α and β, $\alpha \ne \beta$, are in standard position and are coterminal, are $\cos\alpha$ and $\cos\beta$ equal? Explain.

52. If $\cos\alpha = \cos\beta$, $\alpha \ne \beta$, are α and β coterminal? Explain.

53. From the following display on a graphing calculator, explain how you would find $\cot x$ without finding x. Then find $\cot x$ to five decimal places.

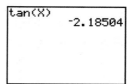

54. From the following display on a graphing calculator, explain how you would find sec x without finding x. Then find sec x to five decimal places.

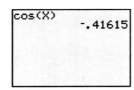

Use a calculator to find the answers to Problems 55–72 to four significant digits.

55. cos 1.539   **56.** sin 37.85°   **57.** csc 26°42′18″

58. sec 107.53°   **59.** cot(−3.86°)   **60.** tan 4.738

61. sec(−245.06°)   **62.** csc(−0.408)   **63.** tan 12°38′27″

64. cot 352°5′55″   **65.** sin 12.48   **66.** cos(−432.18°)

67. csc(−595.62°)   **68.** sin 605°42′75″   **69.** cos 6.77

70. sec 3.55   **71.** tan 482°12′52″   **72.** cot(−567.43°)

73. Which trigonometric functions are not defined when the terminal side of an angle lies along the positive or negative vertical axis? Explain.

74. Which trigonometric functions are not defined when the terminal side of an angle lies along the positive or negative horizontal axis? Explain.

For Problems 75–78, refer to the figure:

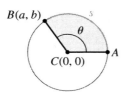

75. In the figure, the coordinates of the center of the circle are (0, 0). If the coordinates of A are (5, 0) and arc length s is exactly 6 units, find:

  (a) The exact radian measure of θ
  (b) The coordinates of B (to three significant digits)

76. In the figure, the coordinates of the center of the circle are (0, 0). If the coordinates of A are (4, 0) and arc length s is exactly 10 units, find:

  (a) The exact radian measure of θ
  (b) The coordinates of B (to three significant digits)

77. In the figure, the coordinates of the center of the circle are (0, 0). If the coordinates of A are (1, 0) and the arc length s is exactly 2 units, find:

  (a) The exact radian measure of θ
  (b) The coordinates of B (to three significant digits)

78. In the figure, the coordinates of the center of the circle are (0, 0). If the coordinates of A are (1, 0) and the arc length s is exactly 4 units, find:

  (a) The exact radian measure of θ
  (b) The coordinates of B (to three significant digits)

79. A circle with its center at the origin in a rectangular coordinate system passes through the point (4, 3). What is the length of the arc on the circle in the first quadrant between the positive horizontal axis and the point (4, 3)? Compute the answer to two decimal places.

80. Repeat Problem 79 with the circle passing through (3, 4).

81. **Solar Energy**   Light intensity I on a solar cell changes with the angle of the sun and is given by the formula in the figure below. Find the intensity in terms of the constant k for $\theta = 0°, \theta = 20°, \theta = 40°, \theta = 60°$, and $\theta = 80°$. Compute each answer to two decimal places.

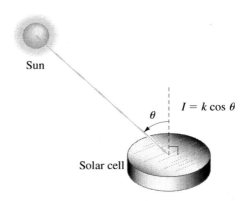

82. **Solar Energy**   In Problem 81, at what angle will the light intensity I be 50% of the vertical intensity?

Sun's Energy and Seasons   The reason we have summers and winters is because the earth's axis of rotation tilts 23.5° away from the perpendicular, as indicated in the figure. The formula given in Problem 83 quantifies this phenomenon.

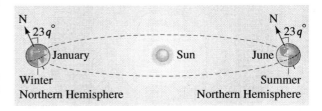

83. The amount of heat energy E from the sun received per square meter per unit of time in a given region on the surface of the earth is approximately proportional to the cosine of the angle θ that the sun makes with the vertical (see the figure on the next page). Thus,

$$E = k \cos \theta$$

where k is the constant of proportionality for a given region. For a region with a latitude of 40°N, compare the energy received at the summer solstice ($\theta = 15°$) with the energy received at the winter solstice ($\theta = 63°$). Express answers in terms of k to two significant digits.

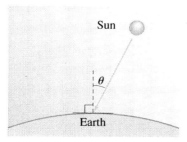

84. For a region with a latitude of 32°N, compare the energy received at the summer solstice ($\theta = 8°$) with the energy received at the winter solstice ($\theta = 55°$). Refer to Problem 83, and express answers in terms of k to two significant digits.

For Problems 85 and 86, refer to the figure:

85. Precalculus: Calculator Experiment   It can be shown that the area of a polygon of n equal sides inscribed in a circle of radius 1 is given by

$$A_n = \frac{n}{2} \sin \left(\frac{360}{n} \right)^{\circ}   \text{Refer to the figure.}$$

(a) Complete the table, giving A_n to five decimal places:

n	6	10	100	1,000	10,000
A_n					

(b) As n gets larger and larger, what number does A_n seem to approach? [*Hint:* What is the area of a circle with radius 1?]

(c) Will an inscribed polygon ever be a circle for any n, however large? Explain.

86. Precalculus: Calculator Experiment   It can be shown that the area of a polygon of n equal sides circumscribed around a circle of radius 1 is given by

$$A_n = n \tan \left(\frac{180}{n} \right)^{\circ}$$

(a) Complete the table, giving A_n to five decimal places:

n	6	10	100	1,000	10,000
A_n					

(b) As n gets larger and larger, what number does A_n seem to approach? [*Hint:* What is the area of a circle with radius 1?]

(c) Will a circumscribed polygon ever be a circle for any n, however large? Explain.

87. Engineering   The figure shows a piston connected to a wheel that turns at 10 revolutions per second (rps). If P is at $(1, 0)$ when $t = 0$, then $\theta = 20\pi t$, where t is time in seconds. Show that

$$x = a + \sqrt{5^2 - b^2} = \cos 20\pi t + \sqrt{25 - (\sin 20\pi t)^2}$$

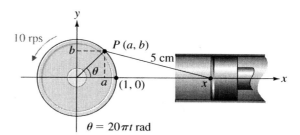

*88. Engineering   In Problem 87, find the position (to two decimal places) of the piston (the value of x) for $t = 0$ and $t = 0.01$ sec.

89. Alternating Current   An alternating current generator produces an electric current (measured in amperes) that is described by the equation

$$I = 35 \sin (48\pi t - 12\pi)$$

where t is time in seconds. (See Example 4 and the figure at the top of the next page.) What is the current I when $t = 0.13$ sec?

90. Alternating Current What is the current I in Problem 89 when $t = 0.310$ sec?

91. Precalculus: Angle of Inclination The **slope** of a nonvertical line passing through points $P_1(x_1, y_1)$ and $P_2(x_2, y_2)$ is given by the formula

$$\text{Slope} = m = \frac{y_2 - y_1}{x_2 - x_1}$$

The angle θ that the line L makes with the x axis, $0° \leq \theta \leq 180°$, is called the **angle of inclination** of the line L (see the figure). Thus,

$$\text{Slope} = m = \tan\theta \qquad 0° \leq \theta < 180°$$

(a) Compute the slopes (to two decimal places) of the lines with angles of inclination 63.5° and 172°.
(b) Find the equation of a line passing through $(-3, 6)$ with an angle of inclination 143°. [*Hint:* Recall, $y - y_1 = m(x - x_1)$.] Write the answer in the form $y = mx + b$, with m and b to two decimal places.

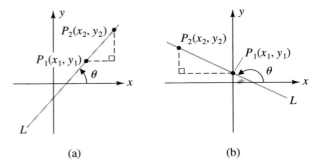

(a)   (b)

92. Precalculus: Angle of Inclination Refer to Problem 91.

(a) Compute the slopes (to two decimal places) of the lines with angles of inclination 89.2° and 179°.
(b) Find the equation of a line passing through $(7, -4)$ with an angle of inclination 101°. Write the answer in the form $y = mx + b$, with m and b to two decimal places.

3.3 EXACT VALUE FOR SPECIAL ANGLES

- Introduction
- Evaluation of Trigonometric Functions for Quadrantal Angles
- Reference Triangle and Angle
- Special 30°–60° and 45° Right Triangles
- Evaluation of Trigonometric Functions for Angles or Real Numbers wih 30°–60° and 45° Reference Triangles

Introduction

Decimal approximations of many numbers are not exact, no matter how many decimal places are computed. For example, 0.5714 is a decimal approximation of $\frac{4}{7}$ and 1.414 is a decimal approximation of $\sqrt{2}$, but neither $\frac{4}{7}$ nor $\sqrt{2}$ can be represented exactly by a finite decimal no matter how many decimal places are computed. In certain formulas and computations it is better to use an exact form rather than a decimal approximation.

Explore/ Discuss 1 Which of the following graphing calculator displays represents cos 45° exactly? Experiment with your own calculator. Do you believe that cos 45° has an exact finite decimal representation? This section will provide an answer to this question.

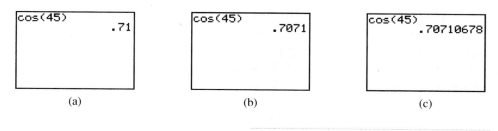

If an angle is an integer multiple of $30°, 45°, \pi/6$ rad, or $\pi/4$ rad, and if a real number is an integer multiple of $\pi/6$ or $\pi/4$ (see Fig. 3.16), then, for those values for which each trigonometric function is defined, the function can be evaluated exactly without the use of any calculator (which is different from finding approximate values using a calculator). With a little practice, you will—mentally—be able to determine these exact values.

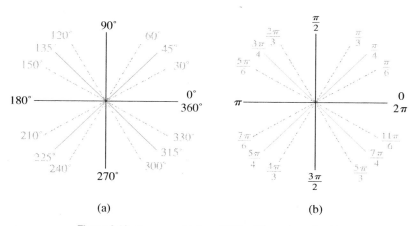

Figure 3.16: Some multiples of $30°, 45°, \pi/6$, and $\pi/4$

Evaluation of Trigonometric Functions for Quadrantal Angles

The easiest angles to deal with are **quadrantal angles**—that is, angles with their terminal side lying along a coordinate axis. These angles are integer multiples of $90°$ or $\pi/2$. It is easy to find coordinates of a point on a coordinate axis. Since any nonorigin point will do, we shall, for convenience, choose points 1 unit from the origin (Fig. 3.17).

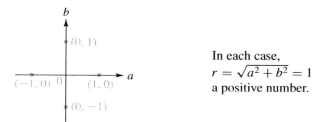

In each case,
$r = \sqrt{a^2 + b^2} = 1$
a positive number.

Figure 3.17: Quadrantal angles points

Evaluation Involving Quadrantal Angles

Example 1   Find:

(a) $\sin 90°$ (b) $\cos \pi$ (c) $\tan(-2\pi)$ (d) $\cot(-180°)$

Solution   For each, visualize the location of the terminal side of the angle relative to Figure 3.16. With a little practice, you should be able to do most of the following calculations mentally.

(a) $\sin 90° \boxed{= \dfrac{b}{r}} = \dfrac{1}{1} = 1$ $(a, b) = (0, 1), \quad r = 1$

(b) $\cos \pi \boxed{= \dfrac{a}{r}} = \dfrac{-1}{1} = -1$ $(a, b) = (-1, 0), \quad r = 1$

(c) $\tan(-2\pi) \boxed{= \dfrac{b}{a}} = \dfrac{0}{1} = 0$ $(a, b) = (1, 0), \quad r = 1$

(d) $\cot(-180°) \boxed{= \dfrac{a}{b}} = \dfrac{-1}{0}$ $(a, b) = (-1, 0), \quad r = 1$
Not defined

Matched Problem 1   Find:

(a) $\sin(3\pi/2)$ (b) $\sec(-\pi)$ (c) $\tan 90°$ (d) $\cot(-270°)$

Explore Discuss 2   In Example 1D, notice that $\cot(-180°)$ is not defined. Discuss other angles in degree measure for which the cotangent is not defined. For what angles in degree measure is the cosecant function not defined?

Reference Triangle and Angle

Because the reference triangle is going to play a very important role in the work that follows, we now restate its definition as well as that of a reference angle.

REFERENCE TRIANGLE AND ANGLE

For a nonquadrantal angle θ:

1. To form a **reference triangle** for θ, drop a perpendicular from a point $P(a, b)$ on the terminal side of θ to the horizontal axis.
2. The **reference angle** α is the acute angle (always taken positive) between the terminal side of θ and the horizontal axis.

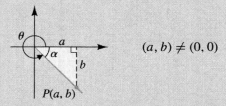

$(a, b) \neq (0, 0)$

Reference Triangles and Angles

Example 2   Sketch the reference triangle and find the reference angle α for each of the following angles:

(a) $\theta = 330°$ (b) $\theta = -315°$ (c) $\theta = -\pi/4$ (d) $\theta = \pi/3$

Solution   (a)

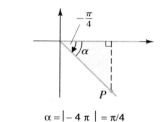

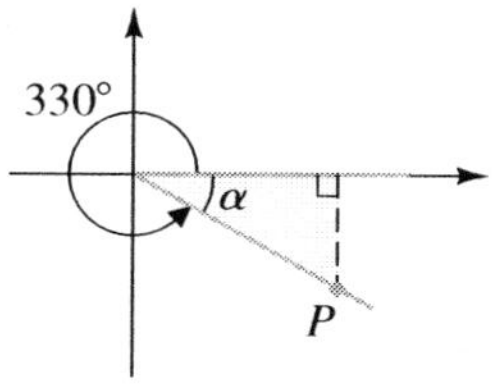

$\alpha = 360° - 330° = 30°$

Figure 3.18

(b)

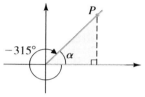

$\alpha = 360° - 315° = 45°$

Figure 3.19

(c)

$\alpha = |-4\pi| = \pi/4$

Figure 3.20

(d)

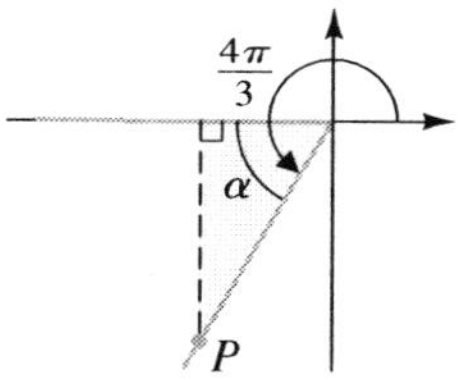

$\alpha = 4\pi/3 - \pi = \pi/3$

Figure 3.21

Matched Problem 2   Sketch the reference triangle and find the reference angle α for each of the following angles:

(a) $\theta = -225°$ (b) $\theta = 420°$ (c) $\theta = -5\pi/6$ (d) $\theta = -2\pi/3$

Special 30°—60° and 45° Right Triangles

If a reference triangle of a given angle is a 30°–60° right triangle or a 45° right triangle, then we will be able to find exact nonorigin coordinates on the terminal side of the given angle.

If we take a 30°–60° right triangle, we note that it is one-half of an equilateral triangle, as indicated in Figure 3.22. Since all sides are equal in an equilateral triangle, we can apply the Pythagorean theorem to obtain a useful relationship among the three sides of the original triangle:

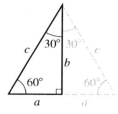

$$b = \sqrt{c^2 - a^2}$$
$$= \sqrt{(2a)^2 - a^2} \quad \text{Since } c = 2a$$
$$= \sqrt{3a^2}$$
$$= a\sqrt{3}$$

Figure 3.22

Similarly, using the Pythagorean theorem on a 45° right triangle, we obtain the following (see Fig. 3.23):

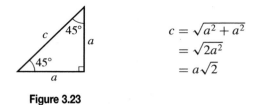

$$c = \sqrt{a^2 + a^2}$$
$$= \sqrt{2a^2}$$
$$= a\sqrt{2}$$

Figure 3.23

We summarize these results in Figure 3.24, along with some frequently used special cases. The ratios of these special triangles should be learned, since they will be used often in this and subsequent sections. The two triangles shown in blue are the easiest to remember. The others can be obtained from these by multiplying or dividing the length of each side by the same nonzero quantity.

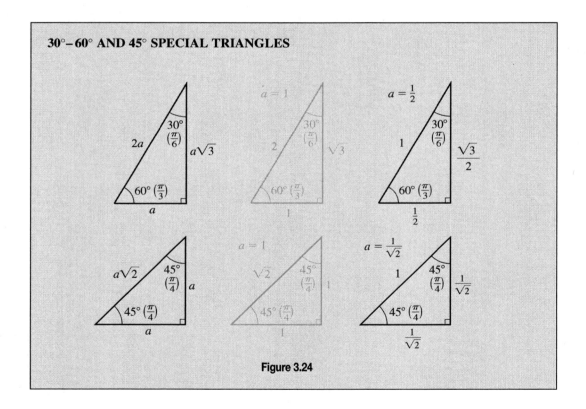

Figure 3.24

Evaluation of Trigonometric Functions for Angles or Real Numbers with 30°–60° and 45° Reference Triangles

If an angle θ has a 30°–60° or 45° reference triangle, then it is easy to find exact coordinates of a point P on the terminal side of θ and the exact distance of P from the origin. Then, using the definitions of the six trigonometric functions given in Section 3.2, we can find the exact value of any of the six functions for the given θ. Several examples will illustrate the process.

Exact Evaluation for Special Angles and Real Numbers

Example 3 Evaluate exactly:

(a) $\sin 30°$, $\cos(\pi/6)$, $\cot(\pi/6)$ (b) $\cos 45°$, $\tan(\pi/4)$, $\csc(\pi/4)$

Solution (a) Use the special 30°–60° triangle (Fig. 3.25) as the reference triangle for $\theta = 30°$ and $\theta = \pi/6$. Use the sides of the reference triangle to determine $P(a, b)$ and r; then use Definition 1 from Section 3.2.

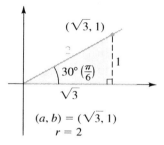

$$\sin 30° = \frac{b}{r} = \frac{1}{2}$$

$$\cos \frac{\pi}{6} = \frac{a}{r} = \frac{\sqrt{3}}{2}$$

$$\cot \frac{\pi}{6} = \frac{a}{b} = \frac{\sqrt{3}}{1} = \sqrt{3}$$

$(a, b) = (\sqrt{3}, 1)$
$r = 2$

Figure 3.25

(b) Use the special 45° triangle (Fig. 3.26) as the reference triangle for $\theta = 45°$ and $\theta = \pi/4$. Use the sides of the reference triangle to determine $P(a, b)$ and r; then use the appropriate definition from Section 3.2.

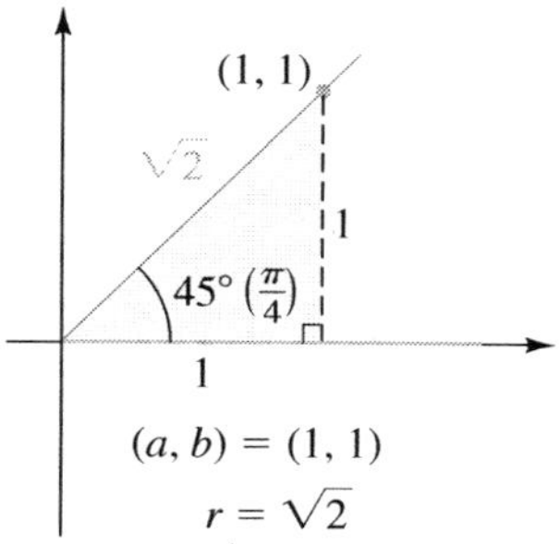

$$\cos 45° = \frac{a}{r} = \frac{1}{\sqrt{2}} \text{*}$$

$$\tan \frac{\pi}{4} = \frac{b}{a} = \frac{1}{1} = 1$$

$$\csc \frac{\pi}{4} = \frac{r}{b} = \frac{\sqrt{2}}{1} = \sqrt{2}$$

$(a, b) = (1, 1)$
$r = \sqrt{2}$

Figure 3.26

Matched Problem 3 Evaluate exactly:

(a) $\cos 60°$, $\sin(\pi/3)$, $\tan(\pi/3)$ (b) $\sin 45°$, $\cot(\pi/4)$, $\sec(\pi/4)$

*Whether we rationalize a denominator or not depends entirely on what we want to do with the answer. Leave answers in unrationalized form unless directed otherwise.

Before proceeding with examples of reference triangles in quadrants other than the first quadrant, it is useful to recall the multiples of $\pi/3$ (60°), $\pi/6$ (30°), and $\pi/4$ (45°). See Figure 3.27.

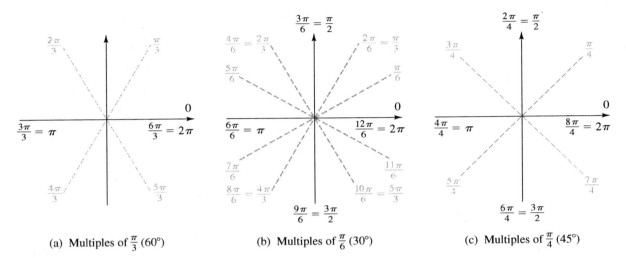

(a) Multiples of $\frac{\pi}{3}$ (60°)   (b) Multiples of $\frac{\pi}{6}$ (30°)   (c) Multiples of $\frac{\pi}{4}$ (45°)

Figure 3.27: Multiples of special angles

Exact Evaluation for Special Angles and Real Numbers

Example 4   Evaluate exactly:

(a) $\sin 210°$ (b) $\cos(2\pi/3)$ (c) $\cot(-5\pi/6)$ (d) $\csc(-240°)$

Solution   Each angle has a 30°–60° or 45° reference triangle. Locate it, determine $P(a, b)$ and r, and then evaluate. (Recall, we label the horizontal and vertical sides of the reference triangle as a and b, respectively; consequently, one or the other may be negative depending on the quadrant containing the terminal side of θ.)

(a) $\sin 210° = \dfrac{-1}{2} = -\dfrac{1}{2}$ (b) $\cos \dfrac{2\pi}{3} = \dfrac{-1}{2} = -\dfrac{1}{2}$

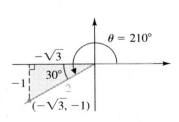

Figure 3.28

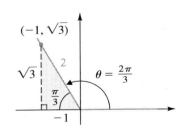

Figure 3.29

(c) $\cot\left(-\dfrac{5\pi}{6}\right) = \dfrac{-\sqrt{3}}{-1} = \sqrt{3}$

(d) $\csc(-240°) = \dfrac{2}{\sqrt{3}}$

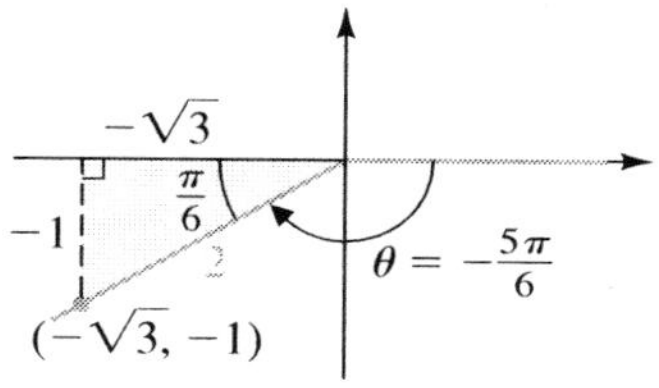

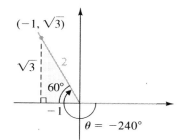

Figure 3.30

Figure 3.31

Matched Problem 4

Evaluate exactly:

(a) $\tan 210°$ (b) $\sin(2\pi/3)$ (c) $\csc(25\pi/6)$ (d) $\sec(2240°)$

Now let us reverse the problem. That is, we are given the exact value of one of the six trigonometric functions that corresponds to one of the special reference triangles, and we must find θ.

Finding Special Angles θ

Example 5

Find the least positive θ in degree and radian measure for which each is true.

(a) $\sin\theta = \sqrt{3}/2$ (b) $\cos\theta = -1/\sqrt{2}$

Solution

(a) Draw a reference triangle (Fig. 3.32) in the first quadrant with side opposite reference angle $\sqrt{3}$ and hypotenuse 2. Observe that this is a special 30°–60° triangle:

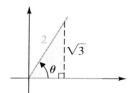

$\theta = 60°$ or $\dfrac{\pi}{3}$

Figure 3.32

(b) Draw a reference triangle (Fig. 3.33) in the second quadrant with side adjacent reference angle -1 and hypotenuse $\sqrt{2}$. Observe that this is a special 45° triangle:

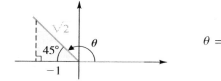

$\theta = 180° - 45° = 135°$ or $\dfrac{3\pi}{4}$

Figure 3.33

Matched Problem 5   Repeat Example 5 for:

(a) $\tan \theta = 1/\sqrt{3}$

(b) $\sec \theta = -\sqrt{2}$

We conclude this section with a summary of special values in Table 3.3. Some people memorize this table; others use the definition in Section 3.2 and special triangles.

Table 3.3 *Special Values*

θ	$\sin \theta$	$\csc \theta$	$\cos \theta$	$\sec \theta$	$\tan \theta$	$\cot \theta$
0° or 0	0	N.D.	1	1	0	N.D.
30° or $\pi/6$	1/2	2	$\sqrt{3}/2$	$2/\sqrt{3}$	$1/\sqrt{3}$	$\sqrt{3}$
45° or $\pi/4$	$1/\sqrt{2}$	$\sqrt{2}$	$1/\sqrt{2}$	$\sqrt{2}$	1	1
60° or $\pi/3$	$\sqrt{3}/2$	$2/\sqrt{3}$	1/2	2	$\sqrt{3}$	$1/\sqrt{3}$
90° or $\pi/2$	1	1	0	N.D.	N.D.	0

N.D. = Not defined

The special angle values for sine and cosine are easily remembered if you observe the (unexpected) pattern after completing Table 3.4 in Explore/Discuss 3.

Explore Discuss 5   Fill in the sine column in Table 3.4 with a pattern of values similar to those in the cosine column. Discuss how the two columns are generated and how they are related.

Table 3.4 *Memory Aid*

θ	$\sin \theta$	$\cos \theta$
0° or 0		$\sqrt{4}/2 = 1$
30° or $\pi/6$		$\sqrt{3}/2$
45° or $\pi/4$		$\sqrt{2}/2 = 1\sqrt{2}$
60° or $\pi/3$		$\sqrt{1}/2 = 1/2$
90° or $\pi/2$		$\sqrt{0}/2 = 0$

Answers to Matched Problems

1. (a) -1 (b) -1 (c) Not defined   (d) 0

2. (a)

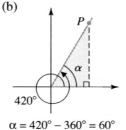

$\alpha = 225° - 180° = 45°$

(b)

$\alpha = 420° - 360° = 60°$

(c)

$\alpha = \pi - 5\pi/6 = \pi/6$

(d)

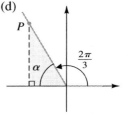

$\alpha = \pi - 2\pi/3 = \pi/3$

3. (a) $1/2, \sqrt{3}/2\sqrt{3}$ (b) $1/\sqrt{2}, 1, \sqrt{2}$
4. (a) $1/\sqrt{3}$ (b) $\sqrt{3}/2$ (c) -2 (d) -2
5. (a) $30°$ or $\pi/6$ (b) $135°$ or $3\pi/4$

Exercises for Section 3.3

Do not use a calculator for any of the problems in these exercises.

Sketch the reference triangle and find the reference angle a for each of the following angles.

1. $\theta = 60°$ 2. $\theta = 45°$ 3. $\theta = -60°$

4. $\theta = -45°$ 5. $\theta = \dfrac{-\pi}{3}$ 6. $\theta = \dfrac{-\pi}{4}$

7. $\theta = \dfrac{3\pi}{4}$ 8. $\theta = \dfrac{5\pi}{6}$ 9. $\theta = -210°$

10. $\theta = -150°$ 11. $\theta = \dfrac{-5\pi}{4}$ 12. $\theta = \dfrac{-5\pi}{3}$

In Problems 13–30, find the exact value of each trigonometric function.

13. $\sin 0°$ 14. $\cos 0°$ 15. $\tan 0$

16. $\cot 0$ 17. $\cos (60°)$ 18. $\sin (30°)$

19. $\cot (45°)$ 20. $\tan (30°)$ 21. $\sec \dfrac{\pi}{6}$

22. $\csc \dfrac{\pi}{3}$ 23. $\sin \dfrac{-\pi}{2}$ 24. $\cos \dfrac{-3\pi}{2}$

25. $\cot \pi$ 26. $\tan \dfrac{\pi}{2}$ 27. $\cos \dfrac{-3\pi}{4}$

28. $\sin \dfrac{-\pi}{3}$ 29. $\tan (-60°)$ 30. $\cot (-30°)$

In Problems 31–42, find the exact value of each trigonometric function.

31. $\sin \dfrac{5\pi}{4}$ 32. $\cos \dfrac{7\pi}{4}$

33. $\tan \dfrac{5\pi}{3}$ 34. $\cot \dfrac{11\pi}{6}$

35. $\sec \dfrac{-3\pi}{2}$ 36. $\csc (-2\pi)$

37. $\cos (-210°)$ 38. $\sin (-300°)$

39. $\cot 405°$ 40. $\tan 480°$

41. $\csc (-495°)$ 42. $\sec (-510°)$

In Problems 43–46, find all angles θ, $0 \le \theta \le 2\pi$ for which the following functions are not defined. Explain why.

43. tangent   44. cotangent

45. cosecant   46. secant

In each graphing calculator display in Problems 47–50, indicate which values are not exact and find the exact value.

47.
```
sin(π/6)
          .5000
sin(-45°)
         -.7071
cos(0)
         1.0000
```

48.
```
cos(90°)
         0.0000
sin(2π/3)
          .8660
sin(π/6)
          .5000
```

49.
```
tan(45°)
         1.0000
tan(180°)
         0.0000
tan(-π/3)
        -1.7321
```

50.
```
sin(-150°)
         -.5000
tan(-150°)
          .5774
tan(5π/4)
         1.0000
```

In Problems 51–56, find the least positive θ in (a) Degree measure   (b) Radian measure for which each is true.

51. $\sin \theta = \dfrac{1}{2}$ 52. $\cos \theta = \dfrac{1}{\sqrt{2}}$

53. $\cos \theta = \dfrac{-1}{2}$ 54. $\sin \theta = -\dfrac{1}{\sqrt{2}}$

55. $\tan \theta = -\sqrt{3}$ 56. $\cot \theta = -1$

57. Find the exact value of all the angles between $0°$ and $360°$ for which $\sin \theta = -\sqrt{3}/2$.

58. Find the exact value of all the angles between $0°$ and $360°$ for which $\tan \theta = -\sqrt{3}$.

59. Find the exact value of all the angles between $0°$ rad and 2π rad for which $\cot \theta = -\sqrt{3}$.

60. Find the exact value of all the angles between 0 rad and 2π rad for which $\cos \theta = -\sqrt{3}/2$.

For each graphing calculator display in Problems 61–64, find the least positive exact X in radian measure that produces the result shown.

61.

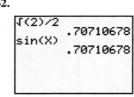

62.

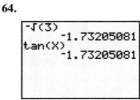

63.

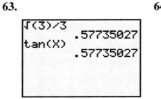

64.

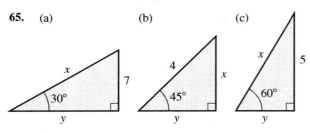

66. (a)   (b)   (c)

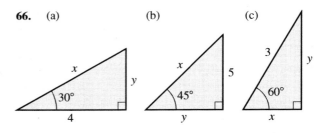

Later, we will show that the area of an n-sided regular polygon inscribed in a circle of radius r (such as in the figure) is given by

$$A = \frac{nr^2}{2} \sin \frac{2\pi}{n}$$

Find the exact values of x and y in Problems 65 and 66.

65. (a)   (b)   (c)

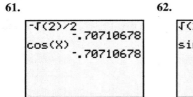

Use this formula to find the exact areas of the polygons defined in Problems 67–70. Assume each radius is exact.

67. $n = 3$, $r = 2$ cm   **68.** $n = 4$, $r = 5$ ft

69. $n = 6$, $r = 10$ in.   **70.** $n = 8$, $r = 4$ mm

3.4   INTRODUCTION TO PERIODIC FUNCTIONS

The World's Largest Ferris Wheel

To celebrate the millennium, British Airways funded construction of the "London Eye," the world's largest ferris wheel.[1] The wheel is located on the south bank of the river Thames, in London, England, measures 450 feet in diameter, and carries up to 800 passengers in 32 capsules. It turns continuously, completing a single rotation once every 30 minutes. This is slow enough for people to hop on and off while it turns.

Ferris Wheel Height As a Function of Time

Suppose you hop on this ferris wheel at time $t = 0$ and ride it for two full turns. Let $f(t)$ be your height above the ground, measured in feet as a function of t, the number of minutes you have been riding. We can figure out some values of $f(t)$.

Let's imagine that the wheel is turning in the counterclockwise direction. At time $t = 0$ you have just boarded the wheel, so your height is 0 ft above the ground (not counting the height of your seat). Thus, $f(0) = 0$. Since the wheel turns all the way around once every 30 minutes, after 7.5 minutes the wheel has turned one-quarter of the way around. Thinking of the wheel as a giant clock, this means you have been carried from the 6 o'clock position to the 3 o'clock position, as shown in Figure 3.34. You are now halfway up the wheel, or 225 feet above the ground, so $f(7.5) = 225$.

---

[1]http://british-airways-london-eye.visit-london-england.com, accessed May 23, 2002.

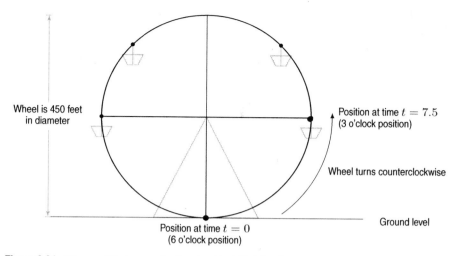

Figure 3.34: The world's largest ferris wheel is 450 ft in diameter and turns around once every 30 minutes. Seats not drawn to scale

After 15 minutes, the wheel has turned halfway around, so you are now at the top, in the 12 o'clock position. Thus, $f(15) = 450$. And after 22.5 minutes, the wheel has turned three quarters of the way around, bringing you into the 9 o'clock position. You have descended from the top of the wheel halfway down to the ground, and you are once again 225 feet above the ground. Thus, $f(22.5) = 225$. (See Figures 3.35 and 3.36.) Finally, after 30 minutes, the wheel has turned all the way around, bringing you back to ground level, so $f(30) = 0$.

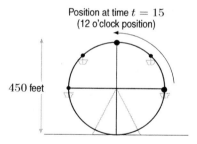

Figure 3.35: At time $t = 15$, the wheel has turned halfway around

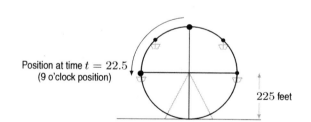

Figure 3.36: At time $t = 22.5$, the wheel has turned three quarters of the way around

The Second Time Around On the Wheel

Since the wheel turns without stopping, at time $t = 30$ it begins its second turn. Thus, at time $t = 37.5$, the wheel has again turned one quarter of the way around, and $f(37.5) = 225$. Similarly, at time $t = 45$ the wheel has again turned halfway around, bringing you back up to the very top. Likewise, at time $t = 52.5$, the wheel has carried you halfway back down to the ground. This means that $f(45) = 450$ and $f(52.5) = 225$. Finally, at time $t = 60$, the wheel has completed its second full turn and you are back at ground level, so $f(60) = 0$.

Repeating Values of the Ferris Wheel Function

Notice that the values of $f(t)$ in Table 3.5 begin repeating after 30 minutes. This is because the second turn is just like the first turn, except that it happens 30 minutes later. If you ride the wheel for more full turns, the values of $f(t)$ continue to repeat at 30-minute intervals.

Table 3.5 *Values of $f(t)$, your height above the ground t minutes after boarding the wheel*

t (minutes)	0	7.5	15	22.5	30	37.5	45	52.5	
$f(t)$ (feet)	0	225	450	225	0	225	450	225	
t (minutes)	60	67.5	75	82.5	90	97.5	105	112.5	120
$f(t)$ (feet)	0	225	450	225	0	225	450	225	0

Graphing the Ferris Wheel Function

The data from Table 3.5 are plotted in Figure 3.37. The graph begins at $y = 0$ (ground level), rises to $y = 225$ (halfway up the wheel) and then to $y = 450$ (the top of the wheel). The graph then falls to $y = 225$ and then down to $y = 0$. This cycle then repeats itself three more times, once for each rotation of the wheel.

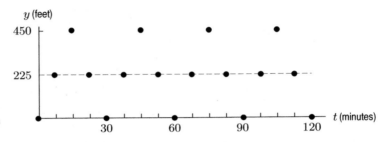

Figure 3.37: Values of $f(t)$, the ferris wheel height function, at 7.5 minute intervals

Filling in the Graph of the Ferris Wheel Function

It is tempting to connect the points in Figure 3.37 with straight lines, but this is not correct. Consider the first 7.5 minutes of your ride, starting at the 6 o'clock position and ending at the 3 o'clock position. (See Figure 3.38). Halfway through this part of the ride, the wheel has turned halfway from the 6 o'clock to the 3 o'clock position. However, as is clear from Figure 3.38, your seat rises less than half the vertical distance from $y = 0$ to $y = 225$. At the same time, the seat glides more than half the horizontal distance. If the points in Figure 3.37 were connected with straight lines, $f(3.75)$ would be halfway between $f(0)$ and $f(7.5)$, which is incorrect.

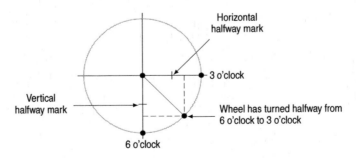

Figure 3.38: As the wheel turns half the way from 6 o'clock to 3 o'clock, the seat rises less than half the vertical distance but glides more than half the horizontal distance

The graph of $f(t)$ in Figure 3.39 is a smooth curve that repeats itself. It looks the same from $t = 0$ to $t = 30$ as from $t = 30$ to $t = 60$, or from $t = 60$ to $t = 90$, or from $t = 90$ to $t = 120$.

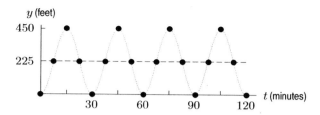

Figure 3.39: The graph of $y = f(t)$ is a smooth wave-shaped curve

Periodic Functions: Period, Midline, and Amplitude

The ferris wheel function, f, is said to be *periodic*. The smallest time interval during which a function completes one full cycle is called its *period* and is represented as a horizontal distance in Figure 3.40.

We can think about the period in terms of horizontal shifts. If the graph of f is shifted to the left by 30 units, the resulting graph looks exactly the same. That is,

$$\underbrace{\text{Graph of } f \text{ shifted left by 30 units}}_{f(t+30)} \quad \text{is the same as} \quad \underbrace{\text{Original graph}}_{f(t)},$$

so, for all values of t,

$$f(t + 30) = f(t).$$

In general, we make the following definition:

A function f is **periodic** if its values repeat at regular intervals. Graphically, this means that if the graph of f is shifted horizontally by c units, the new graph is identical to the original. In function notation, periodic means that, for all t in the domain of f,

$$f(t + c) = f(t).$$

The smallest positive constant c for which this relationship holds for all values of t is called the **period** of f.

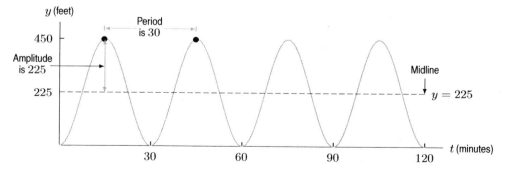

Figure 3.40: The graph of $y = f(t)$ showing the amplitude, period, and midline

In Figure 3.40, the dashed horizontal line is the *midline* of the graph of f. The *amplitude* of a wave-like periodic function is the distance between its maximum and the midline (or the distance between the midline and the minimum). Thus the amplitude of f is 225 because the ferris wheel's maximum height is 450 feet and its midline is at 225 feet. The amplitude is represented graphically as a vertical distance. (See Figure 3.40.) In general:

> The **midline** of a periodic function is the horizontal line midway between the function's maximum and minimum values. The **amplitude** is the vertical distance between the function's maximum (or minimum) value and the midline.

Exercises and Problems for Section 3.4

Exercises

In Exercises 1–8, do the functions appear to be periodic with period less than 4?

1.

t	0	1	2	3	4	5	6
$f(t)$	1	5	7	1	5	7	1

2.

r	0	π	2π	3π	4π	5π	6π	7π
$q(r)$	0	1	0	-1	1	0	1	0

3.

4.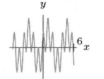

5.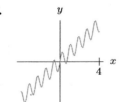

6.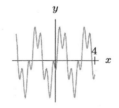

7.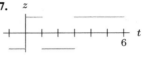

8.

In Exercises 9–12, estimate the period of the periodic functions.

9.

t	0	1	2	3	4	5	6
$f(t)$	12	13	14	12	13	14	12

10.

z	1	11	21	31	41	51	61	71	81
$g(z)$	5	3	2	3	5	3	2	3	5

11.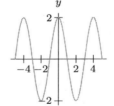

12.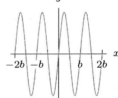

Problems

You board the London ferris wheel described in this section. In Problems 13–15, graph $h = f(t)$, your height in feet above the ground t minutes after the wheel begins to turn. Label the period, the amplitude, and the midline of each graph, as well as both axes. In each case, first determine an appropriate interval for t, with $t \geq 0$.

13. The London ferris wheel has increased its rotation speed. The wheel completes one full revolution every ten minutes. You get off when you reach the ground after having made two complete revolutions.

14. Everything is the same as Problem 13 (including the rotation speed) except the wheel has a 600 foot diameter.

15. The London ferris wheel is rotating at twice the speed as the wheel in Problem 13.

Problem 16–18 involve different ferris wheels. Graph $h = f(t)$. Label the period, the amplitude, and the midline for each graph. In each case, first determine an appropriate interval for t, with $t \geq 0$.

16. A ferris wheel is 50 meters in diameter and boarded from a platform that is 5 meters above the ground. The six o'clock position on the ferris wheel is level with the loading platform. The wheel completes one full revolution every 8 minutes. You make two complete revolutions on the wheel, starting at $t = 0$.

17. A ferris wheel is 20 meters in diameter and boarded from a platform that is 4 meters above the ground. The six o'clock position on the ferris wheel is level with the loading platform. The wheel completes one full revolution every 2 minutes. At $t = 0$ you are in the twelve o'clock position. You then make two complete revolutions and any additional part of a revolution needed to return to the boarding platform.

18. A ferris wheel is 35 meters in diameter and boarded at ground level. The wheel completes one full revolution every 5 minutes. At $t = 0$ you are in the three o'clock position and ascending. You then make two complete revolutions and return to the boarding platform.

The graphs in Problems 19–22 describe your height, $h = f(t)$, above the ground on different ferris wheels, where h is in meters and t is time in minutes. You boarded the wheel before $t = 0$. For each graph, determine the following: your position and direction at $t = 0$, how long it takes the wheel to complete one full revolution, the diameter of the wheel, at what height above the ground you board the wheel, and the length of time the graph shows you riding the wheel. The boarding platform is level with the bottom of the wheel.

19. h (meters)

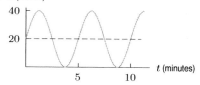

20. h (meters)

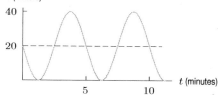

21. h (meters)

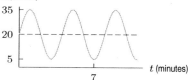

22. h (meters)

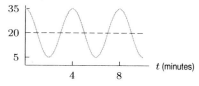

Problems 23–26 concern a weight suspended from the ceiling by a spring. (See Figure 3.41.) Let d be the distance in centimeters from the ceiling to the weight. When the weight is motionless, $d = 10$. If the weight is disturbed, it begins to bob up and down, or *oscillate*. Then d is a periodic function of t, time in seconds, so $d = f(t)$.

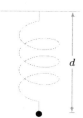

Figure 3.41

23. Determine the midline, period, amplitude, and the minimum and maximum values of f from the graph in Figure 3.42. Interpret these quantities physically; that is, use them to describe the motion of the weight.

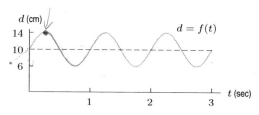

Figure 3.42

24. A new experiment with the same weight and spring is represented by Figure 3.43. Compare Figure 3.43 to Figure 3.42. How do the oscillations differ? For both figures, the weight was disturbed at time $t = -0.25$ and then left to move naturally; determine the nature of the initial disturbances.

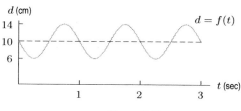

Figure 3.43

25. The weight in Problem 23 is gently pulled down to a distance of 14 cm from the ceiling and released at time $t = 0$. Sketch its motion for $0 \le t \le 3$.

26. Figures 3.44 and 3.45 describe the motion of two different weights, A and B, attached to two different springs. Based on these graphs, which weight:

(a) Is closest to the ceiling when not in motion?
(b) Makes the largest oscillations?
(c) Makes the fastest oscillations?

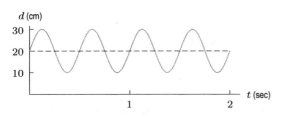

Figure 3.44: Weight A

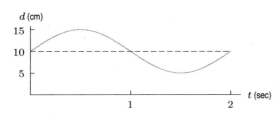

Figure 3.45: Weight B

27. The temperature of a chemical reaction oscillates between a low of 30°C and a high of 110°C. The temperature is at its lowest point when $t = 0$ and completes one cycle over a five-hour period.

(a) Sketch the temperature, T, against the elapsed time, t, over a ten-hour period.
(b) Find the period, the amplitude, and the midline of the graph you drew in part (a).

28. In the US, household electricity is in the form of *alternating current* (AC) at 155.6 volts and 60 hertz. This means that the voltage cycles from -155.6 volts to $+155.6$ volts and back to -155.6 volts, and that 60 cycles occur each second. Suppose that at $t = 0$ the voltage at a given outlet is at 0 volts.

(a) Sketch $V = f(t)$, the voltage as a function of time, for the first 0.1 seconds.

(b) State the period, the amplitude, and the midline of the graph you made in part (a). Describe the physical significance of these quantities.

29. Table 3.6 gives data from a vibrating string experiment, with time, t, in seconds, and height, $h = f(t)$, in centimeters. Find the midline, amplitude and period of f.

Table 3.6

t	0	.1	.2	.3	.4	.5	.6	.7	.8	.9	1
h	2	2.6	3	3	2.6	2	1.4	1	1	1.4	2

30. Table 3.7 gives the height $h = f(t)$ in feet of a weight on a spring where t is time in seconds. Find the midline, amplitude and period of the function f.

Table 3.7

t	0	1	2	3	4	5	6	7
h	4.0	5.2	6.2	6.5	6.2	5.2	4.0	2.8

t	8	9	10	11	12	13	14	15
h	1.8	1.5	1.8	2.8	4.0	5.2	6.2	6.5

31. Table 3.8 gives the number of white blood cells (in 10,000s) in a patient with chronic myelogenous leukemia with nearly periodic relapses. Plot these data and estimate the midline, amplitude and period.

Table 3.8

Day	0	10	40	50	60	70	75	80	90
WBC	0.9	1.2	10	9.2	7.0	3.0	0.9	0.8	0.4
Day	100	110	115	120	130	140	145	150	160
WBC	1.5	2.0	5.7	10.7	9.5	5.0	2.7	0.6	1.0
Day	170	175	185	195	210	225	230	240	255
WBC	2.0	6.0	9.5	8.2	4.5	1.8	2.5	6.0	10.0

32. Use a calculator or a computer to decide whether each of the following functions is periodic or not.

(a) $f(x) = \sin(x/\pi)$ (b) $f(x) = \sin(\pi/x)$
(c) $f(x) = x \sin x$ (d) $f(x) = e^{-x} \sin x$
(e) $f(x) = \pi + \sin x$ (f) $f(x) = \sin(e^{-x})$
(g) $f(x) = \sin(x + \pi)$

3.5 CIRCULAR FUNCTIONS

- Definition of Circular Functions
- Domain and Range for Sine and Cosine Functions
- Periodic Properties

- Fundamental Identities
- Circular Functions and Trigonometric Functions
- Evaluating Circular Functions

Our treatment of trigonometric functions has progressed from the concrete to the abstract, which follows the historical development of the subject. We first defined trigonometric ratios relative to right triangles—a procedure used by the ancient Greeks. We then expanded the meaning of these functions by using generalized angles in standard positions in a rectangular coordinate system.

We now turn to the modern, more abstract definition of these functions, a definition involving real number domains, not angles or triangles. This is the preferred and most useful definition for advanced mathematics and the sciences, including calculus. We will be able to quickly observe some very useful trigonometric properties and relationships that were not as apparent using the angle approach.

Definition of Circular Functions

If we graph the equation $a^2 + b^2 = 1$ in a rectangular coordinate system, we obtain a circle with center at the origin and radius 1 called the **unit circle.** Using this circle, we define the **circular functions** with real number domains, as follows.

Definition 1

CIRCULAR FUNCTIONS

Let x be an arbitrary real number and let U be the unit circle with equation $a^2 + b^2 = 1$. Start at $(1, 0)$ and proceed counterclockwise if x is positive and clockwise if x is negative around the unit circle until an arc length of $|x|$ has been covered. Let $P(a, b)$ be the point at the terminal end of the arc.

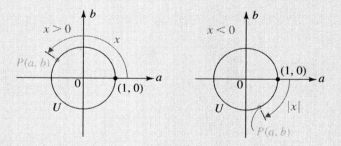

The following six **circular functions*** are defined in terms of the "coordinates of P:

$$y = \sin x = b \qquad y = \cos x = a \qquad y = \tan x = \frac{b}{a}$$

$$y = \csc x = \frac{1}{b} \qquad y = \sec x = \frac{1}{a} \qquad y = \cot x = \frac{a}{b}$$

The independent variable is x and the dependent variable is y.

---

*Following common usage, we also refer to circular functions as trigonometric functions.

Remarks   1. The circular function definitions do not involve any angles.

2. The circular function definitions use standard function notation

$$y = f(x)$$

with f replaced by the name of a particular circular function; for example, $y = \sin x$ actually means $y = \sin(x)$.

3. When we write $y = f(x) = x^2 - 1$, the expression on the right has a recipe for evaluating f (square x and subtract 1). When we write $y = f(x) = \sin x$, the expression on the right only identifies the function; for its evaluation we must refer to the circular function definition.

Explore/ Discuss 1

(a) For the function $y = f(x) = 3 - x^2$, describe the process in words for determining y for each real value x.

(b) For the function $y = h(x) = \sin x$, describe the process in words (in terms of the circle-based definition of the sine function) for determining y for each real value x.

We will now investigate a few important properties of the circular functions that are easily observed from their definitions. In the next chapter we will graph the circular functions and discuss many additional properties.

Domain and Range for Sine and Cosine Functions

Since each real number x can be associated with an arc $|x|$ units in length (counterclockwise if x is positive and clockwise if x is negative), the domain of each circular function is the set of real numbers for which the function is defined.

We now investigate the domains and ranges of the sine and cosine functions. (The domains and ranges of the other four circular functions will be covered in detail later.) Referring to the definition of circular functions, observe that

$$a = \cos x \qquad \text{and} \qquad b = \sin x$$

Thus, as in Figure 3.46, the coordinates of a point P at the end of an arc of length $|x|$, starting at $(1, 0)$, are

$$P(\cos x, \sin x)$$

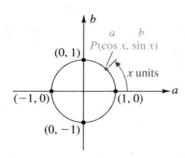

Figure 3.46

It is clear that $\cos x$ and $\sin x$ exist for each real number x, since $(\cos x, \sin x)$ are the coordinates of the point P on the unit circle corresponding to the arc $|x|$ length . Thus, the domain of each function is the set of all real numbers.

What about the range of each function? As $P(\cos x, \sin x)$ moves around the unit circle, the abscissa of the point, $\cos x = a$, and the ordinate of the point, $\sin x = b$, both vary between -1 and 1. Thus, we conclude that the range of each function is the set of all real numbers y such that $-1 \leq y \leq 1$.

The above results are summarized in the box below:

DOMAIN AND RANGE FOR SINE AND FOR COSINE
Domain: All real numbers
Range: $-1 \le y \le 1$, y a real number

Finding Domain Values That Correspond to a Given Range Value

Example 1   Find the domain values of the sine function, $-2\pi \le x \le 2\pi$, that have a range value -1. That is, find x, $-2\pi \le x \le 2\pi$, such that $\sin x = -1$.

Solution   Refer to Figure 3.46 to see that $\sin x = -1$ at the point $(0, -1)$. Thus, for any domain value x associated with an arc starting at $(1, 0)$ and terminating at $(0, -1)$, we have $\sin x = -1$. For the interval $-2\pi \le x \le 2\pi$, $\sin x = -1$ for $x = -\pi/2$ and $x = 3\pi/2$, as indicated in Figure 3.47.

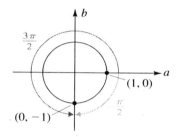

Figure 3.47

Matched Problem 1   Find the domain values of the cosine function, $-2\pi \le x \le 2\pi$ that have a range value -1. That is, find $x - 2\pi \le x \le 2\pi$, such that $\cos x = -1$.

Periodic Properties

Explore/ Discuss 2   Using Figure 3.46, explore the behavior of $P(\cos x, \sin x)$ as x moves around the unit circle in either direction. For what values of x will the coordinates repeat? Conclusions?

The circumference of the unit circle is

$$C = 2\pi r = 2\pi(1) = 2\pi$$

Thus, for a given value x (see Fig. 3.46), if we add or subtract 2π, we will return to exactly the same point P with the same coordinates. And we conclude that

$$\sin(x + 2\pi) = \sin x \qquad \text{and} \qquad \cos(x + 2\pi) = \cos x$$
$$\sin(x - 2\pi) = \sin x \qquad \text{and} \qquad \cos(x - 2\pi) = \cos x$$

In general, if we add any integer multiple of 2π to x, we will return to exactly the same point P. Thus, for k any integer $(\ldots, -3, -2, -1, 0, 1, 2, 3, \ldots)$,

$$\sin(x + 2k\pi) = \sin x \quad \text{and} \quad \cos(x + 2k\pi) = \cos x$$

Functions with this kind of repetitive behavior are called **periodic functions**. In general:

PERIODIC FUNCTIONS

A function f is **periodic** if there is a positive real number p such that
$$f(x + p) = f(x)$$
for all x in the domain of f. The smallest such positive p, if it exists, is called **the period of f**.

From the definition of a periodic function, we conclude that:

Both the sine function and cosine function have a period of 2π.

The other four circular functions also have periodic properties, which we discuss in detail later.

Using Periodic Properties

Example 2   If $\cos x = -0.0315$, what is the value of each of the following?
(a) $\cos(x + 2\pi)$ (b) $\cos(x - 2\pi)$ (c) $\cos(x + 18\pi)$ (d) $\cos(x - 34\pi)$

Solution   All are equal to -0.0315, because the cosine function is periodic with period 2π. That is, $\cos(x + 2k\pi) = \cos x$ for *all* integers k. In part (a), $k = 1$; in part (b), $k = -1$; in part (c), $k = -9$; and in part (d), $k = -17$.

Matched Problem 2   If $\sin x = 0.7714$, what is the value of each of the following?
(a) $\sin(x + 2\pi)$ (b) $\sin(x - 2\pi)$ (c) $\sin(x + 14\pi)$ (d) $\sin(x - 26\pi)$

The periodic properties of the circular functions are of paramount importance in the development of further mathematics as well as the applications of mathematics. As we will see in the next chapter, the circular functions are made to order for the analysis of real-world periodic phenomena: light, sound, electrical, and water waves; motion in buildings during earthquakes; motion in suspension systems in automobiles; planetary motion; business cycles; and so on.

Fundamental Identities

Returning to the definition of the circular functions and noting that

$$\sin x = b \quad \text{and} \quad \cos x = a$$

we can obtain the following useful relationships among the six functions:

$$\csc x = \frac{1}{b} = \frac{1}{\sin x} \tag{1}$$

$$\sec x = \frac{1}{a} = \frac{1}{\cos x} \tag{2}$$

$$\cot x = \frac{a}{b} = \frac{1}{b/a} = \frac{1}{\tan x} \tag{3}$$

$$\tan x = \frac{b}{a} = \frac{\sin x}{\cos x} \tag{4}$$

$$\cot x = \frac{a}{b} = \frac{\cos x}{\sin x} \tag{5}$$

Because the terminal points of x and $-x$ are symmetric with respect to the horizontal axis (see Fig. 3.48), we have the following sign properties:

$$\sin(-x) = -b = -\sin x \tag{6}$$

$$\cos(-x) = a = \cos x \tag{7}$$

$$\tan(-x) = \frac{-b}{a} = -\frac{b}{a} = -\tan x \tag{8}$$

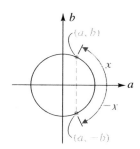

Figure 3.48

Finally, because $(a, b) = (\cos x, \sin x)$ is on the unit circle $a^2 + b^2 = 1$, it follows that

$$(\cos x)^2 + (\sin x)^2 = 1$$

which is usually written in the form

$$\sin^2 x + \cos^2 x = 1 \tag{9}$$

where $\sin^2 x$ and $\cos^2 x$ are concise ways of writing $(\sin x)^2$ and $(\cos x)^2$, respectively.

Caution   Note that $(\cos x)^2 \neq \cos x^2$ and $(\sin x)^2 \neq \sin x^2$.

Equations (1)–(9) are called **fundamental identities.** They hold true for all replacements of x by real numbers (or angles in degree or radian measure, as we will see before the conclusion of this section) for which both sides of an equation are defined.

Use of Identities

Example 3   Simplify each expression using the fundamental identities.

(a) $\dfrac{\sin^2 x + \cos^2 x}{\tan x}$ (b) $\dfrac{\sin(-x)}{\cos(-x)}$

Solution   (a) $\dfrac{\sin^2 x + \cos^2 x}{\tan x}$ Use identity (9).

$= \dfrac{1}{\tan x}$ Use identity (3).

$= \cot x$

(b) $\dfrac{\sin(-x)}{\cos(-x)}$ Use identity (4).

$= \tan(-x)$ Use identity (8).

$= -\tan x$

Matched Problem 3   Simplify each expression using the fundamental identities.

(a) $\dfrac{1 - \cos^2 x}{\sin^3 x}$ (b) $\tan(-x)\cos(-x)$

Some of the fundamental identities will be used in Section 3.6 as aids to graphing some of the trigonometric functions. A detailed discussion of identities is found in Chapter 4.

Circular Functions and Trigonometric Functions

We now show how the earlier definitions of the trigonometric functions (involving angle domains) can be related to the circular functions (involving real number domains and the unit circle). To this end, let us look at the radian measure of an angle θ subtended by an arc of x units on the unit circle (Fig. 3.49).

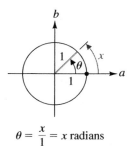

$$\theta = \frac{x}{1} = x \text{ radians}$$

Figure 3.49

We see that for the unit circle, the angle subtended by an arc of x units has a radian measure of x. Thus, every real number can be associated with an arc of x units on the unit circle or a central angle of x radians on the same circle (if x is positive, we go counterclockwise; and if x is negative, we go clockwise). Notice that the point on the terminal end of the arc of x units is also on the terminal side of the angle of x radians. This provides the following very useful relationships between the previously defined trigonometric functions with angle domains and the circular functions with real number domains:

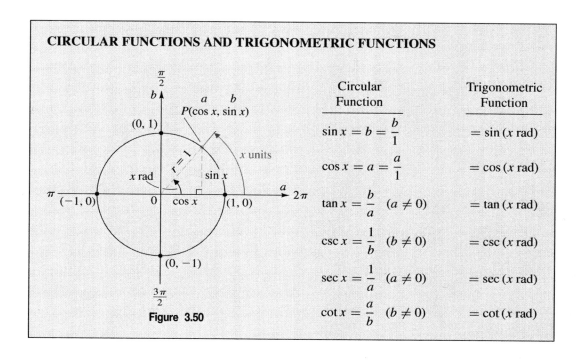

CIRCULAR FUNCTIONS AND TRIGONOMETRIC FUNCTIONS

Circular Function	Trigonometric Function
$\sin x = b = \dfrac{b}{1}$	$= \sin(x \text{ rad})$
$\cos x = a = \dfrac{a}{1}$	$= \cos(x \text{ rad})$
$\tan x = \dfrac{b}{a} \quad (a \neq 0)$	$= \tan(x \text{ rad})$
$\csc x = \dfrac{1}{b} \quad (b \neq 0)$	$= \csc(x \text{ rad})$
$\sec x = \dfrac{1}{a} \quad (a \neq 0)$	$= \sec(x \text{ rad})$
$\cot x = \dfrac{a}{b} \quad (b \neq 0)$	$= \cot(x \text{ rad})$

Figure 3.50

The information in this box, which relates circular functions with trigonometric functions, is very useful and should be understood. We will use it to develop a number of properties that hold simultaneously for the circular functions and the trigonometric functions. (For example, the fundamental identities discussed above hold for all real numbers x or angles in degree or radian measure for which the functions are defined.)

Evaluating Circular Functions

Because circular functions are related to trigonometric functions, we can evaluate circular functions by the procedures we used to evaluate trigonometric functions.

If x is an integer multiple of $\pi/4$ or $\pi/6$, we can find exact values of the six circular functions when they are defined. Corresponding coordinates of points on the unit circle can be found by using appropriate reference triangles and angles. (Recall the special 45° and 30°–60° triangles in Section 3.3.) Using these relationships, we can determine coordinates of points that correspond to integer multiples of $\pi/4$ or $\pi/6$. Figure 3.51 shows these coordinates for multiples ranging from 0 to 2π.

Note that if you learn the coordinates for the points corresponding to $\pi/6$, $\pi/4$, and $\pi/3$ in the first quadrant, you can easily obtain the coordinates of the corresponding points in the other three quadrants by symmetry and reflection across the coordinate axis. To evaluate the six circular functions exactly for integer multiples of $\pi/6$ or $\pi/4$, refer directly to Figure 3.51 or proceed as in Section 3.3 to relate the real number x to an angle of x radians.

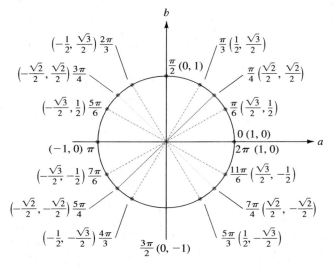

Unit circle $a^2 + b^2 = 1$

Figure 3.51 Multiples of $\pi/6$ and $\pi/4$ on a unit circle

Evaluating Circular Functions Exactly

Example 4   Find each exactly:

(a) $\sin \dfrac{8\pi}{3}$ (b) $\sec \left(-\dfrac{5\pi}{6} \right)$ (c) $\tan 7\pi$

Solution   (a) Refer directly to Figure 3.51 or the fact that

$$\sin \frac{8\pi}{3} = \sin \left(\frac{8\pi}{3} \, \text{rad} \right)$$

and proceed using reference triangles as in Section 3.3. In either case,

$$\sin \frac{8\pi}{3} = \frac{\sqrt{3}}{2}$$

(b) Refer directly to Figure 3.51 or the fact that

$$\sec \left(-\frac{5\pi}{6} \right) = \sec \left(-\frac{5\pi}{6} \, \text{rad} \right)$$

and proceed using reference triangles as in Section 3.3. In either case,

$$\sec \left(-\frac{5\pi}{6} \right) = -\frac{2}{\sqrt{3}}$$

(c) 7π corresponds to the point $(-1, 0)$. Thus,

$$\tan 7\pi = \frac{0}{-1} = 0$$

Matched Problem 4

Find each exactly:

(a) $\cos \dfrac{13\pi}{6}$

(b) $\csc\left(-\dfrac{5\pi}{4}\right)$

(c) $\cot(-3\pi)$

To evaluate circular functions using a calculator, set the calculator in radian mode and proceed as in Section 3.3.

Calculator Evaluation of Circular Functions

Example 5

Evaluate to four significant digits:

(a) $\sin(-13.72)$

(b) $\sec 22.33$

Solution

(a) $\sin(-13.72) = -0.9142$ Set in radian mode.

(b) $\sec 22.33\boxed{= \dfrac{1}{\cos 22.33}} = -1.060$ Set in radian mode.

Matched Problem 5

Evaluate to four significant digits using a calculator:

(a) $\cos 505.3$

(b) $\cot(-0.003211)$

Periodic Properties

Example 6

Evaluate $\cos x$ to two significant digits for:

(a) $x = 1.4$

(b) $x = 1.4 + 2\pi$

(c) $x = 1.4 - 2\pi$

(d) $x = 1.4 + 20\pi$

(e) $x = 1.4 - 8\pi$

Solution

All have the same value because the cosine function is periodic with a period of 2π. That is, $\cos(x + 2k\pi) = \cos x$ for all integers k. Using a calculator (set in radian mode to evaluate real numbers), we obtain:

(a) $\cos 1.4 = 0.17$

(b) $\cos(1.4 + 2\pi) = 0.17$

(c) $\cos(1.4 - 2\pi) = 0.17$

(d) $\cos(1.4 + 20\pi) = 0.17$

(e) $\cos(1.4 - 8\pi) = 0.17$

Matched Problem 6

Evaluate $\sin x$ to two significant digits for:

(a) $x = -3.2$

(b) $x = -3.2 + 2\pi$

(c) $x = -3.2 - 2\pi$

(d) $x = -3.2 + 22\pi$

(e) $x = -3.2 - 12\pi$

Answers to   1. $-\pi, \pi$ 2. All 0.7714   3. (a) $\csc x$ (b) $-\sin x$
Matched   4. (a) $\sqrt{3}/2$ (b) $\sqrt{2}$ (c) Not defined
Problems   5. (a) -0.8793 (b) -311.4 6. All 0.058

Exercises for Section 3.5

Figure 3.50 is repeated here for convenient reference.

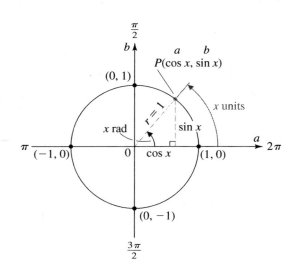

1. Starting with the circumference of the unit circle, 2π, find:

(a) $\frac{1}{2}$ circumference   (b) $\frac{3}{4}$ circumference

2. Starting with the circumference of the unit circle, 2π, find:

(a) $\frac{1}{4}$ circumference   (b) $\frac{1}{8}$ circumference

3. Referring to the figure, state the coordinates of P for the indicated values of x:

(a) $x = 0$ (b) $x = \pi/2$ (c) $x = -3\pi/2$
(d) $x = \pi$ (e) $x = -2\pi$ (f) $x = 5\pi/2$

4. Referring to the figure, state the coordinates of P for the indicated values of x:

(a) $x = 2\pi$ (b) $x = -\pi/2$ (c) $x = -\pi$
(d) $x = 3\pi/2$ (e) $x = -5\pi/2$ (f) $x = -3\pi$

5. Given $y = \sin x$, how does y vary for the indicated variation in x?

(a) x varies from 0 to $\pi/2$
(b) x varies from $\pi/2$ to π
(c) x varies from π to $3\pi/2$
(d) x varies from $3\pi/2$ to 2π
(e) x varies from 2π to $5\pi/2$

6. Given $y = \cos x$, how does y vary for the indicated variation in x?

(a) x varies from 0 to $\pi/2$
(b) x varies from $\pi/2$ to π
(c) x varies from π to $3\pi/2$
(d) x varies from $3\pi/2$ to 2π
(e) x varies from 2π to $5\pi/2$

7. Given $y = \cos x$, how does y vary for the indicated variation in x?

(a) x varies from 0 to $-\pi/2$
(b) x varies from $-\pi/2$ to $-\pi$
(c) x varies from $-\pi$ to $-3\pi/2$
(d) x varies from $-3\pi/2$ to -2π
(e) x varies from -2π to $-5\pi/2$

8. Given $y = \sin x$, how does y vary for the indicated variation in x?

(a) x varies from 0 to $-\pi/2$
(b) x varies from $-\pi/2$ to $-\pi$
(c) x varies from $-\pi$ to $-3\pi/2$
(d) x varies from $-3\pi/2$ to -2π
(e) x varies from -2π to $-5\pi/2$

Find the exact values of x from the indicated interval that satisfy the indicated equation or condition. (Refer to the figure at the beginning of the exercise.)

9. $\sin x = 1$, $0 \leq x \leq 4\pi$

10. $\cos x = 1$, $0 \leq x \leq 4\pi$

11. $\sin x = 0$, $0 \leq x \leq 4\pi$

12. $\cos x = 0$, $0 \leq x \leq 4\pi$

13. $\tan x = 0$, $0 \leq x \leq 4\pi$

14. $\cot x = 0$, $0 \leq x \leq 4\pi$

15. $\sin x = -1$, $0 \leq x \leq 4\pi$

16. $\cos x = -1$, $0 \leq x \leq 4\pi$

17. $\cos x = 1$, $-2\pi \leq x \leq 2\pi$

18. $\sin x = 1$, $-2\pi \leq x \leq 2\pi$

19. $\cos x = 0$, $-2\pi \leq x \leq 2\pi$

20. $\sin x = 0$, $-2\pi \leq x \leq 2\pi$

21. $\tan x$ not defined, $\quad 0 \le x \le 4\pi$

22. $\cot x$ not defined, $\quad 0 \le x \le 4\pi$

23. $\csc x$ not defined, $\quad 0 \le x \le 4\pi$

24. $\sec x$ not defined, $\quad 0 \le x \le 4\pi$

In Problems 25–36, determine each to one significant digit. Use only the figure below, the definition of circular functions, and a calculator if necessary for multiplication and division.

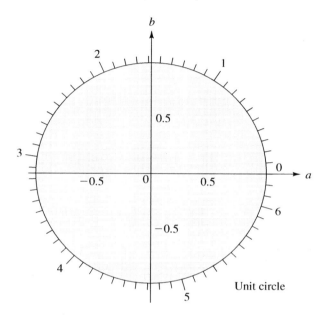

Unit circle

25. $\sin 0.8$

26. $\cos 0.8$

27. $\cos 2.3$

28. $\sin 5.5$

29. $\sin(-0.9)$

30. $\cos(-2)$

31. $\sec 2.2$

32. $\csc 3.8$

33. $\tan 0.8$

34. $\cot 2.8$

35. $\cot(-0.4)$

36. $\tan(-4)$

In Problems 37–48, evaluate to four significant digits using a calculator.

37. $\cos 2.718$

38. $\sin(-1.414)$

39. $\tan(-5.543)$

40. $\csc 24.56$

41. $\sec(-43.86)$

42. $\cot 124.6$

43. $\csc 231.2$

44. $\sec(-0.1015)$

45. $\sin 0.02055$

46. $\cos(-3,000)$

47. $\cot(-5,000)$

48. $\tan 453.8$

In Problems 49–52, a point $P(a, b)$ starts at $(1, 0)$ and moves around a unit circle for the distance and direction indicated. Explain how you would find the coordinates of point P at its final position, and how you would determine which quadrant

P is in. Find the coordinates of P to four decimal places and the quadrant for the final position of P.

49. 0.898 unit clockwise

50. 2.037 units clockwise

51. 26.77 units counterclockwise

52. 44.86 units counterclockwise

Evaluate Problems 53–58 exactly.

53. $\cos \dfrac{3\pi}{4}$
54. $\sin \dfrac{2\pi}{3}$
55. $\csc\left(-\dfrac{\pi}{4}\right)$

56. $\tan\left(-\dfrac{7\pi}{6}\right)$
57. $\tan\left(-\dfrac{5\pi}{2}\right)$
58. $\cot(-3\pi)$

59. If $\sin x = 0.9525$, what is the value of each of the following?
   (a) $\sin(x + 2\pi)$
   (b) $\sin(x - 2\pi)$
   (c) $\sin(x + 10\pi)$
   (d) $\sin(x - 6\pi)$

60. If $\cos x = -0.0379$, what is the value of each of the following?
   (a) $\cos(x + 2\pi)$
   (b) $\cos(x - 2\pi)$
   (c) $\cos(x + 8\pi)$
   (d) $\cos(x - 12\pi)$

61. Evaluate $\tan x$ and $(\sin x)/(\cos x)$ to two significant digits for:
   (a) $x = 1$
   (b) $x = 5.3$
   (c) $x = -2.376$

62. Evaluate $\cot x$ and $(\cos x)/(\sin x)$ to two significant digits for:
   (a) $x = -1$
   (b) $x = 8.7$
   (c) $x = -12.64$

63. Evaluate $\sin(-x)$ and $-\sin x$ to two significant digits for:
   (a) $x = 3$
   (b) $x = -12.8$
   (c) $x = 407$

64. Evaluate $\cos(-x)$ and $\cos x$ to two significant digits for:
   (a) $x = 5$
   (b) $x = -13.4$
   (c) $x = -1,003$

65. Evaluate $\sin^2 x + \cos^2 x$ to two significant digits for:
   (a) $x = 1$
   (b) $x = -8.6$
   (c) $x = 263$

66. Evaluate $1 - \sin^2 x$ and $\cos^2 x$ to two significant digits for:
   (a) $x = 14$
   (b) $x = -16.3$
   (c) $x = 766$

Simplify each expression using the fundamental identities.

67. $\sin x \csc x$
68. $\cos x \sec x$

69. $\cot x \sec x$
70. $\tan x \csc x$

71. $\dfrac{\sin x}{1 - \cos^2 x}$
72. $\dfrac{\cos x}{1 - \sin^2 x}$

73. $\cot(-x)\sin(-x)$
74. $\tan(-x)\cos(-x)$

Problems 75 and 76 show the coordinates of a point on a unit circle in a graphing calculator window. Let s be the length of the least positive arc from (1, 0) to the point. Find s to three decimal places.

75.

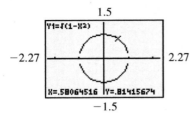

76.

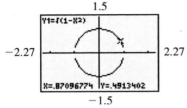

For Problems 77 and 78, fill the blanks in the Reason column with the appropriate identity, (1)–(9).

77. Statement   **Reason**

$$\tan^2 x + 1 = \left(\frac{\sin x}{\cos x}\right)^2 + 1 \qquad \text{(a)}_____$$

$$= \frac{\sin^2 x}{\cos^2 x} + 1 \qquad \text{Algebra}$$

$$= \frac{\sin^2 x + \cos^2 x}{\cos^2 x} \qquad \text{Algebra}$$

$$= \frac{1}{\cos^2 x} \qquad \text{(b)}_____$$

$$= \left(\frac{1}{\cos^2 x}\right)^2 \qquad \text{Algebra}$$

$$= \sec^2 x \qquad \text{(c)}_____$$

78. Statement   **Reason**

$$\cot^2 x + 1 = \left(\frac{\cos x}{\sin x}\right)^2 + 1 \qquad \text{(a)}_____$$

$$= \frac{\cos^2 x}{\sin^2 x} + 1 \qquad \text{Algebra}$$

$$= \frac{\cos^2 x + \sin^2 x}{\sin^2 x} \qquad \text{Algebra}$$

$$= \frac{1}{\sin^2 x} \qquad \text{(b)}_____$$

$$= \left(\frac{1}{\sin x}\right)^2 \qquad \text{Algebra}$$

$$= \csc^2 x \qquad \text{(c)}_____$$

79. What is the period of the cosecant function?

80. What is the period of the secant function?

81. Precalculus: Pi Estimate   With s_n as shown in the figure, a sequence of numbers is formed as indicated. Compute the first five terms of the sequence to six decimal places, and compare the fifth term with the value of $\pi/2$.

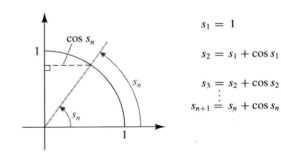

$$s_1 = 1$$
$$s_2 = s_1 + \cos s_1$$
$$s_3 = s_2 + \cos s_2$$
$$\vdots$$
$$s_{n+1} = s_n + \cos s_n$$

82. Precalculus: Pi Estimate   Repeat Problem 81 using $s_1 = 0.5$ as the first term of the sequence.

3.6 GRAPHS OF TRIG FUNCTIONS

- Graphs of $y = \sin x$ and $y = \cos x$
- Graphs of $y = \tan x$ and $y = \cot x$
- Graphs of $y = \csc x$ and $y = \sec x$
- Graphing with a Graphing Calculator

In this section we will discuss the graphs of the six trigonometric functions introduced earlier in this Chapter. We will also discuss the domains, ranges, and periodic properties of these functions. Section 3.5 on circular functions will prove particularly important in our work.

Although it appears that there is a lot to remember in this section, you mainly need to be familiar with the graphs and properties of the sine, cosine, and tangent functions. The reciprocal relationships we discussed in Section 3.5 will enable you to determine the graphs and properties of the other three trigonometric functions from the sine, cosine, and tangent functions.

Graphs of $y = \sin x$ and $y = \cos x$

First, we consider

$$y = \sin x \qquad x \text{ a real number} \tag{1}$$

The graph of the sine function is the graph of the set of all ordered pairs of real numbers (x, y) that satisfy equation (1). How do we find these pairs of numbers? To help make the process clear, we refer to a function machine with the unit circle definition inside (Fig. 3.52).

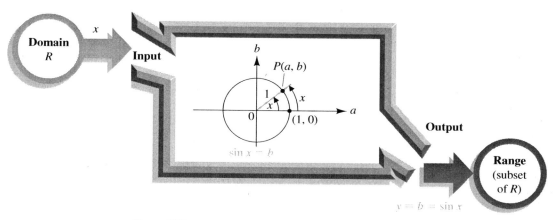

Figure 3.52: Sine function machine ($R =$ All real numbers)

We are interested in graphing, in an xy coordinate system, all ordered pairs of real numbers (x, y) produced by the function machine. We could resort to point-by-point plotting using a calculator, which becomes tedious and tends to obscure some important properties. Instead, we choose to speed up the process by using some of the properties discussed in Section 3.5 and by observing how $y = \sin x = b$ varies as $P(a, b)$ moves around the unit circle. We know that the domain of the sine function is the set of all real numbers R, its range is the set of all real numbers y such that $-1 \leq y \leq 1$, and its period is 2π.

Because the sine function is periodic with period 2π, we will concentrate on the graph over one period, from 0 to 2π. Once we have the graph for one period, we can complete as much of the rest of the graph as we wish by repeating the graph to the left and to the right.

Figure 3.53 illustrates how $y = \sin x = b$ varies as x increases from 0 to 2π and $P(a, b)$ moves around the unit circle.

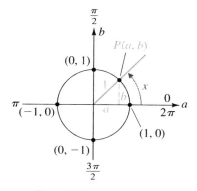

Figure 3.53: $y = \sin x = b$

As x increases	$y = \sin x = b$
from 0 to $\pi/2$	increases from 0 to 1
from $\pi/2$ to π	decreases from 1 to 0
from π to $3\pi/2$	decreases from 0 to -1
from $3\pi/2$ to 2π	increases from -1 to 0

The information in Figure 3.53 can be translated into a graph of $y = \sin x$, $0 \le x \le 2\pi$, as shown in Figure 3.54. (Where the graph is uncertain, fill in with calculator values.)

To complete the graph of $y = \sin x$ over any interval desired, we need only to repeat the final graph in Figure 3.54 to the left and to the right as far as we wish. The next box summarizes what we now know about the graph of $y = \sin x$ and its basic properties.

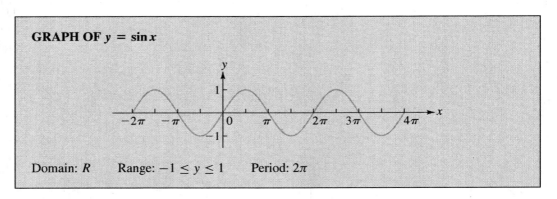

GRAPH OF $y = \sin x$

Domain: R Range: $-1 \le y \le 1$ Period: 2π

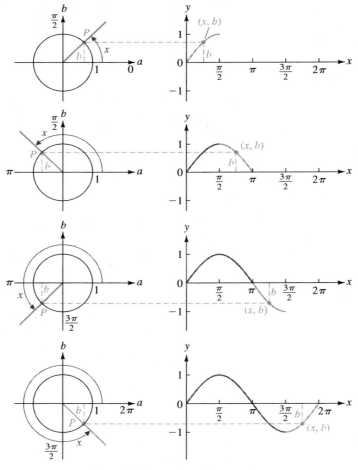

Figure 3.54: $y = \sin x$, $0 \le x \le 2\pi$

Both the x and y axes are real number lines. Because the domain of the sine function is all real numbers, the graph of $y = \sin x$ extends without limit in both horizontal directions. Also, because the range is $-1 \le y \le 1$, no point on the graph can have a y coordinate greater than 1 or less than -1.

Proceeding in the same way for the cosine function, we can obtain its graph. Figure 3.55 shows how $y = \cos x = a$ varies as x increases from 0 to 2π.

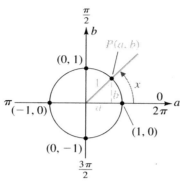

Figure 3.55: $y = \cos x = a$

As x increases	$y = \cos x = a$
from 0 to $\pi/2$	decreases from 1 to 0
from $\pi/2$ to π	decreases from 0 to -1
from π to $3\pi/2$	increases from -1 to 0
from $3\pi/2$ to 2π	increases from 0 to 1

Using the results of Figure 3.55 and the fact that the cosine function is periodic with period 2π (and filling in with calculator values where necessary), we obtain the graph of $y = \cos x$ over any interval desired. The next box shows a portion of the graph of $y = \cos x$ and summarizes some of the properties of the cosine function.

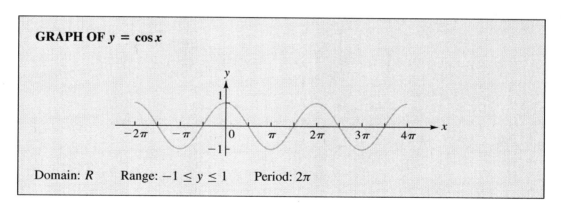

GRAPH OF $y = \cos x$

Domain: R Range: $-1 \le y \le 1$ Period: 2π

The basic characteristics of the sine and cosine graphs should be learned so that the curves can be sketched quickly. In particular, you should be able to answer the following questions:

(a) How often does the graph repeat (what is the period)?
(b) Where are the x intercepts?
(c) Where are the y intercepts?
(d) Where do the high and low points occur?
(e) What are the symmetry properties relative to the origin, y axis, x axis?

**Explore/
Discuss 1**

(a) Discuss how the graphs of the sine and cosine functions are related.
(b) Can one be obtained from the other by a horizontal shift? Explain how.

Graphs of $y = \tan x$ and $y = \cot x$

We first discuss the graph of $y = \tan x$. Later, because $\cot x = 1/(\tan x)$, we will be able to get the graph of $y = \cot x$ from the graph of $y = \tan x$ using reciprocals of ordinates.

From Figure 3.56 we can see that whenever $P(a, b)$ is on the horizontal axis of the unit circle (that is, whenever $x = k\pi$, k an integer), then $(a, b) = (\pm 1, 0)$ and $\tan x = b/a = 0/(\pm 1) = 0$. These values of x are the x intercepts of the graph of $y = \tan x$; that is, where the graph crosses the x axis.

$$x \text{ intercepts: } \quad x = k\pi \qquad k \text{ an integer}$$

Thus, as a first step in graphing $y = \tan x$, we locate the x intercepts with solid dots along the x axis, as indicated in Figure 3.57.

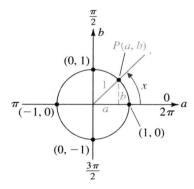

Figure 3.56: $y = \tan x = \dfrac{b}{a}$

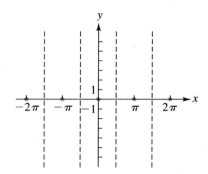

Figure 3.57: x intercepts and vertical asymptotes for $y = \tan x$

Also, from Figure 3.56 we can see that whenever $P(a, b)$ is on the vertical axis of the unit circle (that is, whenever $x = \pi/2 + k\pi$, k an integer), then $(a, b) = (0, \pm 1)$ and $\tan x = b/a = \pm 1/0$, which is not defined. There can be no points plotted for these values of x. Thus, as a second step in graphing $y = \tan x$, we draw dashed vertical lines through each of these points on the x axis where $\tan x$ is not defined; the graph cannot touch these lines (see Fig. 3.57). These dashed lines will become guidelines, called *vertical asymptotes,* which are very helpful for sketching the graph of $y = \tan x$.

$$\text{Vertical asymptotes: } \quad x = \frac{\pi}{2} + k\pi \qquad k \text{ an integer}$$

We next investigate the behavior of the graph of $y = \tan x$ over the interval $0 \leq x < \pi/2$. Two points are easy to plot: $\tan 0 = 0$ and $\tan (\pi/4) = 1$. What happens to $\tan x$ as x approaches $\pi/2$ from the left? [Remember that $\tan (\pi/2)$ is not defined.] When x approaches $\pi/2$ from the left, $P(a, b)$ approaches $(0, 1)$ and stays in the first quadrant. Thus, a approaches 0 through positive values and b approaches 1. What happens to $y = \tan x$ in this process? In Example 1, we perform a calculator experiment that suggests an answer.

Calculator Experiment

Example 1   Form a table of values for $y = \tan x$ with x approaching $\pi/2 \approx 1.570\,796\,3$ from the left (through values less than $\pi/2$). Any conclusions?

Solution   We create a table as follows:

x	0	0.5	1	1.5	1.57	1.5707	1.570 796 3
$\tan x$	0	0.5	1.6	14.1	1,256	10,381	37,320,535

Conclusion: As x approaches $\pi/2$ from the left, $y = \tan x$ appears to increase without bound.

Matched Problem 1

Repeat Example 1, but with x approaching $-\pi/2 \approx -1.570\,796\,3$ from the right. Any conclusions?

Figure 3.58a shows the results of the analysis in Example 1: $y = \tan x$ increases without bound when x approaches $\pi/2$ from the left.

Now we examine the behavior of the graph of $y = \tan x$ over the interval $-\pi/2 < x \le 0$. Because of the identity $\tan(-x) = -\tan x$ (see Section 3.5), we can reflect the graph of $y = \tan x$ for $0 \le x < \pi/2$ through the origin to obtain the full graph over the interval $-\pi/2 < x < \pi/2$ (Fig. 3.58b).

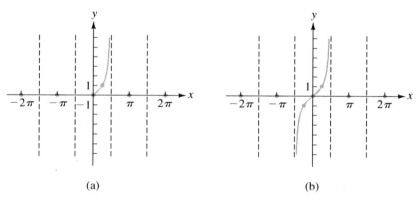

(a)   (b)

Figure 3.58: $y = \tan x$

Proceeding in the same way for the other intervals between the asymptotes (the dashed vertical lines), it appears that the tangent function is periodic with period π. We confirm this as follows: If (a, b) are the coordinates of P associated with x (see Fig. 3.59), then using unit circle symmetry and congruent reference triangles, $(-a, -b)$ are the coordinates of the point Q associated with $x + \pi$. Consequently,

$$\tan(x + \pi) = \frac{-b}{-a} = \frac{b}{a} = \tan x$$

We conclude that the tangent function is periodic with period π. In general,

$$\tan(x + k\pi) = \tan x \qquad k \text{ an integer}$$

for all values of x for which both sides of the equation are defined.

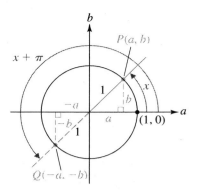

Figure 3.59: $\tan(x + \pi) = \tan x$

Now, to complete as much of the general graph of $y = \tan x$ as we wish, all we need to do is to repeat the graph in Figure 3.58b to the left and to the right over intervals of π units. The main characteristics of the graph of $y = \tan x$ should be learned so that the graph can be sketched quickly. The figure in the next box summarizes the above discussion.

GRAPH OF $y = \tan x$

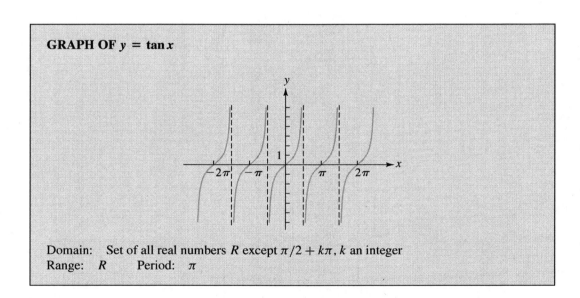

Domain: Set of all real numbers R except $\pi/2 + k\pi$, k an integer
Range: R Period: π

To graph $y = \cot x$, we recall that

$$\cot x = \frac{1}{\tan x}$$

and proceed by taking reciprocals of ordinate values in the graph of $y = \tan x$. Note that the x intercepts for the graph of $y = \tan x$ become vertical asymptotes for the graph of $y = \cot x$ and the vertical asymptotes for the graph of $y = \tan x$ become x intercepts for the graph of $y = \cot x$. The graph of $y = \cot x$ is shown in the following box. Again, you should learn the main characteristics of this function so that its graph can be sketched readily.

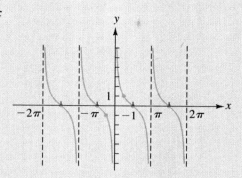

GRAPH OF $y = \cot x$

Domain: Set of all real numbers R except $k\pi$, k an integer
Range: R Period: π

Explore/ Discuss 2

(a) Discuss how the graphs of the tangent and cotangent functions are related.

(b) Explain how the graph of one can be obtained from the graph of the other by horizontal shifts and/or reflections across an axis or through the origin.

Graphs of $y = \csc x$ and $y = \sec x$

Just as we obtained the graph of $y = \cot x$ by taking reciprocals of the ordinate values in the graph of $y = \tan x$, since

$$\csc x = \frac{1}{\sin x} \qquad \text{and} \qquad \sec x = \frac{1}{\cos x}$$

we can obtain the graphs of $y = \csc x$ and $y = \sec x$ by taking reciprocals of ordinate values in the respective graphs of $y = \sin x$ and $y = \cos x$.

The graphs of $y = \csc x$ and $y = \sec x$ are shown in the next two boxes. Note that, because of the reciprocal relationship, vertical asymptotes occur at the x intercepts of $\sin x$ and $\cos x$, respectively. It is helpful to first draw the graphs of $y = \sin x$ and $y = \cos x$, then draw vertical asymptotes through the x intercepts.

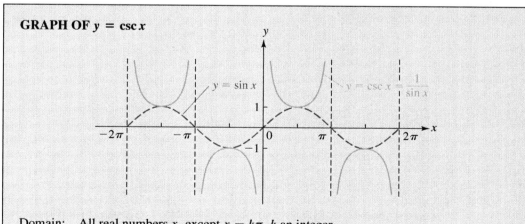

GRAPH OF $y = \csc x$

Domain: All real numbers x, except $x = k\pi$, k an integer
Range: All real numbers y such that $y \leq -1$ or $y \geq 1$
Period: 2π

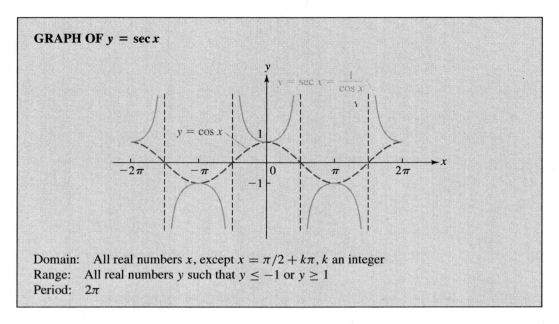

GRAPH OF $y = \sec x$

Domain: All real numbers x, except $x = \pi/2 + k\pi$, k an integer
Range: All real numbers y such that $y \le -1$ or $y \ge 1$
Period: 2π

Calculator Experiment

Example 2   To verify some points on the graph of $y = \csc x$, $0 < x < \pi$ we use a calculator to form the following table:

x	0.001	0.01	0.1	1.57	3.00	3.13	3.14
$\csc x$	1,000	100	10	1	7.1	86.3	628

Matched Problem 2   To verify some points on the graph of $y = \sec x$, $-\pi/2 < x < \pi/2$, complete the following table using a calculator:

x	−1.57	−1.56	−1.4	0	1.4	1.56	1.57
$\sec x$							

Graphing with a Graphing Calculator*

We determined the graphs of the six basic trigonometric functions by analyzing the behavior of the functions, exploiting relationships between the functions, and plotting only a few points. We refer

---

* Material that requires a graphing utility (that is, a graphing calculator or graphing software for a computer) is included in the text and exercise sets in this and subsequent chapters. This material is clearly identified with the icon shown in the margin. Any or all of the graphing utility material may be omitted without loss of continuity. Treatments are generic in nature. If you need help with your specific calculator, refer to your user's manual or to the graphing calculator supplement that accompanies this text.

to this process as curve sketching; one of the major objectives of this course is that you master this technique.

Graphing calculators also can be used to sketch graphs of functions; their accuracy depends on the screen resolution of the calculator. The smallest darkened rectangular area on the screen that the calculator can display is called a *pixel*. Most graphing calculators have a resolution of about 50 pixels per inch, which results in rough, but useful sketches. Note that the graphs shown earlier in this section were created using sophisticated computer software and printed at a resolution of about 1,000 pixels per inch.

The portion of the xy coordinate plane displayed on the screen of a graphing calculator is called the **viewing window** and is determined by the **range** and **scale** for x and for y. Figure 3.60 illustrates a **standard viewing window** using the following range and scale:

$$\text{xmin} = -10 \qquad \text{xmax} = 10 \qquad \text{xscl} = 1$$
$$\text{ymin} = -10 \qquad \text{ymax} = 10 \qquad \text{yscl} = 1$$

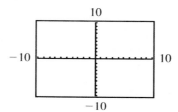

Figure 3.60: Standard viewing window

Most graphing calculators do not display labels on the axes. We have added numeric labels on each side of the viewing window to make the graphs easier to read. Now we want to see what the graphs of the trigonometric functions will look like on a graphing calculator.

Trigonometric Graphs on a Graphing Calculator

Example 3   Use a graphing calculator to graph the functions

$$y = \sin x \qquad y = \tan x \qquad y = \sec x$$

for $-2\pi \le x \le 2\pi$, $-5 \le y \le 5$. Display each graph in a separate viewing window.

Solution   First, set the calculator to the radian mode. Most calculators remember this setting, so you should have to do this only once. Next, enter the following values:

$$\text{xmin} = -2\pi \qquad \text{xmax} = 2\pi \qquad \text{xscl} = 1$$
$$\text{ymin} = -5 \qquad \text{ymax} = 5 \qquad \text{yscl} = 1$$

This defines a viewing window ranging from -2π to 2π on the horizontal axis and from -5 to 5 on the vertical axis with tick marks one unit apart on each axis. Now enter the function $y = \sin x$ and draw the graph (see Fig. 3.61a). Repeat for $y = \tan x$ and $y = \sec x = 1/(\cos x)$ to obtain the graphs in Figures 3.61b and 3.61c.

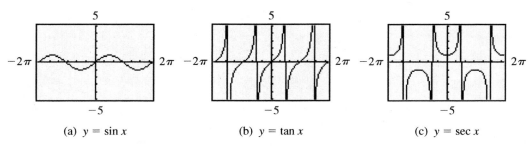

(a) $y = \sin x$ (b) $y = \tan x$ (c) $y = \sec x$

Figure 3.61: Graphing calculator graphs of trigonometric functions

Matched Problem 3

Repeat Example 3 for:

(a) $y = \cos x$ (b) $y = \cot x$ (c) $y = \csc x$

In Figures 3.61b and 3.61c, it appears that the calculator has also drawn the vertical asymptotes for these functions, but this is not the case. Most graphing calculators calculate points on a graph and connect these points with line segments. The last point plotted to the left of the asymptote and the first plotted to the right of the asymptote will usually have very large y coordinates. If these y coordinates have opposite sign, then the calculator will connect the two points with a nearly vertical line segment, which gives the appearance of an asymptote. There is no harm in this as long as you understand that the calculator is not performing any analysis to identify asymptotes; it is simply connecting points with line segments. If you wish, you can set the calculator in dot mode to plot the points without the connecting line segments, as illustrated in Figure 3.62. Unless stated to the contrary, we will use connected mode.

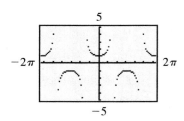

Figure 3.62: Graph of $y = \sec x$ in the plot-points-only mode

Answers to Matched Problems

1.

x	0	-0.5	-1	-1.5	-1.57	-1.5707	$-1.570\ 796\ 3$
$\tan x$	0	-0.5	-1.6	-14.1	$-1{,}256$	$-10{,}381$	$-37{,}320{,}535$

Conclusion: As x approaches $-\pi/2$ from the right, $y = \tan x$ appears to decrease without bound.

2.

x	-1.57	-1.56	-1.4	0	1.4	1.56	1.57
$\sec x$	$1{,}256$	92.6	5.9	1	5.9	92.6	$1{,}256$

3. (a) $y = \cos x$ (b) $y = \cot x$

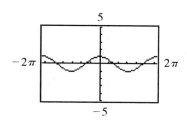   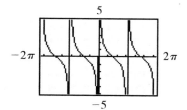

(c) $y = \csc x$

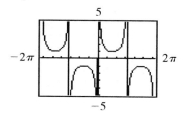

Exercises for Section 3.6

1. What are the periods of the cosine, secant, and tangent functions?

2. What are the periods of the sine, cosecant, and cotangent functions?

3. How far does the graph of each of the following functions deviate from the x axis?

    (a) $\sin x$ **(b)** $\cot x$ **(c)** $\sec x$

4. How far does the graph of each of the following functions deviate from the x axis?

    (a) $\cos x$ **(b)** $\tan x$ **(c)** $\csc x$

In Problems 5–10, what are the x intercepts for the graph of each function over the interval $-2\pi \leq x \leq 2\pi$?

5. $\cos x$ **6.** $\sin x$ **7.** $\tan x$

8. $\cot x$ **9.** $\sec x$ **10.** $\csc x$

11. For what values of x, $-2\pi \leq x \leq 2\pi$, are the following not defined?

    (a) $\sin x$ **(b)** $\cot x$ **(c)** $\sec x$

12. For what values of x, $-2\pi \leq x \leq 2\pi$, are the following not defined?

    (a) $\cos x$ **(b)** $\tan x$ **(c)** $\csc x$

13. Use a calculator and point-by-point plotting to produce an accurate graph of $y = \cos x$, $0 \leq x \leq 1.6$, using domain values $0, 0.1, 0.2, \ldots, 1.5, 1.6$.

14. Use a calculator and point-by-point plotting to produce an accurate graph of $y = \sin x$, $0 \leq x \leq 1.6$, using domain values $0, 0.1, 0.2, \ldots, 1.5, 1.6$.

In Problems 15–20, make a sketch of each trigonometric function without looking at the text or using a calculator. Label each point where the graph crosses the x axis in terms of π.

15. $y = \sin x$, $-2\pi \leq x \leq 2\pi$

16. $y = \cos x$, $-2\pi \leq x \leq 2\pi$

17. $y = \tan x$, $0 \leq x \leq 2\pi$

18. $y = \cot x$, $0 < x < 2\pi$

19. $y = \csc x$, $-\pi \leq x \leq \pi$

20. $y = \sec x$, $-\pi \leq x \leq \pi$

Problems 21–26 require the use of a graphing utility. These problems provide a preliminary exploration into the relationships of the graphs of $y = A \sin x$, $y = A \cos x$, $y = \sin Bx$, $y = \cos Bx$, $y = \sin(x + C)$, and $y = \cos(x + C)$ relative to the graphs of $y = \sin x$ and $y = \cos x$. The topic is discussed in detail in the next section.

21. **(a)** Graph $y = A \sin x (-2\pi \leq x \leq 2\pi, -3 \leq y \leq 3)$ for $A = -2, 1, 3$, all in the same viewing window.

    (b) Do the x intercepts change? If so, where?

    (c) How far does each graph deviate from the x axis? Experiment with other values of A.

(d) Describe how the graph of $y = \sin x$ is changed by changing the values of A in $y = A \sin x$.

22. (a) Graph $y = A \cos x$ $(-2\pi \le x \le 2\pi, -3 \le y \le 3)$ for $A = -3, 1, 2$, all in the same viewing window.
(b) Do the x intercepts change? If so, where?
(c) How far does each graph deviate from the x axis? Experiment with other values of A.
(d) Describe how the graph of $y = \cos x$ is changed by changing the values of A in $y = A \cos x$.

23. (a) Graph $y = \cos Bx$ $(-\pi \le x \le \pi, -2 \le y \le 2)$ for $B = 1, 2, 3$, all in the same viewing window.
(b) How many periods of each graph appear in this viewing window? Experiment with additional positive values of B.
(c) Based on your experiments in part (b), how many periods of the graph of $y = \cos nx$, n a positive integer, would appear in this viewing window?

24. (a) Graph $y = \sin Bx$ $(-\pi \le x \le \pi, -2 \le y \le 2)$ for $B = 1, 2, 3$, all in the same viewing window.
(b) How many periods of each graph appear in this viewing window? Experiment with additional positive values of B.
(c) Based on your experiments in part (b), how many periods of the graph of $y = \sin nx$, n a positive integer, would appear in this viewing window?

25. (a) Graph
$$y = \sin(x + C)$$
$(-2\pi \le x \le 2\pi, -2 \le y \le 2)$ for $C = -\pi/2, 0, \pi/2$, all in the same viewing window. Experiment with additional values of C.
(b) Describe how the graph of $y = \sin x$ is changed by changing the values of C in $y = \sin(x + C)$.

26. (a) Graph
$$y = \cos(x + C)$$
$(-2\pi \le x \le 2\pi, -2 \le y \le 2)$ for $C = -\pi/2, 0, \pi/2$, all in the same viewing window. Experiment with additional values of C.
(b) Describe how the graph of $y = \cos x$ is changed by changing the values of C in $y = \cos(x + C)$.

27. Try to calculate each of the following on your calculator. Explain the problem.
(a) $\cot 0$ **(b)** $\tan(\pi/2)$ **(c)** $\csc \pi$

28. Try to calculate each of the following on your calculator. Explain the problem.
(a) $\tan(-\pi/2)$ **(b)** $\cot(-\pi)$ **(c)** $\sec(\pi/2)$

Problems 29–32 require the use of a graphing utility.

29. In applied mathematics certain formulas, derivations, and calculations are simplified by replacing tan x with x for small x. What justifies this procedure? To find out, graph $y_1 = \tan x$ and $y_2 = x$ in the same viewing window for $-1 \le x \le 1$ and $-1 \le y \le 1$.
(a) What do you observe about the two graphs when x is close to 0, say $-0.5 \le x \le 0.5$?
(b) Complete the table to three decimal places (use the table feature on your graphing utility if it has one):

x	-0.3	-0.2	-0.1	0.0	0.1	0.2	0.3
$\tan x$							

(c) Is it valid to replace tan x with x for small x if x is in degrees? Graph $y_1 = \tan x$ and $y_2 = x$ in the same viewing window with the calculator set in degree mode for $-45° \le x \le 45°$ and $-5 \le y \le 5$, and explain the results after exploring the graphs using TRACE.

30. In applied mathematics certain formulas, derivations, and calculations are simplified by replacing sin x with x for small x. What justifies this procedure? To find out, graph $y_1 = \sin x$ and $y_2 = x$ in the same viewing window for $-1 \le x \le 1$ and $-1 \le y \le 1$.
(a) What do you observe about the two graphs when x is close to 0, say $-0.5 \le x \le 0.5$?
(b) Complete the table to three decimal places (use the table feature on your graphing utility if it has one):

x	-0.3	-0.2	-0.1	0.0	0.1	0.2	0.3
$\sin x$							

(c) Is it valid to replace sin x with x for small x if x is in degrees? Graph $y_1 = \sin x$ and $y_2 = x$ in the same viewing window with the calculator set in degree mode for $-10° \le x \le 10°$ and $-1 \le y \le 1$, and explain the results after exploring the graphs using TRACE.

31. Set your graphing utility in radian and parametric (Par) modes. Make the entries as indicated in the figure to obtain the indicated graph (set Tmax and Xmax to 2π and set Xscl to $\pi/2$). The parameter T represents a central angle in the unit circle of T radians or an arc length of T on the unit circle starting at $(1, 0)$. As T moves from 0 to 2π, the point $P(\cos T, \sin T)$ moves counterclockwise around the unit circle starting at $(1, 0)$ and ending at $(1, 0)$, and the point $P(T, \sin T)$ moves along the sine curve from $(0, 0)$ to $(2\pi, 0)$. Use TRACE to observe this behavior on each curve.

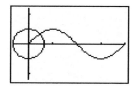

Now use [TRACE] and move back and forth between the unit circle and the graph of the sine function for various values of T as T increases from 0 to 2π. Discuss what happens in each case.

32. Repeat Problem 31 with $y_{2T} = \cos T$.

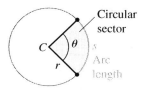

CHAPTER THREE REVIEW

Degrees and Radians

An angle of **radian measure** 1 is a central angle of a circle subtended by an arc having the same length as the radius. The **radian measure** of a central angle subtending an arc of length s in a circle of radius r is $\theta = s/r$ radians (rad). **Radian and degree measure** are related by

$$\frac{\theta_d}{180°} = \frac{\theta_r}{\pi \text{ rad}}$$

An angle with its vertex at the origin and initial side along the positive x axis is in **standard position.** Two angles are **coterminal** if their terminal sides coincide when both angles are placed in their standard position in the same coordinate system. The arc length and the area of a **circular sector** (see Fig. 3.63) are given by

	Radian Measure	Degree Measure
Arc length	$s = r\theta$	$s = \dfrac{\pi}{180}r\theta$
Area	$A = \dfrac{1}{2}r^2\theta$	$A = \dfrac{\pi}{360}r^2\theta$

Figure 3.63

Trigonometric Functions

Trigonometric Functions with Angle Domains

For an arbitrary angle θ:

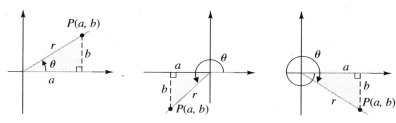

Figure 3.64

$$\sin \theta = \frac{b}{r} \qquad\qquad \csc \theta = \frac{r}{b} \quad b \neq 0 \qquad r = \sqrt{a^2 + b^2} > 0$$

$$\cos \theta = \frac{a}{r} \qquad\qquad \sec \theta = \frac{r}{a} \quad a \neq 0 \qquad P(a, b) \text{ is an arbitrary}$$
$$\qquad\qquad\qquad\qquad\qquad\qquad\qquad\qquad\qquad \text{point on the terminal side}$$
$$\tan \theta = \frac{b}{a} \quad a \neq 0 \qquad \cot \theta = \frac{a}{b} \quad b \neq 0 \qquad \text{of } \theta, (a, b) \neq (0, 0)$$

Domains: Sets of all possible angles for which the ratios are defined
Ranges: Subsets of the set of real numbers

The right triangle formed by dropping a perpendicular from $P(a, b)$ to the horizontal axis is called the **reference triangle** associated with the angle θ.

Trigonometric Functions with Real Number Domains

For x any real number, we define

$$\sin x = \sin (x \text{ rad}) \qquad \csc x = \csc (x \text{ rad})$$
$$\cos x = \cos (x \text{ rad}) \qquad \sec x = \sec (x \text{ rad})$$
$$\tan x = \tan (x \text{ rad}) \qquad \cot x = \cot (x \text{ rad})$$

Domains: Subsets of the set of real numbers
Ranges: Subsets of the set of real numbers

If x is any real number or any angle in degree or radian measure, then the following **reciprocal relationships** hold (division by 0 excluded).

$$\csc x = \frac{1}{\sin x} \qquad \sec x = \frac{1}{\cos x} \qquad \cot x = \frac{1}{\tan x}$$

Exact Value for Special Angles and Real Numbers

Reference Triangle and Angle

For a nonquadrantal angle θ (see Fig. 3.65):

1. To form a **reference triangle** for θ, drop a perpendicular from a point $P(a, b)$ on the terminal side of θ to the horizontal axis.
2. The **reference angle** α is the acute angle (always taken positive) between the terminal side of θ and the horizontal axis.

If the reference triangle for an angle or a real number θ is a 30°–60° right triangle or a 45° right triangle, then the relationships in Figure 3.66 can be used to find exact values of the trigonometric functions of θ.

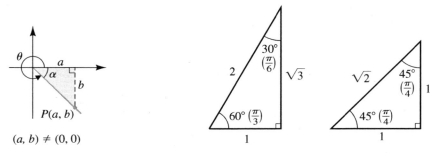

$(a, b) \neq (0, 0)$

Figure 3.65

Figure 3.66

These exact values are summarized in Table 3.9.

Table 3.9   *Special Values*

θ	$\sin\theta$	$\csc\theta$	$\cos\theta$	$\sec\theta$	$\tan\theta$	$\cot\theta$
$0°$ or 0	0	N.D.	1	1	0	N.D.
$30°$ or $\pi/6$	$1/2$	2	$\sqrt{3}/2$	$2/\sqrt{3}$	$1/\sqrt{3}$	$\sqrt{3}$
$45°$ or $\pi/4$	$1/\sqrt{2}$	$\sqrt{2}$	$1/\sqrt{2}$	$\sqrt{2}$	1	1
$60°$ or $\pi/3$	$\sqrt{3}/2$	$2/\sqrt{3}$	$1/2$	2	$\sqrt{3}$	$1/\sqrt{3}$
$90°$ or $\pi/2$	1	1	0	N.D.	N.D.	0

N.D = Not defined

Circular Functions

The **circular functions** for a real number x are defined in terms of the coordinates of a point on a **unit circle;** they are related to the trigonometric functions of an angle of x radians as follows (see Fig. 3.67):

Circular Functions and Trigonometric Functions

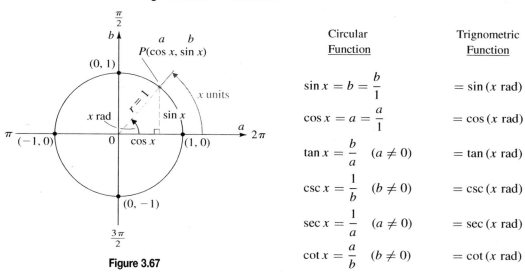

Circular Function	Trignometric Function
$\sin x = b = \dfrac{b}{1}$	$= \sin(x \text{ rad})$
$\cos x = a = \dfrac{a}{1}$	$= \cos(x \text{ rad})$
$\tan x = \dfrac{b}{a}\quad(a \neq 0)$	$= \tan(x \text{ rad})$
$\csc x = \dfrac{1}{b}\quad(b \neq 0)$	$= \csc(x \text{ rad})$
$\sec x = \dfrac{1}{a}\quad(a \neq 0)$	$= \sec(x \text{ rad})$
$\cot x = \dfrac{a}{b}\quad(b \neq 0)$	$= \cot(x \text{ rad})$

Figure 3.67

A function f is **periodic** if there is a positive real number p such that $f(x + p) = f(x)$ for all x in the domain of f. The smallest such positive p, if it exists, is called **the period of f.** Both the sine function and the cosine function have a period of 2π.

The properties of circular functions can be used to establish the following **fundamental identities:**

1. $\csc x = \dfrac{1}{\sin x}$

2. $\sec x = \dfrac{1}{\cos x}$

3. $\cot x = \dfrac{1}{\tan x}$

4. $\tan x = \dfrac{\sin x}{\cos x}$

5. $\cot x = \dfrac{\cos x}{\sin x}$

6. $\sin(-x) = -\sin x$

7. $\cos(-x) = \cos x$

8. $\tan(-x) = -\tan x$

9. $\sin^2 x + \cos^2 x = 1$

Figure 3.68 is useful for finding exact values of the circular functions at multiples of $\pi/6$ and $\pi/4$.

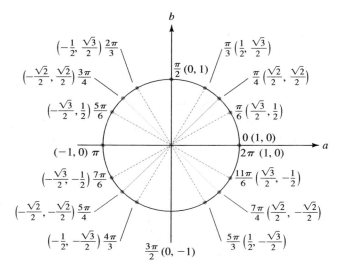

Unit circle $a^2 + b^2 = 1$

Figure 3.68

Basic Graphs

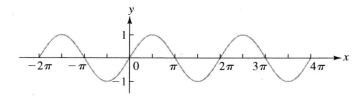

Figure 3.69: Graph of $y = \sin x$

Domain: R Range: $-1 \leq y \leq 1$ Period: 2π

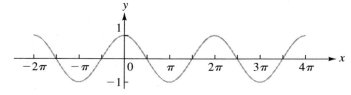

Figure 3.70: Graph of $y = \cos x$

Domain: R Range: $-1 \leq y \leq 1$ Period: 2π

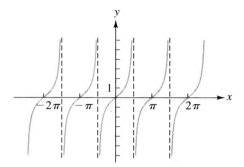

Figure 3.71: Graph of $y = \tan x$

Domain: Set of all real numbers R except $\pi/2 + k\pi$, k an integer
Range: R Period: π

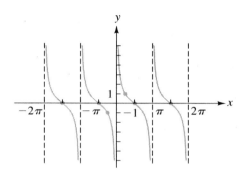

Figure 3.72: Graph of $y = \cot x$

Domain: Set of all real numbers R except $k\pi$, k an integer
Range: R Period: π

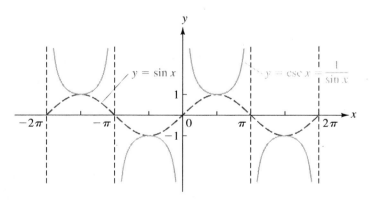

Figure 3.73: Graph of $y = \csc x$

Domain: All real numbers x, except $x = k\pi$, k an integer
Range: All real numbers y such that $y \leq -1$ or $y \geq 1$
Period: 2π

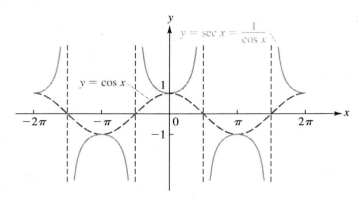

Figure 3.74: Graph of $y = \sec x$

Domain: All real numbers x, except $x = \pi/2 + k\pi$, k an integer
Range: All real numbers y such that $y \leq -1$ or $y \geq 1$
Period: 2π

REVIEW EXERCISES FOR CHAPTER THREE

Work through all the problems in this chapter review and check the answers.

1. Convert to radian measure in terms of π.
   (a) $60°$ (b) $45°$ (c) $90°$

2. Convert to degree measure.
   (a) $\pi/6$ (b) $\pi/2$ (c) $\pi/4$

3. Explain the meaning of a central angle of radian measure 2.

4. Which is larger: an angle of radian measure 1.5 or an angle of degree measure 1.5? Explain.

5. (a) Find the degree measure of 15.26 rad.
   (b) Find the radian measure of $-389.2°$.

*6. Find the velocity V of a point on the rim of a wheel if $r = 25$ ft and $\omega = 7.4$ rad/min.

*7. Find the angular velocity ω of a point on the rim of a wheel if $r = 5.2$ m and $V = 415$ m/hr.

8. Find the value of $\sin \theta$ and $\tan \theta$ if the terminal side of θ contains $P(-4, 3)$.

9. Is it possible to find a real number x such that $\sin x$ is negative and $\csc x$ is positive? Explain.

Evaluate Problems 10–12 to four significant digits using a calculator.

10. (a) $\cot 53°40'$ (b) $\csc 67°10'$

11. (a) $\cos 23.5°$ (b) $\tan 42.3°$

12. (a) $\cos 0.35$ (b) $\tan 1.38$

13. Sketch the reference triangle and find the reference angle α for:
    (a) $\theta = 120°$ (b) $\theta = -\dfrac{7\pi}{4}$

14. Evaluate exactly without a calculator.
    (a) $\sin 60°$ (b) $\cos(\pi/4)$ (c) $\tan 0°$

The following figure from the text is repeated here for use in Problems 15 and 16.

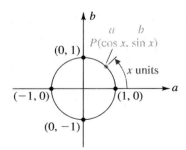

15. Refer to the figure and state the coordinates of P for the indicated values of x.
    (a) $x = -2\pi$ (b) $x = \pi$
    (c) $x = -3\pi/2$ (d) $x = \pi/2$
    (e) $x = -5\pi$ (f) $x = 7\pi/2$

16. Refer to the figure: Given $y = \sin x$, how does y vary for the indicated variations in x?

    (a) x varies from 0 to $\pi/2$
    (b) x varies from $\pi/2$ to π
    (c) x varies from π to $3\pi/2$
    (d) x varies from $3\pi/2$ to 2π
    (e) x varies from 2π to $5\pi/2$
    (f) x varies from $5\pi/2$ to 3π

17. List all angles that are coterminal with $\theta = \pi/6$ rad, $-3\pi \le \theta \le 3\pi$. Explain how you arrived at your answer.

18. What is the degree measure of a central angle subtended by an arc exactly $\frac{7}{60}$ of the circumference of a circle?

19. If the radius of a circle is 4 cm, find the length of an arc intercepted by an angle of 1.5 rad.

20. Convert $212°$ to radian measure in terms of π.

21. Convert $\pi/12$ rad to degree measure.

22. Use a calculator with an automatic radian–degree conversion routine to find:

    (a) The radian measure (to two decimal places) of $-213.23°$
    (b) The degree measure (to two decimal places) of 4.62 rad

23. If the radian measure of an angle is tripled, is the degree measure of the angle tripled? Explain.

24. If $\sin \alpha = \sin \beta, \alpha \ne \beta$, are angles α and β necessarily coterminal? Explain.

25. From the following display on a graphing calculator, explain how you would find $\csc x$ without finding x. Then find $\csc x$ to four decimal places.

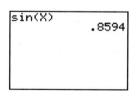

26. Find the tangent of $0, \pi/2, \pi$, and $3\pi/2$.

27. In which quadrant does the terminal side of each angle lie?

    (a) $732°$ **(b)** -7 rad

Evaluate Problems 28–33 to three significant digits using a calculator.

28. $\cos 187.4°$ **29.** $\sec 103°20'$ **30.** $\cot(-37°40')$

31. $\sin 2.39$ **32.** $\cos 5$ **33.** $\cot(-4)$

In Problems 34–42, find the exact value of each without using a calculator.

34. $\cos \dfrac{5\pi}{6}$ **35.** $\cot \dfrac{7\pi}{4}$ **36.** $\sin \dfrac{3\pi}{2}$

37. $\cos \dfrac{3\pi}{2}$ **38.** $\sin \dfrac{-4\pi}{3}$ **39.** $\sec \dfrac{-4\pi}{3}$

40. $\cos 3\pi$ **41.** $\cot 3\pi$ **42.** $\sin \dfrac{-11\pi}{6}$

43. In the following graphing calculator display, indicate which value(s) are not exact and find the exact value.

```
cos(π/3)
            .5000
sin(180°)
          0.0000
tan(-60°)
         -1.7321
```

In Problems 44–47, use a calculator to evaluate each to five decimal places.

44. $\sin 384.0314°$ **45.** $\tan(-198°43'6'')$

46. $\cos 26$ **47.** $\cot(-68.005)$

48. If $\sin \theta = -\frac{4}{5}$ and the terminal side of θ does not lie in the third quadrant, find the exact values of $\cos \theta$ and $\tan \theta$ without finding θ.

49. Find the least positive exact value of θ in radian measure such that $\sin \theta = -\frac{1}{2}$.

50. Find the exact value of each of the other five trigonometric functions if

$$\sin \theta = -\frac{2}{5} \quad \text{and} \quad \tan \theta < 0$$

51. Find all the angles exactly between $0°$ and $360°$ for which $\tan \theta = -1$

52. Find all the angles exactly between 0 and 2π for which $\cos \theta = -\sqrt{3}/2$.

53. In a circle of radius 12.0 cm, find the length of an arc subtended by a central angle of:

    (a) 1.69 rad   **(b)** $22.5°$

54. In a circle with diameter 80 ft, find the area (to three significant digits) of the circular sector with central angle:

    (a) 0.773 rad   **(b)** $135°$

55. Find the distance between Charleston, West Virginia ($38°21'$N latitude) and Cleveland, Ohio ($41°28'$N latitude). Both cities have the same longitude and the radius of the earth is 3,964 mi.

*56. Find the angular velocity of a wheel turning through 6.43 rad in 15.24 sec.

*57. What is meant by a rotating object having an angular velocity of 12π rad/sec?

58. Evaluate $\cos x$ to three significant digits for:
   (a) $x = 7$ (b) $x = 7 + 2\pi$ (c) $x = 7 - 30\pi$

59. Evaluate $\tan(-x)$ and $-\tan x$ to three significant digits for:
   (a) $x = 7$ (b) $x = -17.9$ (c) $x = -2,135$

60. One of the following is not an identity. Indicate which one.

   (a) $\csc x = \dfrac{1}{\sin x}$ (b) $\cot x = \dfrac{1}{\tan x}$

   (c) $\tan x = \dfrac{\sin x}{\cos x}$ (d) $\sec x = \dfrac{1}{\sin x}$

   (e) $\sin^2 x + \cos^2 x = 1$ (f) $\cot x = \dfrac{\cos x}{\sin x}$

61. Simplify: $(\csc x)(\cot x)(1 - \cos^2 x)$

62. Simplify: $\cot(-x)\sin(-x)$

63. A point $P(a, b)$ moves clockwise around a unit circle starting at $(1, 0)$ for a distance of 29.37 units. Explain how you would find the coordinates of the point P at its final position, and how you would determine which quadrant P is in. Find the coordinates to four decimal places and the quadrant.

64. An angle in standard position intercepts an arc of length 1.3 units on a unit circle with center at the origin. Explain why the radian measure of the angle is also 1.3.

65. Which circular functions are not defined for $x = k\pi$, k any integer? Explain.

66. In the following graphing calculator display, find the least positive exact value of x (in radian measure) that produces the indicated result.

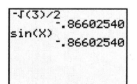

67. The following graphing calculator display shows the coordinates of a point on a unit circle. Let s be the length of the least positive arc from $(1, 0)$ to the point. Find s to four decimal places.

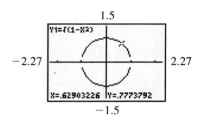

68. A circular sector has an area of 342.5 m² and a radius of 12 m. Calculate the arc length of the sector to the nearest meter.

69. A circle with its center at the origin in a rectangular coordinate system passes through the point $(4, 5)$. What is the length of the arc on the circle in the first quadrant between the positive horizontal axis and the point $(4, 5)$? Compute the answer to two decimal places.

70. **Engineering**   Through how many radians does a pulley with 10 cm diameter turn when 10 m of rope has been pulled through it without slippage? How many revolutions result? (Give answers to one decimal place.)

*71. **Engineering**   If the large gear in the figure completes 5 revolutions, how many revolutions will the middle gear complete? How many revolutions will the small gear complete?

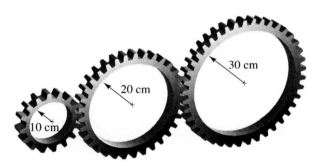

*72. **Engineering**   An automobile is traveling at 70 ft/sec. If the wheel diameter is 27 in., what is the angular velocity in rad/sec?

*73. **Space Science**   A satellite is placed in a circular orbit 1,000 mi above the earth's surface. If the satellite completes one orbit every 114 min and the radius of the earth is 3,964 mi, what is the linear velocity (to three significant digits) of the satellite in miles per hour?

74. **Electric Current**   An alternating current generator produces an electrical current (measured in amperes) that is described by the equation

$$I = 30\sin(120\pi t - 60\pi)$$

where t is time in seconds. What is the current I when $t = 0.015$ sec? (Give answers to one decimal place.)

75. Precalculus   A ladder of length L leaning against a building just touches a fence that is 10 ft high located 2 ft from the building (see the figure).

10 ft

θ

2 ft

(a) Express the length of the ladder in terms of θ.
(b) Describe what you think happens to the length of the ladder L as θ varies between 0 and $\pi/2$ radians.

(c) Complete the table (to two decimal places) using a calculator. (If you have a table-generating calculator, use it.)

θ rad	0.70	0.80	0.90	1.00	1.10	1.20	1.30
L ft	18.14						

(d) From the table, select the angle θ that produces the shortest ladder that satisfies the conditions in the problem. (Calculus techniques can be used on the equation from part (a) to find the angle θ that produces the shortest ladder.)

*76. **Light Waves**   A light wave passing through air strikes the surface of a pool of water so that the angle of incidence is $\alpha = 31.7°$. Find the angle of refraction. (Water has a refractive index of 1.33 and air has a refractive index of 1.00.)

*77. **Light Waves**   A triangular crown glass prism is surrounded by air. If light inside the prism strikes one of its facets, what is the critical angle of incidence α for total reflection? (The refractive index for crown glass is 1.52, and the refractive index for air is 1.00.)

*78. **Bow Waves**   If a boat traveling at 25 mph produces bow waves that separate at an angle of 51°, how fast are the bow waves traveling?

Chapter Four

TRANSFORMATIONS OF TRIGONOMETRIC FUNCTIONS, SINUSOIDAL FUNCTIONS, AND TRIGONOMETRIC EQUATIONS

Trigonometry and algebra skills come together in solving equations that contain trigonometric functions. Graphs of trigonometric functions are studied in detail and further transformations of functions (stretches and compressions) are introduced. From the definitions of the trigonometric functions, we derive identities that relate the trigonometric functions to one another. These identities are used to rewrite expressions, understand graphs, and, in conjunction with algebraic skills, solve equations.

4.1   SOLVING BASIC TRIGONOMETRIC EQUATIONS

Now that you know the values of the trigonometric functions of the special angles and the graphs of the trigonometric functions, you can put that knowledge to use solving equations. The goal of these examples is to help you to think about trigonometric equations by recalling both the sign and values of the trigonometric functions and their graphs in order to determine all of the solutions. We will start with a very simple equation.

Example 1   Solve for x: $\sin x = \dfrac{1}{2}$

Solution   First, it is important to *recognize* that $\frac{1}{2}$ is a number that comes from either a sine or cosine of one of the special angles. From memory, you need to be able to recall that $\sin\left(\frac{\pi}{6}\right) = \frac{1}{2}$, so $\frac{\pi}{6}$ is a solution to the equation.

However, the periodic nature of the sine function should tell you that $\frac{\pi}{6}$ is not the only solution. It is helpful to use the graph of the sine function to determine all of the solutions.

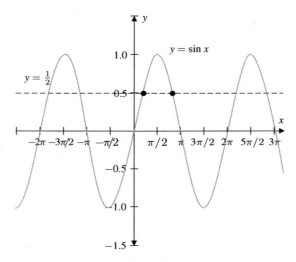

Figure 4.1

In Figure 4.1 you see the graph of $y = \sin x$ and $y = \frac{1}{2}$. Although only part of the graph is visible, it should be obvious that there are infinitely many intersections and there are therefore infinitely many solutions to the equation $\sin x = \frac{1}{2}$.

The first intersection to the right of the y-axis is the point $\left(\frac{\pi}{6}, \frac{1}{2}\right)$. Notice that this same type of point (the one on the increasing side of the sine curve) will occur 2π units later, or at

$$x = \frac{\pi}{6} + 2\pi = \frac{\pi}{6} + \frac{12\pi}{6} = \frac{13\pi}{6}.$$

Also that same type of solution will occur again 4π units after $\frac{\pi}{6}$, or at

$$x = \frac{\pi}{6} + 4\pi = \frac{\pi}{6} + \frac{24\pi}{6} = \frac{25\pi}{6}.$$

Naturally we could go on like this, but a more convenient way of writing down *all* of this type of solution is to say that the solutions occur first at $\frac{\pi}{6}$ and then every 2π units after or before that.

Here is how we say "every 2π": $2\pi(k)$, if k is any integer, but we usually write this $2k\pi$. Thus the solutions to $\sin x = \frac{1}{2}$ that correspond to $\frac{\pi}{6}$ are

$$\frac{\pi}{6} + 2k\pi.$$

That will identify half of the solutions.

The other half of the solutions corresponds to the intersections on the decreasing side of the sine curve. Notice that the first positive one of these occurs between $\frac{\pi}{2}$ and π. This corresponds to the "second quadrant" on the unit circle. This solution will be the second-quadrant angle with reference angle $\frac{\pi}{6}$, namely $\frac{5\pi}{6}$. Solutions of this type also occur every 2π units after or before the first one, so they can all be represented by

$$\frac{5\pi}{6} + 2k\pi.$$

In summary, if $\sin x = \frac{1}{2}$, then $x = \frac{\pi}{6} + 2k\pi$ or $x = \frac{5\pi}{6} + 2k\pi$.

Matched Problem 1   Solve the equation $\sin x = \dfrac{\sqrt{3}}{2}$.

Example 2   Solve the equation $\cos x = -\dfrac{\sqrt{2}}{2}$.

Solution   Once again, recognize that $\frac{\sqrt{2}}{2}$ is a number that comes from either a sine or cosine of one of the special angles. From memory, recall that $\cos\left(\frac{\pi}{4}\right) = \frac{\sqrt{2}}{2}$, so $\frac{\pi}{4}$ will be the reference angle for the solutions to the equation but it is not itself a solution because the $\frac{\sqrt{2}}{2}$ is negative. Once again we turn to the graph, this time the cosine graph.

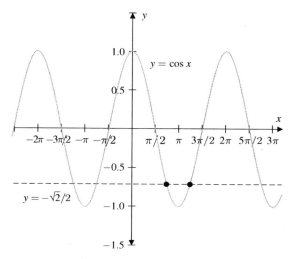

Figure 4.2

In Figure 4.2, notice that the first positive solution occurs on the decreasing portion of the cosine curve between $\frac{\pi}{2}$ and π, so the x value will be the second quadrant version of $\frac{\pi}{4}$, or $\frac{3\pi}{4}$. This solution repeats every 2π units, so all of this type of solution can be written

$$\frac{3\pi}{4} + 2k\pi.$$

There is another type of solution that occurs on the increasing portion of the cosine curve. The first positive one occurs between π and $\frac{3\pi}{2}$, or $\frac{5\pi}{4}$, and this solution occurs every 2π units before and after that, so all of them can be written

$$\frac{5\pi}{4} + 2k\pi.$$

To summarize, if $\cos x = -\frac{\sqrt{2}}{2}$, then $x = \frac{3\pi}{4} + 2k\pi$ or $x = \frac{5\pi}{4} + 2k\pi$.

Matched Problem 2   Solve the equation $\cos x = -\dfrac{1}{2}$.

Example 3   Solve the equation $\tan x = -\sqrt{3}$

Solution   In this equation, recognize that $\sqrt{3}$ is the tangent of $\frac{\pi}{3}$, so $\frac{\pi}{3}$ will be the reference angle.

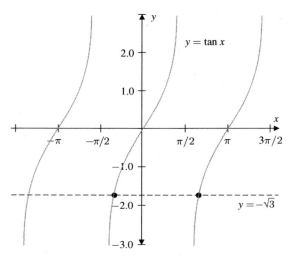

Figure 4.3

From Figure 4.3, we can see that there is only one type of solution. The first one is $-\frac{\pi}{3}$, and because the period of the tangent function is π, another solution will occur every π units after $-\frac{\pi}{3}$, so the complete solution set is

$$x = -\frac{\pi}{3} + k\pi.$$

Matched Problem 3 Solve the equation $\tan x = -1$.

Example 4 Solve the equation $\sin x = -2$

Solution In this equation it is important to be paying attention and to remember that the range of the sine function is only $[-1, 1]$. If you keep this range in mind you will notice right away that it is impossible for $\sin x$ to equal -2, so this equation has no solutions.

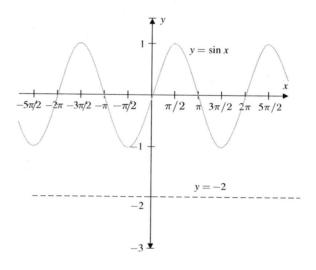

Figure 4.4

In Figure 4.4, you will see that the graph of $y = \sin x$ does not intersect the graph of $y = -2$. Final conclusion: The equation $\sin x = -2$ has no solutions.

Answers to Matched Problem

1. $x = \dfrac{\pi}{3} + 2k\pi, \ x = \dfrac{2\pi}{3} + 2k\pi$

2. $x = \dfrac{2\pi}{3} + 2k\pi, \ x = \dfrac{4\pi}{3} + 2k\pi$

3. $x = -\dfrac{\pi}{4} + k\pi$

Exercises for Section 4.1

Solve each equation, if possible, by using facts about the values of the trig functions. In each case write the complete solution set. Use the graph of the function as an aid.

1. $\sin x = \dfrac{\sqrt{2}}{2}$

2. $\cos x = -\dfrac{1}{2}$

3. $\tan x = \sqrt{3}$

4. $\cos x = \dfrac{\sqrt{3}}{2}$

5. $\tan x = \dfrac{1}{\sqrt{3}}$

6. $\sin x = 1$

7. $\cos x = -1$

8. $\sec x = 1$ (*Hint*: Change sec x to $\dfrac{1}{\cos x}$)

9. $\sin x = 0$

10. $\cos x = 0$

11. $\cos x = -3$

12. $\sin x = \pi$

4.2 TRANSFORMATIONS OF TRIGONOMETRIC FUNCTIONS: SHIFTS AND REFLECTIONS

- Horizontal and Vertical Shifts
- Reflections

In Sections 2.5 and 2.6 we studied transformations of functions. Before we review the specific transformations, remember that *inside* changes to the function produce *horizontal* actions, while *outside* changes to the function produce *vertical* actions. Here is a summary.

Horizontal Shifts

The graph of $y = f(x + k)$ is the graph of $y = f(x)$ shifted horizontally $|k|$ units. If k is positive, the shift is to the left; if k is negative, the shift is to the right.

Example 1 $y = (x - 2)^3$ is the graph of $y = x^3$ shifted 2 units to the right. See Figure 4.5 below.

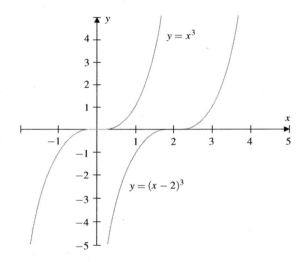

Figure 4.5

Matched Problem 1   If $y = \dfrac{1}{x + 4}$ identify the basic function and the transformation and sketch the graph.

Vertical Shifts

The graph of $y = f(x) + k$ is the graph of $y = f(x)$ shifted vertically $|k|$ units. If k is positive, the shift is up; if k is negative the shift is down.

Example 2 $y = 4 + \sqrt{x}$ is the graph of $y = \sqrt{x}$ shifted 4 units up. See Figure 4.6 below.

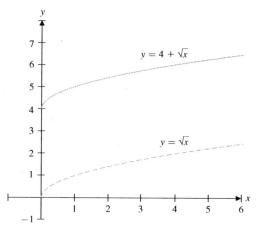

Figure 4.6

Matched Problem 2   If $y = -2 + \sqrt[3]{x}$, identify the basic function and the transformation and sketch the graph.

Horizontal and Vertical Shifts Combined

Example 3 $y = (x + 3)^2 - 2$ is the graph of $y = x^2$ shifted horizontally 3 units to the left and vertically 2 units down. See Figure 4.7 below.

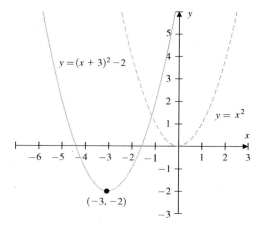

Figure 4.7

Matched Problem 3   If $y = 3 + \sqrt{x - 4}$, identify the basic function and the transformations and sketch the graph.

> **Reflections**
> The graph of $y = f(-x)$ is a reflection of the graph of $y = f(x)$ across the y-axis.
> The graph of $y = -f(x)$ is a reflection of the graph of $y = f(x)$ across the x-axis.

Example 4 $y = \sqrt{-x}$ is the graph of $y = \sqrt{x}$ reflected across the y-axis. See Figure 4.8 below.

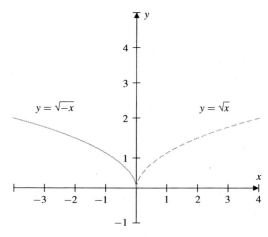

Figure 4.8

Example 5 $y = -x^2$ is the graph of $y = x^2$ reflected across the x-axis. See Figure 4.9 below.

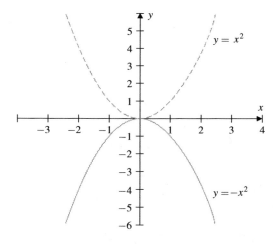

Figure 4.9

Matched Problem 4   If $y = -\sqrt{x}$, identify the basic function and the transformation and sketch the graph.

Characteristics of the Sine and Cosine Graphs

We will now apply these transformations to the sine and cosine functions. In order to do this efficiently, we need to recognize the important characteristics of each graph.

Focus your attention on just the primary cycle of the sine function.

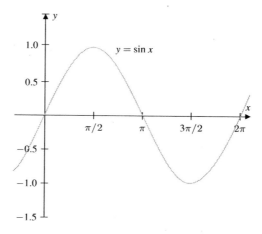

Figure 4.10

As you know from transformations of the library functions, shifts and reflections move the graph around in the coordinate system and every point on the original graph, except perhaps the intercepts, is transformed to a new point. Because of this, when you look at this graph of the sine function, it is helpful to focus on special characteristics. Here are some things to notice about the graph of $y = \sin x$:

- The line $y = 0$ (the x-axis) cuts the graph in half. For this reason, the line $y = 0$ is called the *midline* of $y = \sin x$.
- The graph's maximum is one unit above the midline and its minimum is one unit below the midline. The distance between the midline and the maximum or between the midline and the minimum is called the *amplitude*. For $y = \sin x$ the amplitude is 1.
- One complete cycle goes from $x = 0$ to $x = 2\pi$. The length of one cycle is called the *period* so the period of $y = \sin x$ is 2π.
- Because of its relationship to the quadrants of the unit circle, the graph has four parts, each one corresponding to a quadrant of the unit circle. The length of one of those quarters is the *quarter distance* and for $y = \sin x$ the quarter distance is $\frac{\pi}{2}$.

Characteristics of the Graph of $y = \sin x$

- The midline for $y = \sin x$ is $y = 0$.
- The period for $y = \sin x$ is 2π.
- The amplitude is 1.
- The quarter distance for $y = \sin x$ is $\frac{\pi}{2}$.
- $y = \sin x$ crosses the x-axis at 0, π, and 2π.
- The maximum value is 1. It occurs at $\frac{\pi}{2}$.
- The minimum value is -1. It occurs at $\frac{3\pi}{2}$.
- The cycle begins at 0 and ends at 2π.

Anticipating transformations of this function, we will rewrite these characteristics in more general terms:

Characteristics of a Sine Graph

- The midline is a horizontal line determined by the vertical shift.
- The normal period is 2π. (In Section 4.3, the period will be affected by stretches and compressions.)
- The normal amplitude is 1. (In Section 4.3, the amplitude will be affected by stretches and compressions.)
- The quarter distance is the period divided by 4.
- The beginning of the cycle is determined by the horizontal shift.
- The sine function crosses its midline at the beginning, midpoint, and end of its cycle.
- The maximum value is one amplitude above the midline. It occurs at the first quarter point.
- The minimum value is one amplitude below the midline. It occurs at the third quarter point.
- The end of the cycle is one period after the beginning.

If you know the midline, period, amplitude and beginning, you can determine everything else.

Example 6   For the function $y = 2 + \sin x$, identify the following: midline, amplitude, maximum and minimum values, period, and quarter distance. Also identify the following points: beginning, first quarter point, midpoint, third quarter point, and end. Then graph the function labeling all the points.

Solution   The 2 added to the basic sine function indicates a vertical shift up 2 units. This is the only change in the basic function.
We will use a systematic approach to analyzing the graph.
Midline: $y = 2$ because of the vertical shift up 2 units
Amplitude: 1
Maximum Value: 1 unit above the midline: $2 + 1 = 3$
Minimum Value: 1 unit below the midline: $2 - 1 = 1$
Period: 2π
Beginning: $x = 0$. The point is on the midline, so the y-coordinate is 2.
Quarter Distance: $\frac{\pi}{2}$
First quarter point: $x = \frac{\pi}{2}$. The y-coordinate is the maximum value, 3.
Midpoint: $x = \pi$. The point is on the midline so the y-coordinate is 2.
Third quarter point: $x = \frac{3\pi}{2}$. The y-coordinate is the minimum value, 1.
End: $x = 2\pi$. The point is on the midline so the y-coordinate is 2.
Graph: See Figure 4.11.

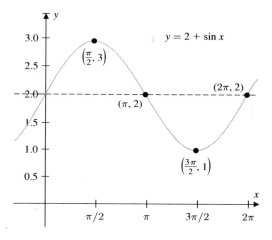

Figure 4.11

Now focus on the cosine graph and its characteristics.

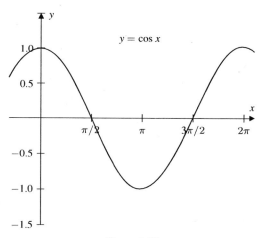

Figure 4.12

Characteristics of the Graph of $y = \cos x$

- The midline for $y = \cos x$ is $y = 0$.
- The period for $y = \cos x$ is 2π.
- The amplitude is 1.
- The quarter distance for $y = \cos x$ is $\frac{\pi}{2}$.
- $y = \cos x$ crosses the x-axis at $\frac{\pi}{2}$ and $\frac{3\pi}{2}$.
- The maximum value is 1. It occurs at 0 and 2π.
- The minimum value is -1. It occurs at π.
- The cycle begins at 0 and ends at 2π.

Now we list the characteristics of a cosine graph in more general terms.

Characteristics of a Cosine Graph

- The midline is a horizontal line determined by the vertical shift.
- The normal period is 2π. (In Section 4.3, the period will be affected by stretches and compressions.)
- The normal amplitude is 1. (In Section 4.3, the amplitude will be affected by stretches and compressions.)
- The quarter distance is the period divided by 4.
- The beginning of the cycle is determined by the horizontal shift.
- The cosine function crosses its midline at the first and third quarter points of its cycle.
- The maximum value is one amplitude above the midline. It occurs at the beginning and end of the cycle.
- The minimum value is one amplitude below the midline. It occurs at the midpoint of the cycle.
- The end of the cycle is one period after the beginning.

Matched Problem 5   For the function $y = -3 + \cos x$, identify the following: midline, amplitude, maximum and minimum values, period, and quarter distance. Also identify the following points: beginning, first quarter point, midpoint, third quarter point, and end. Then graph the function labeling all the points.

Example 7   For the function $y = \sin\left(x + \frac{\pi}{4}\right)$, identify the following: midline, amplitude, maximum and minimum values, period, quarter distance, and horizontal shift. Also identify the following points: beginning, first quarter point, midpoint, third quarter point, and end. Then graph the function labeling all the points.

Solution   This time we have an addition that is an *inside* change, indicating a horizontal shift $\frac{\pi}{4}$ units to the left. This is the only change to the basic function but it will cause the cycle to have a new beginning. We will use the beginning and the quarter distance to determine the other important features of the graph.

Midline: $y = 0$ because there is no vertical shift.

Amplitude: 1

Maximum Value: 1

Minimum Value: -1

Period: 2π

Beginning: $-\frac{\pi}{4}$ because of the horizontal shift $\frac{\pi}{4}$ units to the left. This point is on the midline, so the y-coordinate is 0.

Quarter Distance: Period divided by 4: $\frac{2\pi}{4} = \frac{\pi}{2}$ Notice that the beginning x-value has a denominator of 4. If we leave the quarter distance with this denominator, the addition will be very easy. We will use $\frac{2\pi}{4}$ for the quarter distance.

First Quarter Point: The first quarter point occurs at the beginning plus quarter distance: $-\frac{\pi}{4} + \frac{2\pi}{4} = \frac{\pi}{4}$. This is the maximum point so the y-coordinate is 1.

Midpoint: The midpoint occurs at first quarter point plus quarter distance: $\frac{\pi}{4} + \frac{2\pi}{4} = \frac{3\pi}{4}$. This point is on the midline so the y-coordinate is 0.

Third Quarter Point: The third quarter point occurs at midpoint plus quarter distance: $\frac{3\pi}{4} + \frac{2\pi}{4} = \frac{5\pi}{4}$. This is the minimum point so the y-coordinate is -1.

End: The cycle ends at third quarter point plus quarter distance: $\frac{5\pi}{4} + \frac{2\pi}{4} = \frac{7\pi}{4}$. This point is on the midline so the y-coordinate is 0.

In Figure 4.13 below, notice that tick marks are placed on the x-axis every $\frac{\pi}{4}$ units. This is for accurate scaling and easy location of the points.

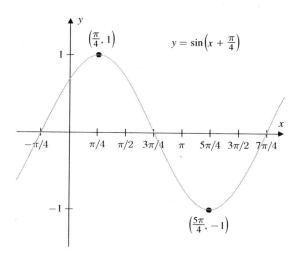

Figure 4.13

Matched Problem 6

For the function $y = \cos\left(x + \frac{\pi}{4}\right)$, identify the following: midline, amplitude, maximum and minimum values, period, quarter distance, and horizontal shift. Also identify the following points: beginning, first quarter point, midpoint, third quarter point, and end. Then graph the function, labeling all the points.

Example 8

For the function $y = -3 + \cos\left(x - \frac{\pi}{3}\right)$, identify the following: midline, amplitude, maximum and minimum values, period, quarter distance, and horizontal shift. Also identify the following points: beginning, first quarter point, midpoint, third quarter point, and end. Then graph the function, labeling all the points.

Solution

Here we have two transformations. The graph is shifted $\frac{\pi}{3}$ units to the right and 3 units down.

Midline: $y = -3$ because of the vertical shift

Amplitude: 1

Maximum Value: 1 unit above the midline, -2.

Minimum Value: 1 unit below the midline, -4.

Period: 2π

Beginning: Because of the horizontal shift, the cycle begins at $\frac{\pi}{3}$. The y-coordinate is the maximum value, -2.

Quarter Distance: The quarter distance is the period divided by 4: $\frac{2\pi}{4} = \frac{\pi}{2}$.

For ease of calculation, we write the beginning and the quarter distance with the same denominator, in this case 6. The **beginning** is $\frac{\pi}{3} = \frac{2\pi}{6}$, and the **quarter distance** is $\frac{\pi}{2} = \frac{3\pi}{6}$.

First quarter point: Beginning plus quarter distance: $\frac{2\pi}{6} + \frac{3\pi}{6} = \frac{5\pi}{6}$. The point is on the midline so the y-coordinate is -3.

Midpoint: First quarter point plus quarter distance: $\frac{5\pi}{6} + \frac{3\pi}{6} = \frac{8\pi}{6} = \frac{4\pi}{3}$. The y-coordinate is the minimum value, -4.

Third quarter point: Midpoint plus quarter distance: $\frac{8\pi}{6} + \frac{3\pi}{6} = \frac{11\pi}{6}$. The point is on the midline so the y-coordinate is -3.

End: Third quarter point plus quarter distance: $\frac{11\pi}{6} + \frac{3\pi}{6} = \frac{14\pi}{6} = \frac{7\pi}{3}$. The y-coordinate is the maximum value, -2.

In Figure 4.14 below, notice that tick marks are placed on the x-axis every $\frac{\pi}{6}$ units. This is for accurate scaling and easy location of the points.

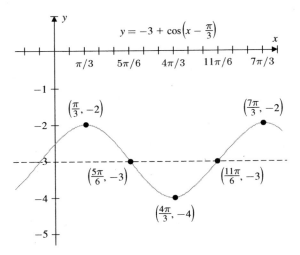

Figure 4.14

Matched Problem 7	For the function $y = 1 + \sin\left(x - \frac{\pi}{8}\right)$, identify the following: midline, amplitude, maximum and minimum values, period, quarter distance, and horizontal shift. Also identify the following points: beginning, first quarter point, midpoint, third quarter point, and end. Then graph the function, labeling all the points.

Reflections

Recall that the sine function is odd so that $\sin(-x) = -\sin x$. The cosine function is even so $\cos(-x) = \cos x$. Because of this, reflections about the y-axis can be expressed either as a function without a reflection (in the case of a cosine) or as a reflection about the x-axis (in the case of a sine). For this reason, we will examine only vertical reflections.

Example 9	For the function $y = 2 - \sin x$, identify the following: midline, amplitude, maximum and minimum values, period, and quarter distance. Also identify the following points: beginning, first quarter point, midpoint, third quarter point, and end. Then graph the function labeling all the points.

Notice that the function can be rewritten as $y = -\sin x + 2$. There are two transformations, a reflection about the x-axis and a vertical shift 2 units up.

Midline: $y = 2$ because of the vertical shift.

Amplitude: 1

Maximum Value: 1 unit above the midline, 3.

Minimum Value: 1 unit below the midline, 1.

Period: 2π

Beginning: The cycle begins at 0 and the point is on the midline so the y-coordinate is 2.

First quarter point: The x-coordinate $\frac{\pi}{2}$ and because of the vertical reflection, the y-coordinate is the minimum value, 1.

Midpoint: The x-coordinate π and the point is on the midline so the y-coordinate is 2.

Third quarter point: The x-coordinate is $\frac{3\pi}{2}$ and the y-coordinate is the maximum value, 3.

End: The x-coordinate is 2π and the point is on the midline so the y-coordinate is 2.

Graph: See Figure 4.15.

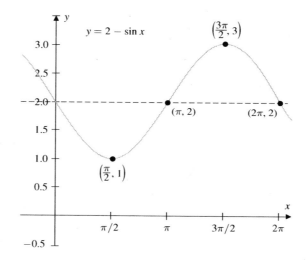

Figure 4.15

Matched Problem 8

For the function $y = -1 - \cos x$, identify the following: midline, amplitude, maximum and minimum values, period, and quarter distance. Also identify the following points: beginning, first quarter point, midpoint, third quarter point, and end. Then graph the function labeling all the points.

Answers to Matched Problems

After sketching graph using transformations, check with calculator

1. $y = \dfrac{1}{x}$, Shifted horizontally 4 units left
2. $y = \sqrt[3]{x}$, Shifted vertically 2 units down
3. $y = \sqrt{x}$, Shifted horizontally 4 units right and vertically 3 units up
4. $y = \sqrt{x}$, Reflected across the x-axis

Matched problem	5	6	7	8
Midline	$y = -3$	$y = 0$	$y = 1$	$y = -1$
Amplitude	1	1	1	1
Max. value	-2	1	2	0
Min. value	-4	-1	0	-2
Period	2π	2π	2π	2π
Begin	$(0, -2)$	$\left(-\frac{\pi}{4}, 1\right)$	$\left(\frac{\pi}{8}, 1\right)$	$(0, -2)$
1st quarter pt.	$\left(\frac{\pi}{2}, -3\right)$	$\left(\frac{\pi}{4}, 0\right)$	$\left(\frac{5\pi}{8}, 2\right)$	$\left(\frac{\pi}{2}, -1\right)$
Midpoint	$(\pi, -4)$	$\left(\frac{3\pi}{4}, -1\right)$	$\left(\frac{9\pi}{8}, 1\right)$	$(\pi, 0)$
3rd quarter pt.	$\left(\frac{3\pi}{2}, -3\right)$	$\left(\frac{5\pi}{4}, 0\right)$	$\left(\frac{13\pi}{8}, 0\right)$	$\left(\frac{3\pi}{2}, -1\right)$
End	$(2\pi, -2)$	$\left(\frac{7\pi}{4}, 1\right)$	$\left(\frac{17\pi}{8}, 1\right)$	$(2\pi, -2)$

Exercises for Section 4.2

For problems 1–4, identify the basic function, state the transformations, and sketch the graph. Mark all the important points on the graph. Check by using your graphing calculator.

1. $y = -(x - 3)^2$ **2.** $y = \dfrac{1}{x + 1} - 4$

3. $y = (x + 3)^3 + 1$ **4.** $y = 2 + \sqrt{-x}$

5. Consider these functions:

    (a) $f(x) = \cos x + 1$ **(b)** $g(x) = \cos(x + 1)$

    Are they the same or are they different? Why?

6. Consider these functions:

    (a) $f(x) = \sin x + 2$ **(b)** $g(x) = \sin(x + 2)$
    (c) $h(x) = \sin(x) + 2$ **(d)** $j(x) = (\sin x) + 2$
    (e) $k(x) = 2 + \sin x$

    Which of these (if any) are the same? Give reasons for your answer.

For the primary cycle of each of the functions in problems 7–16, identify:

    Vertical Shift (if any)
    Horizontal Shift (if any)
    Reflection (if any)

    Midline
    Amplitude
    Maximum Value
    Minimum Value
    Period
    Beginning
    Quarter Distance
    First Quarter Point
    Midpoint
    Third Quarter Point
    End

Without using your graphing calculator, graph each function by hand, labeling each of the important points and lines.

7. $y = 3 + \sin x$ **8.** $y = \cos x - 4$

9. $y = 3 - \sin x$ **10.** $y = -4 - \cos x$

11. $y = \cos\left(x - \dfrac{\pi}{4}\right)$ **12.** $y = \sin\left(x - \dfrac{\pi}{4}\right)$

13. $y = -\sin\left(x + \dfrac{\pi}{3}\right)$ **14.** $y = -\cos\left(x + \dfrac{\pi}{8}\right)$

15. $y = 2 + \cos\left(x + \dfrac{\pi}{6}\right)$ **16.** $y = -3 + \sin\left(x - \dfrac{\pi}{12}\right)$

4.3 TRANSFORMATIONS OF TRIGONOMETRIC FUNCTIONS: STRETCHES AND COMPRESSIONS

- Vertical Stretches and Compressions
- Horizontal Stretches and Compressions

In Section 4.2 we reviewed horizontal and vertical shifts and reflections. Recall that these were accomplished by means of inside and outside additions, subtractions, or negatives. There are two other arithmetic operations, multiplication and division, and these will also transform a function. Before we investigate, remember that *inside* changes to the function produce *horizontal* results, while *outside* changes to the function produce *vertical* results.

Outside Multiplication

Example 1   Use a graphing calculator to graph $y = 2 \sin x$ and compare it to the graph of $y = \sin x$.

Notice that the basic function, $\sin x$, is multiplied by 2. This is an outside multiplication and that means that all the original outputs are doubled. Maximums will be twice as high, minimums will be twice as low, but zeros will stay the same.

Here are the two graphs together: (See Figure 4.16)

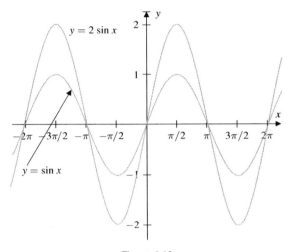

Figure 4.16

As we expected, the graph of $y = 2 \sin x$ reaches a maximum of 2 and a minimum of -2 and it has the same zeros as $y = \sin x$. The graph has been *stretched vertically*. The amplitude of $y = 2 \sin x$ is 2, but the period and all other characteristics of $y = \sin x$ have stayed the same.

Example 2   Use a graphing calculator to graph $y = \frac{1}{2} \sin x$ and compare it to the graph of $y = \sin x$.

This time the basic function, $\sin x$, is multiplied by $\frac{1}{2}$. This means that each of the original outputs is cut in half. Maximums and minimums will be half of their original value but again zeros will stay the same.

Here are the two graphs together: (See Figure 4.17)

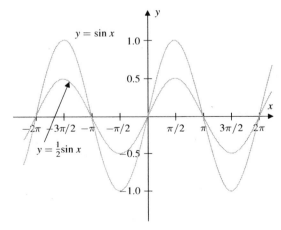

Figure 4.17

As we expected, the graph of $y = \frac{1}{2} \sin x$ reaches a maximum of only $\frac{1}{2}$ and a minimum of $-\frac{1}{2}$ and it has the same zeros as $y = \sin x$. The graph has been *compressed vertically*. The amplitude of $y = \frac{1}{2} \sin x$ is $\frac{1}{2}$, but the period and all other characteristics of $y = \sin x$ have stayed the same.

Matched Problem 1

Using a graphing calculator to graph $y = \cos x$ and then $y = 3 \cos x$ and $y = \frac{1}{3} \cos x$ on the same coordinate system. Use a window of -2π to 2π on the x-axis and -3.5 to 3.5 on the y-axis. Compare the results to those of Examples 1 and 2. Which function produces a vertical stretch of $y = \cos x$ and which one produces a vertical compression?

> **Vertical Stretches and Compressions**
> The graph of $y = A \sin x$ or $y = A \cos x$ is the graph of $y = \sin$ or $y = \cos x$ stretched or compressed vertically.
> The amplitude of the graph is $|A|$.
> The graph is stretched if $|A| > 1$ and the graph is compressed if $0 < |A| < 1$.

Inside Multiplication

Example 3

Use a graphing calculator to graph $y = \cos(2x)$ and compare it to the graph of $y = \cos x$.

Notice that the input, x, is multiplied by 2. This is an inside multiplication and it should produce a horizontal effect on the graph. If an input is doubled before the cosine is applied, output values will occur *sooner* than they did before. Maximums and minimums will be the same but they will occur in different locations.

Here are the two graphs together: (See Figure 4.18)

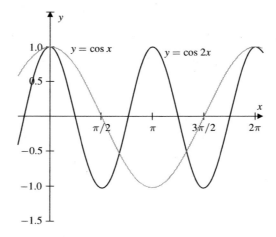

Figure 4.18

Observe that the maximum and minimum values are still the same but now two complete cycles fit into the same interval as one cycle did in the basic function. The graph of $y = \cos(2x)$ is a *horizontal compression* of the graph of $y = \cos x$.

The *period* of $y = \cos(2x)$ is π. Notice that the period is the original period, 2π, divided by 2.

Example 4 Use a graphing calculator to graph $y = \cos\left(\frac{x}{2}\right)$ and compare it to the graph of $y = \cos x$.

Notice that the input, x, is divided by 2 (or multiplied by $\frac{1}{2}$). If each input is cut in half before applying the cosine function then the output values will occur *later* than they did before. Again, maximums and minimums will be the same but they will occur in different locations.

Here are the two graphs together:

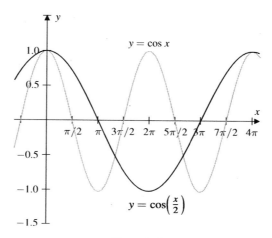

Figure 4.19

Observe that once again the maximum and minimum values are still the same but now the interval for one complete cycle is twice as long as it was for the basic function.

The graph of $y = \cos\left(\frac{x}{2}\right)$ is a *horizontal stretch* of the graph of $y = \cos x$.

The *period* of $y = \cos(2x)$ is 4π. Notice that the period, 4π, is the original period, 2π, divided by $\frac{1}{2}$, or multiplied by 2.

Matched Problem 2 Use a graphing calculator to graph $y = \sin x$ and then $y = \sin(2x)$ and $y = \sin\left(\frac{x}{2}\right)$ on the same coordinate system. Use the same window as in Figure 4.19 above. Compare the results to those of Examples 3 and 4. Which function produces a horizontal stretch of $y = \sin x$ and which one produces a horizontal compression?

Horizontal Stretches and Compressions

The graph of $y = \sin(Bx)$ or $y = \cos(Bx)$, where $B > 0$, is the graph of $y = \sin x$ or $y = \cos x$ stretched or compressed horizontally.

The period of the graph is $\frac{2\pi}{B}$.

The graph is compressed if $B > 1$ and the graph is stretched if $0 < B < 1$.

Vertical and Horizontal Stretches and Compressions Together

Example 5

Without using your graphing calculator, graph one complete cycle of $y = 2\sin\left(\frac{x}{3}\right)$. Identify all of the important points on the graph.

In this function there is an outside multiplication by 2 and that indicates a vertical stretch. There is also an inside multiplication by $\frac{1}{3}$ and that indicates a horizontal stretch. Here is an analysis of the graph's characteristics:

Midline: $y = 0$

Amplitude: 2

Maximum: 2

Minimum: -2

Period: The period is $\frac{2\pi}{B}$ and $B = \frac{1}{3}$, so the period is $\frac{2\pi}{\frac{1}{3}} = 2\pi(3) = 6\pi$.

Beginning: $(0, 0)$

Quarter distance: Period divided by 4: $\frac{6\pi}{4} = \frac{3\pi}{2}$

First Quarter Point: $\left(\frac{3\pi}{2}, 2\right)$

Midpoint: $x = \frac{3\pi}{2} + \frac{3\pi}{2} = \frac{6\pi}{2} = 3\pi$. The point is $(3\pi, 0)$

Third Quarter Point: $x = \frac{6\pi}{2} + \frac{3\pi}{2} = \frac{9\pi}{2}$. The point is $\left(\frac{9\pi}{2}, -2\right)$.

End: $x = \frac{9\pi}{2} + \frac{3\pi}{2} = \frac{12\pi}{2} = 6\pi$. The point is $(6\pi, 0)$

Graph: Tick marks are every $\frac{3\pi}{2}$ units. See Figure 4.20.

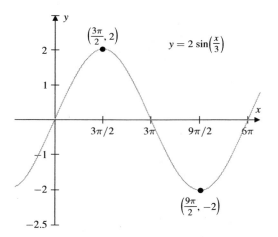

Figure 4.20

Matched Problem 3

Without using your graphing calculator, graph one complete cycle of $y = \frac{1}{3}\cos(2x)$. Identify the transformations, find the quarter distance and use it to identify all of the important points on the graph.

Stretches and Compressions Applied to Algebraic Functions

Stretches and compressions can also be applied to algebraic functions.

Stretches and Compressions

- The graph of $y = A f(x)$ is the graph of $y = f(x)$ stretched or compressed vertically by a factor of $|A|$.
- The graph is stretched if $|A| > 1$ and the graph is compressed if $0 < |A| < 1$.
- The graph of $y = f(Bx)$ is the graph of $y = f(x)$ stretched or compressed horizontally by a factor of $\frac{1}{|B|}$.
- The graph is compressed if $|B| > 1$ and the graph is stretched if $0 < |B| < 1$.

You may be wondering why we didn't include stretches and compressions when we first studied transformations. Stretches and compressions are most easily recognized in sine and cosine graphs. As we will see in the next example, a transformation of an algebraic function might be considered either a vertical or a horizontal stretch.

Example 6   Use your graphing calculator to graph $y = (2x)^2$ and compare it to the graph of $y = x^2$.

Notice that the input, x, is multiplied by 2. This is an inside multiplication and it indicates a *horizontal compression* by a factor of 1/2. Look at the graphs together:

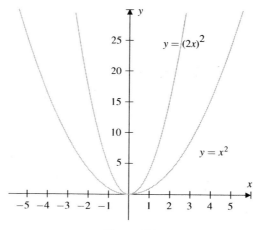

Figure 4.21

Observe that when you look at the new graph, you might see a graph that has been compressed horizontally or you might see a graph that has been stretched vertically. Here is why.

Rewrite the function by expanding $(2x)^2$:

$$y = (2x)^2$$
$$= 4x^2$$

In $y = (2x)^2$, we see a horizontal compression, but in $y = 4x^2$ we see a vertical stretch. This means that with many functions, a vertical stretch can be written and seen as a horizontal compression and a horizontal stretch can be written and viewed as a vertical compression. Because it is usually easier to work with vertical transformations, it is a good idea to rewrite an inside multiplication or division as an outside multiplication or division, as long as it is easy to do so.

Example 7   Use your graphing calculator to graph $y = \frac{1}{3x}$ and compare it to the graph of $y = \frac{1}{x}$.
First rewrite the function:

$$y = \frac{1}{3x} = \frac{1}{3} \cdot \frac{1}{x}$$

The basic function, $\frac{1}{x}$, has been multiplied by $\frac{1}{3}$, which means the graph has been compressed vertically by a factor of $\frac{1}{3}$.
Here are the two graphs:

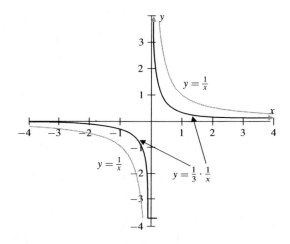

Figure 4.22

Several Transformations at Once

When several transformations are applied to a function, care must be taken to clearly identify the numbers and operations that cause the transformation. A combination that has horizontal shifts and a horizontal stretch or compression can be misleading.

Example 8   Given the function $y = \sqrt{2x - 8}$, identify the basic function and the transformations.
The library function here is $y = \sqrt{x}$. At first glance, it might seem that the -8 indicates a horizontal shift 8 units to the right. However, one look at the graph shows that this is not the case.
From the graph, there is a horizontal shift but it is only 4 units to the right. The reason for this is that because there is also a multiplication by 2, there is a horizontal compression as well as the horizontal shift. When that happens, the number multiplying x must be factored out of the expression

so that the actual shift can be clearly seen. In other words, the function must be rewritten:

$$y = \sqrt{2x - 8} = \sqrt{2(x - 4)}$$

Now the shift is clearly only 4 units to the right and the graph is compressed horizontally by $\frac{1}{2}$.

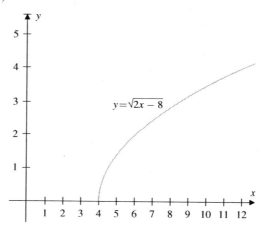

Figure 4.23

Matched Problem 4

Given the function $y = \frac{2}{3x - 6}$, identify the basic function and the transformations.

Here is a summary of function transformations.

Summary of Transformations

The function $y = A\,f\,(B\,(x - h)) + k$ has transformations identified by A, B, h, and k. The graph is the graph of $y = f(x)$

- Vertically stretched or compressed by a factor of $|A|$. If $|A| > 1$, then the graph is stretched and if $0 < |A| < 1$, the graph is compressed.
- Reflected across the x-axis if A is negative.
- Vertically shifted k units. If $k > 0$, the graph shifts up; if $k < 0$, the graph shifts down.
- Horizontally stretched or compressed by a factor of $\frac{1}{|B|}$. If $|B| > 1$, the graph is compressed and if $0 < |B| < 1$, the graph is stretched.
- Reflected across the y-axis if B is negative.
- Horizontally shifted h units. If $h > 0$, the graph shifts to the right; if $h < 0$, the graph shifts to the left.

Although this summary works for all functions, it is worthwhile to rewrite it for the sine and cosine functions because they have special characteristics.

Summary of Transformations for Sine and Cosine
For the functions $y = A \sin(B(x - h)) + k$ and $y = A \cos(B(x - h)) + k$, $B > 0$

- $y = k$ is the midline.
- $|A|$ is the amplitude.
- If A is negative, the graph is reflected across the x-axis
- $\frac{2\pi}{|B|}$ is the period.
- h is the horizontal shift.

Example 9   Without using your graphing calculator, graph one complete cycle of $y = 3 \sin(4x - \pi) + 1$. Identify all of the important points on the graph.

First, rewrite the function so that each transformation is clearly identifiable. In this case, factor out the 4:

$$y = 3 \sin(4x - \pi) + 1 = 3 \sin\left(4\left(x - \frac{\pi}{4}\right)\right) + 1$$

Midline: $y = 1$
Amplitude: 3
Maximum: 4
Minimum: -2
Period: The period is $\frac{2\pi}{B}$ and $B = 4$, so the period is $\frac{2\pi}{4} = \frac{\pi}{2}$.
Horizontal Shift: $\frac{\pi}{4}$ to the right
Quarter distance: Period divided by 4: $\frac{\frac{\pi}{2}}{4} = \frac{\pi}{8}$
Beginning: $x = \frac{\pi}{4}$ or $\frac{2\pi}{8}$. The point is $\left(\frac{\pi}{4}, 1\right)$.
First Quarter Point: $\left(\frac{3\pi}{8}, 4\right)$
Midpoint: $x = \frac{4\pi}{8} = \frac{\pi}{2}$. The point is $\left(\frac{\pi}{2}, 1\right)$.
Third Quarter Point: $\left(\frac{5\pi}{8}, -2\right)$
End: $x = \frac{6\pi}{8} = \frac{3\pi}{4}$. The point is $\left(\frac{3\pi}{4}, 1\right)$
Graph: Tick marks are every $\frac{\pi}{8}$ units.

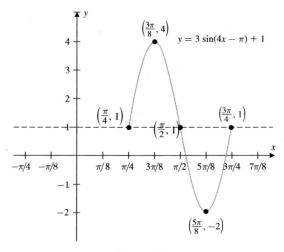

Figure 4.24

Matched Problem 5   Graph one complete cycle of $y = 2\cos(3x - \pi) - 4$. Identify all of the important points on the graph.

Example 10   Graph one complete cycle of $y = -4\cos(2\pi x) + 2$. Identify all of the important points on the graph.

Midline: $y = 2$
Amplitude: 4
Reflection: Across the x-axis
Maximum: 6
Minimum: -2
Period: The period is $\frac{2\pi}{B}$ and $B = 2\pi$, so the period is $\frac{2\pi}{2\pi} = 1$.
Horizontal Shift: None
Quarter distance: Period divided by 4: $\frac{1}{4}$
Beginning: $(0, -2)$
First Quarter Point: $\left(\frac{1}{4}, 2\right)$
Midpoint: $x = \frac{2}{4} = \frac{1}{2}$. The point is $\left(\frac{1}{2}, 6\right)$.
Third Quarter Point: $\left(\frac{3}{4}, 2\right)$
End: $(1, -2)$
Graph: See Figure 4.25.

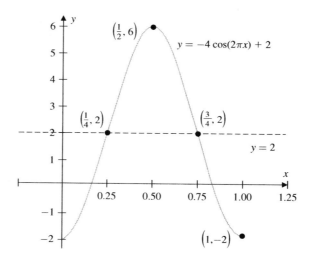

Figure 4.25

Matched Problem 6   Graph one complete cycle of $y = -\sin(4\pi x) - 2$. Identify all of the important points on the graph.

Transformations with the Graph of a Function

Example 11   The function $y = f(x)$ is graphed in Figure 4.26. Graph the function $g(x) = -2f(x - 1) + 3$.

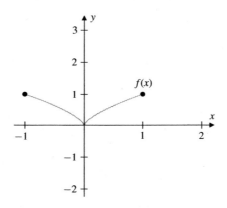

Figure 4.26

Even though we do not have a formula for $f(x)$, we have the graph and can identify the transformations based on what we know about $g(x)$. To correctly identify the transformations, work from the inside out.

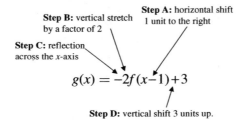

In Figure 4.27 below, each step is shown as a separate graph.

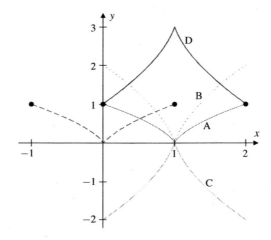

Figure 4.27

Answers to Matched Problems

1. $y = 3\cos x$ vertical stretch, $y = \frac{1}{3}\cos x$ vertical compression
2. $y = \sin(2x)$ horizontal compression, $y = \sin\left(\frac{1}{2}x\right)$ horizontal stretch
4. $y = \frac{1}{x}$, horizontal shift 2 units right, vertical compression by $\frac{2}{3}$

Matched problem	3	5	6
Transformation	compression both		
Midline	$y = 0$	$y = -4$	$y = -2$
Amplitude	$1/3$	2	1
Reflection	none	none	across x-axis
Max. value	$1/3$	-2	-1
Min. value	$-1/3$	-6	-3
Period	π	$\frac{2\pi}{3}$	$\frac{1}{2}$
Quarter distance	$\frac{\pi}{4}$	$\frac{\pi}{6}$	$\frac{1}{8}$
Begin	$(0, \frac{1}{3})$	$(\frac{\pi}{3}, -2)$	$(0, -2)$
1stquarter pt.	$(\frac{\pi}{4}, 0)$	$(\frac{\pi}{2}, -4)$	$(\frac{1}{8}, -3)$
Midpoint	$(\frac{\pi}{2}, -\frac{1}{3})$	$(\frac{2\pi}{3}, -6)$	$(\frac{1}{4}, -2)$
3rdquarter pt.	$(\frac{3\pi}{4}, 0)$	$(\frac{5\pi}{6}, -4)$	$(\frac{3}{8}, -1)$
End	$(\pi, \frac{1}{3})$	$(\pi, -2)$	$(\frac{1}{2}, -2)$

Exercises and Problems for Section 4.3

Exercises A

In Exercises 1–4, graph and label $f(x)$, $4f(x)$, $-\frac{1}{2}f(x)$ $-5f(x)$ on the same axes.

1. $f(x) = -x^2 + 7x$ **2.** $f(x) = \sqrt{x}$

3. $f(x) = \ln x$ **4.** $f(x) = e^x$

5. Fill in all the blanks in Table 4.1 for which you have sufficient information.

Table 4.1

x	-3	-2	-1	0	1	2	3
$f(x)$	-4	-1	2	3	0	-3	-6
$f(-x)$							
$-f(x)$							
$f(x) - 2$							
$f(x - 2)$							
$f(x) + 2$							
$f(x + 2)$							
$2f(x)$							
$-f(x)/3$							

6. Using Table 4.2, make tables for the following transformations of f on an appropriate domain.

  (a) $\frac{1}{2}f(x)$ (b) $-2f(x + 1)$ (c) $f(x) + 5$
  (d) $f(x - 2)$ (e) $f(-x)$ (f) $-f(x)$

Table 4.2

x	-3	-2	-1	0	1	2	3
$f(x)$	2	3	7	-1	-3	4	8

7. Using Table 4.3, create a table of values for
  (a) $f(-x)$ (b) $-f(x)$ (c) $3f(x)$
  (d) Which of these tables from parts (a), (b), and (c) represents an even function?

Table 4.3

x	-4	-3	-2	-1	0	1	2	3	4
$f(x)$	13	6	1	-2	-3	-2	1	6	13

8. Figure 4.28 is a graph of $y = x^{3/2}$. Match the following functions with the graphs in Figure 4.29.
  (a) $y = x^{3/2} - 1$ (b) $y = (x - 1)^{3/2}$
  (c) $y = 1 - x^{3/2}$ (d) $y = \frac{3}{2}x^{3/2}$

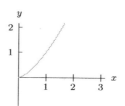

Figure 4.28

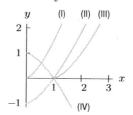

Figure 4.29

9. Using Figure 4.30, match the functions (i)–(v) with a graph (a)–(i).

(i) $y = 2f(x)$ (ii) $y = \frac{1}{3}f(x)$

(iii) $y = -f(x) + 1$ (iv) $y = f(x + 2) + 1$

(v) $y = f(-x)$

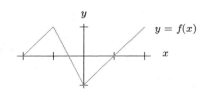

Figure 4.30

(a)   (b)

(c)   (d)

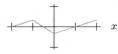

(e)   (f)

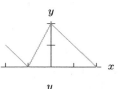

(g)   (h)

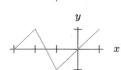

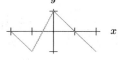

(i)

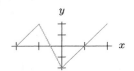

10. Using Figure 4.31, graph the following functions.

(a) $y = -f(x) + 2$ (b) $y = 2f(x)$

(c) $y = f(x - 3)$ (d) $y = -\frac{1}{2}f(x + 1) - 3$

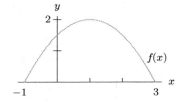

Figure 4.31

Without a calculator, graph the transformations in Exercises 11–16. Label at least three points.

11. $y = f(x + 3)$ if $f(x) = |x|$

12. $y = f(x) + 3$ if $f(x) = |x|$

13. $y = -g(x)$ if $g(x) = x^2$

14. $y = g(-x)$ if $g(x) = x^2$

15. $y = 3h(x)$ if $h(x) = 2^x$

16. $y = 0.5h(x)$ if $h(x) = 2^x$

Problems A

17. The number of gallons of paint, $n = f(A)$, needed to cover a house is a function of the surface area, in ft^2. Match each story to one expression.

(a) I figured out how many gallons I needed and then bought two extra gallons just in case.
(b) I bought enough paint to cover my house twice.
(c) I bought enough paint to cover my house and my welcome sign, which measures 2 square feet.

(i) $2f(A)$ (ii) $f(A + 2)$ (iii) $f(A) + 2$

18. Let $R = P(t)$ be the number of rabbits living in the national park in month t. (See Example 5 on page 5.) What do the following expressions represent?

(a) $P(t + 1)$ (b) $2P(t)$

19. The US population in millions is $P(t)$ today and t is in years. Match each statement (I)–(IV) with one of the formulas (a)–(h).

I. The population 10 years before today.

II. Today's population plus 10 million immigrants.

III. Ten percent of the population we have today.

IV. The population after 100,000 people have emigrated.

(a) $P(t) - 10$ (b) $P(t - 10)$
(c) $0.1P(t)$ (d) $P(t) + 10$
(e) $P(t + 10)$ (f) $P(t)/0.1$
(g) $P(t) + 0.1$ (h) $P(t) - 0.1$

20. Without a calculator, match each formula (a)–(e) with a graph in Figure 4.32. There may be no answer or several answers.

(a) $y = 3 \cdot 2^x$ (b) $y = 5^{-x}$ (c) $y = -5^x$
(d) $y = 2 - 2^{-x}$ (e) $y = 1 - \left(\frac{1}{2}\right)^x$

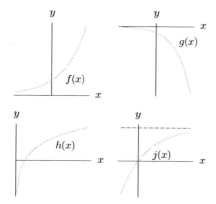

Figure 4.32

21. Using Figure 4.33, graph each of the following functions on separate sets of axes, together with the graph of the original function. Label intercepts and asymptotes.

(a) $y = 3f(x)$ (b) $y = f(x-1)$
(c) $y = f(x) - 1$ (d) $y = -2f(x)$
(e) $y = \frac{1}{2}f(x+2) - 1$ (f) $y = -f(-x)$

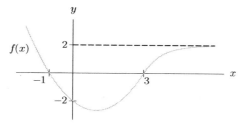

Figure 4.33

22. Let $f(x) = 2^x$. Find possible formulas for the transformations of f in (a)–(d). *Example:* The graph in Figure 4.34 appears to be f flipped across the y-axis. Because the horizontal asymptote is at $y = -3$ instead of $y = 0$, it appears that f is shifted downward by 3 units. Therefore, $y = f(-x) - 3 = 2^{-x} - 3$.

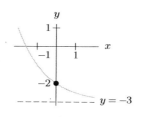

Figure 4.34

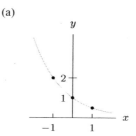

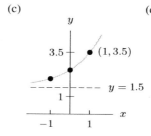

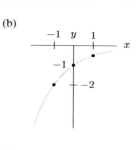

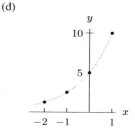

23. Graph the transformations (a) – (f) of the function f given in Figure 4.35. Label the new positions of the points A and B and the horizontal asymptote.

(a) $y = 2f(x)$ (b) $y = f(-x)$
(c) $y = -f(x)$ (d) $y = f(x+3)$
(e) $y = f(x) + 3$ (f) $y = \frac{1}{2}f(x)$

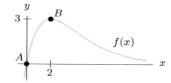

Figure 4.35

24. Using Figure 4.35, find formulas, in terms of f, for the following transformations of f.

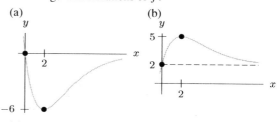

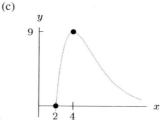

25. Using Figure 4.36, find formulas, in terms of f, for the horizontal and vertical shifts of the graph of f in parts (a)–(c). What is the equation of each asymptote?

26. In Figure 4.37 the point b is labeled on the x-axis. On the y-axis, locate and label the output values:

   (a) $f(b)$ **(b)** $-2f(b)$ **(c)** $-2f(-b)$

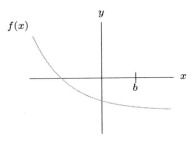

Figure 4.37

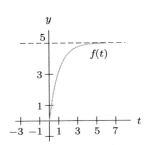

Figure 4.36

27. The average rate of change of $r(n)$ between $n = 2$ and $n = 3$ is 6. What is the average rate of change of $2r(n)$ between $n = 2$ and $n = 3$?

28. Figure 4.38 gives a graph of $y = f(x)$. Consider the transformations $y = \frac{1}{2}f(x)$ and $y = 2f(x)$. Which points on the graph of $y = f(x)$ stay fixed under these transformations? Compare the intervals on which all three functions are increasing and decreasing.

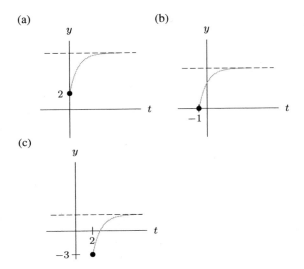

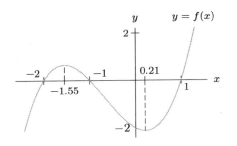

Figure 4.38

Exercises B

1. Using Table 4.4, make a table of values for $f(\frac{1}{2}x)$ for an appropriate domain.

Table 4.4

x	-3	-2	-1	0	1	2	3
$f(x)$	2	3	7	-1	-3	4	8

2. Fill in all the blanks in Table 4.5 for which you have sufficient information.

Table 4.5

x	-3	-2	-1	0	1	2	3
$f(x)$	-4	-1	2	3	0	-3	-6
$f(\frac{1}{2}x)$							
$f(2x)$							

3. Graph $m(x) = e^x$, $n(x) = e^{2x}$, and $p(x) = 2e^x$ on the same axes and describe how the graphs of $n(x)$ and $p(x)$ compare with that of $m(x)$.

4. Graph $y = h(3x)$ if $h(x) = 2^x$.

In Exercises 5–7, graph and label $f(x)$, $f(\frac{1}{2}x)$, and $f(-3x)$ on the same axes between $x = -2$ and $x = 2$.

5. $f(x) = e^x + x^3 - 4x^2$

6. $f(x) = e^{x+7} + (x-4)^3 - (x+2)^2$

7. $f(x) = \ln(x^4 + 3x^2 + 4)$

8. Using Figure 4.39, match each function to a graph (if any) that represents it:

  (i) $y = f(2x)$ (ii) $y = 2f(2x)$ (iii) $y = f(\frac{1}{2}x)$

$y = f(x)$

Figure 4.39

(a)

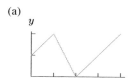

(b)

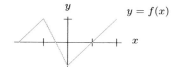

(c)

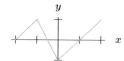

(d)

(e)

(f)

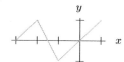

(g)

(h)

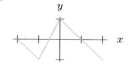

(i)

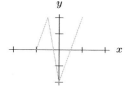

Problems B

9. Every day I take the same taxi over the same route from home to the train station. The trip is x miles, so the cost for the trip is $f(x)$. Match each story in (a)–(d) to a function in (i)–(iv) representing the amount paid to the driver.

  (a) I received a raise yesterday, so today I gave my driver a five dollar tip.

  (b) I had a new driver today and he got lost. He drove five extra miles and charged me for it.

  (c) I haven't paid my driver all week. Today is Friday and I'll pay what I owe for the week.

  (d) The meter in the taxi went crazy and showed five times the number of miles I actually traveled.

  (i) $5f(x)$ (ii) $f(x) + 5$
  (iii) $f(5x)$ (iv) $f(x + 5)$

10. Let $A = f(r)$ be the area of a circle of radius r.

  (a) Write a formula for $f(r)$.

  (b) Which expression represents the area of a circle whose radius is increased by 10%? Explain.

  (i) $0.10f(r)$ (ii) $f(r + 0.10)$ (iii) $f(0.10r)$
  (iv) $f(1.1r)$ (v) $f(r) + 0.10$

  (c) By what percent does the area increase if the radius is increased by 10%?

11. Figure 4.40 shows $f(x) = e^x$ in the window $-3 \le x \le 3$

and $-1 \le y \le 5$. For what window does Figure 4.41 represent the function:

  (a) $g(x) = e^{3x}$?   **(b)** $h(x) = e^{0.4x}$?

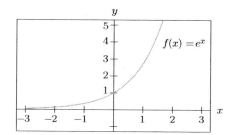

Figure 4.40

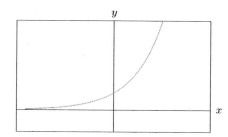

Figure 4.41

12. **(a)** Graph $f(x) = e^x$ and $g(x) = f(4x) = e^{4x}$ in the window $-2 \le x \le 2$ and $-5 \le y \le 10$.

(b) Using new x-values and the original y-values, graph g so that it looks like the original graph of f. What are the new x-values?

(c) With the same y-values, find another set of new x-values so that the graph of f looks like the original graph of g.

13. Graph the following transformations of the function f given in Figure 4.42. Relabel points A and B as well as the horizontal asymptote:

(a) $y = f(2x)$ **(b)** $y = f\left(-\dfrac{x}{3}\right)$

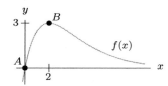

Figure 4.42

14. Figure 4.43 shows a transformation of the function, f, in Figure 4.42. Find a formula for the function in Figure 4.43 in terms of f.

Figure 4.43

15. Using Figure 4.44, graph the following functions on separate sets of axes, together with the graph of the original function. Label any intercepts or special points.

(a) $y = f(3x)$ **(b)** $y = f(-2x)$ **(c)** $y = f(\frac{1}{2}x)$

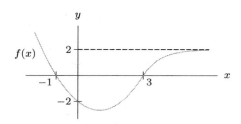

Figure 4.44

16. This problem investigates the effect of a horizontal stretch on the zeros of a function.

(a) Graph $f(x) = 4 - x^2$. Mark the zeros of f on the graph.

(b) Graph and find a formula for $g(x) = f(0.5x)$. What are the zeros of $g(x)$?

(c) Graph and find a formula for $h(x) = f(2x)$. What are the zeros of $h(x)$?

(d) Without graphing, what are the zeros of $f(10x)$?

17. The log function has the property that the graph resulting from a horizontal stretch can also be obtained by a vertical shift.

(a) Graph $f(x) = \log x$ and $g(x) = \log(10x)$ and determine the vertical shift.

(b) Explain how you could have predicted the answer to part (a) from the properties of logarithms.

(c) If $h(x) = \log(ax)$, what is the vertical shift k making $h(x) = \log(x) + k$?

18. In Figure 4.45, the point c is labeled on the x-axis. On the y-axis, locate and label output values:

(a) $g(c)$ **(b)** $2g(c)$ **(c)** $g(2c)$

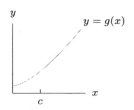

Figure 4.45

In Problems 19–20, state which graph represents

     (a) $f(x)$ **(b)** $f(-2x)$ **(c)** $f(-\frac{1}{2}x)$ **(d)** $f(2x)$

19.

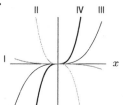

20.

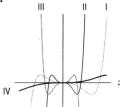

21. A company projects a total profit, $P(t)$ dollars, in year t. Explain the economic meaning of $r(t) = 0.5P(t)$ and $s(t) = P(0.5t)$.

22. You are a banker with a table showing year-end values of \$1 invested at an interest rate of 1% per year, compounded annually, for a period of fifty years.

   (a) Can this table be used to show 1% monthly interest charges on a credit card? Explain.

   (b) Can this table be used to show values of an annual interest rate of 5%? Explain.

23. The von Bertalanffy growth model predicts the mean length L of a fish of age t (in years):[1]

$$L = f(t) = L_\infty \left(1 - e^{-k(t+t_0)}\right), \text{ for constant } L_\infty, k, t_0.$$

Let $L_\infty = 40$, $t_0 = 1/12$, and $k = 0.5$. The lengths of two related species are given by $L = g(t) = 1.5 f(t)$, and $L = h(t) = f(t/2)$.

   (a) Graph f, labeling any asymptotes or axis intercepts. Describe in words what the graph tells you about the growth of these fish.

   (b) Graph g together with f, labeling any asymptotes or axis intercepts. Describe in words how the two species differ.

   (c) Repeat part (b), with h instead of g.

Exercises C

1. Sinusoidal functions are functions that can be written in the form:

$$y = A \sin(B(x - h)) + k \quad \text{or} \quad y = A \cos(B(x - h)) + k$$

Using these functions, identify each of the following:

   (a) The equation of the midline.

   (b) The amplitude.

   (c) The period.

   (d) The horizontal shift.

2. For the function $f(x) = 2 \sin x$, explain in words the transformation and its effect on the graph.

3. For the function $f(x) = \cos(3x)$, explain in words the transformation and its effect on the graph.

4. For the function $g(x) = \cos\left(x - \frac{\pi}{2}\right) + 3$, explain in words the transformations and their effect on the graph.

5. If $f(x)$ is any function, identify the transformations in the function $g(x) = \frac{1}{3} f(2x + 2) - 1$.

6. If $f(x) = 2(x - 3)^3 - 4$, identify the basic functions and identify each of the transformations, stating its effect on the graph.

7. If $f(x) = -\frac{1}{2}\sqrt{x + 5} + 7$, identify the basic functions and identify each of the transformations, stating its effect on the graph.

8. The graph of $f(x)$ in Figure 4.46 represents a transformation of $y = \sin x$. State the transformations and write a possible formula for $f(x)$.

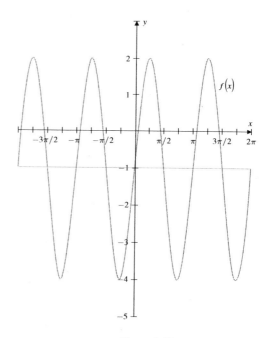

Figure 4.46

[1]*Introduction to Tropical Fish Stock Assessment* by Per Sparre, Danish Institute for Fisheries Research, and Siebren C. Venema, FAO Fisheries Department, available at http://www.fao.org/docrep/W5449E/w5449e00.htm.

For problems 9 – 18, identify any shifts, reflections, stretches or compressions. Then find each of the following for the primary cycle:

Midline
Amplitude
Maximum Value
Minimum Value
Period
Beginning
Quarter Distance
First Quarter Point
Midpoint
Third Quarter Point
End

Graph the primary cycle for each function without using your graphing calculator, labeling each of the important points and lines.

9. $f(x) = \sin\left(\frac{1}{2}x\right)$ **10.** $f(x) = 2\sin x$

11. $y = -\frac{1}{2}\cos(x)$ **12.** $y = -3\cos x$

13. $g(x) = \cos\left(x - \frac{\pi}{2}\right) + 3$ **14.** $f(x) = \cos(3x)$

15. $h(x) = -\sin(3x) + 2$ **16.** $k(x) = \frac{1}{3}\sin\left(x + \frac{\pi}{4}\right)$

17. $y = \frac{1}{2}\cos\left(\frac{1}{2} - \pi\right) - 1$ **18.** $y = 3\sin(2x + \pi)$

4.4   SINUSOIDAL FUNCTIONS

Section 3.4 introduced $f(t)$, your height above the ground while riding a ferris wheel. The graph of f looks like a transformation of $y = \sin\theta$. Transformations of the sine and cosine are called *sinusoidal* functions, and can be expressed in the form

$$y = A\sin(B(t - h)) + k \qquad \text{and} \qquad y = A\cos(B(t - h)) + k,$$

where A, B, h, and k are constants. Their graphs resemble the graphs of sine and cosine, but may also be shifted, flipped, or stretched. These transformations may change the period, amplitude, and midline of the function as well as its value at $t = 0$.

From Section 6.4 we know the following:

> The functions of $y = A\sin t$ and $y = A\cos t$ have **amplitude** $|A|$. If A is negative, the graph is reflected across the t-axis.
>
> The **midline** of the functions $y = \sin t + k$ and $y = \cos t + k$ is the horizontal line $y = k$.

Period

Next, we consider the effect of the constant B. We usually have $B > 0$.

Example 1   Graph $y = \sin t$ and $y = \sin 2t$ for $0 \le t \le 2\pi$. Describe any similarities and differences. What are their periods?

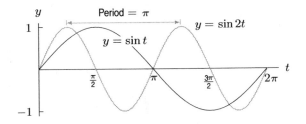

Figure 4.47 The functions $y = \sin t$ and $y = \sin 2t$ have different periods

Solution   The graphs are in Figure 4.47. The two functions have the same amplitude and midline, but their periods are different. The period of $y = \sin t$ is 2π, but the period of $y = \sin 2t$ is π. This is because the factor of 2 causes a horizontal compression, squeezing the graph twice as close to the y-axis.

If $B > 0$ the function $y = \sin(Bt)$ resembles the function $y = \sin t$ except that it is stretched or compressed horizontally. The constant B determines how many cycles the function completes on an interval of length 2π. For example, we see from Figure 4.47 that the function $y = \sin 2t$ completes two cycles on the interval $0 \leq t \leq 2\pi$. The constant B is called the *angular frequency* of the function.

Since, for $B > 0$, the graph of $y = \sin(Bt)$ completes B cycles on the interval $0 \leq t \leq 2\pi$, each cycle has length $2\pi/B$. The period is thus $2\pi/B$. In general, for B of any sign, we have:

The functions of $y = \sin(Bt)$ and $y = \cos(Bt)$ have **period** $P = 2\pi/|B|$.

Example 2   Find possible formulas for the functions f and g shown in Figures 4.48 and 4.49.

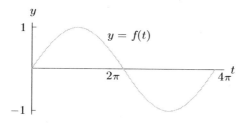

Figure 4.48 This function has period 4π

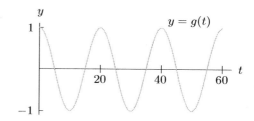

Figure 4.49 This function has period 20

Solution   The graph of f resembles the graph of $y = \sin t$ except that its period is $P = 4\pi$. Using $P = 2\pi/B$ gives

$$4\pi = \frac{2\pi}{B} \qquad \text{so} \qquad B = \frac{1}{2}.$$

Thus, $f(t) = \sin\left(\frac{1}{2}t\right)$.

The function g resembles the function $y = \cos t$ except that its period is $P = 20$. This gives

$$20 = \frac{2\pi}{B} \qquad \text{so} \qquad B = \frac{\pi}{10}.$$

Thus, $g(t) = \cos\left(\frac{\pi}{10}t\right)$.

Example 3   Household electrical power in the US is provided in the form of alternating current. Typically the voltage cycles smoothly between $+155.6$ volts and -155.6 volts 60 times per second.[2] Use a cosine function to model the alternating voltage.

---

[2]A voltage cycling between $+155.6$ volts and -155.6 volts has an average magnitude, over time, of 110 volts.

Solution   If V is the voltage at time, t, in seconds, then V begins at $+155.6$ volts, drops to -155.6 volts, and then climbs back to $+155.6$ volts, repeating this process 60 times per second. We use a cosine with amplitude $A = 155.6$. Since the function alternates 60 times in one second, the period is $1/60$ of a second. We know that $P = 2\pi/B = 1/60$, so $B = 120\pi$. We have $V = 155.6 \cos{(120\pi t)}$.

Example 4   Describe in words the function $y = 300 \cos{(0.2\pi t)} + 600$ and sketch its graph.

Solution   This function resembles $y = \cos t$ except that it has an amplitude of 300, a midline of $y = 600$, and a period of $P = 2\pi/(0.2\pi) = 10$. See Figure 4.50.

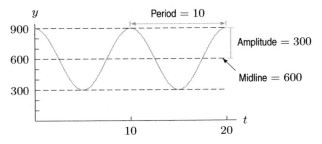

Figure 4.50 The function $y = 300 \cos{(0.2\pi t)} + 600$

Horizontal Shift

Figure 4.51 shows the graphs of two trigonometric functions, f and g, with period $P = 12$. The graph of f resembles a sine function, so a possible formula for f is $f(t) = \sin Bt$. Since the period of f is 12, we have $12 = 2\pi/B$, so $B = 2\pi/12$, so $f(t) = \sin{(\pi t/6)}$.

The graph of g looks like the graph of f shifted to the right by 2 units. Thus a possible formula for g is

$$g(t) = f(t - 2),$$

or

$$g(t) = \sin\left(\frac{\pi}{6}(t - 2)\right).$$

Notice that we can also write the formula for $g(t)$ as

$$g(t) = \sin\left(\frac{\pi}{6}t - \frac{\pi}{3}\right),$$

but $\pi/3$ is *not* the horizontal shift in the graph! To pick out the horizontal shift from the formula, we must write the formula in factored form, that is, as $\sin B(t - h)$.

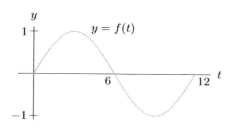
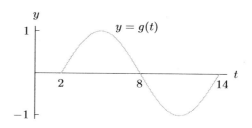

Figure 4.51 The graphs of two trigonometric functions f and g, related by a horizontal shift

---

The graphs of $y = \sin(B(t - h))$ and $y = \cos(B(t - h))$ are the graphs of $y = \sin Bt$ and $y = \cos Bt$ **shifted horizontally** by h units.

Example 5   Describe in words the graph of the function $g(t) = \cos(3t - \pi/4)$.

Solution   Write the formula for g in the form $\cos(B(t - h))$ by factoring 3 out from the expression $3t - \pi/4$ to get $g(t) = \cos(3(t - \pi/12))$. The period of g is $2\pi/3$ and the graph is the graph of $f = \cos 3t$ shifted $\pi/12$ units to the right, as shown in Figure 4.52.

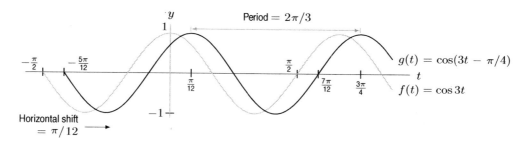

Figure 4.52 The graphs of $g(t) = \cos\left(3t - \frac{\pi}{4}\right)$ and $f(t) = \cos 3t$

Summary of Transformations

The parameters A, B, h, and k determine the graph of a transformed sine or cosine function.

For the **sinusoidal** functions
$$y = A \sin(B(t - h)) + k \qquad \text{and} \qquad y = A \cos(B(t - h)) + k,$$

- $|A|$ is the amplitude
- h is the horizontal shift
- $|B|$ is the angular frequency; that is, the number of cycles completed in $0 \leq t \leq 2\pi$.
- $2\pi/|B|$ is the period
- $y = k$ is the midline

Example 6 The temperature, T, in °C, of the surface water in a pond varies according to the graph in Figure 4.53. If t is the number of hours since sunrise at 6 am, find a possible formula for $T = f(t)$.

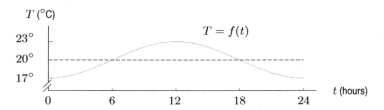

Figure 4.53 Surface water temperature of a pond since sunrise

Solution The graph of $T = f(t)$ resembles a cosine function with amplitude $|A| = 3$, period $= 24$ and midline $k = 20$. Compared to $y = \cos t$, there is no horizontal shift, but the graph has been reflected across the midline, so A is negative, $A = -3$. We have

$$24 = \frac{2\pi}{B} \qquad \text{so} \qquad B = \frac{2\pi}{24} = \frac{\pi}{12}.$$

So a possible formula for f is

$$T = f(t) = -3\cos\left(\frac{\pi}{12}t\right) + 20.$$

Phase Shift

In Example 5, we factored $(3t - \pi/4)$ to write the function as $g(t) = \cos(3(t - \pi/12))$. This allowed us to recognize the horizontal shift, $\pi/12$. However, in most physical applications, the quantity $\pi/4$, known as the *phase shift*, is more important than the horizontal shift. The phase shift enables us to calculate the fraction of a full period that the curve has been shifted. For instance, in Example 5, the wave has been shifted

$$\frac{\text{Phase shift}}{2\pi} = \frac{\pi/4}{2\pi} = \frac{1}{8} \text{ of a full period,}$$

and the graph of g in Figure 4.54 is the graph of $f(t) = \cos 3t$ shifted $1/8$ of its period to the right.

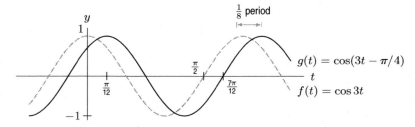

Figure 4.54 The graph of $g(t) = \cos\left(3t - \frac{\pi}{4}\right)$ has phase shift $\frac{\pi}{4}$ relative to $f(t) = \cos 3t$

Phase shift is significant because in many applications, such as optical interference, we want to know if two waves reinforce or cancel each other. For two waves of the same period, a phase shift of 0 or 2π tells us that the two waves reinforce each other; a phase shift of π tells us that the two waves cancel. Thus, the phase shift tells us the relative positions of two waves of the same period.[3]

Using the Transformed Sine and Cosine Functions

Sinusoidal functions are used to model oscillating quantities. Starting with $y = A \sin(B(t - h)) + k$ or $y = A \cos(B(t - h)) + k$, we calculate values of the parameters A, B, h, k.

Example 7 A rabbit population in a national park rises and falls each year. It is at its minimum of 5000 rabbits in January. By July, as the weather warms up and food grows more abundant, the population triples in size. By the following January, the population again falls to 5000 rabbits, completing the annual cycle. Use a trigonometric function to find a possible formula for $R = f(t)$, where R is the size of the rabbit population as a function of t, the number of months since January.

Solution Notice that January is month 0, so July is month 6. The five points in Table 4.6 have been plotted in Figure 4.55 and a curve drawn in. This curve has midline $k = 10,000$, amplitude $|A| = 5000$, and period $= 12$ so $B = 2\pi/12 = \pi/6$. It resembles a cosine function reflected across its midline. Thus, a possible formula for this curve is

$$R = f(t) = -5000 \cos\left(\frac{\pi}{6}t\right) + 10,000.$$

There are other possible formulas.

Table 4.6 *Rabbit population over time*

t (month)	R
0	5000
6	15,000
12	5000
18	15,000
24	5000

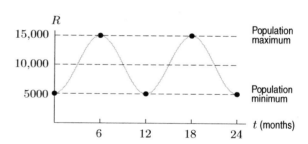

Figure 4.55 The number of rabbits, R, as a function of time in months, t, for $0 \le t \le 24$

Now let's return to the ferris wheel example in Section 3.4.

Example 8 Use the sinusoidal function $f(t) = A \sin(B(t - h)) + k$ to represent your height above ground while riding the ferris wheel.

Solution The diameter of the ferris wheel is 450 feet, so the midline is $k = 225$ and the amplitude, A, is also 225. The period of the ferris wheel is 30 minutes, so

$$B = \frac{2\pi}{30} = \frac{\pi}{15}.$$

[3]The phase shift which tells us that two waves cancel is independent of their period. The horizontal shift that gives the same information is not independent of period.

Figure 4.56 shows a sine graph shifted 7.5 minutes to the right because we reach $y = 225$ (the 3 o'clock position) when $t = 7.5$. Thus, the horizontal shift is $h = 7.5$, so

$$f(t) = 225 \sin\left(\frac{\pi}{15}(t - 7.5)\right) + 225.$$

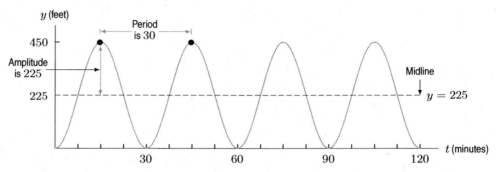

Figure 4.56 Graph of the ferris wheel height function $f(t) = 225 \sin\left(\frac{\pi}{15}(t - 7.5)\right) + 225$

This formula can be checked at some particular values of t. For example, when $t = 0$, we have the correct starting height:

$$f(0) = 225 + 225 \sin\left(\frac{\pi}{15}(0 - 7.5)\right) = 225 + 225 \sin\left(-\frac{\pi}{2}\right) = 225 - 225 = 0.$$

There are other possible formulas for the function graphed in Figure 4.56. For example, we could have used a cosine reflected about its midline, as in Example 7. (See Problem 28.)

Exercises and Problems for Section 4.4

Exercises

In Exercises 1–4, state the period, amplitude, and midline.

1. $y = 7 \sin(4(t + 7)) - 8$

2. $y = 6 \sin(t + 4)$

3. $y = \pi \cos(2t + 4) - 1$

4. $2y = \cos(8(t - 6)) + 2$

In Exercises 5–6, what are the horizontal and phase shifts?

5. $y = 2 \cos(3t + 4) - 5$

6. $y = -4 \cos(7t + 13) - 5$

7. Let $f(x) = \sin(2\pi x)$ and $g(x) = \cos(2\pi x)$. State the periods, amplitudes, and midlines of f and g.

Without a calculator, graph one period of the functions in Exercises 8–11.

8. $y = \sin\left(\frac{1}{2}t\right)$

9. $y = 4 \cos\left(t + \frac{\pi}{4}\right)$

10. $y = 5 - \sin t$

11. $y = \cos(2t) + 4$

12. Which of the following functions are periodic? Justify your answers. State the periods of those that are periodic.

   (a) $y = \sin(-t)$ **(b)** $y = 4 \cos(\pi t)$
   (c) $y = \sin(t) + t$ **(d)** $y = \sin(t/2) + 1$

In Exercises 13–20, find formulas for the trigonometric functions.

13.

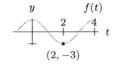

14.

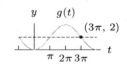

15.

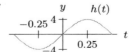

16.

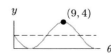

17.

18.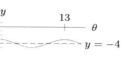

19.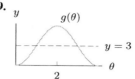

20.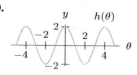

Problems B

21. Figure 4.57 shows $y = \sin x$ and $y = \sin 2x$. Which graph is $y = \sin x$? Identify the points a to e.

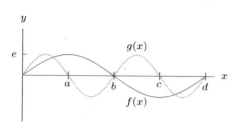

Figure 4.57

22. Describe in words how you can obtain the graph of $y = \cos(5t + \frac{\pi}{4})$ from the graph of $y = \cos(5t)$.

23. A person's blood pressure, P, (in millimeters of mercury, abbreviated mm Hg) is given, for time, t, in seconds, by

$$P = 100 - 20\cos\left(\frac{8\pi}{3}t\right),$$

Graph this function. State the period and amplitude and explain the practical significance of these quantities.

In Problems 24–25, find a formula, using the sine function, for your height above ground after t minutes on the ferris wheel, Graph the function to check that it is correct.

24. A ferris wheel is 35 meters in diameter and boarded at ground level. The wheel completes one full revolution every 5 minutes. At $t = 0$ you are in the three o'clock position and ascending.

25. A ferris wheel is 20 meters in diameter and boarded in the six o'clock position from a platform that is 4 meters above the ground. The wheel completes one full revolution every 2 minutes. At $t = 0$ you are in the twelve o'clock position.

The graphs in Problems 26–27 show your height h meters above ground after t minutes on various ferris wheels. Using the sine function, find a formula for h as a function of t.

26.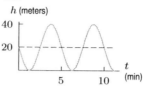

27.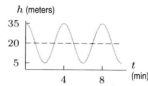

28. Find formula of the form $y = A\cos(B(t - h)) + k$ for the graph in Figure 4.56.

29. The London ferris wheel has diameter 450 feet and one complete revolution takes 30 minutes.

(a) Find the rate (in degrees per minute) that the London ferris wheel is rotating.

(b) Let t, the time in minutes, be 0 when you are in the 6 o'clock position. Write θ, measured from the 3 o'clock position, as a function of t.

(c) Find a formula for the ferris wheel function, $h = f(t)$, giving your height in feet above the ground.

(d) Graph $h = f(t)$. What are the period, midline, and amplitude?

30. The following formulas give animal populations as functions of time, t, in years. Describe the growth of each population in words.

(a) $P = 1500 + 200t$ (b) $P = 2700 - 80t$
(c) $P = 1800(1.03)^t$ (d) $P = 800e^{-0.04t}$
(e) $P = 230\sin\left(\frac{2\pi}{7}t\right) + 3800$

31. A population of animals oscillates between a low of 1300 on January 1 ($t = 0$) and a high of 2200 on July 1 ($t = 6$).

(a) Find a formula for the population, P, in terms of the time, t, in months.

(b) Interpret the amplitude, period, and midline of the function $P = f(t)$.

(c) Use a graph to estimate when $P = 1500$.

32. Find a possible formula for the trigonometric function whose values are in the following table.

x	0	.1	.2	.3	.4	.5	.6	.7	.8	.9	1
$g(x)$	2	2.6	3	3	2.6	2	1.4	1	1	1.4	2

For Problems 33–36, let $f(x) = \sin(2\pi x)$ and $g(x) = \cos(2\pi x)$. Find a possible formula in terms of f or g for the graph.

33.

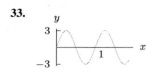

34.

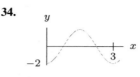

35.

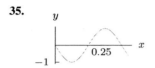

36.

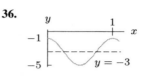

37. A company sells $S(t)$ thousand electric blankets in month t (with $t = 0$ being January), where

$$S(t) \approx 72.25 + 41.5 \sin\left(\frac{\pi t}{6} + \frac{\pi}{2}\right).$$

Graph this function over one year. Find its period and amplitude and explain their practical significance.

38. The pressure, P (in lbs/ft^2), in a pipe varies over time. Five times an hour, the pressure oscillates from a low of 90 to a high of 230 and then back to a low 90. The pressure at $t = 0$ is 90.

  (a) Graph $P = f(t)$, where t is time in minutes. Label your axes.
  (b) Find a possible formula for $P = f(t)$.
  (c) By graphing $P = f(t)$ for $0 \le t \le 2$, estimate when the pressure first equals 115 lbs/ft^2.

39. Table 4.7 gives the population, P, in thousands, of Somerville, MA, with t in years since 1920.[4]

  (a) Graph the data in Table 4.7.
  (b) Based on the data, a researcher decides the population varies in an approximately periodic way with time. Do you agree?
  (c) On your graph, sketch in a sine curve that fits your data as closely as possible. Your sketch should capture the overall trend of the data but need not pass through all the data points. [Hint: Start by choosing a midline.]
  (d) Find a formula for the curve you drew in part (c).
  (e) According to the US census, the population of Somerville in 1910 was 77, 236. How well does this agree with the value given by your formula?

Table 4.7

t	0	10	20	30	40	50	60	70
P	93	104	102	102	95	89	77	76

40. Table 4.8 shows the average daily maximum temperature in degrees Fahrenheit in Boston each month.[5]

  (a) Plot the average daily maximum temperature as a function of the number of months past January.
  (b) What are the amplitude and period of the function?
  (c) Find a trigonometric approximation of this function.
  (d) Use your formula to estimate the daily maximum temperature for October. How well does this estimate agree with the data?

Table 4.8

Month	Jan	Feb	Mar	Apr	May	Jun
Temperature	36.4	37.7	45.0	56.6	67.0	76.6
Month	Jul	Aug	Sep	Oct	Nov	Dec
Temperature	81.8	79.8	72.3	62.5	47.6	35.4

41. The website arXiv.org is used by scientists to share research papers. Figure 4.58 shows usage[6] of this site, $n = f(t)$, the number of new connections on day t, where $t = 0$ is Monday, August 5, 2002.

  (a) The graph suggests that f is approximately periodic with a period of 7 days. However, f is not exactly periodic. How can you tell?
  (b) Why might the usage of the arXiv.org website lend itself to being modeled by a periodic function?
  (c) Find a trigonometric function that gives a reasonable approximation for f. Explain what the period, amplitude, and midline of your function tell you about the usage of the arXiv.org website.

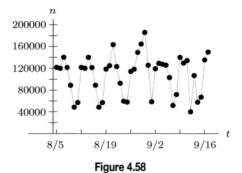

Figure 4.58

---

[4]From the US census.

[5]Statistical Abstract of the United States.

[6]Data obtained from usage statistics made available at the arXive.org site. Usage statistics for August 28, 2002, are unavailable and have been estimated.

42. Table 4.9 gives US petroleum imports, P, in quadrillion BTUs, for t in years since 1900. Plot the data on $73 \leq t \leq 92$ and find a trigonometric function $f(t)$ that approximates US petroleum imports as a function of t.

Table 4.9

t	73	74	75	76	77	78	79	80	81	82
P	14.2	14.5	14	16.5	18	17	17	16	15	14
t	83	84	85	86	87	88	89	90	91	92
P	13	15	12	14	16	17	18	17	16	16

43. An flight from La Guardia Airport in New York City to Logan Airport in Boston has to circle Boston several times before landing. Figure 4.59 shows the graph of the distance, d, of the plane from La Guardia as a function of time t. Construct a function $f(t)$ whose graph approximates this one. Do this by using different formulas on the intervals $0 \leq t \leq 1$ and $1 \leq t \leq 2$.

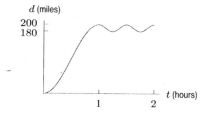

Figure 4.59

4.5 SOLVING TRIGONOMETRIC EQUATIONS

In Section 4.1, you solved the simplest of trigonometric equations by making use of the special values of trigonometric functions and using the graphs to determine the complete solution set. Now that you have studied transformations of trigonometric functions, we return to solving equations. We will start with an equation that is related to the first equation you solved in Section 4.1.

Example 1 Solve for x: $\sin(2x) = \frac{1}{2}$

Solution First, note the difference between this equation and the first example from Section 4.1, $\sin x = \frac{1}{2}$. In this equation we have a doubled argument but the output is still the same. Thinking graphically, recall that the doubled argument (*inside* change) produced a change in the period of the graph and that the new period is $\frac{2\pi}{2} = \pi$. This will change the solutions to the equation. Look at the graphs for each equation side by side.

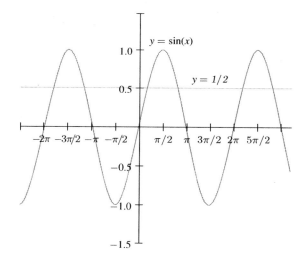

Figure 4.60 $\sin x = \dfrac{1}{2}$

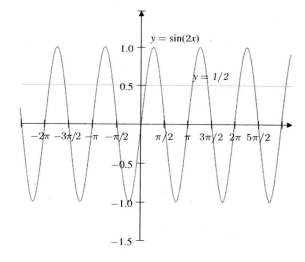

Figure 4.61 $\sin(2x) = \dfrac{1}{2}$

In Figure 4.60, notice that there are only two solutions in the interval $[0, 2\pi]$, whereas in Figure 4.61, there are four solutions in the same interval. The solutions to our new equation occur twice as frequently because of the change of period and that comes from the doubled argument.

To solve the equation, we will build on your experience with the first equation. First, we will deal the one thing that makes this equation different from the ones you have already solved - the doubled argument. Remember that one of the strategies in problem-solving is to "create a similar but simpler problem". The equation would be much easier to think about if we did not have a doubled argument, so our first step is to change the name of the argument from $2x$ to a single variable. We can choose any name at all, let's call it u. Thus we start with the assignment: let $u = 2x$.

The equation now becomes

$$\sin u = \frac{1}{2}$$

This is a similar but simpler equation that you can already solve. In fact the solutions to this equation are

$$u = \frac{\pi}{6} + 2k\pi \qquad \text{or} \qquad u = \frac{5\pi}{6} + 2k\pi$$

At this point, substitute back so that u is replaced with $2x$:

$$2x = \frac{\pi}{6} + 2k\pi \qquad \text{or} \qquad 2x = \frac{5\pi}{6} + 2k\pi$$

Now, divide each equation by 2 to solve for x:

$$\frac{2x}{2} = \frac{\frac{\pi}{6} + 2k\pi}{2} \qquad \text{or} \qquad \frac{2x}{2} = \frac{\frac{5\pi}{6} + 2k\pi}{2}$$

Simplify:

$$x = \frac{\pi}{12} + k\pi \qquad \text{or} \qquad x = \frac{5\pi}{12} + k\pi$$

Let's take a moment to verify graphically the first two positive solutions, $\frac{\pi}{12}$ and $\frac{5\pi}{12}$, graphically. In decimal form, these are approximately 0.2617993878 and 1.308996939.

In Figure 4.62, notice that the first positive solution on the graph is less than $\frac{\pi}{4}$ (or $\frac{3\pi}{12}$) and the second positive solution is greater than $\frac{\pi}{4}$. Our first two solutions are consistent with this observation.

Next, find the first intersection graphically. You should get $x = 0.26179939$, which corresponds to the decimal value of $\frac{\pi}{12}$.

Find the second intersection. You should get $x = 1.3089969$, which corresponds to the decimal value of $\frac{5\pi}{12}$.

Sometimes, it is necessary to identify the solutions within a specified interval, usually $[0, 2\pi]$. To do this, let $k = 0, 1, 2$, etc. until you reach the end of the interval. Note that $2\pi = \frac{24\pi}{12}$.

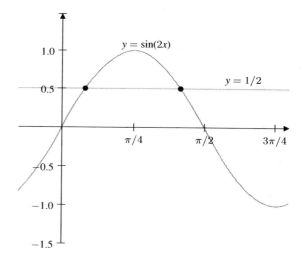

k	$x = \dfrac{\pi}{12} + k\pi$	$x = \dfrac{5\pi}{12} + k\pi$
0	$\dfrac{\pi}{12}$	$\dfrac{5\pi}{12}$
1	$\dfrac{13\pi}{12}$	$\dfrac{17\pi}{12}$
	$\dfrac{25\pi}{12}$	$\dfrac{29\pi}{12}$
2	$\dfrac{25\pi}{12} > \dfrac{24\pi}{12}$, so $\dfrac{25\pi}{12}$ is not a solution	$\dfrac{29\pi}{12} > \dfrac{24\pi}{12}$, so $\dfrac{29\pi}{12}$ is not a solution

Figure 4.62

Thus, the four solutions in the interval $[0, 2\pi]$ are $\left\{ \frac{\pi}{12}, \frac{5\pi}{12}, \frac{13\pi}{12}, \frac{17\pi}{12} \right\}$.

To verify this graphically, look at Figure 4.61 and notice that, indeed, there are exactly four solutions in the interval $[0, 2\pi]$.

Matched Problem 1

Solve the equation $\sin(3\theta) = \frac{\sqrt{3}}{2}$.

Example 2

Solve the equation $\sqrt{2} \cos\left(\frac{x}{3}\right) = -1$.

Solution

The obvious first step in solving this equation is to divide both sides by $\sqrt{2}$. This gives

$$\cos\left(\frac{x}{3}\right) = -\frac{1}{\sqrt{2}}$$

Once again, the argument of the cosine function, instead of being a single variable, is now $\frac{x}{3}$, so we will create a simpler equation by using the substitution $u = \frac{x}{3}$. We now have the simpler equation

$$\cos u = -\frac{1}{\sqrt{2}}$$

As in Section 4.1, recall that $\cos\left(\frac{\pi}{4}\right) = \frac{1}{\sqrt{2}}$, so $\frac{\pi}{4}$ will be the reference angle for the solutions to the equation but it is not itself a solution because the $\frac{1}{\sqrt{2}}$ is negative.

The graph of the cosine function is negative in the 2nd and 3rd quadrants, so the values we want are $\frac{3\pi}{4}$ and $\frac{5\pi}{4}$. So far, then, we have

$$u = \frac{3\pi}{4} + 2k\pi \qquad \text{or} \qquad u = \frac{5\pi}{4} + 2k\pi$$

Now substitute back so that u is replaced with $\frac{x}{3}$:

$$\frac{x}{3} = \frac{3\pi}{4} + 2k\pi \qquad \text{or} \qquad \frac{x}{3} = \frac{5\pi}{4} + 2k\pi$$

To solve for x, multiply both sides by 3:

$$x = \frac{9\pi}{4} + 6k\pi \qquad \text{or} \qquad x = \frac{15\pi}{4} + 6k\pi$$

Matched Problem 2   Solve the equation $2\cos\left(\frac{x}{4}\right) - \sqrt{2} = 0$.

Example 3   Solve the equation $-2\sin\left(2x + \frac{\pi}{4}\right) + 5 = 0$

Solution   Begin by subtracting 5 and dividing by -2:

$$\sin\left(2x + \frac{\pi}{4}\right) = \frac{5}{2}$$

Now stop and think. The sine function associated with the left side of the equation has been transformed horizontally but not vertically, so its amplitude is still 1. This means that the function cannot achieve a value as large as 2.5, so there cannot be any solutions to this equation.

Conclusion: The equation $-2\sin\left(2x + \frac{\pi}{4}\right) + 5 = 0$ has **no** solutions.

Answers to Matched Problems   1. $x = \frac{\pi}{9} + \frac{2k\pi}{3}$ or $x = \frac{2\pi}{9} + \frac{2k\pi}{3}$ 2. $x = \pi + 8k\pi$ or $x = 7\pi + 8k\pi$

Exercises for Section 4.5

For Problems 1–10, solve the equation, if possible. If a solution exists, give the general solution. If a solution does not exist, give a reason. You may wish to check your answers graphically.

1. $\sin(2x) = -\frac{1}{2}$

2. $\cos(3x) = 1$

3. $\cos(3\theta) = \frac{1}{2}$

4. $\sin(4x) = 0$

5. $\cos\left(\frac{1}{2}x\right) = 0$

6. $\sin\left(\frac{1}{8}\theta\right) = -\frac{\sqrt{3}}{2}$

7. $\tan(8x) = 1$

8. $-3\tan\left(\frac{x}{2}\right) = \sqrt{3}$

9. $5\sin\left(\frac{t}{3}\right) + 5 = 0$

10. $6\cos(4x) = 0$

11. $3\cos(5x) = 3$

12. $-2\sin(4t) = 0$

13. $2\sin(4x) - 6 = 0$

14. $3\cos(2x) + 5 = 0$

For Problems 15–16, find the general solution and also find the solutions on the interval $[0, 2\pi]$.

15. $\sin(3\theta) = 0$

16. $2\cos(2x) = 1$

17. The electromotive force V in volts, in an electric circuit at t seconds is given by the formula:

$$V = \cos 2\pi t$$

Find the smallest positive value of t where $0 \le t \le \frac{1}{2}$ for each of the following values of V.

(a) $V = 0$ **(b)** $V = 2.5$ **(c)** $V = 0.5$

4.6 FUNDAMENTAL IDENTITIES AND THEIR USE

- Fundamental Identities
- Evaluating Trigonometric Functions
- Converting to Equivalent Forms

Trigonometric functions have many uses. In addition to solving real-world problems, they are used in the development of mathematics—analytic geometry, calculus, and so on. Whatever their use, it is often of value to be able to change a trigonometric expression from one form to an equivalent form. This involves the use of identities. An equation in one or more variables is said to be an **identity** if the left side is equal to the right side for all replacements of the variables for which both sides are defined. The equation

$$x^2 - x - 6 = (x - 3)(x + 2)$$

is an identity, while

$$x^2 - x - 6 = 2x$$

is not. The latter is called a **conditional equation,** since it holds only for certain values of x and not for all values for which both sides are defined.

In this chapter we will develop a number of very useful classes of trigonometric identities, and you will get practice in using these identities to convert a variety of trigonometric expressions into equivalent forms. You will also get practice in using the identities directly to solve several other types of problems.

Fundamental Identities

Our first encounter with trigonometric identities was in Section 3.5, where we established several fundamental forms. We restate and name these identities in the box for convenient reference. These fundamental identities will be used very frequently in the work that follows.

FUNDAMENTAL TRIGONOMETRIC IDENTITIES

For x any real number or angle in degree or radian measure for which both side are defined:

Reciprocal identities

$$\csc x = \frac{1}{\sin x} \qquad \sec x = \frac{1}{\cos x} \qquad \cot x = \frac{1}{\tan x}$$

Quotient identities

$$\tan x = \frac{\sin x}{\cos x} \qquad \cot x = \frac{\cos x}{\sin x}$$

Identities for negatives

$$\sin(-x) = -\sin x \qquad \cos(-x) = \cos x \qquad \tan(-x) = -\tan x$$

Pythagorean identities

$$\sin^2 x + \cos^2 x = 1 \qquad \tan^2 x + 1 = \sec^2 x \qquad 1 + \cot^2 x = \csc^2 x$$

The second and third Pythagorean identities were established in Problems 77 and 78 in Exercise 3.5. An easy way to remember them is suggested in Explore/Discuss 1.

Explore/ Discuss 1

Discuss an easy way to remember the second and the third Pythagorean identities based on the first. [*Hint:* Divide through the first Pythagorean identity by appropriate expressions.]

Evaluating Trigonometric Functions

Suppose we know that $\cos x = -\frac{4}{5}$ and $\tan x = \frac{3}{4}$. How can we find the exact values of the remaining trigonometric functions of x without finding x and without using reference triangles? We use fundamental identities.

Using Fundamental Identities

Example 1

If $\cos x = -\frac{4}{5}$ and $\tan x = \frac{3}{4}$, use the fundamental identities to find the exact values of the remaining four trigonometric functions at x.

Solution

Find $\sec x$: $\sec x = \dfrac{1}{\cos x} = \dfrac{1}{-\frac{4}{5}} = -\dfrac{5}{4}$

Find $\cot x$: $\cot x = \dfrac{1}{\tan x} = \dfrac{1}{\frac{3}{4}} = \dfrac{4}{3}$

Find $\sin x$:   We can start with either a Pythagorean identity or a quotient identity. We choose the quotient identity $\tan x = (\sin x)/(\cos x)$ changed to the form

$$\sin x = (\cos x)(\tan x) = \left(-\frac{4}{5}\right)\left(\frac{3}{4}\right) = -\frac{3}{5}$$

Find $\csc x$: $\csc x = \dfrac{1}{\sin x} = \dfrac{1}{-\frac{3}{5}} = -\dfrac{5}{3}$

Matched Problem 1

If $\sin x = -\frac{4}{5}$ and $\cot x = -\frac{3}{4}$, use the fundamental identities to find the exact values of the remaining four trigonometric functions at x.

Using Fundamental Identities

Example 2

Use the fundamental identities to find the exact values of the remaining trigonometric functions of x, given

$$\cos x = \frac{-4}{\sqrt{17}} \qquad \text{and} \qquad \tan x < 0$$

Solution

Find $\sin x$:   We start with the Pythagorean identity

$$\sin^2 x + \cos^2 x = 1$$

and solve for $\sin x$:

$$\sin x = \pm\sqrt{1 - \cos^2 x}$$

Since both cos x and tan x are negative, x is associated with the second quadrant, where sin x is positive; hence,

$$\sin x = \sqrt{1 - \cos^2 x}$$

$$= \sqrt{1 - \left(\frac{-4}{\sqrt{17}}\right)^2}$$

$$= \sqrt{\frac{1}{17}} = \frac{1}{\sqrt{17}} \quad ^*$$

Find sec x: $\sec x = \dfrac{1}{\cos x} = \dfrac{1}{-4/\sqrt{17}} = -\dfrac{\sqrt{17}}{4}$

Find csc x: $\csc x = \dfrac{1}{\sin x} = \dfrac{1}{1/\sqrt{17}} = \sqrt{17}$

Find tan x: $\tan x = \dfrac{\sin x}{\cos x} = \dfrac{1/\sqrt{17}}{-4/\sqrt{17}} = -\dfrac{1}{4}$

Find cot x: $\cot x = \dfrac{1}{\tan x} = \dfrac{1}{-\frac{1}{4}} = -4$

Matched Problem 2   Use the fundamental identities to find the exact values of the remaining trigonometric functions of x, given:

$$\tan x = -\frac{\sqrt{21}}{2} \qquad \text{and} \qquad \cos x > 0$$

Converting to Equivalent Forms

One of the most important and frequent uses of the fundamental identities is the conversion of trigonometric forms into equivalent simpler or more useful forms. A couple of examples will illustrate the process.

Simplifying Trigonometric Expressions

Example 3   Use fundamental identities and appropriate algebraic operations to simplify the following expression:

$$\frac{1}{\cos^2 \alpha} - 1$$

---

*An equivalent answer is $1/\sqrt{17} = \sqrt{17}/(\sqrt{17}\sqrt{17}) = \sqrt{17}/17$, a form in which we have rationalized (eliminated radicals in) the denominator. Whether we rationalize the denominator or not depends entirely on what we want to do with the answer—sometimes an unrationalized form is more useful than a rationalized form. For the remainder of this book, you should leave answers to matched problems and exercises unrationalized, unless directed otherwise.

Solution   We start by forming a single fraction:

$$\frac{1}{\cos^2 \alpha} - 1 = \frac{1 - \cos^2 \alpha}{\cos^2 \alpha} \qquad \text{Algebra}$$

$$= \frac{\sin^2 \alpha}{\cos^2 \alpha} \qquad \text{Pythagorean identity}$$

$$= \left(\frac{\sin \alpha}{\cos \alpha}\right)^2 \qquad \text{Algebra}$$

$$= \tan^2 \alpha \qquad \text{Quotient identity}$$

Key Algebraic Steps:

$$\frac{1}{b^2} - 1 = \frac{1}{b^2} - \frac{b^2}{b^2} = \frac{1 - b^2}{b^2} \quad \text{and} \quad \frac{a^2}{b^2} = \left(\frac{a}{b}\right)^2$$

Matched Problem 3   Use fundamental identities and appropriate algebraic operations to simplify the following expression:

$$\frac{\sin^2 \theta}{\cos^2 \theta} + 1$$

Converting a Trigonometric Expression to an Equivalent Form

Example 4   Using fundamental identities, write the following expression in terms of sines and cosines, and then simplify:

$$\frac{\tan x - \cot x}{\tan x + \cot x}$$

Write the final answer in terms of the cosine function.

Solution

$$\frac{\tan x - \cot x}{\tan x + \cot x} = \frac{\dfrac{\sin x}{\cos x} - \dfrac{\cos x}{\sin x}}{\dfrac{\sin x}{\cos x} + \dfrac{\cos x}{\sin x}} \qquad \begin{array}{l}\text{Change to sines}\\\text{and cosines.}\end{array}$$

$$= \frac{(\sin x \cos x)\left(\dfrac{\sin x}{\cos x} - \dfrac{\cos x}{\sin x}\right)}{(\sin x \cos x)\left(\dfrac{\sin x}{\cos x} + \dfrac{\cos x}{\sin x}\right)} \qquad \begin{array}{l}\text{Multiply numerator}\\\text{and denominator by}\\\text{the least common}\\\text{denominator of all}\\\text{internal fractions.}\end{array}$$

$$= \frac{\sin^2 x - \cos^2 x}{\sin^2 x + \cos^2 x} \qquad \text{Algebra}$$

$$= \frac{1 - \cos^2 x - \cos^2 x}{1} \qquad \begin{array}{l}\text{Pythagorean}\\\text{identities}\end{array}$$

$$= 1 - 2\cos^2 x \qquad \text{Algebra}$$

Key Algebraic Steps:

$$\frac{\dfrac{a}{b} - \dfrac{b}{a}}{\dfrac{a}{b} + \dfrac{b}{a}} = \frac{ab\left(\dfrac{a}{b} - \dfrac{b}{a}\right)}{ab\left(\dfrac{a}{b} + \dfrac{b}{a}\right)} = \frac{a^2 - b^2}{a^2 + b^2}$$

Matched Problem 4

Using fundamental identities, write the following expression in terms of sines and cosines, and then simplify:

$$1 + \frac{\tan z}{\cot z}$$

Answers to Matched Problems

1. $\csc x = -\frac{5}{4}$, $\tan x = -\frac{4}{3}$, $\cos x = \frac{3}{5}$, $\sec x = \frac{5}{3}$
2. $\cot x = -2/\sqrt{21}$, $\sec x = \frac{5}{2}$, $\cos x = \frac{2}{5}$, $\sin x = -\sqrt{21}/5$, $\csc x = -5/\sqrt{21}$
3. $\sec^2 \theta$ 4. $\sec^2 z$

Exercises for Section 4.6

1. List the reciprocal identities and identities for negatives without looking at the text.

2. List the quotient identities and Pythagorean identities without looking at the text.

3. One of the following equations is an identity and the other is a conditional equation. Identify each, and explain the difference between the two.

   (1) $3(2x - 3) = 3(3 - 2x)$

   (2) $3(2x - 3) = 6x - 9$

4. One of the following equations is an identity and the other is a conditional equation. Identify each, and explain the difference between the two.

   (1) $\sin x + \cos x = 1$

   (2) $\sin^2 x = 1 - \cos^2 x$

In Problems 5–10, use the fundamental identities to find the exact values of the remaining trigonometric functions of x, given the following:

5. $\sin x = 2/\sqrt{5}$ and $\cos x = 1/\sqrt{5}$

6. $\sin x = \sqrt{5}/3$ and $\tan x = \sqrt{5}/2$

7. $\cos x = 1/\sqrt{10}$ and $\csc x = -\sqrt{10}/3$

8. $\cos x = \sqrt{7}/4$ and $\cot x = -\sqrt{7}/3$

9. $\tan x = 1/\sqrt{15}$ and $\sec x = -4/\sqrt{15}$

10. $\cot x = 2/\sqrt{21}$ and $\csc x = 5/\sqrt{21}$

In Problems 11–22, simplify each expression using the fundamental identities.

11. $\tan u \cot u$

12. $\sec x \cos x$

13. $\tan x \csc x$

14. $\sec \theta \cot \theta$

15. $\dfrac{\sec^2 x - 1}{\tan x}$

16. $\dfrac{\csc^2 v - 1}{\cot v}$

17. $\dfrac{\sin^2 \theta}{\cos \theta} + \cos \theta$

18. $\dfrac{1}{\csc^2 x} + \dfrac{1}{\sec^2 x}$

19. $\dfrac{1}{\sin^2 \beta} - 1$

20. $\dfrac{1 - \sin^2 u}{\cos u}$

21. $\dfrac{(1 - \cos x)^2 + \sin^2 x}{1 - \cos x}$

22. $\dfrac{\cos^2 x + (\sin x + 1)^2}{\sin x + 1}$

23. If an equation has an infinite number of solutions, is it an identity? Explain.

24. Does an identity have an infinite number of solutions? Explain.

In Problems 25–30, use the fundamental identities to find the exact values of the remaining trigonometric functions of x, given the following:

25. $\sin x = 2/5$ and $\cos x < 0$

26. $\cos x = 3/4$ and $\tan x < 0$

27. $\tan x = -1/2$ and $\sin x > 0$

28. $\cot x = -3/2$ and $\csc x > 0$

29. $\sec x = 4$ and $\cot x > 0$

30. $\csc x = -3$ and $\sec x < 0$

In Problems 31 and 32, is it possible to use the given information to find the exact values of the remaining trigonometric functions? Explain.

31. $\sin x = 1/3$ and $\csc x > 0$

32. $\tan x = 2$ and $\cot x > 0$

33. For the following graphing calculator displays, find the value of the final expression without finding x or using a calculator:

(a)   **(b)**

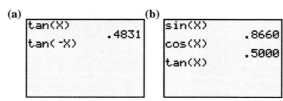

34. For the following graphing calculator displays, find the value of the final expression without finding x or using a calculator:

(a)   **(b)**

Using fundamental identities, write the expressions in Problems 35–44 in terms of sines and cosines, and then simplify.

35. $\csc(-y)\cos(-y)$

36. $\sin(-\alpha)\sec(-\alpha)$

37. $\cot x \cos x + \sin x$

38. $\cos u + \sin u \tan u$

39. $\dfrac{\cot(-\theta)}{\csc \theta} + \cos \theta$

40. $\sin y - \dfrac{\tan(-y)}{\sec y}$

41. $\dfrac{\cot x}{\tan x} + 1$

42. $\dfrac{1 + \cot^2 y}{\cot^2 y}$

43. $\sec w \csc w - \sec w \sin w$

44. $\csc \theta \sec \theta - \csc \theta \cos \theta$

45. If $\sin x = \frac{2}{5}$, find:

  (a) $\sin^2(x/2) + \cos^2(x/2)$ **(b)** $\csc^2(2x) - \cot^2(2x)$

46. If $\cos x = \frac{3}{7}$, find:

  (a) $\sin^2(2x) + \cos^2(2x)$ **(b)** $\sec^2(x/2) - \tan^2(x/2)$

Each of the following is an identity in certain quadrants. Indicate which quadrants.

47. $\sqrt{1 - \cos^2 x} = \sin x$ **48.** $\sqrt{1 - \sin^2 x} = \cos x$

49. $\sqrt{1 - \sin^2 x} = -\cos x$ **50.** $\sqrt{1 - \cos^2 x} = -\sin x$

51. $\sqrt{1 - \sin^2 x} = |\cos x|$ **52.** $\sqrt{1 - \cos^2 x} = |\sin x|$

53. $\dfrac{\sin x}{\sqrt{1 - \sin^2 x}} = \tan x$ **54.** $\dfrac{\sin x}{\sqrt{1 - \sin^2 x}} = -\tan x$

Precalculus: Trigonometric Substitution In calculus, problems are frequently encountered that involve radicals of the forms $\sqrt{a^2 - u^2}$ and $\sqrt{a^2 + u^2}$. It is very useful to be able to make trigonometric substitutions and use fundamental identities to transform these expressions into nonradical forms. Problems 55–58 involve such transformations. (Recall from algebra that $\sqrt{N^2} = N$ if $N \geq 0$ and $\sqrt{N^2} = -N$ if $N < 0$.)

55. In the expression $\sqrt{a^2 - u^2}, a > 0$, let $u = a \sin x$, $-\pi/2 < x < \pi/2$. After using an appropriate fundamental identity, write the given expression in a final form free of radicals.

56. In the expression $\sqrt{a^2 - u^2}, a > 0$, let $u = a \cos x$, $0 < x < \pi$. After using an appropriate fundamental identity, write the given expression in a final form free of radicals.

57. In the expression $\sqrt{a^2 + u^2}, a > 0$, let $u = a \tan x$, $0 < x < \pi/2$. After using an appropriate fundamental identity, write the given expression in a final form free of radicals.

58. In the expression $\sqrt{a^2 + u^2}, a > 0$, let $u = a \cot x$, $0 < x < \pi/2$. After using an appropriate fundamental identity, write the given expression in a final form free of radicals.

Precalculus: Parametric Equations Suppose we are given the parametric equations of a curve,

$$\begin{cases} x = \cos t \\ y = \sin t \end{cases} \qquad 0 \leq t \leq 2\pi$$

[The parameter t is assigned values and the corresponding points $(\cos t, \sin t)$ are plotted in a rectangular coordinate system.] These parametric equations can be transformed into a standard rectangular form free of the parameter t by use of the fundamental identities as follows:

$$x^2 + y^2 = \cos^2 t + \sin^2 t = 1$$

Thus,
$$x^2 + y^2 = 1$$
is the nonparametric equation for the curve. The latter is the equation of a circle with radius 1 and center at the origin. Refer to this discussion for Problems 59 and 60.

59. (a) Transform the parametric equations (by suitable use of a fundamental identity) into nonparametric form.

$$\begin{cases} x = 5\cos t \\ y = 2\sin t \end{cases} \quad 0 \le t \le 2\pi$$

Hint: First write the parametric equations in the following form, then square and add:

$$\begin{cases} \dfrac{x}{5} = \cos t \\ \dfrac{y}{2} = \sin t \end{cases} \quad 0 \le t \le 2\pi$$

(b) Graph the parametric equations from part (a) in a graphing utility. Observe that the graph is an ellipse that is wider than it is high.

60. (a) Transform the parametric equations (by suitable use of a fundamental identity) into nonparametric form.

$$\begin{cases} x = 3\cos t \\ y = 4\sin t \end{cases} \quad 0 \le t \le 2\pi$$

(b) Graph the parametric equations from part (a) in a graphing utility. Observe that the graph is an ellipse that is higher than it is wide.

4.7 USING IDENTITIES TO REWRITE EXPRESSIONS

Conditional Equations and Identities

Remember that the definition of an equation tells us that an equation is a statement that says two algebraic equations are equal. However, does "equal" mean "all the time" or "some of the time"?

Examine these two equations

1. $4(x - 3) = 0$ 2. $4(x - 3) = 4x - 12$

Although the left side of each equation is the same, these two equations are very different. Notice that Equation 1 is an equation in which the left side is **not** equal to the right side *all the time*. It is an equation that is true only *some of the time*; it can be solved for x and there is just one solution, $x = 3$.

Equation 1 is an example of a *conditional equation* – an equation that is true for some value(s) of the variable but not true for others.

Equation 2, on the other hand, is an equation in which the left side is equal to the right side *all the time*. In fact, because this equation is true all the time, it is an example of an important property – the distributive property. An equation that is true for all values of x is called an *identity* and if we have an identity the left and right hand sides are (under certain circumstances) interchangeable.

> **Definition**
> An *identity* is an equation that is true for all values of the variable for which both sides are defined.

Example 1   Verify that $2(x - 3)^2 - 14 = 2x^2 - 12x + 4$ is an identity by:

(a) Constructing a table to show that both sides produce the same value for the same x. This is called *numerical evidence*.

(b) Graphing the left and right sides to show that the graphs are the same. This is called *graphical evidence*.

(c) Expanding and simplifying the left side to show that the expressions are the same. This is called verifying (or proving) the identity algebraically.

Solution
(a) First, use your calculator to make a table with $Y_1 = 2(x - 3)^2 - 14$ and $Y_2 = 2x^2 - 12x + 4$. Set the TBLSTART $= -10$ and Δ TBL $= 1$.

x	$Y_1 = 2(x - 3)^2 - 14$	$Y_2 = 2x^2 - 12x + 4$
-10	324	324
-9	274	274
-8	228	228
-7	186	186
-6	148	148
-5	114	114
-4	84	84
-3	58	58
-2	36	36
-1	18	18
0	4	4

x	$Y_1 = 2(x - 3)^2 - 14$	$Y_2 = 2x^2 - 12x + 4$
1	-6	-6
2	-12	-12
3	-14	-14
4	-12	-12
5	-6	-6
6	4	4
7	18	18
8	36	36
9	58	58
10	84	84
11	114	114

Observation: The tables produced by the two functions are the same. This *suggests*, but doesn't prove, that the equation is an identity.

(b) Next, create a graph for the function corresponding to each side. Use the window Xmin $= -5$, Xmax $= 10$, Ymin $= -20$, Ymax $= 20$. Here are the two graphs:

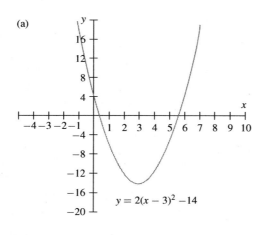
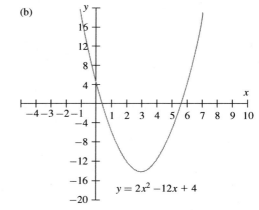

Figure 4.63

Observation: Examining Figures 4.63(a) and 4.63(b), the graphs of the two functions appear to be the same. This also suggests, but does not prove, that the equation is an identity.

Conclusion: The tables and the graphs provide numerical and graphical *evidence* that the equation is an identity.

(c) Now verify the identity algebraically by expanding and simplifying the left side:

$$2(x - 3)^2 - 14 = 2(x^2 - 6x + 9) - 14$$
$$= 2x^2 - 12x + 18 - 14$$
$$= 2x^2 - 12x + 4$$

Final conclusion: The equation $2(x - 3)^2 - 14 = 2x^2 - 12x + 4$ is an identity.

Note that graphs and tables can sometimes be unreliable, so the only sure way to verify or prove an identity is through algebraic or other mathematical properties.

Example 2   Use graphical and numerical evidence to support the statement that $\tan x = \frac{\sin x}{\cos x}$ is an identity. Is the identity true for all values of x?

Solution   (a) Numerical evidence: Let $Y_1 = \tan x$ and $Y_2 = \sin(x)/\cos(x)$. Set the TBLSTART $= -10$ and ΔTBL $= 1$.

x	$Y_1 = \tan x$	$Y_2 = \sin(x)/\cos(x)$
-10	$-.6484$	$-.6484$
-9	$.45232$	$.45232$
-8	6.7997	6.7997
-7	$-.8714$	$-.8714$
-6	$.29101$	$.29101$
-5	3.3805	3.3805
-4	-1.158	-1.158
-3	$.14255$	$.14255$
-2	2.185	2.185
-1	-1.557	-1.557
0	0	0

x	$Y_1 = \tan x$	$Y_2 = \sin(x)/\cos(x)$
1	1.5574	1.5574
2	-2.185	-2.185
3	$-.1425$	$-.1425$
4	1.1578	1.1578
5	-3.381	-3.381
6	$-.291$	$-.291$
7	$.87145$	$.87145$
8	-6.8	-6.8
9	$-.4523$	$-.4523$
10	$.64836$	$.64836$
11	-226	-226

Observation: The tables produced by the two functions are the same. The table seems to imply that the equation is true for all values of x.

(b) Graphical evidence: Use this window: Xmin $= -7$, Xmax $= 7$, Xscl $= \pi/2$, Ymin $= -8$, Ymax $= 8$

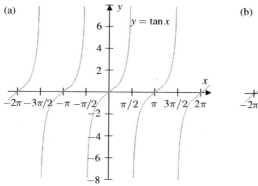
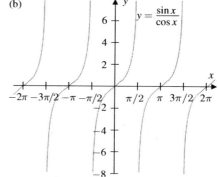

Figure 4.64

Observation: From Figures 4.64(a) and 4.64(b), the graphs of the two functions appear to be the same. The presence of vertical asymptotes at odd multiples of $\frac{\pi}{2}$ suggests that if $x = \frac{\pi}{2}$, neither function is defined. In fact, if you use $\boxed{\text{2nd}}$ CALC 1: VALUE and type $\pi/2$, the calculator is unable to return a value.

Conclusion: The tables and the graphs support the statement that $\tan x = \frac{\sin x}{\cos x}$ is an identity that is true for all values of x in the domain of each side.

Example 3   Use graphical and numerical evidence to formulate a conjecture about whether $\frac{x^2-4}{x-2} = x+2$ is an identity. If it appears to be an identity, prove it algebraically and state whether it is true for all values of x.

Solution   (a) Numerical evidence: Let $Y_1 = (x^2-4)/(x-2)$ and $Y_2 = x+2$. Set the TBLSTART $= -10$ and ΔTBL $= 1$.

x	$Y_1 = (x^2-4)/(x-2)$	$Y_2 = x+2$
-10	-8	-8
-9	-7	-7
-8	-6	-6
-7	-4	-4
-6	-5	-5
-5	-3	-3
-4	-2	-2
-3	-1	-1
-2	0	0
-1	1	1
0	2	2

x	$Y_1 = (x^2-4)/(x-2)$	$Y_2 = x+2$
1	3	3
2	ERROR	4
3	5	5
4	6	6
5	7	7
6	8	8
7	9	9
8	10	10
9	11	11
10	12	12
11	13	13

Observation: The tables produced by the two functions are the same except that when $x = 2$, Y_1 is not defined and $Y_2 = 4$. This suggests that the equation is an identity *except* when $x = 2$.

(b) Graphical evidence: Use ZOOM 6:ZStandard

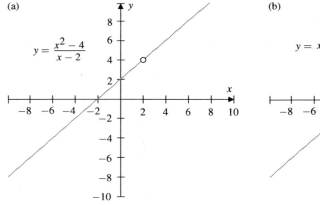
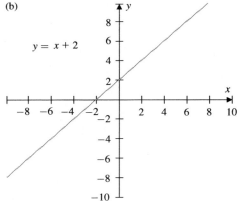

Figure 4.65

Observation: From Figures 4.65(a) and 4.65(b), the graphs of the two functions appear to be the same. Your graphing calculator will not show a hole at $x = 2$. However, if you have the graph of Y_1 and try $\boxed{\text{2nd}}$ CALC 1: VALUE and type 2, the calculator is unable to return a value. Once again, this suggests that the equation is an identity *except* when $x = 2$.

Conclusion: The tables and the graphs *suggest* that the equation is an identity for all values of x except 2.

(c) Now verify the identity algebraically by factoring and reducing the left side:

$$\frac{x^2 - 4}{x - 2} = \frac{(x + 2)(x - 2)}{(x - 2)}$$
$$= x + 2 \quad \text{if } x \neq 2.$$

Final conclusion: The equation $\frac{x^2-4}{x-2} = x + 2$ is an identity if $x \neq 2$.

VERIFYING TRIGONOMETRIC IDENTITIES

- Verifying Identities
- Testing Identities Using a Graphing Utility

We now use the experience gained in the last section to verify identities. If we start with an equation that is not a known identity, how do we proceed? A graphing utility will be helpful in this case.

Verifying Identities

We will now verify (prove) some given trigonometric identities; this process will be helpful to you if you want to convert a trigonometric expression into a form that may be more useful. Verifying a trigonometric identity is different from solving an equation. When solving an equation you use properties of equality such as adding the same quantity to each side or multiplying both sides by a nonzero quantity. These operations are not valid in the process of verifying identities because, at the start, we do not know that the left and right expressions are equal.

VERIFYING AN IDENTITY

To verify an identity, start with the expression on one side and, through a sequence of valid steps involving the use of known identities or algebraic manipulation, convert that expression into the expression on the other side.

Caution

When verifying an identity, *do not* add the same quantity to each side, multiply both sides by the same nonzero quantity, or square (or take the square root of) both sides.

The following examples illustrate some of the techniques used to establish certain identities. To become proficient in the process, it is important that you work many problems on your own.

Example 4   Verify the identity: $\csc(-x) = -\csc x$

Verification

$$\csc(-x) = \frac{1}{\sin(-x)} \quad \text{Reciprocal identity}$$

$$= \frac{1}{-\sin x} \quad \text{Identity for negatives}$$

$$= -\frac{1}{\sin x} \quad \text{Algebra}$$

$$= -\csc x \quad \text{Reciprocal identity}$$

Matched Problem 1 Verify the identity: $\sec(-x) = \sec x$

Example 5 Verify the identity: $\tan x \sin x + \cos x = \sec x$

Verification

$$\tan x \sin x + \cos x = \frac{\sin x}{\cos x} \sin x + \cos x \quad \text{Quotient identity}$$

$$= \frac{\sin^2 x + \cos^2 x}{\cos x} \quad \text{Algebra}$$

$$= \frac{1}{\cos x} \quad \text{Pythagorean identity}$$

$$= \sec x \quad \text{Reciprocal identity}$$

Key Algebraic Steps:

$$\frac{a}{b}a + b = \frac{a^2}{b} + b = \frac{a^2 + b^2}{b}$$

Matched Problem 2 Verify the identity: $\cot x \cos x + \sin x = \csc x$

To verify an identity, proceed from one side to the other, or both sides to the middle, making sure all steps are reversible. Even though there is no fixed method of verification that works for all identities, there are certain steps that help in many cases.

SOME SUGGESTIONS FOR VERIFYING IDENTITIES

Step 1 Start with the more complicated side of the identity and transform it into the simpler side.

Step 2 Try using basic or other known identities.

Step 3 Try algebraic operations such as multiplying, factoring, combining fractions, or splitting fractions.

Step 4 If other stpes fail, try expressing each function in terms of sine and cosine functions; then perform appropriate algebraic operations.

Step 5 At each step, keep the other side of the identity in mind. This often reveals what you should do in order to get there.

Example 6   Verify the identity: $\dfrac{\cot^2 x - 1}{1 + \cot^2 x} = 1 - 2\sin^2 x$

Verification

$$\dfrac{\cot^2 x - 1}{1 + \cot^2 x} = \dfrac{\dfrac{\cos^2 x}{\sin^2 x} - 1}{1 + \dfrac{\cos^2 x}{\sin^2 x}}$$
   Convert to sines and cosines.

$$= \dfrac{(\sin^2 x)\left(\dfrac{\cos^2 x}{\sin^2 x} - 1\right)}{(\sin^2 x)\left(1 + \dfrac{\cos^2 x}{\sin^2 x}\right)}$$
   Multiply numerator and denominator by $\sin^2 x$. the LCD of all secondary fractions.

$$= \dfrac{\cos^2 x - \sin^2 x}{\sin^2 x + \cos^2 x}$$
   Algebra

$$= \dfrac{1 - \sin^2 x - \sin^2 x}{1}$$
   Pythagorean identities, twice

$$= 1 - 2\sin^2 x$$
   Algebra

(See Explore–Discuss 1 for a shorter sequence of steps.)

Key Algebraic Steps:

$$\dfrac{\dfrac{b^2}{a^2} - 1}{1 + \dfrac{b^2}{a^2}} = \dfrac{a^2\left(\dfrac{b^2}{a^2} - 1\right)}{a^2\left(1 + \dfrac{b^2}{a^2}\right)} = \dfrac{b^2 - a^2}{a^2 + b^2}$$

Matched Problem 3   Verify the identity: $\dfrac{\tan^2 x - 1}{1 + \tan^2 x} = 1 - 2\cos^2 x$

Explore/ Discuss 1   Can you verify the identity in Example 6

$$\dfrac{\cot^2 x - 1}{1 + \cot^2 x} = 1 - 2\sin^2 x$$

using another sequence of steps? The following start, using Pythagorean identities, leads to a shorter verification:

$$\dfrac{\cot^2 x - 1}{1 + \cot^2 x} = \dfrac{\csc^2 x - 1 - 1}{\csc^2 x}$$

Example 7   Verify the identity:

$$\frac{1 + \cos x}{\sin x} + \frac{\sin x}{1 + \cos x} = 2 \csc x$$

Verification

$$\frac{1 + \cos x}{\sin x} + \frac{\sin x}{1 + \cos x} = \frac{(1 + \cos x)^2 + \sin^2 x}{(\sin x)(1 + \cos x)} \qquad \text{Algebra}$$

$$= \frac{1 + 2 \cos x + \cos^2 x + \sin^2 x}{(\sin x)(1 + \cos x)} \qquad \text{Algebra}$$

$$= \frac{1 + 2 \cos x + 1}{(\sin x)(1 + \cos x)} \qquad \text{Pythagorean identity}$$

$$= \frac{2 + 2 \cos x}{(\sin x)(1 + \cos x)} \qquad \text{Algebra}$$

$$= \frac{2(1 + \cos x)}{(\sin x)(1 + \cos x)} \qquad \text{Algebra}$$

$$= \frac{2}{\sin x} \qquad \text{Cancel common factor by division.}$$

$$= 2 \csc x \qquad \text{Reciprocal identity}$$

Key Algebraic Steps:

$$\frac{1 + b}{a} + \frac{a}{1 + b} = \frac{(1 + b)^2 + a^2}{a(1 + b)} = \frac{1 + 2b + b^2 + a^2}{a(1 + b)}$$

and

$$\frac{2 + 2b}{a(1 + b)} = \frac{2(1 + b)}{a(1 + b)} = \frac{2}{a}$$

Matched Problem 4   Verify the identity: $\dfrac{1 + \sin x}{\cos x} + \dfrac{\cos x}{1 + \sin x} = 2 \sec x$

Example 8   Verify the identity

$$\csc x + \cot x = \frac{\sin x}{1 - \cos x}$$

(a) Going from left to right   (b) Going from right to left

Verification   (a) Going from left to right:

$$\csc x + \cot x = \frac{1}{\sin x} + \frac{\cos x}{\sin x}$$ Convert to sines and cosines.

$$= \frac{1 + \cos x}{\sin x}$$ Algebra

$$= \frac{(\sin x)(1 + \cos x)}{\sin^2 x}$$ We need a $\sin x$ on top, so we multiply numerator and denominator by $\sin x$.

$$= \frac{(\sin x)(1 + \cos x)}{1 - \cos^2 x}$$ Pythagorean identity

$$= \frac{(\sin x)(1 + \cos x)}{(1 - \cos x)(1 + \cos x)}$$ Factor denominator.

$$= \frac{\sin x}{1 - \cos x}$$ Cancel common factor by division.

Key Algebraic Steps:

$$\frac{1}{a} + \frac{b}{a} = \frac{1 + b}{a} = \frac{a(1 + b)}{a^2} \quad \text{and} \quad \frac{a(1 + b)}{1 - b^2} = \frac{a(1 + b)}{(1 - b)(1 + b)} = \frac{a}{1 - b}$$

(b) Going from right to left:

$$\frac{\sin x}{1 - \cos x} = \frac{(\sin x)(1 + \cos x)}{(1 - \cos x)(1 + \cos x)}$$ Multiply numerator and denominator by $1 + \cos x$ so that we can take advantage of the Pythagorean identity.

$$= \frac{(\sin x)(1 + \cos x)}{1 - \cos^2 x}$$ Algebra

$$= \frac{(\sin x)(1 + \cos x)}{\sin^2 x}$$ Pythagorean identity

$$= \frac{1 + \cos x}{\sin x}$$ Cancel common factor.

$$= \frac{1}{\sin x} + \frac{\cos x}{\sin x}$$ Algebra

$$= \csc x + \cot x$$ Fundamental identities.

Key Algebraic Steps:

$$\frac{a}{1 - b} = \frac{a(1 + b)}{(1 - b)(1 + b)} = \frac{a(1 + b)}{1 - b^2} \quad \text{and} \quad \frac{a(1 + b)}{a^2} = \frac{1 + b}{a} = \frac{1}{a} + \frac{b}{a}$$

Matched Problem 5   Verify the identity

$$\sec m + \tan m = \frac{\cos m}{1 - \sin m}$$

(a) Going from left to right   (b) Going from right to left

Testing Identities Using a Graphing Utility

Given an equation, it is not always easy to tell whether it is an identity or a conditional equation. A graphing utility puts us on the right track with little effort.

Example 6   Use a graphing utility to test whether each equation is an identity. If an equation appears to be an identity, verify it. If the equation does not appear to be an identity, find a value of x for which both sides are defined but are not equal.

(a) $\dfrac{\sin x}{1 - \cos^2 x} = \sec x$ 　　　　　(b) $\dfrac{\sin x}{1 - \cos^2 x} = \csc x$

Solution   (a) Graph both sides of the equation in the same viewing window (Fig. 4.66). The graphs do not match; therefore, the equation is not an identity. The left side is not equal to the right side for $x = 1$, for example.

(b) Graph both sides of the equation in the same viewing window (Fig. 4.67). Use $\boxed{\text{TRACE}}$ and check the values of each function for different values of x. The equation appears to be an identity, which we now verify:

$$\frac{\sin x}{1 - \cos^2 x} = \frac{\sin x}{\sin^2 x} = \frac{1}{\sin x} = \csc x$$

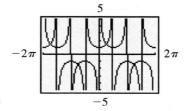

Figure 4.66

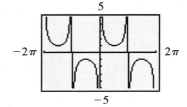

Figure 4.67

Matched Problem 6   Repeat Example 9 for the following two equations:

(a) $\tan x + 1 = (\sec x)(\sin x - \cos x)$

(b) $\tan x - 1 = (\sec x)(\sin x - \cos x)$

Answers to Matched Problems

1. $\sec(-x) = \dfrac{1}{\cos(-x)} = \dfrac{1}{\cos x} = \sec x$

2. $\cot x \cos x + \sin x = \dfrac{\cos^2 x}{\sin x} + \sin x = \dfrac{\cos^2 x + \sin^2 x}{\sin x}$

$$= \frac{1}{\sin x} = \csc x$$

3. $\dfrac{\tan^2 x - 1}{1 + \tan^2 x} = \dfrac{\dfrac{\sin^2 x}{\cos^2 x} - 1}{1 + \dfrac{\sin^2 x}{\cos^2 x}} = \dfrac{(\cos^2 x)\left(\dfrac{\sin^2 x}{\cos^2 x} - 1\right)}{(\cos^2 x)\left(1 + \dfrac{\sin^2 x}{\cos^2 x}\right)}$

$\qquad = \dfrac{\sin^2 x - \cos^2 x}{\cos^2 x + \sin^2 x} = \dfrac{1 - \cos^2 x - \cos^2 x}{1}$

$\qquad = 1 - 2\cos^2 x$

4. $\dfrac{1 + \sin x}{\cos x} + \dfrac{\cos x}{1 + \sin x} = \dfrac{(1 + \sin x)^2 + \cos^2 x}{(\cos x)(1 + \sin x)}$

$\qquad = \dfrac{1 + 2\sin x + \sin^2 x + \cos^2 x}{(\cos x)(1 + \sin x)}$

$\qquad = \dfrac{2 + 2\sin x}{(\cos x)(1 + \sin x)} = \dfrac{2}{\cos x} = 2\sec x$

5. (a) Going from left to right:

$$\sec m + \tan m = \dfrac{1}{\cos m} + \dfrac{\sin m}{\cos m} = \dfrac{1 + \sin m}{\cos m}$$

$$= \dfrac{(\cos m)(1 + \sin m)}{\cos^2 m} = \dfrac{(\cos m)(1 + \sin m)}{1 - \sin^2 m}$$

$$= \dfrac{(\cos m)(1 + \sin m)}{(1 - \sin m)(1 + \sin m)} = \dfrac{\cos m}{1 - \sin m}$$

(b) Going from right to left:

$$\dfrac{\cos m}{1 - \sin m} = \dfrac{(\cos m)(1 + \sin m)}{(1 - \sin m)(1 + \sin m)} = \dfrac{(\cos m)(1 + \sin m)}{1 - \sin^2 m}$$

$$= \dfrac{(\cos m)(1 + \sin m)}{\cos^2 m} = \dfrac{1 + \sin m}{\cos m}$$

$$= \dfrac{1}{\cos m} + \dfrac{\sin m}{\cos m} = \sec m + \tan m$$

6. (a) Not an identity; the left side is not equal to the right side for $x = 0$, for example:

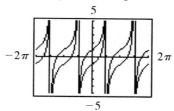

6. (b)

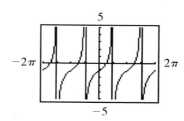

The equation appears to be an identity, which is verified as follows:

$$(\sec x)(\sin x - \cos x) = \frac{1}{\cos x}(\sin x - \cos x)$$

$$= \frac{\sin x}{\cos x} - \frac{\cos x}{\cos x}$$

$$= \tan x - 1$$

Exercises for Section 4.7

In Problems 1–26, verify each identity.

1. $\cos x \sec x = 1$

2. $\sin x \csc x = 1$

3. $\tan x \cos x = \sin x$

4. $\cot x \sin x = \cos x$

5. $\tan x = \sin x \sec x$

6. $\cot x = \cos x \csc x$

7. $\csc(-x) = -\csc x$

8. $\sec(-x) = \sec x$

9. $\dfrac{\sin \alpha}{\cos \alpha \tan \alpha} = 1$

10. $\dfrac{\cos \alpha}{\sin \alpha \cot \alpha} = 1$

11. $\dfrac{\cos \beta \sec \beta}{\tan \beta} = \cot \beta$

12. $\dfrac{\tan \beta \cot \beta}{\sin \beta} = \csc \beta$

13. $(\sec \theta)(\sin \theta + \cos \theta) = \tan \theta + 1$

14. $(\csc \theta)(\cos \theta + \sin \theta) = \cot \theta + 1$

15. $\dfrac{\cos^2 t - \sin^2 t}{\sin t \cos t} = \cot t - \tan t$

16. $\dfrac{\cos \alpha - \sin \alpha}{\sin \alpha \cos \alpha} = \csc \alpha - \sec \alpha$

17. $\dfrac{\cos \beta}{\cot \beta} + \dfrac{\sin \beta}{\tan \beta} = \sin \beta + \cos \beta$

18. $\dfrac{\tan u}{\sin u} - \dfrac{\cot u}{\cos u} = \sec u - \csc u$

19. $\sec^2 \theta - \tan^2 \theta = 1$

20. $\csc^2 \theta - \cot^2 \theta = 1$

21. $(\sin^2 x)(1 + \cot^2 x) = 1$

22. $(\cos^2 x)(\tan^2 x + 1) = 1$

23. $(\csc \alpha + 1)(\csc \alpha - 1) = \cot^2 \alpha$

24. $(\sec \beta - 1)(\sec \beta + 1) = \tan^2 \beta$

25. $\dfrac{\sin t}{\csc t} + \dfrac{\cos t}{\sec t} = 1$

26. $\dfrac{1}{\sec^2 m} + \dfrac{1}{\csc^2 m} = 1$

27. How does solving a conditional equation differ from verifying an identity (both in one variable)?

28. Is $(1 - \cos^2 x)/(\sin x) = \sin x$ an identity for all real values of x? Explain.

In Problems 29–60, verify each identity.

29. $\dfrac{1 - (\cos \theta - \sin \theta)^2}{\cos \theta} = 2 \sin \theta$

30. $\dfrac{1 - (\sin \theta - \cos \theta)^2}{\sin \theta} = 2 \cos \theta$

31. $\dfrac{\tan w + 1}{\sec w} = \sin w + \cos w$

32. $\dfrac{\cot y + 1}{\csc y} = \cos y + \sin y$

33. $\dfrac{1}{1 - \cos^2 \theta} = 1 + \cot^2 \theta$

34. $\dfrac{1}{1 - \sin^2 \theta} = 1 + \tan^2 \theta$

35. $\dfrac{\sin^2 \beta}{1 - \cos \beta} = 1 + \cos \beta$

36. $\dfrac{\cos^2 \beta}{1 + \sin \beta} = 1 - \sin \beta$

37. $\dfrac{2 - \cos^2 \theta}{\sin \theta} = \csc \theta + \sin \theta$

38. $\dfrac{2 - \sin^2 \theta}{\cos \theta} = \sec \theta + \cos \theta$

39. $\tan x + \cot x = \sec x \csc x$

40. $\dfrac{\csc x}{\cot x + \tan x} = \cot x$

41. $\dfrac{1 - \csc x}{1 + \csc x} = \dfrac{\sin x - 1}{\sin x + 1}$

42. $\dfrac{1 - \cos x}{1 + \cos x} = \dfrac{\sec x - 1}{\sec x + 1}$

43. $\csc^2 \alpha - \cos^2 \alpha - \sin^2 \alpha = \cot^2 \alpha$

44. $\sec^2 \alpha - \sin^2 \alpha - \cos^2 \alpha = \tan^2 \alpha$

45. $(\sin x + \cos x)^2 - 1 = 2 \sin x \cos x$

46. $\sec x - 2 \sin x = \dfrac{(\sin x - \cos x)^2}{\cos x}$

47. $(\sin u - \cos u)^2 + (\sin u + \cos u)^2 = 2$

48. $(\tan x - 1)^2 + (\tan x + 1)^2 = 2 \sec^2 x$

49. $\sin^4 x - \cos^4 x = 1 - 2 \cos^2 x$

50. $\sin^4 x + 2 \sin^2 x \cos^2 x + \cos^4 x = 1$

51. $\dfrac{\sin \alpha}{1 - \cos \alpha} - \dfrac{1 + \cos \alpha}{\sin \alpha} = 0$

52. $\dfrac{1 + \cos \alpha}{\sin \alpha} + \dfrac{\sin \alpha}{1 + \cos \alpha} = 2 \csc \alpha$

53. $\dfrac{\cos^2 n - 3 \cos n + 2}{\sin^2 n} = \dfrac{2 - \cos n}{1 + \cos n}$

54. $\dfrac{\sin^2 n + 4 \sin n + 3}{\cos^2 n} = \dfrac{3 + \sin n}{1 - \sin n}$

55. $\dfrac{1 - \cot^2 x}{\tan^2 x - 1} = \cot^2 x$

56. $\dfrac{\tan^2 x - 1}{1 - \cot^2 x} = \tan^2 x$

57. $\sec^2 x + \csc^2 x = \sec^2 x \csc^2 x$

58. $\tan^2 x - \sin^2 x = \tan^2 x \sin^2 x$

59. $\dfrac{1 + \sin t}{\cos t} = \dfrac{\cos t}{1 - \sin t}$

60. $\dfrac{\sin t}{1 - \cos t} = \dfrac{1 + \cos t}{\sin t}$

61. (a) Graph both sides of the following equation in the same viewing window for $-\pi \le x \le \pi$. Is the equation an identity over the interval $-\pi \le x \le \pi$? Explain.

$$\sin x = x - \frac{x^3}{3!} + \frac{x^5}{5!} - \frac{x^7}{7!}$$

(b) Extend the interval in part (a) to $-2\pi \le x \le 2\pi$. Now, does the equation appear to be an identity? What do you observe?

62. (a) Graph both sides of the following equation in the same viewing window for $-\pi \le x \le \pi$. Is the equation an identity over the interval $[-\pi, \pi]$? Explain.

$$\cos x = 1 - \frac{x^2}{2!} + \frac{x^4}{4!} - \frac{x^6}{6!} + \frac{x^8}{8!}$$

(b) Extend the interval in part (a) to $-2\pi \le x \le 2\pi$. Now, does the equation appear to be an identity? What do you observe?

In Problems 63–70, use a graphing utility to test whether each equation is an identity. If an equation appears to be an identity, verify it. If an equation does not appear to be an identity, find a value of x for which both sides are defined but are not equal.

63. $\dfrac{\cos x}{\sin (-x) \cot (-x)} = 1$

64. $\dfrac{\sin x}{\cos x \tan (-x)} = 1$

65. $\dfrac{\cos (-x)}{\sin x \cot (-x)} = 1$

66. $\dfrac{\sin (-x)}{\cos (-x) \tan (-x)} = -1$

67. $\dfrac{\cos x}{\sin x + 1} - \dfrac{\cos x}{\sin x - 1} = 2 \csc x$

68. $\dfrac{\tan x}{\sin x + 2 \tan x} = \dfrac{1}{\cos x - 2}$

69. $\dfrac{\cos x}{1 - \sin x} + \dfrac{\cos x}{1 + \sin x} = 2 \sec x$

70. $\dfrac{\tan x}{\sin x - 2 \tan x} = \dfrac{1}{\cos x - 2}$

In Problems 71–76, verify each identity.

71. $\dfrac{\sin x}{1 - \cos x} - \cot x = \csc x$

72. $\dfrac{\cos x}{1 - \sin x} - \tan x = \sec x$

73. $\dfrac{\cot \beta}{\csc \beta + 1} = \dfrac{\csc \beta - 1}{\cot \beta}$

74. $\dfrac{\tan \beta}{\sec \beta - 1} = \dfrac{\sec \beta + 1}{\tan \beta}$

75. $\dfrac{3 \cos^2 m + 5 \sin m - 5}{\cos^2 m} = \dfrac{3 \sin m - 2}{1 + \sin m}$

76. $\dfrac{2 \sin^2 z + 3 \cos z - 3}{\sin^2 z} = \dfrac{2 \cos z - 1}{1 + \cos z}$

In Problems 77 and 78, verify each identity. (The problems involve trigonometric functions with two variables. Be careful with the terms you combine and simplify.)

77. $\dfrac{\sin x \cos y + \cos x \sin y}{\cos x \cos y - \sin x \sin y} = \dfrac{\tan x + \tan y}{1 - \tan x \tan y}$

78. $\dfrac{\tan \alpha + \tan \beta}{1 - \tan \alpha \tan \beta} = \dfrac{\cot \alpha + \cot \beta}{\cot \alpha \cot \beta - 1}$

4.8 DOUBLE-ANGLE AND HALF-ANGLE IDENTITIES

- Double-Angle Identities
- Half-Angle Identities

We now develop another important set of identities called **double-angle** and **half-angle identities.** We can obtain these identities directly from the sum and difference identities. In spite of names involving the word *angle,* the new identities hold for real numbers as well.

Double-Angle Identities

If we start with the sum identity for sine,

$$\sin(x + y) = \sin x \cos y + \cos x \sin y$$

and let $y = x$, we obtain

$$\sin(x + x) = \sin x \cos x + \cos x \sin x$$

or

$$\sin 2x = 2 \sin x \cos x \tag{1}$$

Similarly, if we start with the sum identity for cosine,

$$\cos(x + y) = \cos x \cos y - \sin x \sin y$$

and let $y = x$, we obtain

$$\cos(x + x) = \cos x \cos x - \sin x \sin x$$

or

$$\cos 2x = \cos^2 x - \sin^2 x \tag{2}$$

Now, using the Pythagorean identities in the two forms

$$\cos^2 x = 1 - \sin^2 x \tag{3}$$

$$\sin^2 x = 1 - \cos^2 x \tag{4}$$

and substituting (3) into (2), we obtain

$$\cos 2x = 1 - \sin^2 x - \sin^2 x$$
$$\cos 2x = 1 - 2 \sin^2 x \tag{5}$$

Substituting (3) into (2), we obtain

$$\cos 2x = \cos^2 x - (1 - \cos^2 x)$$
$$\cos 2x = 2 \cos^2 x - 1 \tag{6}$$

A double-angle identity can be developed for the tangent function in the same way by starting with the sum identity for tangent. This is left as an exercise for you to do. We list these double-angle identities for convenient reference.

DOUBLE-ANGLE IDENTITIES

For x any real number or angle in degree or radian measure for which both sides are defined:

$$\sin 2x = 2 \sin x \cos x \qquad \cos 2x = \cos^2 x - \sin^2 x$$

$$\tan 2x = \frac{2 \tan x}{1 - \tan^2 x} \qquad\qquad = 1 - 2 \sin^2 x$$

$$= 2 \cos^2 x - 1$$

The double-angle formulas for cosine, written in the following forms, are used in calculus to transform power forms to nonpower forms:

$$\sin^2 x = \frac{1 - \cos 2x}{2} \qquad \cos^2 x = \frac{1 + \cos 2x}{2}$$

Explore/ Discuss 1

(a) Show that the following equations are **not** identities:

$$\sin 2x = 2 \sin x \qquad \cos 2x = 2 \cos x \qquad \tan 2x = 2 \tan x$$

(b) Graph $y_1 = \sin 2x$ and $y_2 = 2 \sin x$ in the same viewing window. What can you conclude? Repeat the process for the other two equations in part (a).

Example 1

Verify the identity: $\quad \sin 2x = \dfrac{2 \tan x}{1 + \tan^2 x}$

Verification

We start with the right side:

$$\frac{2 \tan x}{1 + \tan^2 x} = \frac{2 \left(\dfrac{\sin x}{\cos x} \right)}{1 + \dfrac{\sin^2 x}{\cos^2 x}} \qquad \text{Quotient identity}$$

$$= \frac{2 \sin x \cos x}{\cos^2 x + \sin^2 x} \qquad \text{Multiply numerator and denominator by } \cos^2 x.$$

$$= \frac{\sin 2x}{1} \qquad \text{Double-angle and Pythagorean identities}$$

$$= \sin 2x$$

Matched Problem 1

Verify the identity: $\quad \cos 2x = \dfrac{1 - \tan^2 x}{1 + \tan^2 x}$

Example 2   Find the exact value of $\cos 2x$ and $\tan 2x$ if $\sin x = \frac{4}{5}, \pi/2 < x < \pi$.

Solution   First draw a reference triangle in the second quadrant, and find $\cos x$ and $\tan x$ (see Fig. 4.68).

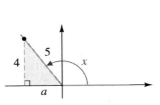

Figure 4.68

$$a = \sqrt{5^2 - 4^2} = 3$$

$$\sin x = \frac{4}{5}$$

$$\cos x = -\frac{3}{5}$$

$$\tan x = -\frac{4}{3}$$

$$\cos 2x = 1 - 2\sin^2 x$$ Use double-angle identity and the results above.

$$= 1 - 2\left(\frac{4}{5}\right)^2$$

$$= \frac{7}{25}$$

$$\tan 2x = \frac{2\tan x}{1 - \tan^2 x}$$ Use double-angle identity and the preceding results.

$$= \frac{2\left(-\frac{4}{3}\right)}{1 - \left(-\frac{4}{3}\right)^2}$$

$$= \frac{24}{7}$$

**Matched
Problem 2**   Find the exact value of $\sin 2x$ and $\cos 2x$ if $\tan x = -\frac{3}{4}, -\pi/2 < x < 0$.

Half-Angle Identities

Half-angle identities are simply double-angle identities in an alternative form. We start with the double-angle identity for cosine in the form

$$\cos 2u = 1 - 2\sin^2 u$$

and let $u = x/2$. Then

$$\cos x = 1 - 2\sin^2 \frac{x}{2}$$

Now solve for $\sin (x/2)$ to obtain a half-angle formula for the sine function:

$$2\sin^2 \frac{x}{2} = 1 - \cos x$$

$$\sin^2 \frac{x}{2} = \frac{1 - \cos x}{2}$$

$$\sin \frac{x}{2} = \pm\sqrt{\frac{1 - \cos x}{2}} \qquad (7)$$

In identity (7), the choice of the sign is determined by the quadrant in which $x/2$ lies.

Now we start with the double-angle identity for cosine in the form

$$\cos 2u = 2\cos^2 u - 1$$

and let $u = x/2$. We then obtain a half-angle formula for the cosine function:

$$\cos x = 2\cos^2 \frac{x}{2} - 1$$

$$2\cos^2 \frac{x}{2} = 1 + \cos x$$

$$\cos^2 \frac{x}{2} = \frac{1 + \cos x}{2}$$

$$\cos \frac{x}{2} = \pm\sqrt{\frac{1 + \cos x}{2}} \tag{8}$$

In identity (8), the choice of the sign is again determined by the quadrant in which $x/2$ lies.

To obtain a half-angle identity for the tangent function, we can use the quotient identity and the half-angle formulas for sine and cosine:

$$\tan \frac{x}{2} = \frac{\sin \frac{x}{2}}{\cos \frac{x}{2}} = \frac{\pm\sqrt{\dfrac{1 - \cos x}{2}}}{\pm\sqrt{\dfrac{1 + \cos x}{2}}} = \pm\sqrt{\frac{1 - \cos x}{1 + \cos x}} \tag{9}$$

where the sign is determined by the quadrant in which $x/2$ lies.

We now list all the half-angle identities for convenient reference. Two of the half-angle identities for tangent are left as Problems 27 and 28 in Exercise 4.8.

HALF-ANGLE IDENTITIES

For x any real number or angle in degree or radian measure for which both sides are defined:

$$\sin \frac{x}{2} = \pm\sqrt{\frac{1 - \cos x}{2}} \qquad \cos \frac{x}{2} = \pm\sqrt{\frac{1 + \cos x}{2}}$$

$$\tan \frac{x}{2} = \pm\sqrt{\frac{1 - \cos x}{1 + \cos x}} = \frac{\sin x}{1 + \cos x} = \frac{1 - \cos x}{\sin x}$$

where the sign is determined by the quadrant containing $x/2$.

**Explore/
Discuss 2**

(a) Show that the following equations are **not** identities:

$$\sin \frac{x}{2} = \frac{1}{2}\sin x \qquad \cos \frac{x}{2} = \frac{1}{2}\cos x \qquad \tan \frac{x}{2} = \frac{1}{2}\tan x$$

(b) Graph $y_1 = \sin(x/2)$ and $y_2 = \frac{1}{2}\sin x$ in the same viewing window. What can you conclude? Repeat the process for the other two equations in part (a).

Using a Half-Angle Identity

Example 3   Find cos 165° exactly by means of a half-angle identity.

Solution
$$\cos 165° = \cos \frac{330°}{2} = -\sqrt{\frac{1 + \cos 330°}{2}}$$

The negative square root is used since 165° is in the second quadrant and cosine is negative there. We complete the evaluation by noting that the reference triangle for 330° is a 30°–60° triangle in the fourth quadrant (see Fig. 4.69).

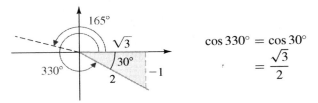

$$\cos 330° = \cos 30°$$
$$= \frac{\sqrt{3}}{2}$$

Figure 4.69

Thus,

$$\cos 165° = -\sqrt{\frac{1 + \sqrt{3}/2}{2}} = -\frac{\sqrt{2 + \sqrt{3}}}{2}$$

Matched Problem 3   Find the exact value of sin 165° using a half-angle identity.

Using Half-Angle Identities

Example 4   Find the exact value of sin $(x/2)$, cos $(x/2)$, and tan $(x/2)$ if sin $x = \frac{3}{5}$, $\pi < x < 3\pi/2$.

Solution   Draw a reference triangle in the third quadrant and find cos x (see Fig. 4.70).

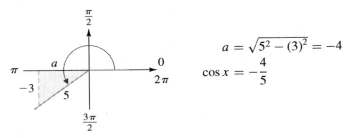

$$a = \sqrt{5^2 - (3)^2} = -4$$
$$\cos x = -\frac{4}{5}$$

Figure 4.70

If $\pi < x < 3\pi/2$, then

$$\pi/2 < x/2 < 3\pi/4 \qquad \text{Divide each member of } \pi < x < 3\pi/2 \text{ by 2.}$$

Thus, $x/2$ is in the second quadrant, where sine is positive and cosine and tangent are negative. Using half-angle identities, we obtain

$$\sin \frac{x}{2} = \sqrt{\frac{1 - \cos x}{2}} \qquad\qquad \cos \frac{x}{2} = -\sqrt{\frac{1 + \cos x}{2}}$$

$$= \sqrt{\frac{1 - \left(-\frac{4}{5}\right)}{2}} \qquad\qquad = -\sqrt{\frac{1 + \left(-\frac{4}{5}\right)}{2}}$$

$$= \sqrt{\frac{9}{10}} \quad \text{or} \quad \frac{3\sqrt{10}}{10} \qquad\qquad = -\sqrt{\frac{1}{10}} \quad \text{or} \quad \frac{-\sqrt{10}}{10}$$

$$\tan \frac{x}{2} = \frac{\sin (x/2)}{\cos (x/2)}$$

$$= \frac{3\sqrt{10}/10}{-\sqrt{10}/10} = -3$$

Matched Problem 4

Find the exact value for $\sin (x/2)$, $\cos (x/2)$, and $\tan (x/2)$ if $\cot x = -\frac{4}{3}$, $\pi/2 < x < \pi$.

Verifying an Identity

Example 5

Verify the identity: $\quad \cos^2 \dfrac{x}{2} = \dfrac{\tan x + \sin x}{2 \tan x}$

Verification

$$\cos^2 \frac{x}{2} = \frac{1 + \cos x}{2} \qquad\qquad \text{Square both sides of the half-angle identity for cosine.}$$

$$= \frac{\tan x}{\tan x} \cdot \frac{1 + \cos x}{2} \qquad\qquad \text{Algebra}$$

$$= \frac{\tan x + \tan x \cos x}{2 \tan x} \qquad\qquad \text{Algebra}$$

$$= \frac{\tan x + \sin x}{2 \tan x} \qquad\qquad \text{Quotient identity and algebra}$$

Matched Problem 5

Verify the identity: $\quad \sin^2 \dfrac{x}{2} = \dfrac{\tan x - \sin x}{2 \tan x}$

Answers to Matched Problems

1. $\dfrac{1 - \tan^2 x}{1 + \tan^2 x} = \dfrac{1 - \dfrac{\sin^2 x}{\cos^2 x}}{1 + \dfrac{\sin^2 x}{\cos^2 x}} = \cos^2 x - \sin^2 x = \cos 2x$

2. $\sin 2x = \dfrac{24}{25}; \cos 2x = \dfrac{7}{25}$ (3.) $\dfrac{\sqrt{2 - \sqrt{3}}}{2}$

4. $\sin (x/2) = 3\sqrt{10}/10, \cos (x/2) = \sqrt{10}/10, \tan (x/2) = 3$

5. $\sin^2 \dfrac{x}{2} = \dfrac{1 - \cos x}{2} = \dfrac{\tan x}{\tan x} \cdot \dfrac{1 - \cos x}{2} = \dfrac{\tan x - \sin x}{2 \tan x}$

Exercises for Section 4.8

Evaluate each side of the indicated identity for $x = 60°$ (thus verifying it for one particular case).

1. $\sin 2x = 2 \sin x \cos x$

2. $\cos 2x = \cos^2 x - \sin^2 x$

3. $\tan 2x = \dfrac{2 \tan x}{1 - \tan^2 x}$

4. $\sin \dfrac{x}{2} = \pm\sqrt{\dfrac{1 - \cos x}{2}}$

Use half-angle identities to find the exact value of Problems 5–8. Do not use a calculator.

5. $\sin 105°$ 6. $\cos 105°$

7. $\tan 15°$ 8. $\tan 75°$

In Problems 9–12, graph y_1 and y_2 in the same viewing window. Then use ⬜ TRACE ⬜ to compare the two graphs.

9. $y_1 = 2 \sin x \cos x, \; y_2 = \sin 2x, \; -2\pi < x < 2\pi$

10. $y_1 = \cos^2 x - \sin^2 x, \; y_2 = \cos 2x, \; -2\pi < x < 2\pi$

11. $y_1 = \dfrac{2 \tan x}{1 - \tan^2 x}, \; y_2 = \tan 2x, \; -\pi < x < \pi$

12. $y_1 = \dfrac{\sin x}{1 + \cos x}, \; y_2 = \tan \dfrac{x}{2}, \; -2\pi < x < 2\pi$

In Problems 13–30, verify each identity.

13. $\sin 2x = (\tan x)(1 + \cos 2x)$

14. $(\sin x + \cos x)^2 = 1 + \sin 2x$

15. $2 \sin^2 \dfrac{x}{2} = \dfrac{\sin^2 x}{1 + \cos x}$

16. $2 \cos^2 \dfrac{x}{2} = \dfrac{\sin^2 x}{1 - \cos x}$

17. $(\sin \theta - \cos \theta)^2 = 1 - \sin 2\theta$

18. $\sin 2\theta = (\sin \theta + \cos \theta)^2 - 1$

19. $\cos^2 \dfrac{w}{2} = \dfrac{1 + \cos w}{2}$ 20. $\sin^2 \dfrac{w}{2} = \dfrac{1 - \cos w}{2}$

21. $\cot \dfrac{\alpha}{2} = \dfrac{1 + \cos \alpha}{\sin \alpha}$

22. $\cot \dfrac{\alpha}{2} = \dfrac{\sin \alpha}{1 - \cos \alpha}$

23. $\dfrac{\cos 2t}{1 - \sin 2t} = \dfrac{1 + \tan t}{1 - \tan t}$

24. $\cos 2t = \dfrac{1 - \tan^2 t}{1 + \tan^2 t}$

25. $\tan 2x = \dfrac{2 \tan x}{1 - \tan^2 x}$

26. $\sin 2x = \dfrac{2 \tan x}{1 + \tan^2 x}$

27. $\tan \dfrac{x}{2} = \dfrac{\sin x}{1 + \cos x}$

28. $\tan \dfrac{x}{2} = \dfrac{1 - \cos x}{\sin x}$

29. $\sec^2 x = (\sec 2x)(2 - \sec^2 x)$

30. $2 \csc 2x = \dfrac{1 + \tan^2 x}{\tan x}$

In Problems 31–34, use the given information to find the exact value of $\sin 2x$, $\cos 2x$, and $\tan 2x$. Check your answer with a calculator.

31. $\sin x = \frac{7}{25}, \quad \pi/2 < x < \pi$

32. $\cos x = -\frac{8}{17}, \quad \pi/2 < x < \pi$

33. $\cot x = -\frac{12}{35}, \quad -\pi/2 < x < 0$

34. $\tan x = -\frac{20}{21}, \quad -\pi/2 < x < 0$

In Problems 35–40, use the given information to find the exact value of $\sin (x/2)$ and $\cos (x/2)$. Check your answer with a calculator.

35. $\cos x = \frac{1}{4}, \quad 0° < x < 90°$

36. $\sin x = \frac{\sqrt{21}}{5}, \quad 0° < x < 90°$

37. $\tan x = -\sqrt{8}, \quad 90° < x < 180°$

38. $\cot x = -\frac{3}{\sqrt{7}}, \quad 90° < x < 180°$

39. $\csc x = -\frac{5}{\sqrt{24}}, \quad -90° < x < 0°$

40. $\sec x = -\frac{3}{2}, \quad -90° < x < 0°$

Your friend is having trouble finding exact values of $\sin\theta$ and $\cos\theta$ from the information given in Problems 41 and 42, and comes to you for help. Instead of just working the problems, you guide your friend through the solution process using the following questions (a)–(e). What is the correct response to each question for each problem?

(a) The angle 2θ is in which quadrant? How do you know?

(b) How can you find $\sin 2\theta$ and $\cos 2\theta$? Find each.

(c) Which identities relate $\sin\theta$ and $\cos\theta$ with either $\sin 2\theta$ or $\cos 2\theta$?

(d) How would you use the identities in part (c) to find $\sin\theta$ and $\cos\theta$ exactly, including the correct sign?

(e) What are the exact values for $\sin\theta$ and $\cos\theta$?

41. Find the exact values of $\sin\theta$ and $\cos\theta$, given $\sec 2\theta = -\frac{5}{4}$, $0° < \theta < 90°$.

42. Find the exact values of $\sin\theta$ and $\cos\theta$, given $\tan 2\theta = -\frac{4}{3}$, $0° < \theta < 90°$.

43. In applied mathematics, approximate forms are often substituted for exact forms to simplify formulas or computations. Graph each side of each statement below in the same viewing window, $-\pi/2 \le x \le \pi 2$, to show that the approximation is valid for x close to to 0. Use $\boxed{\text{TRACE}}$ and describe what happens to the approximation as x gets closer to 0.

(a) $\sin 2x \approx 2 \sin x$ (b) $\sin \dfrac{x}{2} \approx \dfrac{1}{2} \sin x$

44. Repeat Problem 43 for:

(a) $\tan 2x \approx 2 \tan x$ (b) $\tan \dfrac{x}{2} \approx \dfrac{1}{2} \tan x$

In Problems 45–48, graph y_1 and y_2 in the same viewing window for $-2\pi \le x \le 2\pi$ and state the intervals for which y_1 and y_2 are identical.

45. $y_1 = \sin\dfrac{x}{2}$, $y_2 = \sqrt{\dfrac{1 - \cos x}{2}}$

46. $y_1 = \sin\dfrac{x}{2}$, $y_2 = -\sqrt{\dfrac{1 - \cos x}{2}}$

47. $y_1 = \cos\dfrac{x}{2}$, $y_2 = -\sqrt{\dfrac{1 + \cos x}{2}}$

48. $y_1 = \cos\dfrac{x}{2}$, $y_2 = \sqrt{\dfrac{1 + \cos x}{2}}$

In Problems 49–54, use the given information to find the exact value of $\sin x$, $\cos x$, and $\tan x$. Check your answer with a calculator.

49. $\sin 2x = \frac{55}{73}$, $0 < x < \pi/4$

50. $\cos 2x = -\frac{28}{53}$, $\pi/4 < x < \pi/2$

51. $\tan 2x = -\frac{28}{45}$, $\pi/4 < x < \pi/2$

52. $\cot 2x = -\frac{55}{48}$, $-\pi/4 < x < 0$

53. $\sec 2x = \frac{65}{33}$, $-\pi/4 < x < 0$

54. $\csc 2x = \frac{65}{33}$, $0 < x < \pi/4$

In Problems 55–60, verify each identity.

55. $\sin 3x = 3 \sin x - 4 \sin^3 x$

56. $\cos 3x = 4 \cos^3 x - 3 \cos x$

57. $\sin 4x = (\cos x)(4 \sin x - 8 \sin^3 x)$

58. $\cos 4x = 8 \cos^4 x - 8 \cos^2 x + 1$

59. $\tan 3x = \dfrac{3 \tan x - \tan^3 x}{1 - 3 \tan^2 x}$

60. $4 \sin^4 x = 1 - 2 \cos 2x + \cos^2 2x$

In Problems 61–66, graph $f(x)$, find a simpler function $g(x)$ that has the same graph as $f(x)$, and verify the identity $f(x) = g(x)$. [Assume $g(x) = k + A\, t(Bx)$, where $t(x)$ is one of the six basic trigonometric functions.]

61. $f(x) = \csc x + \cot x$ **62.** $f(x) = \csc x - \cot x$

63. $f(x) = \dfrac{\cot x}{1 + \cos 2x}$

64. $f(x) = \dfrac{1}{\cot x \sin 2x - 1}$

65. $f(x) = \dfrac{1 + 2 \cos 2x}{1 + 2 \cos x}$

66. $f(x) = \dfrac{1 - 2 \cos 2x}{2 \sin x - 1}$

Problems 67 and 68 refer to the following identity for n a positive integer (this identity is established in more advanced mathematics):

$$\frac{1}{2} + \cos x + \cdots + \cos nx = \frac{\sin\left(\dfrac{2n + 1}{2}x\right)}{2 \sin\left(\dfrac{1}{2}x\right)}$$

67. Graph each side of the equation for $n = 2$, $-2\pi \le x \le 2\pi$.

68. Graph each side of the equation for $n = 3$, $-2\pi \le x \le 2\pi$.

69. Sports—Javelin Throw In physics it can be shown that the theoretical horizontal distance d a javelin will travel (see the figure) is given approximately by

$$d = \frac{v_0^2 \sin\theta \cos\theta}{16}$$

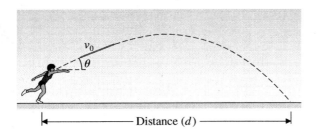

Distance (d)

where v_0 is the initial velocity of the javelin (in feet per second). (Air resistance and athlete height are ignored.)

(a) Write the formula in terms of the sine function only by using a suitable identity.

(b) Use the resulting equation from part (a) to determine the angle θ that will produce the maximum horizontal distance d for a given initial speed v_0. Explain your reasoning. This result is an important consideration for shot-putters, archers, and javelin and discus throwers.

(c) A world-class javelin thrower can throw the javelin with an initial velocity of 100 ft/sec. Graph the equation from part (a), and use a built-in routine to find the maximum distance d and the angle θ (in degrees) that produces the maximum distance. Describe what happens to d as θ goes from 0° to 90°.

70. Precalculus: Geometry An n-sided regular polygon is inscribed in a circle of radius r (see Figure 4.71).

Figure 4.71

(a) Show that the area of the n-sided polygon is given by

$$A_n = \frac{1}{2}nr^2 \sin \frac{2\pi}{n}$$

[*Hint:* Area of triangle = (Base)(Height)/2. A double-angle identity is useful.]

(b) For a circle of radius 1, use the formula from part (a) to complete Table 4.10 (to six decimal places).

(c) What does A_n seem to approach as n increases without bound?

(d) How close can A_n be made to get to the actual area of the circle? Will A_n ever equal the exact area of the circle for any chosen n, however large? Explain. (In calculus, the area of the circumscribed circle, π, is called the *limit* of A_n as n increases without bound.

Symbolically, we write $\lim_{n\to\infty} A_n = \pi$. The limit concept is fundamental to the development of calculus.)

Table 4.10

n	10	100	1,000	10,000
A_n				

71. Construction An animal shelter is to be constructed using two 4 ft by 8 ft sheets of exterior plywood for the roof (see Figure 4.72). We are interested in approximating the value of θ that will give the maximum interior volume. [*Note:* The interior volume is the area of the triangular end, $bh/2$, times the length of the shelter, 8 ft.]

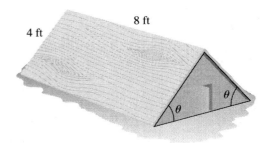

Figure 4.72

(a) Show that the interior volume is given by

$$V = 64 \sin 2\theta$$

(b) Explain how you can determine from the equation in part (a) the value of θ that produces the maximum volume, and find θ and the maximum volume.

(c) Complete Table 4.11 (to one decimal place) and find the maximum volume in the table and the value of θ that produces it. (Use the table feature in your calculator if it has one.)

Table 4.11

θ (deg)	30	35	40	45	50	55	60
V (ft³)	55.4						

(d) Graph the equation in part (a) on a graphing utility, $0° \le \theta \le 90°$, and use a built-in routine to find the maximum volume and the value of θ that produces it.

*72. Construction A new road is to be constructed from resort P to resort Q, turning at a point R on the horizontal line through resort P, as indicated in Figure 4.73.

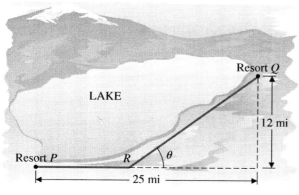

Figure 4.73

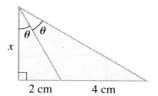

Figure 4.74

(a) Show that the length of the road from P to Q through R is given by

$$d = 25 + 12 \tan \frac{\theta}{2}$$

(b) Because of the lake, θ is restricted to $40° \le \theta \le 90°$. What happens to the length of the road as θ varies between $40°$ and $90°$?

(c) Complete Table 4.12 (to one decimal place) and find the maximum and minimum length of the road. (Use a table-generating feature on your calculator if it has one.)

Table 4.12

θ (deg)	40	50	60	70	80	90
d (mi)	29.4					

(d) Graph the equation in part (a) for the restrictions in part (b); then use a built-in routine to determine the maximum and minimum length of the road.

73. Engineering   Find the exact value of x in Figure 4.74; then find x and θ to three decimal places. [*Hint:* Use $\tan 2\theta = (2 \tan \theta)/(1 - \tan^2 \theta)$.]

74. Engineering   Find the exact value of x in Figure 4.75; then find x and θ to three decimal places. [*Hint:* Use $\cos 2\theta = 2 \cos^2 \theta - 1$.]

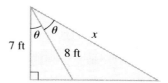

Figure 4.75

**75. Geometry   In part (a) of the figure, M and N are the midpoints of the sides of a square. Find the exact value of $\cos \theta$. [*Hint:* The solution uses the Pythagorean theorem, the definitions of sine and cosine, a half-angle identity, and some auxiliary lines as drawn in part (b) of Figure 4.76.]

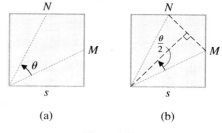

(a)   (b)

Figure 4.76

4.9 USING IDENTITIES AND ALGEBRA TO SOLVE TRIGONOMETRIC EQUATIONS

Now that you know some useful identities for rewriting trigonometric expressions, you can use them as well as your knowledge of algebraic properties to solve equations.

Example 1   Solve for x: $\sin x = \cos x$

Solution   A reasonable first step would be to get all expressions on one side of the equation but there are two ways to do this, subtraction and division. If we use subtraction, we get

$$\sin x - \cos x = 0$$

and there is some doubt about the next step.

On the other hand if we use division, we must be sure that we are not dividing by zero. If we divide by $\cos x$, we can only do so if $x \neq \frac{\pi}{2} + k\pi$ because those are the values of x that make $\cos x = 0$. We only need to worry about those values if they are solutions to the equation. Notice that if $x = \frac{\pi}{2}$, then $\sin x = 1$ and $\cos x = 0$, so that $\sin x \neq \cos x$. The same is true for $x = \frac{3\pi}{2}$ so we can go ahead and divide both sides of this equation by $\cos x$:

$$\frac{\sin x}{\cos x} = 1$$

Now use the identity $\frac{\sin x}{\cos x} = \tan x$:

$$\tan x = 1$$

The primary solution to this equation is $x = \frac{\pi}{4}$ and the period of the tangent function is π, so the solution set for our equation is

$$x = \frac{\pi}{4} + k\pi$$

Check:

$$x = \frac{\pi}{4}: \quad \sin\left(\frac{\pi}{4}\right) \overset{?}{=} \cos\left(\frac{\pi}{4}\right)$$

$$\frac{\sqrt{2}}{2} = \frac{\sqrt{2}}{2}$$

Let's also check the solutions graphically. Using your calculator, let $Y_1 = \sin(x)$ and $Y_2 = \cos(x)$.

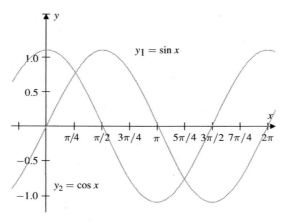

Figure 4.77

In Figure 4.77 we can clearly see that $\frac{\pi}{4}$ is a solution. On your graphing calculator, if you use choosing [2nd] CALC, 5: INTERSECT. You should get $x = .78539816$, which is an 8 decimal-place approximation of $\frac{\pi}{4}$.

Matched Problem 1   Solve the equation $\sin x + \cos x = 0$. Check the solutions by substitution and graphically.

Example 2   Solve for x: $\sin 2x = \cos x$

Solution   First, it is important to recognize that the two expressions in the equation have different arguments. On the left side of the equation, the argument of the sine is $2x$, while on the right side of the equation, the cosine's argument is just x. For this reason, a logical first step would be to use the double-angle identity for sine to rewrite $\sin 2x$:

$$\sin 2x = \cos x$$
$$2 \sin x \cos x = \cos x$$

At this point it might be very tempting to divide both sides of the equation by $\cos x$, but remember that you can only divide both sides of an equation by the same *non-zero* number. If $\cos x = 0$, that strategy is not only illegal, it will also cause us to lose some of the solutions to the equation. Instead of dividing, subtract $\cos x$ from both sides and then factor:

$$2 \sin x \cos x - \cos x = 0$$
$$\cos x \, (2 \sin x - 1) = 0$$

Now recall from algebra the *Zero-Product Property*: If the product of two or more quantities is equal to zero, then at least one of the quantities must be zero. We can now use the zero-product property to set each factor equal to zero:

$$\cos x = 0 \quad \text{or} \quad 2 \sin x - 1 = 0$$

Notice that each of these is the type of equation we solved in Section 4.1. They require us to remember values of trig functions.

If $\cos x = 0$, then $x = \dfrac{\pi}{2} + 2k\pi$ or $x = \dfrac{3\pi}{2} + 2k\pi$

If $2 \sin x - 1 = 0$, then $\sin x = \dfrac{1}{2}$ and $x = \dfrac{\pi}{6} + 2k\pi$ or $x = \dfrac{5\pi}{6} + 2k\pi$

In summary, the solutions to the equation $\sin 2x = \cos x$ are

$$x = \frac{\pi}{2} + 2k\pi, \quad x = \frac{3\pi}{2} + 2k\pi, \quad x = \frac{\pi}{6} + 2k\pi, \quad \text{and } x = \frac{5\pi}{6} + 2k\pi.$$

Notice that we can write the first two solutions more compactly as $x = \dfrac{\pi}{2} + k\pi$.

You should check the primary solutions in the original equation:

$$x = \frac{\pi}{6}: \quad \sin\left(2 \cdot \frac{\pi}{6}\right) \stackrel{?}{=} \cos\left(\frac{\pi}{6}\right) \qquad x = \frac{\pi}{2}: \quad \sin\left(2 \cdot \frac{\pi}{2}\right) \stackrel{?}{=} \cos\left(\frac{\pi}{2}\right)$$

$$\sin\left(\frac{\pi}{3}\right) \stackrel{?}{=} \cos\left(\frac{\pi}{6}\right) \qquad\qquad\qquad \sin(\pi) \stackrel{?}{=} \cos\left(\frac{\pi}{2}\right)$$

$$\frac{\sqrt{3}}{2} = \frac{\sqrt{3}}{2} \qquad\qquad\qquad\qquad\qquad 0 = 0$$

The other two checks are left to you.

Let's also check these solutions graphically. On your calculator, graph $Y_1 = \sin(2x)$ and $Y_2 = \cos(x)$. Here are the two graphs:

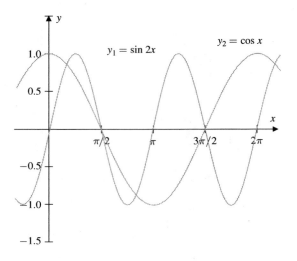

Figure 4.78

In Figure 4.78, notice that the solutions $\frac{\pi}{2}$ and $\frac{3\pi}{2}$ are clearly points of intersection. Check the first positive intersection on your calculator by choosing $\boxed{\text{2nd}}$ CALC, 5: INTERSECT. You should get $x = .52359878$, which is an 8 decimal-place approximation of $\frac{\pi}{6}$. Finally, if you check the solution between $\frac{\pi}{2}$ and π, you should get a decimal approximation of $\frac{5\pi}{6}$.

Matched Problem 2   Solve the equation $\sin x = \sin 2x$. Check the solutions by substitution and graphically.

Answers to Matched Problems

1. $x = \frac{3\pi}{4} + k\pi$

2. $x = k\pi$ or $x = \frac{\pi}{3} + 2k\pi$, $x = \frac{5\pi}{3} + 2k\pi$

Exercises for Section 4.9

Solve each equation. Check your answers by substitution and graphically.

1. $\sin x\,(2\cos x + 1) = 0$

2. $\tan x(\sqrt{2}\sin x - 1) = 0$

3. $(\tan x - 1)(\sin x - 2) = 0$

4. $(2\sin x - \sqrt{3})(\cos x + 1) = 0$

5. $2\cos x - \cos x \sin x = 0$

6. $\tan x \cos x + \cos x = 0$

7. $\sqrt{3}\cos x = \sin x$

8. $\sqrt{3}\cos 3x = \sin 3x$

9. $\dfrac{\sin x}{\tan x} = 1$

10. $\dfrac{\cot x}{\cos x} = -1$

11. $\sin 2x + \sqrt{3}\sin x = 0$

12. $\cos 2x = \sin x - \sin^2 x$

CHAPTER FOUR REVIEW

An equation in one or more variables is said to be an **identity** if the left side is equal to the right side for all replacements of the variables for which both sides are defined. If the left side is equal to the right side only for certain values of the variables and not for all values for which both sides are defined, then the equation is called a **conditional equation.**

Fundamental Identities and Their Use

Fundamental Trigonometric Identities

For x any real number or angle in degree or radian measure for which both sides are defined:

Reciprocal identities

$$\csc x = \frac{1}{\sin x} \qquad \sec x = \frac{1}{\cos x} \qquad \cot x = \frac{1}{\tan x}$$

Quotient identities

$$\tan x = \frac{\sin x}{\cos x} \qquad \cot x = \frac{\cos x}{\sin x}$$

Identities for negatives

$$\sin(-x) = -\sin x \qquad \cos(-x) = \cos x \qquad \tan(-x) = -\tan x$$

Pythagorean identities

$$\sin^2 x + \cos^2 x = 1 \qquad \tan^2 x + 1 = \sec^2 x \qquad 1 + \cot^2 x = \csc^2 x$$

Verifying Trigonometric Identities

When **verifying an identity,** start with the expression on one side and through a sequence of valid steps involving the use of known identities or algebraic manipulation, convert that expression into the expression on the other side. *Do not* add the same quantity to each side, multiply each side by the same nonzero quantity, or square or take the square root of both sides.

Some Suggestions for Verifying Identities

Step 1 Start with the more complicated side of the identity and transform it into the simpler side.
Step 2 Try using basic or other known identities.
Step 3 Try algebraic operations such as multiplying, factoring, combining fractions, or splitting fractions.
Step 4 If other steps fail, try expressing each function in terms of sine and cosine functions; then perform appropriate algebraic operations.
Step 5 At each step, keep the other side of the identity in mind. This often reveals what you should do in order to get there.

Double-Angle and Half-Angle Identities

Double-Angle Identities

For x any real number or angle in degree or radian measure for which both sides are defined:

$$\sin 2x = 2 \sin x \cos x \qquad \cos 2x = \cos^2 x - \sin^2 x$$

$$\tan 2x = \frac{2 \tan x}{1 - \tan^2 x} \qquad \qquad = 1 - 2 \sin^2 x$$

$$= 2 \cos^2 x - 1$$

Half-Angle Identities

For x any real number or angle in degree or radian measure for which both sides are defined:

$$\sin \frac{x}{2} = \pm \sqrt{\frac{1 - \cos x}{2}} \qquad \cos \frac{x}{2} = \pm \sqrt{\frac{1 + \cos x}{2}}$$

$$\tan \frac{x}{2} = \pm \sqrt{\frac{1 - \cos x}{1 + \cos x}} = \frac{\sin x}{1 + \cos x} = \frac{1 - \cos x}{\sin x}$$

where the sign is determined by the quadrant in which $x/2$ lies.

REVIEW EXERCISES FOR CHAPTER FOUR

Work through all the problems in this chapter review and check the answers. Answers to all review problems appear in the back of the book; following each answer is an italic number that indicates the section in which that type of problem is discussed. Where weaknesses show up, review the appropriate sections in the text.

1. One of the following equations is an identity and the other is a conditional equation. Identify which, and explain the difference between the two.

    (1) $(x - 3)(x + 2) = x^2 - x - 6$

    (2) $(x - 3)(x + 2) = 0$

Verify each identity in Problems 2–10 without looking at a table of identities.

2. $\csc x \sin x = \sec x \cos x$

3. $\cot x \sin x = \cos x$

4. $\tan x = -\tan(-x)$

5. $\dfrac{\sin^2 x}{\cos x} = \sec x - \cos x$

6. $\dfrac{\csc x}{\cos x} = \tan x + \cot x$

7. $(\cos^2 x)(\cot^2 x + 1) = \cot^2 x$

8. $\dfrac{\sin \alpha \csc \alpha}{\cot \alpha} = \tan \alpha$

9. $\dfrac{\sin^2 u - \cos^2 u}{\sin u \cos u} = \tan u - \cot u$

10. $\dfrac{\sec \theta - \csc \theta}{\sec \theta \csc \theta} = \sin \theta - \cos \theta$

11. Using $\cos(x + y) = \cos x \cos y - \sin x \sin y$, show that $\cos(x + 2\pi) = \cos x$.

12. Using $\sin(x + y) = \sin x \cos y + \cos x \sin y$, show that $\sin(x + \pi) = -\sin x$.

In Problems 13 and 14, verify each identity for the indicated value.

13. $\cos 2x = 1 - 2 \sin^2 x, x = 30°$

14. $\sin \dfrac{x}{2} = \pm \sqrt{\dfrac{1 - \cos x}{2}}, x = \dfrac{\pi}{2}$

*15. Write $\sin 8t \sin 5t$ as a sum or difference.

*16. Write $\sin w + \sin 5w$ as a product.

Verify each identity in Problems 17–20.

17. $\dfrac{1 - \cos^2 t}{\sin^3 t} = \csc t$

18. $\dfrac{(\cos \alpha - 1)^2}{\sin^2 \alpha} = \dfrac{1 - \cos \alpha}{1 + \cos \alpha}$

19. $\dfrac{1 - \tan^2 x}{1 - \tan^4 x} = \cos^2 x$

20. $\cot^2 x \cos^2 x = \cot^2 x - \cos^2 x$

21. The equation $\sin x = 0$ is true for an infinite number of values ($x = k\pi$, k any integer). Is this equation an identity? Explain.

22. Explain how you would use a graphing utility to show that $\sin x = 0$ is not an identity; then do it.

23. For the following graphing calculator displays, find the value of the final expression without finding x or using a calculator.

(a)

```
cos(X)
cos(-X)       .9394
```

(b)

```
(cos(X))²
(sin(X))²     .8824
```

24. Is $1/(\sin x) = \csc x$ an identity for all real values of x? Explain.

25. Explain how to use a graphing utility to show that $\sin(x - 3) = \sin x - \sin 3$ is not an identity; then do it.

26. Explain how to show that $\sin(x - 3) = \sin x - \sin 3$ is not an identity without graphing; then do it.

Verify the identities in Problems 27–41. Use the list of identities inside the front cover if necessary.

27. $\dfrac{\sin x}{1 - \cos x} = (\csc x)(1 + \cos x)$

28. $\dfrac{1 - \tan^2 x}{1 - \cot^2 x} = 1 - \sec^2 x$

29. $\tan(x + \pi) = \tan x$

30. $1 - (\cos\beta - \sin\beta)^2 = \sin 2\beta$

31. $\dfrac{\sin 2x}{\cot x} = 1 - \cos 2x$

32. $\dfrac{2\tan x}{1 + \tan^2 x} = \sin 2x$

33. $2\csc 2x = \tan x + \cot x$

34. $\csc x = \dfrac{\cot(x/2)}{1 + \cos x}$

35. $\dfrac{\sin(x - y)}{\sin(x + y)} = \dfrac{\tan x - \tan y}{\tan x + \tan y}$

36. $\csc 2x = \dfrac{\tan x + \cot x}{2}$

37. $\dfrac{2 - \sec^2 x}{\sec^2 x} = \cos 2x$

38. $\tan\dfrac{x}{2} = \dfrac{\sec x - 1}{\tan x}$

*39. $\dfrac{\sin t + \sin 5t}{\cos t + \cos 5t} = \tan 3t$

*40. $\dfrac{\sin x + \sin y}{\cos x - \cos y} = \cot\dfrac{x - y}{2}$

*41. $\dfrac{\cos x - \cos y}{\cos x + \cos y} = -\tan\dfrac{x + y}{2}\tan\dfrac{x - y}{2}$

Evaluate Problems 42 and 43 exactly using an appropriate identity.

*42. $\sin 165° \sin 15°$ ***43.** $\cos 165° - \cos 75°$

44. Use fundamental identities to find the exact values of the remaining trigonometric functions of x, given

$$\cos x = -\frac{2}{3} \quad\text{and}\quad \tan x < 0$$

45. Find the exact values of $\sin 2x$, $\cos 2x$, and $\tan 2x$, given $\tan x = \frac{4}{3}$ and $0 < x < \pi/2$. Do not use a calculator.

46. Find the exact values of $\sin(x/2)$, $\cos(x/2)$, and $\tan(x/2)$, given $\cos x = -\frac{5}{13}$ and $-\pi < x < -\pi/2$. Do not use a calculator.

47. Use a sum or difference identity to convert $y = \tan(x + \pi/4)$ into a form involving $\sin x$, $\cos x$, and/or $\tan x$. Check the results using a graphing utility and $\boxed{\text{TRACE}}$.

48. Write $y = \cos 1.5x \cos 0.3x - \sin 1.5x \sin 0.3x$ in terms of a single trigonometric function. Check the result by entering the original equation in a graphing utility as y_1 and the converted form as y_2. Then graph y_1 and y_2 in the same viewing window. Use $\boxed{\text{TRACE}}$ to compare the two graphs.

49. Graph $y_1 = \sin(x/2)$ and $y_2 = -\sqrt{(1 - \cos x)/2}$ in the same viewing window for $-2\pi \le x \le 2\pi$, and indicate the subinterval(s) for which y_1 and y_2 are identities.

50. Use a graphing utility to test whether each equation below is an identity. If the equation appears to be an identity, verify it. If the equation does not appear to be an identity, find a value of x for which both sides are defined but are not equal.

(a) $\dfrac{\sin^2 x}{1 + \sin x} = 1 - \sin x$

(b) $\dfrac{\cos^2 x}{1 + \sin x} = 1 - \sin x$

51. Find the exact values of $\sin x$, $\cos x$, and $\tan x$, given $\sec 2x = -\frac{13}{12}$ and $-\pi/2 < x < 0$. Do not use a calculator.

Verify the identities in Problems 52 and 53.

52. $\dfrac{\cot x}{\csc x + 1} = \dfrac{\csc x - 1}{\cot x}$

53. $\cot 3x = \dfrac{3 \tan^2 x - 1}{\tan^3 x - 3 \tan x}$

54. Use the definition of sine, cosine, and tangent on a unit circle to prove that

$$\tan x = \frac{\sin x}{\cos x}$$

55. Prove that the cosine function has a period of 2π.

56. Prove that the cotangent function has a period of π.

57. By letting

$$x + y = u \qquad \text{and} \qquad x - y = v$$

in $\sin x \sin y = \frac{1}{2}\left[\cos(x - y) - \cos(x + y)\right]$, show that

$$\cos v - \cos u = 2 \sin \frac{u + v}{2} \sin \frac{u - v}{2}$$

In Problems 58–62, graph $f(x)$, find a simpler function $g(x)$ that has the same graph as $f(x)$, and verify the identity $f(x) = g(x)$. [Assume $g(x) = k + A\,t(Bx)$, where $t(x)$ is one of the six trigonometric functions.]

58. $f(x) = \dfrac{3 \sin^2 x}{1 - \cos x} + \dfrac{\tan^2 x \cos^2 x}{1 + \cos x}$

59. $f(x) = \dfrac{\sin x}{\cos x - \sin x} + \dfrac{\sin x}{\cos x + \sin x}$

60. $f(x) = 3 \sin^2 x + \cos^2 x$

61. $f(x) = \dfrac{3 - 4 \cos^2 x}{1 - 2 \sin^2 x}$

62. $f(x) = \dfrac{2 + \sin x - 2 \cos x}{1 - \cos x}$

In Problems 63 and 64, graph y_1 and y_2 in the same viewing window for $-2\pi \le x \le 2\pi$, and state the interval(s) where the graphs of y_1 and y_2 coincide. Use TRACE .

63. $y_1 = \tan \dfrac{x}{2},\ y_2 = \sqrt{\dfrac{1 - \cos x}{1 + \cos x}}$

64. $y_1 = \tan \dfrac{x}{2},\ y_2 = -\sqrt{\dfrac{1 - \cos x}{1 + \cos x}}$

*65. Graph $y_1 = 2 \cos 30\pi x \sin 2\pi x$ and $y_2 = 2 \sin 2\pi x$ for $0 \le x \le 1$ and $-2 \le y \le 2$.

*66. Repeat Problem 65 after converting y_1 to a sum or difference.

67. Precalculus: Trigonometric Substitution In the expression $\sqrt{u^2 - a^2}$, $a > 0$, let $u = a \sec x$, $0 < x < \pi/2$, simplify, and write in a form that is free of radicals.

68. Precalculus: Angle of Intersection of Two Lines Use the results of Problem 63 in Exercise 4.3 to find the acute angle of intersection (to the nearest $0.1°$) between the two lines $y = 4x + 5$ and $y = \frac{1}{3}x - 2$.

*69. Engineering Find the exact value of x in Figure 4.79; then find x and θ to three decimal places.

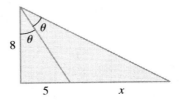

Figure 4.79

*70. Analytic Geometry Find the radian measure of the angle θ in Figure 4.80 (to three decimal places) if A has coordinates $(2, 6)$ and B has coordinates $(4, 4)$. [*Hint:* Label the angle between OB and the x axis as α; then use an appropriate sum identity.]

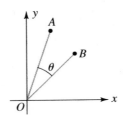

Figure 4.80

*71. Architecture An art museum is being designed with a triangular skylight on the roof, as indicated in Figure 4.81. The facing of the museum is light granite and the top edge, excluding the skylight ridge, is to receive a black granite trim as shown. The total length of the trim depends on the choice of the angle θ for the skylight. All other dimensions are fixed.

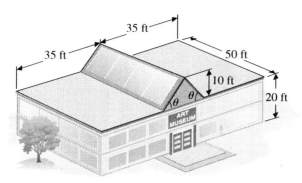

Figure 4.81

(a) Show that the total length L of the black granite trim is given by

$$L = 240 + 40 \tan \frac{\theta}{2}$$

(b) Because of lighting considerations, θ is restricted to $30° \le \theta \le 60°$. Describe what you think happens to L as θ varies from $30°$ to $60°$.

(c) Complete Table 4.13 (to one decimal place) and select the maximum and minimum length of the trim. (Use a table-generating feature on your calculator if it has one.)

Table 4.13

θ	30	35	40	45	50	55	60
L(ft)	250.7						

(d) Graph the equation in part (a) for the restrictions in part (b). Then determine the maximum and minimum lengths of the trim.

*72. Music   One tone is given by $y = 0.3 \cos 120\pi t$ and another by $y = -0.3 \cos 140\pi t$. Write their sum as a product. What is the beat frequency if both notes are sounded together?

*73. Music   Use a graphing utility with the viewing window set to $0 \le t \le 0.2$, $-0.8 \le y \le 0.8$, to graph the indicated equations.

  (a) $y_1 = 0.3 \cos 120\pi t$
  (b) $y_2 = -0.3 \cos 140\pi t$
  (c) $y_3 = y_1 + y_2$ and $y_4 = 0.6 \sin 10\pi t$
  (d) Repeat part (c) using the product form of y_3 from Problem 72.

*74. Physics   The equation of motion for a weight suspended from a spring is given by

$$y = -8 \sin 3t - 6 \cos 3t$$

where y is displacement of the weight from its equilibrium position in centimeters and t is time in seconds. Write this equation in the form $y = A \sin(Bt + C)$; keep A positive, choose C positive and as small as possible, and compute C to two decimal places. Indicate the amplitude, period, frequency, and phase shift.

*75. Physics   Use a graphing utility to graph

$$y = -8 \sin 3t - 6 \cos 3t$$

for $-2\pi/3 \le t \le 2\pi/3$, approximate the t intercepts in this interval to two decimal places, and identify the intercept that corresponds to the phase shift determined in Problem 74.

Chapter Five

QUADRATIC, POWER, POLYNOMIAL, AND RATIONAL FUNCTIONS

This chapter begins with a study of quadratic functions. We investigate the properties of quadratic functions and their graphs, solve related equations, and study applications. Power functions are introduced next as the basic building blocks of polynomial and rational functions.

5.1 QUADRATIC FUNCTIONS

A baseball is "popped" straight up by a batter. The height of the ball above the ground is given by the function $y = f(t) = -16t^2 + 64t + 3$, where t is time in seconds after the ball leaves the bat and y is in feet. See Figure 5.1. Although the path of the ball is straight up and down, the graph of its height as a function of time is concave down. The ball goes up fast at first and then more slowly because of gravity.

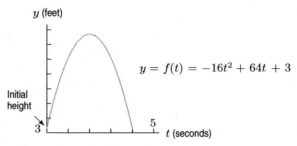

Figure 5.1: The height of a ball t seconds after being "popped up".
(Note: This graph does not represent the ball's path)

The baseball height function is an example of a *quadratic function*, whose general form is $y = ax^2 + bx + c$.

Finding the Zeros of a Quadratic Function

A natural question to ask is when the ball hits the ground. The graph suggests that $y = 0$ when $t \approx 4$. We can phrase the question symbolically: For what value of t does $f(t) = 0$? Input values of t which make the output $f(t) = 0$ are called *zeros* of f. It is easy to find the zeros of a quadratic function if its formula can be factored (see Appendix to review factoring).

Example 1   Find the zeros of $f(x) = x^2 - x - 6$.

Solution   To find the zeros, set $f(x) = 0$ and solve for x by factoring:

$$x^2 - x - 6 = 0$$
$$(x - 3)(x + 2) = 0.$$

Thus the zeros are $x = 3$ and $x = -2$.

Some quadratic functions can be expressed in *factored form*,

$$q(x) = a(x - r)(x - s),$$

where a, r, and s are constants, $a \neq 0$. Note that r and s are zeros of the function q. The factored form of the function f in Example 1 is $f(x) = (x - 3)(x + 2)$.

We can also find the zeros of a quadratic function by using the quadratic formula. (See the Tools section to review the quadratic formula.)

Example 2   Find the zeros of $f(x) = x^2 - x - 6$ by using the quadratic formula.

Solution   We must solve the equation $x^2 - x - 6 = 0$. For this equation, $a = 1$, $b = -1$, and $c = -6$. Thus

$$x = \frac{-b \pm \sqrt{b^2 - 4ac}}{2a} = \frac{-(-1) \pm \sqrt{(-1)^2 - 4(1)(-6)}}{2(1)}$$

$$= \frac{1 \pm \sqrt{25}}{2} = 3 \text{ or } -2.$$

The zeros are $x = 3$ and $x = -2$, the same as we found by factoring.

The zeros of a function occur at the x-intercepts of its graph. Not every quadratic function has x-intercepts, as we see in the next example.

Example 3   Figure 5.2 shows a graph of $h(x) = -\frac{1}{2}x^2 - 2$. What happens if we try to use algebra to find its zeros?

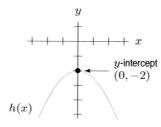

Figure 5.2

Solution   To find the zeros, we solve the equation

$$-\frac{1}{2}x^2 - 2 = 0$$

$$-\frac{1}{2}x^2 = 2$$

$$x^2 = -4$$

$$x = \pm\sqrt{-4}.$$

Since $\sqrt{-4}$ is not a real number, there are no real solutions, so h has no real zeros. This corresponds to the fact that the graph of h in Figure 5.2 does not cross the x-axis.

Concavity and Quadratic Functions

Unlike a linear function, whose graph is a straight line, a quadratic function has a graph which is either concave up or concave down.

Example 4   Let $f(x) = x^2$. Find the average rate of change of f over the intervals of length 2 between $x = -4$ and $x = 4$. What do these rates tell you about the concavity of the graph of f?

Solution   Between $x = -4$ and $x = -2$, we have

$$\text{Average rate of change of } f = \frac{f(-2) - f(-4)}{-2 - (-4)} = \frac{(-2)^2 - (-4)^2}{-2 + 4} = -6.$$

Between $x = -2$ and $x = 0$, we have

$$\text{Average rate of change of } f = \frac{f(0) - f(-2)}{0 - (-2)} = \frac{0^2 - (-2)^2}{0 + 2} = -2.$$

Between $x = 0$ and $x = 2$, we have

$$\text{Average rate of change of } f = \frac{f(2) - f(0)}{2 - 0} = \frac{2^2 - 0^2}{2 - 0} = 2.$$

Between $x = 2$ and $x = 4$, we have

$$\text{Average rate of change of } f = \frac{f(4) - f(2)}{4 - 2} = \frac{4^2 - 2^2}{4 - 2} = 6.$$

Since these rates are increasing, we expect the graph of f to be bending upward. Figure 5.3 confirms that the graph is concave up.

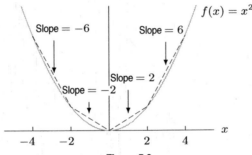

Figure 5.3

Example 5   A high diver jumps off a 10-meter springboard. For h in meters and t in seconds after the diver leaves the board, her height above the water is given by

$$h = f(t) = -4.9t^2 + 8t + 10.$$

See Figure 5.4.

(a) Find and interpret the domain and range of the function and the intercepts of the graph.
(b) Identify the concavity.

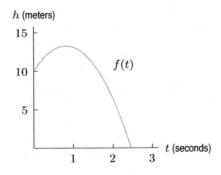

Figure 5.4: Height of diver as a function of time

Solution (a) The diver enters the water when her height is 0. This occurs when

$$h = f(t) = -4.9t^2 + 8t + 10 = 0.$$

Using the quadratic formula to solve this equation, we find $t = 2.462$ seconds. The domain is the interval of time the diver is in the air, namely $0 \le t \le 2.462$. To find the range of f, we look for the largest and smallest outputs for h. From the graph, the diver's maximum height appears to occur at about $t = 1$, so we estimate the largest output value for f to be

$$f(1) = -4.9 \cdot 1^2 + 8 \cdot 1 + 10 = 13.1 \text{ meters}$$

Thus, the range of f is approximately $0 \le f(t) \le 13.1$.
The vertical intercept of the graph is

$$f(0) = -4.9 \cdot 0^2 + 8 \cdot 0 + 10 = 10 \text{ meters}.$$

The diver's initial height is 10 meters (the height of the springboard). The horizontal intercept is the point where $f(t) = 0$, which we found in part (a). The diver enters the water approximately 2.462 seconds after leaving the springboard.

(b) In Figure 5.4, we see that the graph is bending downward over its entire domain, so it is concave down. This is confirmed by Table 5.1, which shows that the rate of change, $\Delta h / \Delta t$, is decreasing.

Table 5.1

t (sec)	h (meters)	Rate of change $\Delta h / \Delta t$
0	10	
		5.55
0.5	12.775	
		0.65
1.0	13.100	
		−4.25
1.5	10.975	
		−9.15
2.0	6.400	

Exercises and Problems for Section 5.1

Exercises

1. Find the zeros of $Q(r) = 2r^2 - 6r - 36$ by factoring.

2. Find the zeros of $Q(x) = 5x - x^2 + 3$ using the quadratic formula.

In Exercises 3–8, find the zeros of the function algebraically.

3. $y = 2x^2 + 5x + 2$

4. $y = 4x^2 - 4x - 8$

5. $y = 7x^2 + 16x + 4$

6. $y = 9x^2 + 6x + 1$

7. $y = -17x^2 + 23x + 19$

8. $y = 89x^2 + 55x + 34$

9. Find two quadratic functions with zeros $x = 1, x = 2$.

10. Solve for x using the quadratic formula and demonstrate your solution graphically:

    (a) $6x - \frac{1}{3} = 3x^2$ (b) $2x^2 + 7.2 = 5.1x$

11. Without a calculator, graph $y = 3x^2 - 16x - 12$ by factoring and plotting zeros.

12. Is there a quadratic function with zeros $x = 1, x = 2$ and $x = 3$?

Problems

13. Use the quadratic formula to find the time at which the baseball in Figure 5.1 hits the ground.

14. Determine the concavity of the graph of $f(x) = 4 - x^2$ between $x = -1$ and $x = 5$ by calculating average rates of change over intervals of length 2.

15. Graph a quadratic function which has all the following properties: concave up, y-intercept is -6, zeros at $x = -2$ and $x = 3$.

16. Let $V(t) = t^2 - 4t + 4$ represent the velocity of an object in meters per second.
(a) What is the object's initial velocity?
(b) When is the object not moving?
(c) Identify the concavity of the velocity graph.

17. The percentage of schools with interactive videodisc players[1] each year from 1992 to 1996 is shown in Table 5.2. If x is in years since 1992, show that this data set can be approximated by the quadratic function $p(x) = -0.8x^2 + 8.8x + 7.2$. What does this model predict for the year 2004? How good is this model for predicting the future?

Table 5.2

Year	1992	1993	1994	1995	1996
Percentage	8	14	21	29.1	29.3

18. A ball is thrown into the air. Its height (in feet) t seconds later is given by $h(t) = 80t - 16t^2$.
(a) Evaluate and interpret $h(2)$.
(b) Solve the equation $h(t) = 80$. Interpret your solutions and illustrate them on a graph of $h(t)$.

19. Without a calculator, graph the following function by factoring and plotting zeros:
$$y = -4cx + x^2 + 4c^2 \quad \text{for} \quad c > 0$$

20. Let $f(x) = x^2$ and $g(x) = x^2 + 2x - 8$.
(a) Graph f and g in the window $-10 \le x \le 10, -10 \le y \le 10$. How are the two graphs similar? How are they different?
(b) Graph f and g in the window $-10 \le x \le 10, -10 \le y \le 100$. Why do the two graphs appear more similar on this window than on the window from part (a)?
(c) Graph f and g in the window $-20 \le x \le 20, -10 \le y \le 400$, the window $-50 \le x \le 50, -10 \le y \le 2500$, and the window $-500 \le x \le 500, -2500 \le y \le 250,000$. Describe the change in appearance of f and g on these three successive windows.

21. A relief package is dropped from an airplane moving at a speed of 500 km/hr. Since the package is initially released with this forward horizontal velocity, it follows a parabolic path (instead of dropping straight down). The graph in Figure 5.5 shows the height of the package, h, as a function of the horizontal distance, d, it has traveled since it was dropped.
(a) From what height was the package released?
(b) How far away from the spot above which it was released does the package hit the ground?
(c) Write a formula for $h(d)$. [Hint: The package starts falling at the maximum of the parabola].

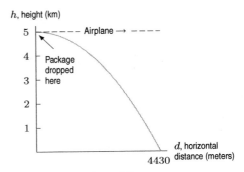

Figure 5.5

22. (a) Fit a quadratic function to the first three data points in Table 5.3. Use the fifth point as a check.
(b) Find the formula for a linear function that passes through the second two data points.
(c) Compare the value of the linear function at $x = 3$ to the value of the quadratic at $x = 3$.
(d) Compare the values of the linear and quadratic functions at $x = 50$.
(e) For approximately what x values do the quadratic and linear function values differ by less than 0.05? Using a calculator or computer, graph both functions on the same axes and estimate an answer.

Table 5.3

x	0	1	2	3	50
y	1.0	3.01	5.04	7.09	126.0

23. Plot the functions $y = 2x$ and $y = x^2 + 1$. Is one graph always above the other? Make a conjecture involving an inequality between these two functions. Show algebraically why your conjecture is true.

[1]Data from R. Famighetti, ed. *The World Almanac and Book of Facts: 1999*. (New Jersey: Funk and Wagnalls, 1998).

5.2 THE FAMILY OF QUADRATIC FUNCTIONS

In Section 5.1 we looked at the example of a baseball which is popped up by a batter. The height of the ball above the ground was modeled by the quadratic function $y = f(t) = -16t^2 + 64t + 3$, where t is time in seconds after the ball leaves the bat, and y is in feet. The function is graphed in Figure 5.6.

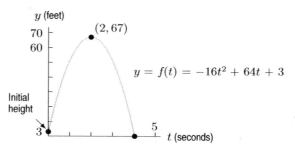

Figure 5.6: Height of baseball at time t

The point on the graph with the largest y value appears to be $(2, 67)$. (We show this in Example 5 in this section.) This means that the baseball reaches its maximum height of 67 feet 2 seconds after being hit. The maximum point $(2, 67)$ is called the *vertex*.

The graph of a quadratic function is called a *parabola*; its maximum (or minimum, if the parabola opens upward) is the vertex.

The Vertex of a Parabola

The graph of the function $y = x^2$ is a parabola with vertex at the origin. All other functions in the quadratic family turn out to be transformations of this function. Let's first graph a quadratic function of the form $y = a(x - h)^2 + k$ and locate its vertex.

Example 1 Let $f(x) = x^2$ and $g(x) = -2(x + 1)^2 + 3$.

(a) Express the function g in terms of the function f.
(b) Sketch a graph of f. Transform the graph of f into the graph of g.
(c) Multiply out and simplify the formula for g.
(d) Explain how the formula for g can be used to obtain the vertex of the graph of g.

Solution

(a) Since $f(x + 1) = (x + 1)^2$, we have

$$g(x) = -2f(x + 1) + 3.$$

(b) The graph of $f(x) = x^2$ is shown in Figure 5.7. The graph of g is obtained from the graph of f in four steps, as shown in Figure 5.7.
(c) Multiplying out gives $g(x) = -2(x^2 + 2x + 1) + 3 = -2x^2 - 4x + 1$
(d) The vertex of the graph of f is $(0, 0)$. In Step 1 the vertex shifts 1 unit to the left (because of the $(x + 1)$ in the formula), and in Step 4 the vertex shifts 3 units up (because of the $+3$ in the formula). Thus, the vertex of the graph of g is at $(-1, 3)$.

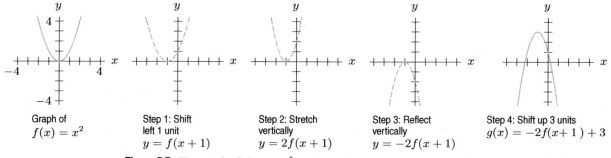

| Graph of $f(x) = x^2$ | Step 1: Shift left 1 unit $y = f(x+1)$ | Step 2: Stretch vertically $y = 2f(x+1)$ | Step 3: Reflect vertically $y = -2f(x+1)$ | Step 4: Shift up 3 units $g(x) = -2f(x+1)+3$ |

Figure 5.7: The graph of $f(x) = x^2$, on the left, is transformed in four steps into the graph of $g(x) = -2(x+1)^2 + 3$, on the right

In general, the graph of $g(x) = a(x - h)^2 + k$ is obtained from the graph of $f(x) = x^2$ by shifting horizontally $|h|$ units, stretching vertically by a factor of a (and reflecting vertically over the x-axis if $a < 0$), and shifting vertically $|k|$ units. In the process, the vertex is shifted from $(0, 0)$ to the point (h, k). The graph of the function is symmetrical about a vertical line through the vertex, called the *axis of symmetry*.

Formulas for Quadratic Functions

The function g in Example 1 can be written in two ways:

$$g(x) = -2(x + 1)^2 + 3$$

and

$$g(x) = -2x^2 - 4x + 1.$$

The first version is helpful for understanding the graph of the quadratic function and finding its vertex. In general, we have the following:

The **standard form** for a **quadratic function** is

$$y = ax^2 + bx + c, \quad \text{where } a, \ b, \ c \text{ are constants}, a \neq 0.$$

The **vertex form** is

$$y = a(x - h)^2 + k, \quad \text{where } a, \ h, \ k \text{ are constants}, a \neq 0.$$

The graph of a quadratic function is called a **parabola**. The parabola

- Has vertex (h, k)
- Has axis of symmetry $x = h$
- Opens upward if $a > 0$ or downward if $a < 0$

Thus, any quadratic function can be expressed in both standard form and vertex form. To convert from vertex form to standard form, we multiply out the squared term. To convert from standard form to vertex form, we *complete the square*.

Example 2   Put these quadratic functions into vertex form by completing the square and then graph them.

(a) $s(x) = x^2 - 6x + 8$ (b) $t(x) = -4x^2 - 12x - 8$

Solution   (a) To complete the square, find the square of half of the coefficient of the x-term, $(-6/2)^2 = 9$. Add and subtract this number after the x-term:

$$s(x) = \underbrace{x^2 - 6x + 9}_{\text{Perfect square}} - 9 + 8,$$

so

$$s(x) = (x - 3)^2 - 1.$$

The vertex of s is $(3, -1)$ and the axis of symmetry is the vertical line $x = 3$. There is no vertical stretch since $a = 1$, and the parabola opens upward. See Figure 5.8.

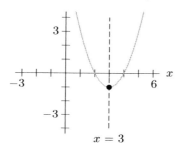

Figure 5.8: $s(x) = x^2 - 6x + 8$

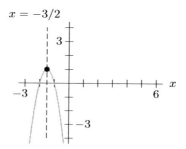

Figure 5.9: $t(x) = -4x^2 - 12x - 8$

(b) To complete the square, first factor out -4, the coefficient of x^2, giving

$$t(x) = -4(x^2 + 3x + 2).$$

Now add and subtract the square of half the coefficient of the x-term, $(3/2)^2 = 9/4$, inside the parentheses. This gives

$$t(x) = -4\left(\underbrace{x^2 + 3x + \frac{9}{4}}_{\text{Perfect square}} - \frac{9}{4} + 2 \right)$$

$$t(x) = -4\left(\left(x + \frac{3}{2}\right)^2 - \frac{1}{4} \right)$$

$$t(x) = -4\left(x + \frac{3}{2}\right)^2 + 1.$$

The vertex of t is $(-3/2, 1)$, the axis of symmetry is $x = -3/2$, the vertical stretch factor is 4, and the parabola opens downward. See Figure 5.9.

Finding a Formula From a Graph

If we know the vertex of a quadratic function and one other point, we can use the vertex form to find its formula.

Example 3   Find the formula for the quadratic function graphed in Figure 5.10.

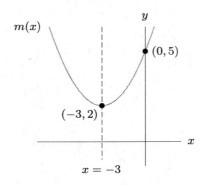

Figure 5.10

Solution   Since the vertex is given, we use the form $m(x) = a(x - h)^2 + k$ and find a, h, and k. The vertex is $(-3, 2)$, so $h = -3$ and $k = 2$. Thus,

$$m(x) = a(x - (-3))^2 + 2,$$

so

$$m(x) = a(x + 3)^2 + 2.$$

To find a, use the y-intercept $(0, 5)$. Substitute $x = 0$ and $y = m(0) = 5$ into the formula for $m(x)$ and solve for a:

$$5 = a(0 + 3)^2 + 2$$
$$3 = 9a$$
$$a = \frac{1}{3}.$$

Thus, the formula is

$$m(x) = \frac{1}{3}(x + 3)^2 + 2.$$

If we want the formula in standard form, we multiply out:

$$m(x) = \frac{1}{3}x^2 + 2x + 5.$$

Example 4   Find the equation of the parabola in Figure 5.11 using the factored form.

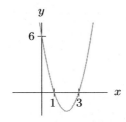

Figure 5.11

Solution   Since the parabola has x-intercepts at $x = 1$ and $x = 3$, its formula can be written as

$$y = a(x - 1)(x - 3).$$

Substituting $x = 0$, $y = 6$ gives

$$6 = a(3)$$
$$a = 2.$$

Thus, the equation is

$$y = 2(x - 1)(x - 3).$$

Multiplying out gives $y = 2x^2 - 8x + 6$.

Applications of Quadratic Functions

In applications, it is often useful to find the maximum or minimum value of a quadratic function. First, we return to the baseball example which started this section.

Example 5   For t in seconds, the height of a baseball in feet is given by the formula

$$y = f(t) = -16t^2 + 64t + 3.$$

Using algebra, find the maximum height reached by the baseball and the time at which the ball reaches the ground.

Solution   To find the maximum height, complete the square to find the vertex:

$$\begin{aligned}
y = f(t) &= -16(t^2 - 4t) + 3 \\
&= -16(t^2 - 4t + 4 - 4) + 3 \\
&= -16(t^2 - 4t + 4) - 16(-4) + 3 \\
&= -16(t - 2)^2 + 16 \cdot 4 + 3 \\
&= -16(t - 2)^2 + 67.
\end{aligned}$$

Thus, the vertex is at the point $(2, 67)$. This means that the ball reaches it maximum height of 67 feet at $t = 2$ seconds.

The time at which the ball hits the ground is found by solving $f(t) = 0$. We have

$$-16(t - 2)^2 + 67 = 0$$
$$(t - 2)^2 = \frac{67}{16}$$
$$t - 2 = \pm\sqrt{\frac{67}{16}} \approx \pm 2.046.$$

The solutions are $t \approx -0.046$ and $t \approx 4.046$. Since the ball was thrown at $t = 0$, we want $t \geq 0$. Thus, the ball hits the ground approximately 4.046 seconds after being hit.

Example 6   A city decides to make a park by fencing off a section of riverfront property. Funds are allotted to provide 80 meters of fence. The area enclosed will be a rectangle, but only three sides will be enclosed by fence—the other side will be bound by the river. What is the maximum area that can be enclosed in this way?

Solution   Two sides are perpendicular to the bank of the river and have equal length, which we call h. The other side is parallel to the bank of the river. Call its length b. See Figure 5.12. Since the fence is 80 meters long,

$$2h + b = 80$$
$$b = 80 - 2h.$$

The area of the park, A, is the product of the lengths of two adjacent sides, so

$$A = bh = (80 - 2h)h$$
$$= -2h^2 + 80h.$$

The function $A = -2h^2 + 80h$ is quadratic. Since the coefficient of h^2 is negative, the parabola opens downward and we have a maximum at the vertex. The zeros of this quadratic function are $h = 0$ and $h = 40$, so the axis of symmetry, which is midway between the zeros, is $h = 20$. The vertex of a parabola occurs on its axis of symmetry. Thus, substituting $h = 20$ gives the maximum area:

$$A = (80 - 2 \cdot 20)20 = (80 - 40)20 = 40 \cdot 20 = 800 \text{ meter}^2.$$

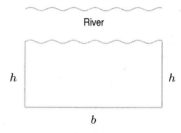

Figure 5.12

Exercises and Problems for Section 5.2

Exercises

1. The vertex of the parabola in Example 3 is $(-3, 2)$ and the y-intercept is $(0, 5)$. We used the vertex form of a quadratic to find its formula. Now use the standard form to obtain the same result.

2. The intercepts of the parabola in Example 4 are $x = 1$, $x = 3$, and $y = 6$. We used the factored form of a quadratic to find its equation. Now use the vertex form to obtain the same result.

In Exercises 3–8, find a formula for the parabola.

3.

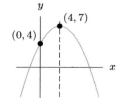

4.

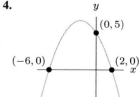

5.

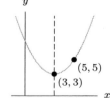

6.

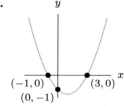

7.

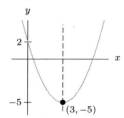

8.

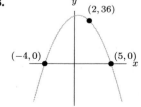

9. Sketch the quadratic functions given in standard form. Identify the values of the parameters a, b, and c. Label the zeros, axis of symmetry, vertex, and y-intercept.

   (a) $g(x) = x^2 + 3$ (b) $f(x) = -2x^2 + 4x + 16$

10. Put in vertex form by completing the square and graph without a calculator: $y - 12x = 2x^2 + 19$.

11. Complete the square on $r(x) = x^2 - 12x + 28$. Find the vertex and axis of symmetry.

12. Find the vertex and axis of symmetry of the graph of $v(t) = t^2 + 11t - 4$.

13. Find the vertex and axis of symmetry of the graph of $w(x) = -3x^2 - 30x + 31$.

14. Find a formula for the quadratic function f with zeros at $x = 1$ and $x = 2$ and vertex at $(3/2, -1)$.

15. By completing the square, find the zeros of $y = x^2 + 8x + 5$ exactly.

16. Show that the function $y = -x^2 + 7x - 13$ has no real zeros.

Problems

17. Let $f(x) = x^2$ and let $g(x) = (x - 3)^2 + 2$.
    (a) Give the formula for g in terms of f, and describe the relationship between f and g in words.
    (b) Is g a quadratic function? If so, find its standard form and the parameters a, b, and c.
    (c) Graph g, labeling all important features.

18. (a) Graph $h(x) = -2x^2 - 8x - 8$.
    (b) Compare the graphs of $h(x)$ and $f(x) = x^2$. How are these two graphs related? Be specific.

19. Graph $y = x^2 - 10x + 25$ and $y = x^2$. Use a shift transformation to explain the relationship between the two graphs.

20. Let f be a quadratic function whose graph is a concave up parabola with a vertex at $(1, -1)$, and a zero at the origin.
    (a) Graph $y = f(x)$.
    (b) Determine a formula for $f(x)$.
    (c) Determine the range of f.
    (d) Find any other zeros.

21. If we know a quadratic function f has a zero at $x = -1$ and vertex at $(1, 4)$, do we have enough information to find a formula for this function? If your answer is yes, find it; if not, give your reasons.

22. Suppose $f(x) = ax^2 + bx + c$, with $a \neq 0$. Without any calculation, explain briefly why

$$f\left(\frac{-b + \sqrt{b^2 - 4ac}}{2a}\right) = f\left(\frac{-b - \sqrt{b^2 - 4ac}}{2a}\right) = 0.$$

23. Gwendolyn, a pleasant parabola, was taking a peaceful nap when her dream turned into a nightmare: she dreamt that a low-flying pterodactyl was swooping towards her. Startled, she flipped over the horizontal axis, darted up (vertically) by three units, and to the left (horizontally) by two units. Finally she woke up and realized that her

equation was $y = (x - 1)^2 + 3$. What was her equation before she had the bad dream?

24. Table 5.4 shows the percentage US households engaged in gardening[2] each year from 1990 to 1993.
    (a) Show that this data can be approximated by the quadratic function $q(x) = -\frac{1}{2}x^2 - \frac{3}{2}x + 80$, where x is in years since 1990.
    (b) According to this model, when was the percentage highest? What was that percentage?
    (c) When is the percentage predicted to be 50%?
    (d) What does this model predict for the year 2000? 2005?
    (e) Is this a good model?

Table 5.4

Year	1990	1991	1992	1993
Percentage	80	78	75	71

25. A tomato is thrown vertically into the air at time $t = 0$. Its height, $d(t)$ (in feet), above the ground at time t (in seconds) is given by

$$d(t) = -16t^2 + 48t.$$

   (a) Graph $d(t)$.
   (b) Find t when $d(t) = 0$. What is happening to the tomato the first time $d(t) = 0$? The second time?
   (c) When does the tomato reach its maximum height?
   (d) What is the maximum height that the tomato reaches?

26. An espresso stand finds that its weekly profit is a function of the price, x, it charges per cup. If x is in dollars, the weekly profit is $P(x) = -2900x^2 + 7250x - 2900$ dollars.
    (a) Approximate the maximum profit and the price per cup that produces that profit.

[2]Data from *The American Almanac: 1995 – 1996*. (Texas: The Reference Press, 1995).

(b) Which function, $P(x - 2)$ or $P(x) - 2$, gives a function that has the same maximum profit? What price per cup produces that maximum profit?

(c) Which function, $P(x + 50)$ or $P(x) + 50$, gives a function where the price per cup that produces the maximum profit remains unchanged? What is the maximum profit?

27. If you have a string of length 50 cm, what are the dimensions of the rectangle of maximum area that you can enclose with your string? Explain your reasoning. What about a string of length k cm?

28. A football player kicks a ball at an angle of $37°$ above the ground with an initial speed of 20 meters/second. The height, h, as a function of the horizontal distance traveled, d, is given by:

$$h = 0.75d - 0.0192d^2.$$

(a) Graph the path the ball follows.
(b) When the ball hits the ground, how far is it from the spot where the football player kicked it?

(c) What is the maximum height the ball reaches during its flight?
(d) What is the horizontal distance the ball has traveled when it reaches its maximum height?[3]

29. A ballet dancer jumps in the air. The height, $h(t)$, in feet, of the dancer at time t, in seconds since the start of the jump, is given by[4]

$$h(t) = -16t^2 + 16Tt,$$

where T is the total time in seconds that the ballet dancer is in the air.

(a) Why does this model apply only for $0 \le t \le T$?
(b) When, in terms of T, does the maximum height of the jump occur?
(c) Show that the time, T, that the dancer is in the air is related to H, the maximum height of the jump, by the equation

$$H = 4T^2.$$

5.3 SOLVING EQUATIONS THAT ARE QUADRATIC IN FORM

In the previous sections, you worked with quadratic functions and solved quadratic equations using several methods. Now we turn our attention to equations that are not, strictly speaking, quadratic, but can still be solved by using the same methods. These equations can all be written in the following form:

$$au^2 + bu + c = 0$$

where u is some other expression. The variable factor in the first term is the square of the variable factor in the second term. We call these equations *quadratic in form* and we can solve them for u by factoring or by using the quadratic formula. After that we have additional steps.

Example 1   Solve for x: $x^8 - 17x^4 + 16 = 0$

Solution   First, notice the exponents in this equation and recall that $(x^4)^2 = x^8$. This means that the variable factor in the first term is the square of the variable factor in the second term so this equation is quadratic in form. Recall from Section 4.5 that we can use a substitution to "create a similar but simpler problem". The substitution is motivated by a desire to have the equation look quadratic. We can do this if we use the substitution: $u = x^4$

The equation now becomes

$$u^2 - 17u + 16 = 0$$

We solve this quadratic equation by factoring:

$$(u - 1)(u - 16) = 0$$

$$u - 1 = 0 \quad \text{or} \quad u - 16 = 0$$

$$u = 1 \quad \text{or} \quad u = 16$$

---

[3]Adapted from R. Halliday, D. Resnick, and K. Krane, *Physics*. (New York: Wiley, 1992), p. 58.
[4]K. Laws, *The Physics of Dance*. (Schirmer, 1984).

Now substitute back so that u is replaced with x^4:

$$x^4 = 1 \quad \text{or} \quad x^4 = 16$$

Now solve each of these equations (real solutions only, not complex):

$$x = \pm 1 \quad \text{or} \quad x = \pm 2$$

Thus the equation $x^8 - 17x^4 + 16 = 0$ has four solutions and the solution set is: $\{-2, -1, 1, 2\}$
Graphical check:

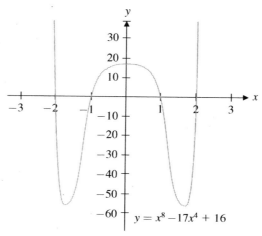

Figure 5.13

Figure 5.13 shows the graph of $y = x^8 - 17x^4 + 16$. To solve the equation $x^8 - 17x^4 + 16 = 0$ graphically, we look for the zeros or x-intercepts of the function. We can see from Figure 5.13 that the graph crosses the x-axis at $-2, -1, 1,$ and 2 so each solution we found is correct.

Matched Problem 1

Solve the equation $x^4 - 13x^2 + 36 = 0$. Check your solution graphically.

Example 2

Solve for t: $(t + 5)^2 + 4(t + 5) - 5 = 0$

Solution

Of course, we *could* expand and combine like terms. However, notice that the variable factor in the first term, $(t + 5)^2$, is the square of the variable factor in the second term, $(t + 5)$, so we can treat this as quadratic in form.

Let $u = t + 5$:
$$u^2 + 4u - 5 = 0$$
Factor: $\quad (u + 5)(u - 1) = 0$
Solve for u : $\quad u + 5 = 0 \quad \text{or} \quad u - 1 = 0$
$\qquad\qquad\quad u = -5 \quad \text{or} \quad u = 1$
Substitute back: $\quad t + 5 = -5 \quad \text{or} \quad t + 5 = 1$
Solve for t : $\quad t = -10 \quad \text{or} \quad t = -4$

Thus the solution set for the equation $(t + 5)^2 + 4(t + 5) - 5 = 0$ is $\{-10, -4\}$.

**Matched
Problem 2**   Solve the equation $(k - 4)^2 - 4(k - 4) - 12 = 0$ for k.

Trigonometric Equations

Example 3   Solve for x: $2 \sin^2 x + \sin x - 1 = 0$.

Solution   This equation looks a bit different and the first thing we have to remember is that $\sin^2 x$ means $(\sin x)^2$, so once again the variable factor in the first term is the square of the variable factor in the second term and the equation is quadratic in form.

$$\begin{array}{lll} \text{Let } u = \sin x : & 2u^2 + u - 1 = 0 \\ \text{Factor:} & (2u - 1)(u + 1) = 0 \\ \text{Solve for } u : & 2u - 1 = 0 \text{ or } u + 1 = 0 \\ & u = \dfrac{1}{2} \text{ or } u = -1 \\ \text{Substitute back:} & \sin x = \dfrac{1}{2} \text{ or } \sin x = -1 \end{array}$$

We now have trigonometric equations to solve using trigonometry facts (if you need to review, see Section 4.1):

If $\sin x = \dfrac{1}{2}$ then $x = \dfrac{\pi}{6} + 2k\pi$, $x = \dfrac{5\pi}{6} + 2k\pi$.

If $\sin x = -1$ then $x = \dfrac{3\pi}{2} + 2k\pi$.

Thus the solution set for the equation $2 \sin^2 x + \sin x - 1 = 0$ is

$$\left\{ \dfrac{\pi}{6} + 2k\pi, \; \dfrac{5\pi}{6} + 2k\pi, \; \dfrac{3\pi}{2} + 2k\pi \right\}.$$

Graphical check:

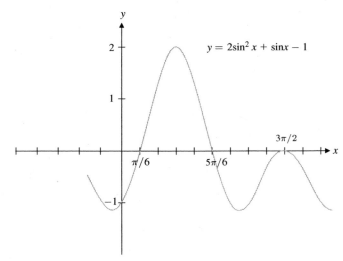

Figure 5.14

Figure 5.14 shows that the zeros of the function $y = 2\sin^2 x + \sin x - 1$ on its first positive cycle are $\frac{\pi}{6}$, $\frac{5\pi}{6}$, and $\frac{3\pi}{2}$.

Matched Problem 3

Solve the equation $2\cos^2 x - \cos x - 1 = 0$ for x.

Example 4

Solve for x: $\cos(2x) = \sin x$

Solution

Notice that the argument of the cosine function is $2x$ whereas the argument of the sine function is x. We can make the argument of the two functions the same if we use an identity for $\cos(2x)$. Recall, however, that there are three versions of this identity:

$$\cos(2x) = \cos^2 x - \sin^2 x$$
$$\cos(2x) = 2\cos^2 x - 1$$
$$\cos(2x) = 1 - 2\sin^2 x$$

Looking at these three versions and also at the equation we want to solve, which has a $\sin x$, the best choice would be the version of the identity that has only sines in it.
We will replace $\cos(2x)$ with $1 - 2\sin^2 x$:

$$1 - 2\sin^2 x = \sin x$$

Notice that this equation is quadratic in $\sin x$. Rewrite the equation in standard form:

$$2\sin^2 x + \sin x - 1 = 0$$

Notice that this is the equation from Example 3, so looking back to that example, we see that the solutions are $x = \frac{\pi}{6} + 2k\pi$, $x = \frac{5\pi}{6} + 2k\pi$, and $x = \frac{3\pi}{2} + 2k\pi$.

Matched Problem 4

Solve the equation $\cos(2x) = \cos x$ for x.

Example 5

Solve for x: $3\cos x = 2\sin^2 x$

Solution

In this equation there are two different trigonometric functions, so, using the strategy of the previous example, we look for an identity that will allow us to work with only one function. We can use the Pythagorean Identity to rewrite $\sin^2 x$ in terms of $\cos^2 x$:

$$\sin^2 x = 1 - \cos^2 x$$

Now the equation becomes:

$$3\cos x = 2(1 - \cos^2 x)$$
$$3\cos x = 2 - 2\cos^2 x$$

This equation is now quadratic in $\cos x$, so rewrite in standard form. For ease, make the leading coefficient positive.

$$2\cos^2 x + 3\cos x - 2 = 0$$

Because the equation is quadratic in $\cos x$, we substitute $u = \cos x$:

$$2u^2 + 3u - 2 = 0$$

Factor: $(2u - 1)(u + 2) = 0$

Solve for u : $2u - 1 = 0 \quad$ or $\quad u + 2 = 0$

$$u = \frac{1}{2} \quad \text{or} \quad u = -2$$

Substitute back: $\cos x = \dfrac{1}{2} \quad$ or $\quad \cos x = -2$

Remember that the range of $\cos x$ is $[-1, 1]$, so the equation $\cos x = -2$ has no solutions. The solutions to $\cos x = \frac{1}{2}$ are $x = \frac{\pi}{3} + 2k\pi$ or $x = \frac{5\pi}{3} + 2k\pi$.

Thus the solutions to the equation $3\cos x = 2\sin^2 x$ are $x = \frac{\pi}{3} + 2k\pi$ and $x = \frac{5\pi}{3} + 2k\pi$.

Observation: Although we have found all the solutions to this equation, let's see what the steps would look like if we omitted the substitution step.

We arrived at the equation

$$2\cos^2 x + 3\cos x - 2 = 0$$

Notice that this equation is *quadratic in* $\cos(x)$. We can factor:

$$(2\cos x - 1)(\cos x + 2) = 0$$

Now solve for $\cos x$:

$$2\cos x - 1 = 0 \quad \text{or} \quad \cos x + 2 = 0$$

$$\cos x = \frac{1}{2} \quad \text{or} \quad \cos x = -2$$

Notice that these are the same equations we obtained after substituting back in our example above. The rest of the steps are the same.

You might try omitting the substitution step as you try more examples.

Matched Problem 5

Solve the equation $5\sin x - 1 = 2\cos^2 x$ for x.

Example 6

Solve for θ: $\sin^2(2\theta) = 1$

Solution

You might be tempted to start this solution by using the double-angle identity for sine. However, because there is no other function in the equation, let's put the equation in standard form:

$$\sin^2(2\theta) - 1 = 0$$

This is the difference of two squares, so factor:

$$(\sin(2\theta) + 1)(\sin(2\theta) - 1) = 0$$

Solve for $\sin(2\theta)$:

$$\sin(2\theta) + 1 = 0 \quad \text{or} \quad \sin(2\theta) - 1 = 0$$
$$\sin(2\theta) = -1 \quad \text{or} \quad \sin(2\theta) = 1$$

Solve for 2θ:

$$2\theta = \frac{3\pi}{2} + 2k\pi \quad \text{or} \quad 2\theta = \frac{\pi}{2} + 2k\pi$$

Notice that these can be combined:

$$2\theta = \frac{\pi}{2} + k\pi$$

Now solve for θ:

$$\theta = \frac{\pi}{4} + \frac{k\pi}{2}$$

Thus the solutions to the equation $\sin^2(2\theta) = 1$ are $\theta = \frac{\pi}{4} + \frac{k\pi}{2}$.

Alternate Method:

Recall that to solve an equation such as $u^2 = 16$, we can take square roots and get $u = \pm 4$. If we use this strategy on

$$\sin^2(2\theta) = 1$$

we get

$$\sin(2\theta) = \pm 1$$

or

$$\sin(2\theta) = -1 \quad \text{or} \quad \sin(2\theta) = 1$$

This is the same outcome we got above, so either strategy will lead to the same conclusion.

Matched Problem 6

Solve the equation $\cos^2(3t) = 1$ for t.

Answers to Matched Problems

1. $x = \pm 2,\ x = \pm 3$

2. $k = 2,\ k = 10$

3. and 4. $x = 2k\pi,\ x = \frac{2\pi}{3} + 2k\pi,\ x = \frac{4\pi}{3} + 2k\pi$

5. $x = \frac{\pi}{6} + 2k\pi,\ x = \frac{5\pi}{6} + 2k\pi$

6. $t = \frac{k\pi}{3}$

Exercises for Section 5.3

For problems 1–22, solve the equation (real number solutions only). Check your answers.

1. $x^4 - 26x^2 + 25 = 0$

2. $x^6 + 9x^3 + 8 = 0$

3. $(w + 6)^2 - 7(w + 6) + 10 = 0$

4. $(t - 10)^2 - 3(t - 10) - 40 = 0$

5. $4\sin^2 x - 1 = 0$

6. $2\cos^2 x - 1 = 0$

7. $\sec^2 x - 2 = 0$

8. $4\cos^2 x - 4\cos x + 1 = 0$

9. $2\sin^2 x - \sin x - 1 = 0$

10. $\sin^2 x - 3 = 2\sin x$

11. $2\sin^2(2x) - \sin(2x) - 1 = 0$

12. $\sin^2(2x) - 3 = 2\sin(2x)$

13. $\sin^2 x = 4 - 2\cos^2 x$

14. $2\cos^2 x + \sin x = 1$

15. $2\sin^2 t + \sin(2t) = 0$

16. $\cos^2(\theta) = \dfrac{1}{2}\sin(2\theta)$

17. $\cos(2x) + \cos(x) = 2$

18. $\cos(2\theta) + \sin^2(\theta) = 0$

19. $\cos(2t) + \cos(t) = 0$

20. $2\cos^2 x + 3\sin x = 0$

21. $3\tan^3 x - \tan x = 0$

22. $\tan^5 x = 9\tan x$

5.4 POWER FUNCTIONS

Proportionality and Power Functions

The following two examples introduce proportionality and power functions.

Example 1   The area, A, of a circle is proportional to the square of its radius, r:

$$A = \pi r^2.$$

Example 2   The weight, w, of an object is inversely proportional to the square of the object's distance, d, from the earth's center:[5]

$$w = \frac{k}{d^2} = kd^{-2}.$$

For an object with weight 44 pounds on the surface of the earth, which is about 3959 miles from the earth's center, we get the data listed in Table 5.5 and graphed in Figure 5.15.

Table 5.5 *Weight of an object, w, inversely proportional to the square of the objects's distance, d, from the earth's center*

d, miles	$w = f(d)$, lbs
4000	43.3
5000	27.8
6000	19.2
7000	14.1
8000	10.8

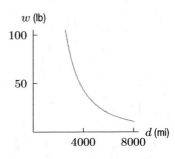

Figure 5.15: Weight, w, inversely proportional to the square of the object's distance, d, from the earth's center

---

[5]There is a distinction between mass and weight. For example, an astronaut in orbit may be weightless, but he still has mass.

A quantity y is (directly) **proportional to a power** of x if

$$y = kx^n, \qquad k \text{ and } n \text{ are constants.}$$

A quantity y is **inversely proportional** to x^n if

$$y = \frac{k}{x^n}, \qquad k \text{ and } n \text{ are constants, with } n > 0.$$

The functions in Examples 1 and 2 are power functions. Generalizing, we define:

A **power function** is a function of the form

$$f(x) = kx^p, \qquad \text{where } k \text{ and } p \text{ are constants.}$$

Example 3   Which of the following functions are power functions? For each power function, state the value of the constants k and p in the formula $y = kx^p$.

(a) $f(x) = 13\sqrt[3]{x}$ (b) $g(x) = 2(x+5)^3$ (c) $u(x) = \sqrt{\dfrac{25}{x^3}}$ (d) $v(x) = 6 \cdot 3^x$

Solution   The functions f and u are power functions; the functions g and v are not.

(a) The function $f(x) = 13\sqrt[3]{x}$ is a power function because we can write its formula as

$$f(x) = 13x^{1/3}.$$

Here, $k = 13$ and $p = 1/3$.

(b) Although the value of $g(x) = 2(x+5)^3$ is proportional to the cube of $x + 5$, it is *not* proportional to a power of x. We cannot write $g(x)$ in the form $g(x) = kx^p$; thus, g is not a power function.

(c) We can rewrite the formula for $u(x) = \sqrt{25/x^3}$ as

$$u(x) = \frac{\sqrt{25}}{\sqrt{x^3}} = \frac{5}{(x^3)^{1/2}} = \frac{5}{x^{3/2}} = 5x^{-3/2}.$$

Thus, u is a power function. Here, $k = 5$ and $p = -3/2$.

(d) Although the value of $v(x) = 6 \cdot 3^x$ is proportional to a power of 3, the power is not a constant—it is the variable x. In fact, $v(x) = 6 \cdot 3^x$ is an exponential function, not a power function. Notice that $y = 6 \cdot x^3$ is a power function. However, $6 \cdot x^3$ and $6 \cdot 3^x$ are quite different.

The Effect of the Power p

We now study functions whose constant of proportionality is $k = 1$ so that we can focus on the effect of the power p.

Graphs of the Special Cases $y = x^0$ and $y = x^1$

The power functions corresponding to $p = 0$ and $p = 1$ are both linear. The graph of $y = x^0 = 1$ is a horizontal line through the point $(1, 1)$. The graph of $y = x^1 = x$ is a line through the origin with slope $+1$.

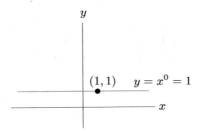

Figure 5.16: Graph of $y = x^0 = 1$

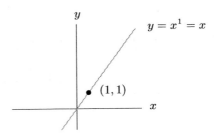

Figure 5.17: Graph of $y = x^1 = x$

Positive Integer Powers: $y = x^3,\ x^5,\ x^7\ldots$, and $y = x^2,\ x^4, x^6\ldots$

The graphs of all power functions with p a positive even integer have the same characteristic $\bigcup$-shape and are symmetric about the y-axis. For instance, the graphs of $y = x^2$ and $y = x^4$ in Figure 5.18 are similar in shape, although the graph of $y = x^4$ is flatter near the origin and steeper away from the origin than the graph of $y = x^2$.

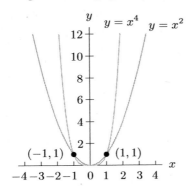

Figure 5.18: Graphs of positive even powers of x are $\bigcup$-shaped

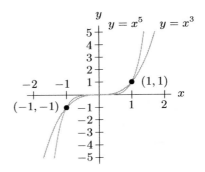

Figure 5.19: Graphs of positive odd powers of x are "chair"-shaped

The graphs of power functions with p a positive odd integer resemble the side view of a chair and are symmetric about the origin. Figure 5.19 shows the graphs of $y = x^3$ and $y = x^5$. The graph of $y = x^5$ is flatter near the origin and steeper far from the origin than the graph of $y = x^3$.

Negative Integer Powers: $y = x^{-1}, x^{-3}, x^{-5}, \ldots$ and $y = x^{-2}, x^{-4}, x^{-6}, \ldots$

For negative powers, if we rewrite

$$y = x^{-1} = \frac{1}{x}$$

and

$$y = x^{-2} = \frac{1}{x^2},$$

then it is clear that as $x > 0$ increases, the denominators increase and the functions decrease. The graphs of power functions with odd negative powers, $y = x^{-3}$, x^{-5}, ... resemble the graph of $y = x^{-1} = 1/x$. The graphs of even integer powers, $y = x^{-4}$, x^{-6}, ... are similar in shape to the graph of $y = x^{-2} = 1/x^2$. See Figures 5.20 and 5.21.

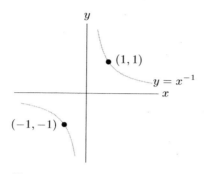

Figure 5.20: Graph of $y = x^{-1} = 1/x$ **Figure 5.21**: Graph of $y = x^{-2} = 1/x^2$

We see in Figures 5.20 and 5.21 that $y = 0$ is a horizontal asymptote and $x = 0$ is a vertical asymptote for the graphs of $y = 1/x$ and $y = 1/x^2$.

Numerically, the values of $1/x$ and $1/x^2$ can be made as close to zero as we like by choosing a sufficiently large x. See Table 5.6. Graphically, this means that the curves $y = 1/x$ and $y = 1/x^2$ get closer and closer to the x-axis for large values of x. We write $y \to 0$ as $x \to \infty$.

Table 5.6 *Values of x^{-1} and x^{-2} approach zero as x grows large*

x	0	10	20	30	40	50
$y = 1/x$	Undefined	0.1	0.05	0.033	0.025	0.02
$y = 1/x^2$	Undefined	0.01	0.0025	0.0011	0.0006	0.0004

On the other hand, as x gets close to zero, the values of $1/x$ and $1/x^2$ get very large. See Table 5.7. Graphically, this means that the curves $y = 1/x$ and $y = 1/x^2$ get very close to the y-axis as x gets close to zero.

Table 5.7 *Values of x^{-1} and x^{-2} grow large as x approaches zero from the positive side*

x	0.1	0.05	0.01	0.001	0.0001	0
$y = 1/x$	10	20	100	1000	10,000	Undefined
$y = 1/x^2$	100	400	10,000	1,000,000	100,000,000	Undefined

Graphs of Positive Fractional Powers: $y = x^{1/2}, x^{1/3}, x^{1/4}, \dots$

Figure 5.22 shows the graphs of $y = x^{1/2}$ and $y = x^{1/4}$. These graphs have the same shape, although $y = x^{1/4}$ is steeper near the origin and flatter away from the origin than $y = x^{1/2}$. The same can be said about the graphs of $y = x^{1/3}$ and $y = x^{1/5}$ in Figure 5.23. In general, if n is a positive integer, then the graph of $y = x^{1/n}$ resembles the graph of $y = x^{1/2}$ if n is even; if n is odd, the graph resembles the graph of $y = x^{1/3}$.

Notice that the graphs of $y = x^{1/2}$ and $y = x^{1/3}$ bend in a direction opposite to that of the graphs of $y = x^2$ and x^3. For example, the graph of $y = x^2$ is concave up, but the graph of $y = x^{1/2}$ is concave down. However, all these functions become infinitely large as x increases.

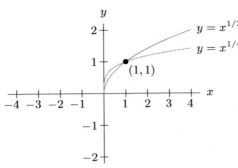

Figure 5.22: The graphs of $y = x^{1/2}$ and $y = x^{1/4}$

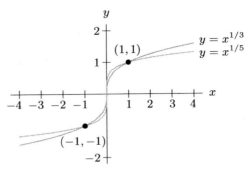

Figure 5.23: The graphs of $y = x^{1/3}$ and $y = x^{1/5}$

Example 4   The radius of a sphere is directly proportional to the cube root of its volume. If a sphere of radius 18.2 cm has a volume of $25{,}252.4$ cm^3, what is the radius of a sphere whose volume is $30{,}000$ cm^3?

Solution   Since the radius of the sphere is proportional to the cube root of its volume, we know that

$$r = kV^{1/3}, \qquad \text{for } k \text{ constant.}$$

We also know that $r = 18.2$ cm when $V = 25{,}252.4$ cm^3, therefore

$$18.2 = k(25{,}252.4)^{1/3}$$

giving

$$k = \frac{18.2}{(25{,}252.4)^{1/3}} \approx 0.620.$$

Thus, when $V = 30{,}000$, we get $r = 0.620(30{,}000)^{1/3} \approx 19.3$, so the radius of the sphere is approximately 19.3 cm.

Finding the Formula for a Power Function

As is the case for linear and exponential functions, the formula of a power function can be found from two points on its graph.

Example 5   Water is leaking out of a container with a hole in the bottom. Torricelli's Law states that at any instant, the velocity v with which water escapes from the container is a power function of d, the depth of the water at that moment. When $d = 1$ foot, then $v = 8$ ft/sec; when $d = 1/4$ foot, then $v = 4$ ft/sec. Express v as a function of d.

Solution   Torricelli's Law tells us that $v = kd^p$, where k and p are constants. The fact that $v = 8$ when $d = 1$, gives $8 = k(1)^p$, so $k = 8$, and therefore $v = 8d^p$. Also $v = 4$ when $d = 1/4$, so

$$4 = 8 \left(\frac{1}{4} \right)^p .$$

Rewriting $(1/4)^p = 1/4^p$, we can solve for 4^p:

$$4 = 8 \cdot \frac{1}{4^p}$$

$$4^p = \frac{8}{4} = 2.$$

Since $4^{1/2} = 2$, we must have $p = 1/2$. Therefore we have $v = 8d^{1/2}$. *Note*: Toricelli's Law is often written in the form $v = \sqrt{2gd}$, where $g = 32$ ft/sec^2 is the acceleration due to gravity.

Exercises and Problems for Section 5.4

Exercises

In Exercises 1–6, is y a power function of x? If so, write it in the form $y = kx^p$.

1. $y = 6x^3 + 2$

2. $3y = 9x^2$

3. $y - 1 = 2x^2 - 1$

4. $y = 4(x + 7)^2$

5. $y = 4(x - 2)(x + 2) + 16$ **6.** $y - 9 = (x + 3)(x - 3)$

Do the power functions in Exercises 7–10 appear to have odd, even, or fractional powers?

7. 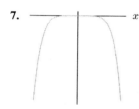   **8.**

9. 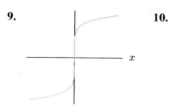   **10.**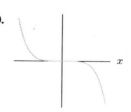

In Exercises 11–13, find a power function through the two points.

11. $(1, 5)$ $(3, 27)$ **12.** $(7, 8)$ $(1, 0.7)$ **13.** $(6, 17)$ $(1, 2)$

14. Suppose y is directly proportional to x. If $y = 6$ when $x = 4$, find the constant of proportionality and write the

formula for y as a function of x. Use your formula to find x when $y = 8$.

15. Suppose y is inversely proportional to x. If $y = 6$ when $x = 4$, find the constant of proportionality and write the formula for y as a function of x. Use your formula to find x when $y = 8$.

16. Suppose c is directly proportional to the square of d. If $c = 45$ when $d = 3$, find the constant of proportionality and write the formula for c as a function of d. Use your formula to find c when $d = 5$.

17. Suppose c is inversely proportional to the square of d. If $c = 45$ when $d = 3$, find the constant of proportionality and write the formula for c as a function of d. Use your formula to find c when $d = 5$.

In Problems 18–21, find possible formulas for the power functions.

18.

x	0	1	2	3
$j(x)$	0	2	16	54

19.

x	2	3	4	5
$f(x)$	12	27	48	75

20.

x	-6	-2	3	4
$g(x)$	36	$4/3$	$-9/2$	$-32/3$

21.

x	-2	$-1/2$	$1/4$	4
$h(x)$	$-1/2$	-8	-32	$-1/8$

Problems

22. Compare the graphs of $y = x^{-2}$, $y = x^{-4}$, and $y = x^{-6}$. Describe the similarities and differences.

23. Describe the behavior of $y = x^{-10}$ and $y = -x^{10}$ as

   (a) $x \to 0$ **(b)** $x \to \infty$ **(c)** $x \to -\infty$

24. Describe the behavior of $y = x^{-3}$ and $y = x^{1/3}$ as

   (a) $x \to 0$ from the right   **(b)** $x \to \infty$

25. If $f(x) = kx^p$, p an integer, show that f is an even function if p is even, and an odd function if p is odd.

26. Three ounces of broiled ground beef contains 245 calories.[6] Is the number of calories directly or inversely proportional to the number of ounces? Explain your reasoning and write a formula for the proportion. How many calories are there in 4 ounces of broiled hamburger?

27. **(a)** One of the graphs in Figure 5.24 is $y = x^n$ and the other is $y = x^{1/n}$, where n is a positive integer. Which is which? How do you know?

   (b) What are the coordinates of point A?

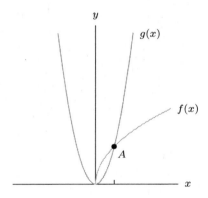

Figure 5.24

28. Figure 5.25 shows $g(x)$, a mystery power function.

   (a) If you learn that the point $(-1, 3)$ lies on its graph, do you have enough information to write a formula for $g(x)$?

   (b) If you are told that the point $(1, -3)$ also lies on the graph, what new deductions can you make?

   (c) If the point $(2, -96)$ lies on the graph g, in addition to the points already given, state three other points which also lie on it.

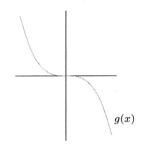

Figure 5.25

29. Figure 5.26 is a graph of the power function $y = c(t)$. Is $c(t) = 1/t$ the only possible formula for c? Could there be others?

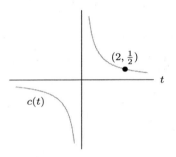

Figure 5.26

30. A 30-second commercial during Super Bowl XXXVI in 2002 cost advertisers $2.0 million. For the first Super Bowl in 1967, an advertiser could have purchased approximately 22.989 minutes of advertising time for the same amount of money.[7]

   (a) Assuming that cost is proportional to time, find the cost of advertising, in dollars/second, during the 1967 and 2002 Super Bowls.

   (b) How many times more expensive was Super Bowl advertising in 2002 than in 1967?

31. A group of friends rent a house at the beach for spring break. If nine of them share the house, it costs $150 each. Is the cost to each person directly or inversely proportional to the number of people sharing the house? Explain your reasoning and write a formula for the proportion. How many people are needed to share the house if each student wants to pay a maximum of $100 each?

32. Driving at 55 mph, it takes approximately 3.5 hours to drive from Long Island to Albany, NY. Is the time the drive takes directly or inversely proportional to the speed? Explain your reasoning and write a formula for the

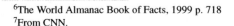

[6]The World Almanac Book of Facts, 1999 p. 718
[7]From CNN.

proportion. To get to Albany in 3 hours, how fast would you have to drive?

33. On a map, 1/2 inch represents 5 miles. Is the map distance between two locations directly or inversely proportional to the actual distance which separates the two locations? Explain your reasoning and write a formula for the proportion. How far apart are two towns if the distance between these two towns on the map is 3.25 inches?

34. The circulation time of a mammal—that is, the average time it takes for all the blood in the body to circulate once and return to the heart—is governed by the equation

$$t = 17.4m^{1/4}$$

where m is the body mass of the mammal in kilograms, and t is the circulation time in seconds.[8]

(a) Complete Table 5.8 which shows typical body masses in kilograms for various mammals.[9]
(b) If the circulation time of one mammal is twice that of another, what is the relationship between their body masses?

Table 5.8

Animal	Body mass (kg)	Circulation time (sec)
Blue whale	91000	
African elephant	5450	
White rhinoceros	3000	
Hippopotamus	2520	
Black rhinoceros	1170	
Horse	700	
Lion	180	
Human	70	

35. A volcano erupts in a powerful explosion. The sound from the explosion is heard in all directions for many hundreds of kilometers. The speed of sound is about 340 meters per second.

(a) Fill in Table 5.9 showing the distance, d, that the sound of the explosion has traveled at time t. Write a formula for d as a function t.
(b) How long after the explosion will a person living 200 km away hear the explosion?
(c) Fill Table 5.9 showing the land area, A, over which the explosion can be heard as a function of time. Write a formula for A as a function of t.
(d) The average population density around the volcano is 31 people per square kilometer. Write a formula

for P as function of t, where P is the number of people who have heard the explosion at time t.
(e) Graph the function $P = f(t)$. How long will it take until 1 million people have heard the explosion?

Table 5.9

Time, t	5 sec	10 sec	1 min	5 min
Distance, d (km)				
Area, A (km^2)				

36. The thrust, T, delivered by a ship's propeller is proportional[10] to the square of the propeller rotation speed, R, times the fourth power of the propeller diameter, D.

(a) Write a formula for T in terms of R and D.
(b) What happens to the thrust if the propeller speed is doubled?
(c) What happens to the thrust if the propeller diameter is doubled?
(d) If the propeller diameter is increased by 50%, by how much can the propeller speed be reduced to deliver the same thrust?

37. Two oil tankers crash in the Pacific ocean. The spreading oil slick has a circular shape, and the radius of the circle is increasing at 200 meters per hour.

(a) Express the radius of the spill, r, as a power function of time, t, in hours since the crash.
(b) Express the area of the spill, A, as a power function of time, t.
(c) Clean-up efforts begin 7 hours after the spill. How large an area is covered by oil at that time?

38. The following questions involve the behavior of the power function $y = x^{-p}$, for p a positive integer. If a distinction between even and odd values of p is significant, the significance should be indicated.

(a) What is the domain of $y = x^{-p}$? What is the range?
(b) What symmetries does the graph of $y = x^{-p}$ have?
(c) What is the behavior of $y = x^{-p}$ as $x \to 0$?
(d) What is the behavior of $y = x^{-p}$ for large positive values of x? For large negative values of x?

39. Let $f(x) = 16x^4$ and $g(x) = 4x^2$.

(a) If $f(x) = g(h(x))$, find a possible formula for $h(x)$, assuming $h(x) \le 0$ for all x.
(b) If $f(x) = j(2g(x))$, find a possible formula for $j(x)$, assuming $j(x)$ is a power function.

40. When an aircraft flies horizontally, its *stall velocity* (the minimum speed required to keep the aircraft aloft) is directly proportional to the square root of the quotient of

[8]K. Schmidt-Nielsen, *Scaling–Why is animal size so important?* (Cambridge, England: Cambridge University Press, 1984).
[9]R. McNeill Alexander, *Dynamics of Dinosaurs and Other Extinct Giants.* (New York: Columbia University Press, 1989).
[10]Gillner, Thomas C., *Modern Ship Design*, (US Naval Institute Press, 1972).

its weight by its wing area. If a breakthrough in materials science allowed the construction of an aircraft with the same weight but twice the wing area, would the stall velocity increase or decrease? By what percent?

41. Consider the power function $y = t(x) = k \cdot x^{p/3}$ where p is any integer, $p \neq 0$.

  (a) For what values of p does $t(x)$ have domain restrictions? What are those restrictions?
  (b) What is the range of $t(x)$ if p is even? If p is odd?
  (c) What symmetry does the graph of $t(x)$ exhibit if p is even? If p is odd?

42. A person's weight, w, on a planet of radius d is given by

$$w = kd^{-2}, \quad k > 0,$$

where the constant k depends on the masses of the person and the planet.

  (a) A man weighs 180 lb on the surface of the earth. How much does he weigh on the surface of a planet whose mass is the same the earth's, but whose radius is three times as large? One-third as large?
  (b) What fraction of the earth's radius must an equally massive planet have if, on this planet, the weight of the man in part (a) is one ton?

43. One of Kepler's three laws of planetary motion states that the square of the period, P, of a body orbiting the sun is proportional to the cube of its average distance, d, from the sun. The earth has a period of 365 days and its distance from the sun is approximately 93,000,000 miles.

  (a) Find P as a function of d.
  (b) The planet Jupiter has an average distance from the sun of 483,000,000 miles. How long in earth days is a Jupiter year?

5.5 POLYNOMIAL FUNCTIONS

A *polynomial function* is a sum of power functions whose exponents are nonnegative integers. We use what we learned about power functions to study polynomials.

Example 1 You make five separate deposits of $1000 each into a savings account, one deposit per year, beginning today. What annual interest rate gives a balance in the account of $6000 five years from today? (Assume the interest rate is constant over these five years.)

Solution Let r be the annual interest rate. Our goal is to determine what value of r gives you $6000 in five years. In year $t = 0$, you make a $1000 deposit. One year later, you have $1000 plus the interest earned on that amount. At that time, you add another $1000.

To picture how this works, imagine the account pays 5% annual interest, compounded annually. Then, after one year, your balance would be

$$\text{Balance} = (100\% \text{ of Initial deposit}) + (5\% \text{ of Initial deposit}) + \text{Second deposit}$$
$$= 105\% \text{ of } \underbrace{\text{Initial deposit}}_{\$1000} + \underbrace{\text{Second deposit}}_{\$1000}$$
$$= 1.05(1000) + 1000.$$

Let x represent the annual growth factor, $1 + r$. For example, if the account paid 5% interest, then $x = 1 + 0.05 = 1.05$. We write the balance after one year in terms of x:

$$\text{Balance after one year} = 1000x + 1000.$$

After two years, you would have earned interest on the first-year balance. This gives

$$\text{Balance after earning interest} = (\underbrace{1000x + 1000}_{\text{First-year balance}})x = 1000x^2 + 1000x.$$

The third $1000 deposit brings your balance to

$$\text{Balance after two years} = 1000x^2 + 1000x + \underbrace{1000.}_{\text{Third deposit}}$$

A year's worth of interest on this amount, plus the fourth $1000 deposit, brings your balance to

$$\text{Balance after three years} = \underbrace{(1000x^2 + 1000x + 1000)}_{\text{Second-year balance}}x + \underbrace{1000}_{\text{Fourth deposit}}$$

$$= 1000x^3 + 1000x^2 + 1000x + 1000.$$

The pattern is this: Each of the $1000 deposits grows to $1000x^n$ by the end of its nth year in the bank. Thus,

$$\text{Balance after five years} = 1000x^5 + 1000x^4 + 1000x^3 + 1000x^2 + 1000x.$$

If the interest rate is chosen correctly, then the balance will be $6000 in five years. This gives us

$$1000x^5 + 1000x^4 + 1000x^3 + 1000x^2 + 1000x = 6000.$$

Dividing by 1000 and moving the 6 to the left side, we have the equation

$$x^5 + x^4 + x^3 + x^2 + x - 6 = 0.$$

Solving this equation for x determines how much interest we must earn. Using a computer or calculator, we find where the graph of $Q(x) = x^5 + x^4 + x^3 + x^2 + x - 6$ crosses the x-axis. Figure 5.27 shows that this occurs at $x \approx 1.0614$. Since $x = 1 + r$, this means $r = 0.0614$. So the account must earn 6.14% annual interest[11] for the balance to be $6000 at the end of five years.

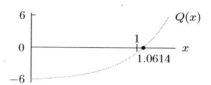

Figure 5.27: Finding where $Q(x)$ crosses the x-axis, for $x \geq 0$

You may wonder if Q crosses the x-axis more than once. For $x \geq 0$, graphing Q on a larger scale suggests that Q increases for all values of x and crosses the x-axis only once. For $x > 1$, we expect Q to be an increasing function, because larger values of x indicate higher interest rates and therefore larger values of $Q(x)$. Having crossed the axis once, the graph of Q does not "turn around" to cross it again.

The function $Q(x) = x^5 + x^4 + x^3 + x^2 + x - 6$ is the sum of power functions; Q is called a *polynomial*. (Note that the expression -6 can be written as $-6x^0$, so it, too, is a power function.)

A General Formula for the Family of Polynomial Functions

The general formula for a polynomial function can be written as

$$p(x) = a_n x^n + a_{n-1} x^{n-1} + \cdots + a_1 x + a_0,$$

[11]This is 6.14% interest per year, compounded annually.

where n is called the *degree* of the polynomial and a_n is the *leading coefficient*. For example, the function

$$g(x) = 3x^2 + 4x^5 + x - x^3 + 1,$$

is a polynomial of degree 5 because the term with the highest power is $4x^5$. It is customary to write a polynomial with the powers in decreasing order from left to right:

$$g(x) = 4x^5 - x^3 + 3x^2 + x + 1.$$

The function g has one other term, $0 \cdot x^4$, which we don't bother to write down. The values of g's coefficients are $a_5 = 4$, $a_4 = 0$, $a_3 = -1$, $a_2 = 3$, $a_1 = 1$, and $a_0 = 1$. In summary:

The general formula for the family of polynomial functions can be written as

$$p(x) = a_n x^n + a_{n-1} x^{n-1} + \cdots + a_1 x + a_0,$$

where n is a positive integer called the **degree** of p and where $a_n \neq 0$.

- Each power function $a_n x^n$ in this sum is called a **term**.
- The constants $a_n, a_{n-1}, \ldots, a_0$ are called **coefficients**.
- The term a_0 is called the **constant term**. The highest-powered term, $a_n x^n$, is called the **leading term**.
- To write a polynomial in **standard form**, we arrange its terms from highest power to lowest power, going from left to right.

Like the power functions from which they are built, polynomials are defined for all values of x. Except for polynomials of degree zero (whose graphs are horizontal lines), the graphs of polynomials do not have horizontal or vertical asymptotes. The shape of the graph depends on its degree; typical graphs are shown in Figure 5.28.

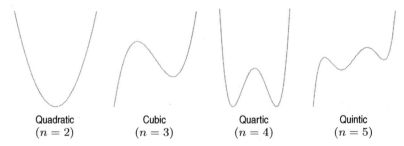

| Quadratic | Cubic | Quartic | Quintic |
| ($n = 2$) | ($n = 3$) | ($n = 4$) | ($n = 5$) |

Figure 5.28: Graphs of typical polynomials of degree n

The Long-Run Behavior of Polynomial Functions

We have seen that, as x grows large, $y = x^2$ increases fast, $y = x^3$ increases faster, and $y = x^4$ increases faster still. In general, power functions with larger positive powers eventually grow much faster than those with smaller powers. This tells us about the behavior of polynomials for large x. For instance, consider the polynomial $g(x) = 4x^5 - x^3 + 3x^2 + x + 1$. Provided x is large enough, the absolute value of the term $4x^5$ is much larger than the absolute value of the other terms combined. For example, if $x = 100$,

$$4x^5 = 4(100)^5 = 40,000,000,000,$$

and the other terms in $g(x)$ are

$$-x^3 + 3x^2 + x + 1 = -(100)^3 + 3(100)^2 + 100 + 1$$
$$= -1,000,000 + 30,000 + 100 + 1 = -969,899.$$

Therefore $p(100) = 39,999,030,101$, which is approximately equal to the value of the $4x^5$ term. In general, if x is large enough, the most important contribution to the value of a polynomial p is made by the leading term; we can ignore the lower-powered terms.

> When viewed on a large enough scale, the graph of the polynomial $p(x) = a_n x^n + a_{n-1} x^{n-1} + \cdots + a_1 x + a_0$ looks like the graph of the power function $y = a_n x^n$. This behavior is called the **long-run behavior** of the polynomial.

Example 2   Find a window in which the graph of $f(x) = x^3 + x^2$ resembles the power function $y = x^3$.

Solution   Figure 5.29 gives the graphs of $f(x) = x^3 + x^2$ and $y = x^3$. On this scale, f does not look like a power function. On the larger scale in Figure 5.30, the graph of f resembles the graph of $y = x^3$. On this larger scale, the "bumps" in the graph of f are too small to be seen. On an even larger scale, as in Figure 5.31, the graph of f is indistinguishable from the graph of $y = x^3$.

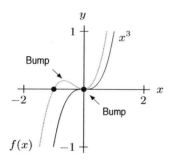
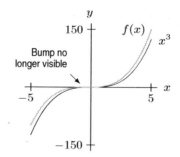
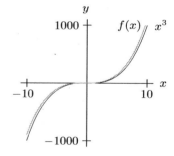

Figure 5.29: On this scale, $f(x) = x^3 + x^2$ does not look like a power function

Figure 5.30: On this scale, $f(x) = x^3 + x^2$ resembles the power function $y = x^3$

Figure 5.31: On this scale, $f(x) = x^3 + x^2$ is nearly indistinguishable from $y = x^3$

Zeros of Polynomials

The *zeros* of a polynomial p are values of x for which $p(x) = 0$. The zeros are also the x-intercepts, because they tell us where the graph of p crosses the x-axis. Factoring can sometimes be used to find the zeros of a polynomial; however, the numerical and graphical method of Example 1 can always be used. In addition, the long-run behavior of the polynomial can give us clues as to how many zeros (if any) there may be.

Example 3   Given the polynomial

$$q(x) = 3x^6 - 2x^5 + 4x^2 - 1,$$

where $q(0) = -1$, is there a reason to expect a solution to the equation $q(x) = 0$? If not, explain why not. If so, how do you know?

Solution   The equation $q(x) = 0$ must have at least two solutions. We know this because on a large scale, q looks like the power function $y = 3x^6$. (See Figure 5.32.) The function $y = 3x^6$ takes on large positive values as x grows large (either positive or negative). Since the graph of q is smooth and unbroken, it must cross the x-axis at least twice to get from $q(0) = -1$ to the positive values it attains as $x \to \infty$ and $x \to -\infty$.

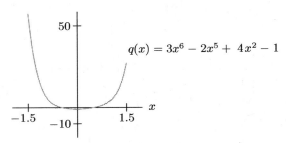

$$q(x) = 3x^6 - 2x^5 + 4x^2 - 1$$

Figure 5.32: Graph must cross x-axis at least twice since $q(0) = -1$ and $q(x)$ looks like $3x^6$ for large x

A sixth degree polynomial such as q in Example 3 can have as many as six real zeros. We consider the zeros of a polynomial in more detail in Section 5.6.

Exercises and Problems for Section 5.5

Exercises

Are the functions in Exercises 1–6 polynomials? If so, of what degree?

1. $y = 4x^2 + 2$

2. $y = 5^x - 2$

3. $y = 5 + x$

4. $y = 4x^2 - 7\sqrt{x^9} + 10$

5. $y = 4x^4 - 3x^3 + 2e^x$

6. $y = 7t^6 - 8t + 7.2$

7. Estimate the zeros of $f(x) = x^4 - 3x^2 - x + 2$.

8. Estimate the minimum value of $g(x) = x^4 - 3x^3 - 8$.

Describe in words the long-run behavior as $x \to \infty$ of the functions in Exercises 9–12. What power function does each resemble?

9. $y = 16x^3 - 4023x^2 - 2$

10. $y = 4x^4 - 2x^2 + 3$

11. $y = 3x^3 + 2x^2/x^{-7} - 7x^5 + 2$

12. $y = 5x^2/x^{3/2} + 2$

Problems

13. Let $u(x) = -\frac{1}{5}(x - 3)(x + 1)(x + 5)$ and $v(x) = -\frac{1}{5}x^2(x - 5)$.

    (a) Graph u and v for $-10 \le x \le 10$, $-10 \le y \le 10$. How are the graphs similar? How are they different?

    (b) Compare the graphs of u and v on the window $-20 \le x \le 20$, $-1600 \le y \le 1600$, the window $-50 \le x \le 50$, $-25{,}000 \le y \le 25{,}000$, and the window $-500 \le x \le 500$, $-25{,}000{,}000 \le y \le 25{,}000{,}000$. Discuss.

14. Compare the graphs of $f(x) = x^3 + 5x^2 - x - 5$ and $g(x) = -2x^3 - 10x^2 + 2x + 10$ on a window that shows all intercepts. How are the graphs similar? Different? Discuss.

15. Find the equation of the line through the y-intercept of $y = x^4 - 3x^5 - 1 + x^2$ and the x-intercept of $y = 2x - 4$.

16. Let $f(x) = \left(\dfrac{1}{50{,}000}\right)x^3 + \left(\dfrac{1}{2}\right)x$.

(a) For small values of x, which term of f is more important? Explain your answer.

(b) Graph $y = f(x)$ for $-10 \leq x \leq 10$, $-10 \leq y \leq 10$. Is this graph linear? How does the appearance of this graph agree with your answer to part (a)?

(c) How large a value of x is required for the cubic term of f to be equal to the linear term?

17. The polynomial function $f(x) = x^3 + x + 1$ is invertible—that is, this function has an inverse.

(a) Graph $y = f(x)$. Explain how you can tell from the graph that f is invertible.

(b) Find $f(0.5)$ and an approximate value for $f^{-1}(0.5)$.

18. If $f(x) = x^2$ and $g(x) = (x + 2)(x - 1)(x - 3)$, find all x for which $f(x) < g(x)$.

19. Let V represent the volume in liters of air in the lungs during a 5-second respiratory cycle. If t is time in seconds, V is given by

$$V = 0.1729t + 0.1522t^2 - 0.0374t^3.$$

(a) Graph this function for $0 \leq t \leq 5$.

(b) What is the maximum value of V on this interval? What is the practical significance of the maximum value?

(c) Explain the practical significance of the t- and V-intercepts on the interval $0 \leq t \leq 5$.

20. Let $C(x)$ be a firm's total cost, in millions of dollars, for producing a quantity x thousand units of an item.

(a) Graph $C(x) = (x - 1)^3 + 1$.

(b) Let $R(x)$ be the revenue to the firm (in millions of dollars) for selling a quantity x thousand units of the good. Suppose $R(x) = x$. What does this tell you about the price of each unit?

(c) Profit equals revenue minus cost. For what values of x does the firm make a profit? Break even? Lose money?

21. The town of Smallsville was founded in 1900. Its population y (in hundreds) is given by the equation

$$y = -0.1x^4 + 1.7x^3 - 9x^2 + 14.4x + 5,$$

where x is the number of years since 1900. Use a the graph in the window $0 \leq x \leq 10$, $-2 \leq y \leq 13$.

(a) What was the population of Smallsville when it was founded?

(b) When did Smallsville become a ghost town (nobody lived there anymore)? Give the year and the month.

(c) What was the largest population of Smallsville after 1905? When did Smallsville reach that population? Again, include the month and year. Explain your method.

22. The volume, V, in milliliters, of 1 kg of water as a function of temperature T is given, for $0 \leq T \leq 30°$C, by:

$$V = 999.87 - 0.06426T + 0.0085143T^2 - 0.0000679T^3.$$

(a) Graph V.

(b) Describe the shape of your graph. Does V increase or decrease as T increases? Does the graph curve upward or downward? What does the graph tell us about how the volume varies with temperature?

(c) At what temperature does water have the maximum density? How does that appear on your graph? (Density = Mass/Volume. In this problem, the mass of the water is 1 kg.)

23. Let f and g be polynomial functions. Are the compositions

$$f(g(x)) \qquad \text{and} \qquad g(f(x))$$

also polynomial functions? Explain your answer.

24. A function that is not a polynomial can often be approximated by a polynomial. For example, for certain x-values, the function $f(x) = e^x$ can be approximated by the fifth-degree polynomial

$$p(x) = 1 + x + \frac{x^2}{2} + \frac{x^3}{6} + \frac{x^4}{24} + \frac{x^5}{120}.$$

(a) Show that $p(1) \approx f(1) = e$. How good is the estimate?

(b) Calculate $p(5)$. How well does $p(5)$ approximate $f(5)$?

(c) Graph $p(x)$ and $f(x)$ together on the same set of axes. Based on your graph, for what range of values of x does $p(x)$ give a good estimate for $f(x)$?

25. Let $f(x) = x - \frac{x^3}{6} + \frac{x^5}{120}$.

(a) Graph $y = f(x)$ and $y = \sin x$ for $-2\pi \leq x \leq 2\pi$, $-3 \leq y \leq 3$.

(b) The graph of f resembles the graph of $\sin x$ on a small interval. Based on the graphs you made in part (a), give the approximate interval.

(c) Your calculator uses a function similar to f in order to evaluate the sine function. How reasonable an approximation does f give for $\sin(\pi/8)$?

(d) Explain how you could use the function f to approximate the value of $\sin\theta$, where $\theta = 18$ radians. [Hint: Use the fact that the sine function is periodic.]

26. Suppose f is a polynomial function of degree n, where n is a positive even integer. For each of the following statements, write *true* if the statement is always true, *false* otherwise. If the statement is false, give an example that illustrates why it is false.

(a) f is an even function.

(b) f has an inverse.

(c) f cannot be an odd function.

(d) If $f(x) \to +\infty$ as $x \to +\infty$, then $f(x) \to -\infty$ as $x \to -\infty$.

27. Table 5.10 gives values of v, the speed of sound (in m/sec) in water as a function of the temperature T (in °C).[12]

(a) An approximate linear formula for v is given by $v = 1402.385 + 5.038813T$. Over what temperature range does this formula agree with the values in Table 5.10 to within 1°C?

(b) The formula in part (a) can be improved by adding the quadratic term $-5.799136 \cdot 10^{-2}T^2$. Repeat part (a) using this adjusted formula.

(c) The formula in part (b) can be further improved by adding the cubic term $3.287156 \cdot 10^{-4}T^3$. Repeat part (a) using this adjusted formula.

(d) The speed of sound in water at 50°C is 1542.6 m/s. If we want to improve our formula still further by adding a quartic (fourth-degree) term, should this term be positive or negative?

Table 5.10

T	0	5	10	15	20	25	30
v	1402.4	1426.2	1447.3	1466.0	1482.4	1496.7	1509.2

5.6 THE SHORT-RUN BEHAVIOR OF POLYNOMIALS

The long-run behavior of a polynomial is determined by its leading term. However, polynomials with the same leading term may have very different short-run behaviors.

Example 1   Compare the graphs of the polynomials f, g, and h given by

$$f(x) = x^4 - 4x^3 + 16x - 16, \quad g(x) = x^4 - 4x^3 - 4x^2 + 16x, \quad h(x) = x^4 + x^3 - 8x^2 - 12x.$$

Solution   Each of these functions is a fourth-degree polynomial, and each has x^4 as its leading term. Thus, all their graphs resemble the graph of x^4 on a large scale. See Figure 5.33.

However, on a smaller scale, the functions look different. See Figure 5.34. Two of the graphs go through the origin while the third does not. The graphs also differ from one another in the number of bumps each one has and in the number of times each one crosses the x-axis. Thus, polynomials with the same leading term look similar on a large scale, but may look dissimilar on a small scale.

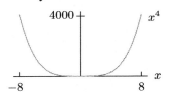

Figure 5.33: On a large scale, the polynomials f, g, and h resemble the power function $y = x^4$

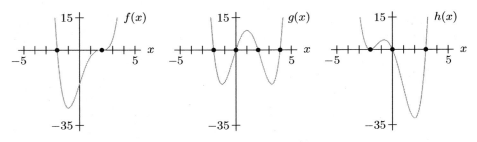

Figure 5.34: On a smaller scale, the polynomials f, g, and h look quite different from each other

---

[12]Data determined using the Marczak formula described at the UK National Physical Laboratory website, http://www.npl.co.uk.

Factored Form, Zeros, and the Short-Run Behavior of a Polynomial

To predict the long-run behavior of a polynomial, we write it in standard form. However, to determine the zeros and the short-run behavior of a polynomial, we write it in factored form, as a product of other polynomials. Some, but not all, polynomials can be factored.

Example 2   Investigate the short-run behavior of the third-degree polynomial $u(x) = x^3 - x^2 - 6x$.

(a) Rewrite $u(x)$ as a product of linear factors.
(b) Find the zeros of $u(x)$.
(c) Describe the graph of $u(x)$. Where does it cross the x-axis? the y-axis? Where is $u(x)$ positive? Negative?

Solution   (a) By factoring out an x and then factoring the quadratic, $x^2 - x - 6$, we rewrite $u(x)$ as

$$u(x) = x^3 - x^2 - 6x = x(x^2 - x - 6) = x(x - 3)(x + 2).$$

Thus, we have expressed $u(x)$ as the product of three linear factors, x, $x - 3$, and $x + 2$.

(b) The polynomial equals zero if and only if at least one of its factors is zero. We solve the equation:

$$x(x - 3)(x + 2) = 0,$$

giving

$$x = 0, \quad \text{or} \quad x - 3 = 0, \quad \text{or} \quad x + 2 = 0,$$

so

$$x = 0, \quad \text{or} \quad x = 3, \quad \text{or} \quad x = -2.$$

These are the zeros, or x-intercepts, of u. To check, evaluate $u(x)$ for these x-values; you should get 0. There are no other zeros.

(c) To describe the graph of u, we give the x- and y-intercepts, and the long-run behavior.

The factored form, $u(x) = x(x - 3)(x + 2)$, shows that the graph crosses the x-axis at $x = 0, 3, -2$. The graph of u crosses the y-axis at $u(0) = 0^3 - 0^2 - 6 \cdot 0 = 0$; that is, at $y = 0$. For large values of x, the graph of $y = u(x)$ resembles the graph of its leading term, $y = x^3$. Figure 5.35 shows where u is positive and where u is negative.

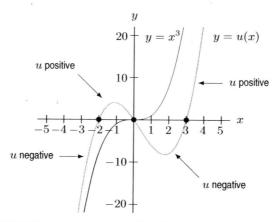

Figure 5.35: The graph of $u(x) = x^3 - x^2 - 6x$ has zeros at $x = -2, 0$, and 3. Its long-run behavior resembles $y = x^3$

In Example 2, each linear factor produced a zero of the polynomial. Now suppose that we do not know the polynomial p, but we do know that it has zeros at $x = 0, -12, 31$. Then we know that the factored form of the polynomial must include the factors $(x - 0)$ or x, and $(x - (-12))$ or $(x + 12)$, and $(x - 31)$. It may include other factors too. In summary:

Suppose p is a polynomial. If the formula for p has a **linear factor**, that is, a factor of the form $(x - k)$, then p has a zero at $x = k$.
Conversely, if p has a **zero** at $x = k$, then p has a linear factor of the form $(x - k)$.

The Number of Factors, Zeros, and Bumps

The number of linear factors is always less than or equal to the degree of a polynomial. For example, a fourth degree polynomial can have no more than four linear factors. This makes sense because if we had another factor in the product and multiplied out, the highest power of x would be greater than four. Since each zero corresponds to a linear factor, the number of zeros is less than or equal to the degree of the polynomial.

We can now say that there is a maximum number of bumps in the graph of a polynomial of degree n. Between any two consecutive zeros, there is a bump because the graph changes direction. In Figure 5.35, the graph, which decreases at $x = 1$, must come back up in order to cross the x-axis at $x = 3$. In summary:

The graph of an nth degree polynomial has at most n zeros and turns at most $(n - 1)$ times.

Multiple Zeros

The functions $s(x) = (x - 4)^2$ and $t(x) = (x + 1)^3$ are both polynomials in factored form. Each is a horizontal shift of a power function. We refer to the zeros of s and t as *multiple zeros*, because in each case the factor contributing the value of $y = 0$ is repeated more than once. For instance, we say that $x = 4$ is a *double zero* of s, since

$$s(x) = (x - 4)^2 = \underbrace{(x - 4)(x - 4)}_{\text{Repeated twice}},$$

Likewise, we say that $x = -1$ is a *triple zero* of t, since

$$t(x) = (x + 1)^3 = \underbrace{(x + 1)(x + 1)(x + 1)}_{\text{Repeated three times}}.$$

The graphs of s and t in Figures 5.36 and 5.37 show typical behavior near multiple zeros.

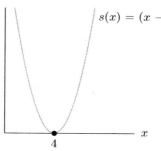

Figure 5.36: Double zero at $x = 4$

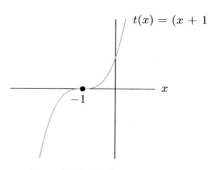

Figure 5.37: Triple zero at $x = -1$

In general:

If p is a polynomial with a repeated linear factor, then p has a **multiple zero**.

- If the factor $(x - k)$ is repeated an even number of times, the graph of $y = p(x)$ does not cross the x-axis at $x = k$, but "bounces" off the x-axis at $x = k$. (See Figure 5.36.)
- If the factor $(x - k)$ is repeated an odd number of times, the graph of $y = p(x)$ crosses the x-axis at $x = k$, but it looks flattened there. (See Figure 5.37.)

Example 3   Describe in words the zeros of the 4th-degree polynomials $f(x)$, $g(x)$, and $h(x)$, in Figure 5.38.

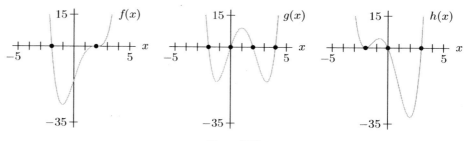

Figure 5.38

Solution   The graph suggests that f has a single zero at $x = -2$. The flattened appearance near $x = 2$ suggests that f has a multiple zero there. Since the graph crosses the x-axis at $x = 2$ (instead of bouncing off it), this zero must be repeated an odd number of times. Since f is 4th degree, f has at most 4 factors, so there must be a triple zero at $x = 2$.

The graph of g has four single zeros. The graph of h has two single zeros (at $x = 0$ and $x = 3$) and a double zero at $x = -2$. The multiplicity of the zero at $x = -2$ is not higher than two because h is of degree $n = 4$.

Finding the Formula for a Polynomial from its Graph

The graph of a polynomial often enables us to find a possible formula for the polynomial.

Example 4   Find a possible formula for the polynomial function f graphed in Figure 5.39.

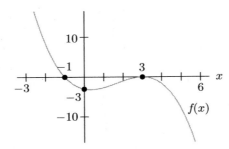

Figure 5.39: Features of the graph lead to a possible formula for this polynomial

Solution   Based on its long-run behavior, f is of odd degree greater than or equal to 3. The polynomial has zeros at $x = -1$ and $x = 3$. We see that $x = 3$ is a multiple zero of even power, because the graph bounces off the x-axis here instead of crossing it. Therefore, we try the formula

$$f(x) = k(x + 1)(x - 3)^2$$

where k represents a stretch factor. The shape of the graph shows that k must be negative.

To find k, we use the fact that $f(0) = -3$, so

$$f(0) = k(0 + 1)(0 - 3)^2 = -3$$

which gives

$$9k = -3 \qquad \text{so} \qquad k = -\frac{1}{3}.$$

Thus, $f(x) = -\frac{1}{3}(x + 1)(x - 3)^2$ is a possible formula for this polynomial.

The formula for f we found in Example 4 is the polynomial of least degree we could have chosen. However, there are other polynomials, such as $y = -\frac{1}{27}(x + 1)(x - 3)^4$, with the same overall behavior as the function shown in Figure 5.39.

Exercises and Problems for Section 5.6

Exercises

1. Use the graph of $g(x)$ in Figure 5.34 to determine the factored form of

$$g(x) = x^4 - 4x^3 - 4x^2 + 16x.$$

2. Use the graph of $f(x)$ in Figure 5.34 to determine the factored form of

$$f(x) = x^4 - 4x^3 + 16x - 16.$$

3. Use the graph of $h(x)$ in Figure 5.34 to determine the factored form of

$$h(x) = x^4 + x^3 - 8x^2 - 12x.$$

4. Factor $f(x) = 8x^3 - 4x^2 - 60x$ completely, and determine the zeros of f.

In Exercises 5–8, find the zeros of the functions.

5. $y = 7(x + 3)(x - 2)(x + 7)$

6. $y = a(x + 2)(x - b)$, where a, b are nonzero constants

7. $y = x^3 + 7x^2 + 12x$

8. $y = (x^2 + 2x - 7)(x^3 + 4x^2 - 21x)$

Without a calculator, graph the polynomials in Exercises 9–10. Label all the x-intercepts and y-intercepts.

9. $f(x) = -5(x^2 - 4)(25 - x^2)$

10. $g(x) = 5(x - 4)(x^2 - 25)$

Problems

11. Without using a calculator, decide which of the equations a–e best describes the polynomial in Figure 5.40.

(a) $y = (x + 2)(x + 1)(x - 2)(x - 3)$
(b) $y = x(x + 2)(x + 1)(x - 2)(x - 3)$
(c) $y = -\frac{1}{2}(x + 2)(x + 1)(x - 2)(x - 3)$
(d) $y = \frac{1}{2}(x + 2)(x + 1)(x - 2)(x - 3)$
(e) $y = -(x + 2)(x + 1)(x - 2)(x - 3)$

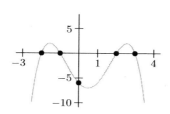

Figure 5.40

Give a possible formula for the polynomials in Problems 12–25.

12.

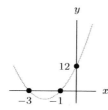

13.

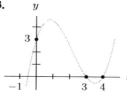

14.

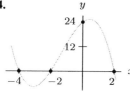

15.

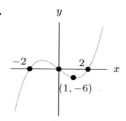

16.

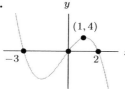

17.

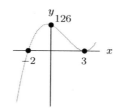

18.

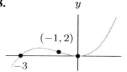

19.

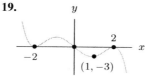

20.

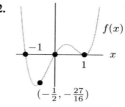

21.

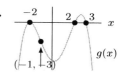

22.

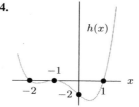

23.

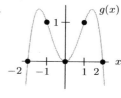

24.

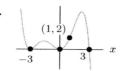

25.

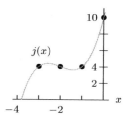

26. Let $u(x) = \frac{1}{8}x^3$ and $v(x) = \frac{1}{8}x(x - 0.01)^2$. Do v and u have the exact same graph? Sketch u and v in the window $-10 \le x \le 10$, $-10 \le y \le 10$. Now do you think that v and u have the same graph? If so, explain why their formulas are different; if not, find a viewing window on which their graphs' differences are prominent.

In Problems 27–32, find possible formulas for polynomials with the given properties.

27. f has degree ≤ 2, $f(0) = f(1) = f(2) = 1$.

28. f has degree ≤ 2, $f(0) = f(2) = 0$ and $f(3) = 3$.

29. f has degree ≤ 2, $f(0) = 0$ and $f(1) = 1$.

30. f is third degree with $f(-3) = 0$, $f(1) = 0$, $f(4) = 0$, and $f(2) = 5$.

31. g is fourth degree, g has a double zero at $x = 3$, $g(5) = 0$, $g(-1) = 0$, and $g(0) = 3$.

32. Least possible degree through the points $(-3, 0)$, $(1, 0)$, and $(0, -3)$.

33. Which of these functions have inverses that are functions? Discuss.

(a) $f(x) = (x - 2)^3 + 4$.   **(b)** $g(x) = x^3 - 4x^2 + 2$.

For Problems 34–39, find the real zeros (if any) of the polynomials.

34. $y = x^2 + 5x + 6$

35. $y = x^4 + 6x^2 + 9$

36. $y = 4x^2 - 1$

37. $y = 4x^2 + 1$

38. $y = 2x^2 - 3x - 3$

39. $y = 3x^5 + 7x + 1$

40. An open-top box is to be constructed from a 6 in by 8 in rectangular sheet of tin by cutting out squares of equal size at each corner, then folding up the resulting flaps.

Let x denote the length of the side of each cut-out square. Assume negligible thickness.

    (a) Find a formula for the volume of the box as a function of x.

    (b) For what values of x does the formula from part (a) make sense in the context of the problem?

    (c) Sketch a graph of the volume function.

    (d) What, approximately, is the maximum volume of the box?

41. You wish to pack a cardboard box inside a wooden crate. In order to have room for the packing materials, you need to leave a 0.5-ft space around the front, back, and sides of the box, and a 1-ft space around the top and bottom of the box. If the cardboard box is x feet long, $(x + 2)$ feet wide, and $(x - 1)$ feet deep, find a formula in terms of x for the amount of packing material needed.

42. Take an 8.5 by 11-inch piece of paper and cut out four equal squares from the corners. Fold up the sides to create an open box. Find the dimensions of the box that has maximum volume.

43. Consider the function $a(x) = x^5 + 2x^3 - 4x$.

    (a) Without using a calculator or computer, what can you say about the graph of a?

    (b) Use a calculator or a computer to determine the zeros of this function to three decimal places.

    (c) Explain why you think that you have all the possible zeros.

    (d) What are the zeros of $b(x) = 2x^5 + 4x^3 - 8x$? Does your answer surprise you?

44. **(a)** Sketch a graph of $f(x) = x^4 - 17x^2 + 36x - 20$ for $-10 \leq x \leq 10, -10 \leq y \leq 10$.

    (b) Your graph should appear to have a vertical asymptote at $x = -5$. Does f actually have a vertical asymptote here? Explain.

    (c) How many zeros does f have? Can you find a window in which all of the zeros of f are clearly visible?

    (d) Write the formula of f in factored form.

    (e) How many turning points does the graph of f have? Can you find a window in which all the turning points of f are clearly visible? Explain.

45. In each of the following cases, find a possible formula for the polynomial f.

    (a) Suppose f has zeros at $x = -2, x = 3, x = 5$ and a y-intercept of 4.

    (b) In addition to the properties in part (a), suppose f has the following long-run behavior: As $x \to \pm\infty$, $y \to -\infty$. [Hint: Assume f has a double zero.]

    (c) In addition to the properties in part (a), suppose f has the following long-run behavior: As $x \to \pm\infty$, $y \to +\infty$.

46. The following statements about $f(x)$ are true:

- $f(x)$ is a polynomial function
- $f(x) = 0$ at exactly four different values of x
- $f(x) \to -\infty$ as $x \to \pm\infty$

For each of the following statements, write *true* if the statement must be true, *never true* if the statement is never true, or *sometimes true* if it is sometimes true and sometimes not true.

    (a) $f(x)$ is an odd function

    (b) $f(x)$ is an even function

    (c) $f(x)$ is a fourth degree polynomial

    (d) $f(x)$ is a fifth degree polynomial

    (e) $f(-x) \to -\infty$ as $x \to \pm\infty$

    (f) $f(x)$ is invertible

5.7 RATIONAL FUNCTIONS

The Average Cost of Producing a Therapeutic Drug

A pharmaceutical company wants to begin production of a new drug. The total cost C, in dollars, of making q grams of the drug is given by the linear function

$$C(q) = 2{,}500{,}000 + 2000q.$$

The fact that $C(0) = 2,500,000$ tells us that the company spends $2,500,000 before it starts making the drug. This quantity is known as the *fixed cost* because it does not depend on how much of the drug is made. It represents the cost for research, testing, and equipment. In addition, the slope of C tells us that each gram of the drug costs an extra $2000 to make. This quantity is known as the *variable cost* per unit. It represents the additional cost, in labor and materials, to make an additional gram of the drug.

The fixed cost of $2.5 million is large compared to the variable cost of $2000 per gram. This means that it is impractical for the company to make a small amount of the drug. For instance, the total cost for 10 grams is

$$C(10) = 2,500,000 + 2000 \cdot 10 = 2,520,000,$$

which works out to an average cost of $252,000 per gram. The company would probably never sell such an expensive drug.

However, as larger quantities of the drug are manufactured, the initial expenditure of $2.5 million seems less significant. The fixed cost averages out over a large quantity. For example, if the company makes 10,000 grams of the drug,

$$\text{Average cost} = \frac{\text{Cost of producing 10,000 grams}}{10,000} = \frac{2,500,000 + 2000 \cdot 10,000}{10,000} = 2250,$$

or $2250 per gram of drug produced.

We define the average cost, $a(q)$, as the cost per gram to produce q grams of the drug:

$$a(q) = \frac{\text{Average cost of}}{\text{producing } q \text{ grams}} = \frac{\text{Total cost}}{\text{Number of grams}} = \frac{C(q)}{q} = \frac{2,500,000 + 2000q}{q}.$$

Figure 5.41 gives a graph of $y = a(q)$ for $q > 0$. The horizontal asymptote reflects the fact that for large values of q, the value of $a(q)$ is close to 2000. This is because, as more of the drug is produced, the average cost gets closer to $2000 per gram. See Table 5.11.

The vertical asymptote of $y = a(q)$ is the y-axis, which tells us that the average cost per gram is very large if a small amount of the drug is made. This is because the initial $2.5 million expenditure is averaged over very few units. We saw that producing only 10 grams costs a staggering $252,000 per gram.

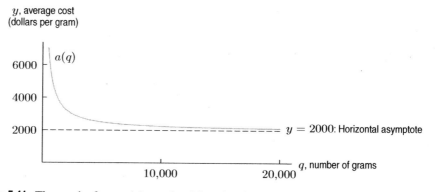

Figure 5.41: The graph of $y = a(q)$, a rational function, has a horizontal asymptote at $y = 2000$ and a vertical asymptote at $q = 0$

Table 5.11   *As quantity q increases, the average cost a(q) draws closer to $2000 per gram*

Quantity, q	Total cost, $C(q) = 2,500,000 + 2000q$	Average cost, $a(q) = C(q)/q$
10,000	$2,500,000 + 20,000,000 = 22,500,000$	2250
50,000	$2,500,000 + 100,000,000 = 102,500,000$	2050
100,000	$2,500,000 + 200,000,000 = 202,500,000$	2025
500,000	$2,500,000 + 1,000,000,000 = 1,002,500,000$	2005

What is a Rational Function?

The formula for $a(q)$ is the ratio of the polynomial $2,500,000 + 2000q$ and the polynomial q. Since $a(q)$ is given by the ratio of two polynomials, $a(q)$ is an example of a *rational function*. In general:

If r can be written as the ratio of polynomial functions $p(x)$ and $q(x)$, that is, if

$$r(x) = \frac{p(x)}{q(x)},$$

then r is called a **rational function**. (We assume that $q(x)$ is not the constant polynomial $q(x) = 0$.)

The Long-Run Behavior of Rational Functions

In the long-run, every rational function behaves like a power function. For example, consider

$$f(x) = \frac{6x^4 + x^3 + 1}{-5x + 2x^2}.$$

Since the long-run behavior of a polynomial is determined by its highest power term, for large x the numerator behaves like $6x^4$ and the denominator behaves like $2x^2$. Thus, the long-run behavior of f is

$$f(x) = \frac{6x^4 + x^3 + 1}{-5x + 2x^2} \approx \frac{6x^4}{2x^2} = 3x^2.$$

See Figure 5.42.

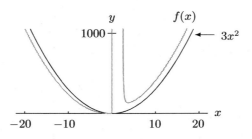

Figure 5.42: In the long-run, the graph of $f(x)$ looks like the graph of $3x^2$

In general, if r is any rational function, then for large enough values of x,

$$r(x) = \frac{a_n x^n + a_{n-1} x^{n-1} + \cdots + a_0}{b_m x^m + b_{m-1} x^{m-1} + \cdots + b_0} \approx \frac{a_n x^n}{b_m x^m} = \frac{a_n}{b_m} x^{n-m}.$$

This means that on a large scale r resembles the function $y = (\frac{a_n}{b_m})x^{n-m}$, which is a power function of the form $y = kx^p$, where $k = a_n/b_m$ and $p = n - m$. In summary:

For large enough values of x (either positive or negative), the graph of the rational function r looks like the graph of a power function. If $r(x) = p(x)/q(x)$, then the **long-run behavior** of $y = r(x)$ is given by

$$y = \frac{\text{Leading term of } p}{\text{Leading term of } q}.$$

Example 1   For positive x, describe the long-run behavior of the rational function

$$r(x) = \frac{x + 3}{x + 2}.$$

Solution   If x is a large positive number, then

$$r(x) = \frac{\text{Big number} + 3}{\text{Same big number} + 2} \approx \frac{\text{Big number}}{\text{Same big number}} = 1.$$

For example, if $x = 100$, we have

$$r(x) = \frac{103}{102} = 1.0098\ldots \approx 1.$$

If $x = 10,000$, we have

$$r(x) = \frac{10,003}{10,002} = 1.00009998\ldots \approx 1,$$

For large positive x-values, $r(x) \approx 1$. Thus, for large enough values of x, the graph of $y = r(x)$ looks like the line $y = 1$, its horizontal asymptote. See Figure 5.43. However, for $x > 0$, the graph of r is above the line since the numerator is larger than the denominator.

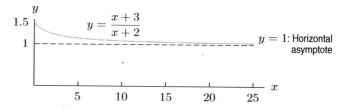

Figure 5.43: For large positive values of x, the graph of $r(x) = (x + 3)/(x + 2)$ looks like the horizontal line $y = 1$

Example 2   For positive x, describe the positive long-run behavior of the rational function

$$g(x) = \frac{3x + 1}{x^2 + x - 2}.$$

Solution   The leading term in the numerator is $3x$ and the leading term in the denominator is x^2. Thus for large enough values of x,

$$g(x) \approx \frac{3x}{x^2} = \frac{3}{x}.$$

Figure 5.44 shows the graphs of $y = g(x)$ and $y = 3/x$. For large values of x, the two graphs are nearly indistinguishable. Both graphs have a horizontal asymptote at $y = 0$.

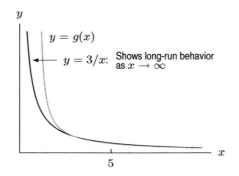

Figure 5.44: For large enough values of x, the function g looks like the function $y = 3x^{-1}$

What Causes Asymptotes?

The graphs of rational functions often behave differently from the graphs of polynomials. Polynomial graphs (except constant functions) cannot level off to a horizontal line like the graphs of rational functions can. In Example 1, the numerator and denominator are approximately equal for large x, producing the horizontal asymptote $y = 1$. In Example 2, the denominator grows faster than the numerator, driving the quotient towards zero.

The rapid rise (or fall) of the graph of a rational function near its vertical asymptote is due to the denominator becoming small (close to zero). It is tempting to assume that any function which has a denominator has a vertical asymptote. However, this is not true. To have a vertical asymptote, the denominator must become close to zero. For example, suppose that

$$r(x) = \frac{1}{x^2 + 3}.$$

The denominator is always greater than 3; it is never 0. We see from Figure 5.45 that r does not have a vertical asymptote.

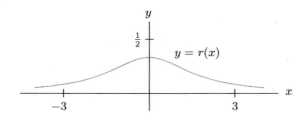

Figure 5.45: The rational function $r(x) = 1/(x^2 + 3)$ has no vertical asymptote

Exercises and Problems for Section 5.7

Exercises

Are the functions in Exercises 1–6 rational functions? If so, write them in the form $p(x)/q(x)$, the ratio of polynomials.

1. $f(x) = \dfrac{x^2}{2} + \dfrac{1}{x}$

2. $f(x) = \dfrac{\sqrt{x} + 1}{x + 1}$

3. $f(x) = \dfrac{4^x + 3}{3^x - 1}$

4. $f(x) = \dfrac{x^2 + 4}{e^x}$

5. $f(x) = \dfrac{x^2}{x - 3} - \dfrac{5}{x - 3}$

6. $f(x) = \dfrac{9x - 1}{4\sqrt{x} + 7} + \dfrac{5x^3}{x^2 - 1}$

Problems

7. Compare and discuss the long-run behaviors of the following functions:

$$f(x) = \frac{x^2 + 1}{x^2 + 5}, \quad g(x) = \frac{x^3 + 1}{x^2 + 5}, \quad h(x) = \frac{x + 1}{x^2 + 5}.$$

8. Give examples of rational functions with even symmetry, odd symmetry, and neither. How does the symmetry of $f(x) = p(x)/q(x)$ depend on the symmetry of $p(x)$ and $q(x)$?

Find the horizontal asymptote, if it exists, of the functions in Problems 9–11.

9. $f(x) = \dfrac{1}{1 + \frac{1}{x}}$

10. $g(x) = \dfrac{(1 - x)(2 + 3x)}{2x^2 + 1}$

11. $h(x) = 3 - \dfrac{1}{x} + \dfrac{x}{x + 1}$

12. Let t be the time in weeks. At time $t = 0$, organic waste is dumped into a pond. The oxygen level in the pond at time t is given by

$$f(t) = \frac{t^2 - t + 1}{t^2 + 1}.$$

Assume $f(0) = 1$ is the normal level of oxygen.

(a) Graph this function.
(b) Describe the shape of the graph. What is the significance of the minimum for the pond?
(c) What eventually happens to the oxygen level?
(d) Approximately how many weeks must pass before the oxygen level returns to 75% of its normal level?

13. Find a formula for $f^{-1}(x)$ given that

$$f(x) = \frac{4 - 3x}{5x - 4}.$$

14. Bronze is an alloy, or mixture, of copper and tin. The alloy initially contains 3 kg copper and 9 kg tin. You add

x kg of copper to this 12 kg of alloy. The concentration of copper in the alloy is a function of x:

$$f(x) = \text{Concentration of copper} = \frac{\text{Total amount of copper}}{\text{Total amount of alloy}}.$$

(a) Find a formula for f in terms of x, the amount of copper added.
(b) Evaluate the following expressions and explain their significance for the alloy:

    (i) $f(\frac{1}{2})$ (ii) $f(0)$ (iii) $f(-1)$

    (iv) $f^{-1}(\frac{1}{2})$ (v) $f^{-1}(0)$

(c) Graph $f(x)$ for $-5 \le x \le 5$, $-0.25 \le y \le 0.5$. Interpret the intercepts in the context of the alloy.
(d) Graph $f(x)$ for $-3 \le x \le 100$, $0 \le y \le 1$. Describe the appearance of your graph for large x-values. Does the appearance agree with what you expect to happen when large amounts of copper are added to the alloy?

15. A chemist is studying the properties of a bronze alloy (mixture) of copper and tin. She begins with 2 kg of an alloy that is one-half tin. Keeping the amount of copper constant, she adds small amounts of tin to the alloy. Letting x be the total amount of tin added, define

$$C(x) = \text{Concentration of tin} = \frac{\text{Total amount of tin}}{\text{Total amount of alloy}}.$$

(a) Find a formula for $C(x)$.
(b) Evaluate $C(0.5)$ and $C(-0.5)$. Explain the physical significance of these quantities.
(c) Graph $y = C(x)$, labeling all interesting features. Describe the physical significance of the features you have labeled.

16. The total cost $C(n)$ for a producer to manufacture n units of a good is given by

$$C(n) = 5000 + 50n.$$

The average cost of producing n units is $a(n) = C(n)/n$.

(a) Evaluate and interpret the economic significance of:
   (i) $C(1)$ (ii) $C(100)$
   (iii) $C(1000)$ (iv) $C(10000)$

(b) Evaluate and interpret the economic significance of:
   (i) $a(1)$ (ii) $a(100)$
   (iii) $a(1000)$ (iv) $a(10000)$

(c) Based on part (b), what trend do you notice in the values of $a(n)$ as n gets large? Explain this trend in economic terms.

17. Figure 5.46 shows the cost function, $C(n)$, from Problem 16, together with a line, l, that passes through the origin.

(a) What is the slope of line l?

(b) How does line l relate to $a(n_0)$, the average cost of producing n_0 units (as defined in Problem 16)?

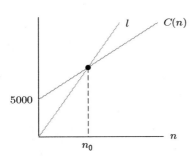

Figure 5.46

18. Typically, the average cost of production (as defined in Problem 16) decreases as the level of production increases. Is this always the case for the goods whose total cost function is graphed in Figure 5.47? Use the result of Problem 17 and explain your reasoning.

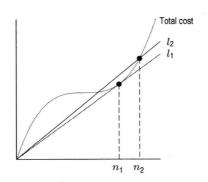

Figure 5.47

19. It costs a company $\$30,000$ to begin production of a good, plus $\$3$ for every unit of the good produced. Let x be the number of units produced by the company.

(a) Find a formula for $C(x)$, the total cost for the production of x units of the good.

(b) Find a formula for the company's average cost per unit, $a(x)$.

(c) Graph $y = a(x)$ for $0 < x \le 50,000$, $0 \le y \le 10$. Label the horizontal asymptote.

(d) Explain in economic terms why the graph of a has the long-run behavior that it does.

(e) Explain in economic terms why the graph of a has the vertical asymptote that it does.

(f) Find a formula for $a^{-1}(y)$. Give an economic interpretation of $a^{-1}(y)$.

(g) The company makes a profit if the average cost of its good is less than $\$5$ per unit. Find the minimum number of units the company can produce and make a profit.

20. The following procedure approximates the cube root of a number. If x is a guess for $\sqrt[3]{2}$, for example, then x^3 equals 2 only if the guess is correct. If $x^3 = 2$ we can also write $x = 2/x^2$. If our guess, x, is less than $\sqrt[3]{2}$, then $2/x^2$ is greater than $\sqrt[3]{2}$. If x is greater than $\sqrt[3]{2}$, then $2/x^2$ is less than $\sqrt[3]{2}$. In either case, if x is an estimate for $\sqrt[3]{2}$, then the average of x and $2/x^2$ provides a better estimate. Define $g(x)$ to be this improved estimate.

(a) Find a possible formula for $g(x)$, expressed as one reduced fraction.

(b) Use $1.26 \approx \sqrt[3]{2}$ as a first guess. Use the function $g(x)$ to estimate the value of $\sqrt[3]{2}$, accurate to five decimal places. Construct a table showing any intermediate results. Explain how you know you have reached the required accuracy.

21. Problem 20 outlines a method of approximating $\sqrt[3]{2}$. An initial guess, x, is averaged with $2/x^2$ to obtain a better guess, denoted by $g(x)$. A better method involves taking a weighted average of x and $2/x^2$.

(a) Let x be a guess for $\sqrt[3]{2}$. Define $h(x)$ by

$$h(x) = \frac{1}{3}\left(x + x + \frac{2}{x^2}\right).$$

Express $h(x)$ as one reduced fraction. Explain why $h(x)$ is referred to as a weighted average.

(b) Explain why $h(x)$ is a better function to use for estimating $\sqrt[3]{2}$ than is $g(x)$. Include specific, numerical examples in your answer.

5.8 THE SHORT-RUN BEHAVIOR OF RATIONAL FUNCTIONS

The short-run behavior of a polynomial can often be determined from its factored form. The same is true of rational functions. If r is a rational function given by

$$r(x) = \frac{p(x)}{q(x)}, \qquad p, q \text{ polynomials,}$$

then the short-run behavior of p and q tell us about the short-run behavior of r.

The Zeros and Vertical Asymptotes of a Rational Function

A fraction is equal to zero if and only if its numerator equals zero (and its denominator does not equal zero). Thus, the rational function $r(x) = p(x)/q(x)$ has a zero wherever p has a zero, provided q does not have a zero there.

Just as we can find the zeros of a rational function by looking at its numerator, we can find the vertical asymptotes by looking at its denominator. A rational function is large wherever its denominator is small. This means that r has a vertical asymptote wherever its denominator has a zero, provided its numerator does not also have a zero there.

Example 1   Find the zeros and vertical asymptotes of the rational function $r(x) = \dfrac{x+3}{x+2}$.

Solution   We see that $r(x) = 0$ if

$$\frac{x+3}{x+2} = 0.$$

This ratio equals zero only if the numerator is zero (and the denominator is not zero), so

$$x + 3 = 0$$
$$x = -3.$$

The only zero of r is $x = -3$. To check, note that $r(-3) = 0/(-1) = 0$. The denominator has a zero at $x = -2$, so the graph of $r(x)$ has a vertical asymptote there.

Example 2   Graph $r(x) = \dfrac{25}{(x+2)(x-3)^2}$, showing all the important features.

Solution   Since the numerator of this function is never zero, r has no zeros, meaning that the graph of r never crosses the x-axis. The graph of r has vertical asymptotes at $x = -2$ and $x = 3$ because this is where the denominator is zero. What does the graph of r look like near its asymptote at $x = -2$? At $x = -2$, the numerator is 25 and the value of the factor $(x-3)^2$ is $(-2-3)^2 = 25$. Thus, near $x = -2$,

$$r(x) = \frac{25}{(x+2)(x-3)^2} \approx \frac{25}{(x+2)(25)} = \frac{1}{x+2}.$$

So, near $x = -2$, the graph of r looks like the graph of $y = 1/(x+2)$. Note that the graph of $y = 1/(x+2)$ is the graph of $y = 1/x$ shifted to the left by 2 units.

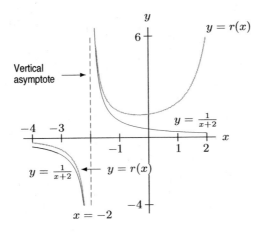

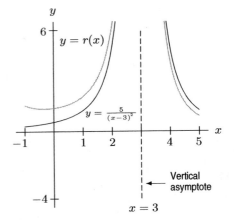

Figure 5.48: The rational function r resembles the shifted power function $1/(x + 2)$ near the asymptote at $x = -2$

Figure 5.49: The rational function r resembles the shifted power function $5/(x - 3)^2$ near the asymptote at $x = 3$

What does the graph of r look like near its vertical asymptote at $x = 3$? Near $x = 3$, the numerator is 25 and value of the factor $(x + 2)$ is approximately $(3 + 2) = 5$. Thus, near $x = 3$,

$$r(x) \approx \frac{25}{(5)(x - 3)^2} = \frac{5}{(x - 3)^2}.$$

Near $x = 3$, the graph of r looks like the the graph of $y = 5/(x - 3)^2$. The graph of $y = 5/(x - 3)^2$ is the graph of $y = 5/x^2$ shifted to the right 3 units. Since

$$r(0) = \frac{25}{(0 + 2)(0 - 3)^2} = \frac{25}{18} \approx 1.4,$$

the graph of r crosses the y-axis at $25/18$. The long-run behavior of r is given by the ratio of the leading term in the numerator to the leading term in the denominator. The numerator is 25 and if we multiply out the denominator, we see that its leading term is x^3. Thus, the long-run behavior of r is given by $y = 25/x^3$, which has a horizontal asymptote at $y = 0$. See Figure 5.50.

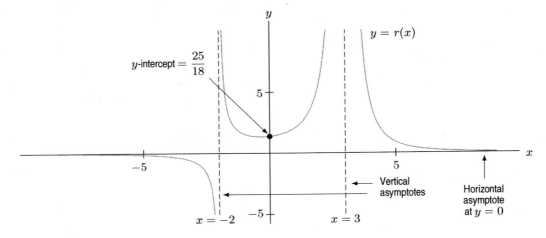

Figure 5.50: A graph of the rational function $r(x) = \dfrac{25}{(x + 2)(x - 3)^2}$, showing intercepts and asymptotes

The Graph of a Rational Function

We can now summarize what we have learned about the graphs of rational functions.

> If r is a rational function given by $r(x) = \dfrac{p(x)}{q(x)}$, where p and q are polynomials with different zeros, then:
> - The **long-run behavior** of r is given by the ratio of the leading terms of p and q.
> - The **zeros** of r are the same as the zeros of the numerator, p.
> - The graph of r has a **vertical asymptote** at each of the zeros of the denominator, q.

If p and q have zeros at the same x-values, the rational function may behave differently.

Can a Graph Cross an Asymptote?

The graph of a rational function never crosses a vertical asymptote. However, the graphs of some rational functions cross their horizontal asymptotes. The difference is that a vertical asymptote occurs where the function is undefined, so there can be no y-value there, whereas a horizontal asymptote represents the limiting value of the function as $x \to \pm\infty$. There is no reason that the function cannot take on this limiting y-value for some finite x-value. For example, the graph of $r(x) = \dfrac{x^2 + 2x - 3}{x^2}$ crosses the line $y = 1$, its horizontal asymptote; the graph does not cross the vertical asymptote, the y-axis. See Figure 5.51.

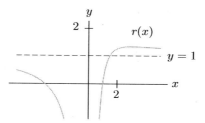

Figure 5.51: A rational function can cross its horizontal asymptote

Rational Functions as Transformations of Power Functions

The average cost function in Section 5.7 can be written as

$$a(q) = \frac{2,500,000 + 2000q}{q} = 2,500,000q^{-1} + 2000.$$

Thus, the graph of a is the graph of the power function $y = 2,500,000q^{-1}$ shifted up 2000 units. Many rational functions can be viewed as translations of power functions.

Finding a Formula for a Rational Function from its Graph

The graph of a rational function can give a good idea of its formula. Zeros of the function correspond to factors in the numerator and vertical asymptotes correspond to factors in the denominator.

Example 3   Find a possible formula for the rational function, $g(x)$, graphed in Figure 5.52.

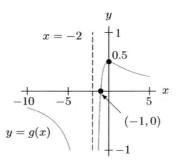

Figure 5.52: The graph of $y = g(x)$ a rational function

Solution   From the graph, we see that g has a zero at $x = -1$ and a vertical asymptote at $x = -2$. This means that the numerator of g has a zero at $x = -1$ and the denominator of g has a zero at $x = -2$. The zero of g does not seem to be a multiple zero because the graph crosses the x-axis instead of bouncing and does not have a flattened appearance. Thus, we conclude that the numerator of g has one factor of $(x + 1)$.

The values of $g(x)$ have the same sign on both sides of the vertical asymptote. Thus, the behavior of g near its vertical asymptote is more like the behavior of $y = 1/(x + 2)^2$ than like $y = 1/(x + 2)$. We conclude that the denominator of g has a factor of $(x + 2)^2$. This suggests

$$g(x) = k \cdot \frac{x + 1}{(x + 2)^2},$$

where k is a stretch factor. To find the value of k, use the fact that $g(0) = 0.5$. So

$$0.5 = k \cdot \frac{0 + 1}{(0 + 2)^2}$$
$$0.5 = k \cdot \frac{1}{4}$$
$$k = 2.$$

Thus, a possible formula for g is $g(x) = \dfrac{2(x + 1)}{(x + 2)^2}$.

When Numerator and Denominator Have the Same Zeros: Holes

The rational function $h(x) = \dfrac{x^2 + x - 2}{x - 1}$ is undefined at $x = 1$ because the denominator equals zero at $x = 1$. However, the graph of h does not have a vertical asymptote at $x = 1$ because the numerator of h also equals zero at $x = 1$. At $x = 1$,

$$h(1) = \frac{x^2 + x - 2}{x - 1} = \frac{1^2 + 1 - 2}{1 - 1} = \frac{0}{0},$$

and this ratio is undefined. What does the graph of h look like? Factoring the numerator of h gives

$$h(x) = \frac{(x - 1)(x + 2)}{x - 1} = \frac{x - 1}{x - 1}(x + 2).$$

For any $x \neq 1$, we can cancel $(x - 1)$ top and bottom and rewrite the formula for h as

$$h(x) = x + 2, \qquad \text{provided } x \neq 1.$$

Thus, the graph of h is the line $y = x + 2$ except at $x = 1$, where h is undefined. The line $y = x + 2$ contains the point $(1, 3)$, but that the graph of h does not. Therefore, we say that the graph of h has a *hole* in it at the point $(1, 3)$. See Figure 5.53.

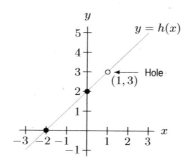

Figure 5.53: The graph of $y = h(x)$ is the line $y = x + 2$, except at the point $(1, 3)$, where it has a hole

Exercises and Problems for Section 5.8

Exercises

In Exercises 1–4, what are the x-intercepts, y-intercepts, and horizontal and vertical asymptotes (if any)?

1. $f(x) = \dfrac{x - 2}{x - 4}$

2. $g(x) = \dfrac{x^2 - 9}{x^2 + 9}$

3. $h(x) = \dfrac{x^2 - 4}{x^3 + 4x^2}$

4. $k(x) = \dfrac{x(4 - x)}{x^2 - 6x + 5}$

For the rational functions in Exercises 5–8, find all zeros and vertical asymptotes and describe the long-run behavior. Then graph the function without a calculator.

5. $y = \dfrac{x + 3}{x + 5}$

6. $y = \dfrac{x + 3}{(x + 5)^2}$

7. $y = \dfrac{x - 4}{x^2 - 9}$

8. $y = \dfrac{x^2 - 4}{x - 9}$

Graph the functions in Exercises 9–10 without a calculator.

9. $y = 2 + \dfrac{1}{x}$

10. $y = \dfrac{2x^2 - 10x + 12}{x^2 - 16}$

11. Let $f(x) = \dfrac{1}{x - 3}$.

    (a) Complete Table 5.12 for x-values close to 3. What happens to the values of $f(x)$ as x approaches 3 from the left? From the right?

Table 5.12

x	2	2.9	2.99	3	3.01	3.1	4
$f(x)$							

    (b) Complete Tables 5.13 and 5.14. What happens to the values of $f(x)$ as x takes very large positive values? As x takes very large negative values?

Table 5.13

x	5	10	100	1000
$f(x)$				

Table 5.14

x	-5	-10	-100	-1000
$f(x)$				

    (c) Without a calculator, graph $y = f(x)$. Give equations for the horizontal and vertical asymptotes.

12. Let $g(x) = \dfrac{1}{(x + 2)^2}$.

    (a) Complete Table 5.15 for x-values close to -2. What happens to the values of $g(x)$ as x approaches -2 from the left? From the right?

Table 5.15

x	-3	-2.1	-2.01	-2	-1.99	-1.9	-1
$g(x)$							

(b) Complete Tables 5.16 and 5.17. What happens to the values of $g(x)$ as x takes very large positive values? As x takes very large negative values?

Table 5.16

x	5	10	100	1000
$g(x)$				

Table 5.17

x	-5	-10	-100	-1000
$g(x)$				

(c) Without a calculator, graph $y = g(x)$. Give equations for the horizontal and vertical asymptotes.

13. Let $F(x) = \dfrac{x^2 - 1}{x^2}$.

(a) Complete Table 5.18 for x-values close to 0. What happens to the values of $F(x)$ as x approaches 0 from the left? From the right?

Table 5.18

x	-1	-0.1	-0.01	0	0.01	0.1	1
$F(x)$							

(b) Complete Tables 5.19 and 5.20. What happens to the values of $F(x)$ as x takes very large positive values? As x takes very large negative values?

Table 5.19

x	5	10	100	1000
$F(x)$				

Table 5.20

x	-5	-10	-100	-1000
$F(x)$				

(c) Without a calculator, graph $y = F(x)$. Give equation for the horizontal and vertical asymptotes.

14. Let $G(x) = \dfrac{2x}{x + 4}$.

(a) Complete Table 5.21 for x-values close to -4. What happens to the values of $G(x)$ as x approaches -4 from the left? From the right?

Table 5.21

x	-5	-4.1	-4.01	-4	-3.99	-3.9	-3
$G(x)$							

(b) Complete Tables 5.22 and 5.23. What happens to the values of $G(x)$ as x takes very large positive values? As x takes very large negative values?

Table 5.22

x	5	10	100	1000
$G(x)$				

Table 5.23

x	-5	-10	-100	-1000
$G(x)$				

(c) Without a calculator, graph $y = G(x)$. Give equations for the horizontal and vertical asymptotes.

Problems

15. Let $f(x) = x^2 + 5x + 6$ and $g(x) = x^2 + 1$.

(a) What are the zeros of f and g?

(b) Let $r(x) = f(x)/g(x)$. Graph r. Does r have zeros? Vertical asymptotes? What is its long-run behavior as $x \to \pm\infty$?

(c) Let $s(x) = g(x)/f(x)$. If you graph s in the window $-10 \le x \le 10$, $-10 \le y \le 10$, it appears to have a zero near the origin. Does it? Does s have a vertical asymptote? What is its long-run behavior?

16. Without a calculator, match the functions (a)–(f) with their graphs in (i)–(vi) by finding the zeros, asymptotes, and end behavior for each function.

(a) $y = \dfrac{-1}{(x - 5)^2} - 1$

(b) $y = \dfrac{x - 2}{(x + 1)(x - 3)}$

(c) $y = \dfrac{2x + 4}{x - 1}$

(d) $y = \dfrac{1}{x + 1} + \dfrac{1}{x - 3}$

(e) $y = \dfrac{1 - x^2}{x - 2}$

(f) $y = \dfrac{1 - 4x}{2x + 2}$

(i)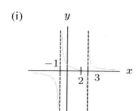

(ii)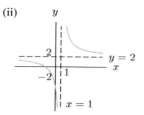

(iii) (iv)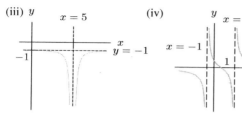

(v) (vi)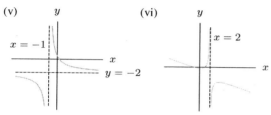

17. Suppose that n is a constant and that $f(x)$ is a function defined when $x = n$. Complete the following sentences.

(a) If $f(n)$ is large, then $\dfrac{1}{f(n)}$ is ...

(b) If $f(n)$ is small, then $\dfrac{1}{f(n)}$ is ...

(c) If $f(n) = 0$, then $\dfrac{1}{f(n)}$ is ...

(d) If $f(n)$ is positive, then $\dfrac{1}{f(n)}$ is ...

(e) If $f(n)$ is negative, then $\dfrac{1}{f(n)}$ is ...

18. (a) Use the results of Problem 17 to graph $y = 1/f(x)$ given the graph of $y = f(x)$ in Figure 5.54.

(b) Find a possible formula for the function in Figure 5.54. Use this formula to check your graph for part (a).

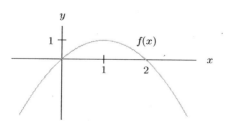

Figure 5.54:

19. Use the graph of f in Figure 5.55 to graph

(a) $y = -f(-x) + 2$ (b) $y = \dfrac{1}{f(x)}$

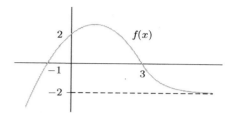

Figure 5.55:

Each of the functions in Problems 20–22 is a transformation of $y = 1/x^p$. For each function, determine p, describe the transformation in words, and graph the function and label any intercepts and asymptotes.

20. $f(x) = \dfrac{1}{x - 3} + 4$

21. $g(x) = -\dfrac{1}{(x - 2)^2} - 3$

22. $h(x) = \dfrac{1}{x - 1} + \dfrac{2}{1 - x} + 2$

Problems 23–25 show a translation of $y = 1/x$.

(a) Find a possible formula for the graph.

(b) Write the formula from part (a) as the ratio of two linear polynomials.

(c) Find the coordinates of the intercepts of the graph.

23. **24.**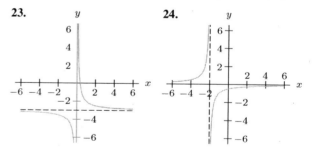

25.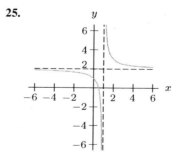

Problems 26–28 show a translation of $y = 1/x^2$.

   (a) Find a formula for the graph.

   (b) Write the formula from part (a) as the ratio of two polynomials.

   (c) Find the coordinates of any intercepts of the graph.

26.   **27.**

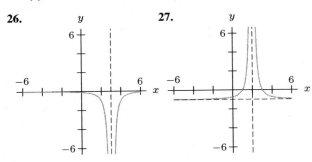

28.

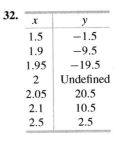

Problems 29–32 give values of translations of either $y = 1/x$ or $y = 1/x^2$. In each case

   (a) Determine if the values are from a translation of $y = 1/x$ or $y = 1/x^2$. Explain your reasoning.

   (b) Find a possible formula for the function.

29.

x	y
2.7	12.1
2.9	101
2.95	401
3	Undefined
3.05	401
3.1	101
3.3	12.1

30.

x	y
−1000	0.499
−100	0.490
−10	0.400
10	0.600
100	0.510
1000	0.501

31.

x	y
−1000	1.000001
−100	1.00001
−10	1.01
10	1.01
100	1.0001
1000	1.000001

32.

x	y
1.5	−1.5
1.9	−9.5
1.95	−19.5
2	Undefined
2.05	20.5
2.1	10.5
2.5	2.5

33. Cut four equal squares from the corners of a $8.5'' \times 11''$ piece of paper. Fold up the sides to create an open box. Find the dimensions of the box with the maximum volume per surface area.

Find possible formulas for the functions in Problems 34–41.

34.   **35.**

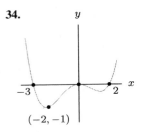
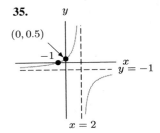

36.   **37.**

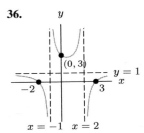
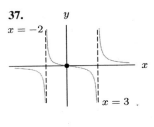

38.   **39.**

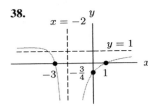
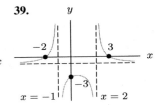

40.

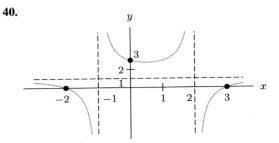

41.

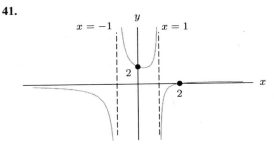

In Problems 42–44, find a possible formula for the rational functions.

42. The graph of $y = f(x)$ has one vertical asymptote, at $x = -1$, and a horizontal asymptote at $y = 1$. The graph of f crosses the y-axis at $y = 3$ and crosses the x-axis once, at $x = -3$.

43. The graph of $y = g(x)$ has two vertical asymptotes: one at $x = -2$ and one at $x = 3$. It has a horizontal asymptote of $y = 0$. The graph of g crosses the x-axis once, at $x = 5$.

44. The graph of $y = h(x)$ has two vertical asymptotes: one at $x = -2$ and one at $x = 3$. It has a horizontal asymp-tote of $y = 1$. The graph of h touches the x-axis once, at $x = 5$.

45. The graph of $f(x) = \dfrac{18 - 11x + x^2}{x - 2}$ is a line with a hole in it. What is the equation of the line? What are the co-ordinates of the hole?

46. The graph of $g(x) = \dfrac{x^3 + 5x^2 + x + 5}{x + 5}$ is a parabola with a hole in it. What is the equation of the parabola? What are the coordinates of the hole?

47. Write a formula for a function, $h(x)$, whose graph is iden-tical to the graph of $y = x^3$, except that the graph of h has a hole at $(2, 8)$. Express the formula as a ratio of two polynomials

CHAPTER SUMMARY

- **Proportionality**
  Direct and indirect.
- **Power Functions**
  $y = kx^p$.
- **Polynomials**
  General formula: $p(x) = a_n x^n + a_{n-1} x^{n-1} + \cdots + a_1 x + a_0$.
  All terms have non-negative, integer exponents. Leading term $a_n x^n$; coefficients $a_0, \ldots, a_n$.
  Long-run behavior: Like $y = a_n x^n$.
  Short-run behavior: Zeros corresponding to each factor; multiple zeros.
- **Rational Functions**
  Ratio of polynomials: $r(x) = \dfrac{p(x)}{q(x)}$.
  Long-run behavior: Horizontal asymptote of $r(x)$:
    Given by ratio of highest-degree terms.

  Short-run behavior: Vertical asymptote of $r(x)$:
    At zeros of $q(x)$ (if $p(x) \neq 0$).
  Short-run behavior: Zeros of $r(x)$:
    At zeros of $p(x)$ (if $q(x) \neq 0$).
- **Comparing Functions**
  Exponential functions eventually dominate power func-tions. Power functions eventually dominate logs.
- **Quadratic Functions**
  Standard form: $y = ax^2 + bx + c$.
  Vertex form: $y = a(x - h)^2 + k$.
    Opening upward if $a > 0$; downward if $a < 0$.
  Vertex (h, k), axis of symmetry $x = h$, maximum, minimum.
    Completing the square.

REVIEW EXERCISES AND PROBLEMS FOR CHAPTER FIVE

Exercises

Do the power functions in Exercises 1–2 appear to have odd, even, or fractional powers?

1.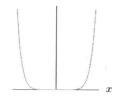

2.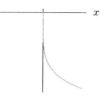

In Exercises 3–4, find possible formulas for the power func-tions with the properties given.

3. $f(1) = \frac{3}{2}$ and $f(2) = \frac{3}{8}$

4. $g\left(-\frac{1}{5}\right) = 25$ and $g(2) = -\frac{1}{40}$

5. Show that the function $u(x) = x(x - 3)(x + 2)$ is a poly-nomial. What is its degree?

For the polynomials in Exercises 6–8, state the degree, the number of terms, and describe the long-run behavior.

6. $y = 2x^3 - 3x + 7$

7. $y = 1 - 2x^4 + x^3$

8. $y = (x + 4)(2x - 3)(5 - x)$

In Exercises 9–10, find the zeros of the functions.

9. $y = (x^2 - 8x + 12)(x - 3)$

10. $y = ax^2(x^2 + 4)(x + 3)$, where a is a nonzero constant.

Are the functions in Exercises 11–12 rational functions? If so, write them in the form $p(x)/q(x)$, the ratio of polynomials.

11. $f(x) = \dfrac{x^3}{2x^2} + \dfrac{1}{6}$

12. $f(x) = \dfrac{x^4 + 3^x - x^2}{x^3 - 2}$

In Exercises 13–14, which function dominates as $x \to \infty$?

13. $y = 12x^3$, $\quad y = 7/x^{-4}$

14. $y = 4/e^{-x}$, $\quad y = 17x^{43}$

Problems

15. Without a calculator, match graphs (i)–(iv) with the functions in Table 5.24.

(i)

(ii)

(v)

(vi)

(iii)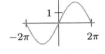

(iv)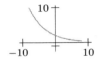

(vii)

(viii)

Table 5.24

(A) $y = 0.5\sin(2x)$	(J) $y = 2\sin(0.5x)$
(B) $y = -\ln x$	(K) $y = \ln(x - 1)$
(C) $y = 10(0.6)^x$	(L) $y = 2e^{-0.2x}$
(D) $y = 2\sin(2x)$	(M) $y = 1/(x - 6)$
(E) $y = \ln(-x)$	(N) $y = (x - 2)/(x^2 - 9)$
(F) $y = -15(3.1)^x$	(O) $y = 1/(x^2 - 4)$
(G) $y = 0.5\sin(0.5x)$	(P) $y = x/(x - 3)$
(H) $y = \ln(x + 1)$	(Q) $y = (x - 1)/(x + 3)$
(I) $y = 7(2.5)^x$	(R) $y = 1/(x^2 + 4)$

Table 5.25

(A)	$y = 0.5\sin(2x)$	(M)	$y = (x + 3)/(x^2 - 4)$
(B)	$y = 2\sin(2x)$	(N)	$y = (x^2 - 4)/(x^2 - 1)$
(C)	$y = 0.5\sin(0.5x)$	(O)	$y = (x + 1)^3 - 1$
(D)	$y = 2\sin(0.5x)$	(P)	$y = -2x - 4$
(E)	$y = (x - 2)/(x^2 - 9)$	(Q)	$y = 3e^{-x}$
(F)	$y = (x - 3)/(x^2 - 1)$	(R)	$y = -3e^x$
(G)	$y = (x - 1)^3 - 1$	(S)	$y = -3e^{-x}$
(H)	$y = 2x - 4$	(T)	$y = 3e^{-x^2}$
(I)	$y = -\ln x$	(U)	$y = 1/(4 - x^2)$
(J)	$y = \ln(-x)$	(V)	$y = 1/(x^2 + 4)$
(K)	$y = \ln(x + 1)$	(W)	$y = (x + 1)^3 + 1$
(L)	$y = \ln(x - 1)$	(X)	$y = 2(x + 2)$

16. Without a calculator, match each graph (i)–(viii) with a functions in Table 5.25

(i)

(ii)

(iii)

(iv)

Find possible polynomial formulas in Problems 17–22.

17.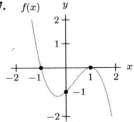

18.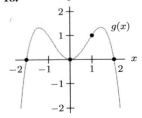

19. 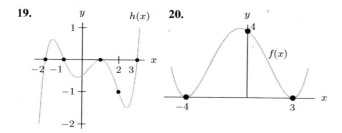   **20.**

21. 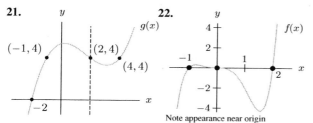   **22.**

Note appearance near origin

23. For each of the following functions, state whether it is even, odd, or neither.

(a) $f(x) = x^2 + 3$ (b) $g(x) = x^3 + 3$
(c) $h(x) = 5/x$ (d) $j(x) = |x - 4|$
(e) $k(x) = \log x$ (f) $l(x) = \log(x^2)$
(g) $m(x) = 2^x + 2$ (h) $n(x) = \cos x + 2$

24. Assume that $x = a$ and $x = b$ are zeros of the second degree polynomial, $y = q(x)$.

(a) Explain what you know and don't know about the graph of q. (Intercepts, vertex, end behavior.)
(b) Explain why a possible formula for $q(x)$ is $q(x) = k(x - a)(x - b)$, with k unknown.

25. (a) Suppose $f(x) = ax^2 + bx + c$. What must be true about the coefficients if f is an even function?
(b) Suppose $g(x) = ax^3 + bx^2 + cx + d$. What must be true about the coefficients if g is an odd function?

26. The gravitational force exerted by a planet is inversely proportional to the square of the distance to the center of the planet. Thus, the weight, w, of an object at a distance, r, from a planet's center is given by

$$w = \frac{k}{r^2}, \quad \text{with } k \text{ constant.}$$

A gravitational force of one ton (2000 lbs) will kill a 150-pound person. Suppose the earth's radius were to shrink with its mass remaining the same. What is the smallest radius at which the 150-pound person could survive? Give your answer as a percentage of the earth's radius.

27. Ship designers usually construct scale models before building a real ship. The formula that relates the speed u

to the hull length l of a ship is

$$u = k\sqrt{l},$$

where k is a positive constant. This constant k varies depending on the ship's design, but scale models of a real ship have the same k as the real ship after which they are modeled.[13]

(a) How fast should a scale model with hull length 4 meters travel to simulate a real ship with hull length 225 meters traveling 9 meters/sec?
(b) A new ship is to be built whose speed is to be 10% greater than the speed of an existing ship with the same design. What is the relationship between the hull lengths of the new ship and the existing ship?

28. The cruising speed V of birds at sea-level (in meters/sec) is determined[14] by the mass M of the bird (in grams), and the surface area S of the wings exposed to the air (in square meters). It is given by

$$V = 0.164\sqrt{\frac{M}{S}}.$$

(a) The mass of a partridge is half the mass of a hawk. Their wing surface areas are typically 0.043 and 0.166 square meters, respectively. Which bird has the faster cruising speed? The cruising speed of the partridge is 15.6 meters/sec. What are the masses of the partridge and the hawk?
(b) The wing surface area of a Canadian goose is typically 12 times that of an American robin, whereas the mass of the goose is 70 times that of the robin. Which bird has the faster cruising speed? The mass and cruising speed of the American robin are typically 80 grams and 9.5 meters/sec, respectively. What are the wing surface areas of the Canadian goose and the American robin?
(c) Use a graphing calculator or computer to plot V against different masses M, for birds with the same surface area of 0.01 square meters—swallows, martins, swifts, and so on. Describe the graph in words. What happens to the cruising speed as the mass increases?
(d) Use a graphing calculator or computer to plot V against different wing surface areas S, for birds with the same mass 784 grams—falcons, hawks, and so on. Describe the graph in words. What happens to the cruising speed as the wing surface area increases?
(e) When a bird dives it draws in its wings. What happens to its cruising speed? Is this realistic?

29. An alcohol solution consists of 5 gallons of pure water and x gallons of alcohol, $x > 0$. Let $f(x)$ be the ratio

[13]R. McNeill Alexander, *Dynamics of Dinosaurs and Other Extinct Giants.* (New York: Columbia University Press, 1989).
[14]H. Tennekes, *The Simple Science of Flight.* (Cambridge: MIT Press, 1996).

of the volume of alcohol to the total volume of liquid. [Note that $f(x)$ is the concentration of the alcohol in the solution.]

(a) Find a possible formula for $f(x)$.
(b) Evaluate and interpret $f(7)$ in the context of the mixture.
(c) What is the zero of f? Interpret your result in the context of the mixture.
(d) Find an equation for the horizontal asymptote of f. Explain its significance in the context of the mixture.

30. The function $f(x)$ defined in Problem 29 gives the concentration of a solution of x gallons of alcohol and 5 gallons of water.

(a) Find a formula for $f^{-1}(x)$.
(b) Evaluate and interpret $f^{-1}(0.2)$ in the context of the mixture.
(c) What is the zero of f^{-1}? Interpret your result in the context of the mixture.
(d) Find an equation for the horizontal asymptote of f^{-1}. Explain its significance in the context of the mixture.

Problems 31–34 show graphs of rational functions of the form

$$y = \frac{(x - A)(x - B)}{(x - C)(x - D)},$$

for different values of the constants A, B, C, and D, with $A \le B$ and $C \le D$. In each case, rank the constants 0, A, B, C, D in order, from least to greatest.

31.

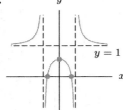

32.

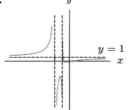

33.

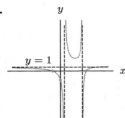

34.

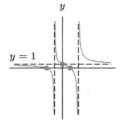

Find possible formulas for the polynomials and rational functions in Problems 35–37.

35. This function has zeros at $x = -3$, $x = 2$, $x = 5$, and a double-zero at $x = 6$. It has a y-intercept of 7.

36. This function has zeros at $x = -3$ and $x = 2$, and vertical asymptotes at $x = -5$ and $x = 7$. It has a horizontal asymptote of $y = 1$.

37. This function has zeros at $x = 2$ and $x = 3$. It has a vertical asymptote at $x = 5$. It has a horizontal asymptote of $y = -3$.

38. Let $f(x) = (x - 3)^2$, $g(x) = x^2 - 4$, $h(x) = x + 1$, and $j(x) = x^2 + 1$. Without a calculator, match the functions described in (a) – (f) to the functions in (i) – (vi). Some of the descriptions may have no matching function or more than one matching function.

(i) $p(x) = \dfrac{f(x)}{g(x)}$ **(ii)** $q(x) = \dfrac{h(x)}{g(x)}$

(iii) $r(x) = f(x)h(x)$ **(iv)** $s(x) = \dfrac{g(x)}{j(x)}$

(v) $t(x) = \dfrac{1}{h(x)}$ **(vi)** $v(x) = \dfrac{j(x)}{f(x)}$

(a) Two zeros, no vertical asymptotes, and a horizontal asymptote.
(b) Two zeros, no vertical asymptote, and no horizontal asymptote.
(c) One zero, one vertical asymptote, and a horizontal asymptote.
(d) One zero, two vertical asymptotes, and a horizontal asymptote.
(e) No zeros, one vertical asymptote, and a horizontal asymptote at $y = 1$.
(f) No zeros, one vertical asymptote, and a horizontal asymptote at $y = 0$.

39. A volunteer was given some objects and asked to judge their weights, where a 98 gram object was assigned the value of 100. Table 5.26 shows the result of such an experiment, where w is the physical weight of the object in grams, and J is the judged weight of the object.[15] This is an example of a "judgment of magnitude" experiment, which is modeled by the power law $J = aw^b$, where a and b are constants.

(a) Estimate a and b.
(b) What does the w-intercept suggest about the value implicitly assigned to an object with no weight?
(c) Someone observes that the doubling of physical weight results in the judged weight being multiplied by 2.6. Is that an accurate observation?

Table 5.26

w	19	33	46	63	74	98	136	212
J	10	25	35	60	90	100	150	280

---

[15]"Elementary Theoretical Psychology" by J. G. Greeno, Addison-Wesley, Massachusetts, 1968.

40. The ancient Greeks placed great importance on a number known as the *golden ratio*, ϕ, which is defined geometrically as follows. Starting with a square, add a rectangle to one side of the square, so that the resulting rectangle has the same proportions as the rectangle that was added. The golden ratio is defined as the ratio of either rectangle's length to its width. (See Figure 5.56.) Given this information, show that $\phi = (1 + \sqrt{5})/2$.

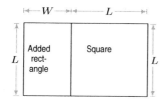

Figure 5.56: Large rectangle has the same proportions as small rectangle

41. The number ϕ, defined in Problem 40, has the property:

$$\phi^k + \phi^{k+1} = \phi^{k+2}.$$

(a) Check that the property holds true for $k = 3$ and $k = 10$.

(b) Show that this property follows from the definition of ϕ.

42. The resolution, r %, of a gamma ray telescope depends on the energy v (in millions of electron volts, or MeVs) of the detected gamma rays.[16] The smaller the value of r, the better the telescope is at distinguishing two gamma ray photons of slightly different energies, and the more detailed observations that can be made. Table 5.27 gives values of r for gamma rays at different energies.

(a) Plot the data in Table 5.27 with r on the vertical axis.

(b) Based on this data, is the telescope better able to distinguish between high-energy photons or low-energy photons?

(c) Fit both power and exponential functions to the data, and give their formulas. Which appears to give the better fit?

(d) The telescope is predicted to grow rapidly worse and worse at distinguishing photons as the energy level drops towards 0 MeV. Which curve, power or exponential, is most consistent with this prediction?

Table 5.27

v, MeV	0.5	0.7	0.9	1.3	1.8	4.0	4.4
r, %	16.0	13.5	12.0	8.5	7.0	4.5	4.0

In Problems 43–48, give the type of functions—linear, exponential, logarithmic, trigonometric, power, or polynomial—that fits the data. Find a possible formula for the function whose values are in each table.

43.

x	−2	−1	0	1	2	3
y	3	−1	3	−1	3	−1

44.

x	1	2	3	4	5
y	8	3	−2	−7	−12

45.

x	−3	−2	−1	0	1	2	3
y	−40	0	12	8	0	0	20

46.

x	−2	−1	0	1	2
y	−24	−3	0	3	24

47.

x	−2	−1	0	1	2	3
y	0.02	0.10	0.5	2.50	12.5	62.5

48.

x	1/100	1/10	1	10	100
y	−2	−1	0	1	2

49. We launch an unpowered spacecraft, initially in free space, so that it hits a planet of radius R. When viewed from a distance, the planet looks like a disk of area πR^2. In the absence of gravity, we would need to aim the spacecraft directly at this disk. However, because of gravity, the planet draws the spacecraft towards it, so that even if we are somewhat off the mark, the spacecraft might still hit its target. Thus, the area we must aim for is actually larger than the apparent area of the planet. This area is called the planet's *capture cross-section*. The more massive the planet, the larger its capture cross-section, because it exerts a stronger pull on passing objects.

A spacecraft with a large initial velocity has a greater chance of slipping past the planet even if its aim is only slightly off, whereas a spacecraft with a low initial velocity has a good chance of drifting into the planet even if its aim is poor. Thus, the planet's capture cross-section is a function of the initial velocity of the spacecraft, v. If the planet's capture cross-section is denoted by A and M is the planet's mass, then it can be shown that, for a positive constant G,

$$A(v) = \pi R^2 \left(1 + \frac{2MG/R}{v^2} \right).$$

(a) Show from the formula for $A(v)$ that, for any initial velocity v,

$$A(v) > \pi R^2.$$

Explain why this makes sense physically.

(b) Consider two planets: The first is twice as massive as the second, and the radius of the second is twice

---

[16]*The LXeGRIT Compton Status and Future Prospects*, E. Aprile, et al., posted at http://arxiv.org as arXiv:astro-ph/0212005v2, December 4, 2002.

the radius of the first. Which has the larger capture cross-section?

(c) The graph of $A(v)$ has both horizontal and vertical asymptotes. Find their equations, and explain their physical significance.

50. A group of x people is tested for the presence of a certain virus. Unfortunately, the test is imperfect and incorrectly identifies some healthy people as being infected and some sick people as being noninfected. There is no way to know when the test is right and when it is wrong. Since the disease is so rare, only 1% of those tested are actually infected.

(a) Write expressions in terms of x for the number of people tested that are actually infected and the number who are not.

(b) The test correctly identifies 98% of all infected people as being infected. (It incorrectly identifies the remaining 2% as being healthy.) Write, in terms of x, an expression representing the number of infected

people who are correctly identified as being infected. (This group is known as the *true-positive* group.)

(c) The test incorrectly identifies 3% of all healthy people as being infected. (It correctly identifies the remaining 97% as being healthy.) Write, in terms of x, an expression representing the number of noninfected people who are incorrectly identified as being infected. (This group is known as the *false-positive* group.)

(d) Write, in terms of x, an expression representing the total number of people the test identifies as being infected, including both true- and false-positives.

(e) Write, in terms of x, an expression representing the fraction of those testing positive who are actually infected. Can this expression be evaluated without knowing the value of x?

(f) Suppose you are among the group of people who test positive for the presence of the virus. Based on your test result, do you think it is likely that you are actually infected?

CHECK YOUR UNDERSTANDING

Are the statements in Problems 1–47 true or false? Give an explanation for your answer.

1. All quadratic functions are power functions.

2. The function $y = 3 \cdot 2^x$ is a power function.

3. Let $g(x) = x^p$. If p is a positive, even integer, then the graph of g passes through the point $(-1, 1)$.

4. Let $g(x) = x^p$. If p is a positive, even integer, then the graph of g is symmetric about the y-axis.

5. Let $g(x) = x^p$. If p is a positive, even integer, then the graph of g is concave up.

6. The graph of $f(x) = x^{-1}$ passes through the origin.

7. The graph of $f(x) = x^{-2}$ has the x-axis as its only asymptote.

8. If $f(x) = x^{-1}$ then $f(x)$ approaches $+\infty$ as x approaches zero.

9. As x grows very large, the values of $f(x) = x^{-1}$ approach zero.

10. The function 2^x eventually grows faster than x^b for any b.

11. The function $f(x) = x^{0.5}$ eventually grows faster than $g(x) = \ln x$.

12. We have $2^x \geq x^2$ on the interval $0 \leq x \leq 4$.

13. The function $f(x) = x^{-3}$ approaches the x-axis faster than $g(x) = e^{-x}$ as x grows very large.

14. The function $f(x) = 3^x$ is an example of a power function.

15. The function $y = 3x$ is an example of a power function.

16. Every quadratic function is a polynomial function.

17. The power of the first term of a polynomial is its degree.

18. Far from the origin, the graph of a polynomial looks like the graph of its highest degree term.

19. A zero of a polynomial p is the value $p(0)$.

20. The zeros of a polynomial are the x-coordinates where its graph intersects the x-axis.

21. The y-intercept of a polynomial $y = p(x)$ can be found by evaluating $p(0)$.

22. For very large x-values $f(x) = 1000x^3 + 345x^2 + 17x + 394$ is less than $g(x) = 0.01x^4$.

23. If $y = f(x)$ is a polynomial of degree n, where n is a positive even number, then f has an inverse.

24. If $y = f(x)$ is a polynomial of degree n, where n is a positive odd number, then f has an inverse.

25. If $p(x)$ is a polynomial and $x - a$ is a factor of p, then $x = a$ is a zero of p.

26. A polynomial of degree n cannot have more than n zeros.

27. The polynomial in Figure 5.57 has a multiple zero at $x = -2$.

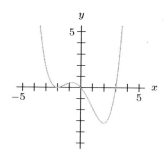

Figure 5.57

28. The polynomial in Figure 5.57 has a multiple zero at $x = 0$.

29. A rational function is the quotient of two polynomials. We assume the denominator is not equal to zero.

30. The function $f(x) = \dfrac{1}{x}$ is a rational function.

31. In order to determine the long-run behavior of a rational function, it is sufficient to consider only the ratio of the highest degree term in the numerator to the highest degree term in the denominator.

32. As x grows through large positive values, $y = \dfrac{x + 18}{x + 9}$ approaches $y = 2$.

33. As x grows through large positive values, $y = \dfrac{2x + 125}{x^2 - 1}$ approaches $y = 0$.

34. As x grows through large positive values, $y = \dfrac{x^3 + 4x^2 - 16x + 12}{4x^3 - 16x + 1}$ has an asymptote at $y = 4$.

35. As x grows through large positive values, $y = \dfrac{1 - 4x^2}{x^2 + 1}$ approaches $y = 0$.

36. As x grows through large positive values, $y = \dfrac{5x}{x + 1}$ approaches $y = -5$.

37. As x grows through large positive values, $y = \dfrac{3x^4 - 6x^3 + 10x^2 - 16x + 7}{-3x + x^2}$ behaves like $y = -x^3$.

38. As x decreases through large negative values, $f(x) = \dfrac{x^3 - 7x^2 + 28x + 76}{-x^2 - 101x + 72}$ approaches positive infinity.

39. A fraction is equal to zero if and only if its numerator equals zero and its denominator does not.

40. The zeros of a function $y = f(x)$ are the values of x that make $y = 0$.

41. The rational function $f(x) = \dfrac{x + 4}{x - 3}$ has a zero at $x = -4$.

42. The rational function $y = \dfrac{x + 2}{x^2 - 4}$ has a zero at $x = -2$.

43. The rational function $g(w) = \dfrac{12}{(w - 2)(w + 3)}$ has exactly two zeros.

44. If $p(x)$ and $q(x)$ have no zeros in common, then the rational function $r(x) = \dfrac{p(x)}{q(x)}$ has an asymptote at each of the zeros of $p(x)$.

45. In general, the rational function $r(x) = \dfrac{p(x)}{q(x)}$ must have at least one zero.

46. Rational functions can never cross an asymptote.

47. The rational function $g(w) = \dfrac{3w - 3}{(w - 12)(w + 4)}$ has a vertical asymptote at $w = 1$.

Chapter Six

COMBINATIONS OF FUNCTIONS, INVERSES, AND INVERSE TRIGONOMETRIC FUNCTIONS

In this chapter we define composition of functions, inverse functions, and combinations of functions. We will then define and investigate the properties of the inverse trigonometric functions and use them in solving equations.

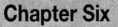

6.1   COMPOSITION OF FUNCTIONS

The Effect of a Drug on Heart Rates

A therapeutic drug has the side effect of raising a patient's heart rate. Table 6.1 gives the relationship between Q, the amount of drug in the patient's body (in milligrams), and r, the patient's heart rate (in beats per minute). We see that the higher the drug level, the faster the heart rate.

Table 6.1   *Heart rate, $r = f(Q)$, as a function of drug level, Q*

Q, drug level (mg)	0	50	100	150	200	250
r, heart rate (beats per minute)	60	70	80	90	100	110

A patient is given a 250 mg injection of the drug. Over time, the level of drug in the patient's bloodstream falls. Table 6.2 gives the drug level, Q, as a function of time, t.

Table 6.2   *Drug level, $Q = g(t)$, as a function of time, t, since the medication was given*

t, time (hours)	0	1	2	3	4	5	6	7	8
Q, drug level (mg)	250	200	160	128	102	82	66	52	42

Since heart rate depends on the drug level and drug level depends on time, the heart rate also depends on time. Tables 6.1 and 6.2 can be combined to give the patient's heart rate, r, as a function of t. For example, according to Table 6.2, at time $t = 0$ the drug level is 250 mg. According to Table 6.1, at this drug level, the patient's heart rate is 110 beats per minute. So $r = 110$ when $t = 0$. The results of similar calculations have been compiled in Table 6.3. Note that many of the entries, such as $r = 92$ when $t = 2$, are estimates.

Table 6.3   *Heart rate, $r = h(t)$, as a function of time, t*

t, time (hours)	0	1	2	3	4	5	6	7	8
r, heart rate (beats per minute)	110	100	92	86	80	76	73	70	68

Now, since

$$r = f(Q) \quad \text{or} \quad \underbrace{\text{Heart rate}}_{r} = f(\underbrace{\text{drug level}}_{Q}),$$

and

$$Q = g(t) \quad \text{or} \quad \underbrace{\text{Drug level}}_{Q} = g(\underbrace{\text{time}}_{t}),$$

we can substitute $Q = g(t)$ into $r = f(Q)$, giving

$$r = f(\underbrace{Q}_{g(t)}) = f(g(t)).$$

The function h in Table 6.3 is said to be the *composition* of the function f and g, written

$$h(t) = f(g(t)).$$

This formula represents the process that we used to find the values of $r = h(t)$ in Table 6.3.

Example 1   Use Tables 6.1 and 6.2 to estimate the values of: (a) $h(0)$ (b) $h(4)$

Solution   (a) If $t = 0$, then

$$r = h(0) = f(g(0)).$$

Table 6.2 shows that $g(0) = 250$, so

$$r = h(0) = f(\underbrace{250}_{g(0)}).$$

We see from Table 6.1 that $f(250) = 110$. Thus,

$$r = h(0) = \underbrace{110}_{f(250)}.$$

As before, this tells us that the patient's heart rate at time $t = 0$ is 110 beats per minute.

(b) If $t = 4$, then

$$h(4) = f(g(4)).$$

Working from the inner set of parentheses outward, we start by evaluating $g(4)$. Table 6.2 shows that $g(4) = 102$. Thus,

$$h(4) = f(\underbrace{102}_{g(4)}).$$

Table 6.1 does not have a value for $f(102)$. But since $f(100) = 80$ and $f(150) = 90$, we estimate that $f(102)$ is close to 80. Thus, we let

$$h(4) \approx \underbrace{80}_{f(102)}.$$

This indicates that four hours after the injection, the patient's heart rate is approximately 80 beats per minute.

> The function $f(g(t))$ is said to be a **composition** of f with g. The function $f(g(t))$ is defined by using the output of the function g as the input to f.

The composite function $f(g(t))$ is only defined for values in the domain of g whose $g(t)$ values are in the domain of f.

Formulas for Composite Functions

A possible formula for $r = f(Q)$, the heart rate as a function of drug level is

$$r = f(Q) = 60 + 0.2Q.$$

A possible formula for $Q = g(t)$, the drug level as a function of time is

$$Q = g(t) = 250(0.8)^t.$$

To find a formula for $r = h(t) = f(g(t))$, the heart rate as a function of time, we use the function $g(t)$ as the input to f. Thus,

$$r = f(\underbrace{\text{input}}_{g(t)}) = 60 + 0.2(\underbrace{\text{input}}_{g(t)}),$$

so

$$r = f(g(t)) = 60 + 0.2g(t).$$

Now, substitute the formula for $g(t)$. This gives

$$r = h(t) = f(g(t)) = 60 + 0.2 \cdot \underbrace{250(0.8)^t}_{g(t)}$$

so

$$r = h(t) = 60 + 50(0.8)^t.$$

We can check the formula against Table 6.3. For example, if $t = 4$

$$h(4) = 60 + 50(0.8)^4 = 80.48.$$

This result is in agreement with the value $h(4) \approx 80$ that we estimated in Table 6.3.

Example 2   Let $p(x) = 2x + 1$ and $q(x) = x^2 - 3$. Suppose $u(x) = p(q(x))$ and $v(x) = q(p(x))$.
(a) Calculate $u(3)$ and $v(3)$.
(b) Find formulas for $u(x)$ and $v(x)$.

Solution   (a) We want

$$u(3) = p(q(3)).$$

We start by evaluating $q(3)$. The formula for q gives $q(3) = 3^2 - 3 = 6$, so

$$u(3) = p(6).$$

The formula for p gives $p(6) = 2 \cdot 6 + 1 = 13$, so

$$u(3) = 13.$$

To calculate $v(3)$, we have

$$
\begin{aligned}
v(3) &= q(p(3)) \\
&= q(7) \qquad \text{Because } p(3) = 2 \cdot 3 + 1 = 7 \\
&= 46 \qquad \text{Because } q(7) = 7^2 - 3
\end{aligned}
$$

Notice that, $v(3) \neq u(3)$. The functions $v(x) = q(p(x))$ and $u(x) = p(q(x))$ are different.
(b) In the formula for u,

$$u(x) = p(\ \underbrace{q(x)}\ )$$
$$\text{Input for } p$$
$$
\begin{aligned}
&= 2q(x) + 1 \qquad \text{Because } p(\text{Input}) = 2 \cdot \text{Input} + 1 \\
&= 2(x^2 - 3) + 1 \qquad \text{Substituting } q(x) = x^2 - 3 \\
&= 2x^2 - 5.
\end{aligned}
$$

Check this formula by evaluating $u(3)$, which we know to be 13:

$$u(3) = 2 \cdot 3^2 - 5 = 13.$$

In the formula for v,

$$v(x) = q(\underbrace{p(x)}_{\text{Input for } q})$$

$$= q(2x + 1) \qquad \text{Because } p(x) = 2x + 1$$
$$= (2x + 1)^2 - 3 \qquad \text{Because } q(\text{Input}) = \text{Input}^2 - 3$$
$$= 4x^2 + 4x - 2.$$

Check this formula by evaluating $v(3)$, which we know to be 46:

$$v(3) = 4 \cdot 3^2 + 4 \cdot 3 - 2 = 46.$$

So far we have considered examples of two functions composed together, but there is no limit on the number of functions that can be composed. Functions can even be composed with themselves.

Example 3 Let $p(x) = \sin x + 1$ and $q(x) = x^2 - 3$. Find a formula in terms of x for $w(x) = p(p(q(x)))$.

Solution We work from inside the parentheses outward. First we find $p(q(x))$, and then input the result to p.

$$w(x) = p(p(q(x)))$$
$$= p(p(x^2 - 3))$$
$$= p(\underbrace{\sin(x^2 - 3) + 1}_{\text{Input for } p})$$
$$= \sin[\sin(x^2 - 3) + 1] + 1. \qquad \text{Because } p(\text{Input}) = \sin(\text{Input}) + 1$$

Composition of Functions Defined by Graphs

So far we have composed functions defined by tables and formulas. In the next example, we compose functions defined by graphs.

Example 4 Let u and v be two functions defined by the graphs in Figure 6.1. Evaluate:

(a) $v(u(-1))$ (b) $u(v(5))$ (c) $v(u(0)) + u(v(4))$

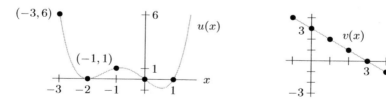

Figure 6.1: Evaluate the composition of functions u and v defined by their graphs

Solution (a) To evaluate $v(u(-1))$, start with $u(-1)$. From Figure 6.1, we see that $u(-1) = 1$. Thus,

$$v(u(-1)) = v(1).$$

From the graph we see that $v(1) = 2$, so

$$v(u(-1)) = 2.$$

(b) Since $v(5) = -2$, we have $u(v(5)) = u(-2) = 0$.

(c) Since $u(0) = 0$, we have $v(u(0)) = v(0) = 3$.

Since $v(4) = -1$, we have $u(v(4)) = u(-1) = 1$.

Thus $v(u(0)) + u(v(4)) = 3 + 1 = 4$.

Decomposition of Functions

Sometimes we reason backward to find the functions which went into a composition. This process is called *decomposition*.

Example 5   Let $h(x) = f(g(x)) = e^{x^2+1}$. Find possible formulas for $f(x)$ and $g(x)$.

Solution   In the formula $h(x) = e^{x^2+1}$, the expression $x^2 + 1$ is in the exponent. Thus, we can take the inside function to be $g(x) = x^2 + 1$. This means that we can write

$$h(x) = e^{\underbrace{x^2 + 1}_{g(x)}} = e^{g(x)}.$$

Then the outside function is $f(x) = e^x$. We check that composing f and g gives h:

$$f(g(x)) = f(x^2 + 1) = e^{x^2+1} = h(x).$$

There are many possible solutions to Example 5. For example, we might choose $f(x) = e^{x+1}$ and $g(x) = x^2$. Then

$$f(g(x)) = e^{g(x)+1} = e^{x^2+1} = h(x).$$

Alternatively, we might choose $f(x) = e^{x^2+1}$ and $g(x) = x$. Although this satisfies the condition that $h(x) = f(g(x))$, it is not very useful, because f is the same as h. This kind of decomposition is referred to as *trivial*. Another example of a trivial decomposition of $h(x)$ is $f(x) = x$ and $g(x) = e^{x^2+1}$.

Example 6   The vertex formula for the family of quadratic functions is

$$p(x) = a(x - h)^2 + k.$$

Decompose the formula into three simple functions. That is, find formulas for u, v, and w where

$$p(x) = u(v(w(x))),$$

Solution   We work from inside the parentheses outward. In the formula $p(x) = a(x - h)^2 + k$, we have the expression $x - h$ inside the parentheses. In the formula $p(x) = u(v(w(x)))$, the innermost function is $w(x)$. Thus, we let

$$w(x) = x - h.$$

In the formula $p(x) = a(x - h)^2 + k$, the first operation done to $x - h$ is squaring. Thus, we let

$$v(\text{Input}) = \text{Input}^2$$
$$v(x) = x^2.$$

So we have

$$v(w(x)) = v(x - h) = (x - h)^2.$$

Finally, to obtain $p(x) = a(x - h)^2 + k$, we multiply $(x - h)^2$ by a and add k. Thus, we let

$$u(\text{Input}) = a \cdot \text{Input} + k$$
$$u(x) = ax + k.$$

To check, we compute

$$
\begin{aligned}
u(v(w(x))) &= u(v(x - h)) & \text{Since } w(x) = x - h \\
&= u(\underbrace{(x - h)^2}_{\text{Input for } u}) & \text{Since } v(x - h) = (x - h)^2 \\
&= a(x - h)^2 + k & \text{Since } u((x - h)^2) = a \cdot (x - h)^2 + k.
\end{aligned}
$$

Functions of Related Quantities

Composition can be used to relate two quantities by means of an intermediate quantity.

Example 7   The formula for the volume of a cube with side s is $V = s^3$. The formula for the surface area of a cube is $A = 6s^2$. Express the volume of a cube, V, as a function of its surface area, A.

Solution   We express V as a function of A by exploiting the fact that V is a function of s, which in turn is expressed as a function of A. To write s as a function of A, we solve $A = 6s^2$ for s

$$s^2 = \frac{A}{6} \qquad \text{so} \qquad s = +\sqrt{\frac{A}{6}} \qquad \text{Because the length of a side of a cube is positive.}$$

Substituting $s = \sqrt{A/6}$ in the formula $V = s^3$ gives V as a function of A:

$$V = s^3 = \left(\sqrt{\frac{A}{6}}\right)^3.$$

Exercises and Problems for Section 6.1

Exercises

1. Use Table 6.4 to construct a table of values for $r(x) = p(q(x))$.

Table 6.4

x	0	1	2	3	4	5
$p(x)$	1	0	5	2	3	4
$q(x)$	5	2	3	1	4	8

2. Let p and q be the functions in Exercise 1. Construct a table of values for $s(x) = q(p(x))$.

3. Using Tables 6.5 and 6.6, complete Table 6.7:

Table 6.5

x	$f(x)$
0	0
$\pi/6$	1/2
$\pi/4$	$\sqrt{2}/2$
$\pi/3$	$\sqrt{3}/2$
$\pi/2$	1

Table 6.6

y	$g(y)$
0	$\pi/2$
1/4	π
$\sqrt{2}/4$	0
1/2	$\pi/3$
$\sqrt{2}/2$	$\pi/4$
3/4	0
$\sqrt{3}/2$	$\pi/6$
1	0

Table 6.7

x	$g(f(x))$
0	
$\pi/6$	
$\pi/4$	
$\pi/3$	
$\pi/2$	

4. Let $f(x) = 3x - 2$ and $h(x) = 3x^2 - 5x + 2$. Find a formula for $f(h(x))$.

Find formulas for the functions in Exercises 5–10 and simplify. Let $f(x) = x^2 + 1$, $g(x) = \frac{1}{x-3}$, and $h(x) = \sqrt{x}$.

5. $f(g(x))$ **6.** $g(f(x))$ **7.** $f(h(x))$

8. $h(f(x))$ **9.** $g(g(x))$ **10.** $g(f(h(x)))$

Find formulas for the functions in Exercises 11–16. Let $m(x) = \frac{1}{x-1}$, $k(x) = x^2$, and $n(x) = \frac{2x^2}{x+1}$.

11. $k(m(x))$ **12.** $m(k(x))$ **13.** $k(n(x))$

14. $m(n(x))$ **15.** $(m(x))^2$ **16.** $n(n(x))$

Problems

In words, give a practical interpretation of the functions in Problems 17–20.

17. $f(h(t))$, where $A = f(r)$ is the area of a circle of radius r and $r = h(t)$ is the radius of the circle at time t.

18. $k(g(t))$, where $L = k(H)$ is the length of a steel bar at temperature H and $H = g(t)$ is temperature at time t.

19. $R(Y(q))$, where R gives a farmer's revenue as a function of corn yield per acre, and Y gives the corn yield as a function of the quantity, q, of fertilizer.

20. $t(f(H))$, where $t(v)$ is the time of a trip at velocity v, and $v = f(H)$ is velocity at temperature H.

21. Complete Table 6.8 given that:

  • f is symmetric about the y-axis (even).

  • g is symmetric about the origin (odd).

  • h is the composition of g with f, that is, $h(x) = g(f(x))$.

Table 6.8

x	-3	-2	-1	0	1	2	3
$f(x)$	0	2	2	0			
$g(x)$	0	2	2	0			
$h(x)$							

22. Complete Table 6.9 given that $h(x) = f(g(x))$.

Table 6.9

x	$f(x)$	$g(x)$	$h(x)$
0	1	2	5
1	9	0	
2		1	

23. Using Figure 6.2, estimate the following:

  (a) $f(g(2))$ **(b)** $g(f(2))$
  (c) $f(f(3))$ **(d)** $g(g(3))$

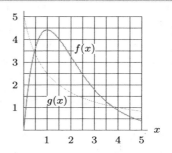

Figure 6.2

In Problems 24–27, use the information from Figures 6.3, and 6.4 to graph the functions.

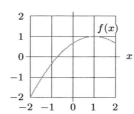
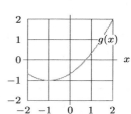

Figure 6.3   **Figure 6.4**

24. $f(g(x))$ **25.** $g(f(x))$ **26.** $f(f(x))$ **27.** $g(g(x))$

28. Complete Tables Table 6.10, Table 6.11, and Table 6.12 given that $h(x) = g(f(x))$. Assume that different values of x lead to different values of $f(x)$.

Table 6.10

x	$f(x)$
-2	4
-1	
0	
1	5
2	1

Table 6.11

x	$g(x)$
1	
2	1
3	2
4	0
5	-1

Table 6.12

x	$h(x)$
-2	
-1	1
0	2
1	
2	-2

29. Use Figure 6.5 to calculate the following:

  (a) $f(f(1))$ **(b)** $g(g(1))$ **(c)** $f(g(2))$ **(d)** $g(f(2))$

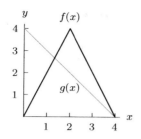

Figure 6.5

30. Use Figure 6.5 to find all solutions to the equations:

   (a) $f(g(x)) = 0$ **(b)** $g(f(x)) = 0$

31. Let $f(x)$ and $g(x)$ be the functions in Figure 6.5.

   (a) Graph the functions $f(g(x))$ and $g(f(x))$.
   (b) On what interval(s) is $f(g(x))$ increasing?
   (c) On what interval(s) is $g(f(x))$ increasing?

32. Find $f(f(1))$ for

$$f(x) = \begin{cases} 2 & \text{if } x \le 0 \\ 3x + 1 & \text{if } 0 < x < 2 \\ x^2 - 3 & \text{if } x \ge 2 \end{cases}$$

33. Using your knowledge of the absolute value function, explain in a few sentences the relationship between the graph of $y = |\sin x|$ and the graph of $y = \sin x$.

34. Graph the following functions for $-2\pi \le x \le 2\pi$.

   (a) $f(x) = \sin x$ **(b)** $g(x) = |\sin x|$
   (c) $h(x) = \sin |x|$ **(d)** $i(x) = |\sin |x||$

   (e) Do any two of these functions have identical graphs? If so, explain why this makes sense.

35. (a) Using what you know about the graph of $y = \sin x$, make predictions about the graph of $y = (\sin x)^2$.
   (b) Using a computer or a graphing calculator, graph $g(x) = (\sin x)^2$, $h(x) = (\cos x)^2$ and $f(x) = g(x) + h(x)$, on the interval $-2\pi \le x \le 2\pi$. What do you observe about the graph of $f(x)$?

In Problems 36–39, find a simplified formula for the difference quotient

$$\frac{f(x + h) - f(x)}{h}.$$

36. $f(x) = x^2 + x$ **37.** $f(x) = \sqrt{x}$

38. $f(x) = \frac{1}{x}$ **39.** $f(x) = 2^x$

40. Let $f(x) = 1/x$. For n a positive integer, define $f_n(x)$ as the composition of f with itself n times. For example, $f_2(x) = f(f(x))$ and $f_3(x) = f(f(f(x)))$.

   (a) Evaluate $f_7(2)$.   **(b)** Evaluate $f_{23}(f_{22}(5))$.

Decompose the functions in Problems 41–48 into two new functions, u and v, where v is the inside function, $u(x) \ne x$, and $v(x) \ne x$.

41. $f(x) = \sqrt{3 - 5x}$ **42.** $F(x) = (2x + 5)^3$

43. $h(x) = x^4 + x^2$ **44.** $j(x) = 1 - \sqrt{x}$

45. $l(x) = 2 + \frac{1}{x}$ **46.** $G(x) = \frac{2}{1 + \sqrt{x}}$

47. $H(x) = 3^{2x-1}$ **48.** $J(x) = 8 - 2|x|$

For Problems 49–53, let $k(x) = x^2 + 2$ and $g(x) = x^2 + 3$. Find a possible formula for the function named.

49. $h(x)$ if $h(k(x)) = (x^2 + 2)^3$.

50. $j(x)$ if $k(j(t)) = \left(\frac{1}{t}\right)^2 + 2$.

51. $f(x)$ if $f(k(v)) = \frac{1}{v^2 + 2}$.

52. $h(x)$ if $h(g(x)) = \frac{1}{x^2 + 3} + 5x^2 + 15$.

53. $j(x)$ if $j(x) = g(g(x))$.

54. Suppose $p(x) = (1/x) + 1$ and $q(x) = x - 2$.

   (a) Let $r(x) = p(q(x))$. Find a formula for $r(x)$ and simplify it.
   (b) Write formulas for $s(x)$ and $t(x)$ such that $p(x) = s(t(x))$, where $s(x) \ne x$ and $t(x) \ne x$.
   (c) Let a be different from 0 and -1. Find a simplified expression for $p(p(a))$.

55. If $s(x) = 5 + \frac{1}{x + 5} + x$, $k(x) = x + 5$, and $s(x) = v(k(x))$, what is $v(x)$?

56. Suppose $u(v(x)) = \frac{1}{x^2 - 1}$ and $v(u(x)) = \frac{1}{(x - 1)^2}$. Find possible formulas for $u(x)$ and $v(x)$.

57. Assume that $f(x) = 3 \cdot 9^x$ and that $g(x) = 3^x$.

   (a) If $f(x) = h(g(x))$, find a formula for $h(x)$.
   (b) If $f(x) = g(j(x))$, find a formula for $j(x)$.

58. You have two money machines, both of which increase any money inserted into them. The first machine doubles your money. The second adds five dollars. The money that comes out is described by $d(x) = 2x$, in the first case, and $a(x) = x + 5$, in the second, where x is the number of dollars inserted. The machines can be hooked up so that the money coming out of one machine goes into the other. Find formulas for each of the two possible composition machines. Is one machine more profitable than the other?

59. Currency traders often move investments from one country to another in order to make a profit. Table 6.13 gives exchange rates for US dollars, Japanese yen, and the European Union's euro.[1] In September, 2002, for example, 1 US dollar purchases 121.5 Japanese yen or 1.02638 European euros. Similarly, 1 European euro purchases 118.377 Japanese yen or 0.97430 US dollar. Suppose

$f(x)$ = Number of yen one can buy with x dollars

$g(x)$ = Number of euros one can buy with x dollars

$h(x)$ = Number of euros one can buy with x yen

(a) Find formulas for f, g, and h.

(b) Evaluate and interpret in terms of currency: $h(f(1000))$.

Table 6.13 *Exchange rate for US dollars, Japanese yen and euros, September 13, 2002*

Amount invested	Dollars purchased	Yen purchased	Euros purchased
1 dollar	1.0000	121.5	1.02638
1 yen	0.00823	1.0000	0.00845
1 euro	0.97430	118.377	1.0000

6.2 INVERSE FUNCTIONS

Definition of Inverse Function

Recall that the statement $f^{-1}(50) = 20$ means that $f(20) = 50$. In fact, the values of f^{-1} are determined in just this way. In general,

> Suppose $Q = f(t)$ is a function with the property that each value of Q determines exactly one value of t. Then f has an **inverse function**, f^{-1} and
> $$f^{-1}(Q) = t \quad \text{if and only if} \quad Q = f(t).$$
> If a function has an inverse, it is said to be **invertible**.

The definitions of the logarithm and of the inverse cosine have the same form as the definition of f^{-1}. Since $y = \log x$ is the inverse function of $y = 10^x$, we have

$$x = \log y \quad \text{if and only if} \quad y = 10^x,$$

and since $y = \cos^{-1} t$ is the inverse function of $y = \cos t$,

$$t = \cos^{-1} y \quad \text{if and only if} \quad y = \cos t.$$

Example 1 Solve the equation $\sin x = 0.8$ using an inverse function.

Solution The solution is $x = \sin^{-1}(0.8)$. A calculator (set in radians) gives $x = \sin^{-1}(0.8) \approx 0.927$.

Example 2 Suppose that g is an invertible function, with $g(10) = -26$ and $g^{-1}(0) = 7$. What other values of g and g^{-1} do you know?

Solution Because $g(10) = -26$, we know that $g^{-1}(-26) = 10$; because $g^{-1}(0) = 7$, we know that $g(7) = 0$.

---

[1]www.x-rates.com, September 13, 2002. Currency exchange rates fluctuate constantly.

Example 3 A population is given by the formula $P = f(t) = 20 + 0.4t$ where P is the number of people (in thousands) and t is the number of years since 1970. Evaluate the following quantities. Explain in words what each tells you about the population.

(a) $f(25)$ (b) $f^{-1}(25)$

(c) Show how to estimate $f^{-1}(25)$ from a graph of f.

Solution (a) Substituting $t = 25$, we have

$$f(25) = 20 + 0.4 \cdot 25 = 30.$$

Thus, in 1995 (year $t = 25$), we have $P = 30$, so the population was 30,000 people.

(b) We have $t = f^{-1}(P)$. Thus, in $f^{-1}(25)$, the 25 is a population. So $f^{-1}(25)$ is the year in which the population reaches 25 thousand. We find t by solving the equation

$$20 + 0.4t = 25$$
$$0.4t = 5$$
$$t = 12.5.$$

Therefore, $f^{-1}(25) = 12.5$, which means that the population reached 25,000 people 12.5 years after 1970, or midway into 1982.

(c) We can estimate $f^{-1}(25)$ by reading the graph of $P = f(t)$ backwards as shown in Figure 6.6.

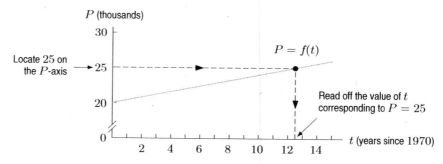

Figure 6.6: Using a graph of the function $P = f(t)$ to read off values of the inverse function $f^{-1}(P)$

Finding a Formula for an Inverse Function

It is sometimes possible to find a formula for an inverse function, f^{-1} from a formula for f. If the function $P = f(t)$ gives the population (in thousands) of a town in year t, then $f^{-1}(P)$ is the year in which the population reaches the value P. In Example 3 we found $f^{-1}(P)$ for $P = 25$. We now perform the same calculations for a general P. Since

$$P = 20 + 0.4t,$$

solving for t gives

$$0.4t = P - 20$$
$$t = \frac{P - 20}{0.4},$$

Table 6.14

t	$P = f(t)$
0	20
5	22
10	24
15	26
20	28

Table 6.15

P	$t = f^{-1}(P)$
20	0
22	5
24	10
26	15
28	20

so

$$f^{-1}(P) = 2.5P - 50.$$

The values in Table 6.14 were calculated using the formula $P = f(t) = 20 + 0.4t$; the values in Table 6.15 were calculated using the formula for $t = f^{-1}(P) = 2.5P - 50$. The table for f^{-1} can be obtained from the table for f by interchanging its columns, because the inverse function reverses the roles of inputs and outputs.

Example 4   Suppose you deposit \$500 into a savings account that pays 4% interest compounded annually. The balance, in dollars, in the account after t years is given by $B = f(t) = 500(1.04)^t$.

(a) Find a formula for $t = f^{-1}(B)$.

(b) What does the inverse function represent in terms of the account?

Solution   (a) To find a formula for f^{-1}, we solve for t in terms of B:

$$B = 500(1.04)^t$$
$$\frac{B}{500} = (1.04)^t$$
$$\log\left(\frac{B}{500}\right) = t \log 1.04 \qquad \text{Taking logs of both sides}$$
$$t = \frac{\log(B/500)}{\log 1.04}.$$

Thus, a formula for the inverse function is

$$t = f^{-1}(B) = \frac{\log(B/500)}{\log 1.04}.$$

(b) The function $t = f^{-1}(B)$ gives the number of years for the balance to grow to \$$B$.

In the previous example the variables of the function $B = f(t)$ had contextual meaning, so the inverse function was written as $t = f^{-1}(B)$. In abstract mathematical examples, a function $y = f(x)$ will often have its inverse function written with x as the independent variable. This situation is shown in the next example.

Example 5   Find the inverse of the function

$$f(x) = \frac{3x}{2x + 1}.$$

Solution   First, we solve the equation $y = f(x)$ for x:

$$y = \frac{3x}{2x + 1}$$
$$2xy + y = 3x$$
$$2xy - 3x = -y$$
$$x(2y - 3) = -y$$
$$x = \frac{-y}{2y - 3} = \frac{y}{3 - 2y}$$

As before, we write $x = f^{-1}(y) = \dfrac{y}{3 - 2y}$.

Since y is now the independent variable, by convention we rewrite the inverse function with x as the independent variable. We have

$$f^{-1}(x) = \frac{x}{3 - 2x}.$$

Noninvertible Functions: Horizontal Line Test

Not every function has an inverse function. A function $Q = f(t)$ has no inverse if it returns the same Q-value for two different t-values. When that happens, the value of t cannot be uniquely determined from the value of Q.

For example, if $q(x) = x^2$ then $q(-3) = 9$ and $q(+3) = 9$. This means that we cannot say what the value $q^{-1}(9)$ would be. (Is it $+3$ or -3?). Thus, q is not invertible. In Figure 6.7, notice that the horizontal line $y = 9$ intersects the graph of $q(x) = x^2$ at two different points: $(-3, 9)$ and $(3, 9)$. This corresponds to the fact that the function q returns $y = 9$ for two different x-values, $x = +3$ and $x = -3$.

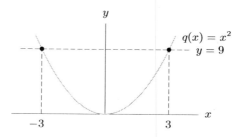

Figure 6.7: The graph of $q(x) = x^2$ fails the horizontal line test

We have the following general result:

The Horizontal Line Test If there is a horizontal line which intersects a function's graph in more than one point, then the function does not have an inverse. If every horizontal line intersects a function's graph at most once, then the function has an inverse.

Evaluating an Inverse Function Graphically

Finding a formula for an inverse function can be difficult. However, this does not mean that the inverse function does not exist. Even without a formula, it may be possible to find values of the inverse function.

Example 6   Let $u(x) = x^3 + x + 1$. Explain why a graph suggests the function u is invertible. Assuming u has an inverse, estimate $u^{-1}(4)$.

Solution   To show that u is invertible, we could try to find a formula for u^{-1}. To do this, we would solve the equation $y = x^3 + x + 1$ for x. Unfortunately, this is difficult. However, the graph in Figure 6.8 suggests that u passes the horizontal line test and therefore that u is invertible. To estimate $u^{-1}(4)$, we find an x-value such that

$$x^3 + x + 1 = 4.$$

In Figure 6.8, the graph of $y = u(x)$ and the horizontal line $y = 4$ intersect at the point $x \approx 1.213$. Thus, tracing along the graph, we estimate $u^{-1}(4) \approx 1.213$.

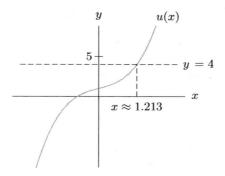

Figure 6.8: The graph of $u(x)$ passes the horizontal line test. Since $u(1.213) \approx 4$, we have $u^{-1}(4) \approx 1.213$

In Example 6, even without a formula for u^{-1}, we can approximate $u^{-1}(a)$ for any value of a.

Example 7   Let $P(x) = 2^x$.

(a) Show that P is invertible.
(b) Find a formula for $P^{-1}(x)$.
(c) Sketch the graphs of P and P^{-1} on the same axes.
(d) What are the domain and range of P and P^{-1}?

Solution   (a) Since P is an exponential function with base 2, it is always increasing, and therefore passes the horizontal line test. (See the graph of P in Figure 6.9.) Thus, P has an inverse function.
(b) To find a formula for $P^{-1}(x)$, we solve for x in the equation

$$2^x = y.$$

We can take the log of both sides to get

$$\log 2^x = \log y$$
$$x \log 2 = \log y$$
$$x = P^{-1}(y) = \frac{\log y}{\log 2}.$$

Thus, we have a formula for P^{-1} with y as the input. To graph P and P^{-1} on the same axes, we write P^{-1} as a function of x:

$$P^{-1}(x) = \frac{\log x}{\log 2} = \frac{1}{\log 2} \cdot \log x = 3.322 \log x.$$

(c) Table 6.16 gives values of $P(x)$ for $x = -3, -2, \ldots, 3$. Interchanging the columns of Table 6.16 gives Table 6.17 for $P^{-1}(x)$. We use these tables to sketch Figure 6.9.

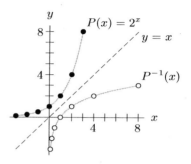

Figure 6.9: The graphs of $P(x) = 2^x$ and its inverse are symmetrical across the line $y = x$

Table 6.16   *Values of* $P(x) = 2^x$

x	$P(x) = 2^x$
-3	0.125
-2	0.25
-1	0.5
0	1
1	2
2	4
3	8

Table 6.17   *Values of* $P^{-1}(x)$

x	$P^{-1}(x)$
0.125	-3
0.25	-2
0.5	-1
1	0
2	1
4	2
8	3

(d) The domain of P, an exponential function, is all real numbers, and its range is all positive numbers. The domain of P^{-1}, a logarithmic function, is all positive numbers and its range is all real numbers.

The Graph, Domain, and Range of an Inverse Function

In Figure 6.9, we see that the graph of P^{-1} is the mirror-image of the graph of P across the line $y = x$. In general, this is true if the x- and y-axes have the same scale. To understand why this occurs, consider how a function is related to its inverse.

If f is an invertible function with, for example, $f(2) = 5$, then $f^{-1}(5) = 2$. Thus, the point $(2, 5)$ is on the graph of f and the point $(5, 2)$ is on the graph of f^{-1}. Generalizing, if (a, b) is any point on the graph of f, then (b, a) is a point on the graph of f^{-1}. Figure 6.10 shows how reflecting the point (a, b) across the line $y = x$ gives the point (b, a). Consequently, the graph of f^{-1} is the reflection of the graph of f across the line $y = x$.

Notice that outputs from a function are inputs to its inverse function. Similarly, outputs from the inverse function are inputs to the original function. This is expressed in the statement $f^{-1}(b) = a$

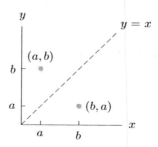

Figure 6.10: The reflection of the point (a, b) across the line $y = x$ is the point (b, a)

if and only if $f(a) = b$, and also in the fact that we can obtain a table for f^{-1} by interchanging the columns of a table for f. Consequently, the domain and range for f^{-1} are obtained by interchanging the domain and range of f. In other words,

Domain of f^{-1} = Range of f and   Range of f^{-1} = Domain of f.

In Example 7, the function P has all real numbers as its domain and all positive numbers as its range; the function P^{-1} has all positive numbers as its domain and all real numbers as its range.

A Property of Inverse Functions

The fact that Tables 6.16 and 6.17 contain the same values, but with the columns switched, reflects the special relationship between the values of $P(x)$ and $P^{-1}(x)$. For the population function in Example 7

$$P^{-1}(2) = 1 \quad \text{and} \quad P(1) = 2 \quad \text{so} \quad P^{-1}(P(1)) = 1,$$

and

$$P^{-1}(0.25) = -2 \quad \text{and} \quad P(-2) = 0.25 \quad \text{so} \quad P^{-1}(P(-2)) = -2.$$

This result holds for any input x, so in general,

$$P^{-1}(P(x)) = x.$$

In addition, $P(P^{-1}(2)) = 2$ and $P(P^{-1}(0.25)) = 0.25$, and for any x

$$P(P^{-1}(x)) = x.$$

Similar reasoning holds for any other invertible function, suggesting the general result:

If $y = f(x)$ is an invertible function and $y = f^{-1}(x)$ is its inverse, then
- $f^{-1}(f(x)) = x$ for all values of x for which $f(x)$ is defined,
- $f(f^{-1}(x)) = x$ for all values of x for which $f^{-1}(x)$ is defined.

This property tell us that composing a function and its inverse function returns the original value as the end result. We can use this property to decide whether two functions are inverses.

Example 8   (a) Check that $f(x) = \dfrac{x}{2x+1}$ and $f^{-1}(x) = \dfrac{x}{1-2x}$ are inverse functions each other.

(b) Graph f and f^{-1} on axes with the same scale. What are the domains and ranges of f and f^{-1}?

Solution   (a) To check that these functions are inverses, we compose

$$f^{-1}(f(x)) = \frac{f(x)}{1 - 2f(x)} = \frac{\dfrac{x}{2x + 1}}{1 - 2\left(\dfrac{x}{2x + 1}\right)}$$

$$= \frac{\dfrac{x}{2x + 1}}{\dfrac{2x + 1}{2x + 1} - \dfrac{2x}{2x + 1}}$$

$$= \frac{\dfrac{x}{2x + 1}}{\dfrac{1}{2x + 1}}$$

$$= x.$$

Similarly, you can check that $f(f^{-1}(x)) = x$.

(b) The graphs of f and f^{-1} in Figure 6.11 are symmetric about the line $y = x$.

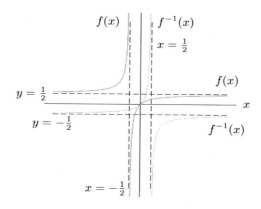

Figure 6.11: The graph of $f(x) = x/(2x + 1)$ and the inverse $f^{-1}(x) = x/(1 - 2x)$

The function $f(x) = x/(2x + 1)$ is undefined at $x = -1/2$, so its domain consists of all real numbers except $-1/2$. Figure 6.11 suggests that f has a horizontal asymptote at $y = 1/2$ which it does not cross and that its range is all real numbers except $1/2$.

Because the inverse function $f^{-1}(x) = x/(1 - 2x)$ is undefined at $x = 1/2$, its domain is all real numbers except $1/2$. Note that this is the same as the range of f. The graph of f^{-1} appears to have a horizontal asymptote which it does not cross at $y = -1/2$ suggesting that its range is all real numbers except $-1/2$. Note that this is the same as the domain of f.

The ranges of the functions f and f^{-1} can be confirmed algebraically.

Restricting the Domain

A function that fails the horizontal line test is not invertible. For this reason, the function $f(x) = x^2$ does not have an inverse function. However, by considering only part of the graph of f, we can eliminate the duplication of y-values. Suppose we consider the half of the parabola with $x \geq 0$.

See Figure 6.12. This part of the graph does pass the horizontal line test because there is only one (positive) x-value for each y-value in the range of f.

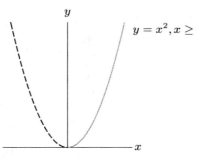

Figure 6.12

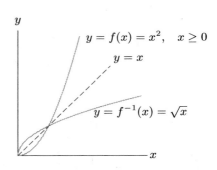

Figure 6.13

We can find an inverse for $f(x) = x^2$ on its restricted domain,[2] $x \geq 0$. Using the fact that $x \geq 0$ and solving $y = x^2$ for x gives

$$x = \sqrt{y}.$$

Thus a formula for the inverse function is

$$x = f^{-1}(y) = \sqrt{y}.$$

Rewriting the formula for f^{-1} with x as the input, we have

$$f^{-1}(x) = \sqrt{x}.$$

The graphs of f and f^{-1} are shown in Figure 6.13. Note that the domain of f is the the range of f^{-1}, and the domain of f^{-1} $(x \geq 0)$ is the range of f.

Exercises and Problems for Section 6.2

Exercises

In Exercises 1–4, use a graph to decide whether or not the function is invertible.

1. $y = x^4 - 6x + 12$

2. $y = x^6 + 2x^2 - 10$

3. $y = \sqrt{x} + x$

4. $y = |x|$

In Exercises 5–8, check that the functions are inverses.

5. $f(x) = \dfrac{x}{4} - \dfrac{3}{2}$ and $g(t) = 4\left(t + \dfrac{3}{2}\right)$

6. $f(x) = 1 + 7x^3$ and $f^{-1}(x) = \sqrt[3]{\dfrac{x-1}{7}}$

7. $g(x) = 1 - \dfrac{1}{x-1}$ and $g^{-1}(x) = 1 + \dfrac{1}{1-x}$

8. $h(x) = \sqrt{2x}$ and $k(t) = \dfrac{t^2}{2}$, for $x, t \geq 0$

Find the inverses of the functions in Exercises 9–21.

9. $h(x) = 12x^3$

10. $h(x) = \dfrac{x}{2x+1}$

11. $k(x) = 3 \cdot e^{2x}$

12. $g(x) = e^{3x+1}$

13. $n(x) = \log(x - 3)$

14. $h(x) = \ln(1 - 2x)$

15. $h(x) = \dfrac{\sqrt{x}}{\sqrt{x}+1}$

16. $f(x) = \dfrac{3 + 2x}{2 - 5x}$

17. $f(x) = \sqrt{\dfrac{4 - 7x}{4 - x}}$

18. $f(x) = \dfrac{\sqrt{x} + 3}{11 - \sqrt{x}}$

19. $p(x) = 2\ln\left(\dfrac{1}{x}\right)$

20. $s(x) = \dfrac{3}{2 + \log x}$

21. $q(x) = \ln(x + 3) - \ln(x - 5)$

---

[2]Technically, changing the domain results in a new function, but we will continue to call it $f(x)$.

Problems

22. If $P = f(t)$ gives the population of a city, in thousands, as a function of time, t, in years, what does $f^{-1}(P)$ represent? What are its units?

23. If $C = f(q)$ gives the cost, in dollars, to manufacture q items, what does $f^{-1}(C)$ represent? What are its units?

24. If $t = g(v)$ represents the time in hours it takes to drive to the next town at velocity v mph, what does $g^{-1}(t)$ represent? What are its units?

25. Let $P = f(t) = 10e^{0.02t}$ give the population in millions at time t in years. Find and interpret $f^{-1}(P)$.

26. Let $C = f(q) = 200 + 0.1q$ give the cost in dollars to manufacture q kg of a chemical. Find and interpret $f^{-1}(C)$.

27. The noise level, N, of a sound in decibels is given by

$$N = f(I) = 10\log\left(\frac{I}{I_0}\right),$$

where I is the intensity of the sound and I_0 is a constant. Find and interpret $f^{-1}(N)$.

Solve the equations in Problems 28–33 exactly. Use an inverse function when appropriate.

28. $7\sin(3x) = 2$

29. $2^{x+5} = 3$

30. $x^{1.05} = 1.09$

31. $\ln(x + 3) = 1.8$

32. $\dfrac{2x + 3}{x + 3} = 8$

33. $\sqrt{x + \sqrt{x}} = 3$

34. Values of f and g are in Table 6.18. Based on this table:

(a) Is $f(x)$ invertible? If not, explain why; if so, construct a table of values of $f^{-1}(x)$ for all values of x for which $f^{-1}(x)$ is defined.

(b) Answer the same question as in part (a) for $g(x)$.

(c) Make a table of values for $h(x) = f(g(x))$, with $x = -3, -2, -1, 0, 1, 2, 3$.

(d) Explain why you cannot define a function $j(x)$ by the formula $j(x) = g(f(x))$.

Table 6.18

x	-3	-2	-1	0	1	2	3
$f(x)$	9	7	6	-4	-5	-8	-9
$g(x)$	3	1	3	2	-3	-1	3

35. Figure 6.14 defines the function f. Rank the following quantities in order from least to greatest: $0, f(0), f^{-1}(0), 3, f(3), f^{-1}(3)$.

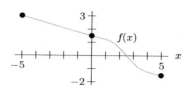

Figure 6.14

36. (a) Explain how to find the formula for an inverse function from the formula for the original function. Illustrate your explanation with an example.

(b) Explain how to obtain the graph of the inverse function from the graph of the original function. Illustrate your explanation with an example.

(c) Describe what kind of symmetry is found between the graph of a function and the graph of its inverse. Illustrate your explanation with at least one example.

37. The function $y = \sin t$ is not invertible because it fails the horizontal line test.

(a) Explain in your own words the way that the domain of $\sin t$ is restricted in order to define the inverse function, $\sin^{-1} y$.

(b) Find some other restriction of the domain and explain why it would be a valid one to use.

38. Let $f(x) = e^x$. Solve each of the following equations exactly for x.

(a) $(f(x))^{-1} = 2$ (b) $f^{-1}(x) = 2$
(c) $f(x^{-1}) = 2$

39. Let $f(x) = e^x$. For each of the following, use the rules of logarithms and exponents (if possible) to find the exact solution to each equation. If this is not possible, use a graph to find an approximate solution.

(a) $f(3x) + f(3x) = 1$ (b) $f(x) + f(3x) = 1$
(c) $f(3x)f(3x) = 2$ (d) $f(x)f(3x) = 2$

40. Find the inverse of each of the following functions. Assume that the functions are defined on domains on which they are invertible.

(a) $f(x) = \arcsin\left(\dfrac{3x}{2-x}\right)$
(b) $g(x) = \ln(\sin x) - \ln(\cos x)$
(c) $h(x) = \cos^2 x + 2\cos x + 1$

41. Simplify the expression $\cos^2(\arcsin t)$, using the property that inverses "undo" each other.

42. Let $Q = 20(0.96)^{t/3}$ be the number of grams of a radioactive substance remaining after t years.

   (a) Describe the behavior of the radioactive substance as a function of time.
   (b) Evaluate $f(8)$. Explain the meaning of this quantity in practical terms.
   (c) Find a formula for $f^{-1}(Q)$ in terms of Q.
   (d) Evaluate $f^{-1}(8)$. Explain the meaning of this quantity in practical terms.

43. (a) What is the formula for the area of a circle in terms of its radius?
   (b) Graph this function for the domain all real numbers.
   (c) What domain actually applies in this situation? On separate axes, graph the function for this domain.
   (d) Find the inverse of the function in part (c).
   (e) Graph the inverse function on the domain you gave in part (c) on the same axes used in part (c).
   (f) If area is a function of the radius, is radius a function of area? Explain carefully.

44. A company believes there is a linear relationship between the consumer demand for its products and the price charged. When the price was $3 per unit, the quantity demanded was 500 units per week. When the unit price was raised to $4, the quantity demanded dropped to 300 units per week. Let $D(p)$ be the quantity per week demanded by consumers at a unit price of $p.

   (a) Estimate and interpret $D(5)$.
   (b) Find a formula for $D(p)$ in terms of p.
   (c) Calculate and interpret $D^{-1}(5)$.
   (d) Give an interpretation of the slope of $D(p)$ in terms of demand.
   (e) Currently, the company can produce 400 units every week. What should be the price of the product be if the company wants to sell all 400 units?
   (f) If the company produced 500 units per week instead of 400 units per week, would its weekly revenues increase, and if so, by how much?

45. Table 6.19 gives the number of cows in a herd.

   (a) Find an exponential function that approximates the data.
   (b) Find the inverse function of the function in part (a).
   (c) When do you predict that the herd will contain 400 cows?

Table 6.19

t (years)	0	1	2
$P(t)$ (cows)	150	165	182

46. Suppose $P = f(t)$ is the population (in thousands) in year t, and that $f(7) = 13$ and $f(12) = 20$,

   (a) Find a formula for $f(t)$ assuming f is exponential.

   (b) Find a formula for $f^{-1}(P)$.
   (c) Evaluate $f(25)$ and $f^{-1}(25)$. Explain what these expressions mean in terms of population.

47. A gymnast at Ringling Brothers, Barnum, & Bailey Circus is fired straight up in the air from a cannon. While she is in the air, a trampoline is moved into the spot where the cannon was. Figure 6.15 is a graph of the gymnast's height, h, as a function of time, t.

   (a) Approximately what is her maximum height?
   (b) Approximately when does she land on the trampoline?
   (c) Restrict the domain of $h(t)$ so that $h(t)$ has an inverse. That is, pick a piece of the graph on which $h(t)$ does have an inverse. Graph this new restricted function.
   (d) Change the story to go with your graph in part (c).
   (e) Graph the inverse of the function in part (c). Explain in your story why it makes sense that the inverse is a function.

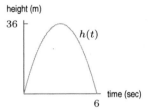

Figure 6.15

48. A 100 ml solution contains 99% alcohol and 1% water. Let $y = C(x)$ be the concentration of alcohol in the solution after x ml of alcohol are removed, so

$$C(x) = \frac{\text{Amount of alcohol}}{\text{Amount of solution}}.$$

   (a) What is $C(0)$?
   (b) Find a formula in terms of x for $C(x)$.
   (c) Find a formula in terms of y for $C^{-1}(y)$.
   (d) Explain the physical significance of $C^{-1}(y)$.

49. (a) How much alcohol do you think should be removed from the 99% solution in Problem 48 in order to obtain a 98% solution? (Make a guess.)
   (b) Express the exact answer to part (a) using the function C^{-1} you found in Problem 62.
   (c) Determine the exact answer to part (a). Are you surprised by your result?

50. Suppose that f, g, and h are invertible and that

$$f(x) = g(h(x)).$$

Find a formula for $f^{-1}(x)$ in terms of g^{-1} and h^{-1}.

51. The von Bertalanffy growth model predicts the mean length L of fish of age t (in years):[3]

$$L = f(t) = L_\infty \left(1 - e^{-k(t+t_0)}\right), \text{ for constant } L_\infty, k, t_0.$$

Find a formula for f^{-1}. Describe in words what f^{-1} tells you about fish. What is the domain of f^{-1}?

6.3 COMBINATIONS OF FUNCTIONS

Like numbers, functions can be combined using addition, subtraction, multiplication, and division.

The Difference of Two Functions Defined by Formulas: A Measure of Prosperity

We can define new functions as the sum or difference of two functions. In Chapter 7, we will discuss Thomas Malthus, who predicted widespread food shortages because he believed that human populations increase exponentially, whereas the food supply increases linearly. We consider a country with population $P(t)$ million in year t. The population is initially 2 million and grows at the rate of 4% per year, so

$$P(t) = 2(1.04)^t.$$

Let $N(t)$ be the number of people (in millions) that the country can feed in year t. The annual food supply is initially adequate for 4 million people and it increases by enough for an additional 0.5 million people every year. Thus

$$N(t) = 4 + 0.5t.$$

This country first experiences shortages in about 78 years. (See Figure 6.16.) When is it most prosperous?

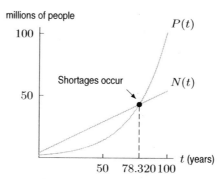

Figure 6.16 Predicted population, $P(t)$, and number of people who can be fed, $N(t)$, over a 100-year period

The answer depends on how we decide to measure prosperity. We could measure prosperity in one of the following ways:

- By the food surplus—that is, the amount of food the country has over and above its needs. This surplus food could be warehoused or exported in trade.
- By the per capita food supply—that is, how much food there is per person. (The term *per capita* means per person, or literally, "per head.") This indicates the portion of the country's wealth each person might enjoy.

[3]*Introduction to Tropical Fish Stock Assessment* by Per Sparre, Danish Institute for Fisheries Research, and Siebren C. Venema, FAO Fisheries Department, available at http://www.fao.org/docrep/W5449E/w5449e00.htm.

First, we choose to measure prosperity in terms of food surplus, $S(t)$, in year t, where

$$S(t) = \underbrace{\text{Number of people that can be fed}}_{N(t)} - \underbrace{\text{Number of people living in the country}}_{P(t)}$$

so

$$S(t) = N(t) - P(t).$$

For example, to determine the surplus in year $t = 25$, we evaluate

$$S(25) = N(25) - P(25).$$

Since $N(25) = 4 + 0.5(25) = 16.5$ and $P(25) = 2(1.04)^{25} \approx 5.332$, we have

$$S(25) \approx 16.5 - 5.332 = 11.168.$$

Thus, in year 25 the food surplus could feed 11.168 million additional people.

We use the formulas for N and P to find a formula for S:

$$S(t) = \underbrace{N(t)}_{4+0.5t} - \underbrace{P(t)}_{2(1.04)^t},$$

so

$$S(t) = 4 + 0.5t - 2(1.04)^t.$$

A graph of S is shown in Figure 6.17. The maximum surplus occurs sometime during the 48th year. In that year, there is surplus food sufficient for an additional 14.865 million people.

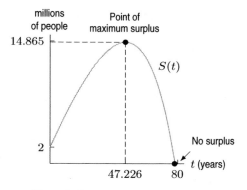

Figure 6.17 Surplus graphed using the formula $S(t) = 4 + 0.5t - 2(1.04)^t$

The Sum and Difference of Two Functions Defined by Graphs

How does the graph of the surplus function S, shown in Figure 6.17, relate to the graphs of N and P in Figure 6.16? Since

$$S(t) = N(t) - P(t),$$

the value of $S(t)$ is represented graphically as the vertical distance between the graphs of $N(t)$ and $P(t)$. See Figure 6.18. Figure 6.19 shows the surplus plotted against time.

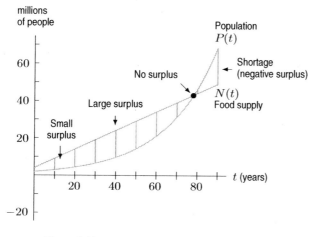

Figure 6.18 Surplus, $S(t) = N(t) - P(t)$, as vertical distance between $N(t)$ and $P(t)$ graphs

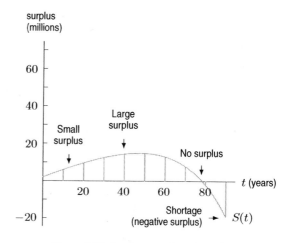

Figure 6.19 Surplus as a function of time

From year $t = 0$ to $t \approx 78.320$, the food supply is more than the population needs. Therefore the surplus, $S(t)$, is positive on this time interval. At time $t = 78.320$, the food supply is exactly sufficient for the population, so $S(t) = 0$, resulting in the horizontal intercept $t = 78.320$ on the graph of $S(t)$ in Figure 6.19. For times $t > 78.320$, the food supply is less than the population needs. Therefore the surplus is negative, representing a food shortage.

In the next example we consider a sum of two functions.

Example 1   Let $f(x) = x$ and $g(x) = \frac{1}{x}$. By adding vertical distances on the graphs of f and g, sketch

$$h(x) = f(x) + g(x) \quad \text{for } x > 0.$$

Solution   The graphs of f and g are shown in Figure 6.20. For each value of x, we add the vertical distances that represent $f(x)$ and $g(x)$ to get a point on the graph of $h(x)$. Compare the graph of $h(x)$ to the values shown Table 6.20.

Table 6.20 *Adding function values*

x	$\frac{1}{4}$	$\frac{1}{2}$	1	2	4
$f(x) = x$	$\frac{1}{4}$	$\frac{1}{2}$	1	2	4
$g(x) = 1/x$	4	2	1	$\frac{1}{2}$	$\frac{1}{4}$
$h(x) = f(x) + g(x)$	$4\frac{1}{4}$	$2\frac{1}{2}$	2	$2\frac{1}{2}$	$4\frac{1}{4}$

Note that as x increases, $g(x)$ decreases towards zero, so the values of $h(x)$ get closer to the values of $f(x)$. On the other hand, as x approaches zero, $h(x)$ gets closer to $g(x)$.

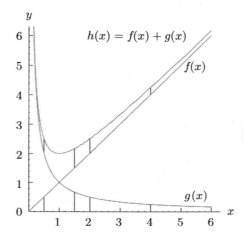

Figure 6.20 Graph of $h(x) = f(x) + g(x)$ constructed by adding vertical distances under f and g

Factoring a Function's Formula into a Product

It is often useful to be able to express a given function as a product of functions.

Example 2   Find exactly all the zeros of the function

$$p(x) = 2^x \cdot 6x^2 - 2^x \cdot x - 2^{x+1}.$$

Solution   We could approximate the zeros by finding the points where the graph of the function p crosses the x-axis. Unfortunately, these solutions are not exact. Alternatively, we can express p as a product. Using the fact that

$$2^{x+1} = 2^x \cdot 2^1 = 2 \cdot 2^x,$$

we rewrite the formula for p as

$$\begin{aligned}
p(x) &= 2^x \cdot 6x^2 - 2^x x - 2 \cdot 2^x \\
&= 2^x(6x^2 - x - 2) \qquad \text{Factoring out } 2^x \\
&= 2^x(2x + 1)(3x - 2) \qquad \text{Factoring the quadratic.}
\end{aligned}$$

Thus p is the product of the exponential function 2^x and two linear functions. Since p is a product, it equals zero if one or more of its factors equals zero. But 2^x is never equal to 0, so $p(x)$ equals zero if and only if one of the linear factors is zero:

$$(2x + 1) = 0 \qquad \text{or} \qquad (3x - 2) = 0$$
$$x = -\frac{1}{2} \qquad\qquad\qquad x = \frac{2}{3}.$$

The Quotient of Functions Defined by Formulas and Graphs: Prosperity

Now let's think about our second proposed measure of prosperity, the per capita food supply, $R(t)$. With this definition of prosperity

$$R(t) = \frac{\text{Number of people that can be fed}}{\text{Number of people living in the country}} = \frac{N(t)}{P(t)}.$$

For example,

$$R(25) = \frac{N(25)}{P(25)} = \frac{16.5}{5.332} \approx 3.1.$$

This means that in year 25, everybody in the country could, on average, have more than three times as much food as he or she needs. The formula for $R(t)$ is

$$R(t) = \frac{N(t)}{P(t)} = \frac{4 + 0.5t}{2(1.04)^t}.$$

From the graph of R in Figure 6.21, we see that the maximum per capita food supply occurs during the 18th year. Notice this maximum prosperity prediction is different from the one made using the surplus function $S(t)$.

However, both prosperity models predict that shortages begin after time $t = 78.320$. This is not a coincidence. The food surplus model predicts shortages when $S(t) = N(t) - P(t) < 0$, or $N(t) < P(t)$. The per capita food supply model predicts shortages when $R(t) < 1$, meaning that the amount of food available per person is less than the amount necessary to feed 1 person. Since $R(t) = \frac{N(t)}{P(t)} < 1$ is true only when $N(t) < P(t)$, the same condition leads to shortages.

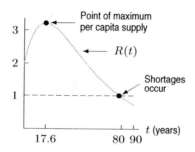

Figure 6.21 Per capita food supply, $R(t) = \frac{N(t)}{P(t)}$

The Quotient of Functions Defined by Tables: Per Capita Crime Rate

Table 6.21 gives the number of violent crimes committed in two cities between 1997 and 2002. It appears that crime in both cities is on the rise and that there is less crime in City B than in City A.

Table 6.21 *Number of violent crimes committed each year in two cities*

Year	1997	1998	1999	2000	2001	2002
t, years since 1997	0	1	2	3	4	5
Crimes in City A	793	795	807	818	825	831
Crimes in City B	448	500	525	566	593	652

Table 6.22 gives the population for these two cities from 1997 to 2002. The population of City A is larger than that of City B and both cities are growing.

Table 6.22 *Population of the two cities*

Year	1997	1998	1999	2000	2001	2002
t, years since 1994	0	1	2	3	4	5
Population of City A	61,000	62,100	63,220	64,350	65,510	66,690
Population of City B	28,000	28,588	29,188	29,801	30,427	31,066

Can we attribute the growth in crime in both cities to the population growth? Can we attribute the larger number of crimes in City A to its larger population? To answer these questions, we consider the per capita crime rate in each city.

Let's define $N_A(t)$ to be the number of crimes in City A during year t (where $t = 0$ means 1997). Similarly, let's define $P_A(t)$ to be the population of City A in year t. Then the per capita crime rate in City A, $r_A(t)$, is given by

$$r_A(t) = \frac{\text{Number of crimes in year } t}{\text{Number of people in year } t} = \frac{N_A(t)}{P_A(t)}.$$

We have defined a new function, $r_A(t)$, as the quotient of $N_A(t)$ and $P_A(t)$. For example, the data in Tables 6.21 and 6.22 shows that the per capita crime rate for City A in year $t = 0$ is

$$r_A(0) = \frac{N_A(0)}{P_A(0)} = \frac{793}{61{,}000} = 1.30\%.$$

Similarly, the per capita crime rate for the year $t = 1$ is

$$r_A(1) = \frac{N_A(1)}{P_A(1)} = \frac{795}{62{,}100} = 1.280\%.$$

Thus, the per capita crime rate in City A actually decreased from 1.30% in 1997 to 1.280% in 1998.

Example 3   (a) Make a table of values for $r_A(t)$ and $r_B(t)$, the per capita crime rates of Cities A and B.
(b) Use the table to decide which city is more dangerous.

Solution   (a) Table 6.23 gives values of $r_A(t)$ for $t = 0, 1, \ldots, 5$. The per capita crime rate in City A declined between 1997 and 2002 despite the fact that the total number of crimes rose during this period. Table 6.23 also gives values of $r_B(t)$, the per capita crime rate of City B, defined by

$$r_B(t) = \frac{N_B(t)}{P_B(t)},$$

where $N_B(t)$ is the number of crimes in City B in year t and $P_B(t)$ is the population of City B in year t. For example, the per capita crime rate in City B in year $t = 0$ is

$$r_B(0) = \frac{N_B(0)}{P_B(0)} = \frac{448}{28{,}000} = 1.6\%.$$

Table 6.23   *Values of $r_A(t)$ and $r_B(t)$, the per capita violent crime rates of Cities A and B*

Year	1997	1998	1999	2000	2001	2002
t, years since 1997	0	1	2	3	4	5
$r_A(t) = N_A(t)/P_A(t)$	1.300%	1.280%	1.276%	1.271%	1.259%	1.246%
$r_B(t) = N_B(t)/P_B(t)$	1.600%	1.749%	1.799%	1.899%	1.949%	2.099%

(b) From Table 6.23, we see that between 1997 and 2002, City A has a lower per capita crime rate than City B. The crime rate of City A is decreasing, whereas the crime rate of City B is increasing. Thus, even though Table 6.21 indicates that there are more crimes committed in City A, Table 6.23 tells us that City B is, in some sense, more dangerous. Table 6.23 also tells us that, even though the number of crimes is rising in both cities, City A is getting safer, while City B is getting more dangerous.

Exercises and Problems for Section 6.3

Exercises

In Exercises 1–6, find a simplified formula for the function. Let $m(x) = 3x^2 - x$, $n(x) = 2x$, and $o(x) = \sqrt{x + 2}$.

1. $f(x) = m(x) + n(x)$

2. $g(x) = (o(x))^2$

3. $h(x) = n(x)o(x)$

4. $i(x) = m(o(x))n(x)$

5. $j(x) = (m(x))/n(x)$

6. $k(x) = m(x) - n(x) - o(x)$

In Exercises 7–12, find the following functions.

(a) $f(x) + g(x)$ (b) $f(x) - g(x)$
(c) $f(x)g(x)$ (d) $f(x)/g(x)$

7. $f(x) = x + 1$ $g(x) = 3x^2$

8. $f(x) = x^2 + 4$ $g(x) = x + 2$

9. $f(x) = x + 5$ $g(x) = x - 5$

10. $f(x) = x^2 + 4$ $g(x) = x^2 + 2$

11. $f(x) = x^3$ $g(x) = x^2$

12. $f(x) = \sqrt{x}$ $g(x) = x^2 + 2$

Problems

13. (a) Graph the functions $f(x) = (x - 4)^2 - 2$ and $g(x) = -(x - 2)^2 + 8$ on the same set of axes.
   (b) Make a table of values for f and g for $x = 0, 1, 2, \ldots, 6$.
   (c) Make a table of values for $y = f(x) - g(x)$ for $x = 0, 1, 2, \ldots, 6$.
   (d) On your graph, sketch the vertical line segment of length $f(x) - g(x)$ for each integer value of x from 0 to 6. Check that the segment lengths agree with the values from part (c).
   (e) Plot the values from your table for the function $y = f(x) - g(x)$ on your graph.
   (f) Simplify the algebraic formulas for $f(x)$ and $g(x)$ given in part (a). Find a formula for the function $y = f(x) - g(x)$.
   (g) Use part (f) to graph $y = f(x) - g(x)$ on the same axes as f and g. Does the graph pass through the points you plotted in part (e)?

14. Use Table 6.24 to make tables of values for $x = -1, 0, 1, 2, 3, 4$ for the following functions.

(a) $h(x) = f(x) + g(x)$ (b) $j(x) = 2f(x)$
(c) $k(x) = (g(x))^2$ (d) $m(x) = g(x)/f(x)$

Table 6.24

x	-1	0	1	2	3	4
$f(x)$	-4	-1	2	5	8	11
$g(x)$	4	1	0	1	4	9

15. Use Table 6.25 to make tables of values for the following functions.

(a) $n(x) = f(x) + g(x)$

(b) $p(x) = 2f(x)g(x) - f(x)$
(c) $q(x) = g(x)/f(x)$

Table 6.25

x	1	2	3	4
$f(x)$	3	4	1	2
$g(x)$	2	1	4	3

16. Use Figure 6.22 to graph the following functions.

(a) $y = g(x) - 3$ (b) $y = g(x) + x$

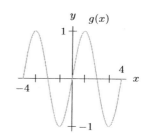

Figure 6.22

17. Let $f(x) = x + 1$ and $g(x) = x^2 - 1$. In parts (a)–(e), write a formula in terms of $f(x)$ and $g(x)$ for the function. Then evaluate the formula for $x = 3$. Write a formula in terms of x for each function. Check your formulas for $x = 3$.

(a) $h(x)$ is the sum of $f(x)$ and $g(x)$.
(b) $j(x)$ is the difference between $g(x)$ and twice $f(x)$.
(c) $k(x)$ is the product of $f(x)$ and $g(x)$.
(d) $m(x)$ is the ratio of $g(x)$ to $f(x)$.
(e) $n(x)$ is defined by $n(x) = (f(x))^2 - g(x)$.

18. Use Figure 6.23 to graph $h(x) = g(x) - f(x)$. On the graph of $h(x)$, label the points whose x-coordinates are $x = a$, $x = b$, and $x = c$. Label the y-intercept.

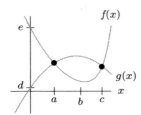

Figure 6.23

19. **(a)** Find possible formulas for the functions in Figure 6.24.
 (b) Let $h(x) = f(x) \cdot g(x)$. Graph $f(x)$, $g(x)$ and $h(x)$ on the same set of axes.

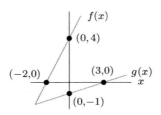

Figure 6.24

20. Sketch two linear functions whose product is the function f graphed in Figure 6.25(a). Explain why this is not possible for the function q graphed in Figure 6.25(b).

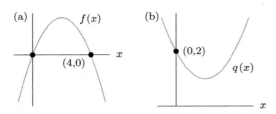

Figure 6.25

21. An average of 50,000 people visit Riverside Park each day in the summer. The park charges \$15.00 for admission. Consultants predict that for each \$1.00 increase in the entrance price, the park would lose an average of 2500 customers per day. Express the daily revenue from ticket sales as a function of the number of \$1.00 price increases. What ticket price maximizes the revenue from ticket sales?

22. Use Figure 6.26 to graph $c(x) = a(x) \cdot b(x)$. [Hint: There is not enough information to determine formulas for a and b but you can use the method of Problem 19.]

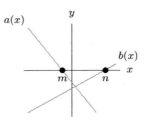

Figure 6.26

23. In Figure 6.27, the line l_2 is fixed and the point P moves along l_2. Define $f(\theta)$ as the y-coordinate of P.
 (a) Find a formula for $f(\theta)$ if $0 < \theta < \pi/2$. [Hint: Use the equation for l_2.]
 (b) Graph $y = f(\theta)$ on the interval $-\pi \le \theta \le \pi$.
 (c) How does the y-coordinate of P change as θ changes? Is $y = f(\theta)$ periodic?

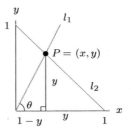

Figure 6.27

24. Find the range for each of the following functions.

 (a) $y = \arccos x$ **(b)** $y = \dfrac{3}{2 - \cos x}$

 (c) $y = \sin\left(\dfrac{1}{1 + x^2}\right)$ **(d)** $y = 4 \sin x \cos x$

 (e) $y = 3^{3 + \sin x}$

25. Graph the following functions for $0 \le x \le 2\pi$.

 (a) $y = x \sin x$ **(b)** $y = (1/x) \sin x$
 (c) $y = \sin(x^2)$ **(d)** $y = (\sin x)^2$
 (e) $y = |\sin x|$ **(e)** $y = e^x \sin x$

26. Graph $y = \sec \theta$, $y = \csc \theta$ and $y = \cot \theta$ for $-\pi \le \theta \le \pi$. Describe and compare the graphs.

27. Describe the similarities and differences between the graphs of $y = \sin(1/x)$ and $y = 1/\sin x$.

28. Let $f(x) = kx^2 + B$ and $g(x) = C^{2x}$ and

$$h(x) = kx^2 C^{2x} + BC^{2x} + C^{2x}.$$

Suppose $f(3) = 7$ and $g(3) = 5$. Evaluate $h(3)$.

29. Is the following statement true or false? If $f(x) \cdot g(x)$ is an odd function, then both $f(x)$ and $g(x)$ are odd functions. Explain your answer.

30. (a) Is the sum of two even functions even, odd, or neither? Justify your answer.
  (b) Is the sum of two odd functions even, odd, or neither? Justify your answer.
  (c) Is the sum of an even and an odd functions even, odd, or neither? Justify your answer.

31. Let $f(t)$ be the number of men and $g(t)$ be the number of women in Canada in year t. Let $h(t)$ be the average income, in Canadian dollars, of women in Canada in year t.

  (a) Find the function $p(t)$ which gives the number of people in Canada in year t.
  (b) Find the total amount of money $m(t)$ earned by Canadian women in year t.

32. Table 6.26 gives $N(t)$, the number of existing warheads, and $P(t)$, the world's population, t years since 1980.

  (a) Assume that $P(t)$ is an exponential function. Based on Table 6.26, find a formula for $P(t)$.
  (b) According to your formula for $P(t)$, by what percent does the population change each year?
  (c) Assume that $N(t)$ is a linear function of time. Based on Table 6.26, find a formula for $N(t)$.
  (d) Construct a table of values for $t = 0, 5, 10, 15$ for the function f defined by the formula:
$$f(t) = \frac{N(t)}{P(t)}.$$
  (e) Is f an exponential function, a linear function, both, or neither? Justify your answer.
  (f) In practical terms, what does the function $f(t)$ represent?

Table 6.26

t, in years	$N(t)$, warheads	$P(t)$, population
0	30,000	
5		4,500,000,000
10	21,000	
15		5,695,300,000

33. Table 6.27 gives data on strawberry production from 1997 through 2001,[4] where t is in years since 1997. Let $f_{CA}(t)$, $f_{FL}(t)$, and $f_{US}(t)$ be the harvested area in year t for strawberries grown in California, Florida, and the US overall, respectively. Likewise, let $g_{CA}(t)$, $g_{FL}(t)$, and $g_{US}(t)$ give the yield in thousands of pounds per acre for these three regions.

  (a) Let $h_{CA}(t) = f_{CA}(t) \cdot g_{CA}(t)$. Create a table of values for $h_{CA}(t)$ for $0 \le t \le 4$. Describe in words what $h_{CA}(t)$ tells you about strawberry production.
  (b) Let $p(t)$ be the fraction of all US strawberries (by weight) grown in Florida and California in year t. Find a formula for $p(t)$ in terms of f_{CA}, f_{FL}, f_{US}. Use Table 6.27 to make a table of values for $p(t)$.

Table 6.27

t	Harvested area (acres)			Yield (1000 lbs per acre)		
	CA	FL	US total	CA	FL	US total
0	22,600	6,100	44,260	59.0	29.0	36.8
1	24,200	6,200	46,010	56.0	26.0	36.3
2	25,800	6,200	46,760	59.5	30.0	40.6
3	27,600	6,300	47,650	59.0	35.0	42.0
4	26,400	6,500	46,100	52.5	26.0	37.8

6.4 INVERSE SINE, COSINE, AND TANGENT FUNCTIONS

- Inverse Sine Function
- Inverse Cosine Function
- Inverse Tangent Function
- Inverse Trigonometric Functions with Angle Ranges
- Summary

In Appendix K, we solved a right triangle (see Figure 6.28) for α as follows:

$$\sin \alpha = \tfrac{3}{5} = 0.6$$
$$\alpha = \sin^{-1} 0.6 \quad \text{or} \quad \arcsin 0.6$$
$$\alpha = 0.64 \text{ rad} \quad \text{or} \quad 36.87° \quad \text{To two deciaml places}$$

In this context, both $\sin^{-1} 0.6$ and $\arcsin 0.6$ represent the acute angle (in either radian or degree measure)whose sine is 0.6. In Appendix K, we said that the concepts behind the inverse

[4]National Agricultural Statistics Service, USDA.

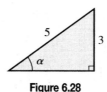

Figure 6.28

function symbols $\sin^{-1}$ (or arcsin), $\cos^{-1}$ (or arccos), and $\tan^{-1}$ (or arctan) would be discussed in greater detail in this chapter. Now the time has come, and we extend the meaning of these symbols so that they apply not only to triangle problems, but to a wide variety of problems that have nothing to do with triangles or angles. That is, we will create another set of tools—a new set of functions—that you can put in your mathematical toolbox for general use on a wide variety of new problems.

After we complete the discussion of inverse trigonometric functions, we will be in a position to solve many types of equations involving trigonometric functions. Trigonometric equations form the subject matter of the last section of this chapter.

In this section we will define the inverse sine, cosine, and tangent functions; look at their graphs; present some basic and useful identities; and consider some applications.

Inverse Sine Function

For a function to have an inverse that is a function, it is necessary that the original function be **one-to-one.** That is, each domain value must correspond to exactly one range value, and each range value must correspond to exactly one domain value. The first condition is satisfied by all functions, but the second condition is not satisfied by some functions. For example, Figure 6.29a illustrates a function that is one-to-one; Figure 6.29b illustrates a function that is not one-to-one.

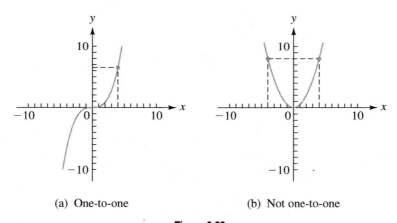

(a) One-to-one   (b) Not one-to-one

Figure 6.29

To form the inverse sine function, we start with the sine function whose graph, domain, and range are indicated in Figure 6.30. Note that the sine function is not one-to-one. Figure 6.31 shows that for the range value $y = 0.5$, for example, there are an unlimited number of domain values x such that $\sin x = 0.5$. Each point where the dashed horizontal line passing through $y = 0.5$ crosses the graph corresponds to a domain value whose sine is 0.5.

How can we restrict the domain of the sine function so that the sine function on this restricted domain becomes one-to-one—that is, so that every horizontal line will pass through at most one

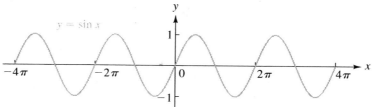

Domain: All real numbers
Range: $-1 \leq y \leq 1$

Figure 6.30 Sine function

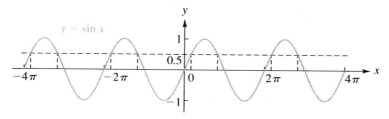

Figure 6.31 $\sin x = 0.5$

point on the graph? Actually, we can do this in an unlimited number of ways. The generally accepted way, however, is illustrated in Figure 6.32.

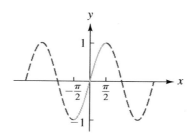

Figure 6.32 $y = \sin x$ is one-to-one for $-\pi/2 \leq x \leq \pi/2$

We use this restricted sine function to define the inverse sine function.

INVERSE SINE FUNCTION

The **inverse sine function** is defined as the inverse of the restricted sine function $y = \sin x$, $-\pi/2 \leq x \leq \pi/2$. Thus,

$$y = \arcsin x$$
$$y = \sin^{-1} x$$

are equivalent to

$$\sin y = x \quad \text{where} -\pi/2 \leq y \leq \pi/2, \quad -1 \leq x \leq 1$$

The inverse sine of x is the number or angle y, $-\pi/2 \leq y \leq \pi/2$, whose sine is x.

To graph $y = \sin^{-1} x$, we take the coordinates of each point on the graph of the restricted sine function and reverse the order. For example, since $(-\pi/2, -1)$, $(0, 0)$, and $(\pi/2, 1)$ are on the graph of the restricted sine function, then $(-1, -\pi/2)$, $(0, 0)$, and $(1, \pi/2)$ are on the graph of the inverse sine function, as shown in Figure 6.33. Using these three points provides us with a quick way of sketching the graph of the inverse sine function. A more accurate graph can be obtained by using a calculator in radian mode and a set of domain values from -1 to 1 (see Problem 39 in the exercises). An instant graph can be obtained using a graphing utility.

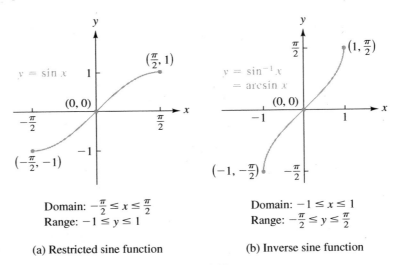

| (a) Restricted sine function | (b) Inverse sine function |

Figure 6.33

We state the important sine–inverse sine identities, which follow from the general properties of inverse functions.

SINE–INVERSE SINE IDENTITIES

$$\sin(\sin^{-1} x) = x \qquad -1 \le x \le 1$$
$$\sin^{-1}(\sin x) = x \qquad -\pi/2 \le x \le \pi/2$$

Explore/ Discuss 1

Use a calculator to evaluate each of the following. Which illustrate a sine–inverse sine identity and which do not? Explain.

(a) $\sin(\sin^{-1} 0.5)$ (b) $\sin(\sin^{-1} 1.5)$ (c) $\sin^{-1}[\sin(-1.3)]$ (d) $\sin^{-1}[\sin(-3)]$

Example 1

Find exact values without using a calculator:

(a) $\sin^{-1}(\sqrt{3}/2)$ (b) $\arcsin(-\frac{1}{2})$ (c) $\sin^{-1}(\sin 1.2)$ (d) $\cos(\sin^{-1} \frac{2}{3})$

Solution

(a) $y = \sin^{-1}(\sqrt{3}/2)$ is equivalent to $\sin y = \sqrt{3}/2$, $-\pi/2 \le y \le \pi/2$. What y between $-\pi/2$ and $\pi/2$ has sine $\sqrt{3}/2$? This y must be associated with a first quadrant reference triangle (see Fig. 6.34):

$$\sin y = \frac{\sqrt{3}}{2}$$

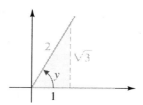

Figure 6.34 Reference triangle is a special
30°–60° triangle, $y = \pi/3$.

Thus,

$$\sin^{-1} \frac{\sqrt{3}}{2} = \frac{\pi}{3}$$

since $\pi/3$ is the only number between $-\pi/2$ and $\pi/2$ with sine equal to $\sqrt{3}/2$.

(b) $y = \arcsin\left(-\frac{1}{2}\right)$ is equivalent to $\sin y = -\frac{1}{2}$, $-\pi/2 \le y \le \pi/2$. What y between $-\pi/2$ and $\pi/2$ has sine $-\frac{1}{2}$? This y must be negative and associated with a fourth quadrant reference triangle (see Fig. 6.35):

$$\sin y = -\frac{1}{2}$$

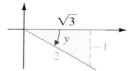

Figure 6.35 Reference triangle is a special
30°–60° triangle, $y = -\pi/6$.

Thus,

$$\arcsin\left(-\frac{1}{2}\right) = -\frac{\pi}{6}$$

[*Note:* y cannot be $11\pi/6$, even though $\sin(11\pi/6) = -\frac{1}{2}$. Why?]

(c) $\sin^{-1}(\sin 1.2) = 1.2$ Sine–inverse sine identity

(d) Let $y = \sin^{-1} \frac{2}{3}$; then $\sin y = \frac{2}{3}$, $-\pi/2 \le y \le \pi/2$. Draw the reference triangle associated with y; then $\cos y = \cos(\sin^{-1} \frac{2}{3})$ can be determined directly from the triangle (after finding the third side) without actually finding y (see Figure 6.36):

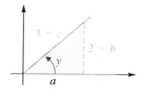

$$a^2 + b^2 = c^2$$
$$a = \sqrt{3^2 - 2^2}$$
$$= \sqrt{5}$$

Figure 6.36

Thus,

$$\cos\left(\sin^{-1} \frac{2}{3}\right) = \cos y = \frac{\sqrt{5}}{3}$$

**Matched
Problem 1**   Find exact values without using a calculator:
(a) $\arcsin(\sqrt{2}/2)$ (b) $\sin^{-1}(-1)$
(c) $\sin[\sin^{-1}(-0.4)]$ (d) $\tan[\sin^{-1}(-1\sqrt{5})]$

Example 2   Find to four significant digits using a calculator:
(a) $\sin^{-1}(0.8432)$ (b) $\arcsin(-0.3042)$
(c) $\sin^{-1} 1.357$ (d) $\cot[\sin^{-1}(-0.1087)]$

Solution   [*Note:* Recall that the keys used to obtain $\sin^{-1}$ vary among different brands of calculators. (Read the user's manual for your calculator.) Two common designations are $\boxed{\sin^{-1}}$ and the combination $\boxed{\text{inv}}\,\boxed{\text{sin}}$. For all these problems set your calculator in radian mode.]
(a) $\sin^{-1}(0.8432) = 1.003$
(b) $\arcsin(-0.3042) = -0.3091$
(c) $\sin^{-1} 1.357 = \text{Error}^5$ 1.357 is not in the domain of $\sin^{-1}$.
(d) $\cot[\sin^{-1}(-0.1087)] = -9.145$

**Matched
Problem 2**   Find to four significant digits using a calculator:
(a) $\arcsin 0.2903$ (b) $\sin^{-1}(-0.7633)$
(c) $\arcsin (-2.305)$ (d) $\sec[\sin^{-1}(-0.3446)]$

Inverse Cosine Function

The generally accepted restriction on the cosine function, which ensures that an inverse will exist, is to have domain values so that $0 \leq x \leq \pi$ (see Figure 6.37).

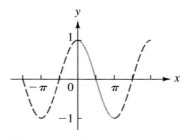

Figure 6.37 $y = \cos x$ is one-to-one for $0 \leq x \leq \pi$

---

[5]Some calculators use a more advanced definition of the inverse sine function involving complex numbers and will display an ordered pair of real numbers as the value of $\sin^{-1}1.357$. You should interpret such a result as an indication that the number entered is not in the domain of the inverse sine function as we have defined it.

INVERSE COSINE FUNCTION

The **inverse cosine function** is defined as the inverse of the restricted cosine function $y = \cos x$, $0 \leq x \leq \pi$. Thus,

$$y = \arccos x$$
$$y = \cos^{-1} x$$

are equivalent to

$$\cos y = x \quad \text{where } 0 \leq y \leq \pi, \quad -1 \leq x \leq 1$$

The inverse cosine of x is the number or angle y, $\quad 0 \leq y \leq \pi$, whose cosine is x.

Figure 6.38 compares the graphs of the restricted cosine function and its inverse. Notice that $(0, 1)$, $(\pi/2, 0)$, and $(\pi, -1)$ are on the restricted cosine graph. Reversing the coordinates gives us three points on the graph of the inverse cosine function.

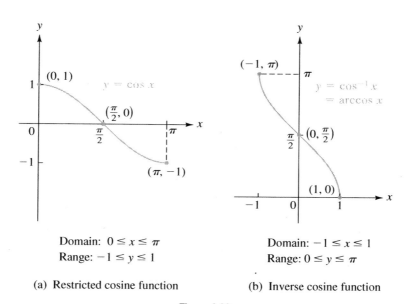

Domain: $0 \leq x \leq \pi$
Range: $-1 \leq y \leq 1$

(a) Restricted cosine function

Domain: $-1 \leq x \leq 1$
Range: $0 \leq y \leq \pi$

(b) Inverse cosine function

Figure 6.38

We complete the discussion by giving the cosine–inverse cosine identities.

COSINE–INVERSE COSINE IDENTITIES

$$\cos(\cos^{-1} x) = x \quad -1 \leq x \leq 1$$
$$\cos^{-1}(\cos x) = x \quad 0 \leq x \leq \pi$$

Explore/
Discuss 2
Use a calculator to evaluate each of the following. Which illustrate a cosine–inverse cosine identity and which do not? Explain.

(a) $\cos(\cos^{-1} 0.5)$ (b) $\cos(\cos^{-1} 1.1)$ (c) $\cos^{-1}(\cos 1.1)$ (d) $\cos^{-1}[\cos(-1)]$

Example 3
Find exact values without using a calculator:

(a) $\cos^{-1} \frac{1}{2}$ (b) $\arccos(-\sqrt{3}/2)$ (c) $\cos(\cos^{-1} 0.7)$ (d) $\sin[\cos^{-1}(-\frac{1}{3})]$

Solution
(a) $y = \cos^{-1} \frac{1}{2}$ is equivalent to $\cos y = \frac{1}{2}, 0 \le y \le \pi$. What y between 0 and π has cosine $\frac{1}{2}$? This y must be associated with a first quadrant reference triangle (see Figure 6.39):

$$\cos y = \frac{1}{2}$$

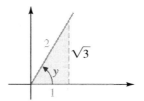

Figure 6.39 Reference triangle is a special 30°–60° triangle, $y = \pi/3$.

Thus,

$$\cos^{-1} \frac{1}{2} = \frac{\pi}{2}$$

(b) $y = \arccos(-\sqrt{3}/2)$ is equivalent to $\cos y = -\sqrt{3}/2, 0 \le y \le \pi$. What y between 0 and π has cosine $-\sqrt{3}/2$? This y must be associated with a second quadrant reference triangle (see Figure 6.40):

$$\cos y = -\frac{\sqrt{3}}{2}$$

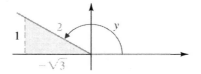

Figure 6.40 Reference triangle is a special 30°–60° triangle, $y = 5\pi/6$.

Thus,

$$\arccos\left(-\frac{\sqrt{3}}{2}\right) = \frac{5\pi}{6}$$

[*Note:* y cannot be $-5\pi/6$, even though $\cos(-5\pi/6) = -\sqrt{3}/2$. Why?]

(c) $\cos(\cos^{-1} 0.7) = 0.7$ Cosine–inverse cosine identity

(d) Let $y = \cos^{-1}(-\frac{1}{3})$; then $\cos y = -\frac{1}{3}, 0 \leq y \leq \pi$. Draw a reference triangle associated with y; then $\sin y = \sin[\cos^{-1}(-\frac{1}{3})]$ can be determined directly from the triangle (after finding the third side) without actually finding y (see Figure 6.41):

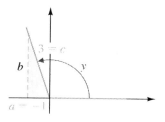

$$a^2 + b^2 = c^2$$
$$a = \sqrt{3^2 - (-1)^2}$$
$$= \sqrt{8} = 2\sqrt{2}$$

Figure 6.41

Thus,

$$\sin\left[\cos^{-1}\left(-\frac{1}{3}\right)\right] = \sin y = \frac{2\sqrt{2}}{3}$$

Matched Problem 3

Find exact values without using a calculator:
(a) $\arccos(\sqrt{2}/2)$ (b) $\cos^{-1}(-1)$ (c) $\cos^{-1}(\cos 3.05)$ (d) $\cot[\cos^{-1}(-1/\sqrt{5})]$

Example 4

Find to four significant digits using a calculator:
(a) $\cos^{-1} 0.4325$ (b) $\arccos(-0.8976)$ (c) $\cos^{-1} 2.137$ (d) $\csc[\cos^{-1}(-0.0349)]$

Solution

Set your calculator in radian mode.
(a) $\cos^{-1} 0.4325 = 1.124$
(b) $\arccos(-0.8976) = 2.685$
(c) $\cos^{-1} 2.137 = $ Error   2.137 is not in the domain of $\cos^{-1}$.
(d) $\csc[\cos^{-1}(-0.0349)] = 1.001$

Matched Problem 4

Find to four significant digits using a calculator:
(a) $\arccos 0.6773$ (b) $\cos^{-1}(-0.8114)$ (c) $\arccos(-1.003)$ (d) $\cot[\cos^{-1}(-0.5036)]$

Example 5

Find the exact value of $\cos(\sin^{-1} \frac{3}{5} - \cos^{-1} \frac{4}{5})$ without using a calculator.

Solution   We use the difference identity for cosine and the procedure outlined in Examples 1D and 3D to obtain

$$\cos(x - y) = \cos x \cos y + \sin x \sin y$$

$$\cos\left(\sin^{-1}\frac{3}{5} - \cos^{-1}\frac{4}{5}\right) = \cos\left(\sin^{-1}\frac{3}{5}\right)\cos\left(\cos^{-1}\frac{4}{5}\right) + \sin\left(\sin^{-1}\frac{3}{5}\right)\sin\left(\cos^{-1}\frac{4}{5}\right)$$

$$= \left(\frac{4}{5}\right) \cdot \left(\frac{4}{5}\right) + \left(\frac{3}{5}\right) \cdot \left(\frac{3}{5}\right)$$

$$= 1$$

Matched Problem 5   Find the exact value of $\sin(2 \cos^{-1}\frac{3}{5})$ without using a calculator.

Inverse Tangent Function

To restrict the tangent function so that every horizontal line will pass through at most one point on its graph, we choose to restrict the domain to the interval $-\pi/2 \le x \le \pi/2$ (see Figure 6.42).

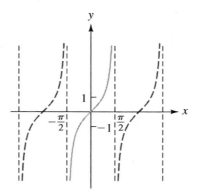

Figure 6.42 $y = \tan x$ is one-to-one for $-\pi/2 < x < \pi/2$

We use this restricted tangent function to define the inverse tangent function.

INVERSE TANGENT FUNCTION

The **inverse tangent function** is defined as the inverse of the restricted tangent function $y = \tan x$, $-\pi/2 < x < \pi/2$. Thus,

$$y = \arctan x$$
$$y = \tan^{-1} x$$

are equivalent to

$$\tan y = x \qquad \text{where} - \pi/2 < y < \pi/2, \quad x \text{ is any real number}$$

The inverse tangent of x is the number or angle y, $-\pi/2 < y < \pi/2$, whose tangent is x.

Figure 6.43 compares the graphs of the restricted tangent function and its inverse. Notice that $(-\pi/4, -1)$, $(0, 0)$, and $(\pi/4, 1)$ are on the restricted tangent graph. Reversing the coordinates gives us three points on the graph of the inverse tangent function. Also note that the vertical asymptotes become horizontal asymptotes.

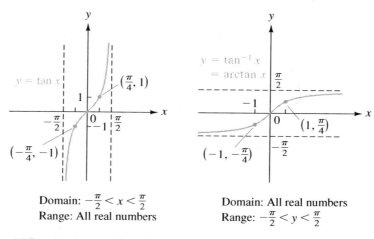

Domain: $-\dfrac{\pi}{2} < x < \dfrac{\pi}{2}$
Range: All real numbers

(a) Restricted tangent function

Domain: All real numbers
Range: $-\dfrac{\pi}{2} < y < \dfrac{\pi}{2}$

(b) Inverse tangent function

Figure 6.43

We now state the tangent–inverse tangent identities.

TANGENT–INVERSE TANGENT IDENTITIES

$$\tan(\tan^{-1} x) = x \qquad \text{for all } x$$
$$\tan^{-1}(\tan x) = x \qquad -\pi/2 < x < \pi/2$$

**Explore/
Discuss 3**

Use a calculator to evaluate each of the following. Which illustrate a tangent–inverse tangent identity and which do not? Explain.

(a) $\tan(\tan^{-1} 25)$ (b) $\tan[\tan^{-1}(-325)]$ (c) $\tan^{-1}(\tan 1.2)$ (d) $\tan^{-1}[\tan(-\pi)]$

Example 6

Find exact values without using a calculator:

(a) $\tan^{-1}(-1/\sqrt{3})$ (b) $\tan^{-1}[\tan(-1.2)]$

Solution

(a) $y = \tan^{-1}(-1/\sqrt{3})$ is equivalent to $\tan y = -1/\sqrt{3}$, where y satisfies $-\pi/2 < y < \pi/2$. What y between $-\pi/2$ and $\pi/2$ has tangent $-1/\sqrt{3}$? This y must be negative and associated with a fourth quadrant reference triangle (see Figure 6.44):

$$\tan y = \frac{-1}{\sqrt{3}}$$

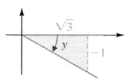

Figure 6.44 Special 30°–60° triangle, $y = -\pi/6$.

Thus,

$$\tan^{-1}\left(-\frac{1}{\sqrt{3}}\right) = -\frac{\pi}{6}$$

[*Note:* y cannot be $11\pi/6$. Why?]

(b) $\tan^{-1}[\tan(-1.2)] = -1.2$ Tangent–inverse tangent identity

---

Matched Problem 6

Find exact values without using a calculator:

(a) $\arctan \sqrt{3}$ (b) $\tan(\tan^{-1} 35)$

Example 7

Find to four significant digits using a calculator:

(a) $\tan^{-1} 3$ (b) $\arctan(-25.45)$

(c) $\tan^{-1} 1,435$ (d) $\sec[\tan^{-1}(-0.1308)]$

Solution

Set calculator in radian mode.

(a) $\tan^{-1} 3 = 1.249$ (b) $\arctan(-25.45) = -1.532$

(c) $\tan^{-1} 1,435 = 1.570$ (d) $\sec[\tan^{-1}(-0.1308)] = 1.009$

Matched Problem 7

Find to four significant digits using a calculator:

(a) $\tan^{-1} 7$ (b) $\arctan(-13.08)$

(c) $\tan^{-1} 735$ (d) $\csc[\tan^{-1}(-1.033)]$

Example 8

Express $\sin(\tan^{-1} x)$ as an algebraic expression in x.

Solution

Let

$$y = \tan^{-1} x \qquad -\frac{\pi}{2} < y < \frac{\pi}{2}$$

or, equivalently,

$$\tan y = x = \frac{x}{1} \qquad -\frac{\pi}{2} < y < \frac{\pi}{2}$$

The two possible reference triangles for y are shown in Figure 6.45.

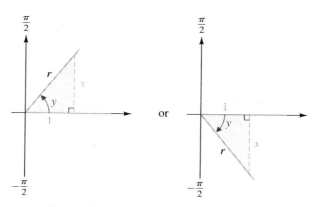

Figure 6.45 Reference triangles for $y = \tan^{-1} x$

In either case,

$$r = \sqrt{x^2 + 1}$$

Thus,

$$\sin(\tan^{-1} x) = \sin y = \frac{x}{r} = \frac{x}{\sqrt{x^2 + 1}}$$

Matched Problem 8   Express $\tan(\arccos x)$ as an algebraic expression in x.

Inverse Trigonometric Functions with Angle Ranges

We first defined trigonometric functions with angle domains, in degree or radian measure, and with real number ranges. Then, we defined the circular functions with real number domains and real number ranges. Technically, the trigonometric functions and the circular functions are not the same: The first are defined in terms of angles and the second in terms of real numbers. The functions, however, are closely related in that every real number in the domain of a circular function can be associated with an angle in either degree or radian measure, and vice versa (Figure 6.46).

In common usage, circular functions are also referred to as trigonometric functions. Thus, we have two sets of trigonometric functions, one with angle domains, in radian or degree measure, and the other with real number domains. (We are free to use the particular trigonometric function that best suits our needs.)

We have a similar situation with inverse trigonometric functions. The inverse trigonometric functions defined in the first part of this section are actually inverse circular functions, with real number domains and ranges. Corresponding to these definitions are inverse trigonometric functions with angle ranges, in degree or radian measure. If the range values are angles in degree measure, we will often use the Greek letter θ (theta) to represent this value. Thus, for example, we may use any of the following three forms, depending on our interest:

Real number range

$$y = \tan^{-1} x \qquad -\frac{\pi}{2} < y < \frac{\pi}{2} \qquad y \text{ is a real number.}$$

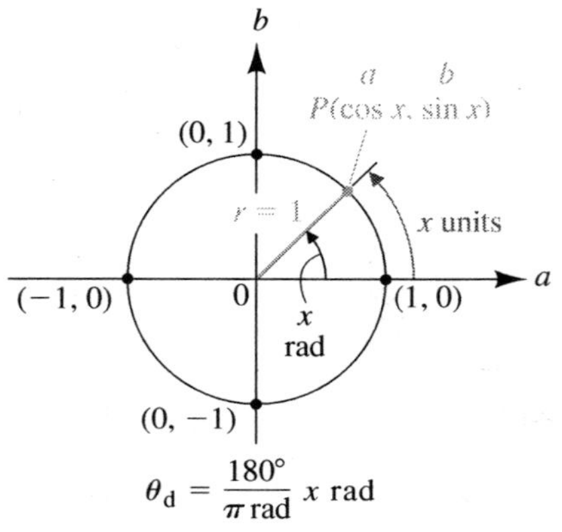

$$\theta_d = \frac{180°}{\pi \text{ rad}} x \text{ rad}$$

Figure 6.46 Real numbers and angles

Angle range in radian measure

$$y = \tan^{-1} x \quad -\frac{\pi}{2} < y < \frac{\pi}{2} \qquad y \text{ is an angle in radian measure.}$$

Angle range in degree measure

$$\theta = \tan^{-1} x \quad -90° < \theta < 90° \qquad \theta \text{ is an angle in degree measure.}$$

Thus, depending on the context, we can write

$$\tan^{-1} 1 = \frac{\pi}{4} \quad \text{or} \quad \tan^{-1} 1 = \frac{\pi}{4} \text{ radian} \quad \text{or} \quad \tan^{-1} 1 = 45°$$

Caution   This discussion does not mean that inverse trigonometric functions are multivalued. If we wish to use the inverse tangent function with a real number range, then $\tan^{-1} 1$ is equal to $\pi/4$ and no other real number. If we wish to use the inverse tangent function with an angle range, then $\tan^{-1} 1$ is the angle with radian measure $\pi/4$ or degree measure $45°$, and no other angle.

Example 9   Find the degree measure of θ.

(a) $\theta = \sin^{-1} \frac{1}{2}$ (Exact value without a calculator.)
(b) $\theta = \tan^{-1}(-1.3025)$ (To two decimal places with a calculator.)

Solution   (a) $\theta = \sin^{-1} \frac{1}{2}$ is equivalent to

$$\sin \theta = \frac{1}{2} \qquad -90° \le \theta \le 90°$$

Thus, $\theta = 30°$
(b) Set calculator in degree mode.

$$\theta = \tan^{-1}(-1.3025) = -52.48°$$

Matched Problem 9   Find the degree measure of θ.
(a) $\theta = \cos^{-1} \frac{1}{2}$ (Exact value without a calculator.)
(b) $\theta = \tan^{-1} 25.08$ (To two decimal places with a calculator.)

Summary

We summarize the definitions of the inverse trigonometric functions in the box for convenient reference.

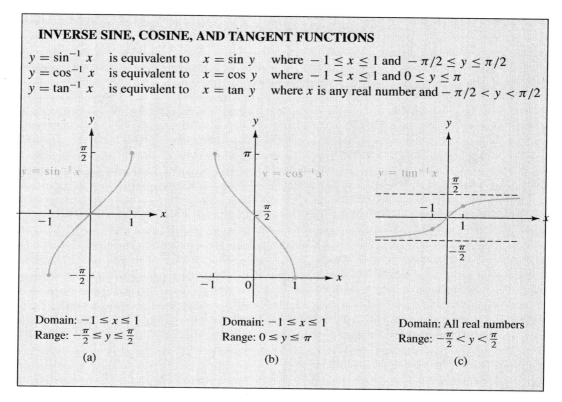

INVERSE SINE, COSINE, AND TANGENT FUNCTIONS

$y = \sin^{-1} x$ is equivalent to $x = \sin y$ where $-1 \le x \le 1$ and $-\pi/2 \le y \le \pi/2$
$y = \cos^{-1} x$ is equivalent to $x = \cos y$ where $-1 \le x \le 1$ and $0 \le y \le \pi$
$y = \tan^{-1} x$ is equivalent to $x = \tan y$ where x is any real number and $-\pi/2 < y < \pi/2$

Domain: $-1 \le x \le 1$
Range: $-\frac{\pi}{2} \le y \le \frac{\pi}{2}$
(a)

Domain: $-1 \le x \le 1$
Range: $0 \le y \le \pi$
(b)

Domain: All real numbers
Range: $-\frac{\pi}{2} < y < \frac{\pi}{2}$
(c)

Answers to Matched Problems

1. (a) $\pi/4$ (b) $-\pi/2$ (c) -0.4 (d) $-\frac{1}{2}$
2. (a) 0.2945 (b) -0.8684 (c) Not defined   (d) 1.065
3. (a) $\pi/4$ (b) π (c) 3.05 (d) $-\frac{1}{2}$
4. (a) 0.8267 (b) 2.517 (c) Not defined   (d) -0.5829
5. $\frac{24}{25}$ 6. (a) $\pi/3$ (b) 35
7. (a) 1.429 (b) -1.494 (c) 1.569 (d) -1.392
8. (a) $\dfrac{\sqrt{1-x^2}}{x}$ 9. (b) $60°$ (b) $87.72°$

Exercises for Section 6.4

Find exact real number values without using a calculator.

1. $\sin^{-1} 0$

2. $\cos^{-1} 0$

3. $\arccos(\sqrt{3}/2)$

4. $\arcsin(\sqrt{3}/2)$

5. $\tan^{-1} 1$

6. $\arctan \sqrt{3}$

7. $\cos^{-1} \frac{1}{2}$

8. $\sin^{-1}(\sqrt{2}/2)$

In Problems 9–14, evaluate to four significant digits using a calculator.

9. $\cos^{-1}(-0.9999)$

10. $\sin^{-1}(-0.0289)$

11. $\tan^{-1} 4.056$

12. $\tan^{-1}(-52.77)$

13. $\arcsin 3.142$

14. $\arccos 1.001$

15. Explain how to find the value of x that produces the result shown in the graphing utility window below, and find it. The utility is in degree mode. Give the answer to six decimal places.

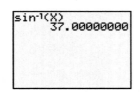

16. Explain how to find the value of x that produces the result shown in the graphing utility window below, and find it. The utility is in radian mode. Give the answer to six decimal places.

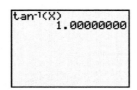

Find exact real number values without using a calculator.

17. $\arccos(-\frac{1}{2})$

18. $\arcsin(\sqrt{2}/2)$

19. $\tan^{-1}(-1)$

20. $\arctan(-\sqrt{3})$

21. $\sin^{-1}(-\sqrt{3}/2)$

22. $\cos^{-1}(-1)$

23. $\cos^{-1}(-\sqrt{3}/2)$

24. $\sin^{-1}(-1)$

25. $\sin[\sin^{-1}(-0.6)]$

26. $\tan(\tan^{-1} 25)$

27. $\cos[\sin^{-1}(-\sqrt{3}/2)]$

28. $\sec[\sin^{-1}(-\sqrt{3}/2)]$

29. $\tan(\sin^{-1}\frac{2}{3})$

30. $\sin(\cos^{-1}\frac{1}{4})$

31. $\cos(\tan^{-1}(-2))$

32. $\sin(\tan^{-1} 10)$

Evaluate to four significant digits using a calculator.

33. $\tan^{-1}(-4.038)$

34. $\arctan(-10.04)$

35. $\sec[\sin^{-1}(-0.0399)]$

36. $\cot[\cos^{-1}(-0.7003)]$

37. $\sqrt{2} + \tan^{-1}\sqrt[3]{5}$

38. $\sqrt{5 + \cos^{-1}(1 - \sqrt{2})}$

Graph Problems 39 and 40 with the aid of a calculator. Plot points using x values $-1.0, -0.8, -0.6, -0.4, -0.2, 0.0,$ 0.2, 0.4, 0.6, 0.8, and 1.0; then join the points with a smooth curve.

39. $y = \sin^{-1} x$

40. $y = \cos^{-1} x$

Find the exact degree measure of θ without a calculator.

41. $\theta = \arccos(-1/2)$

42. $\theta = \arcsin(-\sqrt{2}/2)$

43. $\theta = \tan^{-1}(-1)$

44. $\theta = \arctan(-\sqrt{3})$

45. $\theta = \sin^{-1}(-\sqrt{3}/2)$

46. $\theta = \cos^{-1}(-1)$

47. $\theta = \arcsin(\tan 60°)$

48. $\theta = \arccos(-\tan(-45°))$

49. $\theta = \cos^{-1}(\cos(-60°))$

50. $\theta = \sin^{-1}(\sin 135°)$

In Problems 51–56, find the degree measure of θ to two decimal places using a calculator.

51. $\theta = \tan^{-1} 3.0413$

52. $\theta = \cos^{-1} 0.7149$

53. $\theta = \arcsin(-0.8107)$

54. $\theta = \arccos(-0.7728)$

55. $\theta = \arctan(-17.305)$

56. $\theta = \tan^{-1}(-0.3031)$

57. Evaluate $\cos^{-1}[\cos(-0.3)]$ with a calculator set in radian mode. Explain why this does or does not illustrate a cosine–inverse cosine identity.

58. Evaluate $\sin^{-1}[\sin(-2)]$ with a calculator set in radian mode. Explain why this does or does not illustrate a sine–inverse sine identity.

59. The identity $\sin(\sin^{-1} x) = x$ is valid for $-1 \le x \le 1$.
  (a) Graph $y = \sin(\sin^{-1} x)$ for $-1 \le x \le 1$.
  (b) What happens if you graph $y = \sin(\sin^{-1} x)$ over a wider interval, say $-2 \le x \le 2$? Explain.

60. The identity $\cos(\cos^{-1} x) = x$ is valid for $-1 \le x \le 1$.
  (a) Graph $y = \cos(\cos^{-1} x)$ for $-1 \le x \le 1$.
  (b) What happens if you graph $y = \cos(\cos^{-1} x)$ over a wider interval, say $-2 \le x \le 2$? Explain.

In Problems 61–70, find exact real number values without using a calculator.

61. $\sin[\arccos \frac{1}{2} + \arcsin(1)]$

62. $\cos[\cos^{-1}(-\sqrt{3}/2) - \sin^{-1}(-\frac{1}{2})]$

63. $\sin[2 \sin^{-1}(-\frac{4}{5})]$

64. $\cos\left(\dfrac{\cos^{-1}\frac{1}{3}}{2}\right)$

65. $\cos(\arctan 2 + \arcsin \frac{1}{3})$

66. $\sin(\arccos \frac{2}{5} - \arctan 5)$

67. $\tan(\sin^{-1} \frac{1}{4} - \cos^{-1} \frac{1}{4})$

68. $\tan(\cos^{-1} \frac{3}{4} + \tan^{-1} 3)$

69. $\sin\left(\dfrac{\arctan(-2)}{2}\right)$

70. $\tan(2 \arcsin \frac{3}{5})$

In Problems 71–74, write each as an algebraic expression in x free of trigonometric or inverse trigonometric functions.

71. $\sin(\cos^{-1} x)$, $-1 \leq x \leq 1$

72. $\cos(\sin^{-1} x)$, $-1 \leq x \leq 1$

73. $\tan(\arcsin x)$, $-1 \leq x \leq 1$

74. $\cos(\arctan x)$

Verify each identity in Problems 75 and 76.

75. $\tan^{-1}(-x) = -\tan^{-1} x$

76. $\sin^{-1}(-x) = -\sin^{-1} x$

77. Let $f(x) = \cos^{-1}(2x - 3)$.

    (a) Explain how you would find the domain of f and find it.

    (b) Graph f over the interval $0 \leq x \leq 3$ and explain the result.

78. Let $g(x) = \sin^{-1}\left(\dfrac{x+1}{2}\right)$.

    (a) Explain how you would find the domain of g and find it.

    (b) Graph g over the interval $-4 \leq x \leq 2$ and explain the result.

79. Let $h(x) = 3 + 5 \sin(x - 1)$, $-\pi/2 \leq x \leq 1 + \pi/2$.

    (a) Find $h^{-1}(x)$.

    (b) Explain how x must be restricted in $h^{-1}(x)$.

80. Let $f(x) = 4 + 2 \cos(x - 3)$, $-\pi/2 \leq x \leq 3 + \pi/2$.

    (a) Find $f^{-1}(x)$.

    (b) Explain how x must be restricted in $f^{-1}(x)$.

81. The identity $\sin^{-1}(\sin x) = x$ is valid for $-\pi/2 \leq x \leq \pi/2$.

    (a) Graph $y = \sin^{-1}(\sin x)$ for $-\pi/2 \leq x \leq p/2$.

    (b) What happens if you graph $y = \sin^{-1}(\sin x)$ over a larger interval, say $-2\pi \leq x \leq 2\pi$? Explain.

82. The identity $\cos^{-1}(\cos x) = x$ is valid for $0 \leq x \leq \pi$.

    (a) Graph $y = \cos^{-1}(\cos x)$ for $0 \leq x \leq \pi$.

    (b) What happens if you graph $y = \cos^{-1}(\cos x)$ over a larger interval, say $-2\pi \leq x \leq 2\pi$? Explain.

83. Sonic Boom An aircraft flying faster than the speed of sound produces sound waves that pile up behind the aircraft in the form of a cone. The cone of a level flying aircraft intersects the ground in the form of a hyperbola, and along this curve we experience a *sonic boom* (see the figure). It can be shown that

$$\sin \frac{\theta}{2} = \frac{\text{Speed of sound}}{\text{Speed of aircraft}} \qquad (6.1)$$

where θ is the cone angle. The ratio

$$M = \frac{\text{Speed of aircraft}}{\text{Speed of sound}} \qquad (6.2)$$

is the Mach number. A Mach number of 2.3 would indicate an aircraft moving at 2.3 times the speed of sound. From equations (6.1) and (6.2) we obtain

$$\sin \frac{\theta}{2} = \frac{1}{M}$$

    (a) Write θ in terms of M.

    (b) Find θ to the nearest degree for $M = 1.7$ and for $M = 2.3$.

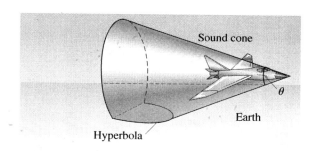

84. Space Science A spacecraft traveling in a circular orbit h miles above the earth observes horizons in each direction (see the figure at the top of the next page), where r is the radius of the earth (3,959 mi).

    (a) Express θ in terms of h and r.

    (b) Find θ, in degrees (to one decimal place), for $h = 425.4$ mi.

    (c) Find the length (to the nearest mile) of the arc subtended by angle θ found in part (b). What percentage (to one decimal place) of the great circle containing the arc does the arc represent? (A **great circle** is any circle on the surface of the earth having the center of the earth as its center.)

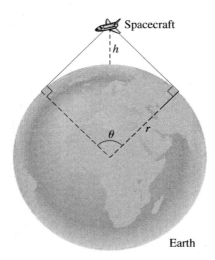

Spacecraft

Earth

*85. **Precalculus: Sports** A particular soccer field is 110 yd by 60 yd, and the goal is 8 yd wide at the end of the field (see the figure). A player is dribbling the ball along a line parallel to and 5 yd inside the side line. Assuming the player has a clear shot all along this line, is there an optimal distance x from the end of the field where the shot should be taken? That is, is there a distance x for which θ is maximum? Parts (a)–(d) will attempt to answer this question.

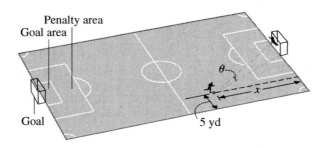

Penalty area
Goal area
Goal
5 yd

(a) Discuss what you think happens to θ as x varies from 0 yd to 55 yd.

(b) Show that

$$\theta = \tan^{-1}\left(\frac{8x}{x^2 + 609}\right)$$

$$\left[\text{Hint:}\quad \tan(\alpha + \beta) = \frac{\tan\alpha + \tan\beta}{1 - \tan\alpha\tan\beta}\text{ is useful.}\right]$$

(c) Complete Table 6.28 (to two decimal places) and select the value of x that gives the maximum value of θ in the table. (If your calculator has a table-generating feature, use it.)

Table 6.28

$x\,(yd)$	10	15	20	25	30	35
$\theta\,(deg)$	6.44					

(d) Graph the equation in part (b) in a graphing utility for $0 \le x \le 55$. Describe what the graph shows. Use a built-in routine to find the maximum θ and the distance x that produces it.

86. **Precalculus: Related Rates** The figure represents a circular courtyard surrounded by a high stone wall. A flood light, located at E, shines into the courtyard. A person walks from the center C along CD to D, at the rate of 6 ft/sec.

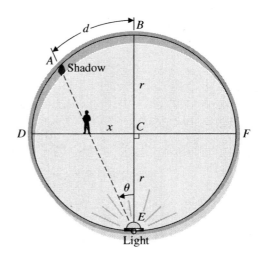

Light

(a) Do you think that the shadow moves along the circular wall at a constant rate, or does it speed up or slow down as the person walks from C to D?

(b) Show that if the person walks x feet from C along CD, then the shadow will move a distance d given by

$$d = 2r\theta = 2r\tan^{-1}\frac{x}{r} \tag{6.3}$$

where θ is in radians. [*Hint:* Draw a line from A to C.] Express x in terms of time t, then for a courtyard of radius $r = 60$ ft, rewrite equation (6.3) in the form

$$d = 120\tan^{-1}\frac{t}{10} \tag{6.4}$$

(c) Using equation (6.4), complete Table 6.29 (to one decimal place). (If you have a calculator with a table-generating feature, use it.)

Table 6.29

s(sec)	0	1	2	3	4	5	6	7	8	9	10
$d(ft)$	0.0	12.0									

(d) From Table 6.29, determine how far the shadow moves during the first second, during the fifth second, and during the tenth second. Is the shadow speeding up, slowing down, or moving uniformly? Explain.

(e) Graph equation (6.2) in a graphing utility for $0 \le t \le 10$. Describe what the graph shows.

*87. Engineering Horizontal cylindrical tanks are buried underground at service stations to store fuel. To determine the amount of fuel in the tank, a "dip stick" is often used to find the depth of the fuel (see the figure).

(a) Show that the volume of fuel x feet deep in a horizontal circular tank L feet long with radius r, $x \le r$, is given by (see the figure)

$$V = \left[r^2 \, \cos^{-1} \frac{r - x}{r} - (r - x) \sqrt{r^2 - (r - x)^2} \right] L$$

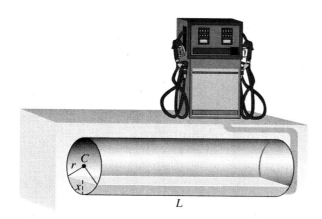

(b) If the fuel in a tank 30 ft long with radius 3 ft is found to be 2 ft deep, how many cubic feet (to the nearest cubic foot) of fuel are in the tank?

(c) The function

$$y_1 = 30 \left[9 \, \cos^{-1} \frac{3 - x}{3} - (3 - x) \sqrt{9 - (3 - x)^2} \right]$$

represents the volume of fuel x feet deep in the tank in part (b). Graph y_1 and $y_2 = 350$ in the same viewing window, and use the built-in intersection routine to find the depth (to one decimal place) when the tank contains 350 ft^3 of fuel.

*88 Engineering In designing mechanical equipment, it is sometimes necessary to determine the length of the belt around two pulleys of different diameters (see the figure).

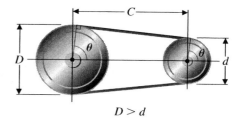

$$D > d$$

(a) Show that the length of the belt around the two pulleys in the figure is given by

$$L = \pi D + (d - D)\theta + 2C \sin \theta$$

where θ (in radians) is given by

$$\theta = \cos^{-1} \frac{D - d}{2C}$$

(b) Find the length of the belt (to one decimal place) if $D = 6$ in., $d = 4$ in., and $C = 10$ in.

(c) The function

$$y_1 = 6\pi - 2 \, \cos^{-1} \frac{1}{x} + 2x \sin \left(\cos^{-1} \frac{1}{x} \right)$$

represents the length of the belt around the two pulleys in part (b) when the centers of the pulleys are x inches apart. Graph y_1 and $y_2 = 40$ in the same viewing window, and use the built-in intersection routine to find the distance between the centers of the pulleys (to one decimal place) when the belt is 40 in. long.

6.5 INVERSE COTANGENT, SECANT, AND COSECANT FUNCTIONS

- Definition of Inverse Cotangent, Secant, and Cosecant Functions
- Calculator Evaluation

Definition of Inverse Cotangent, Secant, and Cosecant Functions

Paralleling the development for the inverse sine, cosine, and tangent functions, we define the inverse cotangent, secant, and cosecant functions as follows.

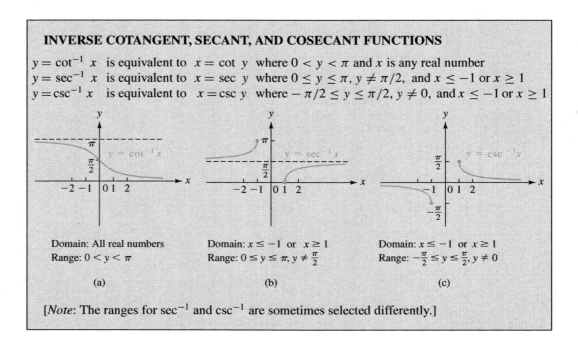

INVERSE COTANGENT, SECANT, AND COSECANT FUNCTIONS

$y = \cot^{-1} x$ is equivalent to $x = \cot y$ where $0 < y < \pi$ and x is any real number
$y = \sec^{-1} x$ is equivalent to $x = \sec y$ where $0 \le y \le \pi$, $y \ne \pi/2$, and $x \le -1$ or $x \ge 1$
$y = \csc^{-1} x$ is equivalent to $x = \csc y$ where $-\pi/2 \le y \le \pi/2$, $y \ne 0$, and $x \le -1$ or $x \ge 1$

Domain: All real numbers
Range: $0 < y < \pi$

(a)

Domain: $x \le -1$ or $x \ge 1$
Range: $0 \le y \le \pi$, $y \ne \dfrac{\pi}{2}$

(b)

Domain: $x \le -1$ or $x \ge 1$
Range: $-\dfrac{\pi}{2} \le y \le \dfrac{\pi}{2}$, $y \ne 0$

(c)

[*Note*: The ranges for $\sec^{-1}$ and $\csc^{-1}$ are sometimes selected differently.]

The functions $y = \cot^{-1} x$, $y = \sec^{-1} x$, and $y = \csc^{-1} x$ are also denoted by $y = \operatorname{arccot} x$, $y = \operatorname{arcsec} x$, and $y = \operatorname{arccsc} x$, respectively.

Explore
Discuss 1

Which of the following are not defined? Why not?

$\cot^{-1}(-0.05)$	$\sec^{-1}(-0.3)$	$\csc^{-1} 0.9$
$\cot^{-1}(-1{,}000{,}000)$	$\sec^{-1}(3.25 \times 10^8)$	$\csc^{-1}(3.25 \times 10^{-8})$

Example 1

Find exact values without using a calculator:

(a) $\operatorname{arccot}(-1)$ (b) $\sec^{-1}(2/\sqrt{3})$

Solution

(a) $y = \operatorname{arccot}(-1)$ is equivalent to $\cot y = -1$, $0 < y < \pi$. What number between 0 and π has cotangent -1? This y must be positive and in the second quadrant (see Figure 6.47):

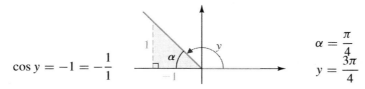

$$\cos y = -1 = -\frac{1}{1}$$

$$\alpha = \frac{\pi}{4}$$

$$y = \frac{3\pi}{4}$$

Figure 6.47

Thus,

$$\operatorname{arccot}(-1) = \frac{3\pi}{4}$$

(b) $y = \sec^{-1}(2/\sqrt{3})$ is equivalent to $\sec y = 2/\sqrt{3}, 0 \le y \le \pi, y \ne \pi/2$. What number between 0 and π has secant $2/\sqrt{3}$? This y is positive and in the first quadrant. We draw a reference triangle, as shown in Figure 6.48.

$$\sec y = \frac{2}{\sqrt{3}} \qquad \text{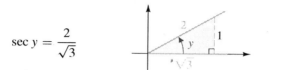} \qquad y = \frac{\pi}{6}$$

Figure 6.48

Thus,

$$\sec^{-1} \frac{2}{\sqrt{3}} = \frac{\pi}{6}$$

Matched Problem 1   Find exact values without using a calculator:

(a) $\operatorname{arccot}(-\sqrt{3})$ (b) $\csc^{-1}(-2)$

Example 2   Find the exact value of $\tan[\sec^{-1}(-3)]$ without using a calculator.

Solution   Let $y = \sec^{-1}(-3)$; then

$$\sec y = -3 \qquad 0 \le y \le \pi, y \ne \pi/2$$

This y is positive and in the second quadrant. Draw a reference triangle, find the third side, and then determine $\tan y$ from the triangle (see Fig. 6.49):

$$\sec y = -3 = -\frac{3}{1} \qquad \text{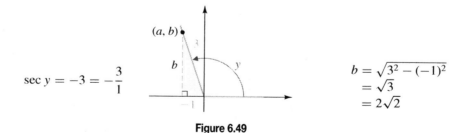} \qquad \begin{aligned} b &= \sqrt{3^2 - (-1)^2} \\ &= \sqrt{3} \\ &= 2\sqrt{2} \end{aligned}$$

Figure 6.49

Thus,

$$\tan[\sec^{-1}(-3)] = \tan y = \frac{b}{a} = \frac{2\sqrt{2}}{-1} = -2\sqrt{2}$$

Matched Problem 2

Find the exact values of $\cot[\csc^{-1}(-\frac{5}{3})]$ without using a calculator.

Calculator Evaluation

Many calculators have keys for sin, cos, tan, $\sin^{-1}$, $\cos^{-1}$, $\tan^{-1}$, or their equivalents. To find sec x, csc x, and cot x using a calculator, we use the reciprocal identities

$$\sec x = \frac{1}{\cos x} \qquad \csc x = \frac{1}{\sin x} \qquad \cot x = \frac{1}{\tan x}$$

How can we evaluate $\sec^{-1}x$, $\csc^{-1}x$, and $\cot^{-1}x$ using a calculator with only $\sin^{-1}$, $\cos^{-1}$, and $\tan^{-1}$ keys? The inverse identities given in the box on the next page are made to order for this purpose.

We will establish the first part of the inverse cotangent identity stated in the box. The inverse secant and cosecant identities are left to you to do (see Problems 67 and 68, in the exercises).

INVERSE COTANGENT, SECANT, AND COSECANT IDENTITIES

$$\cot^{-1} x = \begin{cases} \tan^{-1} \frac{1}{x} & x > 0 \\ \pi + \tan^{-1} \frac{1}{x} & x < 0 \end{cases}$$

$$\sec^{-1} x = \cos^{-1} \frac{1}{x} \qquad x \geq 1 \quad \text{or} \quad x \leq -1$$

$$\csc^{-1} x = \sin^{-1} \frac{1}{x} \qquad x \geq 1 \quad \text{or} \quad x \leq -1$$

Let

$$y = \cot^{-1} x \qquad x > 0$$

Then

$$\cot y = x \qquad 0 < y < \pi/2 \qquad \text{Definition of } \cot^{-1}$$

$$\frac{1}{\tan y} = x \qquad 0 < y < \pi/2 \qquad \text{Reciprocal identity}$$

$$\tan y = \frac{1}{x} \qquad 0 < y < \pi/2 \qquad \text{Algebra}$$

$$y = \tan^{-1} \frac{1}{x} \qquad 0 < y < \pi/2 \qquad \text{Definition of } \tan^{-1}$$

Thus,

$$\cot^{-1} x = \tan^{-1} \frac{1}{x} \qquad \text{for } x > 0$$

Example 3

Use a calculator to evaluate the following as real numbers to three decimal places.

(a) $\cot^{-1} 4.05$ (b) $\csc^{-1}(-12)$

Solution   (a) With the calculator in radian mode,

$$\cot^{-1} 4.05 = \tan^{-1} \frac{1}{4.05} = 0.242$$

(b) With the calculator in radian mode,

$$\csc^{-1}(-12) = \sin^{-1}(-\frac{1}{12}) = -0.083$$

Matched Problem 3   Use a calculator to evaluate the following as real numbers to three decimal places.

(a) $\cot^{-1} 2.314$ (b) $\sec^{-1}(-1.549)$

Answers to Matched Problems

1. (a) $5\pi/6$ (b) $-\pi/6$ 2. $-\frac{4}{3}$
3. (a) 0.408   (b) 2.273

Exercises for Section 6.5

Find the exact real number value of each without using a calculator.

1. $\cot^{-1} \sqrt{3}$ **2.** $\cot^{-1} 0$

3. $\text{arccsc } 1$ **4.** $\text{arcsec } 2$

5. $\sec^{-1} \sqrt{2}$ **6.** $\csc^{-1} 2$

7. $\sin(\cot^{-1} 0)$ **8.** $\cos(\cot^{-1} 1)$

9. $\tan(\csc^{-1} \frac{5}{4})$ **10.** $\cot(\sec^{-1} \frac{5}{3})$

11. $\cot^{-1}(-1)$ **12.** $\sec^{-1}(-1)$

13. $\text{arcsec}(-2)$ **14.** $\text{arccsc}(-\sqrt{2})$

15. $\text{arccsc}(-2)$ **16.** $\text{arccot}(-\sqrt{3})$

17. $\csc^{-1} \frac{1}{2}$ **18.** $\sec^{-1}(-\frac{1}{2})$

19. $\cos[\csc^{-1}(-\frac{5}{3})]$ **20.** $\tan[\cot^{-1}(-1/\sqrt{3})]$

21. $\cot[\sec^{-1}(-\frac{5}{4})]$ **22.** $\sin[\cot^{-1}(-\frac{3}{4})]$

23. $\cos[\sec^{-1}(-2)]$ **24.** $\sin[\csc^{-1}(-2)]$

25. $\cot(\cot^{-1} 33.4]$ **26.** $\sec[\sec^{-1}(-44)]$

27. $\csc[\csc^{-1}(-4)]$ **28.** $\cot[\cot^{-1}(-7.3)]$

Use a calculator to evaluate the following as real numbers to three decimal places.

29. $\sec^{-1} 5.821$ **30.** $\cot^{-1} 2.094$

31. $\cot^{-1} 0.035$ **32.** $\csc^{-1}(-1.003)$

33. $\csc^{-1} 0.847$ **34.** $\sec^{-1}(-0.999)$

35. $\text{arccot}(-3.667)$ **36.** $\text{arccsc } 8.106$

37. $\text{arcsec}(-15.025)$ **38.** $\text{arccot}(-0.157)$

Find the exact degree measure of θ without using a calculator.

39. $\theta = \text{arcsec}(-2)$ **40.** $\theta = \text{arccsc}(-\sqrt{2})$

41. $\theta = \cot^{-1}(-1)$ **42.** $\theta = \text{arccot}(-1/\sqrt{3})$

43. $\theta = \csc^{-1}(-2\sqrt{3})$ **44.** $\theta = \sec^{-1}(-1)$

45. $\theta = \text{arcsec}(\sin 60°)$ **46.** $\theta = \text{arccsc}(\cos 45°)$

47. $\theta = \text{arccsc}(\sec 135°)$ **48.** $\theta = \text{arccot}[\cot(-30°)]$

49. $\theta = \cot^{-1}[\cot(-15°)]$ **50.** $\theta = \sec^{-1}(\sec 100°)$

Find the degree measure to two decimal places using a calculator.

51. $\theta = \cot^{-1} 0.3288$ **52.** $\theta = \sec^{-1} 1.3989$

53. $\theta = \text{arccsc}(-1.2336)$ **54.** $\theta = \text{arcsec}(-1.2939)$

55. $\theta = \text{arccot}(-0.0578)$ **56.** $\theta = \cot^{-1}(-3.2994)$

Find exact values for each problem without using a calculator.

57. $\tan[\csc^{-1}(-\frac{5}{3}) + \tan^{-1} \frac{1}{4}]$

58. $\tan[\tan^{-1} 4 - \sec^{-1}(-\sqrt{5})]$

59. $\tan[2 \cot^{-1}(-\frac{3}{4})]$

60. $\tan[2 \sec^{-1}(-\sqrt{5})]$

In Problems 61–66, write as an algebraic expression in x free of trigonometric or inverse trigonometric functions.

61. $\sin(\cot^{-1}x)$ **62.** $\cos(\cot^{-1}x)$

63. $\csc(\sec^{-1}x)$ **64.** $\tan(\csc^{-1}x)$

65. $\sin(2\cot^{-1}x)$ **66.** $\sin(2\sec^{-1}x)$

67. Show that $\sec^{-1}x = \cos^{-1}(1/x)$ for $x \geq 1$ and $x \leq -1$.

68. Show that $\csc^{-1}x = \sin^{-1}(1/x)$ for $x \geq 1$ and $x \leq -1$.

Problems 69–72 require the use of a graphing utility. Use an appropriate inverse trigonometric identity to graph each function in the viewing window $-5 \leq x \leq 5$, $-\pi \leq y \leq \pi$.

69. $y = \sec^{-1} x$ **70.** $y = \csc^{-1} x$

71. $y = \cot^{-1} x$ [Use two viewing windows, one for $-5 \leq x \leq 0$, and the other for $0 \leq x \leq 5$.]

72. $y = \cot^{-1} x$ [Using one viewing window, $-5 \leq x \leq 5$, graph $y_1 = \pi(x < 0) + \tan^{-1}(1/x)$, where $<$ is selected from the TEST menu. The expression $(x < 0)$ assumes a value of 1 for $x < 0$ and 0 for $x \geq 0$.]

6.6 TRIGONOMETRIC EQUATIONS: AN ALGEBRAIC APPROACH

- Introduction
- Solving Trigonometric Equations Using an Algebraic Approach

Introduction

In Chapter 4 we considered trigonometric equations called identities. These equations are true for all replacements of the variable(s) for which both sides are defined. We now consider another class of equations, called **conditional equations,** which may be true for some replacements of the variable(s) but false for others. For example,

$$\sin x = \cos x$$

is a conditional equation, since it is true for $x = \pi/4$ and false for $x = 0$. (Check both values.)

Explore/ Discuss 1

Consider the simple trigonometric equation

$$\sin x = 0.5$$

Figure 6.50 shows a partial graph of the left and right sides of the equation.

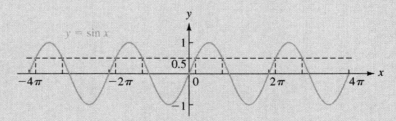

Figure 6.50 $\sin x = 0.5$

(a) How many solutions does the equation have on the interval $(0, 2\pi)$? What are the solutions?
(b) How many solutions does the equation have on the interval $(-\infty, \infty)$? Discuss a method of writing all solutions to the equation.

In this section we will solve conditional trigonometric equations using an algebraic approach. In the next section we will use a graphing utility approach. Solving trigonometric equations using an algebraic approach often requires the use of algebraic manipulation, identities, and some ingenuity. In some cases, an algebraic approach leads to exact solutions. A graphing utility approach uses graphical methods to approximate solutions to any accuracy desired, which is different from finding exact solutions. The graphing utility approach can be used to solve trigonometric equations that are either very difficult or impossible to solve algebraically.

Solving Trigonometric Equations Using an Algebraic Approach

The following suggestions for solving trigonometric equations using an algebraic approach may be helpful:

SUGGESTIONS FOR SOLVING TRIGONOMETRIC EQUATIONS ALGEBRAICALLY

1. Solve for a particular trigonometric function first.
   (a) Try using identities.
   (b) Try algebraic manipulations such as factoring, combining fractions, and so on.
2. After solving for a trigonometric function, solve for the variable.

Several examples should make the algebraic approach clear.

Example 1   Find all solutions exactly for $2 \sin^2 x + \sin x = 0$.

Solution   **Step 1** *Solve for sin x:*

$$2 \sin^2 x + \sin x = 0 \qquad \text{Factor out } \sin x.$$
$$\sin x (2 \sin x + 1) = 0$$
$$\sin x = 0 \qquad \text{or} \quad 2 \sin x + 1 = 0 \qquad ab = 0 \text{ only if } a = 0 \text{ or } b = 0.$$
$$\sin x = -\tfrac{1}{2}$$

Step 2 *Solve each equation over one period* $[0, 2\pi)$:   As an aid to writing all solutions over one period, sketch a graph of $y = \sin x$, $y = 0$, and $y = \frac{1}{2}$ in the same coordinate system, as shown in Figure 6.51.

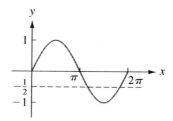

Figure 6.51

$$\sin x = 0 \qquad\qquad \sin x = \tfrac{1}{2}$$
$$x = 0, \pi \qquad\qquad x = \frac{7\pi}{6}, \frac{11\pi}{6}$$

Step 3 *Write an expression for all solutions:*   Because the sine function is periodic with period 2π, all solutions are given by

$$x = \begin{cases} 0 + 2k\pi \\ \pi + 2k\pi \\ 7\pi/6 + 2k\pi \\ 11\pi/6 + 2k\pi \end{cases} \quad k \text{ any integer}$$

Matched Problem 1   Find all solutions exactly for $2\cos^2 x - \cos x = 0$.

Example 2   Approximate all real solutions for $8\sin^2 x = 5 + 10\cos x$. (Compute inverse functions to four decimal places.)

Solution   ***Step 1*** *Solve for sin x and/or cos x:*   Move all nonzero terms to the left of the equal sign and express the left side in terms of $\cos x$:

$$8\sin^2 x = 5 + 10\cos x$$

$$8\sin^2 x - 10\cos x - 5 = 0$$
$$8(1 - \cos^2 x) - 10\cos x - 5 = 0 \quad \sin^2 x = 1 - \cos^2 x$$
$$8\cos^2 x + 10\cos x - 3 = 0 \quad \text{Algebra}$$
$$(2\cos x + 3)(4\cos x - 1) = 0 \quad 8u^2 + 10u - 3 = (2u + 3)(4u - 1)$$
$$2\cos x + 3 = 0 \quad \text{or} \quad 4\cos x - 1 = 0$$
$$\cos x = -\frac{3}{2} \qquad\qquad \cos = \frac{1}{4}$$

Step 2 *Solve each equation over one period* $[0, 2\pi)$:   As an aid to writing all solutions over one period, sketch a graph of $y = \cos x$, $y = -\frac{3}{2}$, and $y = \frac{1}{4}$ in the same coordinate system, as shown in Figure 6.52.

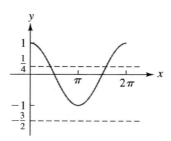

Figure 6.52

Solve the first equation:

$$\cos x = -\frac{3}{2} \qquad \text{No solution } (-\frac{3}{2} \text{ is not in the range of the cosine function}).$$

Solve the second equation:

$$\cos x = \tfrac{1}{4}$$ From Figure 6.52, we see that the solutions are in the first and fourth quadrants.

$$x = \cos^{-1}\tfrac{1}{4} = 1.3181$$ First quadrant solution
$$x = 2\pi - 1.3181 = 4.9651$$ Fourth quadrant solution

$$\cos 1.3181 = 0.2500 \quad \cos 4.9651 = 0.2500$$

(Checks may not be exact because of roundoff errors.)

Step 3 *Write an expression for all solutions:*   Because the cosine function is periodic with period 2π, all solutions are given by

$$x = \begin{cases} 1.3181 + 2k\pi \\ 4.9651 + 2k\pi \end{cases} k \text{ any integer}$$

Matched Problem 2   Approximate all real solutions for $3\cos^2 x + 8\sin x = 7$. (Compute inverse functions to four decimal places.)

Example 3   Find θ in degree measure (to three decimal places) so that

$$8\tan(6\theta + 15) = -64.328 \qquad -90° < 6\theta + 15 < 90°$$

Solution   **Step 1** *Make a substitution:*   Let $u = 6\theta + 15$ to obtain

$$8\tan u = 64.328$$

Step 2 *Solve for tan u:*

$$\tan u = 8.041$$

Step 3 *Solve for u over $-90° < u < 90°$:*   As an aid to writing all solutions for $-90° < u < 90°$, sketch a graph of $y = \tan u$ and $y = -8.041$ in the same coordinate system, as shown in Figure 6.53.

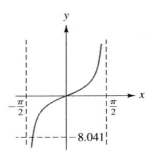

Figure 6.53

The solution is in the fourth quadrant.

$$u = \tan^{-1}(-8.041) = -82.911°$$
$$\tan(-82.911°) = -8.041$$

Step 4 *Solve for* θ:

$$u = -82.911°$$
$$6\theta + 15 = -182.911°$$
$$\theta = -16.319°$$

(A check of θ by substituting in the original problem is left to the reader.)

Matched Problem 3

Find θ in degree measure (to three decimal places) so that

$$5 \sin(2\theta - 5) = -3.045 \qquad 0° \leq 2\theta - 5 \leq 360°$$

Example 4

Find exact solutions for $\sin 2x = \sin x, 0 \leq x < 2\pi$.

Solution

The following solution includes only a few key steps. Sketch graphs as appropriate on scratch paper.

$$\sin 2x = \sin x \qquad \text{Use double-angle identity.}$$
$$2 \sin x \cos x = \sin x$$
$$2 \sin x \cos x - \sin x = 0$$
$$\sin x(2 \cos x - 1) = 0$$

$$\sin x = 0 \qquad \text{or} \qquad 2 \cos x - 1 = 0$$
$$x = 0, \pi \qquad\qquad \cos x = \tfrac{1}{2}$$

$$x = \frac{\pi}{3}, \frac{5\pi}{3}$$

Combining the solutions from each equation, we have $x = 0, \pi/3, \pi, 5\pi/3$.

Matched Problem 4

Find exact solutions for $\sin^2 x = \tfrac{1}{2} \sin 2x, 0 \leq x < 2\pi$.

Example 5

Approximate all real solutions for $\cos 2x = 2(\sin x - 1)$. (Compute inverse functions to four decimal places.)

Solution

Step 1 *Solve for* $\sin x$:

$$\cos 2x = 2(\sin x - 1) \qquad\qquad \text{Use double-angle identity.}$$
$$1 - 2 \sin^2 x = 2 \sin x - 2$$
$$2 \sin^2 x + 2 \sin x - 3 = 0 \qquad\qquad \text{Quadratic in } \sin x, \text{ Left side does}$$
$$\sin x = \frac{-2 \pm \sqrt{4 - 4(2)(-3)}}{4} \qquad \text{not factor using integer coefficients,}$$
$$= -1.822876 \quad \text{or} \quad 0.822876 \qquad \text{so use the quadratic formula.}$$

Step 2 *Solve each equation over one period* $[0, 2\pi)$:   As an aid to writing all solutions on the interval $[0, 2\pi)$, sketch a graph of $y = \sin x$, $y = -1.822876$, and $y = 0.822876$ in the same coordinate system, as shown in Figure 6.54.

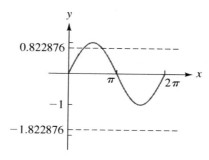

Figure 6.54

Solve the first equation:

$$\sin x = -1.822876 \qquad \text{No solution for this range value.}$$

Solve the second equation:

$$\sin x = 0.822876$$

Figure 6.54 indicates solutions in the first and second quadrants. If the reference angle is α, then $x = \alpha$ or $x = \pi - \alpha$.

$$\alpha = \sin^{-1} 0.822876 = 0.9665$$
$$\pi - \alpha = \pi - 0.9665 = 2.1751$$

Check: $\sin 0.9665 = 0.8229 \qquad \sin 2.1751 = 0.8229$

Step 3 *Write an expression for all solutions:*   Because the sine function is periodic with period 2π, all solutions are given by

$$x = \begin{cases} 0.9665 + 2k\pi \\ 2.1751 + 2k\pi k \end{cases} \qquad k \text{ any integer}$$

Matched Problem 5   Approximate all real solutions for $\cos 2x = 4 \cos x - 2$. (Compute inverse functions to four decimal places.)

Answers to Matched Problems

1. $x = \begin{cases} \pi/3 + 2k\pi \\ \pi/2 + 2k\pi \\ 3\pi/2 + 2k\pi \\ 5\pi/3 + 2k\pi \end{cases} \qquad k \text{ any integer}$

2. $x = \begin{cases} 0.7297 + 2k\pi \\ 2.4119 + 2k\pi \end{cases} \qquad k \text{ any integer}$

3. $\theta = 111.259°, 163.742°$ **4.** $x = 0, \pi/4, \pi, 5\pi/4$

5. $x = \begin{cases} 1.2735 + 2k\pi \\ 5.0096 + 2k\pi \end{cases} \qquad k \text{ any integer}$

Exercises for Section 6.6

In Problems 1–8, find exact solutions over the indicated intervals (x real and θ in degrees).

1. $2\cos x + 1 = 0$, $0 \le x < 2\pi$

2. $2\sin x + 1 = 0$, $0 \le x < 2\pi$

3. $2\cos x + 1 = 0$,   all real x

4. $2\sin x + 1 = 0$,   all real x

5. $\sqrt{2}\sin\theta - 1 = 0$, $0° \le \theta < 360°$

6. $2\cos\theta - \sqrt{3} = 0$, $0° \le \theta < 360°$

7. $\sqrt{2}\sin\theta - 1 = 0$,   all θ

8. $2\cos\theta - \sqrt{3} = 0$,   all θ

In Problems 9–14, solve each to four decimal places (x real and θ in degrees).

9. $4\tan\theta + 15 = 0$, $0° \le \theta < 180°$

10. $2\tan\theta - 7 = 0$, $0° \le \theta < 180°$

11. $5\cos x - 2 = 0$, $0 \le x < 2\pi$

12. $7\cos x - 3 = 0$, $0 \le x < 2\pi$

13. $5.0118\sin x - 3.1105 = 0$,   all real x

14. $1.3224\sin x + 0.4732 = 0$,   all real x

For Problems 15–26, find exact solutions (x real and θ in degrees).

15. $\cos x = \cot x$, $0 \le x < 2\pi$

16. $\tan x = -2\sin x$, $0 \le x < 2\pi$

17. $\cos^2\theta = \frac{1}{2}\sin 2\theta$,   all θ

18. $2\sin^2\theta + \sin 2\theta = 0$,   all θ

19. $\tan(x/2) - 1 = 0$, $0 \le x < 2\pi$

20. $\sec(x/2) + 2 = 0$, $0 \le x < 2\pi$

21. $2\sin^2\theta + 2\cos\theta = -2$, $0° \le \theta < 360°$

22. $2\cos^2\theta + 3\sin\theta = 0$, $0° \le \theta < 360°$

23. $\cos 2\theta + \sin^2\theta = 0$, $0° \le \theta < 360°$

24. $\cos 2\theta + \cos\theta = 0$, $0° \le \theta < 360°$

25. $4\cos^2 2x - 4\cos 2x + 1 = 0$, $0 \le x \le 2\pi$

26. $2\sin^2(x/2) - 3\sin(x/2) + 1 = 0$, $0 \le x \le 2\pi$

Solve Problems 27–30 (x real and θ in degrees). Compute inverse functions to four significant digits.

27. $4\cos^2\theta = 7\cos\theta + 2$, $0° \le \theta \le 180°$

28. $6\sin^2\theta + 5\sin\theta = 6$, $0° \le \theta \le 90°$

29. $\cos 2x + 10\cos x = 5$, $0 \le x < 2\pi$

30. $2\sin x = \cos 2x$, $0 \le x < 2\pi$

Solve Problems 31–36 for all real solutions. Compute inverse functions to four significant digits.

31. $\cos^2 x = 3 - 5\cos x$

32. $2\sin^2 x = 1 - 2\sin x$

33. $\sin^2 x = -2 + 3\cos x$

34. $\cos^2 x = 3 + 4\sin x$

35. $\cos(2x) = 2\cos x$

36. $\cos(2x) = 2\sin x$

37. Explain the difference between evaluating the expression $\cos^{-1}(-0.7334)$ and solving the equation $\cos x = -0.7334$.

38. Explain the difference between evaluating the expression $\tan^{-1}(-5.377)$ and solving the equation $\tan x = -5.377$.

Find exact solutions to Problems 39–42. [Hint: Square both sides at an appropriate point, solve, then eliminate any extraneous solutions at the end.]

39. $\sin x + \cos x = 1$, $0 \le x < 2\pi$

40. $\cos x - \sin x = 1$, $0 \le x < 2\pi$

41. $\sec x + \tan x = 1$, $0 \le x < 2\pi$

42. $\tan x - \sec x = 1$, $0 \le x < 2\pi$

43. Electric Current   An alternating current generator produces a current given by the equation

$$I = 30\sin 120\pi t$$

where t is time in seconds and I is current in amperes. Find the least positive t (to four significant digits) such that $I = 25$ amperes.

44. Electric Current   Find the least positive t in Problem 43 (to four significant digits) such that $I = 10$ amperes.

45. Photography   A polarizing filter for a camera contains two parallel plates of polarizing glass, one fixed and the other able to rotate. If θ is the angle of rotation from the position of maximum light transmission, then the intensity of light leaving the filter is $\cos^2\theta$ times the intensity entering the filter (see the figure). Find the least positive θ (in decimal degrees, to two decimal places) so that the intensity of light leaving the filter is 70% of that entering. [*Hint:* Solve $I \cos^2 \theta = 0.70I$.]

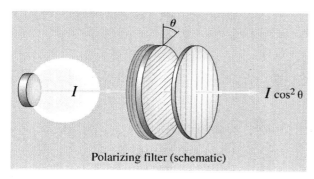

Polarizing filter (schematic)

46. Photography Find θ in Problem 45 so that the light leaving the filter is 40% of that entering.

∗47. Astronomy The planet Mercury travels around the sun in an elliptical orbit given approximately by

$$r = \frac{3.44 \times 10^7}{1 - 0.206 \cos \theta}$$

(see the figure). Find the least positive θ (in decimal degrees, to three significant digits) such that Mercury is 3.78×10^7 mi from the sun.

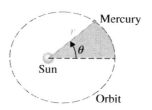

∗48. Astronomy Find the least ositive θ (in decimal degress, to three significant digits) in Problem 47 such that Mercury is 3.09×10^7 mi from the sun.

Precalculus *In Problems 49 and 50, find simultaneous solutions for each system of equations for* $0° \le \theta \le 360°$. *These are* **polar equations,** *which will be discussed in Chapter 7.*

∗ 49. $r = 2 \sin \theta$
$\quad r = 2(1 - \sin \theta)$

∗50. $r = 2 \sin \theta$
$\quad r = \sin 2\theta$

∗51. Precalculus Given the equation $xy = -2$, replace x and y with

$$x = u \cos \theta - v \sin \theta$$
$$y = u \sin \theta + v \cos \theta$$

and simplify the left side of the resulting equation. Find the least positive θ (in degree measure) so that the coefficient of the uv term will be 0.

∗52. Precalculus Repeat Problem 51 for the equation $2xy = 1$.

CHAPTER SUMMARY

- **Composition of Functions**

  Notation: $h(t) = f(g(t))$.

  Domain and range; Decomposition.

- **Inverse Functions**

  Definition: $f^{-1}(Q) = t$ if and only if $Q = f(t)$

  Invertibility; horizontal line test.

  Domain and range of an inverse function.

  Restricting domain of a function to construct and inverse.

- **Combinations of Functions**

  Sums, differences, products, quotients.

- **Inverse Sine, Cosine, and Tangent Functions**

$y = \sin^{-1} x$	is equivalent to	$x = \sin y$
		where $-1 \le x \le 1$ and $-\pi/2 \le y \le \pi/2$
$y = \cos^{-1} x$	is equivalent to	$x = \cos y$
		where $-1 \le x \le 1$ and $0 \le y \le \pi$
$y = \tan^{-1} x$	is equivalent to	$x = \tan y$
		where x is any number and $-\pi/2 < y < \pi/2$

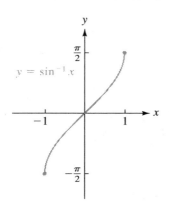

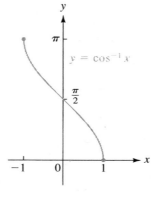

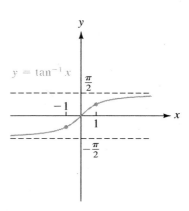

Domain: $-1 \leq x \leq 1$
Range: $-\frac{\pi}{2} \leq y \leq \frac{\pi}{2}$

(a)

Domain: $-1 \leq x \leq 1$
Range: $0 \leq y \leq \pi$

(b)

Domain: All real numbers
Range: $-\frac{\pi}{2} < y < \frac{\pi}{2}$

(c)

The inverse sine, cosine, and tangent functions are also denoted by arcsin x, "arccos x, and arctan x, respectively.

- **Inverse Sine, Cosine, and Tangent Identities**

$$\sin(\sin^{-1} x) = x \qquad -1 \leq x \leq 1$$
$$\sin^{-1}(\sin x) = x \qquad -\pi/2 \leq x \leq \pi/2$$
$$\cos(\cos^{-1} x) = x \qquad -1 \leq x \leq 1$$
$$\cos^{-1}(\cos x) = x \qquad 0 \leq x \leq \pi$$
$$\tan(\tan^{-1} x) = x \qquad \text{for all } x$$
$$\tan^{-1}(\tan x) = x \qquad -\pi/2 < x < \pi/2$$

- **Inverse Cotangent, Secant, and Cosecant Functions**

$y = \cot^{-1} x \qquad$ is equivalent to $\qquad x = \cot y$
  where $0 < y < \pi$ and x is any real number

$y = \sec^{-1} x \qquad$ is equivalent to $\qquad x = \sec y$
  where $0 \leq y \leq \pi$, $y \neq \pi/2$, and $x \leq -1$ or $x \geq 1$

$y = \csc^{-1} x \qquad$ is equivalent to $\qquad x = \csc y$
  where $-\pi/2 \leq y \leq \pi/2$, $y \neq 0$, and $x \leq -1$ or $x \geq 1$

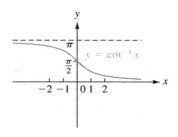

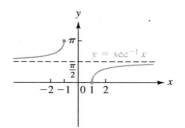

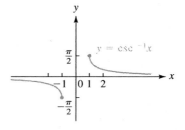

Domain: All real numbers
Range: $0 < y < \pi$

Domain: $x \leq -1$ or $x \geq 1$
Range: $0 \leq y \leq \pi$, $y \neq \frac{\pi}{2}$

Domain: $x \leq -1$ or $x \geq 1$
Range: $-\frac{\pi}{2} \leq y \leq \frac{\pi}{2}$, $y \neq 0$

[*Note:* The ranges for $\sec^{-1}$ and $\csc^{-1}$ are sometimes selected differently.]

- **Inverse Cotangent, Secant, and Cosecant Identities**

$$\cot^{-1} x = \begin{cases} \tan^{-1} \dfrac{1}{x} & x > 0 \\[2mm] \pi + \tan^{-1} \dfrac{1}{x} & x < 0 \end{cases}$$

$$\sec^{-1} x = \cos^{-1} \dfrac{1}{x} \qquad x \geq 1 \text{ or } x \leq -1$$

$$\csc^{-1} x = \sin^{-1} \dfrac{1}{x} \qquad x \geq 1 \text{ or } x \leq -1$$

- **Trigonometric Equations: An Algebraic Approach**

An equation that may be true for some replacements of the variable, but is false for others for which both sides are defined, is called a **conditional equation.** An algebraic approach to solving trigonometric equations can yield exact solutions, and the approach may be aided by the following:

Suggestions for Solving Trigonometric Equations Algebraically

1. Solve for a particular trigonometric function first.
   (a) Try using identities.
   (b) Try algebraic manipulations such as factoring, combining fractions, and so on.
2. After solving for a trigonometric function, solve for the variable.

REVIEW EXERCISES AND PROBLEMS FOR CHAPTER SIX

PART 1 Compositions, Inverses, and Combinations

In Exercises 1–6, let $f(x) = 3x^2$, $g(x) = 9x - 2$, $m(x) = 4x$, and $r(x) = \sqrt{3x}$. Simplify each composite function.

1. $g(f(x))$

2. $f(r(x))$

3. $r(f(x))$

4. $r(g(x))$

5. $f(m(g(x)))$

6. $g(m(f(x)))$

7. Find formulas for the following functions, given that

$$f(x) = x^2 + x, \qquad g(x) = 2x - 3. \qquad h(x) = \frac{x}{1-x}.$$

(a) $f(2x)$ (b) $g(x^2)$ (c) $h(1-x)$
(d) $(f(x))^2$ (e) $g^{-1}(x)$ (f) $(h(x))^{-1}$
(g) $f(x) \cdot g(x)$ (h) $h(f(x))$

In Exercises 8–15, find a formula for the inverse function. Assume these functions are defined on domains on which they are invertible.

8. $f(x) = 3x - 7$

9. $j(x) = \sqrt{1 + \sqrt{x}}$

10. $h(x) = \dfrac{2x + 1}{3x - 2}$

11. $k(x) = \dfrac{3 - \sqrt{x}}{\sqrt{x} + 2}$

12. $g(x) = \dfrac{\ln x - 5}{2 \ln x + 7}$

13. $h(x) = \log\left(\dfrac{x + 5}{x - 4}\right)$

14. $f(x) = \cos \sqrt{x}$

15. $g(x) = 2^{\sin x}$

Problems

16. Using Tables 6.30 and 6.31, evaluate and interpret:

(a) $g(f(23))$ (b) $f(g(5))$

Table 6.30 *Temperature Celsius, $y = f(x)$, as a function of Fahrenheit*

$x°F$	-4	5	14	23	32	41	50
$y°C$	-20	-15	-10	-5	0	5	10

Table 6.31 *Temperature Fahrenheit, $y = g(x)$, as a function of Celsius*

$x°C$	-20	-15	-10	-5	0	5	10
$y°F$	-4	5	14	23	32	41	50

17. Let $f(x) = \dfrac{1}{x + 1}$. Find and simplify $f\left(\dfrac{1}{x}\right) + \dfrac{1}{f(x)}$.

In Problems 18–21, suppose that $f(x) = g(h(x))$. Find possible formulas for $g(x)$ and $h(x)$ (There may be more than one possible answer. Assume $g(x) \neq x$ and $h(x) \neq x$.)

18. $f(x) = (x + 3)^2$

19. $f(x) = \sqrt{1 + \sqrt{x}}$

20. $f(x) = 9x^2 + 3x$

21. $f(x) = \dfrac{1}{x^2 + 8x + 16}$

In Problems 22–25 let $f(x) = x - 3$ and $g(x) = 2x + 5$. Find a formula for $h(x)$.

22. $f(h(x)) = \sqrt{x}$

23. $g(h(x)) = 6x - 7$

24. $h(g(x)) = \dfrac{2x + 5}{1 + \sqrt{2x + 5}}$

25. $h(g(x)) = \dfrac{2x + 6}{1 + \sqrt{2x + 4}}$

Using Figures 6.55 and 6.56, graph the functions in Problems 26–29.

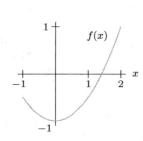

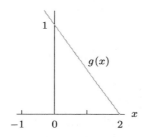

Figure 6.55   **Figure 6.56**

26. $f(x) - g(x)$

27. $f(g(x))$

28. $g(f(x))$

29. $g(f(x - 2))$

Using Figure 6.57, graph the functions in Problems 30–33.

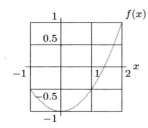

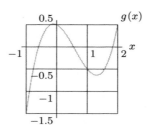

Figure 6.57

30. $f(x) + g(x)$

31. $2g(x)$

32. $g(f(x))$

33. $f(x) - g(x)$

34. The graph of h in Figure 6.58 has a horizontal asymptote at $y = 1.25$. Sketch the following transformations of $h(x)$. For each graph, label the points corresponding to the points P and Q.

(a) $y = -2h(x)$ **(b)** $y = h(-x)$

(c) $y = h(-\frac{1}{2}x)$ **(d)** $y = h^{-1}(x)$

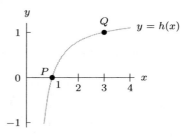

Figure 6.58

35. Using Figure 6.59, match the functions (a)–(g) and graphs (I)–(IV). There may be some functions whose graphs are not shown.

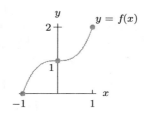

Figure 6.59

(a) $y = -f(x)$ **(b)** $y = f(-x)$

(c) $y = f(-x) - 2$ **(d)** $y = f^{-1}(x)$

(e) $y = -f^{-1}(x)$ **(f)** $y = f(x + 1)$

(g) $y = -(f(x) - 2)$

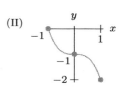

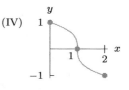

36. Use Figure 6.60.

(a) Evaluate $f(g(a))$.

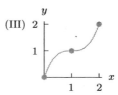

(b) Evaluate $g(f(c))$.
(c) Evaluate $f^{-1}(b) - g^{-1}(b)$.
(d) For what positive value(s) of x is $f(x) \le g(x)$?

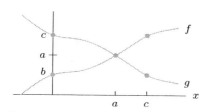

Figure 6.60

37. The rating, r, of an earthquake of intensity I is given by $r = f(I) = \log(I/I_0)$, where I_0 is a constant. Find and interpret $f^{-1}(r)$.

38. A research facility on the Isle of Shoals has 800 gallons of fresh water for a two-month period.

   (a) There are 7 members of the research team and each is allotted 2 gallons of water per day for cooking and drinking. Find a formula for $f(t)$, the amount of fresh water left on the island after t days has elapsed.
   (b) Evaluate and interpret the following expressions
   (i) $f(0)$ (ii) $f^{-1}(0)$
   (iii) t if $f(t) = \dfrac{1}{2}f(0)$ (iv) $800 - f(t)$

39. Let $f(x) = 12 - 4x$, $g(x) = 1/x$, and $h(x) = \sqrt{x - 4}$. Find the domain of the functions:

   (a) $g(f(x))$ **(b)** $h(f(x))$

40. There is a linear relationship between the number of units, $N(x)$, of a product that a company sells and the amount of money, x, spent on advertising. If the company spends $25,000 on advertising, it sells 400 units, and for each additional $5,000 spent, it sells 20 units more.

   (a) Calculate and interpret $N(20,000)$.
   (b) Find a formula for $N(x)$ in terms of x.
   (c) Give interpretations of the slope and the x- and y-intercepts of $N(x)$ if possible.
   (d) Calculate and interpret $N^{-1}(500)$.
   (e) An internal audit reveals that the profit made by the company on the sale of 10 units of its product, before advertising costs have been accounted for, is $2,000. What are the implications regarding the company's advertising campaign? Discuss.

41. The population of a town triples every seven years.

   (a) If the initial population is P_0, find a formula for $P(t)$, the population after t years.
   (b) By approximately what percent does the town's population increase each year?

(c) Find a formula for $P^{-1}(x)$. How is this function useful?
(d) Calculate the doubling time of $P(t)$.

42. A hot brick is removed from a kiln at $200°C$ above room temperature. Over time, the brick cools off. After 2 hours have elapsed, the brick is $20°C$ above room temperature. Let t be the time in hours since the brick was removed from the kiln. Let $y = H(t)$ be the difference between the brick's and the room's temperature at time t. Assume that $H(t)$ is an exponential function.

   (a) Find a formula for $H(t)$.
   (b) How many degrees does the brick's temperature drop during the first quarter hour? During the next quarter hour?
   (c) Find and interpret $H^{-1}(y)$.
   (d) How much time elapses before the brick's temperature is $5°C$ above room temperature?
   (e) Interpret the physical meaning of the horizontal asymptote of $H(t)$.

In Problems 43–49, you hire either Ace Construction or Space Contractors to build office space. Let $f(x)$ be the average total cost in dollars of building x square feet of office space, as estimated by Ace. Let $h(x)$ be the total number of square feet of office space you can build with x dollars, as estimated by Space.

43. Describe in words what the following statement tells you: $f(2000) = 200,000$

44. Let $g(x) = f(x)/x$. Using the information from Problem 43, evaluate $g(2000)$, and describe in words what $g(2000)$ represents. [Hint: Think about the units.]

45. Ace tells you that, due to the economies of scale, "Building twice as much office space always costs less than twice as much." Express this statement symbolically, in terms of f and x. [Hint: If you are building x square feet, how do you represent the cost? How would you represent twice the cost? How do you represent the cost of building twice as many square feet?]

46. Suppose that $q > p$ and $p > 1$. Assuming that the contractor's statement in Problem 45 is correct, rank the following in increasing order, using inequality signs: $f(p)$, $g(p)$, $f(q)$, $g(q)$.

47. What does the statement $h(200,000) = 1500$ tell you?

48. Let $j(x)$ be the average cost in dollars per square foot of office space. Give a formula for $j(x)$. (Your formula will have $h(x)$ in it.)

49. Research reveals that $h(f(x)) < x$ for every value of x you check. Explain the implications of this statement. [Hint: Which company seems more economical?]

In Problems 50–53, let $f(x)$ be an increasing function and let $g(x)$ be a decreasing function. Are the following functions increasing, decreasing, or is it impossible to tell? Explain.

50. $f(f(x))$

51. $g(f(x))$

52. $f(x) + g(x)$

53. $f(x) - g(x)$

54. For a positive integer x, let $f(x)$ be the remainder obtained by dividing x by 3. For example, $f(6) = 0$, because 6 divided by 3 equals 2 with a remainder of 0. Likewise, $f(7) = 1$, because 7 divided by 3 equals 2 with a remainder of 1.

(a) Evaluate $f(8), f(17), f(29), f(99)$.
(b) Find a formula for $f(3x)$.
(c) Is $f(x)$ invertible?
(d) Find a formula in terms of $f(x)$ for $f(f(x))$.
(e) Does $f(x + y)$ necessarily equal $f(x) + f(y)$?

PART 2 Inverse Trigonometric Functions

Evaluate exactly as real numbers.

1. $\tan^{-1}(-1)$

2. $\sin^{-1}(\sqrt{3}/2)$

3. $\arccos 1$

4. $\arctan(-1/\sqrt{3})$

5. $\arcsin \sqrt{2}$

6. $\cos^{-1}(-1/\sqrt{2})$

7. $\csc^{-1}(-2/\sqrt{3})$

8. $\cot^{-1} 0$

9. $\sec^{-1}(-2)$

10. $\csc^{-1}\frac{1}{2}$

Evaluate as a real number to four significant digits.

11. $\sin^{-1} 0.6298$

12. $\arccos(-0.9704)$

13. $\tan^{-1} 23.55$

14. $\cot^{-1}(-1.414)$

Find the degree measure of each to two decimal places.

15. $\theta = \cos^{-1}(-1.025)$

16. $\theta = \arctan 8.333$

17. $\theta = \sin^{-1}(-0.1010)$

In Problems 18–23, find exact solutions over the indicated interval.

18. $2\cos x - \sqrt{3} = 0, \quad 0 \le x < 2\pi$

19. $2\sin^2\theta = \sin\theta, \quad 0° \le \theta < 360°$

20. $4\cos^2 x - 3 = 0, \quad 0 \le x < 2\pi$

21. $2\cos^2\theta + 3\cos\theta + 1 = 0, \quad 0° \le \theta < 360°$

22. $\sqrt{2}\sin 4x - 1 = 0, \quad 0 \le x < \pi/2$

23. $\tan(\theta/2) + \sqrt{3} = 0, \quad -180° < \theta < 180°$

24. Explain how to find the value of x that produces the result shown in the graphing utility display, and find it. The utility is in degree mode. Give the answer to six decimal places.

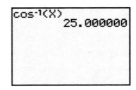

Find exact values for each.

25. $\cos(\cos^{-1} 0.315)$

26. $\tan^{-1}[\tan(-1.5)]$

27. $\sin[\tan^{-1}(-\frac{3}{4})]$

28. $\cot[\arccos(-\frac{2}{3})]$

29. $\csc[\cot^{-1}(-\frac{1}{3})]$

30. $\cos(\text{arccsc } 5)$

In Problems 31–36, evaluate to four significant digits.

31. $\sin^{-1}(\cos 22.37)$

32. $\sin^{-1}(\tan 1.345)$

33. $\sin[\tan^{-1}(-14.00)]$

34. $\csc[\cos^{-1}(-0.4081)]$

35. $\cos(\cot^{-1} 6.823)$

36. $\sec[\text{arccsc}(-25.42)]$

37. Referring to the two displays from a graphing utility below, explain why one of the displays illustrates a sine–inverse sine identity and the other does not.

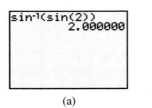 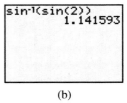

(a)   (b)

Find exact solutions over the indicated interval.

38. $\sin^2\theta = -\cos 2\theta, \quad 0° \le \theta \le 360°$

39. $\sin 2x = \frac{1}{2}, \quad 0 \le x < \pi$

40. $2\cos x + 2 = -\sin^2 x$, $-\pi \le x < \pi$

41. $2\sin^2 \theta - \sin \theta = 0$,   all x

42. $\sin 2x = \sqrt{3}\sin x$,   all real x

43. $2\sin^2 \theta + 5\cos \theta + 1 = 0$, $0° \le \theta < 360°$

44. $3\sin 2x = -2\cos^2 2x$, $0 \le x \le \pi$

Solve for all real x. Compute inverse functions to four significant digits.

45. $\sin x = 0.7088$

46. $\tan x = -4.318$

47. $\sin^2 x + 2 = 4\sin x$

48. $\tan^2 x = 2\tan x + 1$

In Problems 49–56, find all solutions over the indicated interval to three decimal places using a graphing utility.

49. $\sin x = 0.25$, $-\pi \le x \le \pi$

50. $\cot x = -4$, $-\pi \le x \le \pi$

51. $\sec x = 2$, $-\pi \le x \le \pi$

52. $\cos x = x^2$,   all real x

53. $\sin x = \sqrt{x}$, $x \ge 0$

54. $2\sin x \cos 2x = 1$, $0 \le x \le 2\pi$

55. $\sin \dfrac{x}{2} + 3\sin x = 2$, $0 \le x \le 4\pi$

56. $\sin x + 2\sin 2x + 3\sin 3x = 3$, $0 \le x \le 2\pi$

57. Graph $y_1 = \tan(\sin^{-1} x)$ in the window $-2 \le x \le 2$, $-10 \le y \le 10$. What is the domain for y_1? Explain.

58. Given $h(x) = \sin^{-1}\left(\dfrac{x-2}{2}\right)$.

   (a) Explain how you would find the domain of h, and find it.

   (b) Graph h over the interval $-5 \le x \le 5$ and explain the result.

59. Does $\tan^{-1} 23.255$ represent all the solutions to the equation $\tan x = 23.255$? Explain.

In Problems 60 and 61, find exact solutions over the indicated interval.

60. $\cos x = 1 - \sin x$, $0 \le x < 2\pi$

61. $\cos^2 2x = \cos 2x + \sin^2 x$, $0 \le x < \pi$

62. Solve to three significant digits:

$$2 + 2\sin x = 1 + 2\cos^2 x \qquad 0 \le x \le 2\pi$$

Find the exact value

63. $\sin[2\tan^{-1}(-\tfrac{3}{4})]$

64. $\sin(\sin^{-1}\tfrac{3}{5} + \cos^{-1}\tfrac{4}{5})$

Write Problems 65 and 66 as an algebraic expression in x free of trigonometric or inverse trigonometric functions.

65. $\tan(\sin^{-1} x)$

66. $\cos(\tan^{-1} x)$

67. The identity $\tan^{-1}(\tan x) = x$ is valid over the interval $-\pi/2 \le x \le \pi/2$.

   (a) Graph $y = \tan^{-1}(\tan x)$ for $-\pi/2 \le x \le \pi/2$. (Use dot mode.)

   (b) What happens if you graph $y = \tan^{-1}(\tan x)$ over a larger interval, say $-2\pi \le x \le 2\pi$? Explain. (Use dot mode.)

68. **Music**   The note A above middle C has a frequency of 440 Hz. If the intensity I of the sound at a certain point t seconds after the sound is made can be described by the equation

$$I = 0.08\sin 880\pi t$$

find the smallest positive t such that $I = 0.05$. Compute the answer to two significant digits.

69. **Electric Current**   An alternating current generator produces a current given by the equation

$$I = 30\sin 120\pi t$$

where t is time in seconds and I is current in amperes. Find the least positive t (to four significant digits) such that $I = 20$ amperes.

70. **Navigation** A small craft is approaching a large vessel on the course shown in Figure 6.61.

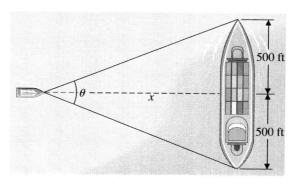

Figure 6.61

   (a) Express the angle θ subtended by the large vessel in terms of the distance x between the two ships.

   (b) Find θ in decimal degrees to one decimal place for $x = 1{,}200$ ft.

*71 Precalculus: Viewing Angle   For advertising purposes, a large brokerage house has a 1.5 ft by 12 ft ticker tape screen mounted 20 ft above the floor on a high wall at an airport terminal (see Figure 6.62). A woman's eyes are 5 ft above the floor. If the best view of the tape is when θ is maximum, how far from the wall should she stand? Parts (a)–(f) explore this problem.

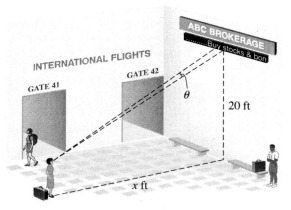

Figure 6.62

(a) Describe what you think happens to θ as x increases from 0 ft to 100 ft.

(b) Show that

$$\theta = \tan^{-1}\frac{1.5x}{x^2 + 247.5} \qquad x \geq 0$$

(c) Complete Table 6.32 (to two decimal places, θ in degrees), and from the table select the maximum θ and the distance x that produces it. (Use a table generator if your calculator has one.)

Table 6.32

x (ft)	0	5	10	15	20	25	30
θ (deg)		1.58					

(d) In a graphing utility, graph the equation in part (b) for $0 \leq x \leq 30$, and describe what the graph shows.

(e) Use a built-in maximum routine in your graphing utility to find the maximum θ and the x that produces it. Find both to two decimal places.

(f) How far away from the wall should the woman stand to have a viewing angle of 2.5°? Solve graphically to two decimal places using a graphing utility.

*72 Engineering   A circular railroad tunnel of radius r is to go through a mountain. The bed for the track is formed by using a chord of the circle of length d as shown in Figure 6.63.

Figure 6.63

(a) Show that the cross-sectional area of the tunnel is given by

$$A = \pi r^2 - r^2 \sin^{-1}\frac{d}{2r} + \frac{d}{4}\sqrt{4r^2 - d^2}$$

(b) Complete Table 6.33 (to the nearest square foot) for $r = 15$ ft and $10 \leq d \leq 20$. (Use a table generator if your calculator has one.)

Table 6.33

d (ft)	8	10	12	14	16	18	20
A (ft^2)	704						

(c) Find the value of d (to one decimal place) that will produce a cross-sectional area of 675 ft^2. Solve graphically using a graphing utility and the built-in intersection routine.

*73 Architecture   The root for a 10 ft wide storage shed is formed by bending a 12 ft wide steel pannel into a circular arc (see Figure 6.64). Approximate (to two decimal places) the height h of the arc.

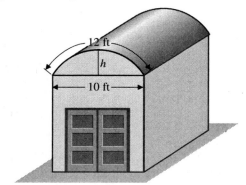

Figure 6.64

74 Physics   The equation of motion for a weight suspended from a spring is given by

$$y = -1.8 \sin 4t - 2.4 \cos 4t$$

where y is displacement of the weight from its equilibrium position (positive direction upwards) and t is time in seconds.

(a) Graph y for $0 \le t \le \pi/2$.

(b) Approximate (to two decimal places) the time(s) t, $0 \le t \le \pi/2$, when the weight is 2 in. above the equilibrium position.

(c) Approximate (to two decimal places) the time(s) t, $0 \le t \le \pi/2$, when the weight is 2 in. below the equilibrium position.

PART 3 Check Your Understanding

Are the statements in Problems 1–19 true or false? Give an explanation for your answer.

1. If $f(x) = x^2$ and $g(x) = \sqrt{x+3}$, then $f(g(x))$ is defined for all x.

2. If $f(x) = x^2$ and $g(x) = \sqrt{x+3}$, then $f(g(6)) = 9$.

3. In general $f(g(x)) = g(f(x))$.

4. The formula for the area of a circle is $A = \pi r^2$ and the formula for the circumference of a circle is $C = 2\pi r$. Then the area of a circle as a function of the circumference is $A = \dfrac{c^2}{2\pi}$.

5. If $f(x) = x^2 + 2$ then $f(f(1)) = 11$.

6. If $h(x) = f(g(x))$, $h(2) = 1\frac{1}{4}$ and $g(2) = \frac{1}{2}$ then $f(x)$ might be equal to $x^2 + 1$.

7. If $f(x) = \dfrac{1}{x}$ then $f(x+h) = \dfrac{1}{x} + \dfrac{1}{h}$.

8. If $f(x) = x^2 + x$, then $\dfrac{f(x+h) - f(x)}{h} = 2x + h$.

9. If $f(x) = x^2$ and $g(x) = \sin x$ then $f(g(x)) = x^2 \sin x$.

10. If there is a vertical line that intersects a graph in more than one point, then the graph does not represent a function.

11. Every function has an inverse.

12. If no horizontal line intersects the graph of a function in more than one point, then the function has an inverse.

13. Most quadratic functions have an inverse.

14. All linear functions of the form $f(x) = mx + b, m \ne 0$ have inverses.

15. Table 6.34 describes y as a function of x.

Table 6.34

x	1	2	3	4	5	6
y	3	4	7	8	5	3

16. Table 6.34 describes a function from x to y that is invertible.

17. The graph in Figure 6.65 is the graph of a function.

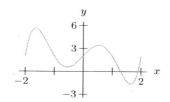

Figure 6.65

18. The function graphed in Figure 6.65 is invertible.

19. For an invertible function g, it is always true that $g^{-1}(g(x)) = x$.

Let $f(x) = \dfrac{1}{x}$, $g(x) = \sqrt{x}$, and $h(x) = x - 5$. Are the statements in Problems 20–29 true or false? Give an explanation for your answer.

20. $f(4) + g(4) = (f + g)(8)$.

21. $\dfrac{h(x)}{f(x)} = \dfrac{x-5}{x}$.

22. $f(4) + g(4) = 2\frac{1}{4}$.

23. $f(g(x))$ is defined for all x.

24. $g(f(x)) = \sqrt{\dfrac{1}{x}}$.

25. $f(x)g(x) = f(g(x))$.

26. $2f(2) = g(1)$.

27. $f(1)g(1)h(1) = -4$.

28. $\dfrac{f(3) + g(3)}{h(3)} = \dfrac{\frac{1}{3} + \sqrt{3}}{-2}$.

29. $4h(2) = h(8)$.

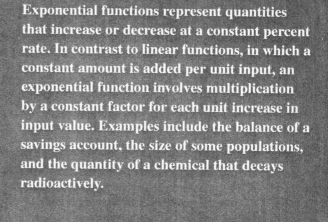

Chapter Seven

EXPONENTIAL FUNCTIONS

Exponential functions represent quantities that increase or decrease at a constant percent rate. In contrast to linear functions, in which a constant amount is added per unit input, an exponential function involves multiplication by a constant factor for each unit increase in input value. Examples include the balance of a savings account, the size of some populations, and the quantity of a chemical that decays radioactively.

7.1 INTRODUCTION TO THE FAMILY OF EXPONENTIAL FUNCTIONS

Growing at a Constant Percent Rate

Linear functions represent quantities that change at a constant rate. In this section we introduce functions that change at a constant *percent* rate, the *exponential functions*.

Salary Raises

Example 1   After graduation from college, you will probably be looking for a job. Suppose you are offered a job at a starting salary of $40,000 per year. To strengthen the offer, the company promises annual raises of 6% per year for at least the first five years after you are hired. Let's compute your salary for the first few years.

If t represents the number of years since the beginning of your contract, then for $t = 0$, your salary is $40,000. At the end of the first year, when $t = 1$, your salary increases by 6% so

$$\text{Salary when } t = 1 = \text{Original salary} + 6\% \text{ of Original salary}$$
$$= 40000 + 0.06 \cdot 40000$$
$$= 42400 \text{ dollars.}$$

After the second year, your salary again increases by 6%, so

$$\text{Salary when } t = 2 = \text{Former salary} + 6\% \text{ of Former salary}$$
$$= 42400 + 0.06 \cdot 42400$$
$$= 44944 \text{ dollars.}$$

Notice that your raise is higher in the second year than in the first since the second 6% increase applies both to the original $40,000 salary and to the $2400 raise given in the first year.

Salary calculations for four years have been rounded and recorded in Table 7.1. At the end of the third and fourth years your salary again increases by 6%, and your raise is larger each year. Not only are you given the 6% increase on your original salary, but your raises earn raises as well.

Table 7.1   *Raise amounts and resulting salaries for a person earning 6% annual salary increases*

Year	Raise amount ($)	Salary ($)
0		40000.00
1	2400.00	42400.00
2	2544.00	44944.00
3	2696.64	47640.64
4	2858.44	50499.08

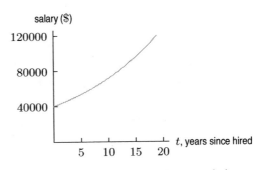

Figure 7.1: Salary over a 20-year period

Figure 7.1 shows salary over a 20-year period assuming that the annual increase remains 6%. Since the rate of change of your salary (in dollars per year) is not constant, the graph of this function is not a line. The salary increases at an increasing rate, giving the graph its upward curve.

Population Growth

Exponential functions provide a reasonable model for many growing populations.

Example 2   During the early 1980s, the population of Mexico increased at a constant annual percent rate of 2.6%. Since the population grew by the same percent each year, it can be modeled by an exponential function.

Let's calculate the population of Mexico for the first few years after 1980. In 1980, the population was 67.38 million. The population grew by 2.6%, so

$$\text{Population in 1981} = \text{Population in 1980} + 2.6\% \text{ of Population in 1980}$$
$$= 67.38 + 0.026(67.38)$$
$$\approx 67.38 + 1.75188$$
$$\approx 69.13188 \text{ million.}$$

Similarly,

$$\text{Population in 1982} = \text{Population in 1981} + 2.6\% \text{ of Population in 1981}$$
$$= 69.13188 + 0.026(69.13188)$$
$$\approx 69.13188 + 1.797$$
$$\approx 70.929 \text{ million.}$$

The calculations for years 1980 through 1984 have been rounded and recorded in Table 7.2. The population of Mexico increased by slightly more each year than it did the year before, because each year the increase is 2.6% of a larger number.

Table 7.2   *Calculated values for the population of Mexico*

Year	ΔP, increase in population	P, population (millions)
1980	—	67.38
1981	1.752	69.132
1982	1.797	70.929
1983	1.844	72.773
1984	1.893	74.666

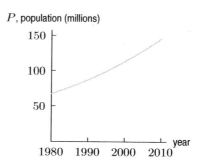

Figure 7.2: The projected population of Mexico, assuming 2.6% annual growth

Figure 7.2 gives a graph of the population of Mexico over a 30-year period, assuming a 2.6% annual growth rate. Notice that this graph curves upwards like the graph in Figure 7.1.

Radioactive Decay

Exponential functions can also model decreasing quantities. A quantity which decreases at a constant percent rate is said to be decreasing exponentially.

Example 3   Carbon-14 is used to estimate the age of organic compounds. Over time, radioactive carbon-14 decays into a stable form. The decay rate is 11.4% every 1000 years. For example, if we begin with a 200 microgram (μg) sample of carbon-14 then

$$\text{Amount remaining after 1000 years} = \text{Initial amount} - 11.4\% \text{ of Initial amount}$$
$$= 200 - 0.114 \cdot 200$$
$$= 177.2.$$

Similarly,

$$\text{Amount remaining after 2000 years} = \text{Amount remaining after 1000 years} - 11.4\% \text{ of } \text{Amount remaining after 1000 years}$$
$$= 177.2 - 0.114(177.2) \approx 156.999,$$

and

$$\text{Amount remaining after 3000 years} = \text{Amount remaining after 2000 years} - 11.4\% \text{ of } \text{Amount remaining after 2000 years}$$
$$= 156.999 - 0.114 \cdot 156.999 \approx 139.101.$$

These calculations are recorded in Table 7.3. During each 1000-year period, the amount of carbon-14 that decays is smaller than in the previous period. This is because we take 11.4% of a smaller quantity each time.

Table 7.3 *The amount of carbon-14 remaining over time*

Years elapsed	Amount decayed (μg)	Amount remaining (μg)
0	—	200.0
1000	22.8	177.2
2000	20.2	156.999
3000	17.898	139.101

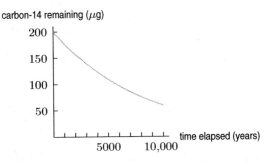

Figure 7.3: Amount of carbon-14 over 10,000 years

Figure 7.3 shows the amount of carbon-14 left from a 200 μg sample over 10,000 years. Because the amount decreases by a smaller amount over each successive time interval, the graph is not linear but bends upwards.

Growth Factors and Percent Growth Rates

The Growth Factor of an Increasing Exponential Function

The salary in Example 1 increases by 6% every year. We say that the annual percent growth rate is 6%. But there is another way to think about the growth of this salary. We know that each year,

$$\text{New salary} = \text{Old salary} + 6\% \text{ of Old salary}.$$

We can rewrite this as follows:

$$\text{New salary} = 100\% \text{ of Old salary} + 6\% \text{ of Old salary}.$$

So

$$\text{New salary} = 106\% \text{ of Old salary}.$$

Since $106\% = 1.06$, we have

$$\text{New salary} = 1.06 \cdot \text{Old salary}.$$

We call the 1.06 the *annual growth factor*.

The Growth Factor of a Decreasing Exponential Function

In Example 3, the carbon-14 changes by -11.4% every 1000 years. The negative growth rate tells us that the quantity of carbon-14 decreases over time. We have

$$\text{New amount} = \text{Old amount} - 11.4\% \text{ of Old amount},$$

which can be rewritten as

$$\text{New amount} = 100\% \text{ of Old amount} - 11.4\% \text{ of Old amount}.$$

So,

$$\text{New amount} = 88.6\% \text{ of Old amount}.$$

Since $88.6\% = 0.886$, we have

$$\text{New amount} = 0.886 \cdot \text{Old amount}.$$

Hence the growth factor is 0.886 per millenium. The fact that the growth factor is less than 1 indicates that the amount of carbon-14 is decreasing, since multiplying a quantity by a factor between 0 and 1 decreases the quantity.

Although it may sound strange to refer to the growth factor, rather than decay factor, of a decreasing quantity, we will use growth factor to describe both increasing and decreasing quantities.

A General Formula for the Family of Exponential Functions

Because it grows at a constant percentage rate each year, the salary, S, in Example 1 is an example of an exponential function. We want a formula for S in terms of t, the number of years since being hired. Since the annual growth factor is 1.06, we know that for each year,

$$\text{New salary} = \text{Previous salary} \cdot 1.06.$$

Thus, after one year, or when $t = 1$,

$$S = \underbrace{40{,}000}_{\text{Previous salary}} \cdot 1.06.$$

Similarly, when $t = 2$,

$$S = \underbrace{40{,}000(1.06)}_{\text{Previous salary}} \cdot 1.06 = 40{,}000(1.06)^2.$$

Here there are *two* factors of 1.06 because the salary has increased by 6% twice. When $t = 3$,

$$S = \underbrace{40{,}000(1.06)^2}_{\text{Previous salary}} \cdot 1.06 = 40{,}000(1.06)^3$$

and continues in this pattern so that after t years have elapsed,

$$S = 40{,}000 \underbrace{(1.06)(1.06)\ldots(1.06)}_{t \text{ factors of } 1.06} = 40{,}000(1.06)^t.$$

After t years the salary has increased by a factor of 1.06 a total of t times. Thus,

$$S = 40{,}000(1.06)^t.$$

These results, which are summarized in Table 7.4, are the same as in Table 7.1. Notice that in this formula we assume that t is an integer, $t \geq 0$, since the raises are given only once a year.

Table 7.4 *Salary after t years*

t (years)	S, salary ($)
0	40,000
1	$40,000(1.06) = 42,400.00$
2	$40,000(1.06)^2 = 44,944.00$
3	$40,000(1.06)^3 = 47,640.64$
t	$40,000(1.06)^t$

This salary formula can be written as

$$S = \text{Initial salary} \cdot (\text{Growth factor})^t.$$

In general, we have:

An **exponential function** $Q = f(t)$ has the formula

$$f(t) = ab^t, \quad b > 0,$$

where a is the initial value of Q (at $t = 0$) and b, the base, is the growth factor: $b > 1$ gives exponential growth, $0 < b < 1$ gives exponential decay. The growth factor is given by

$$b = 1 + r$$

where r is the decimal representation of the percent rate of change.

The constants a and b are called *parameters*. The base b is restricted to positive values because if $b < 0$ then b^t is undefined for some exponents t, for example, $t = 1/2$.

Every function in the form $f(t) = ab^t$ with the input, t, in the exponent is an exponential function, provided $a \neq 0$. Note that if $b = 1$, then $f(t) = a \cdot 1^t = a$ and $f(t)$ is a constant, so when $b = 1$, the function is generally not considered exponential. Graphs showing exponential growth and decay are in Figures 7.4 and 7.5. Notice that in both cases the graph is concave up.

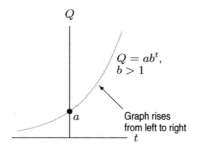

Figure 7.4: Exponential growth: $b > 1$

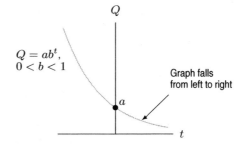

Figure 7.5: Exponential decay: $0 < b < 1$

Example 4   Use the formula $S = 40,000(1.06)^t$ to calculate your salary after 4 years, 12 years, and 40 years.

Solution   After 4 years, $t = 4$, and we have

$$S = 40,000(1.06)^4 \approx \$50,499.08.$$

Notice that this agrees with Table 7.1. After 12 years, $t = 12$, and we have

$$S = 40,000(1.06)^{12} \approx \$80,487.86.$$

After 12 years, the salary has more than doubled from the initial salary of \$40,000. When $t = 40$ we have

$$S = 40,000(1.06)^{40} \approx \$411,428.72.$$

Thus if you work for 40 years and consistently earn 6% annual raises, your salary will be over \$400,000 a year.

Example 5   Carbon-14 decays at a rate of 11.4% every 1000 years. Write a formula for the quantity, Q, of a 200 μg sample remaining as a function of time, t, in thousands of years.

Solution   The growth factor of carbon-14 over 1000 years is $1 - 0.114 = 0.886$. Originally, there are 200 μg, so the quantity remaining after t thousand years is given by

$$Q = 200(0.886)^t.$$

Example 6   Using Example 2 find a formula for P, the population of Mexico (in millions), in year t where $t = 0$ represents the year 1980.

Solution   In 1980, the population of Mexico was 67.38 million, and it was growing at a constant 2.6% annual rate. The growth factor is $b = 1 + 0.026 = 1.026$, and $a = 67.38$, so

$$P = 67.38(1.026)^t.$$

Because the growth factor may change eventually, this formula may not give accurate results for large values of t.

Example 7   What does the formula $P = 67.38(1.026)^t$ predict when $t = 0$? When $t = -5$? What do these values tell you about the population of Mexico?

Solution   If $t = 0$, then, since $(1.026)^0 = 1$, we have

$$P = 67.38(1.026)^0 = 67.38.$$

This makes sense because $t = 0$ stands for 1980, and in 1980 the population was 67.38 million. When $t = -5$ we have

$$P = 67.38(1.026)^{-5} \approx 59.264.$$

To make sense of this number, we must interpret the year $t = -5$ as five years before 1980; that is, as the year 1975. If the population of Mexico had been growing at a 2.6% annual rate from 1975 onward, then it was 59.264 million in 1975.

Example 8   On August 2, 1988, a US District Court judge imposed a fine on the city of Yonkers, New York, for defying a federal court order involving housing desegregation.[1] The fine started at \$100 for the first day and was to double daily until the city chose to obey the court order.

[1]*The Boston Globe*, August 27, 1988.

(a) What was the daily percent growth rate of the fine?

(b) Find a formula for the fine as a function of t, the number of days since August 2, 1988.

(c) If Yonkers waited 30 days before obeying the court order, what would the fine have been?

Solution

(a) Since the fine increased each day by a factor of 2, the fine grew exponentially with growth factor $b = 2$. To find the percent growth rate, we set $b = 1 + r = 2$, from which we find $r = 1$, or 100%. Thus the daily percent growth rate is 100%. This makes sense because when a quantity increases by 100%, it doubles in size.

(b) If t is the number of days since August 2, the formula for the fine, P in dollars, is

$$P = 100 \cdot 2^t.$$

(c) After 30 days, the fine is $P = 100 \cdot 2^{30} \approx 1.074 \cdot 10^{11}$ dollars, or $107,374,182,400.

Exercises and Problems for Section 7.1

Exercises

1. In 1999, the population of a country was 70 million and growing at a rate of 1.9% per year. Assuming the percentage growth rate remains constant, express the population, P, of this country as a function of t, the number of years after 1999.

2. In 2002, the cost of a train ticket from Boston to New York was $62. Assume that the price rises by 10% per year. Make a table showing the price of tickets each year until 2006.

3. The mass, Q, of a sample of Tritium (a radioactive isotope of Hydrogen), decays at a rate of 5.626% per year, t. Write an equation to describe the decay of a 726 gram sample. Graph the decay function.

4. Every year, a lake becomes more polluted, and 2% fewer organisms can live in it. If in 2010 there are one million organisms, write an equation relating O, the number of organisms, to time, t, in years since 2010.

What is the growth factor in Exercises 5–8? Assume time is measured in the units given.

5. A city grows by 28% per decade.

6. A forest shrinks 80% per century.

7. A diamond mine is depleted by 1% per day.

8. Water usage is increasing by 3% per year.

In Exercises 9–14, you start with 500 items. How many will you have after each effect?

9. 10% increase

10. 1% decrease

11. 100% increase

12. 42% decrease

13. 42% increase followed by 42% decrease

14. 42% decrease followed by 42% increase

15. Without a calculator or computer, match each exponential formula to one of the graphs I–VI.

(a) $10(1.2)^t$ (b) $10(1.5)^t$ (c) $20(1.2)^t$
(d) $30(0.85)^t$ (e) $30(0.95)^t$ (f) $30(1.05)^t$

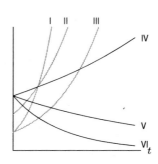

16. The populations, P, of six towns with time t in years are given by.

(i) $P = 1000(1.08)^t$ (ii) $P = 600(1.12)^t$
(iii) $P = 2500(0.9)^t$ (iv) $P = 1200(1.185)^t$
(v) $P = 800(0.78)^t$ (vi) $P = 2000(0.99)^t$

(a) Which towns are growing in size? Which are shrinking?

(b) Which town is growing the fastest? What is the annual percent growth rate for that town?

(c) Which town is shrinking the fastest? What is the annual percent "decay" rate for that town?

(d) Which town has the largest initial population (at $t = 0$)? Which town has the smallest?

Problems

17. In the year 2000, a total of 9.8 million passengers took a cruise vacation.[2] The global cruise industry has been growing at approximately 8% per year for the last decade; assume that this growth rate continues.

  (a) Write a formula to approximate the number, N, of cruise passengers (in millions) t years after 2000.

  (b) How many cruise passengers are predicted in the year 2010? Approximately how many passengers went on a cruise in the year 1990?

18. Radioactive gallium-67 decays by 1.48% every hour; there are 100 milligrams initially.6-1

  (a) Find a formula for the amount of gallium-67 remaining after t hours.

  (b) How many milligrams are left after 24 hours? After 1 week?

19. A typical cup of coffee contains about 100 mg of caffeine and every hour approximately 16% of the amount of caffeine in the body is metabolized and eliminated.

  (a) Write C, the amount of caffeine in the body in mg as a function of t, the number of hours since the coffee was consumed.

  (b) How much caffeine is in the body after 5 hours?

20. (a) The annual inflation rate is 3.5% per year. If a movie ticket costs $7.50, find a formula for p, the price of the ticket t years from today, assuming that movie tickets keep up with inflation.

  (b) According to your formula, how much will movie tickets cost in 20 years?

21. In 1990 the number of people infected by a virus was P_0. Due to a new vaccine, the number of infected people has decreased by 20% each year since 1990. In other words, only 80% as many people are infected each year as were infected the year before. Find a formula for $P = f(n)$, the number of infected people n years after 1990. Graph $f(n)$. Explain, in terms of the virus, why the graph has the shape it does.

22. The value, V, of a $100,000 investment that earns 3% annual interest is given by $V = f(t)$ where t is in years. How much is the investment worth in 3 years?

23. You owe $2000 on a credit card. The card charges 1.5% monthly interest on your balance, and requires a minimum monthly payment of 2.5% of your balance. All transactions (payments and interest charges) are recorded at the end of the month. You make only the minimum required payment every month and incur no additional debt.

  (a) Complete Table 7.5 for a twelve-month period.

  (b) What is your unpaid balance after one year has passed? At that time, how much of your debt have you paid off? How much money in interest charges have you paid your creditors?

Table 7.5

Month	Balance	Interest	Minimum payment
0	$2000.00	$30.00	$50.00
1	$1980.00	$29.70	$49.50
2	$1960.20		
⋮			

24. A quantity increases from 10 to 12. By what percent has it increased? Now suppose that it had increased from 100 to 102. What is the percent increase in this case?

25. The amount (in milligrams) of a drug in the body t hours after taking a pill is given by $A(t) = 25(0.85)^t$.

  (a) What is the initial dose given?

  (b) What percent of the drug leaves the body each hour?

  (c) What is the amount of drug left after 10 hours?

  (d) After how many hours is there less than 1 milligram left in the body?

26. An investment decreases by 5% per year for 4 years. By what total percent does it decrease?

27. Polluted water is passed through a series of filters. Each filter removes 85% of the remaining impurities. Initially, the untreated water contains impurities at a level of 420 parts per million (ppm). Find a formula for L, the remaining level of impurities, after the water has been passed through a series of n filters.

28. The UN Food and Agriculture Organization estimates that 4.2% of the world's natural forests existing in 1990 were gone by the end of the decade. In 1990, the world's forest cover stood at 3843 million hectares.[3]

  (a) How many million hectares of natural forests were lost during the 1990s?

  (b) How many million hectares of natural forests existed in the year 2000?

  (c) Write an exponential formula approximating the number of million hectares of natural forest in the world t years after 1990.

  (d) What was the annual percent decay rate during the 1990s?

---

[2]The Worldwatch Institute, *Vital Signs* 2002 (New York: W.W. Norton & Company, 2002), p. 122.
[3]The Worldwatch Institute, *Vital Signs* 2002 (New York: W.W. Norton & Company, 2002), p. 104.

29. The *Home* section of many Sunday newspapers includes a mortgage table similar to Table 7.6. The table gives the monthly payment per $1000 borrowed for loans at various interest rates and time periods. Determine the monthly payment on a

    (a) $60,000 mortgage at 8% for fifteen years.
    (b) $60,000 mortgage at 8% for thirty years.
    (c) $60,000 mortgage at 10% for fifteen years.
    (d) Over the life of the loan, how much money would be saved on a 15-year mortgage of $60,000 if the rate were 8% instead of 10%?
    (e) Over the life of the loan, how much money would be saved on an 8% mortgage of $60,000 if the term of the loan was fifteen years rather than thirty years?

Table 7.6

Interest rate (%)	15-year loan	20-year loan	25-year loan	30-year loan
8.00	9.56	8.37	7.72	7.34
8.50	9.85	8.68	8.06	7.69
9.00	10.15	9.00	8.40	8.05
9.50	10.45	9.33	8.74	8.41
10.00	10.75	9.66	9.09	8.78
10.50	11.06	9.99	9.45	9.15
11.00	11.37	10.33	9.81	9.53
11.50	11.69	10.67	10.17	9.91

30. Every year, teams from 64 colleges qualify to compete in the NCAA basketball playoffs. For each round, every team is paired with an opponent. A team is eliminated from the tournament once it loses a round. So, at the end of a round, only one half the number of teams move on to the next round. Let $N(r)$ be the number of teams remaining in competition after r rounds of the tournament have been played.

    (a) Find a formula for $N(r)$ and graph $y = N(r)$.
    (b) How many rounds does it take to determine the winner of the tournament?

31. Let $Q(t) = 8(0.87)^t$ give the level of a pollutant (in tons) remaining in a lake after t months. What is the monthly rate of decrease of the pollutant? The annual rate? The daily rate?

32. Figure 7.6 is the graph of $f(x) = 4 \cdot b^x$. Find the slope of the line segment PQ in terms of b.

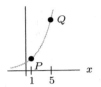

Figure 7.6

33. Let $P(t) = 32(1.047)^t$ give the population of a town (in thousands) in year t. What is the town's annual growth rate? Monthly growth rate? Growth rate per decade?

34. A one-page letter is folded into thirds to go into an envelope. If it were possible to repeat this kind of tri-fold 20 times, how many miles thick would the letter be? (A stack of 150 pieces of stationery is one inch thick; 1 mile = 5280 feet.)

7.2 COMPARING EXPONENTIAL AND LINEAR FUNCTIONS

The exponential function $Q = ab^t$ represents a quantity changing at a constant percent rate. In this section we compare exponential and linear models and we fit exponential models to data from tables and graphs.

Identifying Linear and Exponential Functions From a Table

Table 7.7 gives values of a linear and an exponential functions. Notice that the value of x changes by equal steps of $\Delta x = 5$. The function f is linear because the difference between consecutive values of $f(x)$ is constant: $f(x)$ increases by 15 each time x increases by 5.

Table 7.7 *Two functions, one linear and one exponential*

x	20	25	30	35	40	45
$f(x)$	30	45	60	75	90	105
$g(x)$	1000	1200	1440	1728	2073.6	2488.32

On the other hand, the difference between consecutive values of $g(x)$ is *not* constant:

$$1200 - 1000 = 200$$
$$1440 - 1200 = 240$$
$$1728 - 1440 = 288.$$

Thus, g is not linear. However, the *ratio* of consecutive values of $g(x)$ is constant:

$$\frac{1200}{1000} = 1.2, \quad \frac{1440}{1200} = 1.2, \quad \frac{1728}{1440} = 1.2,$$

and so on. Note that $1200 = 1.2(1000)$, $1440 = 1.2(1200)$, $1728 = 1.2(1440)$. Thus, each time x increases by 5, the value of $g(x)$ increases by a factor of 1.2. This pattern of constant ratios is indicative of exponential functions. In general:

For a table of data that gives y as a function of x and in which Δx is constant:

- If the *difference* of consecutive y-values is constant, the table could represent a linear function.
- If the *ratio* of consecutive y-values is constant, the table could represent an exponential function.

Finding a Formula for an Exponential Function

To find a formula for the exponential function in Table 7.7, we must determine the values of a and b in the formula $g(x) = ab^x$. The table tells us that $ab^{20} = 1000$ and that $ab^{25} = 1200$. Taking the ratio gives

$$\frac{ab^{25}}{ab^{20}} = \frac{1200}{1000} = 1.2.$$

Notice that the value of a cancels in this ratio, so

$$\frac{ab^{25}}{ab^{20}} = b^5 = 1.2.$$

We solve for b by raising each side to the $(1/5)^{\text{th}}$ power:

$$(b^5)^{1/5} = b = 1.2^{1/5} \approx 1.03714.$$

Now that we have the value of b, we can solve for a. Since $g(20) = ab^{20} = 1000$, we have

$$a(1.03714)^{20} = 1000$$
$$a = \frac{1000}{1.03714^{20}} \approx 482.253.$$

Thus, a formula for g is $g(x) = 482.253(1.037)^x$. (Note: We could have used $g(25)$ or any other value from the table to find a.)

Modeling Linear and Exponential Growth Using Two Data Points

If we are given two data points, we can fit either a line or an exponential function to the points. The following example compares the predictions made by a linear model and an exponential model fitted to the same data.

Example 1 At time $t = 0$ years, a species of turtle is released into a wetland. When $t = 4$ years, a biologist estimates there are 300 turtles in the wetland. Three years later, the biologist estimates there are 450 turtles. Let P represent the size of the turtle population in year t.

(a) Find a formula for $P = f(t)$ assuming linear growth. Interpret the slope and P-intercept of your formula in terms of the turtle population.

(b) Now find a formula for $P = g(t)$ assuming exponential growth. Interpret the parameters of your formula in terms of the turtle population.

(c) In year $t = 12$, the biologist estimates that there are 900 turtles in the wetland. What does this indicate about the two population models?

Solution (a) Assuming linear growth, we have $P = f(t) = b + mt$, and

$$m = \frac{\Delta P}{\Delta t} = \frac{450 - 300}{7 - 4} = \frac{150}{3} = 50.$$

Calculating b gives

$$300 = b + 50 \cdot 4$$
$$b = 100,$$

so $P = f(t) = 100 + 50t$. This formula tells us that 100 turtles were originally released into the wetland and that the number of turtles increases at the constant rate of 50 turtles per year.

(b) Assuming exponential growth, we have $P = g(t) = ab^t$. The values of a and b are calculated from the ratio

$$\frac{ab^7}{ab^4} = \frac{450}{300},$$

so

$$b^3 = 1.5.$$

Thus,

$$b = (1.5)^{1/3} \approx 1.145.$$

Using the fact that $g(4) = ab^4 = 300$ to find a gives

$$a(1.145)^4 = 300$$
$$a = \frac{300}{1.145^4} \approx 175, \quad \text{Rounding to the nearest whole turtle}$$

so $P = g(t) = 175(1.145)^t$. This formula tells us that 175 turtles were originally released into the wetland and the number increases at about 14.5% per year.

(c) In year $t = 12$, there are approximately 900 turtles. The linear function from part (a) predicts

$$P = 100 + 50 \cdot 12 = 700 \text{ turtles.}$$

The exponential formula from part (b), however, predicts

$$P = 175(1.145)^{12} \approx 889 \text{ turtles.}$$

The fact that 889 is closer to the observed value of 900 turtles suggests that, during the first 12 years, exponential growth is a better model of the turtle population than linear growth. The two models are graphed in Figure 7.7.

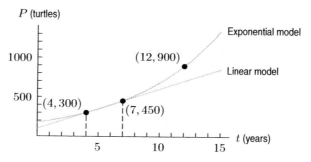

Figure 7.7: Comparison of the linear and exponential models of the turtle population

Similarities and Differences between Linear and Exponential Functions

In some ways the general formulas for linear and exponential functions are similar. If y is a linear function of x and x is a positive integer, we can write $y = b + mx$ as

$$y = b + \underbrace{m + m + m + \cdots + m}_{x \text{ times}}.$$

Similarly, if y is an exponential function of x, so that $y = a \cdot b^x$ and x is a positive integer, we can write

$$y = a \cdot \underbrace{b \cdot b \cdot b \cdot \cdots \cdot b}_{x \text{ times}}.$$

So linear functions involve repeated sums whereas exponential functions involve repeated products. In both cases, x determines the number of repetitions.

There are other similarities between the formulas for linear and exponential functions. The slope m of a linear function gives the rate of change of a physical quantity and the y-intercept gives the starting value. Similarly, in $y = a \cdot b^x$, the value of b gives the growth factor and a gives the starting value.

Example 2 The following tables contain values from an exponential or linear function. For each table, decide if the function is linear or exponential, and find a possible formula for the function.

(a)

x	$f(x)$
0	65
1	75
2	85
3	95
4	105

(b)

x	$g(x)$
0	400
1	600
2	900
3	1350
4	2025

(a) The function values increase by 10 as x increases by 1, so this is a linear function with slope $m = 10$. Since $f(0) = 65$, the vertical intercept is 65. A possible formula is

$$f(x) = 65 + 10x.$$

(b) The function is not linear, since $g(x)$ increases by different amounts as x increases by 1. To determine whether g might be exponential, we look at ratios of consecutive values:

$$\frac{600}{400} = 1.5, \quad \frac{900}{600} = 1.5, \quad \frac{1350}{900} = 1.5, \quad \frac{2025}{1350} = 1.5.$$

Each time x increases by 1, the value of $g(x)$ increases by a factor of 1.5. This is an exponential function with growth factor 1.5. Since $g(0) = 400$, the vertical intercept is 400. A possible formula is

$$g(x) = 400(1.5)^x.$$

Exponential Growth Will Always Outpace Linear Growth in the Long Run

Figure 7.7 shows the graphs of the linear and exponential models for the turtle population from Example 1. The graphs highlight the fact that, although these two graphs remain fairly close for the first ten or so years, the exponential model predicts explosive growth later on.

It can be shown that an exponentially increasing quantity will, in the long run, always outpace a linearly increasing quantity. This fact led the 19th-century clergyman and economist, Thomas Malthus, to make some rather gloomy predictions, which are illustrated in the next example.

Example 3
The population of a country is initially 2 million people and is increasing at 4% per year. The country's annual food supply is initially adequate for 4 million people and is increasing at a constant rate adequate for an additional 0.5 million people per year.

(a) Based on these assumptions, in approximately what year will this country first experience shortages of food?
(b) If the country doubled its initial food supply, would shortages still occur? If so, when? (Assume the other conditions do not change).
(c) If the country doubled the rate at which its food supply increases, in addition to doubling its initial food supply, would shortages still occur? If so, when? (Again, assume the other conditions do not change.)

Solution
Let P represent the country's population (in millions) and N the number of people the country can feed (in millions). The population increases at a constant percent rate, so it can be modeled by an exponential function. The initial population is $a = 2$ million people and the annual growth factor is $b = 1 + 0.04 = 1.04$, so a formula for the population is

$$P = 2(1.04)^t.$$

In contrast, the food supply increases by a constant amount each year and is therefore modeled by a linear function. The initial food supply is adequate for $b = 4$ million people and the growth rate is $m = 0.5$ million per year, so the number of people that can be fed is

$$N = 4 + 0.5t.$$

(a) Figure 7.8(a) gives the graphs of P and N over a 105-year span. For many years, the food supply is far in excess of the country's needs. However, after about 78 years the population has begun to grow so rapidly that it catches up to the food supply and then outstrips it. After that time, the country will suffer from shortages.
(b) If the country can initially feed eight million people rather than four, the formula for N is

$$N = 8 + 0.5t.$$

However, as we see from Figure 7.8(b), this measure only buys the country three or four extra years with an adequate food supply. After 81 years, the population is growing so rapidly that the head start given to the food supply makes little difference.
(c) If the country doubles the rate at which its food supply increases, from 0.5 million per year to 1.0 million per year, the formula for N is

$$N = 8 + 1.0t.$$

Unfortunately the country still runs out of food eventually. Judging from Figure 7.8(c), this happens in about 102 years.

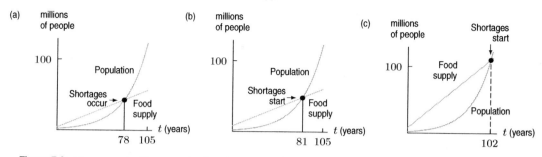

Figure 7.8: These graphs illustrate the fact that an exponentially growing population eventually outstrips a linearly growing food supply

Malthus believed that populations increase exponentially while food production increases linearly. The last example explains his gloomy predictions: Malthus believed that any population eventually outstrips its food supply, leading to famine and war.

Exercises and Problems for Section 7.2

Exercises

1. Explain the difference between linear and exponential growth. That is, without writing down any formulas, describe how linear and exponential functions progress differently from one value to the next.

2. A population has size 100 at time $t = 0$, with t in years.

    (a) If the population grows by 10 people per year, find a formula for the population, P, at time t.

    (b) If the population grows by 10% per year, find a formula for the population, P, at time t.

    (c) Graph both functions on the same axes.

3. A population has size 5000 at time $t = 0$, with t in years.

    (a) If the population decreases by 100 people per year, find a formula for the population, P, at time t.

    (b) If the population decreases by 8% per year, find a formula for the population, P, at time t.

4. In an environment with unlimited resources and no predators, a population tends to grow by the same percentage each year. Should a linear or exponential function be used to model such a population? Why?

5. The following formulas give the populations (in 1000s) of four different cities, A, B, C, and D. Which are changing exponentially? Describe in words how each of these populations is changing over time. Graph those that are exponential.

$$P_A = 200 + 1.3t, \quad P_B = 270(1.021)^t,$$
$$P_C = 150(1.045)^t, \quad P_D = 600(0.978)^t.$$

The tables in Problems 6–9 contain values from an exponential or a linear function. In each problem:

(a) Decide if the function is linear or exponential.

(b) Find a possible formula for each function and graph it.

6.

x	$f(x)$
0	12.5
1	13.75
2	15.125
3	16.638
4	18.301

7.

x	$g(x)$
0	0
1	2
2	4
3	6
4	8

8.

x	$h(x)$
0	14
1	12.6
2	11.34
3	10.206
4	9.185

9.

x	$i(x)$
0	18
1	14
2	10
3	6
4	2

10. Determine which of the functions in Table 7.8 could be linear and which could be exponential. Write formulas for the linear and exponential functions.

Table 7.8

x	-2	-1	0	1	2
$f(x)$	0.43982	1.31947	2.19912	3.07877	3.95842
$g(x)$	1.02711	1.13609	1.25663	1.390	1.537
$h(x)$	0.95338	1.88152	2.72743	3.47375	4.02713

Problems

In Problems 11–14, find formulas for the exponential functions satisfying the given conditions.

11. $h(0) = 3$ and $h(1) = 15$

12. $f(3) = -3/8$ and $f(-2) = -12$

13. $g(1/2) = 4$ and $g(1/4) = 2\sqrt{2}$

14. $g(0) = 5$ and $g(-2) = 10$

For Problems 15–20, find formulas for the exponential functions.

15.

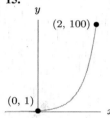

16.
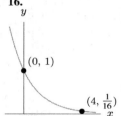

17.
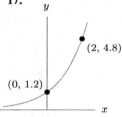

18.
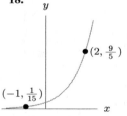

19.
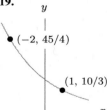

20.
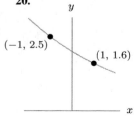

21. Determine whether the function whose values are in Table 7.9 could be exponential. Explain.

Table 7.9

x	1	2	4	5	8	9
$f(x)$	4096	1024	64	16	0.25	0.0625

In Problems 22–25, could the function be linear or exponential or is it neither? Write possible formulas for the linear or exponential functions.

22.

r	1	3	7	15	31
$p(r)$	13	19	31	55	103

23.

x	6	9	12	18	24
$q(x)$	100	110	121	146.41	177.16

24.

x	10	12	15	16	18
$f(x)$	1	2	4	8	16

25.

t	1	2	3	4	5
$g(t)$	512	256	128	64	32

26. Find a possible formula for an exponential function g with $g(1.7) = 6$ and $g(2.5) = 4$.

27. Find a formula (in terms of d) for the exponential function f with $f(1) = 4$ and $f(3) = d$.

28. Suppose $f(-3) = 5/8$ and $f(2) = 20$. Find a formula for f assuming it is:

(a) Linear   (b) Exponential

29. Let $P(t)$ be the population of a country, in millions, t years after 2002, with $P(7) = 3.21$ and $P(13) = 3.75$.

(a) Find a formula for $P(t)$ assuming it is linear. Describe in words the country's annual population growth given this assumption.

(b) Find a formula for $P(t)$ assuming it is exponential. Describe in words the country's annual population growth given this assumption.

30. What is the value of the population at the end of 10 years, given each of the following assumptions? Graph each population against time.

    (a) A population decreases linearly and the decrease is 10% in the first year.

    (b) A population decreases exponentially at the rate of 10% a year.

31. Figure 7.9 shows the balance, P, in a bank account.

    (a) Find a possible formula for $P = f(t)$ assuming the balance grows exponentially.

    (b) What was the initial balance?

    (c) What annual interest rate does the account pay?

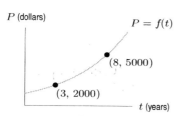

Figure 7.9

32. Let $p(x) = 2 + x$ and $q(x) = 2^x$. Estimate the values of x such that $p(x) < q(x)$.

33. The number of asthma sufferers in the world was about 84 million in 1990 and 130 million in 2001.[4] Let N represent the number of asthma sufferers (in millions) worldwide t years after 1990.

    (a) Write N as a linear function of t. What is the slope? What does it tell you about asthma sufferers?

    (b) Write N as an exponential function of t. What is the growth factor? What does it tell you about asthma sufferers?

    (c) How many asthma sufferers are predicted worldwide in the year 2010 with the linear model? With the exponential model?

34. Table 7.10 gives the approximate number of cell phone subscribers, S, worldwide. Explain why it makes sense to model the growth of S with an exponential function, and find S as an exponential function of t, the number of years since 1995. Interpret the growth rate in terms of cell phone subscribers.[5]

Table 7.10

Year	1995	1996	1997	1998	1999	2000
Subscribers (m.)	91	138	210	320	485	738

35. A 1987 treaty to protect the ozone layer produced dramatic declines in global production, P, of chloroflourocarbons (CFCs). See Figure 7.10.[6] Find a formula for P as an exponential function of the number of years, t, since 1989. What was the annual percent decay rate?

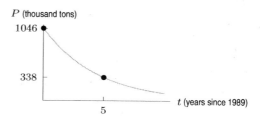

Figure 7.10

36. In 1940, there were about 10 brown tree snakes per square mile on the island of Guam, and in 2002, there were about 20,000 per square mile.[7] Find an exponential formula for the number, N, of brown tree snakes per square mile on Guam t years after 1940. What was, on average, the annual percent increase in the population during this period?

37. Match the stories in (a)–(e) with the formulas in (i)–(v). In each case, state what the variables represent. Assume that the constants P_0, r, B, A are all positive.

    (a) The percent of a lake's surface covered by algae, initially at 35%, was halved each year since the passage of anti-pollution laws.

    (b) The amount of charge on a capacitor in an electric circuit decreases by 30% every second.

    (c) Polluted water is passed through a series of filters. Each filter removes all but 30% of the remaining impurities from the water.

    (d) In 1920, the population of a town was 3000 people. Over the course of the next 50 years, the town grew at a rate of 10% per decade.

    (e) In 1920, the population of a town was 3000 people. Over the course of the next 50 years, the town grew at a rate of 250 people per year.

    (i) $f(x) = P_0 + rx$ (ii) $g(x) = P_0(1 + r)^x$

    (iii) $h(x) = B(0.7)^x$ (vi) $j(x) = B(0.3)^x$

    (v) $k(x) = A(2)^{-x}$

---

[4]www.who.int/inf-fs/en/fact206.html, August 24, 2002.

[5]The Worldwatch Institute, *Vital Signs* 2002 (New York: W.W. Norton & Company, 2002), p. 84.

[6]These numbers reflect the volume of the major CFCs multiplied by their respective ozone-depleting potentials (ODPs), as reported by the United Nations Environmental Programme Ozone Secretariat.

[7]*Science News*, Vol. 162, August 10, 2002, p. 85.

38. A 2002 Lexus costs $61,055 and the car depreciates a total of 46% during its first 7 years.

   (a) Suppose the depreciation is exponential. Find a formula for the value of the car at time t.

   (b) Suppose instead that the depreciation is linear. Find a formula for the value of the car at time t.

   (c) If this were your car and you were trading it in after 4 years, which depreciation model would you prefer (exponential or linear)?

39. On November 27, 1993, the *New York Times* reported that wildlife biologists have found a direct link between the increase in the human population in Florida and the decline of the local black bear population. From 1953 to 1993, the human population increased, on average, at a rate of 8% per year, while the black bear population decreased at a rate of 6% per year. In 1953 the black bear population was 11,000.

   (a) The 1993 human population of Florida was 13 million. What was the human population in 1953?

   (b) Find the black bear population for 1993.

   (c) If this trend continues, when will the black bear population number less than 100?

40. Suppose the city of Yonkers is offered two alternative fines by the judge. (See Example 8 in section 7.1.)

   Penalty A: $1 million on August 2 and the fine increases by $10 million each day thereafter.

   Penalty B: 1 ¢ on August 2 and the fine doubles each day thereafter.

   (a) If the city of Yonkers plans to defy the court order until the end of the month (August 31), compare the fines incurred under Penalty A and Penalty B.

   (b) If t represents the number of days after August 2, express the fine incurred as a function of t under

   (i) Penalty A   (ii) Penalty B

   (c) Assume your formulas in part (b) holds for $t \geq 0$, is there a time such that the fines incurred under both penalties are equal? If so, estimate that time.

7.3 GRAPHS OF EXPONENTIAL FUNCTIONS

As with linear functions, an understanding of the significance of the parameters a and b in the formula $Q = ab^t$ helps us analyze and compare exponential functions.

Graphs of the Exponential Family: The Effect of the Parameter a

In the formula $Q = ab^t$, the value of a tells us where the graph crosses the Q-axis, since a is the value of Q when $t = 0$. In Figure 7.11 each graph has the same value of b but different values of a and thus different vertical intercepts.

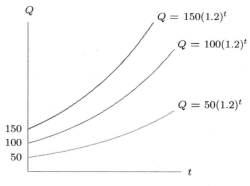

Figure 7.11: Graphs of $Q = a(1.2)^t$ for $a = 50$, 100, and 150

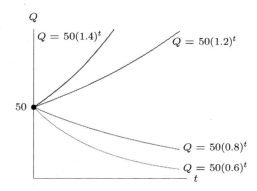

Figure 7.12: Graphs of $Q = 50b^t$ for $b = 0.6$, 0.8, 1.2 and 1.4

Graphs of the Exponential Family: The Effect of the Parameter b

The growth factor, b, is called the *base* of an exponential function. Provided a is positive, if $b > 1$, the graph climbs when read from left to right, and if $0 < b < 1$, the graph falls when read from left to right.

Figure 7.12 shows how the value of b affects the steepness of the graph of $Q = ab^t$. Each graph has a different value of b but the same value of a (and thus the same Q-intercept). For $b > 1$, the greater the value of b, the more rapidly the graph rises. For $0 < b < 1$, the smaller the value of b, the more rapidly the graph falls. In every case, however, the graph is concave up.

Horizontal Asymptotes

The horizontal line $Q = 0$, the t-axis, is a *horizontal asymptote* for the graph of $Q = ab^t$, because Q approaches 0 as t gets large, either positively or negatively. For exponential decay, such as $Q = a(0.6)^t$ in Figure 7.12, the value of Q approaches 0 as t gets large and positive. We write

$$Q \to 0 \quad \text{as} \quad t \to \infty.$$

This means that Q is as close to 0 as we like for all sufficiently large values of t. For exponential growth, the value of Q approaches zero as t grows more negative. See Figure 7.23, Section 7.4. We write

$$Q \to 0 \quad \text{as} \quad t \to -\infty.$$

This means that Q is as close to 0 as we like for all sufficiently large negative values of t. We make the following definition:

The horizontal line $y = k$ is a **horizontal asymptote** of a function, f, if the function values get arbitrarily close to k as x gets large (either positively or negatively or both). We describe this behavior using the notation

$$f(x) \to k \quad \text{as} \quad x \to \infty$$

or

$$f(x) \to k \quad \text{as} \quad x \to -\infty.$$

Example 1   A capacitor is the part of an electrical circuit that stores electric charge. The quantity of charge stored decreases exponentially with time. Stereo amplifiers provide a familiar example: When an amplifier is turned off, the display lights fade slowly because it takes time for the capacitors to discharge. (Thus, it can be unsafe to open a stereo or a computer immediately after it is turned off.)

If t is the number of seconds after the circuit is switched off, suppose that the quantity of stored charge (in micro-coulombs) is given by

$$Q = 200(0.9)^t, \quad t \geq 0,$$

(a) Describe in words how the stored charge changes over time.
(b) What quantity of charge remains after 10 seconds? 20 seconds? 30 seconds? 1 minute? 2 minutes? 3 minutes?
(c) Graph the charge over the first minute. What does the horizontal asymptote of the graph tell you about the charge?

Solution

(a) The charge is initially 200 micro-coulombs. Since $b = 1 + r = 0.9$, we have $r = -0.10$, which means that the charge level decreases by 10% each second.

(b) Table 7.11 gives the value of Q at $t = 0, 10, 20, 30, 60, 120,$ and 180. Notice that as t increases, Q gets closer and closer to, but doesn't quite reach, zero. The charge stored by the capacitor is getting smaller, but never completely vanishes.

(c) Figure 7.13 shows Q over a 60-second interval. The horizontal asymptote at $Q = 0$ corresponds to the fact that the charge gets very small as t increases. After 60 seconds, for all practical purposes, the charge is zero.

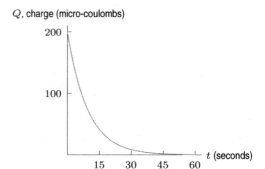

Table 7.11 *Charge (in micro-coulombs) stored by a capacitor over time*

t (seconds)	Q, charge level
0	200
10	69.736
20	24.315
30	8.478
60	0.359
120	0.000646
180	0.00000116

Figure 7.13: The charge stored by a capacitor over one minute

Solving Exponential Equations Graphically

We are often interested in solving equations involving exponential functions. In the following examples, we do this graphically. In Section 8.1, we will see how to solve equations using logarithms.

Example 2

In Example 8, Section 7.1, the fine, P, imposed on the city of Yonkers is given by $P = 100 \cdot 2^t$ where t is the number of days after August 2. In 1988, the annual budget of the city was \$337 million. If the city chose to disobey the court order, at what point would the fine have wiped out the entire annual budget?

Solution

We need to find the day on which the fine reaches \$337 million. That is, we must solve the equation

$$100 \cdot 2^t = 337,000,000.$$

Using a computer or graphing calculator we can graph $P = 100 \cdot 2^t$ to find the point at which the fine reaches 337 million. From Figure 7.14, we see that this occurs between $t = 21$ and $t = 22$. At day $t = 21$, August 23, the fine is:

$$P = 100 \cdot 2^{21} = 209,715,200$$

or just over \$200 million. On day $t = 22$, the fine is

$$P = 100 \cdot 2^{22} = 419,430,400$$

or almost \$420 million—quite a bit more than the city's entire annual budget!

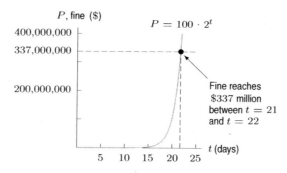

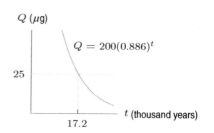

Figure 7.14: The fine imposed on Yonkers exceeds $337 million after 22 days

Figure 7.15: Solving the equation $200(0.886)^t = 25$

Example 3   A 200 μg sample of carbon-14 decays according to the formula

$$Q = 200(0.886)^t$$

where t is in thousands of years. Estimate when there is 25 μg of carbon-14 left.

Solution   We must solve the equation

$$200(0.886)^t = 25.$$

At the moment, we cannot find a formula for the solution to this equation. However, we can estimate the solution graphically. Figure 7.15 shows a graph of $Q = 200(0.886)^t$ and the line $Q = 25$. The amount of carbon-14 decays to 25 micrograms at $t \approx 17.180$. Since t is measured in thousands of years, this means in about 17,180 years.

Fitting Exponential Functions to Data

The data in Table 7.12 gives population data for the Houston Metro Area since 1900. In Section 10.1, we will see how to fit a linear function to data, but Figure 7.16 suggests that it may make more sense to fit an exponential function using *exponential regression*.

Table 7.12   *Population (in thousands) of Houston Metro Area, t years after 1900*

t	N	t	N
0	184	60	1583
10	236	70	2183
20	332	80	3122
30	528	90	3733
40	737	100	4672
50	1070		

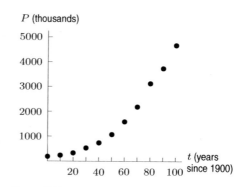

Figure 7.16: Population of Houston Metro Area

One algorithm used by a calculator or computer gives the best fitting exponential function as

$$P = 183.5(1.035)^t.$$

Other algorithms may give different formulas. Figure 7.17 shows this function and the data.

Since the base of this exponential function is 1.035, the population was increasing at a rate of about 3.5% per year between 1900 and 2000.

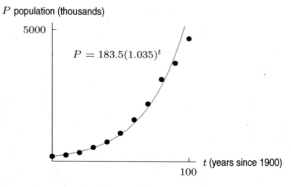

Figure 7.17: The population data since 1900 together with an exponential model

Exercises and Problems for Section 7.3

Exercises

Use Figure 7.18 to answer Exercises 1–4, assuming $A, B, C,$ and D can all be written in the form $y = ab^t$.

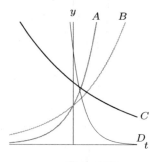

Figure 7.18

1. Which function has the largest value for a?

2. Which two functions have the same value for a?

3. Which function has the smallest value for b?

4. Which function has the largest value for b?

5. Solve $y = 46(1.1)^x$ graphically for x if $y = 91$.

6. Solve $p = 22(0.87)^q$ graphically for q if $p = 10$.

7. Solve $4m = 17(2.3)^w$ graphically for w if $m = 12$.

8. Solve $P/7 = (0.6)^t$ graphically for t if $P = 2$.

9. If $b > 1$, what is the horizontal asymptote of $y = ab^t$ as $t \to -\infty$?

10. If $0 < b < 1$, what is the horizontal asymptote of $y = ab^t$ as $t \to \infty$?

Problems

11. (a) Make a table of values for $f(x) = 2^x$ for $x = -3, -2, -1, 0, 1, 2, 3$.
  (b) Graph $f(x)$. Describe the graph in words.

12. (a) Make a table of values for $f(x) = \left(\dfrac{1}{2}\right)^x$ for $x = -3, -2, -1, 0, 1, 2, 3$.
  (b) Graph $f(x)$. Describe the graph in words.

13. The graphs of $f(x) = (1.1)^x$, $g(x) = (1.2)^x$, and $h(x) = (1.25)^x$ are in Figure 7.19. Explain how you can match these formulas and graphs without a calculator.

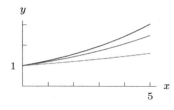

Figure 7.19

14. The graphs of $f(x) = (0.7)^x$, $g(x) = (0.8)^x$, and $h(x) = (0.85)^x$ are in Figure 7.20. Explain how you can match these formulas and graphs without a calculator.

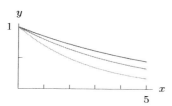

Figure 7.20

15. The city of Baltimore has been declining in population for the last ten years. In the year 2000, the population of Baltimore was 651 thousand and declining at a rate of 1.2% per year. If this trend continues:

(a) Give a formula for the population of Baltimore, P, in thousands, as a function of years, t, since 2000.
(b) What is the predicted population in 2010?
(c) To two decimal places, estimate t when the population is 550 thousand.

16. Let $P = f(t) = 1000(1.04)^t$ be the population of a community in year t.

(a) Evaluate $f(0)$ and $f(10)$. What do these expressions represent in terms of the population?
(b) Using a calculator or a computer, find appropriate viewing windows on which to graph the population for the first 10 years and for the first 50 years. Give the viewing windows you used and sketch the resulting graphs.
(c) If the percentage growth rate remains constant, approximately when will the population reach 2500 people?

17. Suppose y, the number of cases of a disease, is reduced by 10% each year.

(a) If there are initially 10,000 cases, express y as a function of t, the number of years elapsed.
(b) How many cases will there be 5 years from now?
(c) How long does it take to reduce the number of cases to 1000?

18. The earth's atmospheric pressure, P, in terms of height above sea level is often modeled by an exponential decay function. The pressure at sea level is 1013 millibars and that the pressure decreases by 14% for every kilometer above sea level.

(a) What is the atmospheric pressure at 50 km?
(b) Estimate the altitude h at which the pressure equals 900 millibars.

19. Table 7.13 shows the populations of the planet Vulcan, which is growing exponentially, and of the planet Romulus, which is growing linearly.

(a) Find a formula for the population (in millions) of each planet as a function of the number of years since 2010.
(b) Use the formulas to predict the population of each planet in the year 2030.
(c) Estimate the year in which the population of Vulcan reaches 50 million.
(d) Estimate the year in which the population of Vulcan overtakes the population of Romulus.

Table 7.13

Year	2010	2020
Population of Vulcan (millions)	8	12
Population of Romulus (millions)	16	20

20. Consider the exponential functions graphed in Figure 7.21 and the six constants a, b, c, d, p, q.

(a) Which of these constants are definitely positive?
(b) Which of these constants are definitely between 0 and 1?
(c) Which of these constants could be between 0 and 1?
(d) Which two of these constants are definitely equal?
(e) Which one of the following pairs of constants could be equal?

a and p b and d b and q d and q

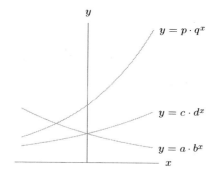

Figure 7.21

21. For which value(s) of a and b is $y = ab^x$ an increasing function? A decreasing function? Concave up?

22. Write a paragraph that compares the function $f(x) = a^x$, where $a > 1$, and $g(x) = b^x$, where $0 < b < 1$. Include graphs in your answer.

23. Set a window of $-4 \leq x \leq 4$, $-1 \leq y \leq 6$ and graph the following functions using several different values of a for each. Include some values of a with $a < 1$.

(a) $y = a2^x$, $0 < a < 5$.
(b) $y = 2a^x$, $0 < a < 5$.

In Problems 24–27, graph $f(x)$, a function defined for all real numbers and satisfying the condition.

24. $f(x) \rightarrow 5$ as $x \rightarrow \infty$

25. $f(x) \rightarrow 3$ as $x \rightarrow -\infty$

26. $f(x) \rightarrow 2$ as $x \rightarrow -\infty$ and $f(x) \rightarrow -1$ as $x \rightarrow \infty$

27. $f(x) \rightarrow 0$ as $x \rightarrow -\infty$ and $f(x) \rightarrow -\infty$ as $x \rightarrow \infty$

In Problems 28–29, graph the function to find horizontal asymptotes.

28. $f(x) = 8 - 2^x$ **29.** $f(x) = 3^{-x^2} + 2$

30. Suppose you use your calculator to graph $y = 1.04^{5x}$. You correctly enter $y = 1.04^{\wedge}(5x)$ and see the graph in Figure 7.22. A friend graphed the function by entering $y = 1.04^{\wedge}5x$ and said, "The graph is a straight line, so I must have the wrong window." Explain why changing the window will not correct your friend's error.

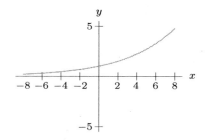

Figure 7.22

31. The population of a colony of rabbits grows exponentially. The colony begins with 10 rabbits; five years later there are 340 rabbits.

(a) Give a formula for the population of the colony of rabbits as a function of the time.
(b) Use a graph to estimate how long it takes for the population of the colony to reach 1000 rabbits.

32. Table 7.14 shows global wind energy generating capacity, W (in megawatts), as a function of the number of years, t, since 1995.[8]

(a) Plot the data and explain why it is reasonable to approximate these data with an exponential function.

(b) Use a calculator or computer to fit an exponential function to these data.
(c) What annual percent growth rate does the exponential model show?

Table 7.14

t	0	1	2	3	4	5	6
W	4780	6070	7640	10,150	13,930	18,100	24,800

33. Global sales of energy-efficient compact fluorescent lamps have been growing approximately exponentially. Table 7.15 shows lamp sales, in millions.[9]

(a) Use a calculator or computer to find the exponential regression function for sales, S (in millions), as a function of the number of years, t, since 1990.
(b) Plot the function with the data. Does it appear to fit the data well?
(c) What annual percent growth rate does the exponential model show?
(d) If this growth rate continues, what sales are predicted in the year 2010?

Table 7.15

Year	1990	1992	1994	1996	1998	2000
Sales (millions)	83	138	206	288	387	528

34. What are the domain and range of the exponential function $Q = ab^t$ where a and b are both positive constants?

35. The functions $f(x) = (\frac{1}{2})^x$ and $g(x) = 1/x$ are similar in that they both tend toward zero as x becomes large. Using your calculator, determine which function, f or g, approaches zero faster.

36. Three scientists, working independently of each other, arrive at the following formulas to model the spread of a species of mussel in a system of fresh water lakes:

$$f_1(x) = 3(1.2)^x, \quad f_2(x) = 3(1.21)^x, \quad f_3(x) = 3.01(1.2)^x,$$

where $f_n(x)$, $n = 1, 2, 3$, is the number of individual mussels (in 1000s) predicted by model number n to be living in the lake system after x months have elapsed.

(a) Graph these three functions for $0 \leq x \leq 60$, $0 \leq y \leq 40,000$.
(b) The graphs of these three models do not seem all that different from each other. But do the three functions make significantly different predictions about the

---

[8]The Worldwatch Institute, *Vital Signs* 2002 (New York: W.W. Norton & Company, 2002), p. 43.
[9]The Worldwatch Institute, *Vital Signs* 2002 (New York: W.W. Norton & Company, 2002), p. 47.

future mussel population? To answer this, graph the difference function, $f_2(x) - f_1(x)$, of the population sizes predicted by models 1 and 2, as well as the difference functions, $f_3(x) - f_1(x)$ and $f_3(x) - f_2(x)$. (Use the same window as in part (a).)

(c) Based on your graphs in part (b), discuss the assertion that all three models are in good agreement as far as long-range predictions of mussel population are concerned. What conclusions can you draw about exponential functions in general?

37. Let f be a piecewise-defined function given by

$$f(x) = \begin{cases} 2^x, & x < 0 \\ 0, & x = 0 \\ 1 - \frac{1}{2}x, & x > 0. \end{cases}$$

(a) Graph f for $-3 \le x \le 4$.
(b) The domain of $f(x)$ is all real numbers. What is its range?
(c) What are the intercepts of f?
(d) What happens to $f(x)$ as $x \to \infty$ and $x \to -\infty$?
(e) Over what intervals is f increasing? Decreasing?

7.4 CONTINUOUS GROWTH AND THE NUMBER e

The Number e

The irrational number $e = 2.71828\ldots$, introduced by Euler[10] in 1727, is often used for the base, b, of the exponential function. Base e is so important that e is called the *natural base*. This may seem mysterious, as what could possibly be natural about using an irrational base such as e? The answer is that the formulas of calculus are much simpler if e is used as the base for exponentials. Since $2 < e < 3$, the graph of $Q = e^t$ lies between the graphs of $Q = 3^t$ and $Q = 2^t$. See Figure 7.23.

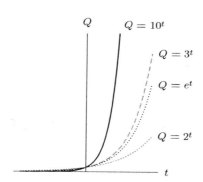

Figure 7.23: Graphs of exponential functions with various bases

Exponential Functions with Base e Represent Continuous Growth

Any positive base b can be written as a power of e:

$$b = e^k.$$

If $b > 1$, then k is positive; if $0 < b < 1$, then k is negative. Then the function $Q = ab^t$ can be rewritten in terms of e:

$$Q = ab^t = a\left(e^k\right)^t = ae^{kt}.$$

The constant k is called the *continuous growth rate*. In general:

---

[10]Leonhard Euler (1707-1783), a Swiss mathematician, introduced e, $f(x)$ notation, π, and i (for $\sqrt{-1}$).

For the exponential function $Q = ab^t$, the **continuous growth rate**, k, is given by solving $e^k = b$. Then

$$Q = ae^{kt}.$$

If a is positive,

- If $k > 0$, then Q is increasing.
- If $k < 0$, then Q is decreasing.

The value of the continuous growth rate, k, may be given as a decimal or a percent. If t is in years, for example, then the units of k are per year; if t is in minutes, then k is per minute.

Example 1   Give the continuous growth rate of each of the following functions and graph each function:

$$P = 5e^{0.2t}, \qquad Q = 5e^{0.3t}, \qquad \text{and} \quad R = 5e^{-0.2t}.$$

Solution   The function $P = 5e^{0.2t}$ has a continuous growth rate of 20%, and $Q = 5e^{0.3t}$ has a continuous 30% growth rate. The function $R = 5e^{-0.2t}$ has a continuous growth rate of -20%. The negative sign in the exponent tells us that R is decreasing instead of increasing.

Because $a = 5$ in all three formulas, all three populations start at 5. Note that the graphs of these functions in Figure 7.24 have the same shape as the exponential functions in Section 7.3 They are concave up and have horizontal asymptotes of $y = 0$. (Note that $P \to 0$ and $Q \to 0$ as $t \to -\infty$, whereas $R \to 0$ as $t \to \infty$.)

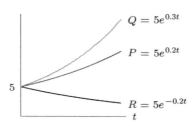

Figure 7.24: Exponential functions with different continuous growth rates

Example 2   A population increases from 7.25 million at a continuous rate of 2.2% per year. Write a formula for the population, and estimate graphically when the population reaches 10 million.

Solution   We express the formula in base e since the continuous growth rate is given. If P is the population (in millions) in year t, then

$$P = 7.3e^{0.022t}.$$

See Figure 7.25. We see that $P = 10$ when $t \approx 14.3$. Thus, it takes about 14.3 years for the population to reach 10 million.

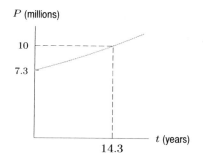

P (millions)

10

7.3

14.3

t (years)

Figure 7.25

Example 3   Caffeine leaves the body at a continuous rate of 17% per hour. How much caffeine is left in the body 8 hours after drinking a cup of coffee containing 100 mg of caffeine?

Solution   If *A* is the amount of caffeine in the body *t* hours after drinking the coffee, then

$$A = 100e^{-0.17t}.$$

After 8 hours, we have $A = 100e^{-0.17(8)} = 25.67$ mg.

Compound Interest

What is the difference between a bank account that pays 12% interest once per year and one that pays 1% interest every month? Imagine we deposit $1000 into the first account. Then, after 1 year, we have (assuming no other deposits or withdrawals)

$$\$1000(1.12) = \$1120.$$

But if we deposit $1000 into the second account, then after 1 year, or 12 months, we have

$$\$1000 \underbrace{(1.01)(1.01)\ldots(1.01)}_{\text{12 months of 1\% monthly interest}} = 1000(1.01)^{12} = \$1126.83.$$

Thus, we earn $6.83 more in the second account than in the first. To see why this happens, notice that the 1% interest we earn in January itself earns interest at a rate of 1% per month. Similarly, the 1% interest we earn in February earns interest, and so does the interest earned in March, April, May, and so on. The extra $6.83 comes from interest earned on interest. This effect is known as *compounding*. We say that the first account earns 12% interest *compounded annually* and the second account earns 12% interest *compounded monthly*.

Nominal Versus Effective Rates

The expression 12% compounded monthly means that interest is added twelve times per year and that 12%/12 = 1% of the current balance is added each time. Banks refer to the 12% as the *annual percentage rate* or APR. We also call the 12% the *nominal rate* (nominal means "in name only"). When the interest is compounded more frequently than once a year, the account effectively earns more than the nominal rate. Thus, we distinguish between nominal rate and *effective annual yield*, or *effective rate*. The effective annual rate tells you how much interest the investment actually earns.

Example 4   What are the nominal and effective annual rates of an account paying 12% interest, compounded annually? Compounded monthly?

Solution   Since an account paying 12% annual interest, compounded annually, grows by exactly 12% in one year, we see that its nominal rate is the same as its effective rate: both are 12%.

The account paying 12% interest, compounded monthly, also has a nominal rate of 12%. On the other hand, since it pays 1% interest every month, after 12 months, its balance increases by a factor of

$$\underbrace{(1.01)(1.01)\ldots(1.01)}_{\text{12 months of 1% monthly growth}} = 1.01^{12} \approx 1.1268250.$$

Thus, effectively, the account earns 12.683% interest in a year.

Example 5   What is the effective annual rate of an account that pays interest at the nominal rate of 6% per year, compounded daily? Compounded hourly?

Solution   Since there are 365 days in a year, daily compounding pays interest at the rate of

$$\frac{6\%}{365} = 0.0164384\% \text{ per day.}$$

Thus, the daily growth factor is

$$1 + \frac{0.06}{365} = 1.000164384.$$

If at the beginning of the year the account balance is P, after 365 days the balance is

$$P \cdot \underbrace{\left(1 + \frac{0.06}{365}\right)^{365}}_{\substack{\text{365 days of} \\ \text{0.0164384\% daily interest}}} = P \cdot (1.0618313).$$

Thus, this account earns interest at the effective annual rate of 6.18313%.

Notice that daily compounding results in a higher rate than yearly compounding (6.183% versus 6%), because with daily compounding the interest has the opportunity to earn interest.

If interest is compounded hourly, since there are $24 \cdot 365$ hours in a year, the balance at year's end is

$$P \cdot \left(1 + \frac{0.06}{24 \cdot 365}\right)^{24 \cdot 365} = P \cdot (1.0618363).$$

The effective rate is now 6.18363% instead of 6.18313%—that is, just slightly better than the rate of the account that compounds interest daily. The effective rate increases with the frequency of compounding.

To summarize:

> If interest at an annual rate of r is compounded n times a year, then r/n times the current balance is added n times a year. Therefore, with an initial deposit of $\$P$, the balance t years later is
>
> $$B = P \cdot \left(1 + \frac{r}{n}\right)^{nt}.$$
>
> Note that r is the nominal rate; for example, $r = 0.05$ if the annual rate is 5%.

Continuous Compounding and the Number *e*

In Example 5 we calculated the effective interest rates for two accounts with a 6% per year nominal interest rate, but different compounding periods. We see that the account with more frequent compounding earns a higher effective rate, though the increase is small.

This suggests that compounding more and more frequently—every minute or every second or many times per second—would increase the effective rate still further. However, there is a limit to how much more an account can earn by increasing the frequency of compounding.

Table 7.16 *Effect of increasing the frequency of compounding*

Compounding frequency	Annual growth factor	Effective annual rate
Annually	1.0600000	6%
Monthly	1.0616778	6.16778%
Daily	1.0618313	6.18313%
Hourly	1.0618363	6.18363%
$\vdots$	$\vdots$	$\vdots$
Continuously	$e^{0.06} \approx 1.0618365$	6.18365%

Table 7.16 shows several compounding periods with their annual growth factors and effective annual rates. As the compounding periods become shorter, the growth factor approaches $e^{0.06}$. Using a calculator, we check that

$$e^{0.06} \approx 1.0618365,$$

which is the final value for the annual growth factors in Table 7.16. If an account with a 6% nominal interest rate delivers this effective yield, we say that the interest has been *compounded continuously*.

In general:

If interest on an initial deposit of $\$P$ is *compounded continuously* at an annual rate r, the balance t years later can be calculated using the formula

$$B = Pe^{rt}.$$

Again, r is the nominal rate, and, for example, $r = 0.06$ when the annual rate is 6%.

It is important to realize that the functions $B = Pe^{0.06t}$ and $B = P(1.0618365)^t$ both give the balance in a bank account growing at a continuous rate of 6% per year. These formulas both represent the *same* exponential function—they just describe it in different ways.[11]

Example 6   Find the effective annual rate if $1000 is deposited at 5% annual interest, compounded continuously.

Solution   The value of the deposit is given by

$$V = 1000e^{0.05t}.$$

To find the effective annual rate, we use the fact that $e^{0.05t} = (e^{0.05})^t$ to rewrite the function as

$$V = 1000(e^{0.05})^t.$$

---

[11]Actually, this isn't precisely true, because we rounded off when we found $b = 1.0618365$. However, we can find b to as many digits as we want, and to this extent the two formulas are the same.

Since $e^{0.05} = 1.05127$, we have

$$V = 1000(1.05127)^t.$$

This tells us that the effective annual rate is 5.127%.

Example 7   Which is better: An account that pays 8% annual interest compounded quarterly or an account that pays 7.95% annual interest compounded continuously?

Solution   The account that pays 8% interest compounded quarterly pays 2% interest 4 times a year. Thus, in one year the balance is

$$P(1.02)^4 \approx P(1.08243),$$

which means the effective annual rate is 8.243%.

    The account that pays 7.95% interest compounded continuously has a year-end balance of

$$Pe^{0.0795} \approx P(1.08275),$$

so the effective annual rate is 8.275%. Thus, 7.95% compounded continuously is better than 8% compounded quarterly.

Exercises and Problems for Section 7.4

Exercises

1. Without a calculator, match the functions $y = 2^x$, $y = 3^x$, and $y = e^x$ with the graphs in Figure 7.26.

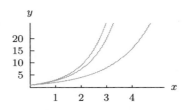

Figure 7.26

2. Without a calculator, match each formula to one of the graphs I–IV in 7.27.

   (a) $e^{-0.01t}$ **(b)** $e^{0.05t}$ **(c)** $e^{-0.10t}$ **(d)** $e^{0.20t}$

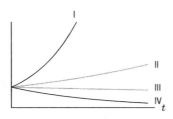

Figure 7.27

3. A population is 25,000 in year $t = 0$ and grows at a continuous rate of 7.5% per year.

   (a) Find a formula for $P(t)$, the population in year t.
   (b) By what percent does the population increase each year? Why is this more than 7.5%?

4. A population grows from its initial level of 22,000 at a continuous growth rate of 7.1% per year.

   (a) Find a formula for $P(t)$, the population in year t.
   (b) By what percent does the population increase each year?

5. The same amount of money is deposited into two different bank accounts paying the same nominal rate, one compounded annually and the other compounded continuously. Which curve in Figure 7.28 corresponds to which compounding method? What is the initial deposit?

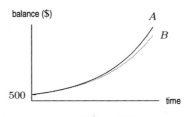

Figure 7.28

6. Find the effective annual yield and the continuous growth rate if $Q = 5500\,e^{0.19t}$.

In Exercises 7–10, what is the balance after 1 year if an account containing $500 earns the stated yearly nominal interest, compounded

(a) Annually   **(b)** Weekly (52 weeks per year)

(c) Every minute (525,600 per year)
(d) Continuously?

7. 1%   **8.** 3%   **9.** 5%   **10.** 8%

Problems

11. A radioactive substance decays at a continuous rate of 14% per year, and 50 mg of the substance is present in the year 2000.

   (a) Write a formula for the amount present, A (in mg), t years after 2000.
   (b) How much will be present in the year 2010?
   (c) Estimate when the quantity drops below 5 mg.

12. In the year 2000, the gross world product, W, (total output in goods and services) was 45 trillion dollars and growing at a continuous rate of 4.6% per year. Write a formula for W, in trillions of dollars, as a function of years, t, since 2000. Estimate the value of t when the gross world product reaches 60 trillion dollars.

13. Without a calculator, match the functions $y = e^x$, $y = 2e^x$, and $y = 3e^x$ to the graphs in Figure 7.29.

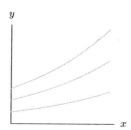

Figure 7.29

14. Without a calculator, match the functions $y = e^x$, $y = e^{-x}$, and $y = -e^x$ to the graphs in Figure 7.30.

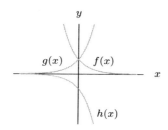

Figure 7.30

15. At time t in years, the value, V, of an investment of $1000 is given by $V = 1000e^{0.02t}$. When is the investment worth $3000?

16. From time $t = 0$, with t in years, a $1200 deposit in a bank account grows according to the formula

$$B = 1200e^{0.03t}.$$

   (a) What is the balance in the account at the end of 100 years?
   (b) When does the balance first go over $50,000?

17. How long does it take an investment to double if it grows according to the formula $V = 537e^{0.015t}$? Assume t is in years.

18. If $5000 is deposited in an account paying a nominal interest rate of 4% per year, how much is in the account 10 years later if interest is compounded

   (a) Annually?
   (b) Continuously?

19. Which is better, an account paying 5.3% interest compounded continuously or an account paying 5.5% interest compounded annually? Justify your answer.

20. Suppose $1000 is deposited into an account paying interest at a nominal rate of 8% per year. Find the balance 3 years later if the interest is compounded

   (a) Monthly   **(b)** Weekly
   (c) Daily   **(d)** Continuously

21. A bank account pays 6% annual interest. As the number of compounding periods increases, the effective interest rate earned also rises.

   (a) Find the annual interest rate earned by the account if the interest is compounded:
     (i) Quarterly   (ii) Monthly
     (iii) Weekly   (iv) Daily
   (b) Evaluate $e^{0.06}$, where $e = 2.71828\ldots$ Explain what your result tells you about the bank account.

In Problems 22–25, what are the nominal and effective annual rates for an account paying the stated annual interest, compounded

   (a) Annually?   **(b)** Quarterly?
   (c) Daily?   **(d)** Continuously?

22. 1%   **23.** 100%   **24.** 3%   **25.** 6%

26. A bank pays interest at the nominal rate of 4.2% per year. What is the effective annual yield if compounding is:

(a) Annual   (b) Monthly   (c) Continuous

27. If you need $25,000 six years from now, what is the minimum amount of money you need to deposit into a bank account that pays 5% annual interest, compounded:

(a) Annually   (b) Monthly   (c) Daily

(d) Your answers get smaller as the number of times of compounding increases. Why is this so?

28. Three different investments are given.

(a) Find the balance of each of the investments after the two-year period.

(b) Rank them from best to worst in terms of rate of return. Explain your reasoning.

- Investment A: $875 deposited at 13.5% per year compounded daily for 2 years.

- Investment B: $1000 deposited at 6.7% per year compounded continuously for 2 years.

- Investment C: $1050 deposited at 4.5% per year compounded monthly for 2 years.

29. Rank the following three bank deposit options from best to worst.

- Bank A: 7% compounded daily

- Bank B: 7.1% compounded monthly

- Bank C: 7.05% compounded continuously

30. An investment grows by 3% per year for 10 years. By what percent does it increase over the 10-year period?

31. An investment grows by 30% over a 5-year period. What is its effective annual percent growth rate?

32. An investment decreases by 60% over a 12-year period. At what effective annual percent rate does it decrease?

33. If the balance, M, at time t in years, of a bank account that compounds its interest payments monthly is given by

$$M = M_0(1.07763)^t.$$

(a) What is the effective annual rate for this account?

(b) What is the nominal annual rate?

34. A sum of $850 is invested for 10 years and the interest is compounded quarterly. There is $1000 in the account at the end of 10 years. What is the nominal annual rate?

35. In the 1980s a northeastern bank experienced an unusual robbery. Each month an armored car delivered cash deposits from local branches to the main office, a trip requiring only one hour. One day, however, the delivery was six hours late. This delay turned out to be a scheme devised by an employee to defraud the bank. The armored car drivers had lent the money, a total of approximately $200,000,000, to arms merchants who then used it as collateral against the purchase of illegal weapons. The interest charged for this loan was 20% per year compounded continuously. How much was the fee for the six-hour period?

7.5   TRANSFORMATIONS OF EXPONENTIAL FUNCTIONS

- Vertical and Horizontal Shifts
- Reflections, Stretches, and Compressions
- Expressing Transformations of Exponential Functions in the Form $y = ab^x$

We studied general transformations of functions in Chapter 2 and transformations of trigonometric functions in Chapter 4. Recall that addition to or subtraction from the formula for the original function yielded a *shift* in its graph. Multiplying the formula for the original function yielded a reflection, stretch, or compression of its graph. Recall also that *inside* changes to the function produce *horizontal* changes in the graph, while *outside* changes to the function produce *vertical* changes in the graph. For example, $y = \sqrt{\frac{1}{2}(x - 4)}$ shows two *inside* changes to the function $y = \sqrt{x}$. The inside subtraction creates a shift of the graph 4 units to the right, and the inside multiplication creates a horizontal stretch by a factor of 2. The function $y = 2x^2 + 5$ shows two *outside* changes to the function $y = x^2$. The outside addition creates a shift in the graph up 5 units, and the outside multiplication creates a vertical stretch by a factor of 2.

In this section, we examine each of these types of transformations for exponential functions, focusing on what happens to the function's formula, to its graph, and to the function's attributes. The function's attributes to be considered are whether it is increasing or decreasing, its range, its horizontal asymptote, and its y-intercept. As we transform an exponential function, we will look at each of these.

Vertical and Horizontal Translations

We start with an example of a vertical shift in the context of a job's salary offer.

Example 1   Recall the job described in Example 1 of Section 7.1. The job had an original salary of $40,000 and a raise of 6% per year. We modeled the salary as $S = 40000(1.06)^t$ where S is salary and t is years since hired. Consider a variation of this job offer. Instead, you receive a sign-on bonus and an annual bonus of $5,000 each year, but the bonus does not earn any raise. The new annual salary is $S_{new} = 5000 + 40000(1.06)^t$. Compare the job offer with and without the $5000 bonus. From your knowledge of *shifts*, how do you think the graph of S_{new} will compare to S?

Solution   The graph of S_{new} is shifted *upward* by 5000.

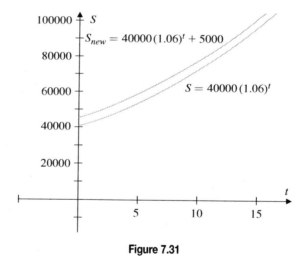

Figure 7.31

The next example involves shifting a graph horizontally.

Example 2   Let us consider another job offer. Again you start at a salary of $40,000, with a 6% raise each year. This time, however, the raise does not begin until you have been at the job two years. Therefore, your salary stays at $40,000 for the first two years and then is $S = 40000(1.06)^{t-2}$, for each year after that, i.e. $t \geq 2$. How does the graph of this salary compare to the original job?

Solution   After the initial two years, the graph is shifted to the right 2 units.

By subtracting two from the input t, an *inside* subtraction, the graph of the original salary moved to the right two units.

As we have seen in Examples 1 and 2, additions to and subtractions from an exponential function behave as we previously learned. An *outside* addition or subtraction moves the graph of the original function up or down. An *inside* addition or subtraction moves the graph of the original function left or right.

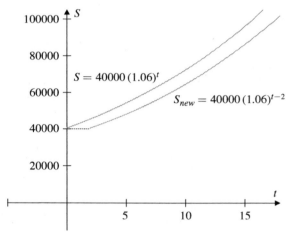

Figure 7.32

Starting with the exponential function $y = e^x$, its attributes are the following. Because its base e is larger than 1, the function is increasing everywhere. Its range is all of the positive numbers, $(0, \infty)$. Recall that the horizontal asymptote of this exponential function is the *x-axis*, which has the equation $y = 0$. As $x \to -\infty$, $y \to 0$. Its y-intercept is the value $e^0 = 1$ and is graphed on the vertical-axis at the point $(0, e^0) = (0, 1)$. Compare that to the function in **Example 3** that undergoes two shifts from $y = e^x$.

Example 3   Consider the function $y = e^{x+3} - 4$ that results from two transformations applied to $y = e^x$. The *inside addition* of 3 tells us that the graph is shifted *left* by 3 units. The *outside subtraction* of 4 indicates that the graph is shifted *down* by 4 units. What are the attributes of this transformed function?

Solution   The function is still increasing everywhere, and its range remains $(0, \infty)$. Its horizontal asymptote has dropped by 4 units, so it is the line $y = -4$. As $x \to -\infty$, $y \to -4$. Its y-intercept is the value $e^{0+3} - 4 = e^3 - 4 \approx 16.1$, approximately located at the point $(0, 16.1)$. The original y-intercept, $(0, 1)$, has moved to the left 3 and down 4, so it is shifted to the point $(-3, -3)$. See Figure 7.33 for the graph of the transformed function.

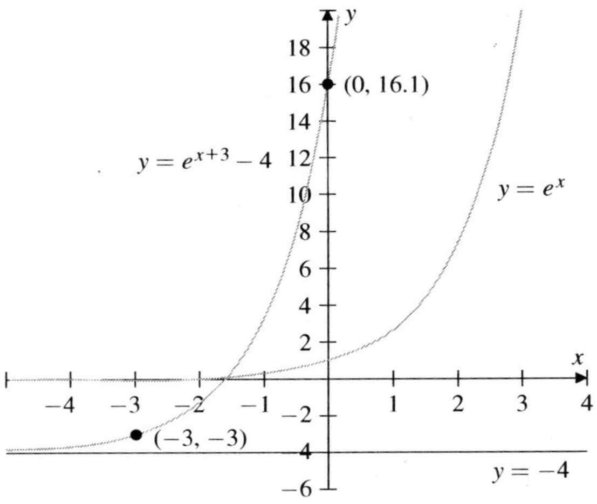

Figure 7.33

Summary of Translations (Shifts) of Exponential Functions

The function $y = b^{(x-h)} + k$ has translations identified by h and k. The graph is shifted from the graph of $y = b^x$.

- Because $+k$ is an *outside change*, the graph shifts vertically $|k|$ units. If $k > 0$, the graph shifts up; if $k < 0$, the graph shifts down.
- Because $(x - h)$ is an *inside change*, the graph shifts horizontally $|h|$ units. If $h > 0$, the graph shifts to the right; if $h < 0$, the graph shifts to the left.
- The new y-intercept is at the point $(0, k + b^{-h})$.
- The original horizontal asymptote $y = 0$ shifts to the line $y = k$.

Matched Problem 1

Sketch the graph of $g(x) = 2^x$. Without using your calculator, sketch the graphs of the following transformed functions, along with $g(x)$, each on a separate coordinate system. Indicate the formula for each function, its range, its horizontal asymptote, its vertical intercept, and the shifted location of the original y-intercept on each sketch.

(a) $y = g(x) - 3$

(b) $y = g(x + 3)$

(c) $y = g(x - 3) + 6$

Matched Problem 2

(a) Write the equation of a function that transforms $y = 2^x$ so that its graph is shifted 4 units upward and 5 units to the left.

(b) What is its range?

(c) What is its horizontal asymptote?

(d) What is its y-intercept?

(e) Where does its original y-intercept point shift?

Example 4   From our knowledge of how a transformation of an exponential function might shift its graph, we are able to examine a graph and write its function formula. The following graph, seen in Figure 7.34, is a transformation of $y = 3^x$. What is its function formula?

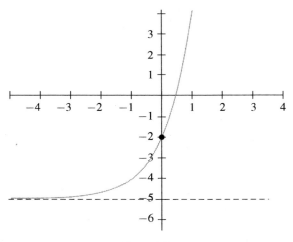

Figure 7.34

Solution   Observe that the graph has a horizontal asymptote at the line $y = -5$. This means that the formula for the function shown in the graph has an *outside* subtraction of 5. Its y intercept is at the point $(0, -2)$, so $-2 = -5 + 3^{-h}$. In this case, we are able to solve for h : $3 = 3^{-h}$, so $h = -1$. The formula for the function graphed in Figure 4.34 is $y = 3^{x-(-1)} - 5 = 3^{x+1} - 5$. For this graph, we were able to solve for h easily. After we have studied logarithms in chapter 8, we will be able to solve for any h in this procedure.

Reflections

Recall that a *reflection* across the *x-axis* comes about when the function is multiplied by –1, giving an *outside* transformation of the function's formula. The transformation $y = -f(x)$ produces a graph that is reflected about the *x-axis*. On the other hand, a *reflection* across the *y-axis* occurs when the input or *x-value* is multiplied by –1, giving an *inside* transformation of the function's formula. This reflection across the *y-axis* occurs when we graph $y = f(-x)$.

Example 5   How do $y = 5^x$ and $y = -5^x$, an *outside* change, compare?

Solution   Recall that the expression -5^x is equivalent to $-(5^x)$. Its base is 5, not –5. With the new, reflected function, each function value is now negative. The range of this reflected function is the negative numbers, $(-\infty, 0)$.

We know that when the base of an exponential function is greater than one (such as a base of 5) and the parameter a from the equation $y = ab^x$ is positive (such as a value of 1), the function is increasing. Thus the original function, $y = 5^x$, is increasing. When we reflect the graph of the function across the *x-axis*, the transformed function is decreasing. The horizontal asymptote has not changed. It is still $y = 0$, and as $x \to -\infty$, $y \to 0$. In addition, the new $y-$intercept is the value $-5^0 = -(5^0) = -1$ and is graphed on the *vertical-axis* at the point $(0, -1)$. The original y-intercept reflected to this new y-intercept.

In summary, both $y = 5^x$ and $y = -5^x$ are graphed in Figure 7.35.

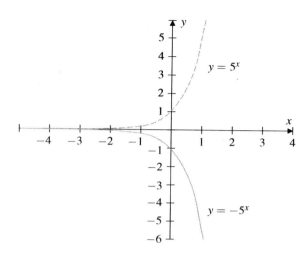

Figure 7.35

Example 6   Next, how do $y = 5^x$ and $y = 5^{-x}$, an *inside* change, compare?

Solution   The graph of $y = 5^{-x}$ is the graph of $y = 5^x$ reflected horizontally across the y-axis. The transformed function is decreasing everywhere. Its range is still the positive numbers, $(0, \infty)$. The x-axis, or $y = 0$, is still the horizontal asymptote, but now as $x \to \infty$, $y \to 0$. The y-intercept has not moved from the point $(0, 1)$.

Observe the graph of $y = 5^{-x}$ below. Confirm its graph with your graphing calculator, and reinforce that graph by typing $y_1 = 5^{\wedge}(-x)$.

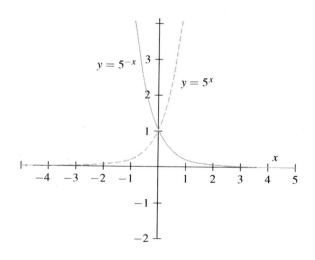

Figure 7.36

This new, transformed function behaves as an exponential function with a base between zero and one. Indeed, that is exactly what it is, as shown by the following equivalent equations.

(1) $y = 5^{-x}$ transformed function

(2) $y = \dfrac{1}{5^x}$ by the definition of a negative exponent

(3) $y = \left(\dfrac{1}{5}\right)^x$ by the rules of exponents

The transformed function is an exponential function with a base of $\frac{1}{5}$. Notice Figure 7.36, comparing the graph of the original function and its *reflection* about the *y-axis*. Again, confirm with your graphing calculator that the graph of $y = \left(\frac{1}{5}\right)^x$ is identical to the graph of $y = 5^{-x}$.

We can now combine the horizontal and vertical shifts with the horizontal and vertical reflections to make a more complex transformation of an exponential function.

Example 7   Consider the function $y = -5^{-x} + 3$. How does it compare to $y = 5^x$?

Solution   To combine several transformations, always work from the inside outward as explained in Figure 7.37. The graphs corresponding to each step are shown in Figure 7.38.

$$g(x) = -\left(5^{-x}\right) + 3$$

Step 1: horizontal reflection about the y-axis

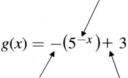

Step 2: vertical reflection about the *x*-axis   Step 3: vertical shift

Figure 7.37

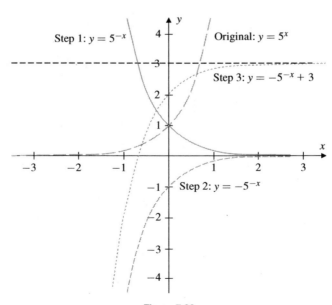

Figure 7.38

Stretches and Compressions

As we saw with polynomial and trigonometric functions, stretches and compressions of the graph of a function occur when the original function is *multiplied* by a number. The vertical changes in scale happen when we multiply on the *outside*, while horizontal changes in scale happen when we multiply on the *inside*. Let's explore with the graphing calculator to see whether we stretch or compress, based on the transforming factor.

Example 8   Begin with the exponential function $y = 2^x$. Write the formulas of the four transformed functions as y_1 to y_4, using factors 3 and $\frac{1}{3}$ and multiplying each of *inside* and *outside*. Using transforming factors of 3 and $\frac{1}{3}$, we have four transformations to try.

Solution $y_1 = 3(2^x), \quad y_2 = \frac{1}{3}(2^x) \quad y_3 = 2^{3x} \quad y_4 = 2^{\frac{x}{3}}$ in any order.

Use your graphing calculator to graph the original function along with each of the four transformed functions, one at a time. You should get the results seen in Figure 7.39.

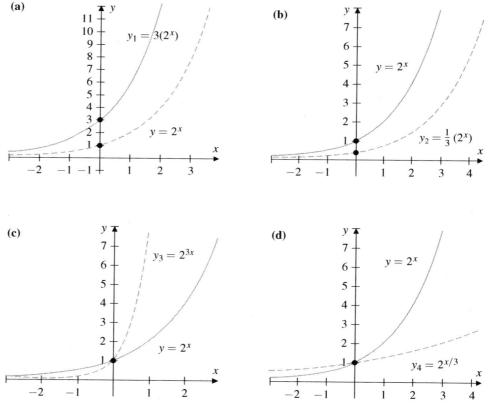

Figure 7.39

Notice that the *outside* multiplication as illustrated in graphs **a** and **b** stretches the graph of the original function vertically when the transforming factor is greater than one and compresses the graph vertically when the transforming factor is between zero and one. On the other hand, the *inside* multiplication as illustrated in graphs **c** and **d** stretches the graph of the original function horizontally when the positive transforming factor is between zero and one and compresses the graph horizontally when the transforming factor is greater than one. The *inside* multiplication preserves the *y*-intercept while the *outside* multiplication does not.

Each of these transformed functions remains increasing, with a range of the positive numbers, $(0, \infty)$. The *x*-axis, or $y = 0$, is still the horizontal asymptote. The outside multiplications, such as $y = 3\,(2^x)$ and $y = \frac{1}{3}\,(2^x)$, shift the *x-coordinate of the y*-intercept by the outside factor.

Example 9   Consider a function that combines some of the above transformations. For example, starting with $y = 2^x$, consider the transformed function $g(x) = -\frac{1}{3}(2^{4x}) + 3$.

$$g(x) = -\frac{1}{3}(2^{4x}) + 3$$

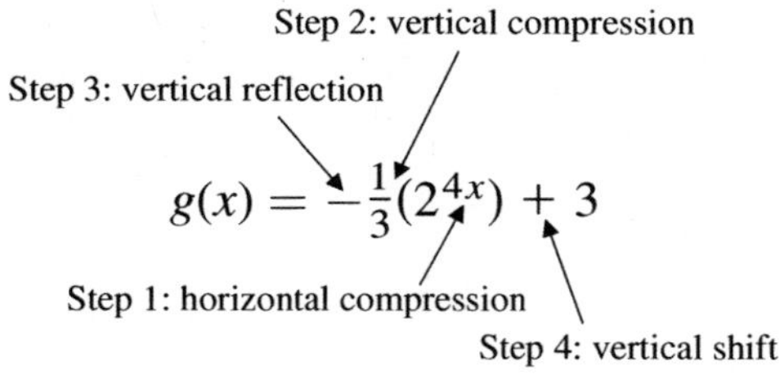

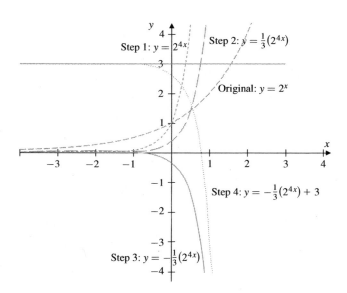

Step 2: vertical compression

Step 3: vertical reflection

$$g(x) = -\frac{1}{3}(2^{4x}) + 3$$

Step 1: horizontal compression

Step 4: vertical shift

Figure 7.40

Figure 7.41

Solution   As Figures 7.40 and 7.41 show, the order of the four transformations is from the inside to the outside. When we consider this transformed function, $g(x) = -\frac{1}{3}(2^{4x}) + 3$, we see a decreasing function with a range of $(-\infty, 3)$. Its horizontal asymptote is the line $y = 3$, and as $x \to -\infty$, $y \to 3$. The original *y*-intercept moved from the point $(0, 1)$ to the point $\left(0, 3 - \frac{1}{3}\right) = \left(0, 2\frac{2}{3}\right)$. This is the new *y*-intercept as well.

Look back at Example 5 of Section 2.6. This example models the temperature of a yam as it bakes as an exponential function. Now this model can be understood in the language of a transformed exponential function similar to ones that we have considered in this section.

Expressing Transformations of Exponential Functions in the Form $y = ab^x$

Consider the exponential function $y = 2^x$ as our starting function. It is exponential, with the parameter a equal to 1 and its base b equal to 2. As we examine some transformations of the function, illustrated in Figure 7.39, we recognize some of the new functions as exponential functions also.

The horizontal compression, such as that seen in Figure 7.39c above, has a function formula of $y = 2^{3x}$. It may be written as an exponential function in the form $y = ab^x$ by the following steps.

(1) $y = 2^{3x}$
(2) $y = (2^3)^x$ by the rules of exponents
(3) $y = 8^x$ evaluating the exponential expression

The transformed function is in exponential form, with an a parameter of 1 and a base b of 8. The transformed function increases faster than the original function because its base, 8, is larger than the original base of 2.

Consider a transformation that shifts the graph of the function horizontally, such as **Example 2.** This new function is an exponential function as well. For the function $y = 2^{x+3}$, the following steps show how it can be written in the form $y = ab^x$.

(1) $y = 2^{x+3}$
(2) $y = 2^x \cdot 2^3$ by the rules of exponents
(3) $y = 2^x \cdot 8$ evaluating the exponential expression
(4) $y = 8 \cdot 2^x$ by the commutative property of multiplication

Thus the transformed function has a base b of 2 and an a parameter of 8. This also illustrates that a horizontal shift is equivalent to a vertical stretch or compression. In this case, a horizontal shift to the left is equivalent to a vertical stretch. It turns out that a horizontal shift to the right is equivalent to a vertical compression.

In applications of an exponential model, especially when the initial value and the growth or decay rate are given, the vertical stretch or compression form of the model's equation is usually used. For example, Example 8 in Section 7.1 and Example 1 in Section 7.3 use this form.

Answers to Matched Problems

1. (a) $y = g(x) - 3 = 2^x - 3$
     Range: $(-3, \infty)$
     Horizontal Asymptote: $y = -3$
     y-intercept: $(0, -2)$
     Shifted y-intercept: $(0, -2)$

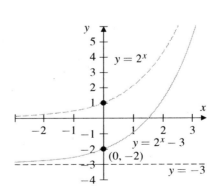

(b) $y = g(x + 3) = 2^{x+3}$
Range: $(0, \infty)$
Horizontal Asymptote: $y = 0$
y-intercept: $(0, 8)$
Shifted y-intercept: $(-3, 1)$

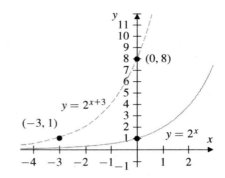

(c) $y = g(x - 3) + 6 = 2^{(x-3)} + 6$
Range: $(6, \infty)$
Horizontal Asymptote: $y = 6$
y-intercept: $(0, 6.125)$
Shifted y-intercept: $(3, 7)$

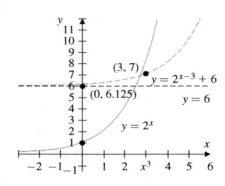

2. (a) $y = 2^{(x+5)} + 4$
   (b) Range: $(4, \infty)$
   (c) Horizontal Asymptote: $y = 4$
   (d) y-intercept: $(0, 36)$
   (e) Original y-intercept shifted to: $(-5, 5)$

Exercises for Section 7.5

1. Let $f(x) = 4^x$, $g(x) = 4^x + 2$, and $h(x) = 4^{x+2}$. What is the relationship between the graph of $f(x)$ and the graphs of $g(x)$ and $h(x)$?

2. Let $f(x) = e^x$, $g(x) = 2e^x$, and $h(x) = e^{2x}$. How do the graphs of $g(x)$ and $h(x)$ compare to the graph of $f(x)$?

For Exercises 3–4, start with the function $k(x) = 4^x$. For each exercise,

(a) Write the formula of the function,
(b) State the location of the transformed y-intercept,
(c) State the equation of the horizontal asymptote, and
(d) State the new y-intercept.
(e) Without a calculator, graph the new function and label the two points and the asymptote.

3. $y = k(x) - 3$

4. $y = k(x + 3)$

5. If $g(x) = -3^{x-2}$, state the basic function and state the transformations. Without a calculator, graph the function and label the graph, the location of the transformed y-intercept and the new y-intercept, and sketch and label the horizontal asymptote.

6. If $y = 3^{-x} + 1$, state the basic function and state the transformations. Without a calculator, graph the function and label the graph, the location of the transformed y-intercept and the new y-intercept, and sketch and label the horizontal asymptote.

For Exercises 7–8, give a formula and graph (without a calculator) for each of the transformations of $f(x) = e^x$. For each graph, label the location of the transformed y-intercept, the new y-intercept, and sketch and label the horizontal asymptote.

7. $y = 3f(-x)$

8. $y = -f(x) - 1$

9. If $y = -e^{-x}$, state the basic function and state the transformations. Without a calculator, graph the function and label the graph, the location of the transformed y-intercept and the new y-intercept, and sketch and label the horizontal asymptote.

10. If $y = -e^x - 2$, state the basic function and state the transformations. Without a calculator, graph the function and label the graph, the location of the transformed y-intercept and the new y-intercept, and sketch and label the horizontal asymptote.

11. (a) If $h(x) = 2^x$, write a formula for the function $y = 3h(x-1)$. State the transformations.
   (b) Without a calculator, graph the new function. Label at least three points.
   (c) Write the new function in the form $y = a \cdot b^x$ and identify a and b.

12. Write the function $y = -5\left(3^{x+4}\right)$ in the form $y = a \cdot b^x$ and identify a and b. Use your calculator to verify numerically and graphically that the two forms represent the same function.

13. Without a calculator, match each formula (a) – (e) with a graph in Figure 7.42. There may be no answer or several answers.

   (a) $y = 3 \cdot 2^x$ (b) $y = 5^{-x}$ (c) $y = -5^x$
   (d) $y = 2 - 2^{-x}$ (e) $y = 1 - \left(\frac{1}{2}\right)^x$

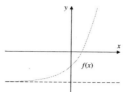
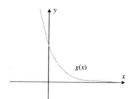
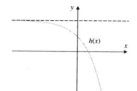
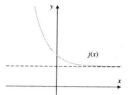

Figure 7.43

15. Let $f(x) = 2^x$. Find possible formulas for the transformations of f in (a)–(d). *Example*: The graph in Figure 7.44 appears to be f flipped across the y-axis. Because the horizontal asymptote is at $y = -3$ instead of $y = 0$, it appears that f is shifted downward by 3 units. Therefore, $y = f(-x) - 3 = 2^{-x} - 3$.

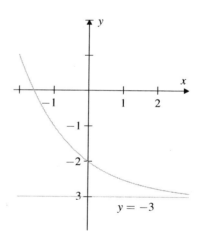

Figure 7.44

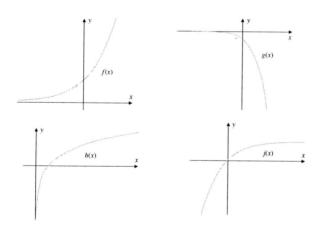

Figure 7.42

14. Without a calculator, match each formula (a)–(e) with a graph in Figure 7.43. There may be no answer or several answers.

   (a) $y = e^{-x}$ (b) $y = e^x - 2$ (c) $y = e^x + 2$
   (d) $y = 2 - e^x$ (e) $y = e^{-x} + 2$

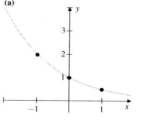
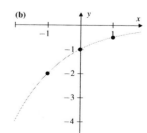

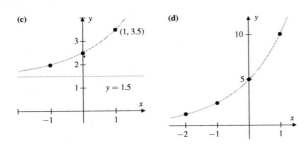

16. Use your calculator to graph $s(x) = 2^x + \left(\frac{1}{2}\right)^x$, $c(x) = 2^x - \left(\frac{1}{2}\right)^x$, and $n(x) = 2^x - \left(\frac{1}{2}\right)^{x-1}$. Based on your visual observations, state whether you think these functions are even, odd, or neither. Show that your statements are true using algebra. That is, prove or disprove statements such as $s(-x) = s(x)$.

17. By applying one or more transformations to a function, you can create a new function that contains a given point. Create two different functions that both have $y = 2^x$ as the basic function and that contain the point $(3, -2)$.

18. Using as many transformations as you like, create two different functions that both have $y = 10^x$ as the basic function and that contain the point $(-5, 3)$.

19. If $t \geq 0$ then $H(t) = 68 + 93e^{-0.094\,t}$ gives the temperature of a cup of coffee in degrees Fahrenheit t minutes after it is brought to class.
  (a) Find formulas for $H(t + 15)$ and $H(t) + 15$.
  (b) Describe in practical terms a situation modeled by the function $H(t + 15)$. What about $H(t) + 15$?
  (c) Which function $H(t + 15)$ or $H(t) + 15$ approaches the same final temperature as the function $H(t)$? What is that temperature?

CHAPTER SUMMARY

- **Exponential Functions**

  Value of $f(t)$ changes at constant percent rate with respect to t.

- **General Formula for Exponential Functions**

  Exponential function: $f(t) = ab^t$, $b > 0$. f increasing for $b > 1$, decreasing for $0 < b < 1$.

  Growth factor: $b = 1 + r$.

  Growth rate: r, percent change as a decimal.

- **Comparing Linear and Exponential Functions**

  An increasing exponential function eventually overtakes any linear function.

- **Graphs of Exponential Functions**

  Concavity; asymptotes; effect of parameters a and b.

Solving exponential equations graphically; fitting exponential functions to data.

- **The Number e**

  Continuous growth: $f(t) = ae^{kt}$.

  f is increasing for $k > 0$, decreasing for $k < 0$.

  Continuous growth rate: k.

- **Compound Interest**

  For compounding n times per year, balance,

  $$B = P\left(1 + \frac{r}{n}\right)^{nt}.$$

  For continuous compounding, $B = Pe^{kt}$.
  Nominal rate, r or k, versus effective rate earned over one year.

REVIEW EXERCISES AND PROBLEMS FOR CHAPTER SEVEN

Exercises

1. A town has population 3000 people at year $t = 0$. Write a formula for the population, P, in year t if the town
  (a) Grows by 200 people per year.
  (b) Grows by 6% per year.
  (c) Grows at a continuous rate of 6% per year.
  (d) Shrinks by 50 people per year.
  (e) Shrinks by 4% per year.
  (f) Shrinks at a continuous rate of 4% per year.

2. The following formulas each describe the size of an animal population, P, in t years since the start of the study. Describe the growth of each population in words.
  (a) $P = 200(1.028)^t$
  (b) $P = 50e^{-0.17t}$
  (c) $P = 1000(0.89)^t$
  (d) $P = 600e^{0.20t}$
  (e) $P = 2000 - 300t$
  (f) $P = 600 + 50t$

3. World poultry production was 69 million tons in the year 2001 and increasing at a continuous rate of 3% per year.[12] Assume that this growth rate continues.

    (a) Write an exponential formula for world poultry production, P, in million tons, as a function of the number of years, t, since 2001.

    (b) Use the formula to estimate world poultry production in the year 2005.

    (c) Use a graph to estimate the year in which world poultry production goes over 90 million tons.

4. A population of fish starts at 8000 fish in the year 2000 and decreases by 5.8% per year.

    (a) Find a formula for the population, P, of fish t years after 2000.

    (b) What population does the formula predict in the year 2005?

    (c) Use a graph to estimate the year in which the population goes below 3000.

5. Without a calculator, match each of the formulas to one of the graphs in Figure 7.45.

    (a) $y = 0.8^t$ **(b)** $y = 5(3)^t$

    (c) $y = -6(1.03)^t$ **(d)** $y = 15(3)^{-t}$

    (e) $y = -4(0.98)^t$ **(f)** $y = 82(0.8)^{-t}$

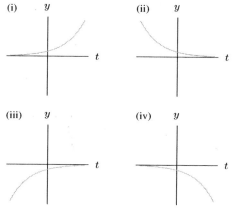

Figure 7.45

6. Without a calculator, match each of the following formulas to one of the graphs in Figure 7.45.

    (a) $y = 8.3e^{-t}$ **(b)** $y = 2.5e^t$ **(c)** $y = -4e^{-t}$

For Exercises 7–11, find a formula for the exponential function.

7.   **8.**

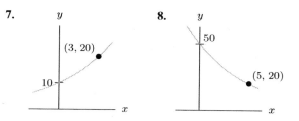

9.   **10.**

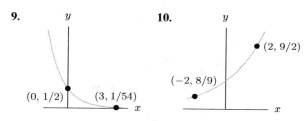

11.

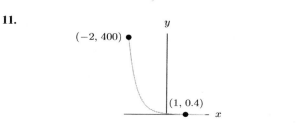

Decide whether the functions in Exercises 12–14 could be linear or exponential or are neither. For those that could be linear or exponential, find a formula.

12.

x	0	1	2	3
$f(x)$	125	150	180	216

13.

x	0	1	2	3
$g(x)$	12.8	11.5	10.2	8.9

14.

x	-2	-1	0	1
$h(x)$	1024	512	256	128

15. An account pays interest at a nominal rate of 8% per year. Find the effective annual yield if interest is compounded

    (a) Monthly   **(b)** Weekly

    (c) Daily   **(d)** Continuously

16. Find a formula for $f(x)$, an exponential function such that $f(-8) = 200$ and $f(30) = 580$.

17. Suppose that $f(x)$ is exponential and that $f(-3) = 54$ and $f(2) = \frac{2}{9}$. Find a formula for $f(x)$.

---

[12]The Worldwatch Institute, *Vital Signs* 2002 (New York: W.W. Norton & Company, 2002), p. 29.

18. Find a formula for $f(x)$, an exponential function such that $f(2) = 1/27$ and $f(-1) = 27$.

19. Find the equation of an exponential curve through the points $(-1, 2)$, $(1, 0.3)$.

20. Graph a function with a horizontal asymptote of $y = 5$.

21. Use a graph to determine any horizontal asymptotes of $y = 3 - e^{-x}$.

Problems

Decide whether the functions in Problems 22–24 could be approximately linear, approximately exponential, or are neither. For those that could be nearly linear or nearly exponential, find a formula.

22.

t	3	10	14
$Q(t)$	7.51	8.7	9.39

23.

t	5	9	15
$R(t)$	2.32	2.61	3.12

24.

t	5	12	16
$S(t)$	4.35	6.72	10.02

25. In 2001 the population of the United States was about 284.8 million and increasing at a rate of 0.9% per year. In what year is the population projected to reach 300 million?

26. There were 178.8 million licensed drivers in the US in 1989 and 187.2 million in 1999.[13] Find a formula for the number, N of licensed drivers in the US as a function of t, the number of years since 1989, assuming growth is

  (a) Linear   **(b)** Exponential

27. The population of a small town increases by a growth factor of 1.134 over a two-year period.

  (a) By what percent does the town increase in size during the two-year period?
  (b) If the town grows by the same percent each year, what is its annual percent growth rate?

28. If t is in years, the formulas for dollar balances of two different bank accounts are:

$$f(t) = 1100(1.05)^t \quad \text{and} \quad g(t) = 1500e^{0.05t}.$$

  (a) Describe in words the bank account modeled by f.
  (b) Describe the account modeled by g. State the effective annual yield.

29. Determine which of the functions given in Table 7.17 is linear and which is exponential. Write a formula for the linear and the exponential function.

Table 7.17

x	$f(x)$	$g(x)$	$h(x)$
-2	4	48	20/3
-1	1	12	16/3
0	0	3	4
1	1	3/4	8/3

30. One of the functions in Table 7.18 is linear and the other is exponential. Find formulas for these functions.

Table 7.18

x	0.21	0.37	0.41	0.62	0.68
$f(x)$	0.03193	0.04681	0.05053	0.07006	0.07564
$g(x)$	3.324896	3.423316	3.448373	3.582963	3.622373

31. If $f(x) = 12 + 20x$ and $g(x) = \frac{1}{2} \cdot 3^x$, for what values of x is $g(x) < f(x)$?

32. A colony of bacteria is growing exponentially. At the end of 3 hours there are 1000 bacteria. At the end of 5 hours there are 4000.

  (a) Write a formula for the population of bacteria at time t, in hours.
  (b) By what percent does the number of bacteria increase each hour?

33. Accion is a non-profit microlending organization which makes small loans to entrepreneurs who do not qualify for bank loans.[14] A New York woman who sells clothes from a cart has the choice of a $1000 loan from Accion to be repaid by $1160 a year later and a $1000 loan from a loan shark with an annual interest rate of 22%, compounded annually.

  (a) What is the annual interest rate charged by Accion?
  (b) To pay off the loan shark for a year's loan of $1000, how much would the woman have to pay?
  (c) Which loan is a better deal for the woman? Why?

34. Two reductions are available on a copy machine: 70% and 85%. A page can be further reduced by copying an already reduced copy.

---

[13]*The World Almanac* 2002 (New York: World Almanac Education Group, Inc., 2002), p. 228.
[14]From *Hemispheres*, December 1998 (United Airlines).

(a) If a 70% reduction is followed by an 85% reduction, what is the overall percent reduction?

(b) Write a formula for the percent reduction if a page is copied n times in succession at 70%.

(c) Estimate the number of times a page has to be copied at 70% reduction before it is less than 10% of its original size.

35. In 1990, the population of a town was 18,500 and it grew by 250 people by the end of the year. By 2000, its population had reached 22,500.

(a) Can this population be best described by a linear or an exponential model, or neither? Explain.

(b) If possible, find a formula for $P(t)$, the population t years after 1990.

36. In 1990, the population of a town was 20,000, and it grew by 4.14% that year. By 2000, the town's population had reached 30,000.

(a) Can this population be best described by a linear or an exponential model, or neither? Explain.

(b) If possible, find a formula for $P(t)$, this population t years after 1990.

37. Forty percent of a radioactive substance decays in five years. By what percent does the substance decay each year?

38. Find the annual growth rates of a quantity which:

(a) Doubles in size every 7 years
(b) Triples in size every 11 years
(c) Grows by 3% per month
(d) Grows by 18% every 5 months

39. Table 7.19 shows the concentration of theophylline, a common asthma drug, in the blood stream as a function of time after injection of a 300 mg initial dose.[15] It is claimed that this data set is consistent with an exponential decay model $C = ab^t$ where C is the concentration and t is the time.

(a) Estimate the values of a and b, using ratios to estimate b. How good is this model?

(b) Use a calculator or computer to find the exponential regression function for concentration as a function of time. Compare answers from parts (a) and (b).

Table 7.19

Time (hours)	0	1	3	5	7	9
Concentration (mg/l)	12.0	10.0	7.0	5.0	3.5	2.5

40. Figure 7.46 gives the voltage, $V(t)$, across a circuit element at time t seconds. For $t < 0$, the voltage is a constant 80 volts; for $t \geq 0$, the voltage decays exponentially.

(a) Find a piecewise formula for $V(t)$.
(b) At what value of t will the voltage reach 0.1?

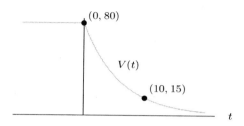

Figure 7.46

41. Hong Kong shifted from British to Chinese rule in 1997. Figure 7.47 shows[16] the number of people who emigrated from Hong Kong during each of the years from 1980 to 1992.

(a) Find an exponential function that approximates the data.

(b) What does the model predict about the number of emigrants in 1997?

(c) Briefly explain why this model is or is not useful to predict emigration in the year 2010.

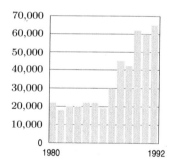

Figure 7.47

42. The annual inflation rate, r, for a five-year period is given in Table 7.20.

(a) By what total percent did prices rise between the start of 1980 and the end of 1984?

(b) What is the average annual inflation rate for this time period?

(c) At the beginning of 1980, a shower curtain costs $20. Make a prediction for the good's cost at the beginning of 1990, using the average inflation rate found in part (b).

[15]Based on D. N. Burghes, I. Huntley, and J. McDonald, *Applying Mathematics*. (Ellis Horwood, 1982).
[16]Adapted from the *New York Times* July 5, 1995.

Table 7.20

t	1980	1981	1982	1983	1984
r	5.1%	6.2%	3.1%	4.7%	3.3%

43. A high-risk investment reports the annual yields in Table 7.21. What is the average annual yield of this investment over the five-year period shown?

Table 7.21

t	1990	1991	1992	1993	1994
Growth	27%	36%	19%	44%	57%

44. The population of Botswana[17] from 1975 to 1990 is shown in Table 7.22.

(a) Fit an exponential growth model, $P = ab^t$, to this data set, where P is the population in millions and t measures the years since 1975 in 5-year intervals—so $t = 1$ corresponds to 1980. Estimate a and b. Plot the data set and $P = ab^t$ on the same graph.

(b) Starting from 1975, how long does it take for the population of Botswana to double? When is the population of Botswana projected to exceed 214 million, the 1975 population of the US?

Table 7.22

Year	1975	1980	1985	1990
Population (millions)	0.755	0.901	1.078	1.285

45. Suppose $300 was deposited into one of five bank accounts and t is time in years. For each verbal description (i)–(v), state which formulas (a)–(e) could represent it.

(a) $B = 300(1.2)^t$ (b) $B = 300(1.12)^t$

(c) $B = 300(1.06)^{2t}$ (d) $B = 300(1.06)^{t/2}$

(e) $B = 300(1.03)^{4t}$

(i) This investment earned 12% annually, compounded annually.

(ii) This investment earned, on average, more than 1% each month.

(iii) This investment earned 12% annually, compounded semi-annually.

(iv) This investment earned, on average, less than 3% each quarter.

(v) This investment earned, on average, more than 6% every 6 months.

46. It is a well-documented fact that the earning power of men is higher than that of women.[18] Table 7.23 gives the median income of year-round full-time workers in the US in thousands of dollars.

(a) Plot the data and connect the points.

(b) Let t be the year. Construct two functions of the form $W(t) = ae^{b(t-1980)}$, one each for the men's and women's earning power data.

(c) Graph the two functions from 1980 to 2000.

(d) Graph the two functions from 1980 to 2030.

(e) Does the graph in part (d) predict women's salaries will catch up with men's?

(f) Do you think it likely that the median salaries of women will ultimately be higher than men's?

Table 7.23

Year	1980	1985	1988	1989	1990
Female	11.591	16.252	18.545	19.643	20.586
Male	19.173	24.999	27.342	28.605	29.172

47. According to a letter to the *New York Times* on April 10, 1993, "... the probability of [a driver's] involvement in a single-car accident increases exponentially with increasing levels of blood alcohol." The letter goes on to state that when a driver's blood-alcohol content (BAC) is 0.15, the risk of such an accident is about 25 times greater than for a nondrinker.

(a) Let p_0 be a nondrinker's probability of being involved in a single-car accident. Let $f(x)$ be the probability of an accident for a driver whose blood alcohol level is x. Find a formula for $f(x)$. (This only makes sense for some values of x.)

(b) At the time of the letter, the legal definition of intoxication was a BAC of 0.1 or higher. According to your formula for $f(x)$, how many times more likely to be involved in a single-car accident was a driver at the legal limit than a nondrinker?

(c) Suppose that new legislation is proposed to change the definition of legal intoxication. The new definition states that a person is legally intoxicated when their likelihood of involvement in a single-car accident is three times that of a non-drinker. To what BAC would the new definition of legal intoxication correspond?

48. In the Fibonacci sequence 1, 1, 2, 3, 5, 8 ..., each term in the sequence is the sum of the two preceding terms. For example, the seventh term in this sequence is the sum of the sixth and fifth terms, $8 + 5 = 13$. Let $f(n)$ be the nth term in the Fibonacci sequence, for $n \geq 1$.

---

[17]*World Population Growth and Aging* by N. Keyfitz, University of Chicago Press, 1990.
[18]Source: The American Almanac, 1992–1993, Table 710.

(a) Complete the table with the first twelve terms of the Fibonacci sequence:

n	1	2	3	4	5	6	7	8	9	10	11	12
$f(n)$	1	1	2	3	5							

(b) Show that $f(n)$ is not an exponential function.
(c) Show, by taking ratios, that for adequately large values of n, the value of $f(n)$ grows at roughly a constant percent rate.
(d) Find an exponential function that approximates $f(n)$ for large values of n (say, $n > 5$).

49. (a) Using a computer or calculator, graph $f(x) = 2^x$.
(b) Find the slope of the line tangent to f at $x = 0$ to an accuracy of two decimals. [Hint: Zoom in on the graph until it is indistinguishable from a line and estimate the slope using two points on the graph.]

(c) Find the slope of the line tangent to $g(x) = 3^x$ at $x = 0$ to an accuracy of two decimals.
(d) Find b (to two decimals) such that the line tangent to the function $h(x) = b^x$ at $x = 0$ has slope 1.

50. With more terms giving a better approximation, it can be shown that

$$e = 1 + \frac{1}{1} + \frac{1}{1 \cdot 2} + \frac{1}{1 \cdot 2 \cdot 3} + \frac{1}{1 \cdot 2 \cdot 3 \cdot 4} + \cdots .$$

(a) Use a calculator to sum the five terms shown.
(b) Find the sum of the first seven terms.
(c) Compare your sums with the calculator's displayed value for e (which you can find by entering $e\hat{\ }1$) and state the number of correct digits in the five and seven term sum.
(d) How many terms of the sum are needed in order to give a nine decimal digit approximation equal to the calculator's displayed value for e?

CHECK YOUR UNDERSTANDING

Are the statements in Problems 1–32 true or false? Give an explanation for your answer.

1. Exponential functions are functions that increase or decrease at a constant percent rate.

2. The independent variable in an exponential function is always found in the exponent.

3. If $y = 40(1.05)^t$ then y is an exponential function of t.

4. The following table shows a function that could be exponential.

x	1	2	4	5	6
y	1	2	4	7	11

5. If your salary, S, grows by 4% each year, then $S = S_0(0.04)^t$ where t is in years.

6. If $f(t) = 4(2)^t$ then $f(2) = 64$.

7. If $f(t) = 3(\frac{2}{5})^t$ then f is a decreasing function.

8. If $Q = f(t) = 1000(0.5)^t$ then when $Q = 125$, $t = 3$.

9. If $Q = f(t) = ab^t$ then a is the initial value of Q.

10. If we are given two data points, we can find a linear function and an exponential function that go through these points.

11. A population that has 1000 members and decreases at 10% per year can be modeled as $P = 1000(0.10)^t$.

12. A positive increasing exponential function always becomes larger than any increasing linear function in the long run.

13. A possible formula for an exponential function that passes through the point $(0, 1)$ and the point $(2, 10)$ is $y = 4.5t + 1$.

14. If a population increases by 50% each year, then in two years it increases by 100%.

15. In the formula $Q = ab^t$, the value of a tells us where the graph crosses the Q-axis.

16. In the formula $Q = ab^t$, if $a > 1$, the graph always rises as we read from left to right.

17. The symbol e represents a constant whose value is approximately 2.71828.

18. If $f(x) \to k$ as $x \to \infty$ we say that the line $y = k$ is a horizontal asymptote.

19. Exponential graphs are always concave up.

20. If there are 110 grams of a substance initially and its decay rate is 3% per minute, then the amount after t minutes is $Q = 110(0.03)^t$ grams.

21. If a population had 200 members at time zero and was growing a 4% per year, then the population size after t years can be expressed as $P = 200(1.04)^t$.

22. If $P = 5e^{0.2t}$, we say the continuous growth rate of the function is 2%.

23. If $P = 4e^{-0.90t}$, we say the continuous growth rate of the function is 10%.

24. If $Q = 3e^{0.2t}$, then when $t = 5$, $Q = 3$.

25. If $Q = Q_0e^{kt}$, with Q_0 positive and k negative, then Q is decreasing.

26. If an investment earns 5% compounded monthly, its effective rate will be more than 5%.

27. If a $500 investment earns 6% per year, compounded quarterly, we can find the balance after three years by evaluating the formula $B = 500(1 + \frac{6}{4})^{3 \cdot 4}$.

28. If interest on a $2000 investment is compounded continuously at 3% per year, the balance after five years is found by evaluating the formula $B = 2000e^{(0.03)(5)}$.

29. Investing $10,000 for 20 years at 5% earns more if interest is compounded quarterly than if it is compounded annually.

30. Investing $P for T years always earns more if interest is compounded continuously than if it is compounded annually.

31. There is no limit to the amount a twenty-year $10,000 investment at 5% interest can earn if the number of times the interest is compounded becomes greater and greater.

32. If you put $1000 into an account that earns 5.5% compounded continuously, then it takes about 18 years for the investment to grow to $2000.

LOGARITHMIC FUNCTIONS

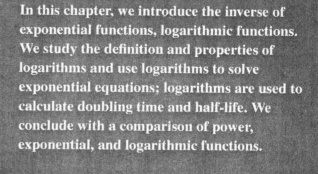

In this chapter, we introduce the inverse of exponential functions, logarithmic functions. We study the definition and properties of logarithms and use logarithms to solve exponential equations; logarithms are used to calculate doubling time and half-life. We conclude with a comparison of power, exponential, and logarithmic functions.

8.1 LOGARITHMS AND THEIR PROPERTIES

What is a Logarithm?

Suppose that a population grows according to the formula $P = 10^t$, where P is the colony size at time t, in hours. When will the population be 2500? We want to solve the following equation for t:

$$10^t = 2500.$$

In Section 7.2, we used a graphical method to approximate t. This time, we introduce a function which returns precisely the exponent of 10 we need.

Since $10^3 = 1000$ and $10^4 = 10,000$, and $1000 < 2500 < 10,000$, the exponent we are looking for is between 3 and 4. But how do we find the exponent exactly?

To answer this question, we define the *common logarithm function*, or simply the *log function*, written $\log_{10} x$, or $\log x$, as follows.

> If x is a positive number,
>
> $$\log x \text{ is the exponent of 10 that gives } x.$$
>
> In other words, if
>
> $$y = \log x \qquad \text{then} \qquad 10^y = x.$$

For example, $\log 100 = 2$, because 2 is the exponent of 10 that gives 100, or $10^2 = 100$.

To solve the equation $10^t = 2500$, we must find the power of 10 that gives 2500. Using the log button on a calculator, we can approximate this exponent. We find

$$\log 2500 \approx 3.398, \qquad \text{which means that} \qquad 10^{3.398} \approx 2500.$$

As predicted, this exponent is between 3 and 4. The precise exponent is $\log 2500$; the approximate value is 3.398. Thus, it takes roughly 3.4 hours for the population to reach 2500.

Example 1   Rewrite the following statements using exponents instead of logs.

(a) $\log 100 = 2$ (b) $\log 0.01 = -2$ (c) $\log 30 = 1.477$

Solution   For each statement, we use the fact that if $y = \log x$ then $10^y = x$.

(a) $2 = \log 100$ means that $10^2 = 100$.
(b) $-2 = \log 0.01$ means that $10^{-2} = 0.01$.
(c) $1.477 = \log 30$ means that $10^{1.477} = 30$. (Actually, this is only an approximation. Using a calculator, we see that $10^{1.477} = 29.9916\ldots$ and that $\log 30 = 1.47712125\ldots$.)

Example 2   Rewrite the following statements using logs instead of exponents.

(a) $10^5 = 100,000$ (b) $10^{-4} = 0.0001$ (c) $10^{0.8} = 6.3096.$

Solution   For each statement, we use the fact that if $10^y = x$, then $y = \log x$.

(a) $10^5 = 100,000$ means that $\log 100,000 = 5$.

(b) $10^{-4} = 0.0001$ means that $\log 0.0001 = -4$.

(c) $10^{0.8} = 6.3096$ means that $\log 6.3096 = 0.8$. (This, too, is only an approximation because $10^{0.8}$ actually equals $6.30957344\ldots$)

Logarithms Are Exponents

Note that logarithms are just exponents! Thinking in terms of exponents is often a good way to answer a logarithm problem.

Example 3   Without a calculator, evaluate the following, if possible:

(a) $\log 1$ (b) $\log 10$ (c) $\log 1{,}000{,}000$

(d) $\log 0.001$ (e) $\log \dfrac{1}{\sqrt{10}}$ (f) $\log(-100)$

Solution

(a) We have $\log 1 = 0$, since $10^0 = 1$.

(b) We have $\log 10 = 1$, since $10^1 = 10$.

(c) Since $1{,}000{,}000 = 10^6$, the exponent of 10 that gives $1{,}000{,}000$ is 6. Thus, $\log 1{,}000{,}000 = 6$.

(d) Since $0.001 = 10^{-3}$, the exponent of 10 that gives 0.001 is -3. Thus, $\log 0.001 = -3$.

(e) Since $1/\sqrt{10} = 10^{-1/2}$, the exponent of 10 that gives $1/\sqrt{10}$ is $-\frac{1}{2}$. Thus $\log(1/\sqrt{10}) = -\frac{1}{2}$.

(f) Since 10 to any power is positive, -100 cannot be written as a power of 10. Thus, $\log(-100)$ is undefined.

Logarithmic and Exponential Functions are Inverses

The operation of taking a logarithm "undoes" the exponential function; the logarithm and the exponential are inverse functions. For example, $\log(10^6) = 6$ and $10^{\log 6} = 6$. In particular

> For any N,
> $$\log(10^N) = N$$
> and for $N > 0$,
> $$10^{\log N} = N.$$

Example 4   Evaluate without a calculator: (a) $\log\left(10^{8.5}\right)$ (b) $10^{\log 2.7}$ (c) $10^{\log(x+3)}$

Solution

Using $\log(10^N) = N$ and $10^{\log N} = N$, we have:

(a) $\log\left(10^{8.5}\right) = 8.5$ (b) $10^{\log 2.7} = 2.7$ (c) $10^{\log(x+3)} = x + 3$

You can check the first two results on a calculator.

Properties of Logarithms

In Chapter 7, we saw how to solve exponential equations such as $100 \cdot 2^t = 337,000,000$, graphically. To use logarithms to solve these equations, we use the properties of logarithms, which are justified in this section.

Properties of the Common Logarithm

- By definition, $y = \log x$ means $10^y = x$.
- In particular,
$$\log 1 = 0 \quad \text{and} \quad \log 10 = 1.$$
- The functions 10^x and $\log x$ are inverses, so they "undo" each other:
$$\log(10^x) = x \qquad \text{for all } x,$$
$$10^{\log x} = x \qquad \text{for } x > 0.$$
- For a and b both positive and any value of t,
$$\log(ab) = \log a + \log b$$
$$\log\left(\frac{a}{b}\right) = \log a - \log b$$
$$\log(b^t) = t \cdot \log b.$$

Example 5   Solve $100 \cdot 2^t = 337,000,000$ for t.

Solution   Dividing both sides of the equation by 100 gives
$$2^t = 3,370,000.$$

Taking logs of both sides gives
$$\log\left(2^t\right) = \log(3,370,000).$$

Since $\log(2^t) = t \cdot \log 2$, we have
$$t \log 2 = \log(3,370,000),$$

so, solving for t, we have
$$t = \frac{\log(3,370,000)}{\log 2} = 21.684.$$

In Example 2, Section 7.3, we found the graphical approximation of between 21 and 22 days as the time for the Yonkers fine to exceed the city's annual budget.

The Natural Logarithm

When e is used as the base for exponential functions, computations are easier with the use of another logarithm function, called log base e. The log base e is used so frequently that it has its own notation: $\ln x$, read as the *natural log of x*. We make the following definition:

For $x > 0$,

$$\ln x \text{ is the power of } e \text{ that gives } x$$

or, in symbols,

$$\ln x = y \quad \text{means} \quad e^y = x,$$

and y is called the **natural logarithm** of x.

Just as the functions 10^x and $\log x$ are inverses, so are e^x and $\ln x$. The function $\ln x$ has similar properties to the common log function:

Properties of the Natural Logarithm

- By definition, $y = \ln x$ means $x = e^y$.
- In particular,

$$\ln 1 = 0 \quad \text{and} \quad \ln e = 1.$$

- The functions e^x and $\ln x$ are inverses, so they "undo" each other:

$$\ln(e^x) = x \qquad \text{for all } x$$
$$e^{\ln x} = x \qquad \text{for } x > 0.$$

- For a and b both positive and any value of t,

$$\ln(ab) = \ln a + \ln b$$
$$\ln\left(\frac{a}{b}\right) = \ln a - \ln b$$
$$\ln(b^t) = t \cdot \ln b.$$

Example 6 Solve for x:

(a) $5e^{2x} = 50$ (b) $3^x = 100$.

Solution   (a) We first divide both sides by 5 to obtain

$$e^{2x} = 10.$$

Taking the natural log of both sides, we have

$$\ln(e^{2x}) = \ln 10$$
$$2x = \ln 10$$
$$x = \frac{\ln 10}{2} \approx 1.151.$$

(b) Taking natural logs of both sides,

$$\ln(3^x) = \ln 100$$
$$x \ln 3 = \ln 100$$
$$x = \frac{\ln 100}{\ln 3} \approx 4.192.$$

Misconceptions and Calculator Errors Involving Logs

It is important to know how to use the properties of logarithms. It is equally important to recognize statements that are *not* true. Beware of the following:

- $\log(a + b)$ is not the same as $\log a + \log b$
- $\log(a - b)$ is not the same as $\log a - \log b$
- $\log(ab)$ is not the same as $(\log a)(\log b)$
- $\log\left(\dfrac{a}{b}\right)$ is not the same as $\dfrac{\log a}{\log b}$
- $\log\left(\dfrac{1}{a}\right)$ is not the same as $\dfrac{1}{\log a}$.

There are no formulas to simplify either $\log(a + b)$ or $\log(a - b)$. Also the expression $\log 5x^2$ is not the same as $2 \cdot \log 5x$, because the exponent, 2, applies only to the x and not to the 5. However, it is correct to write

$$\log 5x^2 = \log 5 + \log x^2 = \log 5 + 2\log x.$$

Using a calculator to evaluate expressions like $\log(\frac{17}{3})$ requires care. On some calculators, entering log 17/3 gives 0.410, which is incorrect. This is because the calculator assumes that you mean $(\log 17)/3$, which is not the same as $\log(17/3)$. Notice also that

$$\frac{\log 17}{\log 3} \approx \frac{1.230}{0.477} \approx 2.579,$$

which is not the same as either $(\log 17)/3$ or $\log(17/3)$. Thus, the following expressions are all different.

$$\log \frac{17}{3} \approx 0.753, \qquad \frac{\log 17}{3} \approx 0.410, \quad \text{and} \quad \frac{\log 17}{\log 3} \approx 2.579.$$

Justification of $\log (a \cdot b) = \log a + \log b$ and $\log (a/b) = \log a - \log b$

If a and b are both positive, we can write $a = 10^m$ and $b = 10^n$, so $\log a = m$ and $\log b = n$. Then, the product $a \cdot b$ can be written

$$a \cdot b = 10^m \cdot 10^n = 10^{m+n}.$$

Therefore $m + n$ is the power of 10 needed to give $a \cdot b$, so

$$\log(a \cdot b) = m + n,$$

which gives

$$\log(a \cdot b) = \log a + \log b.$$

Similarly, the quotient a/b can be written as

$$\frac{a}{b} = \frac{10^m}{10^n} = 10^{m-n}.$$

Therefore $m - n$ is the power of 10 needed to give a/b, so

$$\log\left(\frac{a}{b}\right) = m - n,$$

and thus

$$\boxed{\log\left(\frac{a}{b}\right) = \log a - \log b.}$$

Justification of $\log(b^t) = t \cdot \log b$

Suppose that b is positive, so we can write $b = 10^k$ for some value of k. Then

$$b^t = (10^k)^t.$$

We have rewritten the expression b^t so that the base is a power of 10. Using a property of exponents, we can write $(10^k)^t$ as 10^{kt}, so

$$b^t = (10^k)^t = 10^{kt}.$$

Therefore kt is the power of 10 which gives b^t, so

$$\log(b^t) = kt.$$

But since $b = 10^k$, we know $k = \log b$. This means

$$\log(b^t) = (\log b)t = t \cdot \log b.$$

Thus, for $b > 0$ we have

$$\boxed{\log\left(b^t\right) = t \cdot \log b.}$$

Exercises and Problems for Section 8.1

Exercises

Rewrite the statements in Exercises 1–6 using exponents instead of logs.

1. $\ln 26 = 3.258$ **2.** $\ln(0.646) = -0.437$

3. $\log 19 = 1.279$ **4.** $\log 4 = 0.602$

5. $\ln q = z$ **6.** $\log P = t$

Rewrite the statements in Exercises 7–10 using logs.

7. $10^8 = 100,000,000$ **8.** $e^{-4} = 0.0183$

9. $10^v = \alpha$ **10.** $e^a = b$

Solve the equations in Exercises 11–18 using logs.

11. $2^x = 11$ **12.** $(1.45)^x = 25$

13. $e^{0.12x} = 100$ **14.** $10 = 22(0.87)^q$

15. $48 = 17(2.3)^w$ **16.** $2/7 = (0.6)^{2t}$

17. $0.00012 = 0.001^{m/2}$ **18.** $500 = 25(1.1)^{3x}$

Problems

19. Evaluate 10^n for $n = 3$, $n = 3.5$, $n = 3.48$, $n = 3.477$, and $n = 3.47712$. Based on your answer, estimate the value of log 3000.

20. Evaluate without a calculator.

    (a) $\log 1$ **(b)** $\log 0.1$ **(c)** $\log(10^0)$

    (d) $\log \sqrt{10}$ **(e)** $\log(10^5)$ **(f)** $\log(10^2)$

    (g) $\log\left(\dfrac{1}{\sqrt{10}}\right)$ **(h)** $10^{\log 100}$ **(i)** $10^{\log 1}$

    (j) $10^{\log(0.01)}$

21. Evaluate without a calculator.

    (a) $\ln 1$ **(b)** $\ln e^0$ **(c)** $\ln e^5$

    (d) $\ln \sqrt{e}$ **(e)** $e^{\ln 2}$ **(f)** $\ln\left(\dfrac{1}{\sqrt{e}}\right)$

22. Evaluate without a calculator.

    (a) $\log(\log 10)$ **(b)** $\sqrt{\log 100} - \log \sqrt{100}$

    (c) $\log(\sqrt{10}\sqrt[3]{10}\sqrt[5]{10})$ **(d)** $1000^{\log 3}$

    (e) $0.01^{\log 2}$ **(f)** $\dfrac{1}{\log(1/\log \sqrt[10]{10})}$

23. Express the following in terms of x without logs.

    (a) $\log 100^x$ **(b)** $1000^{\log x}$ **(c)** $\log 0.001^x$

24. Express the following in terms of x without natural logs.

    (a) $\ln e^{2x}$ **(b)** $e^{\ln(3x+2)}$

    (c) $\ln\left(\dfrac{1}{e^{5x}}\right)$ **(d)** $\ln \sqrt{e^x}$

25. True or false?

    (a) $\log AB = \log A + \log B$

    (b) $\dfrac{\log A}{\log B} = \log A - B$

    (c) $\log A \log B = \log A + \log B$

    (d) $p \cdot \log A = \log A^p$

    (e) $\log \sqrt{x} = \frac{1}{2} \log x$

    (f) $\sqrt{\log x} = \log(x^{1/2})$

26. True or false?

    (a) $\ln(ab^t) = t \ln(ab)$ **(b)** $\ln(1/a) = -\ln a$

    (c) $\ln a \cdot \ln b = \ln(a + b)$ **(d)** $\ln a - \ln b = \dfrac{\ln a}{\ln b}$

27. Suppose that $x = \log A$ and that $y = \log B$. Write the following expressions in terms of x and y.

    (a) $\log(AB)$ **(b)** $\log(A^3 \cdot \sqrt{B})$

    (c) $\log(A - B)$ **(d)** $\dfrac{\log A}{\log B}$

    (e) $\log \dfrac{A}{B}$ **(f)** AB

28. Let $p = \log m$ and $q = \log n$. Write the following expressions in terms of p and/or q without using logs.

    (a) m **(b)** n^3

    (c) $\log(mn^3)$ **(d)** $\log \sqrt{m}$

29. Let $p = \ln m$ and $q = \ln n$. Write the following expressions in terms of p and/or q without using logs.

    (a) $\ln(nm^4)$ **(b)** $\ln\left(\dfrac{1}{n}\right)$

    (c) $\dfrac{\ln m}{\ln n}$ **(d)** $\ln(n^3)$

30. A graph of $P = 25(1.075)^t$ is given in Figure 8.1.

    (a) What is the initial value of P (when $t = 0$)? What is the percent growth rate?

    (b) Use the graph to estimate the value of t when $P = 100$.

    (c) Use logs to find the exact value of t when $P = 100$.

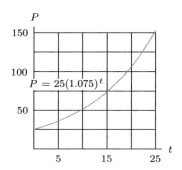

Figure 8.1

31. A graph of $Q = 10e^{-0.15t}$ is given in Figure 8.2.

    (a) What is the initial value of Q (when $t = 0$)? What is the continuous percent decay rate?

    (b) Use the graph to estimate the value of t when $Q = 2$.

    (c) Use logs to find the exact value of t when $Q = 2$.

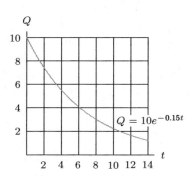

Figure 8.2

In Problems 32–43, solve the equations exactly for x.

32. $5(1.031)^x = 8$

33. $4(1.171)^x = 7(1.088)^x$

34. $3 \log(2x + 6) = 6$

35. $3 \cdot 2^x + 8 = 25$

36. $e^{x+4} = 10$

37. $e^{x+5} = 7 \cdot 2^x$

38. $\log(1 - x) - \log(1 + x) = 2$

39. $\log(2x + 5) \cdot \log(9x^2) = 0$

40. $b^x = c$

41. $ab^x = c$

42. $Pa^x = Qb^x$

43. $Pe^{kx} = Q$

In Problems 44–47, solve the equation exactly for t.

44. $121e^{-0.112t} = 88$

45. $58e^{4t+1} = 30$

46. $17e^{0.02t} = 18e^{0.03t}$

47. $44e^{0.15t} = 50(1.2)^t$

48. Solve each of the following equations exactly for x.

   (a) $e^{2x} + e^{2x} = 1$ **(b)** $2e^{3x} + e^{3x} = b$

49. Evaluate the following pairs of expressions without using a calculator.

   (a) $\log(10 \cdot 100)$ and $\log 10 + \log 100$

   (b) $\log(100 \cdot 1000)$ and $\log 100 + \log 1000$

   (c) $\log\left(\dfrac{10}{100}\right)$ and $\log 10 - \log 100$

   (d) $\log\left(\dfrac{100}{1000}\right)$ and $\log 100 - \log 1000$

   (e) $\log(10^2)$ and $2 \log 10$

   (f) $\log(10^3)$ and $3 \log 10$

50. (a) Write general formulas based on what you observed in Problem 49.

   (b) Apply your formulas to rewrite $\log\left(\dfrac{AB}{C}\right)^p$ at least two different ways.

51. Three students try to solve the equation

$$11 \cdot 3^x = 5 \cdot 7^x.$$

The first student finds that $x = \dfrac{\log(11/5)}{\log(7/3)}$. The second finds that $x = \dfrac{\log(5/11)}{\log(3/7)}$. The third finds that $x = \dfrac{\log 11 - \log 5}{\log 7 - \log 3}$. Which student (or students) is (are) correct? Explain.

52. Given that $10^{1.3} \approx 20$, approximate the value of $\log 200$ without using a calculator.

8.2   LOGARITHMS AND EXPONENTIAL MODELS

The log function is often useful when answering questions about exponential models. Because logarithms "undo" the exponential functions, we use them to solve many exponential equations.

Example 1   In Example 3 Section 7.3 we solved the equation $200(0.886^t) = 25$ graphically, where t is in thousands of years. We found that a 200 microgram sample of carbon-14 decays to 25 micrograms in approximately $17,200$ years. Now solve $200(0.886)^t = 25$ using logarithms.

Solution   First, isolate the power on one side of the equation

$$200(0.886^t) = 25$$
$$0.886^t = 0.125.$$

Take the log of both sides, and use the fact that $\log(0.886^t) = t \log 0.886$. Then

$$\log(0.886^t) = \log 0.125$$
$$t \log 0.886 = \log 0.125$$

so

$$t = \frac{\log 0.125}{\log 0.886} \approx 17.18 \text{ thousand years.}$$

This answer is close to the value we found from the graph, $17,200$.

Example 2   The US population, P, in millions, is currently growing according to the formula

$$P = 263e^{0.009t},$$

where t is in years since 1995. When is the population predicted to reach 300 million?

Solution   We want to solve the following equation for t:

$$263e^{0.009t} = 300.$$

Dividing by 263 gives

$$e^{0.009t} = \frac{300}{263}$$

So $0.009t$ is the power of e which gives 300/263. Thus, by the definition of the natural log,

$$0.009t = \ln\left(\frac{300}{263}\right).$$

Solving for t and evaluating $\ln(300/263)$ on a calculator gives

$$t = \frac{\ln(300/263)}{0.009} = 14.6 \text{ years.}$$

The US population is predicted to reach 300 million during the year 2009.

Example 3   The population of City A begins with 50,000 people and grows at 3.5% per year. The population of City B begins with a larger population of 250,000 people but grows at the slower rate of 1.6% per year. Assuming that these growth rates hold constant, will the population of City A ever catch up to the population of City B? If so, when?

Solution   If t is time measured in years and P_A and P_B are the populations of these two cities, then

$$P_A = 50{,}000(1.035)^t \quad \text{and} \quad P_B = 250{,}000(1.016)^t.$$

We want to solve the equation

$$50{,}000(1.035)^t = 250{,}000(1.016)^t.$$

We first get the exponential terms together by dividing both sides of the equation by $50{,}000(1.016)^t$:

$$\frac{(1.035)^t}{(1.016)^t} = \frac{250{,}000}{50{,}000} = 5.$$

Since $\dfrac{a^t}{b^t} = \left(\dfrac{a}{b}\right)^t$, this gives

$$\left(\frac{1.035}{1.016}\right)^t = 5.$$

Taking logs of both sides and using $\log b^t = t\log b$, we have

$$\log\left(\frac{1.035}{1.016}\right)^t = \log 5$$

$$t \log\left(\frac{1.035}{1.016}\right) = \log 5$$

$$t = \frac{\log 5}{\log(1.035/1.016)} \approx 86.865.$$

Thus, the cities' populations will be equal in just under 87 years. To check this, notice that when $t = 86.865$,

$$P_A = 50,000(1.035)^{86.865} = 992,575$$

and

$$P_B = 250,000(1.016)^{86.865} = 992,572.$$

The answers aren't exactly equal because we rounded off the value of t. Rounding can introduce significant errors, especially when logs and exponentials are involved. Using $t = 86.86480867$, the computed values of P_A and P_B agree to three decimal places.

Doubling Time

Eventually, any exponentially growing quantity doubles, or increases by 100%. Since its percent growth rate is constant, the time it takes for the quantity to grow by 100% is also a constant. This time period is called the *doubling time*.

Example 4   (a) Find the time needed for the turtle population described by the function $P = 175(1.145)^t$ to double its initial size.

(b) How long does this population take to quadruple its initial size? To increase by a factor of 8?

Solution   (a) The initial size is 175 turtles; doubling this gives 350 turtles. We need to solve the following equation for t:

$$175(1.145)^t = 350$$
$$1.145^t = 2$$
$$\log\left(1.145^t\right) = \log 2$$
$$t \cdot \log 1.145 = \log 2$$
$$t = \frac{\log 2}{\log 1.145} \approx 5.119 \text{ years.}$$

We check this by noting that

$$175(1.145)^{5.119} = 350,$$

which is double the initial population. In fact, at any time it takes the turtle population about 5.119 years to double in size.

(b) Since the population function is exponential, it increases by 100% every 5.119 years. Thus it doubles its initial size in the first 5.119 years, quadruples its initial size in two 5.119 year periods, or 10.238 years, and increases by a factor of 8 in three 5.119 year periods, or 15.357 years. We check this by noting that

$$175(1.145)^{10.238} = 700,$$

or 4 times the initial size, and that

$$175(1.145)^{15.357} = 1400,$$

or 8 times the initial size.

Example 5   A population doubles in size every 20 years. What is its continuous growth rate?

Solution   We are not given the initial size of the population, but we can solve this problem without that information. Let the symbol P_0 represent the initial size of the population. We have $P = P_0 e^{kt}$. After 20 years, $P = 2P_0$, and so

$$P_0 e^{k \cdot 20} = 2P_0$$
$$e^{20k} = 2$$
$$20k = \ln 2 \qquad \text{Taking ln of both sides}$$
$$k = \frac{\ln 2}{20} \approx 0.03466.$$

Thus, the population grows at the continuous rate of 3.466% per year.

Half-Life

Just as an exponentially growing quantity doubles in a fixed amount of time, an exponentially decaying quantity decreases by a factor of 2 in a fixed amount of time, called the *half-life* of the quantity.

Example 6   Carbon-14 decays radioactively at a constant annual rate of 0.0121%. Show that the half-life of carbon-14 is about 5728 years.

Solution   We are not given an initial amount of carbon-14, but we can solve this problem without that information. Let the symbol Q_0 represent the initial quantity of carbon-14 present. The growth rate is -0.000121 because carbon-14 is decaying. So the growth factor is $b = 1 - 0.000121 = 0.999879$. Thus, after t years the amount left will be

$$Q = Q_0 (0.999879)^t.$$

We want to find how long it takes for the quantity to drop to half its initial level. Thus, we need to solve for t in the equation

$$\frac{1}{2} Q_0 = Q_0 (0.999879)^t.$$

Dividing each side by Q_0, we have

$$\frac{1}{2} = 0.999879^t.$$

Taking logs

$$\log \frac{1}{2} = \log(0.999879^t)$$
$$\log 0.5 = t \cdot \log 0.999879$$
$$t = \frac{\log 0.5}{\log 0.999879} \approx 5728.143.$$

Thus, no matter how much carbon-14 there is initially, after about 5728 years, half will remain.

Similarly, we can determine the growth rate given the half-life or doubling time.

Example 7   The quantity, Q, of a substance decays according to the formula $Q = Q_0 e^{-kt}$, where t is in minutes. The half-life of the substance is 11 minutes. What is the value of k?

Solution   We know that after 11 minutes, $Q = \frac{1}{2}Q_0$. Thus, solving for k, we get

$$Q_0 e^{-k \cdot 11} = \frac{1}{2}Q_0$$
$$e^{-11k} = \frac{1}{2}$$
$$-11k = \ln \frac{1}{2}$$
$$k = \frac{\ln(1/2)}{-11} \approx 0.06301,$$

so $k = 0.063$ per minute. This substance decays at the continuous rate of 6.301% per minute.

Converting Between $Q = ab^t$ and $Q = ae^{kt}$

Any exponential function can be written in either of the two forms:

$$Q = ab^t \qquad \text{or} \qquad Q = ae^{kt}.$$

If $b = e^k$, so $k = \ln b$, the two formulas represent the same function.

Example 8   Convert the exponential function $P = 175(1.145)^t$ to the form $P = ae^{kt}$.

Solution   Since the new formula represents the same function, we want $P = 175$ when $t = 0$. Thus, substituting $t = 0$, gives $175 = ae^{k(0)} = a$, so $a = 175$. The parameter a in both functions represents the initial population. For all t,

$$175(1.145)^t = 175(e^k)^t,$$

so we must find k such that

$$e^k = 1.145.$$

Therefore k is the power of e which gives 1.145. By the definition of ln, we have

$$k = \ln 1.145 \approx 0.1354.$$

Therefore,

$$P = 175e^{0.1354t}.$$

Example 9   Convert the formula $Q = 7e^{0.3t}$ to the form $Q = ab^t$.

Solution   Using the properties of exponents,

$$Q = 7e^{0.3t} = 7(e^{0.3})^t.$$

Using a calculator, we find $e^{0.3} \approx 1.3499$, so

$$Q = 7(1.3499)^t.$$

Example 10   Assuming t is in years, find the continuous and annual percent growth rates in Examples 8 and 9.

Solution   In Example 8, the annual percent growth rate is 14.5% and the continuous percent growth rate per year is 13.54%. In Example 9, the continuous percent growth rate is 30% and the annual percent growth rate is 34.985%.

Example 11   Find the continuous percent growth rate of $Q = 200(0.886)^t$, where t is in thousands of years.

Solution   Since this function describes exponential decay, we expect a negative value for k. We want

$$e^k = 0.886.$$

Solving for k gives

$$k = \ln(0.886) = -0.12104.$$

So we have $Q = 200e^{-0.12104t}$ and the continuous growth rate is -12.104% per thousand years.

Exponential Growth Problems That Cannot Be Solved By Logarithms

Some equations with the variable in the exponent cannot be solved using logarithms.

Example 12   With t in years, the population of a country (in millions) is given by $P = 2(1.02)^t$, while the food supply (in millions of people that can be fed) is given by $N = 4 + 0.5t$. Determine the year in which the country first experiences food shortages.

Solution   The country starts to experience shortages when the population equals the number of people that can be fed—that is, when $P = N$. We attempt to solve the equation $P = N$ by using logs:

$$2(1.02)^t = 4 + 0.5t$$
$$1.02^t = 2 + 0.25t \qquad \text{Dividing by 2}$$
$$\log 1.02^t = \log(2 + 0.25t)$$
$$t \log 1.02 = \log(2 + 0.25t).$$

Unfortunately, we cannot isolate t, so, this equation cannot be solved using logs. However, we can approximate the solution of the original equation numerically or graphically, as shown in Figure 8.3. The two functions, P and N, are equal when $t \approx 199.381$. Thus, it will be almost 200 years before shortages occur.

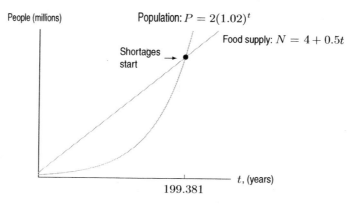

People (millions)

Population: $P = 2(1.02)^t$

Food supply: $N = 4 + 0.5t$

Shortages start

199.381

t, (years)

Figure 8.3: Finding the intersection of linear and exponential graphs

Exercises and Problems for Section 8.2

Exercises

Find the doubling time in Exercises 1–4.

1. A population growing according to $P = P_0 e^{0.2t}$.

2. A city is growing by 26% per year.

3. A bank account is growing by 2.7% per year.

4. A company's profits are increasing by an annual growth factor of 1.12.

Find the half-lives of the substances in Exercises 5–7.

5. Tritium, which decays at a rate of 5.471% per year.

6. Einsteinium-253, which decays at a rate of 3.406% per day.

7. A radioactive substance that decays at a continuous rate of 11% per minute.

In Exercises 8–11, convert to the form $Q = ae^{kt}$.

8. $Q = 4 \cdot 7^t$

9. $Q = 2 \cdot 3^t$

10. $Q = 4 \cdot 8^{1.3t}$

11. $Q = 973 \cdot 6^{2.1t}$

In Exercises 12–15, convert to the form $Q = ab^t$.

12. $Q = 4e^{7t}$

13. $Q = 0.3e^{0.7t}$

14. $Q = \dfrac{14}{5} e^{0.03t}$

15. $Q = e^{-0.02t}$

For Exercises 16–17, write the exponential function in the form $y = ab^t$. Find b accurate to four decimal places. If t is measured in years, give the percent annual growth or decay rate and the continuous percent growth or decay rate per year.

16. $y = 25e^{0.053t}$

17. $y = 100e^{-0.07t}$

For Exercises 18–19, write the exponential function in the form $y = ae^{kt}$. Find k accurate to four decimal places. If t is measured in years, give the percent annual growth rate and the continuous percent growth rate per year.

18. $y = 6000(0.85)^t$

19. $y = 5(1.12)^t$

Problems

20. A population grows from 11000 to 13000 in three years. Assuming the growth is exponential, find the:

    (a) Annual growth rate
    (b) Continuous growth rate
    (c) Why are your answers to parts (a) and (b) different?

21. A population doubles in size every 15 years. Assuming exponential growth, find the

    (a) Annual growth rate
    (b) Continuous growth rate

22. A population increases from 5.2 million at an annual rate of 3.1%. Find the continuous growth rate.

23. If 17% of a radioactive substance decays in 5 hours, what is the half-life of the substance?

Solve the equations in Problems 24–29 if possible. Give an exact solution if there is one.

24. $1.7(2.1)^{3x} = 2(4.5)^x$ **25.** $3^{4\log x} = 5$

26. $5(1.044)^t = t + 10$ **27.** $12(1.221)^t = t + 3$

28. $10e^{3t} - e = 2e^{3t}$

29. $\log x + \log(x - 1) = \log 2$

30. Use algebra to show that the time it takes for a quantity growing exponentially to double is independent of the starting quantity and the time. To do this, let d represent the time it takes for P to double. Show that if P becomes $2P$ at time $t + d$, then d depends only on the growth factor b, but not on the starting quantity a and time t. (Assume $P \neq 0$.)

31. A colony of bacteria grows exponentially. The colony begins with 3 bacteria, but 3 hours after the beginning of the experiment, it has grown to 100 bacteria.

    (a) Give a formula for the number of bacteria as a function of time.

    (b) How long does it take for the colony to triple in size?

32. In 2001, the Internet was linked by a global network of 147 million host computers.[1] The number of host computers has been growing approximately exponentially and was about 1.3 million in 1992.

    (a) Find a formula for the number, N, of internet host computers as an exponential function of t, the number of years since 1992, using the form $N = ae^{kt}$.

    (b) What is the continuous annual percent increase?

    (c) What is the doubling time?

33. The number of cases of sepsis, an immune response to infection or trauma, has been growing exponentially and has doubled in this country in the last 5 years.[2]

    (a) Find the continuous annual percent growth rate in the number of cases.

    (b) If this growth rate continues, how many years will it take for the number of cases to triple?

34. The US census projects the population of the state of Washington using the function $N(t) = 5.4e^{0.013t}$, where $N(t)$ is in millions and t is in years since 1995.

    (a) What is the population's continuous growth rate?

    (b) What is the population of Washington in year $t = 0$?

    (c) How many years is it before the population triples?

    (d) In what year does this model indicate a population of only one person? Is this reasonable or unreasonable?

35. The voltage V across a charged capacitor is given by $V(t) = 5e^{-0.3t}$ where t is in seconds.

    (a) What is the voltage after 3 seconds?

    (b) When will the voltage be 1?

    (c) By what percent does the voltage decrease each second?

36. The half-life of iodine-123 is about 13 hours. You begin with 50 grams of iodine-123.

    (a) Write an equation that gives the amount of iodine-123 remaining after t hours.

    (b) Determine the number of hours needed for your sample to decay to 10 grams.

37. Scientists observing owl and hawk populations collect the following data. Their initial count for the owl population is 245 owls, and the population grows by 3% per year. They initially observe 63 hawks, and this population doubles every 10 years.

    (a) Find a formula for the size of the population of owls in terms of time t.

    (b) Find a formula for the size of the population of hawks in terms of time t.

    (c) Use a graph to find how long it will take for these populations to be equal in number.

38. Figure 8.4 shows the graphs of the exponential functions f and g, and the linear function, h.

    (a) Find formulas for f, g, and h.

    (b) Find the exact value(s) of x such that $f(x) = g(x)$.

    (c) Estimate the value(s) of x such that $f(x) = h(x)$.

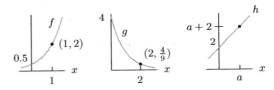

Figure 8.4

39. In 1991, the body of a man was found in melting snow in the Alps of Northern Italy. An examination of the tissue sample revealed that 46% of the carbon-14 present in his body at the time of his death had decayed. The half-life of carbon-14 is approximately 5728 years. How long ago did this man die?

[1]Internet Software Consortium, "Internet Domain Surveys", www.isc.org/ds/, viewed February 20, 2002.
[2]"Improvement seen in Recognizing, Treating Sepsis", Watertown Daily Times, September 25, 2002.

40. In a country where inflation is a concern, prices have risen by 40% over a 5-year period.

(a) By what percent do the prices rise each year?
(b) How long does it take for prices to rise by 5%?
(c) Use a continuous growth rate to model inflation by a function of the form $P = P_0 e^{rt}$.

41. A person's blood alcohol content (BAC) is a measure of how much alcohol is in the blood stream. When the person stops drinking, the BAC declines over time as the alcohol is metabolized. If Q is the amount of alcohol and Q_0 the initial amount, then $Q = Q_0 e^{-t/\tau}$, where τ is known as the *elimination time*. How long does it take for a person's BAC to drop from 0.10 to 0.04 if the elimination time is 2.5 hours?

42. The probability of a transistor failing within t months is given by $P(t) = 1 - e^{-0.016t}$.

(a) What is the probability of failure within the first 6 months? Within the second six months?
(b) Within how many months will the probability of failure be 99.99%?

43. (a) What annual interest rate, compounded continuously, is equivalent to an annual rate of 8%, compounded annually?
(b) What annual interest rate, compounded annually, is equivalent to an annual rate of 6%, compounded continuously?

44. One student deposits $500 into a savings account earning 4.5% annual interest compounded annually. Another deposits $800 into an account earning 3% annual interest compounded annually. When are the balances equal?

45. You deposit $4000 into an account that earns 6% annual interest, compounded annually. A friend deposits $3500 into an account that earns 5.95% annual interest, compounded continuously. Will your friend's balance ever equal yours? If so, when?

46. (a) Find the time required for an investment to triple in value if it earns 4% annual interest, compounded continuously.
(b) Now find the time required assuming that the interest is compounded annually.

47. The temperature, H, in °F, of a cup of coffee t hours after it is set out to cool is given by the equation:

$$H = 70 + 120(1/4)^t.$$

(a) What is the coffee's temperature initially (that is, at time $t = 0$)? After 1 hour? 2 hours?
(b) How long does it take the coffee to cool down to 90°F? 75°F?

48. The size of a population, P, of toads t years after it is introduced into a wetland is given by

$$P = \frac{1000}{1 + 49(1/2)^t}.$$

(a) How many toads are there in year $t = 0$? $t = 5$? $t = 10$?
(b) How long does it take for the toad population to reach 500? 750?
(c) What is the maximum number of toads that the wetland can support?

49. The population of bacteria m doubles every 24 hours. The population of bacteria q grows by 3% per hour. Which has the larger population in the long term?

50. The half-life of substance ϵ is 17 years, and substance s decays at a rate of 30% per decade. Of which substance is there less in the long term?

8.3 THE LOGARITHMIC FUNCTION

The Graph, Domain, and Range of the Common Logarithm

In Section 8.1 we defined the log function (to base 10) for all positive numbers. In other words,

Domain of $\log x$ is all positive numbers.

By considering its graph in Figure 8.5, we determine the range of $y = \log x$. The log graph crosses the x-axis at $x = 1$, because $\log 1 = \log(10^0) = 0$. The graph climbs to $y = 1$ at $x = 10$, because $\log 10 = \log(10^1) = 1$. In order for the log graph to climb to $y = 2$, the value of x must reach 100, or 10^2, and in order for it to climb to $y = 3$, the value of x must be 10^3, or 1000. To reach the modest height of $y = 20$ requires x to equal 10^{20}, or 100 billion billion! The log function increases so slowly that it often serves as a benchmark for other slow-growing functions. Nonetheless, the graph of $y = \log x$ eventually climbs to any value we choose.

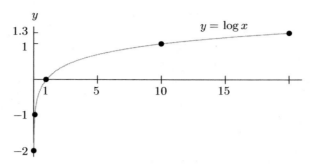

Figure 8.5: The log function grows very rapidly for $0 < x < 1$ and very slowly for $x > 1$. It has a vertical asymptote at $x = 0$

Although x cannot equal zero in the log function, we can choose $x > 0$ to be as small as we like. As x decreases toward zero, the values of $\log x$ get large and negative. For example,

$$\log 0.1 = \log 10^{-1} = -1,$$
$$\log 0.01 = \log 10^{-2} = -2,$$
$$\vdots \qquad \qquad \vdots$$
$$\log 0.0000001 = \log 10^{-7} = -7,$$

and so on. So, small positive values of x give exceedingly large negative values of y. Thus,

$$\text{Range of } \log x \text{ is all real numbers.}$$

The log function is increasing and its graph is concave down, since its rate of change is decreasing.

Graphs of the Inverse Functions $y = \log x$ and $y = 10^x$

The fact that $y = \log x$ and $y = 10^x$ are inverses means that their graphs are related. Looking at Tables 8.1 and 8.2, we see that the point $(0.01, -2)$ is on the graph of $y = \log x$ and the point $(-2, 0.01)$ is on the graph of $y = 10^x$. In general, if the point (a, b) is on the graph of $y = \log x$, the point (b, a) is on the graph of $y = 10^x$. Thus, the graph of $y = \log x$ is the graph of $y = 10^x$ with x and y-axes interchanged. If the x- and y-axes have the same scale, this is equivalent to reflecting the graph of $y = 10^x$ across the diagonal line $y = x$. See Figure 8.6.

Table 8.1	Log function
x	$y = \log x$
0.01	-2
0.1	-1
1	0
10	1
100	2
1000	3

Table 8.2	Exponential function
x	$y = 10^x$
-2	0.01
-1	0.1
0	1
1	10
2	100
3	1000

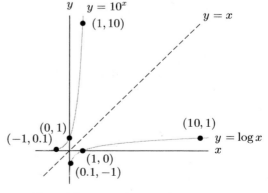

Figure 8.6: The functions $y = \log x$ and $y = 10^x$ are inverses of one another

Asymptotes

In Section 7.3 we saw that the graph of an exponential function has a horizontal asymptote. In Figure 8.6, we see that $y = 10^x$ has horizontal asymptote $y = 0$, because

$$\text{as } x \to -\infty, \quad 10^x \to 0.$$

Correspondingly, as x gets closer to zero, $y = \log x$ takes on larger and larger negative values. We write

$$\text{as } x \to 0^+, \qquad f(x) \to -\infty.$$

The notation $x \to 0^+$ is read "x approaches zero from the right" and means that we are choosing smaller and smaller positive values of x—that is, we are sliding toward $x = 0$ through small positive values. We say the graph of the log function $y = \log x$ has a *vertical asymptote* of $x = 0$.

To describe vertical asympotes in general, we use the notation

$$x \to a^+$$

to mean that x slides toward a from the right (that is, through values larger than a) and

$$x \to a^-$$

to mean that x slides toward a from the left (that is, through values smaller than a).

We summarize the information about both horizontal and vertical asymptotes:

Let $y = f(x)$ be a function and let a be a finite number.

- The graph of f has a **horizontal asymptote** of $y = a$ if

$$f(x) \to a \quad \text{as} \quad x \to \infty \quad \text{or} \quad x \to -\infty \quad \text{or both.}$$

- The graph of f has a **vertical asymptote** of $x = a$ if

$$f(x) \to \infty \quad \text{or} \quad f(x) \to -\infty \quad \text{as} \quad x \to a \quad \text{(from the left or the right or both).}$$

Notice that the process of finding a vertical asymptote is different from the process for finding a horizontal asymptote. Vertical asymptotes occur where the function values grow larger and larger, either positively or negatively, as x approaches a finite value (i.e. where $f(x) \to \infty$ or $f(x) \to -\infty$ as $x \to a$.) Horizontal asymptotes are determined by whether the function values approach a finite number as x takes on large positive or large negative values (i.e., as $x \to \infty$ or $x \to -\infty$).

Graph of Natural Logarithm

In addition to similar algebraic properties, the natural log and the common log have similar graphs.

Example 1   Graph $y = \ln x$ for $0 < x < 10$.

Solution   Values of $\ln x$ are in Table 8.3. Like the common log, the natural log is only defined for $x > 0$ and has a vertical asymptote at $x = 0$. The graph is slowly increasing and concave down.

Table 8.3 *Values of* $\ln x$ *(rounded)*

x	$\ln x$
0	Undefined
1	0
2	0.7
e	1
3	1.1
4	1.4
$\vdots$	$\vdots$

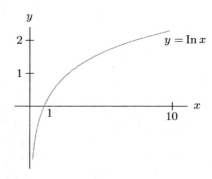

Figure 8.7: Graph of the natural logarithm

The functions $y = \ln x$ and $y = e^x$ are inverses. If the scales on the axes are the same, their graphs are reflections of one another across the line $y = x$. See Figure 8.8.

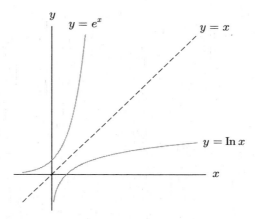

Figure 8.8: The functions $y = \ln x$ and $y = e^x$ are inverses of one another

Chemical Acidity

Logarithms are useful in measuring quantities whose magnitudes vary widely, such as acidity (pH), sound (decibels), and earthquakes (the Richter scale). In chemistry, the acidity of a liquid is expressed using pH. The acidity depends on the hydrogen ion concentration in the liquid (in moles per liter); this concentration is written [H$^+$]. The greater the hydrogen ion concentration, the more acidic the solution. The pH is defined as:

$$pH = -\log[H^+].$$

Example 2   The hydrogen ion concentration of seawater is $[H^+] = 1.1 \cdot 10^{-8}$. Estimate the pH of seawater. Then check your answer with a calculator.

Solution   We want to estimate $pH = -\log(1.1 \cdot 10^{-8})$. Since $1.1 \cdot 10^{-8} \approx 10^{-8}$ and $\log 10^{-8} = -8$, we know that

$$pH = -\log(1.1 \cdot 10^{-8}) \approx -(-8) = 8.$$

Using a calculator, we have

$$\text{pH} = -\log(1.1 \cdot 10^{-8}) = 7.959.$$

Example 3   A vinegar solution has a pH of 3. Determine the hydrogen ion concentration.

Solution   Since $3 = -\log[\text{H}^+]$, we have $-3 = \log[\text{H}^+]$. This means that $10^{-3} = [\text{H}^+]$. So the hydrogen ion concentration is 10^{-3} moles per liter.

Logarithms and Orders of Magnitude

We often compare sizes or quantities by computing their ratios. If A is twice as tall as B, then

$$\frac{\text{Height of } A}{\text{Height of } B} = 2.$$

If one object is 10 times heavier than another, we say it is an *order of magnitude* heavier. If one quantity is two factors of 10 greater than another, we say it is two orders of magnitude greater, and so on. For example, the value of a dollar is two orders of magnitude greater than the value of a penny, because we have

$$\frac{\$1}{\$0.01} = 100 = 10^2.$$

The order of magnitude is the logarithm of their ratio.

Example 4   The sound intensity of a refrigerator motor is 10^{-11} watts/cm^2. A typical school cafeteria has sound intensity of 10^{-8} watts/cm^2. How many orders of magnitude more intense is the sound of the cafeteria?

Solution   To compare the two intensities, we compute their ratio:

$$\frac{\text{Sound intensity of cafeteria}}{\text{Sound intensity of refrigerator}} = \frac{10^{-8}}{10^{-11}} = 10^{-8-(-11)} = 10^3.$$

Thus, the sound intensity of the cafeteria is 1000 times greater than the sound intensity of the refrigerator. The log of this ratio is 3. We say that the sound intensity of the cafeteria is three orders of magnitude greater than the sound intensity of the refrigerator.

Decibels

The intensity of audible sound varies over an enormous range. The range is so enormous that we consider the logarithm of the sound intensity. This is the idea behind the *decibel* (abbreviated dB). To measure a sound in decibels, the sound's intensity, I, is compared to the intensity of a standard benchmark sound, I_0. The intensity of I_0 is defined to be 10^{-16} watts/cm^2, roughly the lowest intensity audible to humans. The comparison between a sound intensity I and the benchmark sound intensity I_0 is made as follows:

$$\text{Noise level in decibels} = 10 \cdot \log\left(\frac{I}{I_0}\right).$$

For instance, let's find the decibel rating of the refrigerator in Example 4. First, we find how many orders of magnitude more intense the refrigerator sound is than the benchmark sound:

$$\frac{I}{I_0} = \frac{\text{Sound intensity of refrigerator}}{\text{Benchmark sound intensity}} = \frac{10^{-11}}{10^{-16}} = 10^5.$$

Thus, the refrigerator's intensity is 5 orders of magnitude more than I_0, the benchmark intensity. We have

$$\text{Decibel rating of refrigerator} = 10 \cdot \underbrace{\text{Number of orders of magnitude}}_{5} = 50 \text{ dB}.$$

Note that 5, the number of orders of magnitude, is the log of the ratio I/I_0. We use the log function because it "counts" the number of powers of 10. Thus if N is the decibel rating, then

$$N = 10 \log\left(\frac{I}{I_0}\right).$$

Example 5   (a) If a sound doubles in intensity, by how many units does its decibel rating increase?

(b) Loud music can measure 110 dB whereas normal conversation measures 50 dB. How many times more intense is loud music than normal conversation?

Solution

(a) Let I be the sound's intensity before it doubles. Once doubled, the new intensity is $2I$. The decibel rating of the original sound is $10 \log(I/I_0)$, and the decibel rating of the new sound is $10 \log(2I/I_0)$. The difference in decibel ratings is given by

$$\text{Difference in decibel ratings} = 10 \log\left(\frac{2I}{I_0}\right) - 10 \log\left(\frac{I}{I_0}\right)$$

$$= 10\left(\log\left(\frac{2I}{I_0}\right) - \log\left(\frac{I}{I_0}\right)\right) \qquad \text{Factoring out 10}$$

$$= 10 \cdot \log\left(\frac{2I/I_0}{I/I_0}\right) \qquad \text{Using the property } \log a - \log b = \log(a/b)$$

$$= 10 \cdot \log 2 \qquad \text{Canceling } I/I_0$$

$$\approx 3.010 \text{ dB} \qquad \text{Because } \log 2 \approx 0.3.$$

Thus, if the sound intensity is doubled, the decibel rating goes up by approximately 3 dB.

(b) If I_M is the sound intensity of loud music, then

$$10 \log\left(\frac{I_M}{I_0}\right) = 110 \text{ dB}.$$

Similarly, if I_C is the sound intensity of conversation, then

$$10 \log\left(\frac{I_C}{I_0}\right) = 50 \text{ dB}.$$

Computing the difference of the decibel ratings gives

$$10 \log\left(\frac{I_M}{I_0}\right) - 10 \log\left(\frac{I_C}{I_0}\right) = 60.$$

Dividing by 10 gives

$$\log\left(\frac{I_M}{I_0}\right) - \log\left(\frac{I_C}{I_0}\right) = 6$$

$$\log\left(\frac{I_M/I_0}{I_C/I_0}\right) = 6 \qquad \text{Using the property } \log b - \log a = \log(b/a)$$

$$\log\left(\frac{I_M}{I_C}\right) = 6 \qquad \text{Canceling } I_0$$

$$\frac{I_M}{I_C} = 10^6 \qquad \log x = 6 \text{ means that } x = 10^6.$$

So $I_M = 10^6 I_C$, which means that loud music is 10^6 times, or one million times, as intense as normal conversation.

Exercises and Problems for Section 8.3

Exercises

1. Without a calculator, match the functions $y = 10^x$, $y = e^x$, $y = \log x$, $y = \ln x$ with the graphs in Figure 8.9.

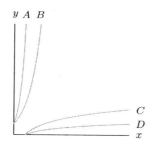

Figure 8.9

2. Without a calculator, match the functions $y = 2^x$, $y = e^{-x}$, $y = 3^x$, $y = \ln x$, $y = \log x$ with the graphs in Figure 8.10.

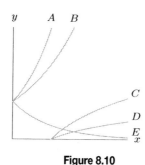

Figure 8.10

3. What is the equation of the asymptote of the graph of $y = 10^x$? Of the graph of $y = 2^x$? Of the graph of $y = \log x$?

4. What is the equation for the asymptote of the graph of $y = e^x$? Of the graph of $y = e^{-x}$? Of the graph of $y = \ln x$?

5. What is the value (if any) of the following?

    (a) 10^{-x} as $x \to \infty$ **(b)** $\log x$ as $x \to 0^+$

6. What is the value (if any) of the following?

    (a) e^x as $x \to -\infty$ **(b)** $\ln x$ as $x \to 0^+$

Graph the functions in Problems 7–10. Label all asymptotes and intercepts.

7. $y = 2 \cdot 3^x + 1$ **8.** $y = -e^{-x}$

9. $y = \log(x - 4)$ **10.** $y = \ln(x + 1)$

In Problems 11–12, graph the function. Identify any vertical asymptotes. State the domain of the function.

11. $y = 2\ln(x - 3)$ **12.** $y = 1 - \ln(2 - x)$

In Exercises 13–17, find the hydrogen ion concentration, $[H^+]$, for the substances.[3] [Hint: pH $= -\log[H^+]$.]

13. Lye, with a pH of 13.

14. Battery acid, with a pH of 1.

15. Baking soda, with a pH of 8.3.

16. Tomatoes, with a pH of 4.5.

17. Hydrochloric acid, with a pH of 0.

---

[3]Data from www.miamisci.org/ph/hhoh.html

Problems

18. Match the graphs (a)–(c) to one of the functions $r(x)$, $s(x)$, $t(x)$ whose values are in the tables.

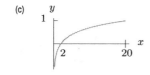

x	2	4	10
$r(x)$	1	1.301	1.699

x	0.5	5	10
$s(x)$	−0.060	0.379	0.699

x	0.1	2	100
$t(x)$	−3	0.903	6

19. Immediately following the gold medal performance of the US women's gymnastic team in the 1996 Olympic Games, an NBC commentator, John Tesh, said of one team member: "Her confidence and performance have grown logarithmically." He clearly thought this was an enormous compliment. Is it a compliment? Is it realistic?

In Problems 20–25, find possible formulas for the functions using logs or exponentials.

20.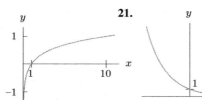

21.

22.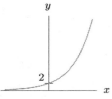

23.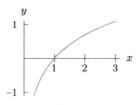

24.

25.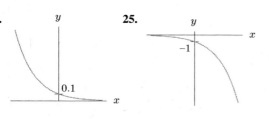

Find the domain of the functions in Problems 26–29.

26. $h(x) = \ln(x^2)$ **27.** $g(x) = (\ln x)^2$

28. $f(x) = \ln(\ln x)$ **29.** $k(x) = \ln(x - 3)$

30. **(a)** Using the definition of pH on page 458, find the concentrations of hydrogen ions in solutions with
    (i) pH $= 2$ (ii) pH $= 4$ (iii) pH $= 7$
(b) A high concentration of hydrogen ions corresponds to an acidic solution. From your answer to part (a), decide if solutions with high pHs are more or less acidic than solutions with low pHs.

31. **(a)** A 12 oz cup of coffee contains about $2.41 \cdot 10^{18}$ hydrogen ions. What is the concentration (moles/liter) of hydrogen ions in a 12 oz cup of coffee? [Hint: One liter equals 30.3 oz. One mole of hydrogen ions equals $6.02 \cdot 10^{23}$ hydrogen ions.]
(b) Based on your answer to part (a) and the formula for pH, what is the pH of a 12 oz cup of coffee?

32. **(a)** The pH of lemon juice is about 2.3. What is the concentration of hydrogen ions in lemon juice?
(b) A person squeezes 2 oz of lemon juice into a cup. Based on your answer to part (a), how many hydrogen ions does this juice contain?

33. Sound A measures 30 decibels and sound B is 5 times as loud as sound A. What is the decibel rating of sound B to the nearest integer?

34. **(a)** Let D_1 and D_2 represent the decibel ratings of sounds of intensity I_1 and I_2, respectively. Using log properties, find a simplified formula for the difference between the two ratings, $D_2 - D_1$, in terms of the two intensities, I_1 and I_2. (Decibels are introduced on page 459.)
(b) If a sound's intensity doubles, how many decibels louder does the sound become?

35. The magnitude of an earthquake is measured relative to the strength of a "standard" earthquake, whose seismic waves are of size W_0. The magnitude, M, of an earthquake with seismic waves of size W is defined to be

$$M = \log\left(\frac{W}{W_0}\right).$$

The value of M is called the *Richter scale* rating of the strength of an earthquake.

(a) Let M_1 and M_2 represent the magnitude of two earthquakes whose seismic waves are of sizes W_1 and W_2, respectively. Using log properties, find a simplified formula for the difference $M_2 - M_1$ in terms of W_1 and W_2.

(b) The 1989 earthquake in California had a rating of 7.1 on the Richter scale. How many times larger were the seismic waves in the 1906 earthquake in San Francisco which measured 8.4 on the Richter scale? Give your answer to the nearest integer.

8.4 TRANSFORMATIONS OF LOGARITHMIC FUNCTIONS

- Stretches, Compressions, and Reflections
- Vertical and Horizontal Shifts

In Section 7.4 we reviewed transformations of exponential functions. Recall that addition to or subtraction from the formula for the original function yielded a shift in its graph. Multiplying the formula for the original function yielded a reflection, stretch, or compression of its graph. Recall also that *inside* changes to the function produce *horizontal* changes in the graph, while *outside* changes to the function produce *vertical* changes in the graph. This section considers transformations applied to a logarithmic function, $f(x) = \log_b(x)$

In this section, the common logarithmic function, $f(x) = \log(x)$, will be the starting point for our discussion of its transformations. Recall that a logarithm with a base other than 10 may be written with base 10 by the following change of base formula for logarithms:

$$\log_b(x) = \frac{\log(x)}{\log(b)}$$

Therefore, this section will use the common logarithm function in all examples, because a logarithmic function with any other base may be rewritten as an equivalent function with base 10, divided by the common logarithm of the original base.

The important attributes of a logarithmic function that we will compare after transformation are the domain, the vertical asymptote, whether the function is increasing or decreasing, and the *x-intercept*. Recall that the function $f(x) = \log(x)$ has a domain $(0, \infty)$. The vertical axis, $x = 0$, is a vertical asymptote of the logarithmic function. As $x \to 0^+$, $\log(x) \to -\infty$. The logarithmic function is increasing everywhere in its domain. Finally, the *x-intercept* is the point $(1, 0)$ because $\log(1) = 0$. Each example in this section will examine what happens to each of these attributes of the logarithmic function after a transformation.

Stretches, Compressions, and Reflections

Example 1   When $f(x) = \log(x)$ is multiplied by a positive constant a, its graph is stretched vertically if $a > 1$ and compressed vertically if $0 < a < 1$. For example, the new function $y = 10 \cdot \log(x)$ has a graph that is stretched vertically compared to $f(x) = \log(x)$. Another function, $y = 0.1 \cdot \log(x)$ is compressed vertically. What are the function attributes of each of the two transformed functions: what is the domain, what is the vertical asymptote, is the function increasing or decreasing, and what is the *x- intercept*? What happens to the graphs of the function?

Solution   See Figure 8.11 to compare the three graphs.

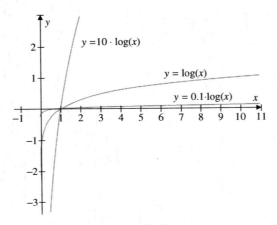

Figure 8.11

Each transformed function has all four attributes in common: a domain of all $x > 0$, a vertical asymptote at the vertical axis, increasing everywhere in its domain, and a *x-intercept* at the point $(1, 0)$. The graph of the function is stretched vertically when $\log(x)$ is multiplied by 10 and compressed vertically when $\log(x)$ is multiplied by 0.1.

Example 2   What are the logarithmic function's attributes if we reflect the graph of the function $f(x) = \log(x)$ over the *horizontal axis*?

Solution   When $f(x) = \log(x)$ is multiplied by negative one, the graph of the function is reflected across the horizontal axis. The domain of the function $f(x) = -\log(x)$ remains $x > 0$, and the function has a vertical asymptote at the *y-axis*, $x = 0$. As $x \to 0^+$, $\log(x) \to +\infty$. The reflected function is now decreasing. Its *x-intercept* remains at the point $(1, 0)$. Putting it all together, $y = -\log(x)$ has a graph as seen in Figure 8.12.

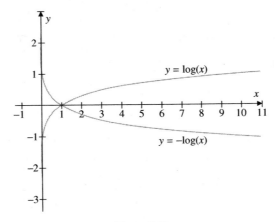

Figure 8.12

As we have seen in both Examples 1 and 2, an *outside* multiplication of $f(x) = \log(x)$ by a constant $a, a > 0$, stretches or compresses its graph but preserves its domain, its *x- intercept*, and its vertical asymptote. If $f(x)$ is multiplied by a negative constant, the nature of its vertical asymptote, $x = 0$, changes. As $x \to 0^+$, $-\log(x) \to \infty$. Also, this transformed function is decreasing.

Example 3   What are the logarithmic function's attributes if we reflect the graph of the function $f(x) = \log(x)$ over the *vertical axis*?

Solution   A reflection of a graph of a function across the *y-axis* comes from the graph of $f(-x)$. In this example, we consider $g(x) = \log(-x)$. First, think of the domain of $g(x)$. The logarithm of a non-positive number is not defined, so the domain of $g(x)$ is $(-\infty, 0)$. Its vertical asymptote is the vertical axis. As $x \to 0^-$, $\log(-x) \to -\infty$. The function is decreasing everywhere on its domain. The function's zero is at $x = -1$, making its *x-intercept* the point $(-1, 0)$. See Figure 8.13 to observe this reflection across the vertical axis.

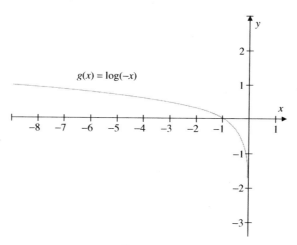

Figure 8.13

Example 4   Next, consider an *inside* multiplication by a positive constant. When we consider, for instance, $y = f(10x) = \log(10x)$, its attributes are as follows: its domain is still $x > 0$ and its vertical asymptote is still the vertical axis. As $x \to 0^+$, $\log(x) \to -\infty$. Also, it remains increasing on its domain. Its *x-intercept*, however, has changed. The following steps derive its zero.

(1) $0 = \log(10x)$ definition of equation to solve to find a function's zero
(2) $10^0 = 10x$ equivalent exponential equation
(3) $1 = 10x$ by the definition of an exponent of zero
(4) $\frac{1}{10} = x$ or $0.1 = x$

The *x-intercept* is the point $(\frac{1}{10}, 0)$. The graph of $y = \log(10x)$ is compressed horizontally by a factor of 10.

**Matched
Problem 1**   Write the formula for the function that horizontally stretches the graph of $y = \log(x)$ by a factor of 10. What is its x-intercept? Graph both the original function and the transformed function with your graphing calculator.

Vertical and Horizontal Shifts

Example 5   Consider the function $y = \log(x) + 1$. Compared to $y = \log(x)$, its graph is a *shift upward* by one unit. See **Figure 8.14** below. The graph of $y = \log(10x)$ is a different logarithmic function's graph, with the point (1,0) shifted up by one unit. In fact, it can be shown that $\log(10x) = \log(x) + 1$ by the following steps.

(1) $\log(10x) = \log(x) + \log(10)$ by rules of logarithms
(2) $\log(10x) = \log(x) + 1$ because $\log(10) = 1$

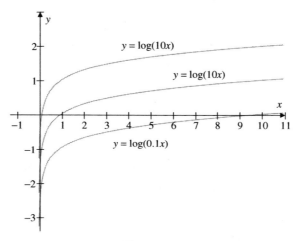

Figure 8.14

**Matched
Problem 2**   Show that $f(x) = \log(0.1x)$ is equivalent to $f(x) = \log(x) - 1$.

Our examination shows that both *inside* multiplication of a logarithmic function by a positive constant and an *outside* addition of a different constant yielded the same transformed function. Any vertical shift of a logarithmic function may also be rewritten as a horizontal stretch or compression.

Example 6   Our last transformation to consider is an *inside* addition of a constant. We expect an *inside* addition to translate or shift the graph of the function to the left or right. Therefore, we expect the new function to have a different domain, vertical asymptote, and *x-intercept*. What are the attributes and the graph of the horizontal shift $y = f(x - 3) = \log(x - 3)$?

Solution

The domain of $y = \log(x - 3)$ is $(3, \infty)$. This transformed function is increasing on its domain. Its vertical asymptote is the vertical line $x = 3$. As $x \to 3^+$, $f(x) \to -\infty$. The zero of the function is 4 as outlined in the following steps.

(1) $0 = \log(x - 3)$ definition of equation to solve to find a function's zero
(2) $10^0 = x - 3$ equivalent exponential equation
(3) $1 = x - 3$ by the definition of an exponent of zero
(4) $4 = x$

The *x-intercept* is at the point (4, 0).

The graph of y is a shift 3 units to the right, compared to $f(x) = \log(x)$. See Figure 8.15 below.

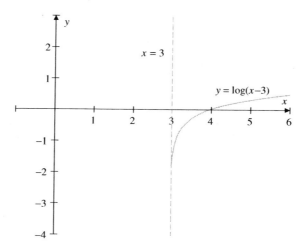

Figure 8.15

Putting It All Together

Example 7

The last example in this section will put together several transformations at once. If we start with $f(x) = \log(x)$, consider $g(x) = 2 \cdot f(3(x + 4)) = 2 \cdot \log(3(x + 4))$. What are the attributes and the graph of this transformed function, $g(x)$?

Solution

The domain of the transformed function is $(-4, \infty)$. Its vertical asymptote is at the vertical line $x = -4$. Because the coefficient 2 is positive, the function is increasing on its domain. Its *x-intercept* is at the point $\left(-3\frac{2}{3}, 0\right)$. In addition, this function has a *y-intercept* at the point $(0, 2\log(12))$.

Considering its graph, this function started with $y = \log(x)$, shifted horizontally 4 units to the left, compressed horizontally by a factor of 3, and stretched vertically by a factor of 2. See Figure 8.16 below to confirm our expectations.

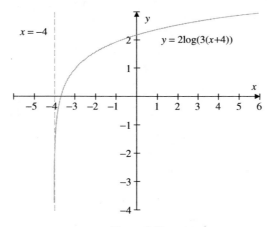

Figure 8.16

Outside changes to a logarithmic function, such as multiplying by a constant, yielded either a reflection across the *x-axis* and/or a vertical stretch or compression to the graph of that log function. An outside addition of a constant gave a vertical shift to the graph. As we have seen with every other function family, an inside change, such as multiplying or adding a constant to the logarithmic argument, gave a horizontal shift, stretch, or compression to the graph of the logarithmic function. Sometimes the function's attributes of its domain, its vertical asymptote, whether it is increasing or decreasing, and its *x-intercept*, remained the same, and sometimes these attributes changed.

Answers to Matched Problems

1. $y = \log(.10x)$
    x-intercept: $(10, 0)$

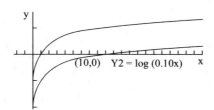

2. $y = \log(0.1x)$
    $= \log .0.1 + \log x$
    $= -1 + \log x$
    $= \log x - 1$

Exercises for Section 8.4

For exercises 1 to 3, start with the function $f(x) = \log(x)$. For each,

  i. write the formula of the function,
  ii. give the domain of the transformed function,
  iii. state the equation of the vertical asymptote,
  iv. state whether the function is increasing or decreasing,
  v. state the new x-intercept, and
  vi. by hand, sketch the new function and label the intercept and the asymptote. Check the graph with your calculator.

1. $y = f(x) - 3$ **2.** $y = -f(x + 3)$

3. $y = f(x - 3) + 3$

For exercises 4 to 6, start with the function $k(x) = \ln(x)$. For each,

  i. write the formula of the function,
  ii. give the domain of the transformed function,
  iii. state the equation of the vertical asymptote,
  iv. state whether the function is increasing or decreasing,
  v. state the new x-intercept, and
  vi. by hand, sketch the new function and label the intercept and the asymptote. Check the graph with your calculator.

4. $y = k(-x) + 2$ **5.** $y = -2k(x)$

6. $y = -2k(x - 2) + 3$

7. If $y = 3\ln(-x)$,

  a. state the basic function,
  b. state the transformations,
  c. graph the function by hand,
  d. label the x-intercept and the asymptote, and
  e. state the domain.

8. If $y = \ln(x - 1) + 2$,

  a. state the basic function,
  b. state the transformation,
  c. graph the function by hand,
  d. label the x-intercept and the asymptote, and
  e. state the domain.

9. Without a calculator, match the graphs in (a) to (d) of Figure 8.17 with the formulas in (i) to (iv).

  (i) $y = -\ln(x)$ (ii) $y = \ln(x)$
  (iii) $y = 2\ln(x)$ (iv) $y = -\ln(x - 2)$

a. 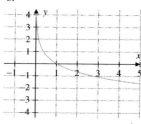   b.

c. 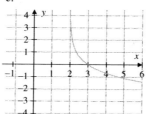   d.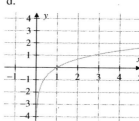

Figure 8.17

10. Without a calculator, match the graphs in (a) to (d) of Figure 8.18 with the formulas in (i) to (vi).

  (i) $y = \ln(-x)$ (ii) $y = e^{-x}$
  (iii) $y = -e^{-x} + 1$ (iv) $y = -\ln(x)$
  (v) $y = \ln(x + 4)$ (vi) $y = e^{x+4}$

a. 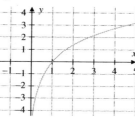   b.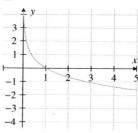

c. 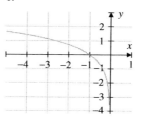   d.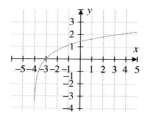

Figure 8.18

8.5 COMPARING POWER, EXPONENTIAL, AND LOG FUNCTIONS

In preceding chapters, we encountered exponential, power, and logarithmic functions. In this section, we compare the long and short-run behaviors of these functions.

Comparing Power Functions

For power functions $y = kx^p$ for large x, the higher the power of x, the faster the function climbs. See Figure 8.19. Not only are the higher powers larger, but they are *much* larger. This is because if $x = 100$, for example, 100^5 is one hundred times as big as 100^4, which is one hundred times as big as 100^3. As x gets larger (written as $x \to \infty$), any positive power of x grows much faster than all lower powers of x. We say that, as $x \to \infty$, higher powers of x *dominate* lower powers.

As x approaches zero (written $x \to 0$), the story is entirely different. Figure 8.20 is a close-up view near the origin. For x between 0 and 1, x^3 is bigger than x^4, which is bigger than x^5. (Try $x = 0.1$ to confirm this.) For values of x near zero, smaller powers dominate.

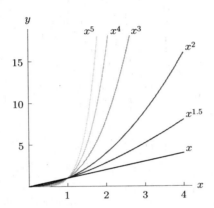

Figure 8.19: For large x: Large powers of x dominate

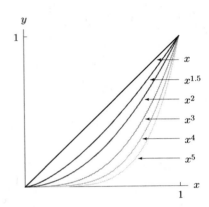

Figure 8.20: For $0 \le x \le 1$: Small powers of x dominate

In Chapter 4 we saw the effect of k on the graph of $f(x) = kx^p$. The coefficient k stretches or compresses the graph vertically; if k is negative, the graph is reflected across the x-axis. How does the value of k affect the long-term growth rate of $f(x) = kx^p$? Is the growth of a power function affected more by the size of the coefficient or by the size of the power?

Example 1 Let $f(x) = 100x^3$ and $g(x) = x^4$ for $x > 0$. Compare the long-term behavior of these two functions using graphs.

Solution For $x < 10$, Figure 8.21 suggests that f is growing faster than g and that f dominates g. Eventually, however, the fact that g has a higher power than f asserts itself. In Figure 8.22, we see that $g(x)$ has caught up to $f(x)$ at $x = 100$. In Figure 8.23, we see that for $x > 100$, values of g are larger than values of f.

Could the graphs of f and g intersect again for some value of $x > 100$? To show that this cannot be the case, solve the equation $g(x) = f(x)$:

$$x^4 = 100x^3$$
$$x^4 - 100x^3 = 0$$
$$x^3(x - 100) = 0.$$

Since the only solutions to this equation are $x = 0$ and $x = 100$, the graphs of f and g do not cross for $x > 100$.

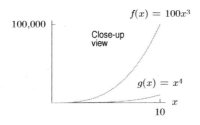

Figure 8.21: On this interval, f climbs faster than g

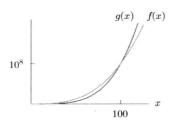

Figure 8.22: On this interval, g catches up to f

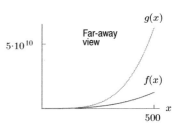

Figure 8.23: On this interval, g ends up far ahead of f

Comparing Exponential Functions and Power Functions

Both power functions and exponential functions can increase at phenomenal rates. For example, Table 8.4 shows values of $f(x) = x^4$ and $g(x) = 2^x$.

Table 8.4 *The exponential function $g(x) = 2^x$ eventually grows faster than the power function $f(x) = x^4$*

x	0	5	10	15	20
$f(x) = x^4$	0	625	10,000	50,625	160,000
$g(x) = 2^x$	1	32	1024	32,768	1,048,576

Despite the impressive growth in the value of the power function $f(x) = x^4$, in the long run $g(x) = 2^x$ grows faster. By the time $x = 20$, the value of $g(20) = 2^{20}$ is over six times as large as $f(20) = 20^4$. Figure 8.24 shows the exponential function $g(x) = 2^x$ catching up to $f(x) = x^4$.

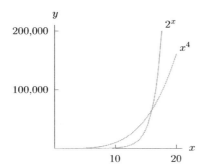

Figure 8.24: The exponential function $y = 2^x$ dominates the power function $y = x^4$

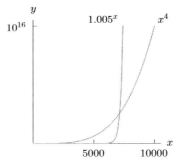

Figure 8.25: The exponential function $y = 1.005^x$ dominates the power function $y = x^4$

But what about a more slowly growing exponential function? After all, $y = 2^x$ increases at a 100% growth rate. Figure 8.25 compares $y = x^4$ to the exponential function $y = 1.005^x$. Despite the fact that this exponential function creeps along at a 0.5% growth rate, at around $x = 7000$, it overtakes the power function. In summary,

> *Any* positive increasing exponential function eventually grows faster than *any* power function.

Decreasing Exponential Functions and Decreasing Power Functions

Just as an increasing exponential function eventually outpaces any increasing power function, an exponential decay function wins the race towards the x-axis. In general:

> *Any* positive decreasing exponential function eventually approaches the horizontal axis faster than any positive decreasing power function.

For example, let's compare the long term behavior of the decreasing exponential function $y = 0.5^x$ with the decreasing power function $y = x^{-2}$. By rewriting

$$y = 0.5^x = \left(\frac{1}{2}\right)^x = \frac{1}{2^x} \quad \text{and} \quad y = x^{-2} = \frac{1}{x^2}$$

we can see the comparison more easily. In the long run, the smallest of these two fractions is the one with the largest denominator. The fact that 2^x is eventually larger than x^2 means that $1/2^x$ is eventually smaller than $1/x^2$.

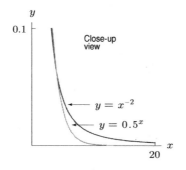

Figure 8.26: Graphs of $y = x^{-2}$ and $y = 0.5^x$

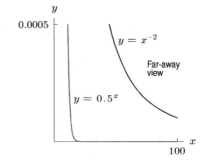

Figure 8.27: Graphs of $y = x^{-2}$ and $y = 0.5^x$

Figure 8.26 shows $y = 0.5^x$ and $y = x^{-2}$. Both graphs have the x-axis as a horizontal asymptote. As x increases, the exponential function $y = 0.5^x$ approaches the x-axis faster than the power function $y = x^{-2}$. Figure 8.27 shows what happens for large values of x. The exponential function approaches the x-axis so rapidly that it becomes invisible compared to $y = x^{-2}$.

Comparing Log and Power Functions

Power functions like $y = x^{1/2}$ and $y = x^{1/3}$ grow quite slowly. However, they grow rapidly in comparison to log functions. In fact:

> *Any* positive increasing power function eventually grows more rapidly than $y = \log x$ and $y = \ln x$.

For example, Figure 8.28 shows the graphs of $y = x^{1/2}$ and $y = \log x$. The fact that exponential functions grow so fast should alert you to the fact that their inverses, the logarithms, grow very slowly. See Figure 8.29.

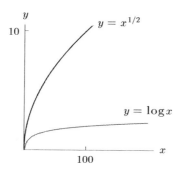

Figure 8.28: Graphs of $y = x^{1/2}$ and $y = \log x$

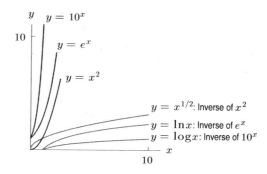

Figure 8.29: Graphs of $y = 10^x$, $y = e^x$, $y = x^2$, $y = x^{1/2}$, $y = \ln x$, and $y = \log x$

Exercises and Problems for Section 8.5

Exercises

1. Can the following formulas be written in the form of an exponential function or a power function? If not, explain why the function does not fit either form.

   (a) $m(x) = 3(3x + 1)^2$ (b) $n(x) = 3 \cdot 2^{3x+1}$
   (c) $p(x) = (5^x)^2$ (d) $q(x) = 5^{(x^2)}$
   (e) $r(x) = 2 \cdot 3^{-2x}$ (f) $s(x) = \dfrac{4}{5x^{-3}}$

2. Without a calculator, match the following functions with the graphs in Figure 8.30.

   (i) $y = x^5$ (ii) $y = x^2$ (iii) $y = x$ (iv) $y = x^3$

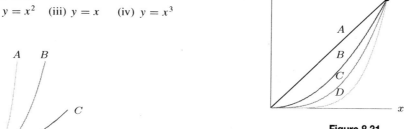

Figure 8.30

3. Let $f(x) = 3^x$ and $g(x) = x^3$.

   (a) Complete the following table of values:

x	-3	-2	-1	0	1	2	3
$f(x)$							
$g(x)$							

   (b) Describe the long-run behaviors of f and g as $x \to -\infty$ and as $x \to +\infty$.

4. Without a calculator, match the following functions with the graphs in Figure 8.31.

   (i) $y = x^5$ (ii) $y = x^2$ (iii) $y = x$ (iv) $y = x^3$

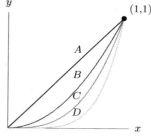

Figure 8.31

In Exercises 5–8, which function dominates as $x \to \infty$?

5. $y = 50x^{1.1}$, $y = 1000x^{1.08}$

6. $y = 4e^x$, $y = 2x^{50}$

7. $y = 7(0.99)^x$, $y = 6x^{35}$

8. $y = ax^3$, $y = bx^2$, $a, b > 0$

Problems

9. The functions $y = x^{-3}$ and $y = 3^{-x}$ both approach zero as $x \to \infty$. Which function approaches zero faster? Support your conclusion numerically.

10. Let $f(x) = x^x$. Is f a power function, an exponential function, both, or neither? Discuss.

In Problems 11–13, find a possible formula for f if f is
    (a) Linear   **(b)** Exponential   **(c)** Power function.

11. $f(1) = 18$ and $f(3) = 1458$

12. $f(1) = 16$ and $f(2) = 128$

13. $f(-1) = \frac{3}{4}$ and $f(2) = 48$

14. The functions $y = x^{-3}$ and $y = e^{-x}$ both approach zero as $x \to \infty$. Which function approaches zero faster? Support your conclusion numerically.

15. **(a)** Match the functions $f(x) = x^2$, $g(x) = 2x^2$, and $h(x) = x^3$ to their graphs in Figure 8.32.
    (b) Do graphs A and B intersect for $x > 0$? If so, for what value(s) of x? If not, explain how you know.
    (c) Do graphs C and A intersect for $x > 0$? If so, for what value(s) of x? If not, explain how you know.

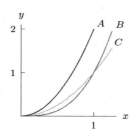

Figure 8.32

16. Match the graphs in Figure 8.33 with the functions $y = kx^{9/16}$, $y = kx^{3/8}$, $y = kx^{5/7}$, $y = kx^{3/11}$.

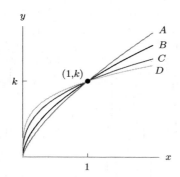

Figure 8.33

17. In Figure 8.34, find the values of m, t, and k.

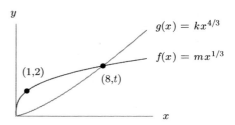

Figure 8.34

18. **(a)** Given $t(x) = x^{-2}$ and $r(x) = 40x^{-3}$, find v such that $t(v) = r(v)$.
    (b) For $0 < x < v$, which is greater, $t(x)$ or $r(x)$?
    (c) For $x > v$, which is greater, $t(x)$ or $r(x)$?

What is the long-run behavior of the functions in Problems 19–30?

19. $y = \dfrac{x^2 + 5}{x^8}$ **20.** $y = \dfrac{5 - t^2}{(7 + t + \sqrt{t})t^5}$

21. $y = \dfrac{x(x + 5)(x - 7)}{4 + x^2}$ **22.** $y = \dfrac{2^x + 3}{x^2 + 5}$

23. $y = \dfrac{2^t + 7}{5^t + 9}$ **24.** $y = \dfrac{3^{-t}}{4^t + 7}$

25. $y = \dfrac{e^x + 5}{x^{100} + 50}$ **26.** $y = \dfrac{e^{2t}}{e^{3t} + 5}$

27. $y = \dfrac{\ln x}{\sqrt{x} + 5}$ **28.** $y = \dfrac{e^t + t^2}{\ln |t|}$

29. $y = \dfrac{e^x - e^{-x}}{2}$ **30.** $y = \dfrac{e^x - e^{-x}}{e^x + e^{-x}}$

31. Table 8.5 gives approximate values for three functions, f, g, and h. One is exponential, one is trigonometric, and one is a power function. Determine which is which and find possible formulas for each.

Table 8.5

x	-2	-1	0	1	2
$f(x)$	4	2	4	6	4
$g(x)$	20.0	2.5	0.0	-2.5	-20.0
$h(x)$	1.33	0.67	0.33	0.17	0.08

32. The period, p, of the orbit of a planet whose average distance (in millions of miles) from the sun is d, is given by $p = kd^{3/2}$, where k is a constant. The average distance from the earth to the sun is 93 million miles.

(a) If the period of the earth's orbit were twice the current 365 days, what would be the average distance from the sun to earth?

(b) Is there a planet in our solar system whose period is approximately twice the earth's?

33. Refer to Problem 32. If the distance between the sun and the earth were halved, how long (in earth days) would a "year" be?

34. (a) The functions in Table 8.6 are of the form $y = a \cdot r^{3/4}$ and $y = b \cdot r^{5/4}$. Explain how you can tell which is which from the values in the table.

(b) Determine the constants a and b.

Table 8.6

r	2.5	3.2	3.9	4.6
$y = g(r)$	15.9	19.1	22.2	25.1
$y = h(r)$	9.4	12.8	16.4	20.2

35. A woman opens a bank account with an initial deposit of $1000. At the end of each year thereafter, she deposits an additional $1000.

(a) The account earns 6% annual interest, compounded annually. Complete Table 8.7.

(b) Does the balance of this account grow linearly, exponentially, or neither? Justify your answer.

Table 8.7

Years elapsed	Start-of-year balance	End-of-year deposit	End-of-year interest
0	$1000.00	$1000	$60.00
1	$2060.00	$1000	$123.60
2	$3183.60	$1000	
3		$1000	
4		$1000	
5		$1000	

36. Suppose the annual percentage rate (APR) paid by the account in Problem 35 is r, where r does not necessarily equal 6%. Define $p_n(r)$ as the balance of the account after n years have elapsed. (For example, $p_2(0.06) = \$3183.60$, because, according to Table 8.7, the balance after 2 years is $3183.60 if the APR is 6%.)

(a) Find formulas for $p_5(r)$ and $p_{10}(r)$.

(b) What is the APR if the woman in Problem 35 has $10,000 in 5 years?

37. Values of f and g are in Table 8.8 and 8.9. One function is of the form $y = a \cdot d^{p/q}$ with $p > q$; the other is of the form $y = b \cdot d^{p/q}$ with $p < q$. Which is which? How can you tell?

Table 8.8

d	2	2.2	2.4	2.6	2.8
$f(d)$	151.6	160.5	169.1	177.4	185.5

Table 8.9

d	10	10.2	10.4	10.6	10.8
$g(d)$	7.924	8.115	8.306	8.498	8.691

CHAPTER SUMMARY

- **Logarithms**

  Common log: $y = \log x$ means $10^y = x$.

  $$\log 10 = 1, \log 1 = 0.$$

  Natural log: $y = \ln x$ means $e^y = x$.

  $$\ln e = 1, \ln 1 = 0.$$

- **Properties of Logs**

  $$\log(ab) = \log a + \log b.$$
  $$\log(a/b) = \log a - \log b.$$
  $$\log(b^t) = t \log b.$$
  $$\log(10^x) = 10^{\log x} = x.$$

- **Converting between base b and base e**

  If $Q = ab^t$ and $Q = ae^{kt}$, then $k = \ln b$.

- **Solving Equations using Logs**

  Solve equations such as $ab^t = c$ and $ae^{kt} = c$ using logs. Not all exponential equations can be solved with logs, e.g. $2^t = 3 + t$.

- **Logarithmic Functions**

  Graph; domain; range; concavity; asymptotes.

- **Applications of Logarithms**

  Doubling time; half life;
  Chemical acidity; orders of magnitude; decibels.

- **Logarithmic Scales**

  Plotting data; log-log scales. Linearizing data and fitting curves to data using logs.

REVIEW EXERCISES AND PROBLEMS FOR CHAPTER EIGHT

Exercises

In Exercises 1–4, convert to the form $Q = ae^{kt}$.

1. $Q = 12(0.9)^t$

2. $Q = 16(0.487)^t$

3. $Q = 14(0.862)^{1.4t}$

4. $Q = 721(0.98)^{0.7t}$

In Exercises , convert to the form $Q = ab^t$.

5. $Q = 7e^{-10t}$

6. $Q = 5e^t$

For Exercises 7–10, use logarithms to solve for t.

7. $3^t = 50$

8. $e^{0.15t} = 25$

9. $40e^{-0.2t} = 12$

10. $5 \cdot 2^t = 100$

11. The following populations, $P(t)$, are given in millions in year t. Describe the growth of each population in words. Give both the percent annual growth rate and the continuous growth rate per year.

(a) $P(t) = 51(1.03)^t$
(b) $P(t) = 15e^{0.03t}$
(c) $P(t) = 7.5(0.94)^t$
(d) $P(t) = 16e^{-0.051t}$
(e) $P(t) = 25(2)^{t/18}$
(f) $P(t) = 10(\frac{1}{2})^{t/25}$

12. A population, $P(t)$ (in millions) in year t, increases exponentially. Suppose $P(8) = 20$ and $P(15) = 28$.

(a) Find a formula for $P(t)$ without using e.
(b) If $P(t) = ae^{kt}$, find k.

13. (a) What is the domain and range of $f(x) = 10^x$? What is the asymptote of $f(x) = 10^x$?

(b) What does your answer to part (a) tell you about the domain, range, and asymptotes of $g(x) = \log x$?

14. Rewrite the following formulas as indicated.

(a) If $f(x) = 5(1.121)^x$, find a and k if $f(x) = ae^{kx}$.
(b) If $g(x) = 17e^{0.094x}$, find a and b if $g(x) = ab^x$.
(c) If $h(x) = 22(2)^{x/15}$, find a and b if $h(x) = ab^x$, and a and k if $h(x) = ae^{kx}$.

15. (a) Let $B = 5000(1.06)^t$ give the balance of a bank account after t years. If the formula for B is written $B = 5000e^{kt}$, estimate the value of k correct to four decimal places. What is the financial meaning of k?

(b) The balance of a bank account after t years is given by the formula $B = 7500e^{0.072t}$. If the formula for B is written $B = 7500b^t$, find b exactly, and give the value of b correct to four decimal places. What is the financial meaning of b?

In Exercises 16–18, find an exact solution for t if possible.

16. $16.3(1.072)^t = 18.5$

17. $13e^{0.081t} = 25e^{0.032t}$

18. $87e^{0.066t} = 3t + 7$

In Exercises 19–21, simplify fully.

19. $\log(100^{x+1})$

20. $\ln(e \cdot e^{2+M})$

21. $\ln(A + B) - \ln(A^{-1} + B^{-1})$

Problems

22. The balance B (in $) in an account after t years is given by $B = 5000(1.12)^t$.
(a) What is the balance after 5 years? 10 years?
(b) When is the balance $10,000? $20,000?

23. The populations (in thousands) of two cities are given by
$$P_1 = 51(1.031)^t \quad \text{and} \quad P_2 = 63(1.052)^t,$$
where t is the number of years since 1980. When does the population of P_1 equal that of P_2?

24. In 1999, the population of the country Erehwon was 50 million people and increasing by 2.9% every year. The population of the country Ecalpon, on other hand, was 45 million people and increasing by 3.2% every year.
(a) For each country, write a formula expressing the population as a function of time t, where t is the number of years since 1999.
(b) Find the value(s) of t, if any, when the two countries have the same population.
(c) When is the population of Ecalpon double that of Erehwon?

25. The following is excerpted from an article that appeared in the January 8, 1990 *Boston Globe*.

Men lose roughly 2 percent of their bone mass per year in the same type of loss that can severely affect women after menopause, a study indicates. "There is a problem with osteoporosis in men that hasn't been appreciated. It's a problem that needs to be recognized and addressed," said Dr. Eric Orwoll, who led the study by the Oregon Health Sciences University. The bone loss was detected at all ages and the 2 percent rate did not appear to vary, Orwoll said.

(a) Assume that the average man starts losing bone mass at age 30. Let M_0 be the average man's bone mass at this age. Express the amount of remaining bone mass as a function of the man's age, a.
(b) At what age will the average man have lost half his bone mass?

26. The number of bacteria present in a culture after t hours is given by the formula $N = 1000e^{0.69t}$.

(a) How many bacteria will there be after $1/2$ hour?
(b) How long before there are $1,000,000$ bacteria?
(c) What is the doubling time?

27. Oil leaks from a tank. At hour $t = 0$ there are 250 gallons of oil in the tank. Each hour after that, 4% of the oil leaks out.

(a) What percent of the original 250 gallons has leaked out after 10 hours? Why is it less than $10 \cdot 4\% = 40\%$?
(b) If $Q(t) = Q_0 e^{kt}$ is the quantity of oil remaining after t hours, find the value of k. What does k tell you about the leaking oil?

28. A population increases from 30,000 to 34,000 over a 5-year period at a constant annual percent growth rate.

(a) By what percent did the population increase in total?
(b) At what constant percent rate of growth did the population increase each year?
(c) At what continuous annual growth rate did this population grow?

29. Radioactive carbon-14 decays according to the function $Q(t) = Q_0 e^{-0.000121t}$ where t is time in years, $Q(t)$ is the quantity remaining at time t, and Q_0 is the amount of present at time $t = 0$. Estimate the age of a skull if 23% of the original quantity of carbon-14 remains.

30. Suppose 2 mg of a drug is injected into a person's bloodstream. As the drug is metabolized, the quantity diminishes at the continuous rate of 4% per hour.

(a) Find a formula for $Q(t)$, the quantity of the drug remaining in the body after t hours.
(b) By what percent does the drug level decrease during any given hour?
(c) The person must receive an additional 2 mg of the drug whenever its level has diminished to 0.25 mg. When must the person receive the second injection?
(d) When must the person receive the third injection?

31. Suppose that $u = \log 2$ and $v = \log 5$.

(a) Find possible formulas for the following expressions in terms of u and/or v. Your answers should not involve logs.

(i) $\log(0.4)$ (ii) $\log 0.25$
(iii) $\log 40$ (iv) $\log \sqrt{10}$

(b) Justify the statement: $\log(7) \approx \frac{1}{2}(u + 2v)$.

32. Solve the following equations. Give approximate solutions if exact ones can't be found.

(a) $e^{x+3} = 8$ (b) $4(1.12^x) = 5$

(c) $e^{-0.13x} = 4$ (d) $\log(x - 5) = 2$
(e) $2\ln(3x) + 5 = 8$ (f) $\ln x - \ln(x - 1) = 1/2$
(g) $e^x = 3x + 5$ (h) $3^x = x^3$
(i) $\ln x = -x^2$

33. Solve for x exactly.

(a) $\dfrac{3^x}{5^{x-1}} = 2^{x-1}$

(b) $-3 + e^{x+1} = 2 + e^{x-2}$

(c) $\ln(2x - 2) - \ln(x - 1) = \ln x$

(d) $9^x - 7 \cdot 3^x = -6$

(e) $\ln\left(\dfrac{e^{4x} + 3}{e}\right) = 1$

(f) $\dfrac{\ln(8x) - 2\ln(2x)}{\ln x} = 1$

Problems 34–35 involve the Rule of 70, which gives quick estimates of the doubling time of an exponentially growing quantity. If $r\%$ is the annual growth rate of the quantity, then the Rule of 70 says

$$\text{Doubling time in years} \approx \frac{70}{r}.$$

34. Use the Rule of 70 by estimate how long it takes a \$1000 investment to double if it grows at the following annual rates: 1%, 2%, 5%, 7%, 10%. Compare with the actual doubling times.

35. Using natural logs, solve for the doubling time for $Q = ae^{kt}$. Use your result to explain why the Rule of 70 works.

36. You want to borrow \$25,000 to buy a Ford Explorer XL. The best available annual interest rate is 6.9%, compounded monthly. Determine how long it will take to pay off the loan if you can only afford monthly payments of \$330. To do this, use the loan payment formula

$$P = \frac{Lr/12}{1 - (1 + (r/12))^{-m}},$$

where P is the monthly payment, L is the amount borrowed, r is the annual interest rate, and m is the number of months the loan is carried.

37. A rubber ball is dropped onto a hard surface from a height of 6 feet, and it bounces up and down. At each bounce it rises to 90% of the height from which it fell.

(a) Find a formula for $h(n)$, the height reached by the ball on bounce n.
(b) How high will the ball bounce on the 12th bounce?
(c) How many bounces before the ball rises no higher than an inch?

38. A manager at Saks Fifth Avenue wants to estimate the number of customers to expect on the last shopping day before Christmas. She collects data from three previous years, and determines that the crowds follow the same general pattern. When the store opens at 10 am, 500 people enter, and the total number in the store doubles every 40 minutes. When the number of people in the store reaches 10,000, security guards need to be stationed at the entrances to control the crowds. At what time should the guards be commissioned?

39. The Richter scale is a measure of the ground motion that occurs during an earthquake. The intensity, R, of an earthquake as measured on the Richter scale is given by

$$R = \log\left(\frac{a}{T}\right) + B$$

where a is the amplitude (in microns) of vertical ground motion, T is the period (in seconds) of the seismic wave,

and B is a constant. Let $B = 4.250$ and $T = 2.5$. Find a if

(a) $R = 6.1$ **(b)** $R = 7.1$
(c) Compare the values of R in parts (a) and (b). How do the corresponding values of a compare?

40. Since $e = 2.718\ldots$ we know that $2 < e < 3$, which means that $2^2 < e^2 < 3^2$. Without using a calculator, explain why

(a) $1 < \ln 3 < 2$ **(b)** $1 < \ln 4 < 2$

CHECK YOUR UNDERSTANDING

Are the statements in Problems 1–29 true or false? Give an explanation for your answer.

1. If x is a positive number, $\log x$ is the exponent of 10 that gives x.

2. If $10^y = x$ then $\log x = y$.

3. The quantity 10^{-k} is a negative number when k is positive. For any n, we have $\log(10^n) = n$.

4. For any n, we have $\log(10^n) = n$.

5. If $n > 0$, then $10^{\log n} = n$.

6. If a and b are positive, $\log\left(\frac{a}{b}\right) = \frac{\log a}{\log b}$.

7. If a and b are positive, $\ln(a + b) = \ln a + \ln b$.

8. For any value a, $\log a = \ln a$.

9. For any value x, $\ln(e^{2x}) = 2x$.

10. The function $y = \log x$ has an asymptote at $y = 0$.

11. The graph of the function $y = \log x$ is concave down.

12. The reflected graph of $y = \log x$ across the line $y = x$ is the graph of $y = 10^x$.

13. If $y = \log\sqrt{x}$ then $y = \frac{1}{2}\log x$.

14. The function $y = \log(b^t)$ is always equal to $y = (\log b)^t$.

15. The values of $\ln e$ and $\log 10$ are both 1.

16. If $7.32 = e^t$ then $t = \frac{7.32}{e}$.

17. If $50(0.345)^t = 4$, then $t = \frac{\log(4/50)}{\log 0.345}$.

18. If $ab^t = n$, then $t = \frac{\log(n/a)}{\log b}$.

19. The doubling time of a quantity $Q = Q_0 e^{kt}$ is the time it takes for any t-value to double.

20. The half-life of a quantity is the time it takes for the quantity to be reduced by half.

21. If the half-life of a substance is 5 hours then there will be $\frac{1}{4}$ of the substance in 25 hours.

22. If $y = 6(3)^t$, then $y = 6e^{(\ln 3)t}$.

23. If a population doubles in size every 20 years, its annual continuous growth rate is 20%.

24. If $Q = Q_0 e^{kt}$, then $t = \frac{\ln(Q/Q_0)}{k}$.

25. Log scales provide a way to graph quantities that have vastly different magnitudes.

26. In a graph made using a log-log scale, consecutive powers of 10 are equally spaced on the horizontal axis and on the vertical axis.

27. One million and one billion differ by one order of magnitude.

28. After fitting a data set with both an exponential function, $y = Ae^{kx}$, and a power function, $y = Bx^n$, we must have $B = A$.

29. Given the points on a cubic curve, $(1, 1)$, $(2, 8)$, $(3, 27)$ and $(4, 64)$ it is not possible to fit an exponential function to this data.

Chapter Nine

MODELING, PARAMETRIC EQUATIONS, AND CONIC SECTIONS

This chapter begins with two sections on mathematical models; in the first, trigonometric functions are used to model phenomena such as electricity usage and fluctuating populations, while in the second, algebraic and transcendental functions are defined and graphs are investigated. The next four sections focus on conic sections—circles, ellipses, and hyperbolas. These shapes cannot be represented by functions but can be represented by implicit equations or by parametric equations, which are also introduced. The chapter concludes by studying the intersections of graphs, which leads to solving a wide variety of equations algebraically and graphically.

9.1 TRIGONOMETRIC MODELS

This section gives examples of mathematical models using trigonometric functions.

Sums of Trigonometric Functions

The first example shows mathematical models involving the sums of trigonometric functions. We see how the identities enable us to predict and explain the observed phenomena.

Example 1   A utility company serves two different cities. Let P_1 be the power requirement in megawatts (mw) for City 1 and P_2 be the requirement for City 2. Both P_1 and P_2 are functions of t, the number of hours elapsed since midnight. Suppose P_1 and P_2 are given by the following formulas:

$$P_1 = 40 - 15\cos\left(\frac{\pi}{12}t\right) \qquad \text{and} \qquad P_2 = 50 + 10\sin\left(\frac{\pi}{12}t\right).$$

(a) Describe the power requirements of each city in words.
(b) What is the maximum total power the utility company must be prepared to provide?

Solution   (a) The power requirement of City 1 is at a minimum of $40 - 15 = 25$ mw at $t = 0$, or midnight. It rises to a maximum of $40 + 15 = 55$ mw at noon and falls back to 25 mw by the following midnight. The power requirement of City 2 is at a maximum of 60 mw at 6 am. It falls to a minimum of 40 mw by 6 pm but by the following morning has climbed back to 60 mw, again at 6 am. Figure 9.1 shows P_1 and P_2 over a two-day period.

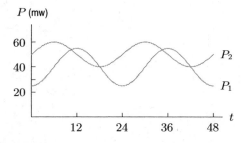

Figure 9.1: Power requirements for cities 1 and 2

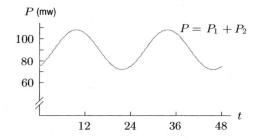

Figure 9.2: Total power demand for both cities combined

(b) The utility company must provide enough power to satisfy the needs of both cities. The total power required is given by

$$P = P_1 + P_2 = 90 + 10\sin\left(\frac{\pi}{12}t\right) - 15\cos\left(\frac{\pi}{12}t\right).$$

The graph of total power in Figure 9.2 looks like a sinusoidal function. It varies between about 108 mw and 72 mw, giving it an amplitude of roughly 18 mw. Since the maximum value of P is about 108 mw, the utility company must be prepared to provide at least this much power at all times. Since the maximum value of P_1 is 55 and the maximum value of P_2 is 60, you might have expected that the maximum value of P would be $55 + 60 = 115$. The reason that this isn't true is that the maximum values of P_1 and P_2 occur at different times. However, the midline of P is a horizontal line at 90, which does equal the midline of P_1 plus the midline of P_2. The period of P is 24 hours because the values of both P_1 and P_2 begin repeating after 24 hours, so their sum repeats that frequently as well.

There are formulas that allow us to take the sum and find an expression for the total power as a sine function:

$$P = P_1 + P_2 = 90 + 10 \sin\left(\frac{\pi}{12}t\right) - 15 \cos\left(\frac{\pi}{12}t\right) = 90 + A \sin(Bt + \phi),$$

where

$$A = \sqrt{10^2 + (-15)^2} = 18.028 \text{ mw.}$$

Since $\cos\phi = 10/18.028 = 0.555$ and $\sin\phi = -15/18.028 = -0.832$, we know ϕ must be in the fourth quadrant. Also,

$$\tan\phi = \frac{-15}{10} = -1.5 \quad \text{and} \quad \tan^{-1}(-1.5) = -0.983,$$

and since -0.983 is in the fourth quadrant, we take $\phi = -0.983$. Thus,

$$P = P_1 + P_2 = 90 + 18 \sin\left(\frac{\pi}{12}t - 0.983\right).$$

The next example shows that the sum of sine or cosine functions is not always sinusoidal.

Example 2   Sketch and describe the graph of $y = \sin 2x + \sin 3x$.

Solution   Figure 9.3 shows that the function $y = \sin 2x + \sin 3x$ is not sinusoidal. It is, however, periodic. Its period seems to be 2π, since it repeats twice on the interval of length 4π shown in the figure.

We can see that the function $y = \sin 2x + \sin 3x$ has period 2π by looking at the periods of $\sin 2x$ and $\cos 3x$. Since the period of $\sin 2x$ is π and the period of $\sin 3x$ is $2\pi/3$, on any interval of length 2π, the function $y = \sin 2x$ completes two cycles and the function $y = \sin 3x$ completes three cycles. Both functions are at the beginning of a new cycle after an interval of 2π, so their sum begins to repeat at this point. (See Figure 9.4.) Notice that even though the maximum value of each of the functions $\sin 2x$ and $\sin 3x$ is 1, the maximum value of their sum is not 2; it is a little less than 2. This is because $\sin 2x$ and $\sin 3x$ achieve their maximum values for different x values.

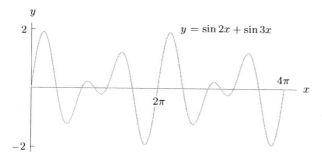

Figure 9.3: A graph of the sum $y = \sin 2x + \sin 3x$

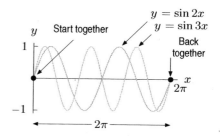

Figure 9.4: Graphs of $y = \sin 2x$ and $y = \sin 3x$ on an interval of 2π

Damped Oscillation

In Problems 23–26 in Section 3.4, we considered a weight attached to the ceiling by a spring. If the weight is disturbed, it begins bobbing up and down; we modeled the weight's motion using a trigonometric function. Figure 9.5 shows such a weight at rest. Suppose d is the displacement in centimeters from the weight's position at rest. For instance, if $d = 5$ then the weight is 5 cm above its rest position; if $d = -5$, then the weight is 5 cm below its rest position.

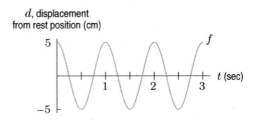

Figure 9.5: The value of d represents the weight's displacement from its at-rest position, $d = 0$

Figure 9.6: The predicted motion of the weight for the first 3 seconds

Imagine that we raise the weight 5 cm above its rest position and release it at time $t = 0$, where t is in seconds. Suppose the weight bobbed up and down once every second for the first few seconds. We could model this behavior by the function

$$d = f(t) = 5\cos(2\pi t).$$

One full cycle is completed each second, so the period is 1, and the amplitude is 5. Figure 9.6 gives a graph of d for the first three seconds of the weight's motion.

This trigonometric model of the spring's motion is flawed, however, because it predicts that the weight will bob up and down forever. In fact, we know that as time passes, the amplitude of the bobbing diminishes and eventually the weight comes to rest. How can we alter our formula to model this kind of behavior? We need an amplitude which decreases over time.

For example, the amplitude of the spring's motion might decrease at a constant rate, so that after 5 seconds, the weight stops moving. In other words, we could imagine that the amplitude is a decreasing linear function of time. Using A to represent the amplitude, this means that $A = 5$ at $t = 0$, and that $A = 0$ at $t = 5$. Thus, $A(t) = 5 - t$. Then, instead of writing

$$d = f(t) = \underbrace{\text{Constant amplitude}}_{5} \cdot \cos 2\pi t,$$

we write

$$d = f(t) = \underbrace{\text{Decreasing amplitude}}_{(5-t)} \cdot \cos 2\pi t$$

so that the formula becomes

$$d = f(t) = (5 - t) \cdot \cos 2\pi t.$$

Figure 9.7 shows a graph of this function.

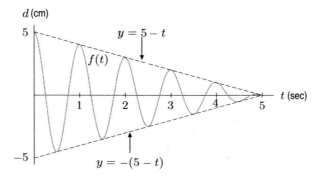

Figure 9.7: Graph of the weight's displacement assuming amplitude is a decreasing linear function of time

While the function $d = f(t) = (5 - t)\cos 2\pi t$ is a better model for the behavior of the spring for $t < 5$, Figure 9.8 shows that this model does not work for $t > 5$. The breakdown in the model occurs because the magnitude of $A(t) = 5 - t$ starts to increase when t grows larger than 5.

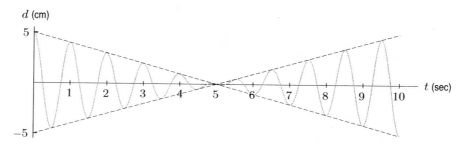

Figure 9.8: The formula $d = f(t) = (5 - t)\cos 2\pi t$ makes inaccurate predictions for values of t larger than 5

To improve the model, we keep the idea of representing the amplitude as a decreasing function of time, but we pick a different decreasing function. The problem with the linear function $A(t) = 5 - t$ is two-fold. It approaches zero too abruptly, and, after attaining zero, it becomes negative. We want a function that approaches zero gradually and does not become negative.

Let's try a decreasing exponential function. Suppose that the amplitude of the spring's motion is halved each second. Then at $t = 0$ the amplitude is 5, and the amplitude at time t is given by

$$A(t) = 5 \left(\frac{1}{2}\right)^t.$$

Thus, a formula for the motion is

$$d = f(t) = \underbrace{5 \left(\frac{1}{2}\right)^t}_{\text{Decreasing amplitude}} \cdot \cos 2\pi t.$$

Figure 9.9 shows a graph of this function. The dashed curves in Figure 9.9 show the decreasing exponential function. (There are two curves, $y = 5(\frac{1}{2})^t$ and $y = -5(\frac{1}{2})^t$, because the amplitude measures distance on both sides of the midline.)

Figure 9.9 predicts that the weight's oscillations diminish gradually, so that at time $t = 5$ the weight is still oscillating slightly. Figure 9.10 shows that the weight continues to make small oscillations long after 5 seconds have elapsed.

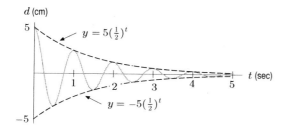

Figure 9.9: A graph of the weight's displacement assuming that the amplitude is a decreasing exponential function of time

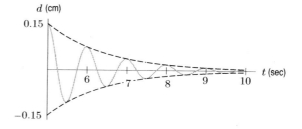

Figure 9.10: Graph showing that the weight is still making small oscillations for $t \geq 5$. Note reduced scale on d-axis; t-axis starts at $t = 5$

If A_0, B, and C, and k are constants, $k > 0$, a function of the form

$$y = A_0 e^{-kt} \cos(Bt) + C \quad \text{or} \quad y = A_0 e^{-kt} \sin(Bt) + C$$

can be used to model an oscillating quantity whose amplitude decreases exponentially according to $A(t) = A_0 e^{-kt}$ where A_0 is the initial amplitude. Our model for the displacement of a weight is in this form with $k = \ln 2$.

Oscillation With a Rising Midline

In the next example, we consider an oscillating quantity which does not have a horizontal midline, but whose amplitude of oscillation is in some sense constant.

Example 3   In Section 4.4, Example 7, we represented a rabbit population undergoing seasonal fluctuations by the function

$$R = f(t) = 10000 - 5000 \cos\left(\frac{\pi}{6} t\right),$$

where R is the size of the rabbit population t months after January. See Figure 9.11. The rabbit population varies periodically about the midline, $y = 10000$. The average number of rabbits is 10,000, but, depending on the time of year, the actual number may be above or below the average.

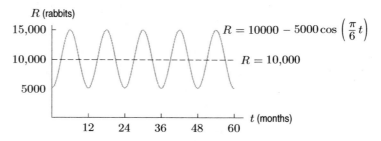

Figure 9.11: The rabbit population over a 5-year (60 month) period

This suggests the following way of thinking about the formula for R:

$$R = \underbrace{10{,}000}_{\text{Average value}} - \underbrace{5000 \cos\left(\frac{\pi}{6} t\right)}_{\text{Seasonal variation}}.$$

Notice that we can't say the average value of the rabbit population is 10,000 unless we look at the population over year-long units. For example, if we looked at the population over the first two months, an interval on which it is always below 10,000, then the average would be less than 10,000.

Now let us imagine a different situation. What if the average, even over long periods of time, does not remain constant? For example, suppose that, due to conservation efforts, there is a steady increase of 50 rabbits per month in the average rabbit population. Thus, instead of writing

$$P = f(t) = \underbrace{10{,}000}_{\text{Constant midline}} - \underbrace{5000 \cos\left(\frac{\pi}{6} t\right)}_{\text{Seasonal variation}},$$

we could write

$$P = f(t) = \underbrace{10{,}000 + 50t}_{\substack{\text{Midline population increasing} \\ \text{by 50 every month}}} - \underbrace{5000 \cos\left(\frac{\pi}{6} t\right)}_{\text{Seasonal variation}}.$$

Figure 9.12 gives a graph of this new function over a five-year period.

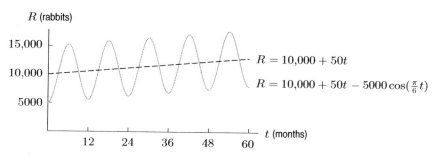

Figure 9.12: A graph of the gradually increasing rabbit population

Acoustic Beats

By international agreement, on a perfectly tuned piano, the A above middle C has a frequency of 440 cycles per second, also written 440 hertz (hz). The lowest-pitched note on the piano (the key at the left-most end) has frequency 55 hertz. Suppose a frequency of 55 hertz is struck on a tuning fork together with a note on an out-of-tune piano, whose frequency is 61 hertz. The intensities, I_1 and I_2, of these two tones are represented by the functions

$$I_1 = \cos(2\pi f_1 t) \qquad \text{and} \qquad I_2 = \cos(2\pi f_2 t),$$

where $f_1 = 55$, and $f_2 = 61$, and t is in seconds. If both tones are sounded at the same time, then their combined intensity is the sum of their separate intensities:

$$I = I_1 + I_2 = \cos(2\pi f_1 t) + \cos(2\pi f_2 t).$$

The graph of this function in Figure 9.13 resembles a rapidly varying sinusoidal function except that its amplitude increases and decreases. The ear perceives this variation in amplitude as a variation in loudness, so the tone appears to waver (or *beat*) in a regular way. This is an example of *acoustic beats*. A piano can be tuned by adjusting it until the beats fade.

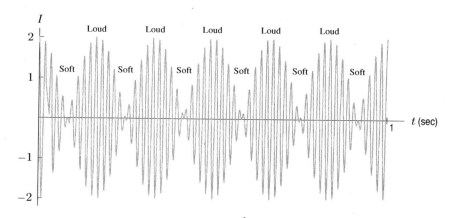

Figure 9.13: A graph of $I = \cos(2\pi f_1 t) + \cos(2\pi f_2 t)$

How can we explain the graph in Figure 9.13? Using the identity for a sum of cosines, we rewrite the intensity as

$$I = \cos(2\pi f_2 t) + \cos(2\pi f_1 t) = 2\cos\frac{2\pi f_2 t + 2\pi f_1 t}{2} \cdot \cos\frac{2\pi f_2 t - 2\pi f_1 t}{2}$$

$$= 2\cos\frac{2\pi \cdot (61 + 55)t}{2} \cdot \cos\frac{2\pi \cdot (61 - 55)t}{2}$$

$$= 2\cos(2\pi \cdot 58t)\cos(2\pi \cdot 3t).$$

We can think of this formula in the following way:

$$I = 2\cos(2\pi \cdot 3t) \cdot \cos(2\pi \cdot 58t) = A(t)p(t),$$

where $A(t) = 2\cos(2\pi \cdot 3t)$ gives a (slowly) changing amplitude and $p(t) = \cos(2\pi \cdot 58t)$ gives a pure tone of 58 hz. Thus, we can think of the tone described by I as having a pitch of 58 hz, which is midway between the tones sounded by the tuning fork and the out-of-tune piano. As the amplitude rises and falls, the tone grows louder and softer, but its pitch remains a constant 58 hz. (See Figure 9.14.)

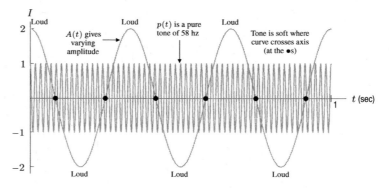

Figure 9.14: The function $A(t) = 2\cos(2\pi \cdot 3t)$ gives a varying amplitude, while the function $p(t) = \cos(2\pi \cdot 58t)$ gives a pure tone of 58 hz

Notice from Figure 9.14 that the function $A(t)$ completes three full cycles on the interval $0 \le t \le 1$. The tone is loudest when $A(t) = 1$ or $A(t) = -1$. Since both of these values occur once per cycle, the tone grows loud six times every second.

Exercises and Problems for Section 9.1

Exercises

1. Graph the function $f(x) = e^{-x}(2\cos x + \sin x)$ on the interval $0 \le x \le 12$. Use a calculator or computer to find the maximum and minimum values of the function.

2. Graph $y = t + 5\sin t$ and $y = t$ on $0 \le t \le 2\pi$. Where do the two graphs intersect if t is not restricted to $0 \le t \le 2\pi$?

Problems

3. A power company serves two different cities, City A and City B. The power requirements of both cities vary in a predictable fashion over the course of a typical day.

(a) At midnight, the power requirement of City A is at a minimum of 40 megawatts. (A megawatt is a unit of power.) By noon the city has reached its maximum power consumption of 90 megawatts and by midnight it once again requires only 40 megawatts. This pattern repeats every day. Find a possible formula for $f(t)$, the power, in megawatts, required by City A as a function of t, in hours since midnight.

(b) The power requirements, $g(t)$ megawatts, of City B differ from those of City A. For t, in hours since midnight,

$$g(t) = 80 - 30\sin\left(\frac{\pi}{12}t\right).$$

Give the amplitude and the period of $g(t)$, and a physical interpretation of these quantities.

(c) Graph and find all t such that

$$f(t) = g(t), \qquad 0 \le t < 24.$$

Interpret your solution(s) in terms of power usage.

(d) Why should the power company be interested in the maximum value of the function

$$h(t) = f(t) + g(t), \qquad 0 \le t < 24?$$

What is the approximate maximum of this function, and approximately when is it attained?

(e) Find a formula for $h(t)$ as a single sine function. What is the exact maximum of this function?

4. John is developing a mathematical model for predicting the value of a stock. From its past behavior, he knows that the value of the stock has a cyclical component which increases for the first three months of each year, falls for the next six, and rises again for the last three. In addition, inflation adds a linear component to the stock's price. John is seeking a model of the form

$$f(t) = mt + b + A\sin\frac{\pi t}{6}.$$

with t in months since Jan 1, 2002. He has the following data:

Date	1/1/02	4/1/02	7/1/02	10/1/02	1/1/03
Price	$20.00	$37.50	$35.00	$32.50	$50.00

(a) Find values of m, b, and A so that f fits the data.

(b) During which month(s) does this stock appreciate the most?

(c) During what period each year is this stock actually losing value?

5. Let $f(x) = \sin\left(\frac{1}{x}\right)$ for $x > 0$, x in radians.

(a) $f(x)$ has a horizontal asymptote as $x \to \infty$. Find the equation for the asymptote and explain carefully why $f(x)$ has this asymptote.

(b) Describe the behavior of $f(x)$ as $x \to 0$. Explain why $f(x)$ behaves in this way.

(c) Is $f(x)$ a periodic function?

(d) Let z_1 be the greatest zero of $f(x)$. Find the exact value of z_1.

(e) How many zeros do you think the function $f(x)$ has?

(f) Suppose a is a zero of f. Find a formula for b, the largest zero of f less than a.

6. Let $f(t) = \cos(e^t)$, where t is measured in radians.

(a) Note that $f(t)$ has a horizontal asymptote as $t \to -\infty$. Find its equation, and explain why f has this asymptote.

(b) Describe the behavior of f as $t \to \infty$. Explain why f behaves this way.

(c) Find the vertical intercept of f.

(d) Let t_1 be the least zero of f. Find t_1 exactly. [Hint: What is the smallest positive zero of the cosine function?]

(e) Find an expression for t_2, the least zero of f greater than t_1.

7. In the July 1993 issue of *Standard and Poor's Industry Surveys* the editors stated:[1]

> The strength (of sales) of video games, seven years after the current fad began, is amazing.... What will happen next year is anything but clear. While video sales ended on a strong note last year, the toy industry is nothing if not cyclical.

(a) Why might sales of video games be cyclical?

(b) Does $s(t) = a\sin(bt)$, where t is time, serve as a reasonable model for the sales graph in Figure 9.15? What about $s(t) = a\cos(bt)$?

(c) Modify your choice in part (b) to provide for the higher amplitude in the years 1985–1992 as compared to 1979–1982.

(d) Graph the function created in part (c) and compare your results to Figure 9.15. Modify your function to improve your approximation.

(e) Use your function to predict sales for 1993.

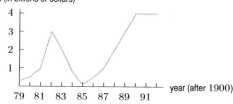

retail sales of games and cartridges (in billions of dollars)

year (after 1900)

Figure 9.15

[1]Source: Nintendo of America

8. Derive the following identity used in an electrical engineering text[2] to represent the received AM signal function. Note that A, ω_c, ω_d are constants and $M(t)$ is a function of time, t.

$$r(t) = (A + M(t)) \cos \omega_c t + I \cos(\omega_c + \omega_d)t$$
$$= ((A + M(t)) + I \cos \omega_d t) \cos \omega_c t$$
$$\quad - I \sin \omega_d t \sin \omega_c t$$

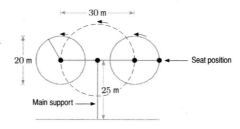

Figure 9.16

9. An amusement park has a giant double ferris wheel as in Figure 9.16. The double ferris wheel has a 30-meter rotating arm attached at its center to a 25-meter main support. At each end of the rotating arm is attached a ferris wheel measuring 20 meters in diameter, rotating in the direction shown in Figure 9.16. The rotating arm takes 6 minutes to complete one full revolution, and each wheel takes 4 minutes to complete a revolution about that wheel's hub. At time $t = 0$ the rotating arm is parallel to the ground and your seat is at the 3 o'clock position of the rightmost wheel.

   (a) Find a formula for $h = f(t)$, your height above the ground in meters, as a function of time in minutes. [Hint: Your height above ground equals the height of your wheel hub above ground plus your height above that hub.]
   (b) Graph $f(t)$. Is $f(t)$ periodic? If so, what is its period?
   (c) Approximate the least value of t such that h is at a maximum value. What is this maximum value?

10. A rope has one free end. If we give the free end a small upward shake, a wiggle travels down the length of the rope. If we repeatedly shake the free end, a periodic series of wiggles travels down the rope. This situation can be described by a wave function:

$$y(x, t) = A \sin(kx - \omega t).$$

Here, x is the distance along the rope in metres; y is the displacement distance perpendicular to the rope; t is time in seconds; A is the amplitude; $2\pi / k$ is the distance from peak to peak, called the wavelength, λ, measured in meters; and $2\pi / \omega$ is the time in seconds for one wavelength to pass by. Suppose $A = 0.06$, $k = 2\pi$, and $\omega = 4\pi$.

   (a) What is the wavelength of the motion?
   (b) How many peaks of the wave pass by a given point each second?
   (c) Construct the graph of this wave from $x = 0$ to $x = 1.5$ m when t is fixed at 0.
   (d) What other values of t would give the same graph as the one found in part (d)?

9.2 ALGEBRAIC AND TRANSCENDENTAL FUNCTIONS

Most of our work in this text has been devoted to certain distinct categories of functions and their properties. For example, we can identify functions that are linear, exponential, sinusoidal, polynomial, or rational, and from that, we can describe certain characteristics of the function and its graph. There are, however, many functions that do not fit into one of the categories that we have studied. The purpose of this section is to investigate a few of these functions and use the tools at our disposal to determine properties of the function and its graph. First, we need some definitions.

> **Definition 1**: A function of one real variable is called *algebraic* if it is defined by the use of variables and constants and any combination of algebraic operations – addition, subtraction, multiplication, division, powers, and roots – that are applied to the variable.

[2]*Modern Digital and Analog Communication Systems* by B. P. Lathi, 2nd ed., page 269.

Example 1   The following functions are all examples of algebraic functions:

$$y = x^2 - 3x + 2, \quad y = x^{-3/5}, \quad y = \sqrt{\frac{x+3}{x^2 - 2x + 1}}, \quad y = 2x + \sqrt{x - 4}$$

> **Definition 2:** A function of one real variable is called *transcendental* if it is not algebraic.

Example 2   The following functions are all examples of transcendental functions:

$$y = 3^x, \quad y = \sin x, \quad y = \tan x, \quad y = \arcsin x, \quad y = \ln x$$

From these definitions, we know that the following function types fit into the *algebraic* classification: linear, quadratic, polynomial, rational, radical. However, exponential functions do not fit into the algebraic category because the exponent is not applied to the variable. Therefore, exponential functions are in the *transcendental* category, as are logarithmic, trigonometric, and inverse trigonometric functions.

Furthermore, any function that is a combination or composition of an algebraic and a transcendental function or two transcendental functions is also transcendental.

Example 3   The following functions are all examples of transcendental functions:

$$y = x + \sin x, \quad y = \frac{\ln x}{x}, \quad y = \sin\left(x^2\right), \quad y = 2x\,e^{-x^2}, \quad y = e^x \cos x, \quad y = \frac{\tan x}{x^2 + 1}$$

Matched Problem 1   Identify each of the following functions as algebraic or transcendental:

(a) $y = x^4$ (b) $y = 4^x$ (c) $y = \dfrac{1}{\sqrt{2 - x}}$ (d) $y = \dfrac{1}{\sqrt{\sin x}}$

We will investigate some functions that we have not studied before and use our knowledge of function properties and algebraic processes to analyze each function and its graph.

Example 4   Create a function that gives the distance between the points $(x, 4)$ and $(2, 3)$. Then analyze the function to determine the domain, range (if possible), intercepts, and symmetry. Use these to graph the function and state the intervals where the function is increasing and where it is decreasing.

Solution   Any point $(x, 4)$, with y-coordinate 4, would be on the line $y = 4$. A reasonable first step here is to sketch a graph showing the location of $(2, 3)$ and the line $y = 4$.

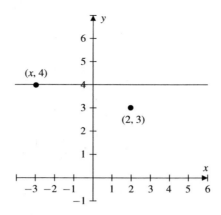

Figure 9.17

Observations:

- From Figure 9.17 it is clear that the closest point to (2, 3) is (2, 4), so the minimum distance should be 1.
- This distance is always positive, so our function should always be positive.
- If $x > 2$ and getting larger, the distance will grow larger. If $x < 2$ and getting smaller (that is, growing in the negative direction), the distance will also grow larger.

Now we can write the distance function. If $(x, 4)$ is any point on the line $y = 4$, then we can use the distance formula to find the distance between $(x, 4)$ and $(2, 3)$:

$$d = \sqrt{(x - 2)^2 + (4 - 3)^2}$$

This is our function and we can simplify it:

$$d(x) = \sqrt{x^2 - 4x + 5}$$

Notice that this function is an algebraic function. We will use our knowledge of the problem situation and our algebraic tools to investigate the properties of this function.

Domain: From the problem description and our sketch in Figure 9.17, we should be able to use any real number for x. To confirm this, we should note that, because of the square root, the radicand must be non-negative, so

$$x^2 - 4x + 5 \geq 0$$

The quadratic expression is not factorable so a sign diagram to solve this inequality is not helpful. Instead we use a graphical approach.

If we graph $y = x^2 - 4x + 5$ (see Figure 9.18), we see that the parabola has its vertex in Quadrant 1 and opens up. This tells us that the values of $x^2 - 4x + 5$ are greater than zero for all x. This confirms that the domain of the function is all real numbers.

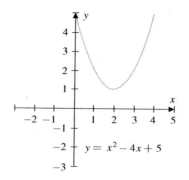

Figure 9.18

Range: From the problem description and our observations above, the distance must always be positive, the smallest distance is 1 and there is no largest distance, so the range is $[1, \infty)$.

Intercepts: To find the vertical intercept, let $x = 0$. We get $d(0) = \sqrt{5}$. Thus the point $\left(0, \sqrt{5}\right)$ is on the graph of the function. This also means that the distance from the point $(0, 4)$ to $(2, 3)$ is $\sqrt{5}$.

To find any x-intercepts, let $d = 0$. However, this would mean that the distance is zero and we have already determined that the smallest distance is 1, so we conclude that there are no x-intercepts.

Symmetry: We can test for symmetry by evaluating $d(-x)$ to see whether $d(-x) = d(x)$ (for symmetry about the vertical axis) or $d(-x) = -d(x)$ (for symmetry about the origin).

$$d(-x) = \sqrt{(-x)^2 - 4(-x) + 5} = \sqrt{x^2 + 4x + 5}$$

We can see from this that neither type of symmetry exists. This should be surprising because, looking at Figure 9.17 and thinking about the fact that our function represents the distance from $(x, 4)$ to $(2, 3)$, it is more logical to suspect that there will be symmetry but it will be about the line $x = 2$ because points on the line at the same distance from $x = 2$ will be the same distance away from the point $(2, 3)$.

Graph: The domain is all real numbers and the range is positive numbers greater than 2, so one possible window is $-10 \leq x \leq 12$ and $0 \leq y \leq 15$.

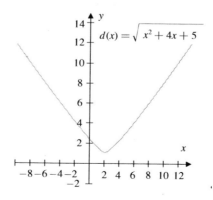

Figure 9.19

Increasing, Decreasing: From the graph, as we expected, the function is decreasing on $(-\infty, 2)$ and increasing on $(2, \infty)$.

Notice also from the graph that we do, indeed, have symmetry about the line $x = 2$.

Comments: The shape of this graph may remind you of the graph of an absolute value function. Notice, however, that the bottom of the graph is rounded in contrast to the sharp point on an absolute value graph. While it is difficult to tell from the graph, this is a curve, not two lines. Calculus provides us with tools to determine concavity.

Example 5   Example 3 in Section 2.2 gave the following *logistic* function $h(t)$, for the height (in centimeters) of a sunflower plant that was measured every day. In this function, t is the number of days since the initial measurement and $t \geq 0$.

$$h(t) = \frac{260}{1 + 24\,(0.9)^t}$$

For this function determine: practical domain and range, intercepts, and asymptotes. Sketch the graph of the function and determine the intervals where the function is concave up and where it is concave down.

Solution   Observations about the problem:

- A sunflower is always growing so the function should be increasing.
- It is likely that the sunflower grows more quickly at first and as it ages its growth rate slows down.
- The sunflower can't grow infinitely tall nor last an infinite number of days.

Observations about the function:

- The function is a transcendental function. It has an exponential component but it is not an exponential function, so it will not have the same characteristics as an exponential function. It is a fraction but it is not a rational function because the denominator is not a polynomial, so it will not have the same characteristics as a rational function.

Determine properties of the function:

Domain: The input variable is the number of days since the initial measurement. Let's assume the sunflower is growing in New Jersey and let's also assume that the sunflower can grow during June, July, August, and September. Then we can give an approximate domain of $0 \leq t \leq 120$.

Range: The initial measurement is taken when $t = 0$ and that gives us

$$h(0) = \frac{260}{1 + 24(0.9)^0} = \frac{260}{25} = 10.4 \text{ cm}$$

From there the sunflower grows and if we assume no more than 120 days, then its height at 120 days would be

$$h(120) = \frac{260}{1 + 24\,(0.9)^{120}} = 259.98 \text{ cm}$$

From these calculations, an approximate range would be $[10.4, \ 260)$.

Intercepts: We already calculated the vertical intercept when we investigated the range. The vertical intercept is $(0, 10.4)$. There are no horizontal intercepts for two reasons: first, the height of the sunflower will never be zero, and second, the function $h(t)$ can never equal zero because its numerator cannot be zero.

Asymptotes: There are no t-values in [0, 120] that cause the function to be undefined so we can assume that there are no vertical asymptotes. For a horizontal asymptote, we look at the behavior of the function as t gets very large. (Note that although we assumed that t could only be as large as 120, we can still learn about the function by looking at long-run behavior.)

Note that as $t \to \infty$, $(0.9)^t \to 0$ because the base is smaller than one. This means that as $t \to \infty$, $\left(1 + 24\,(0.9)^t\right) \to 1$ and $\dfrac{260}{1 + 24\,(0.9)^t} \to \dfrac{260}{1} = 260$. So

As $t \to \infty$, $h(t) \to 260$ and this means that the line $h(t) = 260$ is a horizontal asymptote for the function. For the sunflower, this means that as time goes by, the height of the sunflower gets closer and closer to 260 cm.

Graph:

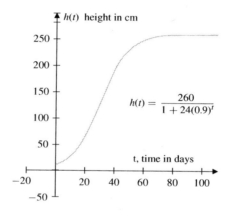

Figure 9.20

As we expected the function is increasing on its domain and increases quickly at first and then the growth rate decreases.

Concavity: We can see from the graph that the function is concave up from $t = 0$ to somewhere between $t = 20$ and $t = 40$ and then the graph becomes concave down. While Calculus will give us the tools to find the exact location of the change from concave up to concave down, we will approximate it and use $t = 30$. So our best estimate is that the function is concave up on $(0, 30)$ and concave down on $(30, 120)$.

Note: Functions of this form: $P(t) = \dfrac{K}{1 + A\,e^{-kt}}$ are called *logistic* functions and are often used to model population growth. The sunflower growth function has base 0.9 instead of base e in the denominator. However, we can change the base from 0.9 to e as follows. If $0.9 = e^b$, then $b = \ln(0.9) \approx -.1054$. This means that the sunflower growth function can be written: $h(t) = \dfrac{260}{1 + 24\,e^{-.1054t}}$, which fits the definition of a logistic function.

Example 6 Let $f(x) = \sin\left(\frac{1}{x}\right)$. Determine the domain and range of $f(x)$. Investigate the intercepts, symmetry, and asymptotes. Graph the function.

Solution Observations:

- The function is transcendental because it is a composition of $y = \frac{1}{x}$ (an algebraic function) and $y = \sin x$ (a transcendental function).

Characteristics of the function:

Domain: Because of $\frac{1}{x}$, x cannot be zero, but every other x value is acceptable. Hence the domain of the function is all real numbers except 0.

Range: Regardless of the size of the input, the sine function can only produce values between -1 and 1, so the range will still be $[-1, 1]$.

Intercepts: Because $x \neq 0$, there is no y-intercept.
To determine x-intercepts, let $y = 0$. We get:

$$\sin\left(\frac{1}{x}\right) = 0$$

To solve this, recall that the sine of anything is zero when the "anything" is an integer multiple of π, so

$$\frac{1}{x} = k\pi, \text{ where } k \text{ is an integer}$$

Now solve for x:

$$x = \frac{1}{k\pi}$$

We could try various values of k to get a sense of the x-intercepts but instead let's analyze this fraction. We can look only at positive values of k because the negative values will simply give the opposite number.
If $k = 1$, then $x = \frac{1}{\pi} \approx 0.3183$.
If $k > 1$, then the denominator becomes an integer multiple of π and the fraction becomes smaller and smaller as k increases.
Remember that k is an integer so the largest x-intercept is $\frac{1}{\pi} \approx 0.3183$ and there are an infinite number of other positive x-intercepts, but they are all smaller than $\frac{1}{\pi}$. This means an infinite number of x-intercepts between 0 and about 0.3.

Symmetry: Both $y = \frac{1}{x}$ and $y = \sin x$ are symmetric about the origin, so it is reasonable to think that the composition is also symmetric about the origin. To check, determine whether $f(-x) = -f(x)$. Begin by substituting $-x$ for x:

$$\sin\left(\frac{1}{-x}\right) = \sin\left(-\frac{1}{x}\right) = -\sin\left(\frac{1}{x}\right)$$

Thus, the function *is* symmetric about the origin.

Asymptotes: Because $x \neq 0$ and the line $x = 0$ is a vertical asymptote for $y = \frac{1}{x}$, it might seem reasonable to think that $x = 0$ is a vertical asymptote for $f(x)$ as well. Remember that the definition of a vertical asymptote says that:

$x = a$ is a vertical asymptote for $f(x)$ if, as x gets very, very close to a, $f(x)$ gets larger and larger in either the positive or negative direction.

To check, we construct a table of values for $f(x)$, letting x get very, very close to zero from both sides.

x	$f(x)$	x	$f(x)$
-0.5	-0.9093	0.5	0.9093
-0.1	0.54402	0.1	-0.544
-0.01	0.50637	0.01	-0.5064
-0.001	-0.8269	0.001	0.82688
-0.0001	0.30561	0.0001	-0.3056
-0.00001	-0.0357	0.00001	0.03575
-0.000001	0.34999	0.000001	-0.35

Observations from the table:
- As x gets very close to zero, $f(x)$ definitely does *not* get arbitrarily large in either direction.
- The values of $f(x)$ shift rapidly between positive and negative numbers. Oscillation is a feature of the sine function but this oscillation must be very rapid.
- Other than rapid changes, there does not appear, from the table, to be a pattern to the behavior of the function.

Conclusion: We can at least say that $x = 0$ is not a vertical asymptote for $f(x)$ and because there are no other candidates, we conclude that there are no vertical asymptotes.

Now we turn our attention to horizontal asymptotes. Recall that horizontal asymptotes are one of the possible long-run behaviors of a function. The definition of a horizontal asymptote says that:

$y = b$ is a horizontal asymptote for $y = f(x)$ if as x gets very, very large in either direction, $f(x)$ gets closer and closer to b.

First, notice that when x gets very, very large, $\frac{1}{x}$ gets very, very small, closer and closer to zero, and the sine of a number very, very close to zero itself gets closer and closer to zero. Thus we form the conjecture that $y = 0$ is a horizontal asymptote for $f(x)$. To support this conjecture, we look at tables for $f(x)$ as x gets large in either direction.

x	$f(x)$		x	$f(x)$
-1	-0.8415		1	0.84147
-10	-0.0998		10	0.09983
-100	-0.01		100	0.01
-1000	-1×10^{-3}		1000	1×10^{-3}
-10000	-1×10^{-4}		10000	1×10^{-4}
-100000	-1×10^{-5}		100000	1×10^{-5}
-1000000	-1×10^{-6}		1000000	1×10^{-6}

Observation: As x gets large in either direction, $\sin\left(\frac{1}{x}\right)$ gets very, very close to zero. Thus $y = 0$ is a horizontal asymptote for the function.

Graph: Our first graph of $y = \sin\left(\frac{1}{x}\right)$ will be on the interval $-5 \leq x \leq 5$.

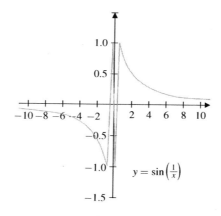

Figure 9.21

This graph gives graphical evidence of the horizontal asymptote but the part of the graph near $x = 0$ is very difficult to see. Here is another graph on the interval $-0.5 \leq x \leq 0.5$

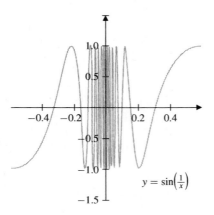

Figure 9.22

In this graph we can more clearly see the x-intercept at $\approx \pm 0.3$ and now we start to see oscillation that becomes more and more rapid as x gets closer to 0. One more graph on the interval $-0.01 \leq x \leq 0.01$

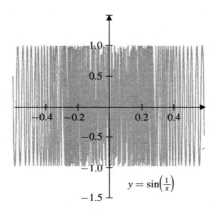

Figure 9.23

At this point the screen is nearly filled with the function and you can just make out the oscillations at the ends of the interval.

Answers to Matched Problem 2

1. (a) algebraic   (b) transcendental   (c) algebraic   (d) transcendental

Exercises for Section 9.2

For problems 1–7, identify the function as either algebraic or transcendental. Analyze the function by investigating the following: domain, range, intercepts, symmetry, and asymptotes. Graph the function on an appropriate viewing window.

1. $f(x) = \sqrt{x^2 - 4}$

2. $h(x) = \sqrt{4 - x^2}$

3. $g(x) = \dfrac{1}{\sqrt{x^2 - 4}}$

4. $k(x) = \dfrac{x^2}{\sqrt{4 - x^2}}$

5. $h(x) = \dfrac{\sin x}{x}$

6. $g(x) = x + \sin x$

7. $f(x) = x \sin x$

8. $f(x) = e^{-x} \sin x$

9. $g(x) = x e^{-x}$

10. $h(x) = x^2 e^{-x}$

11. $f(x) = e^{x^2}$

12. (a) Create a function that gives the *total* distance from the point $(x, 6)$ to $(0, 1)$ and from $(x, 6)$ to $(4, 3)$. Give a sketch and outline your thought process.

   (b) Analyze the function to determine the domain, range (if possible), intercepts, and symmetry.

   (c) Graph the function on an appropriate window.

   (d) State the approximate intervals where the function is increasing and where it is decreasing.

   (e) From the graph determine the value of x that will give a *minimum* total distance and determine what that distance is.

13. (a) Write an expression for the distance from the point (x, y) to the point $(4, 0)$.

   (b) Now suppose the point (x, y) is on the graph of $y = \sqrt{x}$. Use this information to write the distance

expression from part (a) so that it only has one variable, x. Call this function $d(x)$.

   (c) Analyze $d(x)$ to determine the domain, range (if possible), intercepts, and symmetry.

   (d) Graph the function on an appropriate window.

   (e) State the approximate intervals where the function is increasing and where it is decreasing.

   (f) From the graph determine the value of x that will give the *minimum* distance from (x, y) to $(4, 0)$ and determine what that distance is.

14. A particularly infectious form of flu is spreading through a city of 100,000 people. No vaccine is available. The number of people infected, $N(t)$, after t days, is given by the logistic function $N(t) = \dfrac{100{,}000}{1 + 5999 e^{-0.7167t}}$.

   (a) How many people were infected initially?

   (b) For this function determine: practical domain and range, intercepts, and asymptotes.

   (c) Sketch the graph of the function on an appropriate window.

   (d) From the graph, determine the approximate intervals where the function is concave up and where it is concave down.

9.3 PROBLEM-SOLVING

In this section we will work with a variety of problems that will require us to use or construct functions. Some of the problems are typical of those studied in calculus. You will need to use problem-solving skills as well your knowledge of mathematics and function types and behaviors.

In 1957 the mathematician George Polya wrote a little book titled How to Solve It, and the simple ideas in it have been used for solving problems ever since.

Here is a summary of Polya's four steps for problem-solving:

Step 1: Understand the problem. While this may seem obvious, it is often the step that is most ignored. If you are rush into a strategy, you may miss some of the important ideas and details that will enable you to construct an appropriate solution. In order to understand a problem better, you will always need to identify what is unknown and you may need to draw a diagram, make a list of given information and what you want to find, or make a list of various mathematical ideas that may influence the problem. If you are having trouble getting through this step, try creating a *similar* but *simpler* problem.

Step 2: Make a plan. In this step, you outline your proposed solution. This is a good idea because if a problem is long and involved, you may lose track of your strategy in the middle. If you create a roadmap, you can go back and fill in the specifics of the solution later. Also, if you can see two possible methods of solution, this is the time to write them both down. If one doesn't work out, you can try the second method.

Step 3: Carry out the plan. You are most accustomed to this step. Do all the mathematics that you outlined in Step 2, checking for accuracy as you go along.

Step 4: Answer the question and check the result. Once you have carried out the plan in Step 3, write a complete answer to the question and check it for reasonableness. See if it matches your expectations and assumptions about the problem. Always give a complete and thorough answer to the problem.

Example 1

A packaging company is going to make an open-top box in the following way. Start with a piece of cardboard that is 24 inches by 18 inches. Cut equal size squares out of each corner and fold up the sides. The company wants the box to have as large a volume as possible. What size square should be cut out of each corner to accomplish this? What are the dimensions of the resulting box and what is its volume?

Solution

Step 1: Understand the problem: Let's begin by understanding the process of making this box. We will start with a diagram showing the piece of cardboard and the squares cut out of each corner.

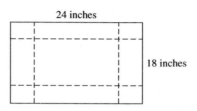

24 inches

18 inches

Figure 9.24

Visualize cutting out the corners and folding up the sides. You might want to make a paper model using various size square cutouts. The size of the square determines the height of the resulting box. The larger the square cutout, the shorter the length and width of the box will be—cutting out the square reduces the original 24 inches by twice the length of the square and the same is true for the 18 inch side.

If the company wants the box to hold as much as possible, then the question becomes: How does the size of the square cutout affect the volume of the box?

Let's try one particular size of cutout. Suppose the square cutout has sides 2 inches long. This means that the length of the box will be

$$\text{Length} = l = 24 - 2(2) = 20 \text{ inches}$$

The width of the box will be

$$\text{Width} = w = 18 - 2(2) = 14 \text{ inches}$$

The height of the box will be 2 inches.

$$\text{Height} = h = 2 \text{ inches}$$

The volume of the box is

$$\begin{aligned} V &= l\,w\,h \\ &= (20 \text{ inches})(14 \text{ inches})(2 \text{ inches}) \\ &= 560 \text{ cubic inches} \end{aligned}$$

So if a 2-inch square is cut out of each corner, the box is $20''$ by $14''$ by $2''$ and has a volume of 560 in^3.

Now suppose the square cutout is 3 inches on a side. The length of the box will be

$$\text{Length} = l = 24 - 2(3) = 18 \text{ inches}$$

The width of the box will be

$$\text{Width} = w = 18 - 2(3) = 12 \text{ inches}$$

The height of the box will be 3 inches.

$$\text{Height} = h = 3 \text{ inches}$$

The volume of the box is

$$V = l\,w\,h$$
$$= (18 \text{ inches})(12 \text{ inches})(3 \text{ inches})$$
$$= 648 \text{ cubic inches}$$

Thus, if a 3-inch square is cut out of each corner, the box is 18″ by 12″ by 3″ and has a volume of 648 in³.

Clearly, cutting a 3-inch square out of each corner results in a box with a larger volume than the box created by cutting a 2-inch square out of each corner.

It might seem that the bigger the square cutout, the larger the volume of the box. However, on reflection, this is impossible. The square cutout cannot be larger than 9 inches because then the two cutouts would use up the entire width of the cardboard. Also, with a 9-inch cutout, the volume would be zero. It is reasonable to think that there must be some size cutout that will make the box as large as possible.

Step 2: Make a Plan: Next, we should make a plan for solving the problem. The plan should involve variables and functions.

The Plan:

1. Call the length of the side of the square cutout x.
2. Express the length, width, and height of the box in terms of x.
3. Use the formula for the volume of the box to express volume as a function of x.
4. Investigate this function – type of function, domain, intercepts.
5. Use the domain and a table to determine a suitable graphing window for the function.
6. Graph the function and find the maximum value.
7. Write a complete answer and check for reasonableness.

Step 3: Carry Out the Plan

1. Let the length of the side of the square cutout be x inches. The diagram now looks like this:

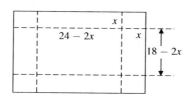

Figure 9.25

2. The length of the box will be

$$l = 24 - 2x \text{ inches}$$

The width of the box will be

$$w = 18 - 2x \text{ inches}$$

The height of the box will be x inches.

$$h = x \text{ inches}$$

3. The volume of the box is

$$V = l\,w\,h$$
$$V(x) = (24 - 2x)(18 - 2x)x$$
$$V(x) = 4x^3 - 84x^2 + 432x$$

4. The volume function is a polynomial of degree 3. It has three zeros, $x = 0$, $x = 9$, and $x = 12$. The leading coefficient is positive, so the long run behavior is ↙ ↗. The graph comes from negative values, goes through the origin, becomes positive until $x = 9$, then becomes negative until $x = 12$, then becomes and stays positive. The domain for the function is all real numbers but the domain for this problem situation is $0 \le x \le 9$. We could exclude the 0 and the 9 but we will leave them in.

5. Looking at a table of values for $V(x)$ on the interval $0 \le x \le 9$, we get:

Table 9.1

x	$V(x) = 4x^3 - 84x^2 + 432x$
0	0
1	352
2	560
3	648
4	640
5	560
6	432
7	280
8	128
9	0

The largest volume on the table is 648 in^3, but the x value that maximizes the volume may not be an integer.

6. Graph:

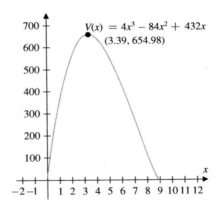

Figure 9.26

Using [2nd] [CALC] 4: MAXIMUM, we see that the maximum point on the interval [0, 9] is approximately (3.39, 654.98).

7. Thus, the box has a maximum volume if the square cutout is 3.39 inches on each side. This is reasonable because it is close to the value that gave the largest volume on the table.

Step 4: Answer the Question and Check the Result: The box should be made by cutting a square of side length 3.39 inches out of each corner and turning up the sides. The length of the box will be 17.22 inches, the width will be 11.22 inches, and the height will be 3.39 inches. The volume of the box will be 654.98 in^3.

Matched Problem 1   Suppose the original piece of cardboard had been 24 inches by 24 inches. How will that change the outcome?

Example 2   A paper cup is designed to fit into a metal holder. It has the shape of a cone with the pointed end down. The cup is 6 inches high and the circular top has a 3 inch radius. Suppose soda is poured into the cup at a constant rate of 1.5 in^3 per second. Is the height of the soda in the cup changing at a constant rate? If not, describe the rate of change of the height of the soda in the cup.

Solution   *Step 1: Understand the problem:* Let's begin by drawing a diagram to help us understand the physical situation. Rather than try to draw a three-dimensional diagram, we can use a cross section of the paper cone.

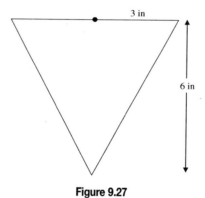

Figure 9.27

If soda is poured into the cup, the soda itself will also have the shape of a cone but will simply be a smaller version of the larger conical container.

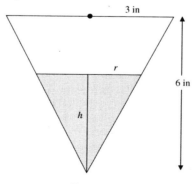

Figure 9.28

Notice that the right-hand half of the cone is a right triangle with height 6 inches and base 3 inches. The right-hand half of the soda-cone is also a right triangle and it shares the same angles as the larger triangle. This makes the two triangles similar triangles. Because the height of the conical cup is twice its radius, the height of the soda, h, will also be twice its radius, r. Thus, we have

$$h = 2r \quad \text{or} \quad r = \frac{1}{2}h$$

Next, we should examine the question for other pieces of information and determine what we want to find.

The soda is being poured into the cup at the constant rate of 1.5 in³/sec. Notice that the units in this rate are cubic inches (V) and seconds (t). This is the rate of change of the volume with respect to time, or $\frac{\Delta V}{\Delta t}$, so we have

$$\frac{\Delta V}{\Delta t} = 1.5$$

Because this rate of change is constant, we can use it to find the volume of the soda in the cup at various times or to write volume as a function of time.

We are being asked about the rate of change of the height of the soda. Experience and observation tell us that the soda will rise more quickly at first because of the small radius at the bottom of the cone and then the soda will rise more slowly as the cup fills because the radius is getting larger. Because of this, we should expect to find that the rate of change of the height of the soda is not constant. To determine this mathematically, note that the rate of change in the height of the soda would be in inches per second, so the variables are h and t and we need to investigate $\frac{\Delta h}{\Delta t}$. To do this, we will need to find the height of the soda at various times and then calculate the average rate of change. To find the height of the soda, we can use the volume formula for a cone.

Step 2: Make a Plan: Our plan should use the volume formula to compute values of h in order to find values of $\frac{\Delta h}{\Delta t}$.

The Plan:

1. Start with the formula for the volume of a cone.
2. Use the relationship between r and h and the relationship between V and t to rewrite the formula so that the variables are h and t.
3. Write the new formula so that h is a function of t.
4. Create a table of values for this function using a chosen time increment.
5. Calculate $\frac{\Delta h}{\Delta t}$ for several time increments in order to understand how the height of the soda is changing.
6. Write a complete answer and check for reasonableness.

Step 3: Carry Out the Plan

1. The formula for the volume of a cone is $V = \frac{1}{3}\pi r^2 h$. This formula contains V, r, and h, but we want a function that has h as a function of t.
2. We know that volume is increasing at the rate of 1.5 in³/sec so if t is measured in seconds, then volume can be written:

$$V = 1.5t$$

We also know that the radius is always half the height, so $r = \frac{1}{2}h$.

If we substitute both of these into the volume formula, we get:

$$1.5t = \frac{1}{3}\pi\left(\frac{h}{2}\right)^2 h$$

This equation now has the desired variables, h and t.

3. Now we need to simplify this and solve for h.

$$1.5t = \frac{\pi}{12}h^3$$

$$\frac{18}{\pi}t = h^3$$

$$h = \sqrt[3]{\frac{18}{\pi}t} = \left(\frac{18}{\pi}t\right)^{1/3}$$

This new equation is a function in which h is a function of t. Note that the function is a power function.

4. We can now choose values of time, t, and use this new function to get values of h. Let's start with $t = 0$ and use an increment of 5 seconds. Here is the table:

Table 9.2

t, sec	h, in
0	0
5	3.06
10	3.86
15	4.41
20	4.86
25	5.23

Before we calculate the average rate of change, it would be helpful to look at a graph of h. Figure 9.29 shows the graph on a window suggested by Table 9.2.

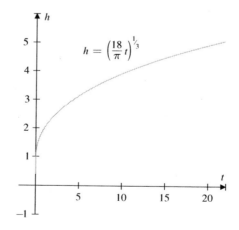

$$h = \left(\frac{18}{\pi}t\right)^{1/3}$$

Figure 9.29

Observation: The graph is increasing, as expected, and concave down. This means that h is increasing more slowly as time increases, also as we expected.

5. Now that we have values for h and t, we can calculate $\frac{\Delta h}{\Delta t}$. Remember that $\frac{\Delta h}{\Delta t} = \frac{h_2 - h_1}{t_2 - t_1}$.

Table 9.3

Time Interval	$\dfrac{\Delta h}{\Delta t}$
[0, 5]	$\dfrac{3.06 - 0}{5 - 0} \approx 0.61\,\text{in/sec}$
[5, 10]	$\dfrac{3.86 - 3.06}{10 - 5} \approx 0.16\ \text{in/sec}$
[10, 15]	$\dfrac{4.41 - 3.86}{15 - 10} \approx 0.11\ \text{in/sec}$
[15, 20]	$\dfrac{4.86 - 4.41}{20 - 15} \approx 0.09\ \text{in/sec}$

Observations: Clearly the height of the soda is not changing at a constant rate. The soda is rising rapidly at first and then more slowly as time goes on.

6. **Answer**: The height of the soda in the cup is not changing at a constant rate, even though the volume of soda in the cup is changing at a constant rate. The average rate of change of the soda's height is larger in the beginning and the height changes more slowly as time goes by, just as we expected.

Matched Problem 2

Suppose the shape of the cup had been a cylinder instead of a cone. How would that change the outcome?

Example 3

Ed and Sarah are buying a house and will need to obtain a mortgage for $150,000. They have decided to get a 30-year variable rate mortgage and have determined that they can afford no more than $1000 for their monthly payment. The formula $P = \dfrac{Ar\,(1 + m)^n}{(1 + m)^n - 1}$ gives the monthly payment P, where A is the amount borrowed, m is the monthly interest rate, and n is the number of months of the loan. What annual interest rates should Ed and Sarah consider in order to stay within their $1000 target payment?

Solution

Step 1: Understand the Problem: First, we need to understand the relationship between Ed and Sarah's requirements and the given formula.

In the formula, A is the amount borrowed, and we know that Ed and Sarah are obtaining a mortgage for $150,000, so

$$A = 150{,}000$$

n is the number of months of the loan and their mortgage will be for 30 years, so

$$n = 30 \times 12 = 360$$

m is the *monthly* interest rate. This is unknown but we must remember that in the end we will want the *annual* interest rate and so must multiply m by 12.

Substituting what we know into the monthly payment formula, we get

$$P = \frac{150000\,m(1 + m)^{360}}{(1 + m)^{360} - 1}$$

We now have a function, which we can call $P(m)$, that gives the monthly payment P in terms of the monthly interest rate m.

$$P(m) = \frac{150000\, m(1 + m)^{360}}{(1 + m)^{360} - 1}$$

Next, before going on to consider the case of Ed and Sarah, we might want to better understand this function. It is a rational function in which the numerator is a polynomial with degree 361 and the denominator is a polynomial with degree 360. Because the degree of the numerator is larger than the degree of the denominator, the function gets larger and larger in the long run as m gets larger and larger. Of course, we would expect a monthly mortgage payment to get larger and larger as the rate continues to increase. The domain of the function for this problem is $m > 0$.

Finally, to get a sense of how the formula works, let's try one interest rate and see how we get the monthly payment.

Suppose the annual interest rate for a 30-year mortgage is $5\frac{1}{4}\%$ or 0.0525. The *monthly* interest rate, m, would be the annual rate divided by 12:

$$m = \frac{0.0525}{12} = 0.004375$$

Then to find the payment, find $P(0.004375)$:

$$P(0.004375) = \frac{150000\,(0.004375)\,(1 + 0.004375)^{360}}{(1 + 0.004375)^{360} - 1}$$
$$= 828.31$$

So if the annual interest is $5\frac{1}{4}\%$, the monthly payment is \$828.31.

Step 2: Make a Plan: We will determine a domain that is practical for this problem and then examine the function numerically and graphically.

Step 3: Carry out the Plan: We should decide what values of m are appropriate for this situation. Considering interest rates at this time, it would be reasonable to consider rates between 5% and 10%. Changing to a decimal and dividing by 12 gives us:

$$0.0042 \leq m \leq 0.0083$$

A table will be helpful in seeing the effect the interest rate has on the monthly payment. On your calculator, set your table to start at 0.004 and set the ΔTbl to 0.0005

Table 9.4

Monthly Interest Rate (decimal), m	Monthly Payment $P(m)$
0.0040	787.00
0.0045	842.30
0.0050	899.33
0.0055	957.99
0.0060	1018.20
0.0065	1079.80
0.0070	1142.80
0.0075	1206.90
0.0080	1272.20

Now, Ed and Sarah want to keep their monthly payment at or below \$1000. From Table 9.4, we can see that $P(m) \leq 1000$ if m is approximately less than 0.0060, but to get an exact solution, we can turn to a graph. From the table, we will use the following window: $0 \le m \le 0.0080$ and $700 \le P(m) \le 1250$. Here is the graph on this window:

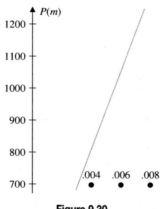

Figure 9.30

Find a more accurate value of m by graphing $P(m) = 1000$ and finding the intersection.

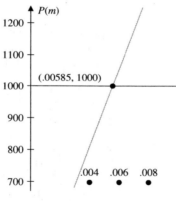

Figure 9.31

As we see in Figure 9.31, the intersection is $(0.00585, 1000)$, which means that if $m \le 0.00585$, then the monthly payment will be no more than $1000. To obtain a complete answer, we change 0.00585 to an annual percentage rate by changing to a percent and multiplying by 12. We get an annual percentage rate of 7.02%.

Step 4: Answer the Question and Check the Result: Ed and Sarah can only afford this mortgage if their annual interest rate stays at or below 7.02%. The answer seems reasonable considering current interest rates and the evidence supplied by the table and graphs.

Matched Problem 3

Suppose Ed and Sarah only needed a mortgage for $110,000. How would this change the outcome?

Answers to Matched Problems

1. The box should be made by cutting a square of side length 4 inches out of each corner and turning up the sides. The length of the box will be 16 inches, the width will be 16 inches, and the height will be 4 inches. The volume of the box will be 1024 in³.

2. This time the height is changing at a constant rate because h is a linear function of t: $h = \frac{1}{6\pi}t$. The height is increasing at about 0.053 in/sec.

3. The function now becomes $P(m) = \dfrac{110000\, m(1 + m)^{360}}{(1 + m)^{360} - 1}$. Solving $P(m) = 1000$ graphically, we get $m = 0.00868699$. Multiplying by 12 and changing to a percent, we get about 10.4%. This means that Ed and Sarah's monthly payment will be no more than $1000 if the interest rate for their mortgage is no more than 10.4%.

Exercises for Section 9.3

1. A construction company wishes to build a rectangular enclosure to store machinery. The site selected borders a river that will be used as one of the sides of the rectangle. Fencing will be needed to form the other three sides (see Figure 9.32.) The company has 600 feet of chain-link fencing. The company's goal is to maximize the area of the enclosure while using only the amount of fence on hand.

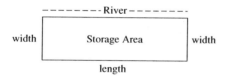

Figure 9.32

(a) Define your variables and use them to clearly label your diagram.

(b) Express the area A of the enclosure as a function of one variable. Explain how you arrived at your function. Identify the type of function.

(c) What is the practical domain of the function for this situation? Explain why.

(d) Use numerical and graphical evidence to approximate the dimensions of the enclosure that has maximum area. Write your observations and conclusions.

(e) Algebraically find the dimensions of the enclosure that will maximize the area enclosed. Be sure to carefully explain your reasoning and also to write a complete answer to the problem.

2. You want to fence a rectangular garden plot by placing a brick wall along one side and wooden fencing along the other three sides (see Figure 9.33.) The brick wall costs $8 per linear foot, while the wooden fence costs $2 per linear foot. You have only $500 to spend on materials and you would like to enclose the largest possible plot.

Figure 9.33

(a) Define your variables and use them to clearly label your diagram.

(b) Express the area as a function of one variable. Explain how you arrived at your function. Identify the type of function.

(c) What is the practical domain of the function for this situation? Explain why.

(d) Use numerical and graphical evidence to approximate the dimensions of the garden plot that has maximum area. Write your observations and conclusions.

(e) Algebraically find the dimensions of the plot that will maximize the garden's area. Be sure to carefully explain your reasoning and also to write a complete answer to the problem.

3. The managers of the construction company in Exercise 1 have used the 600 feet of fencing for another project and have amended their plan for the enclosure. The managers still propose a rectangular enclosure that must have 45000 square feet of area, but building codes require decorative fencing along the river. The decorative fencing costs $30 per linear foot, while the standard fencing used for the rest of the enclosure costs $20 per linear foot. The company's goal is to minimize the cost of the fencing.

(a) Draw a diagram to represent the situation. Define your variables and use them to clearly label your diagram.

(b) Express the cost of the fencing as a function of one variable. Explain how you arrived at your function. Identify the type of function.

(c) What is the practical domain of the function for this situation? Explain why.

(d) Use numerical and graphical evidence to approximate the dimensions of the enclosure that minimize the cost of the fencing. Write your observations and state your conclusions by giving a complete answer to the problem.

4. Your neighbor is creating a rectangular garden but wants to divide it into two halves, one for flowers and one for vegetables. To do this, she will put up a fence around the entire plot and use more of the fencing down the center to create a divider (see Figure 9.34.) She has purchased 540 feet of fencing and wants the largest possible garden area.

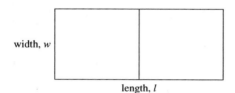

width, *w*

length, *l*

Figure 9.34

(a) Define your variables and use them to clearly label your diagram.

(b) Express the area as a function of one variable. Explain how you arrived at your function. Identify the type of function.

(c) What is the practical domain of the function for this situation? Explain why.

(d) Use numerical and graphical evidence to approximate the dimensions of the garden that has maximum area. Write your observations and conclusions.

(e) Algebraically find the dimensions of the plot that will maximize the garden's area. Be sure to carefully explain your reasoning and also to write a complete answer to the problem.

5. A closed box with a square base has a volume of 20,000 cubic inches (see Figure 9.35). The goal is to minimize the amount of material needed to construct the box.

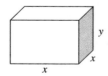

y

x

x

Figure 9.35

(a) Using the variables in Figure 9.35, express the amount of material (surface area) as a function

of one variable. Explain how you arrived at your function. Identify the type of function.

(b) What is the practical domain of the function for this situation? Explain why.

(c) Use numerical and graphical evidence to approximate the dimensions of the box that minimize the amount of material. Write your observations and state your conclusions by giving a complete answer to the problem.

6. A container company must construct a rectangular box with a square base and open top that has a volume of 300 cubic inches. The cardboard used to make the bottom of the box costs \$.08 per square inch, while the cardboard used to make the rest of the box costs \$.05 per square inch. The goal is to minimize the cost of the box while maintaining the volume of 300 cubic inches.

(a) Draw a diagram to represent the situation. Define your variables and use them to clearly label your diagram.

(b) Express the cost of making the box as a function of one variable. Explain how you arrived at your function. Identify the type of function.

(c) What is the practical domain of the function for this situation? Explain why.

(d) Use graphical and numerical evidence to approximate the dimensions of the box that minimize the cost of construction. Write your observations and state your conclusions by giving a complete answer to the problem.

7. A cable TV company is asked to provide service to a customer whose house is located 2 miles from the road along which the cable is buried (see Figure 9.36.) The nearest connection box for the cable is located 5 miles down the road from the house. The cable company has to decide how to install the cable for this customer. They could use a direct line from the connection box to the house - this would be completely off the road. Another possibility would be to follow the road for the 5 miles and then turn off the road for the 2 miles to the house. Or they could choose to follow the road for some distance and then turn off the road and head to the house. Cost will decide since the installation cost is \$10 per mile along the road and \$14 per mile off the road. The goal is to minimize the cost of cable installation.

House

2 miles

5 miles

Connection Box

Road

Figure 9.36

(a) Using Figure 9.36, draw a representative choice for the cable company. Define your variables and use them to clearly label your diagram.
(b) Write the total cost of installation as a function of one variable. Explain how you arrived at your function.
(c) What is the practical domain of the function for this situation? Explain why.
(d) Use numerical and graphical evidence to approximate the spot where the cable should turn off the road so that the cost is a minimum. Write your observations and state your conclusions by giving a complete answer to the problem.

8. The Fair Lawn Theater seats 320 people. When the tickets are priced at $8 the theater sells out. Theater owners have determined that for every dollar increase in the price of a ticket, four more people decide not to buy one. Their goal is to determine the ticket price that will yield the maximum revenue.

   (a) Complete the following table to find out what happens to the revenue collected by the theater if the ticket price is increased.

Table 9.5

x = # of dollars increase in the price of one ticket	p = price of one ticket in dollars	N = number of tickets purchased	R = revenue collected = Np
0	8	320	2560
1	9	316	2844
2	10		
3			

   (b) Express the price of a ticket, p, as a function of x.
   (c) Express the number of people who buy a ticket, N, as a function of x.
   (d) Express the revenue function, R, as a function of x, using (b) and (c). What is the practical domain of the function for this situation? Explain why.
   (e) Use numerical and graphical evidence to find the maximum revenue. Write your observations and conclusions.
   (f) Algebraically find the maximum revenue. Be sure to carefully explain your reasoning and also to write a complete answer to the problem.

9. A charter airline company runs a round-trip flight from Newark to San Francisco. The regular cost of a round-trip ticket is $550. For a group of ten or more, the company will reduce the price of a ticket by an amount equal to $2.50 times the number of people in the group. For example, if there are 20 in the group, then each person's ticket will be reduced by $2.50×20 or $50. In this case each person's ticket will cost $500. The plane holds a maximum of 150 passengers.

   (a) Complete the following table to find out what happens to the revenue collected by the airline company as the size of the group increases.

Table 9.6

x = # of people in the group	Reduction in price of one ticket	p = price of one ticket in dollars	R = revenue collected from the group = Np
Less than 10	0	550	0 to 4950
10	25	525	5250
11	27.50		
12			

   (b) Express the price of a ticket, p, as a function of x.
   (c) Use (b) to express the revenue, R, as a function of x. What kind of function is this? What is the practical domain of the function for this situation? Explain why.
   (d) Use numerical and graphical evidence to find the group size that maximizes the company's revenue. Write your observations and conclusions.
   (e) Algebraically find the group size that maximizes the company's revenue. Be sure to carefully explain your reasoning and also to write a complete answer to the problem.
   (f) Now suppose the company's cost to operate the round trip is given by $C(x) = 9000 + 40x$. The profit is the difference between revenue and cost. Write the profit function, $P(x)$, and use it to find the group size that maximizes the profit.

10. One way to generate income in retirement is by means of an *annuity*. An annuity is a monthly payment for a guaranteed period of time. You must have an amount of money to purchase the annuity. The following formula gives the purchase amount required, A, to receive equal periodic payments of R dollars for each of n periods at a periodic interest rate of i (the periodic interest rate is the annual rate divided by the number of compounding periods in one year.)

$$A = R \left[\frac{1 - (1 + i)^{-n}}{i} \right]$$

For example, if you want to generate an income of $6,000 per month for 20 years, and if you assume an annual interest rate of 6% compounded monthly, you can use the formula to find the amount, A, required to purchase the annuity.

$R = \$6,000$ (the desired monthly payment)
$i = 0.06/12 = 0.005$ (the monthly (periodic) interest rate)
$n = 20(12) = 240$ (the total number of months (periods))
$A = 6000 \left[\dfrac{1 - (1 + 0.005)^{-240}}{0.005} \right] = 837,484.63$

So you must have $837,484.63 at retirement in order to purchase an annuity to generate monthly payments of $6,000 for 20 years at 6% compounded monthly. At the end of the 20 years, there will be nothing left in the account.

(a) Use the formula $A = R \left[\dfrac{1 - (1 + i)^{-n}}{i} \right]$ to find the monthly income a person will generate if he or she retires with savings of $1,200,000 and can use it to purchase an annuity at 4.8% compounded monthly over a period of 30 years. Your answer should be accurate to the nearest whole cent. Show all your steps and give a complete answer.

(b) Using the above formula, find the annual interest rate (to the nearest 100th of a percent) necessary for someone to generate an income of $4,000 per month for 25 years if $800,000 is available to purchase the annuity. Show the equation you solved, give a graphical solution, and write a complete answer.

11. An 18-foot ladder is leaning against the side of a building. A workman slides the bottom of the ladder away from the building at a constant rate of 0.5 feet per second. The bottom of the ladder is initially 5 feet from the building. See Figure 9.37.

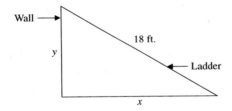

Figure 9.37

(a) Use the constant sliding rate to express x, the distance between the bottom of the ladder and the wall, as a function of time, t.

(b) Assume the top of the ladder remains in contact with the wall as the bottom slides away. The distance between the top of the ladder and the ground is y. Use the triangle in Figure 9.37 to write a relationship between x, y, and the length of the ladder.

(c) Use your answer to (b) to express y as a function of time.

(d) Is the distance y changing at a constant rate? That is, is $\frac{\Delta y}{\Delta t}$ constant? Use tables and graphs to support your reasoning and give a complete answer.

(e) Use the function to find the time when the top of the ladder is 6 feet above the ground. You can use a table or graph to approximate your answer but provide an algebraic solution for the exact answer.

(f) What is the practical domain of the function for this situation? Explain why.

12. Two cars leave the town of Northport at the same time. Car A is traveling north on a straight road at a constant rate of 50 miles per hour. Car B is traveling east on a straight road at a constant rate of 60 miles per hour.

(a) Draw a diagram showing the town and the two straight roads. Use variables to label the distances traveled by Cars A and B and the distance between them.

(b) Express the distance between Car A and Northport as a function of time and express the distance between Car B and Northport as function of time.

(c) Use your diagram to write a relationship among the three distances. Then rewrite this relationship so that the distance between the two cars is a function of time. Simplify this function completely. What type of function is this?

(d) Is this distance changing at a constant rate? Use your knowledge of functions as well as tables and graphs to support your reasoning and give a complete answer.

13. Once again Car A leaves the town of Northport and travels north on a straight road at a constant rate of 50 miles per hour. At the same time that Car A leaves Northport, Car B is 100 miles east of town and is traveling east at a constant rate of 60 miles per hour.

(a) Draw a diagram showing the town and the two straight roads. Use variables to label the distances traveled by Cars A and B and the distance between them.

(b) Express the distance between Car A and Northport as a function of time and express the distance between Car B and its starting point as function of time.

(c) Use your diagram to write a relationship among the three distances. Then rewrite this relationship so that the distance between the two cars is a function of time. Simplify this function as much as possible.

(d) Is this distance changing at a constant rate? Use your knowledge of functions as well as tables and graphs to support your reasoning and give a complete answer.

14. Refer to Figure 9.37 of Exercise 11. Once again, the 18-foot ladder is leaning against the side of a building.

(a) Suppose that initially, when the ladder is at rest, θ, the angle between the ladder and the ground, is 1.2 radians. Find the initial distance x, between the bottom of the ladder and the building.

(b) Now the workman slides the bottom of the ladder away from the building at a constant rate of 0.5 feet per second. Use this rate and your answer to (a) to express the distance x a function of time.

(c) Assume the top of the ladder remains in contact with the wall as the bottom slides away. Use the triangle and trigonometry to write a relationship between θ and x. Then use your answer and your answer to (b) to express θ as a function of time.

(d) Is this angle changing at a constant rate? That is, is $\frac{\Delta\theta}{\Delta t}$ constant? Use tables and graphs to support your reasoning and give a complete answer.

(e) Use the function from (c) to determine the time when the angle is 0.75 radians.

(f) What is the practical domain of the function for this situation? Explain why.

15. A balloon has the shape of a sphere and it is being inflated so that the radius is increasing at the constant rate of 4 cm/sec.

(a) Write the radius of the balloon, r, as a function of time, t.

(b) Write the formula for the volume of a sphere and use your answer to (a) to write volume, V, as a function of t.

(c) Is the volume of the balloon changing at a constant rate? Use tables and graphs to support your reasoning and give a complete answer.

16. A balloon has the shape of a sphere and it is being inflated so that the volume is increasing at the constant rate of 2 in³/sec.

(a) Write the volume of the balloon, V, as a function of time, t.

(b) Write the formula for the volume of a sphere and use your answer to (a) to write the radius, r, as a function of t.

(c) Is the radius of the balloon changing at a constant rate? Use tables and graphs to support your reasoning and give a complete answer.

9.4 PARAMETRIC EQUATIONS

The Mars Pathfinder

On July 4, 1997, the Mars Pathfinder bounced down onto the surface of the red planet, its impact cushioned by airbags. The next day, the Sojourner—a small, six-wheeled robot—rolled out of the spacecraft and began a rambling exploration of the surrounding terrain. Figure 9.38 shows a photograph of the Sojourner and a diagram of the path it took before radio contact was lost.

In Figure 9.38, Sojourner's path is labeled according to the elapsed number of Martian days or *sols* (short for solar periods). The robot's progress was slow because instructions for every movement had to be calculated by NASA engineers and sent from Earth.

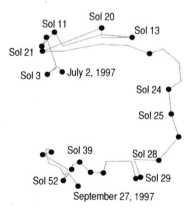

Figure 9.38: The Pathfinder Sojourner robot and the path it followed on the surface of the planet Mars. Image from NASA/Jet Propulsion Laboratory. Diagram adapted from *The New York Times*, July 21, 1998

The Path of the Sojourner Robot

How can Sojourner's path be represented? How can we tell a robot where it should go, how fast, and when? The path in Figure 9.38 is not the graph of a function in the ordinary sense—for instance, it crosses over itself in several different places. However, positions on the path can be determined by knowing t, the elapsed time. In this section, we describe a path by giving the x- and y-coordinates of points on the path as functions of a *parameter* such as t.

Programming a Robot Using Coordinates

One way to program a robot's motion is to send it coordinates to tell it where to go. Imagine that a robot like the Sojourner is moving around the xy-plane.[3] If we choose the origin $(0, 0)$ to be the spot where the robot's spacecraft lands, we can direct its motion by giving it (x, y) coordinates of the points to which it should move.

We select the positive y-axis so that it points north (that is, toward the northern pole of Mars) and the positive x-axis so that it points east. Our units of measurement are meters, so that, the coordinates $(2, 4)$ indicate a point that is 2 meters to the east and 4 meters to the north of the landing site. We program the robot to move to the following points:

$$(0, 0) \quad \rightarrow \quad (1, 1) \quad \rightarrow \quad (2, 2) \quad \rightarrow \quad (2, 3) \quad \rightarrow \quad (2, 4).$$

These points have been plotted in Figure 9.39.

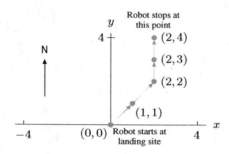

Figure 9.39: The robot is programmed to move along this path

Programming the Robot Using a Parameter

In order to represent the robot's path using a parameter, we need two functions: one for the robot's x-coordinate, $x = f(t)$, and one for its y-coordinate, $y = g(t)$. The function for x describes the robot's east-west motion, and the function for y describes its north-south motion. Together, they are called *parametric equations* for the robot's path.

Example 1   If t is time in minutes, describe the path followed by a robot given by

$$x = 2t, \qquad y = t \qquad \text{for} \quad 0 \le t \le 5.$$

Solution   At time $t = 0$, the robot's position is given by

$$x = 2 \cdot 0 = 0, \qquad y = 0, \qquad \text{so it starts at the point } (0, 0).$$

One minute later, at $t = 1$, its position is given by

$$x = 2 \cdot 1 = 2, \qquad y = 1, \qquad \text{so it has moved to the point } (2, 1).$$

---

[3]The surface of Mars is not as flat as the xy-plane, but this is a useful first approximation.

At time $t = 2$, its position is given by

$$x = 2 \cdot 2 = 4, \qquad y = 2, \qquad \text{so it has moved to the point } (4, 2).$$

The path followed by the robot is given by

$$(0, 0) \quad \rightarrow \quad (2, 1) \quad \rightarrow \quad (4, 2) \quad \rightarrow \quad (6, 3) \quad \rightarrow \quad (8, 4) \quad \rightarrow \quad (10, 5).$$

At time $t = 5$, the robot stops at the point $(10, 5)$ because we have restricted the values of t to the interval $0 \le t \le 5$. In Figure 9.40 we see the path followed by the robot; it is a straight line.

In the previous example, we can use substitution to rewrite the formula for x in terms of y. Since $x = 2t$ and $t = y$, we have $x = 2y$. Thus, the path followed by the robot has the equation

$$y = \frac{1}{2}x.$$

Since the parameter t can be easily eliminated from our equations, you may wonder why we use it. One reason is that it is useful to know when the robot gets to each point. The values of x and y tell us where the robot is, while the parameter t tells us when it gets there. In addition, for some pairs of parametric equations, the parameter t cannot be so easily eliminated.

So far, we have assumed that a robot moves in a straight line between two points. We now imagine that a robot can be continuously redirected along a curved path.

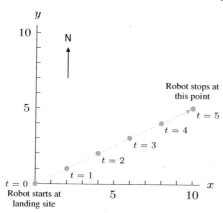

Figure 9.40: Path followed by the robot if $x = 2t$, $y = t$ for $0 \le t \le 5$

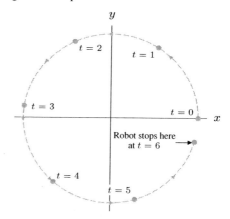

Figure 9.41: Path followed by the robot if $x = \cos t$, $y = \sin t$ for $0 \le t \le 6$

Example 2   A robot begins at the point $(1, 0)$ and follows the path given by the equations

$$x = \cos t, \qquad y = \sin t \qquad \text{where } t \text{ is in minutes}, \quad 0 \le t \le 6.$$

(a) Describe the path followed by the robot.
(b) What happens when you try to eliminate the parameter t from these equations?

Solution   (a) At time $t = 0$, the robot's position is given by

$$x = \cos 0 = 1, \qquad y = \sin 0 = 0$$

so it starts at the point $(1, 0)$, as required. At time $t = 1$, its position is given by

$$x = \cos 1 = 0.54, \qquad y = \sin 1 = 0.84.$$

Thus, the robot has moved west and north. At time $t = 2$, its position is given by

$$x = \cos 2 = -0.42, \qquad y = \sin 2 = 0.91.$$

Now it is farther west and slightly farther north. Continuing, we see that the path followed by the robot is given by

$$(1, 0) \rightarrow (0.54, 0.84) \quad \rightarrow \quad (-0.42, 0.91) \quad \rightarrow \quad (-0.99, 0.14)$$
$$\rightarrow (-0.65, -0.76) \quad \rightarrow \quad (0.28, -0.96) \quad \rightarrow \quad (0.96, -0.28).$$

In Figure 9.41 we see the path followed by the robot; it is circular with a radius of one meter. At the end of 6 minutes the robot has not quite returned to its starting point at $(1, 0)$.

(b) One way to eliminate t from this pair of equations is to use the Pythagorean identity,

$$\cos^2 t + \sin^2 t = 1.$$

Since $x = \cos t$ and $y = \sin t$, we can substitute x and y into this equation:

$$\underbrace{(\cos t)}_{x}{}^2 + \underbrace{(\sin t)}_{y}{}^2 = 1,$$

giving

$$x^2 + y^2 = 1.$$

This is the equation of a circle of radius 1 centered at $(0, 0)$. Attempting to solve for y in terms of x, we have

$$x^2 + y^2 = 1$$
$$y^2 = 1 - x^2$$
$$y = +\sqrt{1 - x^2} \quad \text{or} \quad y = -\sqrt{1 - x^2}.$$

Thus, we obtain two different equations for y in terms of x. The first, $y = +\sqrt{1 - x^2}$, returns positive values for y (as well as 0), while the second returns negative values for y (as well as 0). The first equation gives the top half of the circle, while the second gives the bottom half.

In the previous example, y is not a function of x, because for all x-values (except 1 and -1) there are two possible y values. This confirms what we already knew, because the graph in Figure 9.41 fails the vertical line test.

Different Motions Along the Same Path

It is possible to parameterize the same curve in more than one way, as the following example illustrates.

Example 3   Describe the motion of the robot that follows the path given by

$$x = \cos \frac{1}{2}t, \qquad y = \sin \frac{1}{2}t \qquad \text{for} \quad 0 \leq t \leq 6.$$

Solution   At time $t = 0$, the robot's position is given by

$$x = \cos \left(\frac{1}{2} \cdot 0 \right) = 1, \qquad y = \sin \left(\frac{1}{2} \cdot 0 \right) = 0$$

so it starts at the point $(1, 0)$, as before. After one minute, that is, at time $t = 1$, its position (rounded to thousandths) is given by

$$x = \cos\left(\frac{1}{2} \cdot 1\right) = 0.878, \qquad y = \sin\left(\frac{1}{2} \cdot 1\right) = 0.479.$$

At time $t = 2$ its position is given by

$$x = \cos\left(\frac{1}{2} \cdot 2\right) = 0.540, \qquad y = \sin\left(\frac{1}{2} \cdot 2\right) = 0.841.$$

Continuing, we see that the path followed by the robot is given by

$$(1, 0) \rightarrow (0.878, 0.479) \quad \rightarrow \quad (0.540, 0.841) \quad \rightarrow \quad (0.071, 0.997)$$
$$\rightarrow (-0.416, 0.909) \quad \rightarrow \quad (-0.801, 0.598) \quad \rightarrow \quad (-0.990, 0.141).$$

Figure 9.42 shows the path; it is again circular with a radius of one meter. However, at the end of 6 minutes the robot has not even made it half way around the circle. Because we have multiplied the parameter t by a factor of $1/2$, the robot moves at half its original rate.

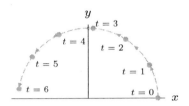

Figure 9.42: Path followed by the robot if $x = \cos \frac{1}{2}t$, $y = \sin \frac{1}{2}t$ for $0 \le t \le 6$

Example 4   Describe the motion of the robot that follows the path given by:

(a) $x = \cos(-t)$, $y = \sin(-t)$ for $0 \le t \le 6$ (b) $x = \cos t$, $y = \sin t$ for $0 \le t \le 10$

Solution   (a) Figure 9.43 shows the robot's path. The robot travels around the circle in the clockwise direction, opposite to that in Examples 2 and 3.

(b) See Figure 9.44. The robot travels around the circle more than once but less than twice, coming to a stop roughly southwest of the landing site.

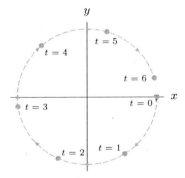

Figure 9.43: Path given by $x = \cos(-t)$, $y = \sin(-t)$ for $0 \le t \le 6$

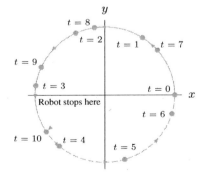

Figure 9.44: Path given by $x = \cos t$, $y = \sin t$ for $0 \le t \le 10$

Other Parametric Curves

Parametric equations can be used to describe extremely complicated motions. For instance, suppose the robot follows the rambling path described by the parametric equations

$$x = 20\cos t + 4\cos(4\sqrt{5}t) \qquad y = 20\sin t + 4\sin(4\sqrt{8}t).$$

See Figure 9.45. The path is roughly circular, and the robot moves in a more or less counterclockwise direction. The dashed circle in Figure 9.45 is given by the parametric equations

$$x = 20\cos t, \qquad y = 20\sin t \qquad \text{for } 0 \leq t \leq 2\pi.$$

The other terms, $4\cos(4\sqrt{5}t)$ and $4\sin(4\sqrt{8}t)$, are responsible for the robot's deviations from the circle.

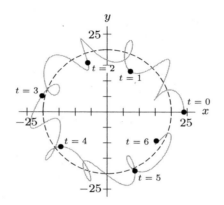

Figure 9.45: Rambling path, parametrically defined

The Archimedean Spiral

In polar coordinates, the Archimedean spiral is the graph of the equation.

$$r = \theta.$$

Since the relationship between polar coordinates and Cartesian coordinates is

$$x = r\cos\theta \qquad \text{and} \qquad y = r\sin\theta,$$

we can write the Archimedean spiral $r = \theta$ as

$$x = \theta\cos\theta \qquad \text{and} \qquad y = \theta\sin\theta.$$

Replacing θ (an angle) by t (a time), we obtain the parametric equations for the spiral in Figure 9.46:

$$x = t\cos t \qquad y = t\sin t.$$

Lissajous Figures

The beautiful curve in Figure 9.47 is called a *Lissajous figure*. Its equations are

$$x = \cos 3t, \qquad y = \sin 5t \qquad \text{for } 0 \leq t \leq 2\pi.$$

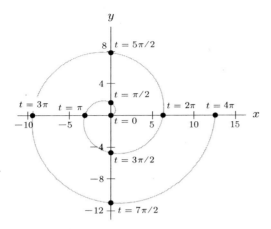

Figure 9.46: Archimedean spiral given by
$x = t \cos t$, $y = t \sin t$, $0 \le t \le 4\pi$

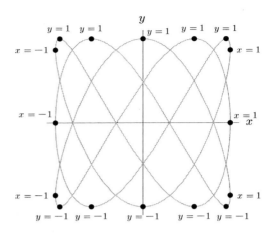

Figure 9.47: Lissajous figure: $x = \cos 3t$, $y = \sin 5t$,
$0 \le t \le 2\pi$

To explain the shape of this Lissajous figure, notice that $y = \sin 5t$ completes five full oscillations on the interval $0 \le t \le 2\pi$. Thus, since the amplitude of $y = \sin 5t$ is 1, the value of y reaches a maximum of 1 at five different values of t. Similarly, the value of y is -1 at another five different values of t. Figure 9.47 shows the curve climbs to a high point of $y = 1$ five times and falls to a low of $y = -1$ five times.

Meanwhile, since $x = \cos 3t$, the value of x oscillates between 1 and -1 a total of 3 times on the interval $0 \le t \le 2\pi$. Figure 9.47 shows that the curve moves to its right boundary, $x = 1$, three times and to its left boundary, $x = -1$, three times.

Foxes and Rabbits

In a wildlife park, foxes prey on rabbits. Suppose F is the number of foxes, R is the number of rabbits, t is the number of months since January 1, and that

$$R = 1000 - 500 \sin\left(\frac{\pi}{6}t\right) \qquad \text{and} \qquad F = 150 + 50 \cos\left(\frac{\pi}{6}t\right).$$

These equations are a parameterization of the curve in Figure 9.48. Since this curve fails the vertical line test, F is not a function of R.

We can use the curve to analyze the relationship between the rabbit population and the fox population. In January, there are 1000 rabbits but they are dying off; in April only 500 rabbits remain. By July the population has rebounded to 1000 rabbits, and by October it has soared to 1500 rabbits. Then the rabbit population begins to fall again; the following April there are once more only 500 rabbits.

The fox population also rises and falls, though not at the same time of year as the rabbits. In January, the fox population numbers 200. By April, it has fallen to 150 foxes. The fox population continues to fall, perhaps because there are so few rabbits to eat at that time. By July, only 100 foxes remain. The fox population then begins to increase again. By October, when the rabbit population is largest, the fox population is growing rapidly, so that by January it has returned to its maximum size of 200 foxes. By this point, though, the rabbit population is already dropping, perhaps because there are so many hungry foxes around. Then the cycle repeats.

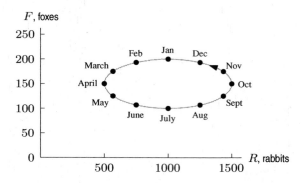

Figure 9.48: The relationship between F, the number of foxes, and R, the number of rabbits

Using Graphs to Parameterize a Curve

Example 5   Figure 9.49 shows the graphs of two functions, $f(t)$ and $g(t)$. Describe the motion of the particle whose coordinates at time t are given by $x = f(t)$, $y = g(t)$.

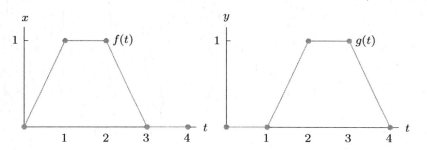

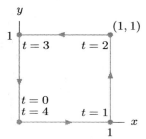

Figure 9.49: Graphs of $x = f(t)$ and $y = g(t)$ used to trace out the path in Figure 9.50

Figure 9.50: Square parameterized by $x = f(t)$, $y = g(t)$ from Figure 9.49

Solution   As t increases from 0 to 1, the x-coordinate increases from 0 to 1, while the y-coordinate stays fixed at 0. The particle moves along the x-axis from $(0, 0)$ to $(1, 0)$. As t increases from 1 to 2, the x-coordinate stays fixed at $x = 1$, while the y-coordinate increases from 0 to 1. Thus, the particle moves along the vertical line from $(1, 0)$ to $(1, 1)$. Between times $t = 2$ and $t = 3$, it moves horizontally backward to $(0, 1)$, and between times $t = 3$ and $t = 4$ it moves down the y-axis to $(0, 0)$. Thus, it traces out the square in Figure 9.50.

Exercises and Problems for Section 9.4

Exercises

Graph the parametric equations in Exercises 1–12. Assume that the parameter is restricted to values for which the functions are defined. Indicate the direction of the curve. Eliminate the parameter, t, to obtain an equation for y as a function of x. Check your sketches by graphing y as a function of x.

1. $x = t + 1$, $y = 3t - 2$

2. $x = 5 - 2t$, $y = 1 + 4t$

3. $x = \sqrt{t}$, $y = 2t + 1$

4. $x = \sqrt{t}$, $y = t^2 + 4$

5. $x = t - 3, \quad y = t^2 + 2t + 1$

6. $x = e^t, \quad y = e^{2t}$

7. $x = e^{2t}, \quad y = e^{3t}$

8. $x = \ln t, \quad y = t^2$

9. $x = t^3, \quad y = 2 \ln t$

10. $x = 2 \cos t, \quad y = 2 \sin t$

11. $x = 3 + \sin t, \quad y = 2 + \cos t$

12. $x = 2 \cos t, \quad y = 3 \sin t$

For Exercises 13–16, describe the motion of a particle whose position at time t is given by $x = f(t)$, $y = g(t)$.

13.

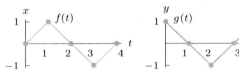

14.

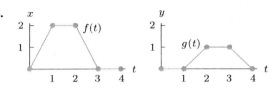

15.

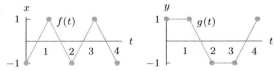

16.

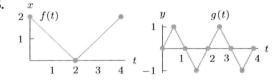

Problems

17. Write two different parameterizations for each of the curves in the xy-plane.

   (a) A parabola whose equation is $y = x^2$.
   (b) The parabola from part (a) shifted to the left 2 units and up 1 unit.

Problems 18–21 give parameterizatisations of the unit circle or a part of it. In each case, describe in words how the circle is traced out, including when and where the particle is moving clockwise and when and where it is moving counterclockwise.

18. $x = \cos t, \quad y = -\sin t$

19. $x = \sin t, \quad y = \cos t$

20. $x = \cos(t^2), \quad y = \sin(t^2)$

21. $x = \cos(\ln t), \quad y = \sin(\ln t)$

22. Describe the similarities and differences among the motions in the plane given by the following three pairs of parametric equations:

   (a) $x = t, \quad y = t^2$ **(b)** $x = t^2, \quad y = t^4$
   (c) $x = t^3, \quad y = t^6$.

23. As t varies, the following parametric equations trace out a line in the plane

$$x = 2 + 3t, \quad y = 4 + 7t.$$

   (a) What part of the line is obtained by restricting t to nonnegative numbers?
   (b) What part of the line is obtained if t is restricted to $-1 \leq t \leq 0$?
   (c) How should t be restricted to give the part of the line to the left of the y-axis?

24. Suppose $a, b, c, d, m, n, p, q > 0$. Match each of the following pairs of parametric equations with one of the lines l_1, l_2, l_3, l_4 in Figure 9.51.

   I. $\begin{cases} x = a + ct, \\ y = -b + dt. \end{cases}$ II. $\begin{cases} x = m + pt, \\ y = n - qt. \end{cases}$

Figure 9.51

25. A bug is crawling around the Cartesian plane. Let $x = f(t)$ be the function denoting the x-coordinate of the bug's position as a function of time, t, and let $y = g(t)$ be the y-coordinate of the bug's position.

   (a) Let $f(t) = t$ and $g(t) = t$. What path does the bug follow?

(b) Now let $f(t) = \cos t$ and $g(t) = \sin t$. What path does the bug follow? What is its starting point? (That is, where is the bug when $t = 0$?) When does the bug get back to its starting point?

(c) Now let $f(t) = \cos t$ and $g(t) = 2 \sin t$. What path does the bug follow? What is its starting point? When does the bug get back to its starting point?

Write a parameterization for the lines in the xy-plane in Problems 26–27.

26. A vertical line through the point $(-2, -3)$.

27. The line through the points $(2, -1)$ and $(1, 3)$.

Graph the Lissajous figures in Problems 28–31 using a calculator or computer.

28. $x = \cos 2t$, $y = \sin 5t$

29. $x = \cos 3t$, $y = \sin 7t$

30. $x = \cos 2t$, $y = \sin 4t$

31. $x = \cos 2t$, $y = \sin \sqrt{3}t$

32. Motion along a straight line is given by a single equation, say, $x = t^3 - t$ where x is distance along the line. It is difficult to see the motion from a plot; it just traces out the x-line, as in Figure 9.52. To visualize the motion, we introduce a y-coordinate and let it slowly increase, giving Figure 9.53. Try the following on a calculator or computer. Let $y = t$. Now plot the parametric equations $x = t^3 - t$, $y = t$ for, say, $-3 \leq t \leq 3$. What does the plot in Figure 9.53 tell you about the particle's motion?

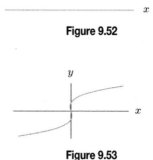

Figure 9.52

Figure 9.53

For Problems 33–34, plot the motion along the x-line by introducing a y-coordinate, as in Problem 32. What does the plot tell you about the particle's motion?

33. $x = \cos t$, $-10 \leq t \leq 10$

34. $x = t^4 - 2t^2 + 3t - 7$, $-3 \leq t \leq 2$

35. A ball is thrown vertically into the air at time $t = 0$. Its height $d(t)$, in feet, above the ground at time t, in seconds, is given by:

$$d(t) = -16t^2 + 48t + 6.$$

(a) Write a parameterization for the curve.

(b) Sketch a graph of the curve.

(c) What is the height of the ball at $t = 0$? Explain how this makes sense.

(d) Does the ball ever reach this height again? If so when? Why?

(e) When does the ball reach its maximum height? What is the maximum height?

9.5 IMPLICITLY DEFINED CURVES AND CIRCLES

In the previous section, we saw that the parametrically defined curve $x = \cos t$, $y = \sin t$ is the circle of radius 1 centered at the origin. Eliminating the parameter t gives the equation

$$x^2 + y^2 = 1.$$

The circle described by the equation $x^2 + y^2 = 1$ is an example of an *implicitly defined* curve. To be explicit is to state a fact outright; to be implicit is to make a statement in a round-about way. If a curve has an equation of the form $y = f(x)$, then we say that y is an *explicit* function of x. However, the equation $x^2 + y^2 = 1$ does not explicitly state that y depends on x. Instead, this dependence is implied by the equation. If we try to solve for y in terms of x, we do not obtain a function. Rather, we obtain *two* functions, one for the top half of the unit circle and one for the bottom half:

$$y = \begin{cases} +\sqrt{1 - x^2} \\ -\sqrt{1 - x^2}. \end{cases}$$

Example 1   Graph the equation $y^2 = x^2$. Can you find an explicit formula for y in terms of x?

Solution   The equation $y^2 = x^2$ is implicit because it does not tell us what y equals, instead, it tells us what y^2 equals. Suppose $x = 2$. What values can y equal? Since

$$y^2 = 2^2 = 4, \qquad \text{we have} \qquad y = 2 \text{ or } -2,$$

because for either of these y-values $y^2 = 4$. What if x is negative? If $x = -3$, we have

$$y^2 = (-3)^2 = 9, \qquad \text{then} \qquad y = 3 \text{ or } -3,$$

because these are the solutions to $y^2 = 9$.

For almost all x-values, there are two y-values, one given by $y = x$ and one by $y = -x$. The only exception is at $x = 0$, because the only solution to the equation $y^2 = 0$ is $y = 0$. Thus, the graph of $y^2 = x^2$ has two parts, given by

$$y = \begin{cases} x \\ -x. \end{cases}$$

When both parts of the graph of $y^2 = x^2$ are plotted together, the resulting graph looks like an X. (See Figure 9.54.)

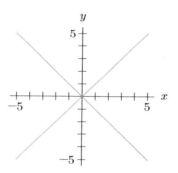

Figure 9.54: Graph of $y^2 = x^2$

Conic Sections

The curves known as *conic sections* include two we are already familiar with, circles and parabolas. They also include *ellipses* and *hyperbolas*. An ellipse is a "squashed" circle; an example is given by Figure 9.48 in Section 9.4. An example of a hyperbola is the graph of the function $y = 1/x$.

Conic sections are so-called because, as was demonstrated by the Greeks, they can be constructed by slicing, or sectioning, a cone. Conic sections arise naturally in physics, since the path of a body orbiting the sun is a conic section. We will study them in terms of parametric and implicit equations. As we have already studied parabolas, we now focus on circles, ellipses and hyperbolas.

Circles

Example 2   Graph the parametric equations

$$x = 5 + 2\cos t \qquad \text{and} \qquad y = 3 + 2\sin t.$$

Solution   We see that x varies between 3 and 7 with a midline of 5 while y varies between 1 and 5 with a midline of 3. Figure 9.55 gives a graph of this function. It appears to be a circle of radius 2 centered at the point $(5, 3)$.

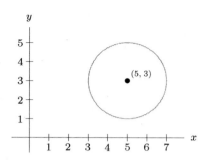

Figure 9.55: The circle defined by $x = 5 + 2\cos t, y = 3 + 2\sin t, 0 \le t \le 2\pi$

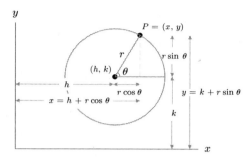

Figure 9.56: A circle of radius r centered at the point (h, k)

Compare Figure 9.55 with Figure 9.56 which shows a circle of radius r centered at the point (h, k). The coordinates of a point $P = (x, y)$, corresponding to an angle θ, are given by

$$x = h + r\cos\theta \qquad \text{and} \qquad y = k + r\sin\theta.$$

The equations in Example 2 are of this form, with t instead of θ and with $h = 5$, $k = 3$, and $r = 2$. This curve is a circle because the point P is always a fixed distance, 2, from the point $(5, 3)$.

For $r > 0$, the parametric equations of a **circle** of radius r centered at the point (h, k) are:
$$x = h + r\cos t \qquad y = k + r\sin t \qquad 0 \le t \le 2\pi.$$

Eliminating the Parameter t in the Equations for a Circle

To eliminate the parameter t from the parametric equations for a circle, we rewrite the equations as

$$x - h = r\cos t \qquad \text{so} \qquad (x - h)^2 = r^2\cos^2 t$$

and

$$y - k = r\sin t \qquad \text{so} \qquad (y - k)^2 = r^2\sin^2 t.$$

Adding these two equations and applying the Pythagorean identity, $\cos^2 t + \sin^2 t = 1$, gives

$$(x - h)^2 + (y - k)^2 = r^2\cos^2 t + r^2\sin^2 t$$
$$= r^2(\cos^2 t + \sin^2 t)$$
$$= r^2.$$

An implicit equation for the **circle** of radius r centered at the point (h, k) is:
$$(x - h)^2 + (y - k)^2 = r^2.$$
This is called the **standard form** of the equation of a circle.

For the unit circle, we have $h = 0$, $k = 0$, and $r = 1$. This gives
$$x^2 + y^2 = 1.$$

Example 3   Write the circle in Example 2 in standard form.

Solution   We have $h = 5$, $k = 3$, and $r = 2$. This gives
$$(x - 5)^2 + (y - 3)^2 = 2^2 = 4.$$

If we expand the equation for the circle in Example 3, we get a quadratic equation in two variables:
$$x^2 - 10x + 25 + y^2 - 6y + 9 = 4,$$
or
$$x^2 + y^2 - 10x - 6y + 30 = 0.$$
Note that the coefficients of x^2 and y^2 (in this case, 1) are equal. Such equations often describe circles; we put them into standard form, $(x - h)^2 + (y - k)^2 = r^2$, by completing the square.

Example 4   Describe in words the curve defined by the equation
$$x^2 + 10x + 20 = 4y - y^2.$$

Solution   Rearranging terms gives
$$x^2 + 10x + y^2 - 4y = -20.$$
We complete the square for the terms involving x and (separately) for the terms involving y:
$$\underbrace{(x^2 + 10x + 25)}_{(x+5)^2} + \underbrace{(y^2 - 4y + 4)}_{(y-2)^2} \underbrace{-25 - 4}_{\substack{\text{Compensating} \\ \text{terms}}} = -20$$
$$(x + 5)^2 + (y - 2)^2 - 29 = -20$$
$$(x + 5)^2 + (y - 2)^2 = 9.$$
This equation is a circle of radius $r = 3$ with center $(h, k) = (-5, 2)$.

Exercises and Problems for Section 9.5

Exercises

What are the center and radius of the circles in Exercises 1–4?

1. $4x^2 + 4y^2 - 9 = 0$

2. $10 - 3(x^2 + y^2) = 0$

3. $(x + 1)^2 + 2(y + 3)^2 = 32 - (x + 1)^2$

4. $\dfrac{4 - (x - 4)^2}{(y - 4)^2} - 1 = 0$

In Exercises 5–12, parameterize the circles.

5. Radius 4, centered at the origin, traversed clockwise starting at $(4, 0)$.

6. Radius 3, centered at the origin, traversed clockwise starting at $(0, 3)$.

7. Radius 5, centered at the origin, traversed counterclockwise starting at $(0, -5)$.

8. Radius 7, centered at the origin, traversed counterclockwise starting at $(-7, 0)$.

9. Radius 5, centered at $(3, 4)$, traversed counterclockwise starting at $(8, 4)$.

10. Radius 4, centered at $(3, 1)$, traversed clockwise starting at $(3, 5)$.

11. Radius 3, centered at $(-1, -2)$, traversed counterclockwise starting at $(-4, -2)$.

12. Radius $\sqrt{5}$, centered at $(-2, 1)$, traversed counterclockwise starting at $(-2, 1 + \sqrt{5})$.

Problems

13. Identify the center and radius for each of the following circles.

   (a) $(x - 2)^2 + (y + 4)^2 = 20$
   (b) $2x^2 + 2y^2 + 4x - 8y = 12$

What curves do the parametric equations in Problems 14–17 trace out? Find an implicit or explicit equation for each curve.

14. $x = 2 + \cos t, \ y = 2 - \sin t$

15. $x = 2 + \cos t, \ y = \cos^2 t$

16. $x = 2 + \cos t, \ y = 2 - \cos t$

17. $x = 4 \sin^2 t, \ y = 3 + \sin t$

State whether the equations in Problems 18–21 represent a curve parametrically, implicitly, or explicitly. Give the two other types of representations for the same curve.

18. $xy = 1 \quad$ for $x > 0$

19. $x = e^t, \quad y = e^{2t} \quad$ for all t

20. $y = \sqrt{4 - x^2}$

21. $x^2 - 2x + y^2 = 0 \quad$ for $y < 0$

22. An ant, starting at the origin, moves at 2 units/sec along the x-axis to the point $(1, 0)$. The ant then moves counterclockwise along the unit circle to $(0, 1)$ at a speed of $3\pi/2$ units/sec, then straight down to the origin at a speed of 2 units/sec along the y-axis.

   (a) Express the ant's coordinates as a function of time, t, in secs.
   (b) Express the reverse path as a function of time.

23. What can you say about the values of a, b and k if the equations

$$x = a + k \cos t, \quad y = b + k \sin t, \qquad 0 \le t \le 2\pi,$$

trace out each of the circles in Figure 9.57?

   (a) C_1 **(b)** C_2 **(c)** C_3

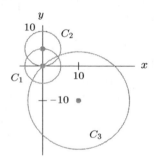

Figure 9.57:

24. In Figure 9.58 a wheel of radius 1 meter rests on the x-axis with its center on the y-axis. There is a spot on the rim at the point $(1, 1)$. At time $t = 0$ the wheel starts rolling on the x-axis in the direction shown at a rate of 1 radian per second. Find parametric equations describing the motion of

   (a) The center of the wheel.
   (b) The motion of the spot on the rim. Plot its path.

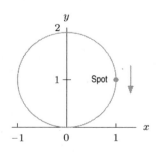

Figure 9.58:

9.6 ELLIPSES

In this section we consider the graph of an ellipse, which is a "squashed" circle.

> The parametric equations of an **ellipse** centered at (h, k) are:
> $$x = h + a \cos t \qquad y = k + b \sin t \qquad 0 \le t \le 2\pi.$$
> We usually take $a > 0$ and $b > 0$.

In the special case where $a = b$, these equations give a circle of radius $r = a$. Thus, a circle is a special kind of ellipse. The parametric equations of an ellipse are transformations of the parametric equations of the unit circle, $x = \cos t$, $y = \sin t$. These transformations have the effect of shifting and stretching the unit circle into an ellipse.

Example 1   Graph the ellipse given by

$$x = 7 + 5 \cos t, \qquad y = 4 + 2 \sin t, \qquad 0 \le t \le 2\pi.$$

Solution   See Figure 9.59. The center of the ellipse is $(h, k) = (7, 4)$. The value $a = 5$ determines the horizontal "radius" of the ellipse, while $b = 2$ determines the vertical "radius". The value of x varies from a maximum of 12 to a minimum of 2 about the vertical midline $x = 7$. Similarly, the value of y varies from a maximum of 6 to a minimum of 2 about the horizontal midline $y = 4$. The ellipse is symmetric about the midlines $x = 7$ and $y = 4$.

In general, the horizontal axis of an ellipse has length $2a$, and the vertical axis has length $2b$. This is similar to a circle, which has diameter $2r$. The difference here is that the diameter of a circle is the same in every direction, whereas the "diameter" of an ellipse depends on the direction.

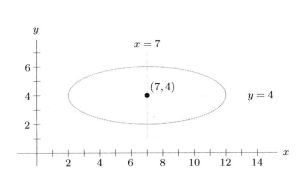

Figure 9.59: The ellipse $x = 7 + 5 \cos t$, $y = 4 + 2 \sin t$, $0 \le t \le 2\pi$

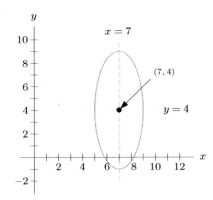

Figure 9.60: $x = 7 + 2 \cos t$, $y = 4 + 5 \sin t$, $0 \le t \le 2\pi$

The longer axis of an ellipse is called the *major* axis and the shorter axis is called the *minor* axis. Either the horizontal or the vertical axis can be the longer axis.

Example 2   Graph the ellipse given by

$$x = 7 + 2\cos t, \qquad y = 4 + 5\sin t, \qquad 0 \le t \le 2\pi.$$

How is this ellipse similar to the one in Example 1? How is it different?

Solution   This ellipse has the same center $(h, k) = (7, 4)$ as the ellipse in Example 1. However, as we see in Figure 9.60, the vertical axis of this ellipse is the longer one and the horizontal axis is the shorter one. This is the opposite of the situation in Example 1.

Eliminating the Parameter t in the Equations for an Ellipse

As with circles, we can eliminate t from the parametric equations for an ellipse. We first rewrite the equation for x as follows:

$$x = h + a\cos t$$
$$x - h = a\cos t$$
$$\frac{x - h}{a} = \cos t.$$

Similarly, we rewrite the equation for y as

$$\frac{y - k}{b} = \sin t.$$

Using the Pythagorean Identity gives

$$\left(\frac{x - h}{a}\right)^2 + \left(\frac{y - k}{b}\right)^2 = \cos^2 t + \sin^2 t = 1.$$

> The implicit equation for an **ellipse** centered at (h, k) and with horizontal axis $2a$ and vertical axis $2b$ is:
>
> $$\frac{(x - h)^2}{a^2} + \frac{(y - k)^2}{b^2} = 1.$$

Exercises and Problems for Section 9.6

Exercises

For the ellipses in Exercises 1–4, find

- **(a)** The coordinates of the center and the "diameter" in the x- and y-directions.
- **(b)** An implicit equation for the ellipse.

1.

2.

3.

4.

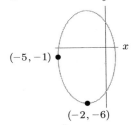

5. Parameterize the ellipse in Exercise 1 counterclockwise, starting at $(12, 0)$.

6. Parameterize the ellipse in Exercise 2 counterclockwise, starting at $(-2, 0)$.

7. Parameterize the ellipse in Exercise 3 clockwise, starting at $(9, 3)$.

8. Parameterize the ellipse in Exercise 4 clockwise, starting at $(-5, -1)$.

9. Compare the ellipse in Example 2 on page 526 with the ellipse given by

$$x = 7 + 2\cos(2t), \quad y = 4 + 5\sin(2t), \quad 0 \le t \le 2\pi.$$

10. Compare the ellipse in Example 2 on page 526 with the ellipse given by

$$x = 7 + 2\cos(-s), \quad y = 4 + 5\sin(-s), \quad 0 \le s \le 2\pi.$$

Problems

By completing the square, rewrite the equations in Problems 11–16 in the form

$$\frac{(x-h)^2}{a^2} + \frac{(y-k)^2}{b^2} = 1.$$

What is the center of the ellipse? The values of a and b?

11. $\dfrac{x^2 - 2x}{4} + y^2 + 4y + \dfrac{13}{4} = 0$

12. $\dfrac{x^2 + 4x}{9} + \dfrac{y^2 + 10y}{25} = -\dfrac{4}{9}$

13. $4x^2 + 16x + y^2 + 2y + 13 = 0$

14. $9x^2 - 54x + 4y^2 - 16y + 61 = 0$

15. $4x^2 - 4x + y^2 + 2y = 2$

16. $9x^2 + 9x + 4y^2 - 4y = \dfrac{131}{4}$

17. For each of the following ellipses, find the center and lengths of the major and minor axes, and graph it.

    (a) $\dfrac{(x+1)^2}{4} + \dfrac{(y-3)^2}{6} = 1$

    (b) $2x^2 + 3y^2 - 6x + 6y = 12$

For positive a, b, the equation of an ellipse can be written in the form

$$\frac{(x-h)^2}{a^2} + \frac{(y-k)^2}{b^2} = 1.$$

In Problems 18–19, rank h, k, a, b, and the number 0 in ascending order (i.e. increasing order). Assume the x- and y-scales are equal.

18.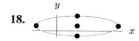

19.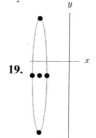

20. If you look at a circular disk, such as a quarter, head on, you see a circle. But if you tilt the disk away from your line of sight, as shown in Figure 9.61, the disk appears elliptical. The length of the apparent ellipse's horizontal axis does not change, but the length of the vertical axis decreases.

    (a) Find a formula for ℓ, the length of the ellipse's vertical axis, in terms of θ, the angle of tilt with respect to the line of sight.
    (b) What does your formula say about the appearance of the coin after being tilted through an angle of $\theta = 0°$? $\theta = 90°$? $\theta = 180°$? Does this make sense?
    (c) Find a formula for the ellipse formed by tilting a disk of radius r through an angle of θ. Assume that the disk is centered at the origin and that the disk is being tilted around the x-axis, so that the length of its horizontal axis does not change.
    (d) The equation $x^2/16 + y^2/7 = 1$ describes an ellipse. If we think of this ellipse as a tilted disk, then what is the disk's radius, and through what angle θ has it been tilted?

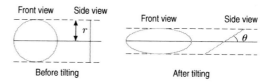

Figure 9.61: At left, front and side views of a circular disc of radius r. At right, the same disk as it appears after being tilted through an angle θ relative to the line of sight.

21. Show, by completing the square, that the equation $Ax^2 - Bx + y^2 = r_0^2$ represents an ellipse, where A, B, and r_0 are constants. (See Problem 22.)

22. Consider the following equation in polar coordinates, where r_0 is a positive constant and where $0 \le \epsilon < 1$ is a constant:

$$r = \frac{r_0}{1 - \epsilon \cos\theta}, \quad 0 \le \theta < 2\pi.$$

    (a) Show, by converting to Cartesian coordinates, that this equation describes an ellipse. You may use the results of Problem 21.

(b) What are the minimum and maximum values of r? At what values of θ do they occur?

(c) Graph the ellipse for $r_0 = 6$ and $\epsilon = 0.5$, labeling the points from part (b) as well as the y-intercepts, that is, the points at $\theta = \pi/2$ and $\theta = 3\pi/2$. What is its center?

(d) Find a formula in terms of r_0 and ϵ for the length of the horizontal axis of the ellipse

(e) The constant ϵ is known as the *eccentricity* of the ellipse. Describe in words the appearance of an ellipse of eccentricity $\epsilon = 0$. What happens to the appearance of the ellipse as the eccentricity gets closer and closer to $\epsilon = 1$?

23. A fuel-efficient way to travel from earth to Mars is to follow a semi-elliptical orbit known as a *Hohmann transfer orbit*.[4] The spacecraft leaves the earth at the point on the ellipse closest to the sun, and arrives at Mars at the point on the ellipse farthest from the sun, as shown in Figure 9.62. Let r_e be the radius of earth's orbit, and r_m the radius of Mars' orbit, and let $2a$ and $2b$ be the respective

lengths of the horizontal and vertical axes of the ellipse.

(a) Orienting the ellipse as shown in the figure, with the sun at the origin, find a formula for this orbit in terms of r_e, r_m, and b.

(b) It can be shown that $b^2 = 2ar_e - r_e^2$. Given this and your answer to part (a), find a formula for b in terms of r_m and r_e.

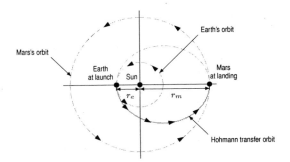

Figure 9.62:

9.7   HYPERBOLAS

We now use another form of the Pythagorean identity to parameterize a curve. With $\tan t = \sin t / \cos t$ and $\sec t = 1/\cos t$, we showed in previous sections that

$$\sec^2 t - \tan^2 t = 1.$$

We use this identity to investigate the curve described by the parametric equations

$$x = \sec t \qquad \text{and} \qquad y = \tan t.$$

By eliminating the parameter t, we get

$$x^2 - y^2 = 1.$$

This implicit equation looks similar to the equation for a unit circle $x^2 + y^2 = 1$. However, the curve it describes is very different. Solving for y, we find that

$$y^2 = x^2 - 1.$$

For large values of x, the values of y^2 and x^2 are very nearly equal. For instance, when $x = 100$, we see that $x^2 = 10,000$ and $y^2 = x^2 - 1 = 9999$. Thus, for large values of x,

$$y^2 \approx x^2,$$
$$y \approx \pm x.$$

The graph of $y = \pm x$ is in Figure 9.54 on page 521; it looks like an X.

---

[4]*Scientific American*, www.sciam.com, March 17, 2000. Note that in an actual Hohmann transfer, the spacecraft would begin in low earth orbit, not from the earth's surface. Timing is critical in order for the two planets to be correctly aligned. Calculations show that at launch, Mars must lead earth by about 45 degrees, which happens only once every 26 months. Note also that the orbits of earth and Mars are actually themselves elliptical, though here we treat them as circular.

What happens for smaller values of x? Writing the equation as $y^2 = x^2 - 1$, shows us that x^2 cannot be less than 1; otherwise y^2 would be negative. See Table 9.7 and Figure 9.63.

Table 9.7 *Points on the graph of the hyperbola, $x^2 - y^2 = 1$*

x	y	Points	x	y	Points
-3	± 2.83	$(-3, 2.83)$ and $(-3, -2.83)$	3	± 2.83	$(3, 2.83)$ and $(3, -2.83)$
-2	± 1.73	$(-2, 1.73)$ and $(-2, -1.73)$	2	± 1.73	$(2, 1.73)$ and $(2, -1.73)$
-1	± 0	$(-1, 0)$ and $(-1, -0)$	1	± 0	$(1, 0)$ and $(1, -0)$
0	Undefined	None			

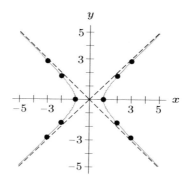

Figure 9.63: A graph of $x^2 - y^2 = 1$. The X-shaped graph of $y^2 = x^2$ has been dashed in

This graph is an example of a *hyperbola*. By analogy to the unit circle, it is called the *unit hyperbola*. It has two branches, one to the right of the y-axis and one to the left. As x grows large in magnitude, either towards $+\infty$ or $-\infty$, the graph approaches the asymptotes, $y^2 = x^2$.

A General Formula for Hyperbolas

We can shift and stretch the unit hyperbola using the equations $x = h + a \sec t$ and $y = k + b \tan t$. This has the effect of centering the hyperbola at the point (h, k).

> The parametric equations for a **hyperbola** centered at (h, k) and opening to the left and right are
> $$x = h + a \sec t \qquad y = k + b \tan t \qquad 0 \le t \le 2\pi.$$
> We usually take $a > 0$ and $b > 0$.

We eliminate the parameter, t, from the parametric equations to obtain the implicit equation

$$\frac{(x - h)^2}{a^2} - \frac{(y - k)^2}{b^2} = 1.$$

Notice that this equation is similar to the general equation for an ellipse.

Example 3   Graph the equation $\dfrac{(x - 4)^2}{9} - \dfrac{(y - 7)^2}{25} = 1$.

Solution   Since $h = 4$ and $k = 7$, we have shifted the unit hyperbola 4 units to the right and 7 units up. We have $a^2 = 9$ and $b^2 = 25$, so $a = 3$ and $b = 5$. Thus, we have stretched the unit hyperbola horizontally by a factor of 3 and vertically by a factor of 5.

To make it easier to draw hyperbolas, we imagine a "unit square" centered at the origin. This unit square helps us locate the vertices and asymptotes of the hyperbola $x^2 - y^2 = 1$. See Figure 9.64. Stretching and shifting the hyperbola causes this square to be transformed into a rectangle centered at the point $(h, k) = (4, 7)$ with width $2a = 6$ and height $2b = 10$. See Figure 9.65. The rectangle enables us to draw the X-shaped asymptotes as diagonal lines through the corners. The vertices of the transformed hyperbola are located at the midpoints of the vertical sides of the rectangle.

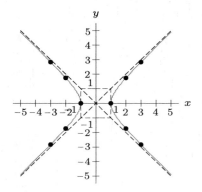

Figure 9.64: The hyperbola $x^2 - y^2 = 1$, with the unit square dashed in

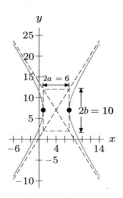

Figure 9.65: A graph of $\frac{(x-4)^2}{9} - \frac{(y-7)^2}{25} = 1$. A rectangle of width $2a = 6$ height $2b = 10$ has been dashed in, centered at the point $(h, k) = (4, 7)$

Note that the ellipse $\frac{(x-4)^2}{9} + \frac{(y-7)^2}{25} = 1$ would exactly fit inside the rectangle in Figure 9.65. In this sense, a hyperbola is an ellipse turned "inside-out."

Example 4   Graph the equation $\dfrac{(y-7)^2}{25} - \dfrac{(x-4)^2}{9} = 1$.

Solution   This equation is similar to that in Example 3, except that the terms have opposite signs. The graph in Figure 9.66 is similar to the one in Figure 9.65 except that it opens up and down instead of right and left.

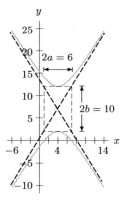

Figure 9.66: A graph of $\frac{(y-7)^2}{25} - \frac{(x-4)^2}{9} = 1$. This graph is similar to the one in Figure 9.65 except that here the hyperbola opens up and down instead of right and left

In summary:

The implicit equation for a **hyperbola**,

$$\frac{(x-h)^2}{a^2} - \frac{(y-k)^2}{b^2} = 1,$$

describes a hyperbola that opens left and right. Its asymptotes are diagonal lines through the corners of a rectangle of width $2a$ and height $2b$ centered at the point (h, k). The graph with equation

$$\frac{(y-k)^2}{b^2} - \frac{(x-h)^2}{a^2} = 1$$

has a similar shape, except that it opens up and down.

Exercises and Problems for Section 9.7

Exercises

For the hyperbolas in Exercises 1–4, find

(a) The coordinates of the vertices of the hyperbola and the coordinates of its center.

(b) The equations of the asymptotes.

(c) An implicit equation for the hyperbola.

1.

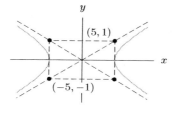

2.

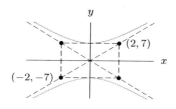

3.

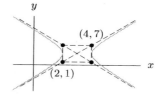

4.

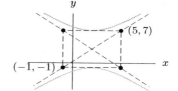

Problems

5. Parameterize the hyperbola in Exercise 1. What t values give the right half?

6. Parameterize the hyperbola in Exercise 2. What t values give the upper half?

7. Parameterize the hyperbola in Exercise 3. What t values give the left half?

8. Parameterize the hyperbola in Exercise 4. What t values give the lower half?

By completing the square, rewrite the equations in Problems 9–14 in the form

$$\frac{(x-h)^2}{a^2} - \frac{(y-k)^2}{b^2} = 1 \text{ or } \frac{(y-k)^2}{b^2} - \frac{(x-h)^2}{a^2} = 1.$$

What is the center, and does the hyperbola open left-right or up-down? What are the values of a and b?

9. $\dfrac{x^2 - 2x}{4} - y^2 + 4y = \dfrac{19}{4}$

10. $\dfrac{y^2 + 2y}{4} - \dfrac{x^2 - 4x}{9} = \dfrac{43}{36}$

11. $x^2 + 2x - 4y^2 - 24y = 39$

12. $9x^2 - 36x - 4y^2 + 8y = 4$

13. $4x^2 - 8x = 36y^2 - 36y - 31$

14. $9y^2 + 6y = 89 + 8x^2 + 24x$

For positive a, b, the equation of a hyperbola can be written in one of the two forms

I. $\dfrac{(x - h)^2}{a^2} - \dfrac{(y - k)^2}{b^2} = 1$

II. $\dfrac{(y - k)^2}{b^2} - \dfrac{(x - h)^2}{a^2} = 1$

In Problems 15–16, which form applies? Rank h, k, a, b, and the number 0 in ascending order (i.e. increasing order). Assume the x- and y-scales are equal.

15.

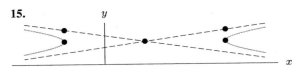

16.

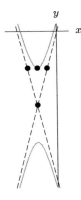

17. For each of the following hyperbolas, find the center, vertices, and asymptotes, and graph it.

(a) $\dfrac{(x + 5)^2}{6} - \dfrac{(y - 2)^2}{4} = 1$

(b) $x^2 - y^2 + 2x = 4y + 17$

18. By scattering positively charged alpha particles off of atoms in gold foil, Earnest Lord Rutherford demonstrated that atoms contain a nucleus of concentrated charge. The scattered alpha particles followed hyperbolic trajectories, as shown in Figure 9.67, and Rutherford was able to measure the angle θ. However, the value of θ alone was not enough for Rutherford to determine whether the nuclear charge is negative or positive. A negatively charged nucleus would exert an attractive force on the alpha particles, and the positively charged nucleus would exert a repulsive force, but in either case, the trajectory would be a hyperbola specified by the angle θ. Note that in Figure 9.67, the incoming particle would pass through the origin if it were not scattered by the nucleus at $(d, 0)$.

(a) The hyperbola is $x^2/a^2 - y^2/b^2 = 1$. Find a formula for b in terms of a and θ.

(b) It turns out that the charge in the nucleus is positive, and that the alpha particles undergo a repulsive force. What must be true about the parameter a?

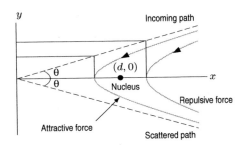

Figure 9.67

9.8 INTERSECTIONS

This section focuses on the points of intersection of two or more graphs. You will use visualization skills, algebraic skills, and critical thinking skills.

Example 1   Find the points of intersection of $y = 2x$ and $y = x^2$.

Solution   First, stop and think about the equations given. The first equation, $y = 2x$, is a straight line through the origin. The second equation, $y = x^2$, is a parabola with vertex at the origin opening up. Creating a mental image of these two on one coordinate system allows us to have an *expectation* of the existence and nature of the solutions. In this case, we can see that there will be two solutions.

To create the graph on your calculator, let $y_1 = 2x$ and $y_2 = x^2$

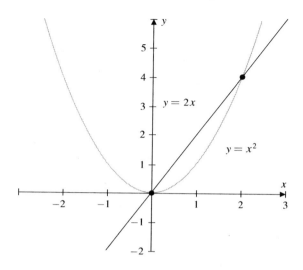

Figure 9.68

It appears that the points of intersection are $(0, 0)$ and $(2, 4)$ but we will also find the points algebraically. This means to solve the *system* of equations

$$y = 2x$$
$$y = x^2$$

We can do this by the method of substitution. In the second equation y is the same as x^2, so we can replace y by x^2 in the first equation. This gives us:

$$x^2 = 2x$$

This equation is quadratic, so write it in standard form:

$$x^2 - 2x = 0$$

Factor the left side and use the zero-product property:

$$x(x - 2) = 0$$
$$x = 0 \text{ or } x = 2$$

Note that this is consistent with our expectations.

Now find the y-coordinates:

If $x = 0$, then $y = 2(0) = 0$ and if $x = 2$, then $y = 2(2) = 4$, so the points are $(0, 0)$ and $(2, 4)$, as we expected.

In summary the points of intersection of $y = 2x$ and $y = x^2$ are $(0, 0)$ and $(2, 4)$.

Matched Problem 1 Find the points of intersection of $y = -x + 2$ and $y = x^2 - 2x$.

Example 2   Find the points of intersection of $y = 2x - 1$ and $y = x^2$.

Solution   Once again, we have a straight line and the same parabola as in Example 1. This time the line has slope 2 but the y-intercept is –1. We may need to see the graph to determine the existence of intersection points. The graph looks like this:

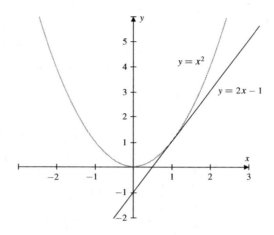

Figure 9.69

It appears that there is only one point of intersection but we will verify algebraically:
Solve the system:

$$y = 2x - 1$$
$$y = x^2$$

Substituting x^2 for y in the first equation gives:

$$x^2 = 2x - 1$$

This is a quadratic equation, so write in standard form and solve by factoring:

$$x^2 - 2x + 1 = 0$$
$$(x - 1)^2 = 0$$
$$x = 1$$

Thus there is only one point of intersection, as we expected. The y-coordinate is 1, so the point of intersection is (1, 1).

In summary, the point of intersection of $y = 2x - 1$ and $y = x^2$ is (1, 1).

Note: When a line touches a curve at one point like this one does, the line is said to be *tangent* to the curve at that point. The line $y = 2x - 1$ is the *tangent line* to the curve $y = x^2$ at the point (1, 1). Tangent lines are very important in the study of calculus.

Example 3   Find the points of intersection of $x^2 + y^2 = 2$ and $y = x^2$.

Solution   Again, stop and think about the equations given. The first equation, $x^2 + y^2 = 2$, is a circle with center at the origin and radius $\sqrt{2}$. The second equation, $y = x^2$, is the same parabola as before. Creating a mental image of these two on one coordinate system, we can see that there will be two solutions.

To create the graph on your calculator, solve the circle equation for y and graph the top and bottom halves separately.

$$y_1 = \sqrt{2 - x^2} \quad \text{and} \quad y_2 = -\sqrt{2 - x^2} \quad \text{and} \quad y_3 = x^2$$

Once you have the graph, use ZOOM 5:SQUARE

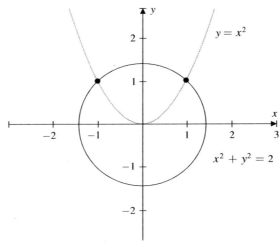

Figure 9.70

We can certainly find the points of intersection graphically using the calculator. Let's find them algebraically by solving the system

$$x^2 + y^2 = 2$$
$$y = x^2$$

We can use substitution. In the second equation y is the same as x^2, so we can replace y by x^2 in the first equation. This gives us:

$$x^2 + (x^2)^2 = 2$$
$$x^2 + x^4 = 2$$

Notice that this equation is quadratic in x^2, so write the equation in standard form:

$$x^4 + x^2 - 2 = 0$$

The left side can be factored:

$$(x^2 + 2)(x^2 - 1) = 0$$

Using the zero-product property, we get:

$$x^2 + 2 = 0 \text{ or } x^2 - 1 = 0$$
$$x^2 = -2 \text{ or } x^2 = 1$$

Because we are considering only real number solutions, the first equation has no solutions. We can, however, solve the second equation by taking square roots:

$$x = \pm 1$$

This is consistent with our expectations and our observations of the two graphs. Now we complete the solution by finding the y-coordinates of the points of intersection.

If $x = -1$ then $y = (-1)^2$ or $y = 1$ and if $x = 1$ then $y = (1)^2$ or $y = 1$.

This gives us the points $(-1, 1)$ and $(1, 1)$.

In summary, the two curves $x^2 + y^2 = 2$ and $y = x^2$ have two points of intersection, $(-1, 1)$ and $(1, 1)$.

Observation: Before leaving this problem, notice that in our solution we used x^2 as a replacement for y. Suppose, instead, that we use y as a replacement for x^2 and generate an equation in y instead of x. Let's see how the solution progresses from the beginning:

$$x^2 + y^2 = 2$$
$$y = x^2$$

We now use the substitution $x^2 = y$. This gives us:

$$y + y^2 = 2$$

Notice that this equation is quadratic in y, so write the equation in standard form:

$$y^2 + y - 2 = 0$$

The left side can be factored:

$$(y + 2)(y - 1) = 0$$

Using the zero-product property, we get:

$$y + 2 = 0 \text{ or } y - 1 = 0$$
$$y = -2 \text{ or } y = 1$$

Now we complete the solution by finding x:

$$x^2 = -2 \text{ or } x^2 = 1$$

The first equation gives us no real solutions and the second equation gives us

$$x = \pm 1$$

So once again we have the two points $(-1, 1)$ and $(1, 1)$.

Example 4   Find the points of intersection of $x^2 + y^2 = 8$ and $y = x^2$.

Solution   This problem is very similar to Example 3. We still have a circle, slightly larger than before, and a parabola, and we still expect two solutions. Here is the graph: The graph offers no surprises, so we now solve the system algebraically.

$$x^2 + y^2 = 8$$
$$y = x^2$$

Using substitution:

$$x^2 + \left(x^2\right)^2 = 8$$
$$x^2 + x^4 = 8$$

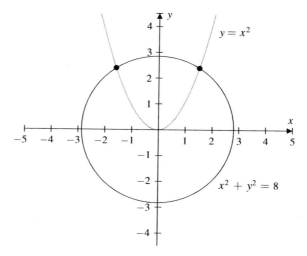

Figure 9.71

Notice that this equation is quadratic in x^2, so write the equation in standard form:

$$x^4 + x^2 - 8 = 0$$

Now we can see the difference between this example and Example 3. The left side of this equation cannot be factored. We will use the quadratic formula, remembering that we are solving for x^2:

$$x^2 = \frac{-1 \pm \sqrt{1 - 4(1)(-8)}}{2(1)}$$

$$x^2 = \frac{-1 \pm \sqrt{33}}{2}$$

$$x^2 = -3.37228 \text{ or } x^2 = 2.37228$$

Once again, we are seeking only real number solutions so we discard the first equation and solve the second:

$$x = \pm\sqrt{2.37228}$$

$$x = \pm 1.54022$$

Finally, the y-coordinates: $y = (\pm 1.54022)^2 = 2.37228$.

In summary, the points of intersection of $x^2 + y^2 = 8$ and $y = x^2$ are (1.54022, 2.37228) and (−1.54022, 2.37228).

Matched Problem 2   Solve the system of equations in Example 4 by substituting y for x^2.

Example 5   Find the points of intersection of the curves $y = \cos(3x)$ and $y = 3 - x^2$.

Solution   This time we have a cosine curve with only a period change and a parabola with vertex at (0, 3) opening down. Graphing the two together we get:

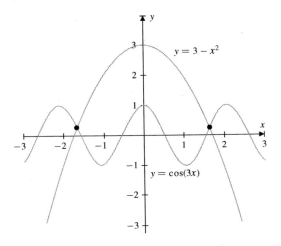

Figure 9.72

To find the points of intersection, we need to solve the system:

$$y = 3 - x^2$$
$$y = \cos(3x)$$

If we use substitution, we get

$$3 - x^2 = \cos(3x)$$

This equation cannot be solved algebraically. Our best tool is a graphical solution using the calculator. Note that the region is symmetric about the y-axis so we only have to find one point and we will also know the other. Using the CALC menu $\boxed{\text{2nd}}$ [CALC] and 5: INTERSECT, we get the point (1.6567768, 0.25509063) so the other point is (−1.6567768, 0.25509063).

Example 6   In a business setting, the break-even point is the point at which Cost = Revenue. Cost includes both fixed costs, such as salaries, building maintenance, and utilities, and variable costs, such as materials and shipping. Revenue is price per unit (which may vary depending on the number of units) times the number of units. Cost and revenue functions can be linear but other functions are also used.

Suppose a company is manufacturing stoves. It has fixed costs of $28,000 and its variable costs are $222 + 0.40x$ dollars per stove, where x is the number of stoves produced. The selling price of the stove is $1250 - 0.60x$ dollars per stove.

(a) Write and graph the cost function $C(x)$.
(b) Write and graph the revenue function $R(x)$.
(c) Find the maximum revenue.
(d) Find the break-even points.
(e) Write and graph the profit function (Profit = Revenue − Cost)
(f) Find the price that will maximize profit.

Solution   (a) Cost = Fixed Costs + Variable Costs
   x = the number of stoves produced and sold
   Fixed costs = 28000
   Variable costs = ($222 + 0.40x$ dollars per stove) times the number of stoves, so
   Variable costs = ($222 + 0.40x$ dollars per stove) x

Therefore,

$$C(x) = 28000 + (222 + 0.40x)\,x = 0.40x^2 + 222x + 28000$$

Note that the cost function is quadratic. To graph this function we need to think about a practical domain. Certainly $x > 0$ and it seems reasonable to assume that a large number of stoves will be made. Arbitrarily, let's choose a domain of $0 \le x \le 1500$. Using the function, then, the range would be about $0 \le C(x) \le 10^6$. The graph looks like this:

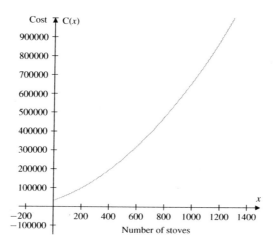

Figure 9.73

Notice that the graph is increasing at an increasing rate. This means that as more stoves are produced, the total cost increases.

(b) Revenue = selling price per stove times the number of stoves
Selling price per stove $= 1250 - 0.60x$ and x is the number of stoves, so

$$R(x) = x\,(1250 - 0.60x) = 1250x - 0.60x^2$$

The revenue function is also quadratic. Its graph on the same domain and range as the cost function looks like this:

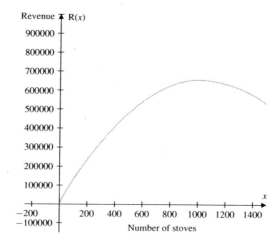

Figure 9.74

Notice that the revenue function increases to a maximum and then decreases.

(c) The maximum revenue can be found either graphically or algebraically. Algebraically, the maximum value occurs at the vertex of the parabola. Using the formula:

$$\text{Vertex:} x = \frac{-b}{2a} = \frac{-1250}{2(-.60)} \approx 1041.67$$
$$R(1041.67) \approx 651,041.67$$

So the maximum revenue is approximately \$651,042 if about 1042 stoves are sold.

(d) To find the break-even point algebraically, we solve the equation

$$\text{Cost} = \text{Revenue}$$
$$0.40x^2 + 222x + 28000 = 1250x - 0.60x^2$$

This equation is quadratic so write it in standard form:

$$x^2 - 1028x + 28000 = 0$$

Using the quadratic formula, we get two solutions:

$$x = 28 \quad \text{or} \quad x = 1000$$

In this case, the company will break even if it makes and sells 28 stoves and again if it makes and sells 1000 stoves. To see why there are two break-even points and what happens in between, we can look at the cost and revenue functions graphed together:

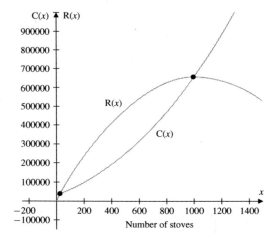

Figure 9.75

If the company makes and sells 28 stoves then the cost and revenue are both \$34,529.60.
If the company makes and sells 1000 stoves, then the cost and revenue are both \$650,000.
In between 28 stoves and 1000 stoves, the revenue is greater than the cost and this means that the company is making a profit.

(e) The profit function is found by

$$\text{Profit} = \text{Revenue} - \text{Cost}$$
$$P(x) = R(x) - -C(x)$$
$$P(x) = (1250x - 0.60x^2) - (0.40x^2 + 222x + 28000)$$
$$P(x) = -x^2 + 1028x - 28000$$

To graph the profit function we can use the same domain as cost and revenue. However, the range can include negative values because negative profit is loss and loss is meaningful in this situation.

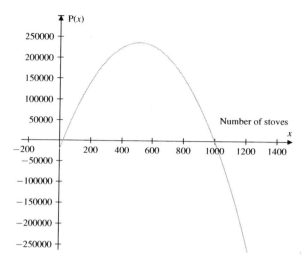

Figure 9.76

(f) To find the price that will maximize profit, we first find the number of stoves that will maximize profit. Once again, this occurs at the vertex of the parabola:

$$x = \frac{-1028}{-2} = 514$$

Thus profit is a maximum if 514 stoves are produced and sold. The price is given by $1250 - 0.60x$ and if $x = 514$, then the selling price should be $941.60.

Answers to Matched Problems   **1.** $(2, 0)$ and $(-1, 3)$ **2.** Answers are the same as those in Example 4.

EXERCISES FOR SECTION 9.8

Exercises

1. Consider the graphs of $y = x^2 - 4$ and $y = 2x - 4$.

   (a) Before graphing the two functions, visualize the graph. Identify each curve and write down your expectations about the number of intersections.

   (b) Graph the two functions on the same coordinate system and sketch this graph. By inspection, what are the intersections points?

   (c) Find the intersection points algebraically. Write down the system you are solving and show the steps you use to solve the system. Write a complete answer.

2. Consider the graphs of $y = x^2 - 4$ and $y = 2x - 5$.

   (a) Graph the two functions on the same coordinate system and sketch this graph. Why is this graph different from the graph in Exercise 1? What is the relationship between this line and curve?

(b) Find the intersection point algebraically. Write down the system you are solving and show the steps you use to solve the system. Write a complete answer.

3. (a) Based on your experience with Exercises 1 and 2, what would you say if you were asked to find the intersection points for $y = x^2 - 4$ and $y = 2x - 10$? Write down you thought process and support your answer with a graph.

(b) Try to find the intersection points algebraically. Explain what happens.

4. Consider again $y = x^2 - 4$. Write the equation of the line that intersects this parabola at $(-1, -3)$ and $(2, 0)$. Show your steps and support your answer with a graph.

5. (a) Consider again $y = x^2 - 4$. The point $(3, 5)$ is on this graph. Write the equation of *any* line that is neither vertical nor horizontal and intersects the parabola at $(3, 5)$. Show your steps and support your answer with a graph.

(b) Using the line you found in part (a), find (algebraically) any other intersection point that your line has with the parabola. Show your steps and support your answer with a graph.

6. Algebraically find the points of intersection of the ellipse $\dfrac{x^2}{4} + \dfrac{y^2}{9} = 1$ and the parabola $y = \dfrac{x^2}{4} - 1$. Show all your steps and support your answer with a graph.

7. Algebraically find the points of intersection of the ellipse $\dfrac{x^2}{4} + \dfrac{y^2}{9} = 1$ and the parabola $y = -x^2$. Show all your steps and support your answer with a graph.

8. Algebraically find the points of intersection of $y = x^2 + 2x - 5$ and $y = -x^2 + 2x + 3$. Show all your steps and support your answer with a graph.

9. Graphically find the points of intersection of $y = e^x$ and $y = x^3 - 2x^2 + x + 2$.

10. In 1963, the population of Nigeria was 55.6 million and increasing by 2.2% per year. Also in 1963, Nigeria's oil production was sufficient for 115.1 million people but by 1980 oil production was sufficient for 107.3 million people.

(a) Write a function that gives the population of Nigeria, $P(t)$, where t is the number of years since 1963.

(b) Write $P(t)$ using base e.

(c) Use $P(t)$ to determine the population of Nigeria in 2000.

(d) Write a linear function that gives the number of people supported by Nigeria's oil production, $N(t)$, where t is the number of years since 1963.

(e) Graph $P(t)$ and $N(t)$ on the same coordinate system using a window appropriate for the graphs between 1963 and 2005.

(f) Write the equation needed to find the intersection of these two functions.

(g) Find the intersection graphically.

(h) Write a few sentences explaining the significance of this intersection to Nigeria.

11. A new high-tech company has fixed weekly costs of $2400 and its variable costs are $100 + 2x$ dollars per item, where x is the number of items produced. The selling price of the item is $180 - 2x$ dollars per item.

(a) Write and graph the cost function $C(x)$.

(b) Write and graph the revenue function $R(x)$.

(c) Find the maximum revenue.

(d) Find (algebraically) the break-even points.

(e) Write and graph the profit function (Profit = Revenue – Cost)

(f) Find the price that will maximize profit.

Review Exercises and Problems for Chapter Nine

Exercises

In Exercises 1–8, decide if the equation represents a circle, an ellipse, or a hyperbola. Give the center and the radius (for a circle) or the values of a and b (for an ellipse or hyperbola) and whether it opens left-right or up-down (for a hyperbola).

1. $x^2 + (y - 3)^2 = 5$

2. $7 - 2(x + 1)^2 = 2(y - 4)^2$

3. $\dfrac{x^2}{4} - \dfrac{(y - 1)^2}{9} = 1$

4. $(x + 1)^2 = 1 - \dfrac{(y + 2)^2}{8}$

5. $9(x - 5)^2 + 4y^2 = 36$

6. $63 + 9x^2 = 7(y - 1)^2$

7. $6 + 2(x + \frac{1}{3})^2 - 3(y - \frac{1}{2})^2 = 0$

8. $\dfrac{4 - 2(x - 1)^2}{(y + 2)^2} = 1$

Write a parameterization for the curves in Exercises 9–16.

9. A circle of radius 3 centered at the origin and traced clockwise.

10. A circle of radius 5 centered at the point (2, 1) and traced counterclockwise.

11. A circle of radius 2 centered at the origin traced clockwise starting from $(-2, 0)$ when $t = 0$.

12. The circle of radius 4 centered at the point (4, 4) starting on the x-axis when $t = 0$.

13. An ellipse centered at the origin and crossing the x-axis at ± 5 and the y-axis at ± 7.

14. A hyperbola crossing the x-axis at $x = \pm 1$ and with asymptotes $y = \pm 2x$.

15. An ellipse centered at the origin, crossing the x-axis at ± 3 and the y-axis at ± 7. Trace counterclockwise, starting from $(-3, 0)$.

16. A hyperbola crossing the y-axis at (0, 7) and (0, 3) and with asymptotes $y = \pm 4x + 5$.

Problems

Write a parameterization for the curves in Problems 17–19.

17. The horizontal line through the point (0, 5).

18. The circle of radius 1 in the xy-plane centered at the origin and traversed counterclockwise.

19. The circle of radius 2 centered at the origin, starting at the point (0, 2) when $t = 0$.

By completing the square, put the equations in Problems 20–23 into one of the following forms

$$\frac{(x - h)^2}{a^2} + \frac{(y - k)^2}{b^2} = 1$$

or

$$\frac{(x - h)^2}{a^2} - \frac{(y - k)^2}{b^2} = 1$$

or

$$\frac{(y - k)^2}{b^2} - \frac{(x - h)^2}{a^2} = 1$$

and decide if it represents a circle, an ellipse, or a hyperbola. Give its center, radius (for a circle), or the values of a and b (for an ellipse or a hyperbola), and whether it opens left-right or up-down (for a hyperbola).

20. $x^2 + 2x + y^2 = 0$

21. $2x^2 + 2y = y^2 + 4x$

22. $6x^2 - 12x + 9y^2 + 6y + 1 = 0$

23. $\dfrac{x^2 - 4x}{2y - y^2} - 1 = 0$

24. On a graphing calculator or a computer, plot $x = 2t/(t^2 + 1)$, $y = (t^2 - 1)/(t^2 + 1)$, first for $-50 \le t \le 50$, and then for $-5 \le t \le 5$. Explain what you see. Is the curve really a circle?

25. Plot the Lissajous figure given by $x = \cos 2t$, $y = \sin t$ using a graphing calculator or computer. Explain why it looks like part of a parabola. [Hint: Use a double angle identity.]

26. A planet P in the xy-plane orbits the star S counterclockwise in a circle of radius 10 units, completing one orbit in 2π units of time. A moon M orbits the planet P counterclockwise in a circle of radius 3 units, completing one orbit in $2\pi/8$ units of time. The star S is fixed at the origin $x = 0$, $y = 0$, and at time $t = 0$ the planet P is at the point (10, 0) and the moon M is at the point (13, 0).

(a) Find parametric equations for the x- and y-coordinates of the planet at time t.

(b) Find parametric equations for the x- and y-coordinates of the moon at time t. [Hint: For the moon's position at time t, take a vector from the sun to the planet at time t and add a vector from the planet to the moon].

(c) Plot the path of the moon in the xy-plane, using a graphing calculator or computer.

CHECK YOUR UNDERSTANDING

Are the statements in Problems 1–13 true or false? Give an explanation for your answer.

1. If the motion of an object is described by $x = \sin(t/2)$ and $y = \cos(t/2), 0 \le t \le 4$, then when $t = \pi$ the object is located at the point (1, 0).

2. If the motion of an object on the unit circle is described by $x = \sin(t/2)$ and $y = \cos(t/2)$, $0 \le t \le 4$, then the object is moving counterclockwise.

3. The graph of $x^2 - y^2 = 0$ is a circle.

4. The graph of $(x + 3)^2 + y^2 = 4$ is a circle of radius 4 centered at $(-3, 0)$.

5. There is only one parameterization of the circle.

6. If the parameter t is eliminated from the parametric equations $x = 2t + 1$ and $y = t - 1$, the resulting equation can be written as $y = \frac{1}{2}(x - 3)$.

7. If a circle is centered at the point $(1, -1)$ and its radius is $\sqrt{5}$, then its equation is $(x - 1)^2 + (y + 1)^2 = 5$.

8. The equation $4x^2 + 9y^2 = 36$ represents a circle.

9. The equations $x = 2\cos t$, $y = \sin t$ parameterize an ellipse.

10. The graph of $\dfrac{(y - k)^2}{b^2} - \dfrac{(x - h)^2}{a^2} = 1$ is a hyperbola that opens up and down.

11. The hyperbolic sine is defined as $\sinh x = \dfrac{e^x + e^{-x}}{2}$.

12. As x approaches infinity, $\cosh x$ approaches $\frac{1}{2}e^x$.

13. An identity that relates $\sinh x$ and $\cosh x$ is $\cosh^2 x + \sinh^2 x = 1$.

Chapter Ten

CURVE FITTING

In this chapter we work with data and look for mathematical functions that can best describe the data. We will use linear, exponential, and power regressions.

10.1 LINEAR REGRESSION

When real data are collected in the laboratory or the field, they are often subject to experimental error. Even if there is an underlying linear relationship between two quantities, real data may not fit this relationship perfectly. However, even if a data set does not perfectly conform to a linear function, we may still be able to use a linear function to help us analyze the data.

Laboratory Data: The Viscosity of Motor Oil

The viscosity of a liquid, or its resistance to flow, depends on the liquid's temperature. Pancake syrup is a familiar example: straight from the refrigerator, it pours very slowly. When warmed on the stove, its viscosity decreases and it becomes quite runny.

The viscosity of motor oil is a measure of its effectiveness as a lubricant in the engine of a car. Thus, the effect of engine temperature is an important determinant of motor-oil performance. Table 10.1 gives the viscosity, v, of motor oil as measured in the lab at different temperatures, T.

Table 10.1 *The measured viscosity, v, of motor oil as a function of the temperature, T*

T, temperature (°F)	v, viscosity (lbs·sec/in²)
160	28
170	26
180	24
190	21
200	16
210	13
220	11
230	9

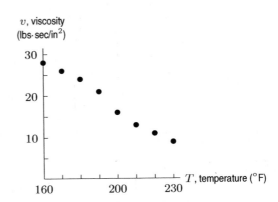

Figure 10.1: The viscosity data from Table 10.1

The *scatter plot* of the data in Figure 10.1 shows that the viscosity of motor oil decreases, approximately linearly, as its temperature rises. To find a formula relating viscosity and temperature, we fit a line to these data points.

Fitting the best line to a set of data is called *linear regression*. One way to fit a line is to draw a line "by eye." Alternatively, many computer programs and calculators compute regression lines. Figure 10.2 shows the data from Table 10.1 together with the computed regression line,

$$v = 75.6 - 0.293T.$$

Notice that none of the data points lie exactly on the regression line, although it fits the data well.

The Assumptions Involved In Finding a Regression Line

When we find a regression line for the data in Table 10.1, we are assuming that the value of v is related to the value of T. However, there may be experimental errors in our measurements. For example, if we measure viscosity twice at the same temperature, we may get two slightly different values. Alternatively, something besides engine temperature could be affecting the oil's viscosity (the oil pressure, for example). Thus, even if we assume that the temperature readings are exact, the viscosity readings include some degree of uncertainty.

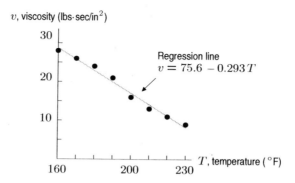

Figure 10.2: A graph of the viscosity data from Table 10.1, together with a regression line (provided by a calculator)

Interpolation and Extrapolation

The formula for viscosity can be used to make predictions. Suppose we want to know the viscosity of motor oil at $T = 196°$F. The formula gives

$$v = 75.6 - 0.293 \cdot 196 \approx 18.2 \text{ lb} \cdot \text{sec/in}^2.$$

To see that this is a reasonable estimate, compare it to the entries in Table 10.1. At 190°F, the measured viscosity was 21, and at 200°F, it was 16; the predicted viscosity of 18.2 is between 16 and 21. See Figure 10.3. Of course, if we measured the viscosity at $T = 196°$F in the lab, we might not get exactly 18.2.

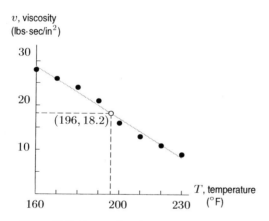

Figure 10.3: Regression line used to predict the viscosity at 196°

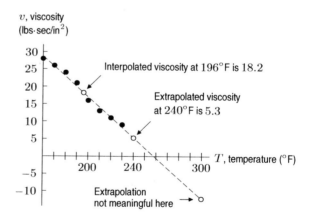

Figure 10.4: The data from Table 10.1 together with the predicted viscosity at $T = 196°$, $T = 240°$, and $T = 300°$

Since the temperature $T = 196°$ is between two temperatures for which v is known (190° and 200°), the estimate of 18.2 is said to be an *interpolation*. If instead we estimate the value of v at a temperature outside the values for T in Table 10.1, our estimate is called an *extrapolation*.

Example 1   Predict the viscosity of motor oil at 240°F and at 300°F.

Solution   At $T = 240°$F, the formula for the regression line predicts that the viscosity of motor oil is

$$v = 75.6 - 0.293 \cdot 240 = 5.3 \text{ lb} \cdot \text{sec/in}^2.$$

This is reasonable. Figure 10.4 shows that the predicted point—represented by an open circle on the graph—is consistent with the trend in the data points from Table 10.1.

On the other hand, at $T = 300°F$ the regression-line formula gives

$$v = 75.6 - 0.293 \cdot 300 = -12.3 \text{ lb} \cdot \text{sec/in}^2.$$

This is unreasonable because viscosity cannot be negative. To understand what went wrong, notice that in Figure 10.4, the open circle representing the point $(300, -12.3)$ is far from the plotted data points. By making a prediction at $300°F$, we have assumed—incorrectly—that the trend observed in laboratory data extended as far as $300°F$.

In general, interpolation tends to be more reliable than extrapolation because we are making a prediction on an interval we already know something about instead of making a prediction beyond the limits of our knowledge.

How Regression Works

How does a calculator or computer decide which line fits the data best? We assume that the value of y is related to the value of x, although other factors could influence y as well. Thus, we assume that we can pick the value of x exactly but that the value of y may be only partially determined by this x-value.

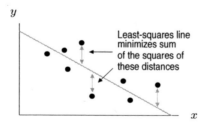

Figure 10.5: A given set of data and the corresponding least-squares regression line

One way to fit a line to the data is shown in Figure 10.5. The line shown was chosen to minimize the sum of the squares of the vertical distances between the data points and the line. Such a line is called a *least-squares line*. There are formulas which a calculator or computer uses to calculate the slope, m, and the y-intercept, b, of the least-squares line.

Correlation

When a computer or calculator calculates a regression line, it also gives a *correlation coefficient, r*. This number lies between -1 and $+1$ and measures how well a particular regression line fits the data. If $r = 1$, the data lie exactly on a line of positive slope. If $r = -1$, the data lie exactly on a line of negative slope. If r is close to 0, the data may be completely scattered, or there may be a non-linear relationship between the variables. (See Figure 10.6.)

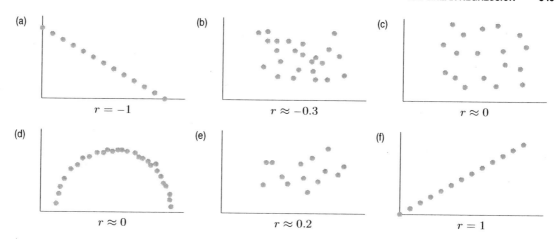

Figure 10.6: Various data sets and correlation coefficients

Example 2   The correlation coefficient for the viscosity data in Table 10.1 on page 546 is $r \approx -0.99$. The fact that r is negative tells us that the regression line has negative slope. The fact that r is close to -1 tells us that the regression line fits the data well.

The Difference between Relation, Correlation, and Causation

It is important to understand that a high correlation (either positive or negative) between two quantities does *not* imply causation. For example, there is a high correlation between children's reading level and shoe size.[1] However, large feet do not cause a child to read better (or vice versa). Larger feet and improved reading ability are both a consequence of growing older.

Notice also that a correlation of 0 does not imply that there is no relationship between x and y. For example, in Figure 10.6(d) there is a relationship between x and y-values, while Figure 10.6(c) exhibits no apparent relationship. Both data sets have a correlation coefficient of $r \approx 0$. Thus a correlation of $r = 0$ usually implies there is no linear relationship between x and y, but this does not mean there is no relationship at all.

Exercises and Problems for Section 10.1

Exercises

1. Table 10.2 shows the number of calories burned per minute by a person walking at 3 mph.

   (a) Make a scatter plot of this data.
   (b) Draw a regression line by eye.
   (c) Roughly estimate the correlation coefficient by eye.

Table 10.2

Body weight (lb)	100	120	150	170	200	220
Calories	2.7	3.2	4.0	4.6	5.4	5.9

2. The rate of oxygen consumption for Colorado beetles increases with temperature. See Table 10.3.
   (a) Make a scatter plot of this data.
   (b) Draw an estimated regression line by eye.
   (c) Use a calculator or computer to find the equation of the regression line. (Alternatively, find the equation of your line in part (b).) Round constants in the equation to the nearest integer.
   (d) Interpret the slope and each intercept of the regression equation.

[1]From *Statistics*, 2ed, by David Freedman. Robert Pisani, Roger Purves, Ani Adhikari, p. 142 (New York: W.W.Norton, 1991).

(e) Interpret the correlation between temperature and oxygen rate.

Table 10.3

°C	10	15	20	25	30
Oxygen consumption rate	90	125	200	300	375

3. Match the r values with scatter plots in Figure 10.7.

$$r = -0.98, \quad r = -0.5, \quad r = -0.25,$$
$$r = 0, \quad r = 0.7, \quad r = 1.$$

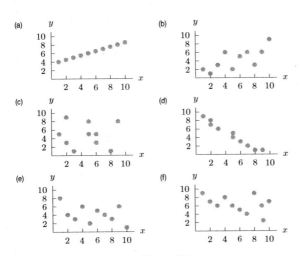

Figure 10.7

4. An ecologist tracked 145 deer that were born in 1992. The number of deer, d, living each subsequent year is recorded in Table 10.4.

   (a) Make a scatter plot of this data. Let $t = 0$ represent 1992.
   (b) Draw by eye a good fitting line and estimate its equation. (Round the coefficients to integers.)
   (c) Use a calculator or computer to find the equation of the least squares line. (Round the coefficients to integers.)
   (d) Interpret the slope and each intercept of the line.
   (e) Interpret the correlation between the year and the number of deer born in 1992 that are still alive.

Table 10.4

Year	1992	1993	1994	1995	1996	1997	1998	1999	2000
Deer	145	144	134	103	70	45	32	22	4

5. Table 10.5 shows the IQ of ten students and the number of hours of TV each watches per week.

   (a) Make a scatter plot of the data.
   (b) By eye, make a rough estimate of the correlation coefficient.
   (c) Use a calculator or computer to find the least squares regression line and the correlation coefficient. Your values should be correct to four decimal places.

Table 10.5

IQ	110	105	120	140	100	125	130	105	115	110
TV	10	12	8	2	12	10	5	6	13	3

6. Table 10.6 gives the data on hand strength collected from college freshman using a grip meter.

   (a) Make a scatter plot of these data treating the strength of the preferred hand as the independent variable.
   (b) Draw a line on your scatter plot that is a good fit for these data and use it to find an approximate equation for the regression line.
   (c) Using a graphing calculator or computer, find the equation of the least squares line.
   (d) What would the predicted grip strength in the non-preferred hand be for a student with a preferred hand strength of 37?
   (e) Discuss interpolation and extrapolation using specific examples in relation to this regression line.
   (f) Discuss why r, the correlation coefficient, is both positive and close to 1.
   (g) Why do the points tend to cluster into two groups on your scatter plot?

Table 10.6 *Hand strength for 20 students in kilograms*

Preferred	28	27	45	20	40	47	28	54	52	21
Nonpreferred	24	26	43	22	40	45	26	46	46	22
Preferred	53	52	49	45	39	26	25	32	30	32
Nonpreferred	47	47	41	44	33	20	27	30	29	29

7. In baseball, Henry Aaron holds the record for the greatest number of home-runs hit in the major leagues. Table 10.7 shows his cumulative yearly record [2] from the start of his career, 1954, until 1973.

   (a) Plot Aaron's cumulative number of home runs H on the vertical axis, and the time t in years along the horizontal axis, where $t = 1$ corresponds to 1954.
   (b) By eye draw a straight line that fits these data well and find its equation.

---

[2]Adapted from "Graphing Henry Aaron's home-run output" by H. Ringel, The Physics Teacher, January 1974, page 43.

(c) Use a calculator or computer to find the equation of the regression line for these data. What is the correlation coefficient, r, to 4 decimal places? To 3 decimal places? What does this tell you?

(d) What does the slope of the regression line mean in terms of Henry Aaron's home-run record?

(e) From your answer to part (d), how many home-runs do you estimate Henry Aaron hit in each of the years 1974, 1975, 1976, and 1977? If you were told that Henry Aaron retired at the end of the 1976 season, would this affect your answers?

Table 10.7 *Henry Aaron's cumulative home-run record, H, from 1954 to 1973, with t in years since 1953*

t	1	2	3	4	5	6	7	8	9	10
H	13	40	66	110	140	179	219	253	298	342
t	11	12	13	14	15	16	17	18	19	20
H	366	398	442	481	510	554	592	639	673	713

8. Table 10.8 shows men's and women's world records for swimming distances from 50 meters to 1500 meters.[3]

(a) What values would you add to Table 10.8 to represent the time taken by both men and women to swim 0 meters?

(b) Plot men's time against distance, with time t in seconds on the vertical axis and distance d in meters on the horizontal axis. It is claimed that a straight line models this behavior well. What is the equation for that line? What does its slope represent? On the same graph, plot women's time against distance and find the equation of the straight line that models this behavior well. Is this line steeper or flatter than the men's line? What does that mean in terms of swimming? What are the values of the vertical intercepts? Do these values have a practical interpretation?

(c) On another graph plot the women's times against the men's times, with women's times, w, on the vertical axis and men's times, m, on the horizontal axis. It should look linear. How could you have predicted this linearity from the equations you found in part (b)? What is the slope of this line and how can it be interpreted? A newspaper reporter claims that the women's records are about 8% slower than the men's. Do the facts support this statement? What is the value of the vertical intercept? Does this value have a practical interpretation?

Table 10.8 *Men's and women's world swimming records*

Distance (m)	50	100	200	400	800	1500
Men (sec)	21.64	47.84	104.06	220.17	459.16	874.56
Women (sec)	24.13	53.77	116.78	243.85	496.22	952.10

10.2   FITTING EXPONENTIALS AND POLYNOMIALS TO DATA

In Section 10.1 we used linear regression to find the equation for a line of best fit for a set of data. In this section, we fit an exponential or a power function to a set of data.

The Spread of AIDS

The data in Table 10.9 give the total number of deaths in the US from AIDS from 1981 to 1996. Figure 10.8 suggests that a linear function may not give the best possible fit for these data.

Fitting an Exponential

We first fit an exponential function to the data[4] in Table 10.9

$$N = ae^{kt},$$

[3]Data from "The World Almanac and Book of Facts: 2002," World Almanac Education Group, Inc., New York, 2002.
[4]*HIV/AIDS Surveillance Report*, Year-end Edition, Vol 9, No 2, Table 13, US Department of Health and Human Services, Centers for Disease Control and Prevention, Atlanta. Data does not include 450 people whose dates of death are unknown.

where N is the total number of deaths t years after 1980.

Table 10.9 *Domestic deaths from AIDS, 1981–96*

t	N	t	N
1	159	9	90039
2	622	10	121577
3	2130	11	158193
4	5635	12	199287
5	12607	13	243923
6	24717	14	292586
7	41129	15	340957
8	62248	16	375904

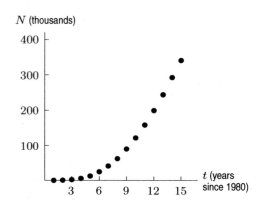

Figure 10.8: Domestic deaths from AIDS, 1981–96

Using exponential regression on a calculator or computer, we obtain

$$N \approx 630e^{0.47t}.$$

Figure 10.9 shows how the graph of this formula fits the data points.

Fitting a Power Function

Now we fit the AIDS data with a power function of the form

$$N = at^p,$$

where a and p are constants. Some scientists have suggested that a power function may be a better model for the growth of AIDS than an exponential function.[5] Using power function regression on a calculator or a computer, we obtain

$$N \approx 107t^{3.005}.$$

Figure 10.9 shows the graph of this power function with the data.

Which Function Best Fits the Data?

Both the exponential function

$$N = 630e^{0.47t}$$

and the power function

$$N = 107t^{3.005}$$

fit the AIDS data reasonably well. By visual inspection alone, the power function arguably provides the better fit. If we fit a linear function to the original data we get

$$N = -97311 + 25946t.$$

Even this linear function gives a possible fit for $t \geq 4$, that is, for 1984 to 1996. (See Figure 10.9.)

---

[5]"Risk behavior-based model of the cubic growth of acquired immunodeficiency syndrome in the United States", by Stirling A. Colgate, E. Ann Stanley, James M. Hyman, Scott P. Layne, and Alifford Qualls, in *Proc. Natl. Acad. Sci. USA*, Vol 86, June 1989, Population Biology.

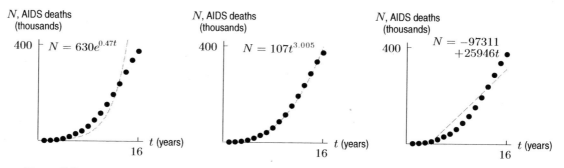

Figure 10.9: The AIDS data since 1980 together with an exponential model, a power-function model, and a linear model

Despite the fact that all three functions fit the data reasonably well up to 1996, it's important to realize that they give wildly different predictions for the future. If we use each model to estimate the total number of AIDS deaths by the year 2010 (when $t = 30$), the exponential model gives

$$N = 630e^{(0.47)30} \approx 837{,}322{,}467, \quad \text{about triple the current US population;}$$

the power model gives

$$N = 107(30)^{3.005} \approx 2{,}938{,}550, \quad \text{or about 1\% of the current population;}$$

and the linear model gives

$$N = -97311 + 25946 \cdot 30 \approx 681{,}069, \quad \text{or about 0.25\% of the current population.}$$

Which function is the best predictor of the future? To explore this question, let us add some more recent data to our previous data on AIDS deaths. See Table 10.10.

Table 10.10 *Domestic deaths from AIDS, 1997–2000*

t	N
17	406444
18	424841
19	442013
20	457258

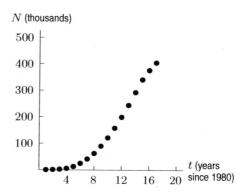

Figure 10.10: Domestic deaths from AIDS, 1981–2000

When data from the entire period from 1981 to 2000 are plotted together (see Figure 10.10), we see that the rate of increase of AIDS deaths reaches a peak sometime around 1995 and then begins to taper off. Since none of the three types of functions we have used to model AIDS deaths exhibit this type of behavior, some other type of function is needed to describe the number of AIDS deaths accurately over the entire 19-year period.

This example illustrates that while a certain type of function may fit a set of data over a short period of time, care must be taken when using a mathematical model to make predictions about the future. An understanding of the processes leading to the data is crucial in answering any long-term question.

Exercises and Problems for Section 10.2

Exercises

1. Find a formula for the power function $f(x)$ such that $f(1) = 1$ and $f(2) = c$.

2. Find a formula for the power function $g(x)$.

x	2	3	4	5
g(x)	4.5948	7.4744	10.5561	13.7973

3. Find a formula for an exponential function $h(x)$.

x	2	3	4	5
h(x)	4.5948	7.4744	10.5561	13.7973

4. Anthropologists suggest that the relationship between the body weight and brain weight of primates can be modeled with a power function. Table 10.11 lists various body weights and the corresponding brain weights of different primates.[6]

   (a) Using Table 10.11, find a power function that gives the brain weight, Q (in mg), as a function of the body weight, b (in gm).
   (b) The Erythrocebus (Patas monkey) has a body weight of 7800 gm. Estimate its brain weight.

Table 10.11

b	6667	960	6800	9500	1088
Q	56,567	18,200	110,525	120,100	20,700
b	2733	3000	6300	1500	665
Q	78,250	58,200	96,400	31,700	25,050

5. Students in the School of Forestry & Environmental Studies at Yale University collected data measuring Sassafras trees. Table 10.12 lists the diameter at breast height (dbh, in cm) and the total dry weight (w, in gm) of different trees.[7]

   (a) Find a power function that fits the data.
   (b) Predict the total weight of a tree with a dbh of 20 cm.
   (c) If a tree has a total dry weight of 100,000 gm, what is its expected dbh?

Table 10.12

dbh	5	23.4	11.8	16.7	4.2	5.6
w	5,353	169,290	30,696	76,730	3,436	5,636
dbh	3.8	4.3	6.5	21.9	17.7	25.5
w	14,983	2,098	7,364	177,596	100,848	171,598

6. According to the National Marine Fisheries Service, the Maine lobster catch (in millions of pounds) has greatly increased in the past 30 years.[8] See Table 10.13. With t in years since 1965, use a calculator or computer to fit the data with

   (a) A power function of the form $y = at^b$.
   (b) A quadratic function of the form $y = at^2 + bt + c$.
   (c) Discuss which is a better fit and why.

Table 10.13

Year	1970	1975	1980	1985	1990	1995	2000
t	5	10	15	20	25	30	35
Lobster	17	19	22	20	27	36	56

7. Recently, the use of one-way pagers has been declining due to the popularity of cell phones.[9] The number of users is given in Table 10.14 and plotted in Figure 10.11, along with a quadratic regression function.

   (a) How well does the graph of the quadratic function fit the data?
   (b) Find a cubic regression function. Does it fit better?

Table 10.14

Year	1990	1991	1992	1993	1994	1995
Users, millions	10	12	15	19	25	32
Year	1996	1997	1998	1999	2000	
Users, millions	38	43	44	43	37	

[6]http://mac-huwis.lut.ac.uk/ wis/lectures/primate-adaptation/10PrimateBrains.pdf (December 15, 2002).
[7]www.yale.edu/fes519b/totoket/allom/allom.htm (December 15, 2002).
[8]Adapted from *The New York Times*, p.16, May 31, 2001.
[9]*The New York Times*, p.16, April 11, 2002.

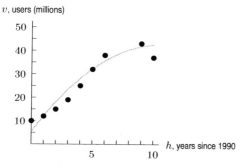

v, users (millions)

h, years since 1990

Figure 10.11

8. In this problem you will fit a quartic polynomial to the AIDS data.

(a) With N as the total number of AIDS deaths t years after 1980, use a calculator or computer to fit the data in Table 10.9 of this section with a polynomial of the form

$$N = at^4 + bt^3 + ct^2 + dt + e.$$

(b) Graph the data and your quartic for $0 \le t \le 16$. Comment on the fit.

(c) Graph the data and your quartic for $0 \le t \le 30$. Comment on the predictions made by this model.

Problems

9. The managers of a furniture store have compiled data showing the daily demand for recliners at various prices.

(a) In Table 10.15, fill in the revenue generated by selling the number of recliners at the corresponding price.

(b) Find the quadratic function that best fits the data.

(c) According to the function you found, what price should the store charge for their recliners to maximize revenue? What is the maximum revenue?

Table 10.15

Recliner price ($)	399	499	599	699	799
Demand (recliners)	62	55	47	40	34
Revenue ($)					

10. The population (in thousands) of the Houston-Galveston-Brazoria metro area [10] is in Table 10.16.

(a) Find an exponential function that fits the data. Let t be in years since 1990.

(b) Find a power function that fits the data.

(c) Does one function fit the data better than the other? If so, which one?

(d) Use the power function to compute the Houston-Galveston-Brazoria population in 1975 and in 2010. Which estimate do you expect to be closer to the actual population at the time?

Table 10.16

Year	1940	1950	1960	1970	1980	1990	2000
Population	737	1070	1583	2183	3122	3733	4672

11. The US export of edible fishery produce, in thousands of metric tons, is shown in Table 10.17.[11] With t in years since 1935, fit the data with a function of the form

(a) $y = at^b$ (b) $y = ab^t$

(c) $y = at^2 + bt + c$

(d) Discuss the reliability for estimating 2005 exports with each function.

Table 10.17

Year	1940	1945	1950	1955	1960	1965	1970
Fish export	66	62	55	50	31	50	73
Year	1975	1980	1985	1990	1995	2000	
Fish export	109	275	305	883	929	982	

12. The data in Table 10.17 show a big jump in fish exports between 1985 and 1990. This suggests fitting a piecewise defined function. With t in years since 1935, fit a quadratic function to the data from

(a) 1940 to 1985   (b) 1990 to 2000

(c) Write a piecewise defined function using parts (a) and (b). Graph the function and the data.

13. According to the US Census Bureau, the 2001 mean income by age is given in Table 10.18.[12]

(a) Choose the best type of function to fit the data: linear, exponential, power, or quadratic.

(b) Using a mid-range age value for each interval, find an equation to fit the data.

(c) Interpolation estimates incomes for ages within the range of the data. Predict the income of a 37-year old.

---

[10]From the US Census Bureau.
[11]http://www.st.nmfs.gov/st1/trade/trade2001.pdf, p. 17, December 15, 2002.
[12]www.census.gov, December 15, 2002.

(d) Extrapolation estimates incomes outside the range of data. Use your function to predict the income of a 10-year old. Is it reasonable?

Table 10.18

Age	Median salary, dollars
15 to 24	21,120
25 to 34	34,521
35 to 44	42,404
45 to 54	46,657
55 to 64	46,751
65 to 74	48,687
75 + years	43,360

14. Table 10.19 gives N, the number of transistors per integrated circuit chip, t years after 1970.[13]

(a) Plot N versus t and fit an exponential curve to the data.

(b) According to the formula of your curve of best fit, approximately how often does the number of transistors double?

Table 10.19

Chip name	t	N
4004	1	2,250
8008	2	2,500
8080	4	5,000
8086	8	29,000
80286	12	120,000
80386	15	275,000
80486	19	1,180,000
Pentium	23	3,100,000
Pentium II	27	7,500,000
Pentium III	29	24,000,000
Pentium 4	30	42,000,000

15. German physicist Arnd Leike of the University of Munich won the 2002 Ig Nobel prize in Physics for experiments with beer foam conducted with his students.[14] The data in Table 10.20 give the height (in cm) of beer foam after t seconds for three different types of beer, Erdinger Weissbier, Augustinerbräu München, and Budweiser Budvar. The heights are denoted h_e, h_a, and h_b, respectively.

(a) Plot these points and fit exponential functions to them. Give the equations in the form $h = h_0 e^{-t/\tau}$.

(b) What does the value of h_0 tell you for each type of beer? What does the value of τ tell you for each type of beer?

Table 10.20

t	h_e	h_a	h_b	t	h_e	h_a	h_b
0	17.0	14.0	14.0	120	10.7	6.0	7.0
15	16.1	11.8	12.1	150	9.7	5.3	6.2
30	14.9	10.5	10.9	180	8.9	4.4	5.5
45	14.0	9.3	10.0	210	8.3	3.5	4.5
60	13.2	8.5	9.3	240	7.5	2.9	3.5
75	12.5	7.7	8.6	300	6.3	1.3	2.0
90	11.9	7.1	8.0	360	5.2	0.7	0.9
105	11.2	6.5	7.5				

16. Table 10.21 gives the development time t (in days) for eggs of the pea weevil (*Bruchus pisorum*) at temperature H (°C).[15]

(a) Plot these data and fit a power function.

(b) Ecologists define the development rate $r = 1/t$ where t is the development time. Plot r against H, and fit a linear function.

(c) At a certain temperature, the value of r drops to 0 and pea weevil eggs will not develop. What is this temperature according to the model from part (a)? part (b)? Which model's prediction do you think is more reasonable?

Table 10.21

H, °C	10.7	14.4	16.2	18.1	21.4	23.7	24.7	26.9
t, days	38.0	19.5	15.6	9.6	9.5	7.3	4.5	4.5

17. (a) Using the data in Table 10.9 in this section, plot $\ln N$ against t. If the original data were exponential, the points would lie on a line.

(b) Fit a line to the graph from part (a).

(c) From the equation of the line, obtain the formula for N as an exponential function of t.

18. (a) Let $N = at^p$, with a, p constant. Explain why if you plot $\ln N$ against $\ln t$, you get a line.

---

[13]The Intel Corporation, http://www.intel.com/research/silicon/mooreslaw.htm.

[14]Find this and other Ig Nobel announcements at http://ignobel.com/ig/ig-pastwinners.html. The Ig Nobel prize is a spoof of the Nobel prize and honors researchers whose achievements "cannot or should not be reproduced." The data here is taken from *Demonstration of the Exponential Decay Law Using Beer Froth*, Arnd Leike, European Journal of Physics, vol. 23, January 2002, pp. 21-26.

[15]Data from a website created by Dr. Alexei A. Sharov at the Virginia Polytechnic Institute, http://www.ento.vt.edu/ sharov/PopEcol/lec8/quest8.html. The site attributes the data to Smith, A. M., 1992, Environ. Entomol. 21:314-321.

(b) To decide if a function of the form $N = at^p$ fits some data, you plot $\ln N$ against $\ln t$. Explain why this plot is useful.

19. (a) Using the data in Table 10.9 in this section plot $\ln N$ against $\ln t$. If a power function fitted the original data, the points would lie on a line

(b) Fit a line to the graph from part (a).

(c) From the equation of the line, obtain the formula for N as a power function of t.

20. If y and x are given by the following graphs, find equations for y in terms of x.

(a)
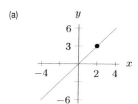

(b)
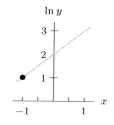

(c)
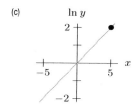

(d)
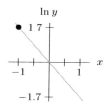

(e)
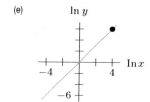

(f)
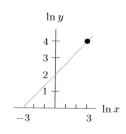

21. On a piece of paper draw a straight line through the origin with slope 2 in the first quadrant. What is the equation of the function represented by your straight line in each of the following cases?

(a) The horizontal axis is labeled x and the vertical axis is labeled y.

(b) The horizontal axis is labeled $\ln x$ and the vertical axis is labeled $\ln y$.

(c) The horizontal axis is labeled x and the vertical axis is labeled $\ln y$.

22. An analog radio dial can be measured in millimeters from left to right. Although the scale of the dial can be different from radio to radio, Table 10.22 gives typical measurements.

(a) Which radio band data appear linear? Graph and connect the data points for each band.

(b) Which radio band data appear exponential?

(c) Find a possible formula for the FM station number in terms of x.

(d) Find a possible formula for the AM station number in terms of x.

Table 10.22

x, millimeters	5	15	25	35	45	55
FM (mhz)	88	92	96	100	104	108
AM (khz/10)	53	65	80	100	130	160

23. In this problem, we will determine whether or not the compact disc data from Table 10.23 can be well modeled using a power function of the form $l = kc^p$, where l and c give the number of LPs and CDs (in millions) respectively, and where k and p are constant.

(a) Based on the plot of the data in Figure 10.12, what do you expect to be true about the sign of the power p?

(b) Fit a power function to the data. One data point may have to be omitted. Which point and why?

(c) Let $y = \ln l$ and $x = \ln c$. Find a linear formula for y in terms of x by making substitutions in the equation $l = kc^p$.

(d) Transform the data in Table 10.23 to create a table comparing $x = \ln c$ and $y = \ln l$. What data point must be omitted?

(e) Plot your transformed data from part (d). Based on your plot, do you think a power function gives a good fit to the data? Explain.

24. (a) Find a linear function that fits the data in Table 10.24. How good is the fit?

(b) The data in the table was generated using the power function $y = 5x^3$. Explain why (in this case) a linear function gives such a good fit to a power function. Does the fit remain good for other values of x?

Table 10.24

x	2.00	2.01	2.02	2.03	2.04	2.05
y	40.000	40.603	41.212	41.827	42.448	43.076

Sales of Compact Discs

Table 10.23 shows the fall in the sales of vinyl long-playing records (LPs) and the rise of compact discs (CDs) during for the years 1982 through 1993.[16]

Table 10.23 *CD and LP sales*

t, years since 1982	c, CDs (millions)	l, LPs (millions)
0	0	244
1	0.8	210
2	5.8	205
3	23	167
4	53	125
5	102	107
6	150	72
7	207	35
8	287	12
9	333	4.8
10	408	2.3
11	495	1.2

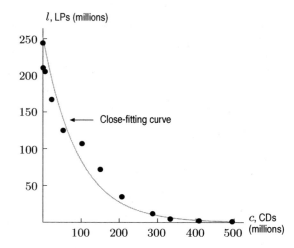

Figure 10.12: The number of LPs sold, l, as a function of number of CDs sold, c

[16]Data from Recording Industry Association of America, Inc., 1998

Appendices

A   EXPONENTS

Positive Integer Exponents

Repeated addition leads to multiplication. For example,

$$\underbrace{2 + 2 + 2 + 2 + 2}_{\text{5 terms in sum}} = 5 \times 2.$$

Similarly, repeated multiplication leads to *exponentiation*. For example,

$$\underbrace{2 \times 2 \times 2 \times 2 \times 2}_{\text{5 factors in product}} = 2^5.$$

Here, 5 is the *exponent* of 2, and 2 is called the *base*. Notice that 2^5 is not the same as 5^2, because $2^5 = 32$ and $5^2 = 25$.

In general, if a is a real number and n is a positive integer, then we define exponentiation as an abbreviation for multiplication:

$$\underbrace{a \cdot a \cdot a \cdots \cdot a}_{n \text{ factors}} = a^n.$$

It's worth noticing that $a^1 = a$, because here we have only 1 factor of a.

Exponent Rules

There are five basic facts, called exponent rules, which follow as a direct consequence of the definition of exponents. These rules are summarized in the following box.

Exponent Rules

If a and b are real numbers and m and n are positive integers,

1. $a^n \cdot a^m = a^{n+m}$ 　　　　 2. $\dfrac{a^n}{a^m} = a^{n-m}$ 　　　　 3. $(a^m)^n = a^{m \cdot n}$

4. $(ab)^n = a^n b^n$ 　　　　 5. $\left(\dfrac{a}{b}\right)^n = \dfrac{a^n}{b^m}$

The explanation of all five rules are very straightforward. If you forget one of the rules, you should be able to immediately rederive it using the following logic.

For exponent rule 1, we have

$$a^n \cdot a^m = \underbrace{a \cdot a \cdot a \cdots \cdot a}_{n \text{ factors}} \; \underbrace{a \cdot a \cdot a \cdots \cdot a}_{m \text{ factors}} = \underbrace{a \cdot a \cdot a \cdots \cdot a}_{n + m \text{ factors}} = a^{n+m}.$$

For example, $2^3 \cdot 2^5 = (2 \cdot 2 \cdot 2) \cdot (2 \cdot 2 \cdot 2 \cdot 2 \cdot 2) = 2^8$, and $8 = 3 + 5$.

For exponent rule 2, suppose n and m are positive integers and $n > m$. Then the m factors of a in the denominator cancel with some of the n factors of a in the numerator, leaving only $n - m$ factors of a:

$$\frac{a^n}{a^m} = \frac{\overbrace{a \cdot a \cdot a \cdot a \cdots a}^{n \text{ factors of } a}}{\underbrace{a \cdot a \cdots a}_{m \text{ factors of } a}} = \frac{\overbrace{\not{a} \cdot \not{a} \cdots \not{a}}^{m \text{ factors of } a \text{ cancel}} \cdot \overbrace{a \cdots a}^{\substack{n\text{-}m \text{ factors} \\ \text{of } a \text{ are left} \\ \text{after cancelling}}}}{\underbrace{\not{a} \cdot \not{a} \cdots \not{a}}_{m \text{ factors of } a \text{ cancel}}} = \underbrace{a \cdot a \cdot a \cdots a}_{n - m \text{ factors}} = a^{n-m}$$

For example,

$$\frac{4^5}{4^3} = \frac{4 \cdot 4 \cdot 4 \cdot 4 \cdot 4}{4 \cdot 4 \cdot 4} = \frac{\cancel{4} \cdot \cancel{4} \cdot \cancel{4} \cdot 4 \cdot 4}{\cancel{4} \cdot \cancel{4} \cdot \cancel{4}} = 4 \cdot 4 = 4^2 = 4^{5-3},$$

For exponent rule 3,

$$(a^m)^n = \underbrace{(a \cdot a \cdot a \cdots a)}_{m \text{ factors of } a}{}^n = \overbrace{\underbrace{(a \cdot a \cdot a \cdots a)}_{m \text{ factors of } a}\underbrace{(a \cdot a \cdot a \cdots a)}_{m \text{ factors of } a} \cdots \underbrace{(a \cdot a \cdot a \cdots a)}_{m \text{ factors of } a}}^{\substack{\text{The } m \text{ factors of } a \text{ are multiplied } n \text{ times,} \\ \text{giving a total of } m \cdot n \text{ factors of } a}} = a^{m \cdot n}.$$

For example,

$$(a^2)^3 = (\underbrace{a \cdot a}_{2 \text{ factors of } a})^3 = \underbrace{(a \cdot a)(a \cdot a)(a \cdot a)}_{3 \text{ times 2 factors of } a} = a^6.$$

An alternative explanation for rule 3 uses rule 1:

$$\left(a^m\right)^n = \underbrace{a^m \cdot a^m \cdots a^m}_{n \text{ factors of } a^m} = a^{\overbrace{m + m + \cdots + m}^{n \text{ terms in sum}}} = a^{m \cdot n}.$$

For example, $(2^5)^3 = 2^5 \cdot 2^5 \cdot 2^5 = 2^{5+5+5} = 2^{15}$, and $15 = 5 \cdot 3$.

To justify exponent rule 4, we use the commutative property of multiplication, which states that the order in which numbers are multiplied together does not affect the result. For example, $2 \cdot 9 \cdot 13 = 13 \cdot 2 \cdot 9 = 9 \cdot 13 \cdot 2 = 234$.

$$(a \cdot b)^n = \underbrace{(a \cdot b)(a \cdot b)(a \cdot b) \cdots (a \cdot b)}_{n \text{ factors of } (a \cdot b)} = \underbrace{\overbrace{(a \cdot a \cdot a \cdots a)}^{n \text{ factors of } a} \cdot \overbrace{(b \cdot b \cdot b \cdots b)}^{n \text{ factors of } b}}_{\substack{\text{Since we can rearrange the order using the} \\ \text{commutative property of multiplication}}} = a^n \cdot b^n.$$

For example, $(5 \cdot 8)^2 = (5 \cdot 8)(5 \cdot 8) = (5 \cdot 5)(8 \cdot 8) = 5^2 \cdot 8^2 = 1600$.

For exponent rule 5,

$$\left(\frac{a}{b}\right)^n = \underbrace{\left(\frac{a}{b}\right) \cdot \left(\frac{a}{b}\right) \cdot \left(\frac{a}{b}\right) \cdots \left(\frac{a}{b}\right)}_{n \text{ factors of } a/b} = \frac{\overbrace{a \cdot a \cdot a \cdots a}^{n \text{ factors of } a}}{\underbrace{b \cdot b \cdot b \cdots b}_{n \text{ factors of } b}} = \frac{a^n}{b^n}.$$

For example, $\left(\frac{2}{7}\right)^3 = \left(\frac{2}{7}\right) \cdot \left(\frac{2}{7}\right) \cdot \left(\frac{2}{7}\right) = \frac{2 \cdot 2 \cdot 2}{7 \cdot 7 \cdot 7} = \frac{2^3}{7^3} = \frac{8}{343}$.

Be aware of the following notational conventions:

$$ab^n = a(b^n), \qquad \text{but } ab^n \neq (ab)^n,$$
$$-b^n = -(b^n), \qquad \text{but } -b^n \neq (-b)^n,$$
$$-ab^n = (-a)(b^n).$$

For example, $-2^4 = -(2^4) = -16$, but $(-2)^4 = (-2)(-2)(-2)(-2) = +16$. Also, be sure to realize that for values of n other than 0 and 1,

$$(a + b)^n \neq a^n + b^n \qquad \text{Power of a sum} \neq \text{Sum of powers.}$$

Rational Exponents

The natural definition for exponentiation as an abbreviation for multiplication holds for positive integers only. For example, 4^5 means 4 multiplied times itself 5 times, but we cannot use the same definition for 4^0 or 4^{-1} or $4^{1/2}$. We must choose a definition for exponents which are not positive integers.

The five exponent rules follow from the definition of positive integer exponents. Therefore, it makes sense to choose a definition for exponents like 0, −1, 1/2 which is consistent with the five exponent rules. The definitions are summarized in the following box. After the box, explanations are given for these choices of definition.

Definitions For Exponentiation

If a is a real number and m and n are positive integers:[1]

- $a^0 = 1$ (for $a \neq 0$)
- $a^{-n} = \frac{1}{a^n}$ (for $a \neq 0$)
- $a^{1/n} = \sqrt[n]{a}$ (if n is even, then we assume $a \geq 0$.)
- $a^{m/n} = \sqrt[n]{a^m} = (\sqrt[n]{a})^m$ (if n is even, then we assume $a^m \geq 0$.)

To understand the definition of a^0, consider the following example. If we apply exponent rule 1 when one of the exponents is $m = 0$, and $a \neq 0$, then

$$a^n \cdot a^m = a^n \cdot a^0 = a^{n+0} = a^n,$$

so

$$a^n \cdot a^0 = a^n.$$

Notice that if we divide both sides of the equation by a^n, we get $a^0 = 1$. Therefore, if we want exponent rule 1 to hold for any exponent, including $m = 0$, we must define $a^0 = 1$, for $a \neq 0$. (We leave 0^0 undefined.)

Next we define a^{-n}, where n is a positive integer. Consider the following example. By the definition of a^2 and a^5,

$$\frac{a^2}{a^5} = \frac{a \cdot a}{a \cdot a \cdot a \cdot a \cdot a} = \frac{\not{a} \cdot \not{a}}{\not{a} \cdot \not{a} \cdot a \cdot a \cdot a} = \frac{1}{a^3}.$$

Alternatively, if we apply exponent rule 2, we see that the result is a negative exponent:

$$\frac{a^2}{a^5} = a^{2-5} = a^{-3}.$$

Therefore, if we want exponent rule 2 to hold for any exponent, including negative numbers, we must define $a^{-3} = \frac{1}{a^3}$. In general, $a^{-n} = \frac{1}{a^n}$. Notice that, in particular, $a^{-1} = \frac{1}{a}$.

Example 1   Use the rules of exponents to simplify the following:

(a) $3b(2b)^3(b^{-1})$

(b) $\dfrac{y^4(x^3 y^{-2})^2}{2x^{-1}}$

(c) $\left(\dfrac{2^{-3}}{L}\right)^{-2}$

(d) $\dfrac{5(2s+1)^4(s+3)^{-2}}{2s+1}$

(e) $-2^2 p^0 (-3q)^4$

(f) $(-z)^{-n}$

---

[1] When we write a fractional power, we assume that the base is restricted to the values for which the power is defined.

Solution

(a) $3b(2b)^3 \left(b^{-1}\right) = 3b^1(2^3b^3)b^{-1} = 3 \cdot 8 \cdot b^1 b^3 b^{-1} = 3 \cdot 8 \cdot b^{3+(-1)+1} = 24b^3$

(b) $\dfrac{y^4 \left(x^3 y^{-2}\right)^2}{2x^{-1}} = \dfrac{y^4 x^6 y^{-4}}{2x^{-1}} = \dfrac{y^{(4-4)} x^{(6-(-1))}}{2} = \dfrac{y^0 x^7}{2} = \dfrac{x^7}{2}$

(c) $\left(\dfrac{2^{-3}}{L}\right)^{-2} = \dfrac{2^{(-3)(-2)}}{L^{-2}} = \dfrac{2^6}{L^{-2}} = 64L^2$ (Note that $\dfrac{1}{L^{-2}} = \dfrac{L^0}{L^{-2}} = L^{0-(-2)} = L^2$.)

(d) $\dfrac{5(2s+1)^4(s+3)^{-2}}{(2s+1)} = \dfrac{5(2s+1)^{4-1}}{(s+3)^2} = \dfrac{5(2s+1)^3}{(s+3)^2}$

(e) $-2^2 p^0 (-3q)^4 = -4 \cdot 1(-3)^4 q^4 = -4(81)q^4 = -324q^4.$

(f) $(-z)^{-n} = \dfrac{1}{(-z)^n} = \dfrac{(-1)^n}{z^n}.$

Before explaining the definitions for fractional exponents, we review some notation:

Let n be an integer greater than 1:

- For $a \geq 0$,

  $\sqrt{a}$ is the positive number whose square is a.

  $\sqrt[n]{a}$ is the positive number whose n^{th} power is a.

- For $a < 0$,

  If n is even, $\sqrt[n]{a}$ is not a real number.

  If n is odd, $\sqrt[n]{a}$ is the negative number whose n^{th} power is a.

We say that $\sqrt[n]{a}$ is the **n^{th} root of a**.

For example, $\sqrt{49} = 7$ because $7^2 = 49$. Likewise, $\sqrt[3]{125} = 5$ because $5^3 = 125$, and $\sqrt[5]{32} = 2$ because $2^5 = 32$. Similary, $\sqrt[3]{-27} = -3$ because $(-3)^3 = -27$, and $\sqrt{-9}$ is not a real number, because the square of no real number is negative. When $\sqrt[n]{a}$ and $\sqrt[n]{b}$ are real numbers with $b \neq 0$, the rules for radicals are as follows:

$$\sqrt[n]{ab} = \sqrt[n]{a}\sqrt[n]{b}, \qquad \sqrt[n]{\dfrac{a}{b}} = \dfrac{\sqrt[n]{a}}{\sqrt[n]{b}}$$

Example 2   Simplify the following radicals:

(a) $\sqrt{36}$ (b) $\sqrt[3]{-8x^6}$ (c) $\sqrt{\dfrac{16R^8}{25}}$ (d) $\sqrt[4]{16u^8 w^{12}}$

Solution

(a) $\sqrt{36} = +6$ (Notice that the answer is the positive root, not ± 6.)

(b) $\sqrt[3]{-8x^6} = \sqrt[3]{-8} \cdot \sqrt[3]{x^6} = -2x^2$ (c) $\sqrt{\dfrac{16R^8}{25}} = \dfrac{\sqrt{16R^8}}{\sqrt{25}} = \dfrac{\sqrt{16}\sqrt{R^8}}{\sqrt{25}} = \dfrac{4R^4}{5}$

(d) $\sqrt[4]{16u^8 w^{12}} = \sqrt[4]{16}\sqrt[4]{u^8}\sqrt[4]{w^{12}} = 2u^2 w^3$, because $2^4 = 16$, $(u^2)^4 = u^8$, and $(w^3)^4 = w^{12}$.

Special case: n-th root of a^n

If n is odd,

$$\sqrt[n]{a^n} = a \qquad \text{by definition.}$$

If n is even,

$$\sqrt[n]{a^n} = |a| = \begin{cases} a & \text{if } a \geq 0 \\ -a & \text{if } a < 0 \end{cases}.$$

Example 3   Simplify:

(a) $\sqrt[4]{(-1)^4}$

(b) $\sqrt{9x^2}$

Solution   (a) $\sqrt[4]{(-1)^4} = \sqrt[4]{1} = 1$ (Notice that in this case $\sqrt[n]{a^n} \neq a$.)

(b) $\sqrt{9x^2} = 3|x|$ (since x can be either positive or negative).

To see why fractional exponents are defined in the way they are, we again consider the consequences of the exponent rules. Suppose we evaluate an expression with a fractional exponent, such as $(a^{1/2})^2$, for $a \geq 0$. If we apply exponent rule 3, we get

$$(a^{1/2})^2 = a^{(1/2) \cdot 2} = a^1 = a, \quad \text{so} \quad (a^{1/2})^2 = a.$$

Taking the square root of both sides results in $a^{1/2} = \sqrt{a}$. Therefore, if we want exponent rule 3 to hold for any exponent, including fractions, we must define $a^{1/2} = \sqrt{a}$. In general, $a^{1/n} = \sqrt[n]{a}$. Note that when n is even, then a must be non-negative, and $a^{1/n} \geq 0$.

We can extend this explanation to an expression such as $(a^{1/3})^2$. Since $a^{1/3} = \sqrt[3]{a}$, we must have $(a^{1/3})^2 = (\sqrt[3]{a})^2$. Exponent rule 3 gives

$$(a^{1/3})^2 = a^{(1/3) \cdot 2} = a^{2/3}.$$

Therefore, if we want exponent rule 3 to hold for any exponent, including fractions, we must define $a^{2/3} = (\sqrt[3]{a})^2$. In general, $a^{m/n} = (\sqrt[n]{a})^m$. Because multiplication is commutative, we have

$$a^{m/n} = a^{m \cdot (1/n)} = a^{(1/n) \cdot m}$$
$$= (a^m)^{1/n} = (a^{1/n})^m$$
$$\text{so} \quad a^{m/n} = \sqrt[n]{a^m} = (\sqrt[n]{a})^m.$$

We have chosen these definitions so that exponent rules hold for any rational exponent.

Example 4   Find $(27)^{2/3}$.

Solution $(27)^{2/3} = \sqrt[3]{27^2} = \sqrt[3]{729} = 9$, or, equivalently, $(27)^{2/3} = \left(27^{\frac{1}{3}}\right)^2 = \left(\sqrt[3]{27}\right)^2 = 3^2 = 9$.

Example 5   Simplify:

(a) $\left(\dfrac{M^{1/5}}{3N^{-1/2}}\right)^2$

(b) $\dfrac{3u^2\sqrt{uw}}{w^{1/3}}$

Solution

(a) $\left(\dfrac{M^{1/5}}{3N^{-1/2}}\right)^2 = \dfrac{\left(M^{1/5}\right)^2}{\left(3N^{-1/2}\right)^2} = \dfrac{M^{2/5}}{3^2 N^{-1}} = \dfrac{M^{2/5}N}{9}$

(b) $\dfrac{3u^2\sqrt{u}\,w}{w^{1/3}} = \dfrac{3u^2 u^{1/2}w}{w^{1/3}} = 3u^{(2+1/2)}w^{(1-1/3)} = 3u^{5/2}w^{2/3}$

Calculator Note: Some calculators will not compute $a^{m/n}$ for $m \neq 1$ when a is negative, even if n is odd. For example, though $(-1)^{2/3}$ is well defined, a calculator may display "error."

Example 6   Evaluate, if possible:

(a) $(-2197)^{2/3}$

(b) $(-256)^{3/4}$

Solution

(a) To find $(-2197)^{2/3}$ on a calculator, we can first evaluate $(-2197)^{1/3}$, and then square the result. This gives 169.

(b) $(-256)^{3/4}$ is not a real number since $(-256)^{1/4}$ is not real.

Irrational and Variable Exponents

The rules for exponents given for integer and fractional exponents apply also when the exponent is an irrational number, as in $x^{\sqrt{3}}$, or a variable, as in 5^x.

Example 7   Simplify:

(a) $p^{\sqrt{2}} \cdot p^{\sqrt{8}}$

(b) $\sqrt{\dfrac{x^{3\pi}}{x^{\pi}}}$

Solution

(a) $p^{\sqrt{2}} \cdot p^{\sqrt{8}} = p^{(\sqrt{2}+\sqrt{8})} = p^{(\sqrt{2}+2\sqrt{2})} = p^{3\sqrt{2}}$

(b) $\sqrt{\dfrac{x^{3\pi}}{x^{\pi}}} = \left(\dfrac{x^{3\pi}}{x^{\pi}}\right)^{1/2} = \left(x^{3\pi - \pi}\right)^{1/2} = \left(x^{2\pi}\right)^{1/2} = x^{2\pi(1/2)} = x^{\pi}$

Example 8   Simplify:

(a) $-3^x \cdot 3^{-x}$

(b) $\dfrac{4^p}{2^p}$

(c) $\dfrac{a^{2/3}(a^k)(a^k)}{a}$

(d) $\dfrac{f^{2y}g^y}{f^{3y}}$

Solution

(a) $-3^x \cdot 3^{-x} = -(3^x)(3^{-x}) = -(3^{x-x}) = -(3^0) = -1$

(b) $\dfrac{4^p}{2^p} = \left(\dfrac{4}{2}\right)^p = 2^p$

(c) $\dfrac{a^{2/3}\left(a^k\right)\left(a^k\right)}{a} = a^{2/3}\left(a^k\right)\left(a^k\right)\left(a^{-1}\right) = a^{((2/3)+k+k-1)} = a^{2k-1/3}$

(d) $\dfrac{f^{2y}g^y}{f^{3y}} = \left(\dfrac{f^2 g}{f^3}\right)^y = \left(\dfrac{g}{f}\right)^y$

Problems for Section A

For Problems 1–16, evaluate without a calculator.

1. 4^3 2. $(-5)^2$ 3. 11^2 4. 10^4

5. $(-1)^{12}$ 6. $(-1)^{13}$ 7. $\dfrac{5^3}{5^2}$ 8. $\dfrac{5^3}{5}$

9. $\dfrac{10^8}{10^5}$ 10. $\dfrac{6^4}{6^4}$ 11. 8^0 12. $\sqrt{4}$

13. $\sqrt{4^2}$ 14. $\sqrt{4^3}$ 15. $\sqrt{4^4}$ 16. $\sqrt{(-4)^2}$

For Problems 17–44, simplify the following expressions.

17. $\sqrt{x^4}$ 18. $\sqrt{y^8}$ 19. $\sqrt{w^8 z^4}$ 20. $\sqrt{x^5 y^4}$

21. $\sqrt{16x^3}$ 22. $\sqrt{49w^9}$ 23. $\sqrt{25x^3 z^4}$ 24. $\sqrt{r^2}$

25. $\sqrt{r^3}$ 26. $\sqrt{r^4}$ 27. $\sqrt{36t^2}$ 28. $\sqrt{64s^7}$

29. $\sqrt{50x^4 y^6}$ 30. $\sqrt{48u^{10} v^{12} y^5}$ 31. $\sqrt{8m}\sqrt{2m^3}$ 32. $\sqrt{6s^2 t^3 v^5}\sqrt{6st^5 v^3}$

33. $(32)^{1/5}$ 34. $(16)^{1/2}$ 35. $16^{1/4}$ 36. $16^{3/4}$

37. $16^{5/4}$ 38. $16^{5/2}$ 39. 3^{-1} 40. 3^{-2}

41. $3^{-(3/2)}$ 42. 25^{-1} 43. 25^{-2} 44. $25^{-(3/2)}$

Evaluate the quantities in Problems 45–59 mentally.

45. $\dfrac{1}{7^{-2}}$ 46. $\dfrac{2^7}{2^3}$ 47. $(-1)^{445}$ 48. -11^2

49. $(-2)(3^2)$ 50. $(5^0)^3$ 51. $2.1(10^3)$ 52. $\sqrt[3]{-125}$

53. $\sqrt{(-4)^2}$ 54. $(-1)^3 \sqrt{36}$ 55. $(0.04)^{1/2}$ 56. $(-8)^{2/3}$

57. $(1/27)^{-1/3}$ 58. $0.125^{1/3}$ 59. $100^{5/2}$

Simplify the expressions in Problems 60–77 and leave without radicals.

60. $(0.1)^2 (4xy^2)^2$ 61. $3(3^{x/2})^2$ 62. $(4L^{2/3} P)^{3/2} (P)^{-3/2}$

63. $7(5w^{1/2})(2w^{1/3})$ 64. $\left(S\sqrt{16xt^2}\right)^2$ 65. $\sqrt{e^{2x}}$

66. $(3AB)^{-1}(A^2 B^{-1})^2$ 67. $e^{kt} \cdot e^3 \cdot e$ 68. $\sqrt{M+2}(2+M)^{3/2}$

69. $(3x\sqrt{x^3})^2$ 70. $x^e (x^e)^2$ 71. $(y^{-2} e^y)^2$

72. $\dfrac{4x^{(3\pi+1)}}{x^2}$ 73. $\dfrac{4A^{-3}}{(2A)^{-4}}$ 74. $\dfrac{a^{n+1} 3^{n+1}}{a^n 3^n}$

75. $\dfrac{12u^3}{3(uv^2 w^4)^{-1}}$ 76. $(A^{-1} + b^{-1})^{-1}$ 77. $\left(\dfrac{35(2b+1)^9}{7(2b+1)^{-1}}\right)^2$

(Do not expand $(2b+1)^9$.)

If possible, evaluate the quantities in Problems 78–86. Check your answers with a calculator.

78. $(-32)^{3/5}$ 79. $-32^{3/5}$ 80. $-625^{3/4}$

81. $(-625)^{3/4}$ 82. $(-1728)^{4/3}$ 83. $64^{3/2}$

84. $-64^{3/2}$ 85. $(-64)^{3/2}$ 86. $81^{5/4}$

Determine whether the statements in Problems 87–96 are true or false.

87. $t^3 t^4 = t^{12}$ 88. $(u+v)^{-1} = \dfrac{1}{u} + \dfrac{1}{v}$

89. $-4w^2 - 3w^3 = -w^2(4 + 3w)$ 90. $5z^{-4} = \dfrac{1}{5z^4}$

91. $x^2 y^5 = (xy)^{10}$ 92. $(p^3)^8 = p^{11}$

93. $\sqrt[3]{-64b^3c^6} = -4bc^2$

94. $\dfrac{m^8}{2m^2} = \dfrac{1}{2}m^4$

95. $5u^2 + 5u^3 = 10u^5$

96. $(3r)^2 9s^2 = 81r^2 s^2$

B   MULTIPLYING ALGEBRAIC EXPRESSIONS

The *distributive property* for real numbers a, b, and c tells us that

$$a(b + c) = ab + ac,$$

and

$$(b + c)a = ba + ca.$$

We use the distributive property and the rules of exponents to multiply algebraic expressions involving parentheses. This process is sometimes referred to as *expanding* the expression.

Example 1   Multiply the following expressions and simplify.

(a) $3x^2\left(x + \dfrac{1}{6}x^{-3}\right)$

(b) $\left((2t)^2 - 5\right)\sqrt{t}$

(c) $2^x(3^x + 2^{x-1})$

Solution

(a) $3x^2\left(x + \dfrac{1}{6}x^{-3}\right) = (3x^2)(x) + (3x^2)\left(\dfrac{1}{6}x^{-3}\right) = 3x^3 + \dfrac{1}{2}x^{-1}$

(b) $\left((2t)^2 - 5\right)\sqrt{t} = (2t)^2(\sqrt{t}) - 5\sqrt{t} = (4t^2)(t^{1/2}) - 5t^{1/2} = 4t^{5/2} - 5t^{1/2}$

(c) $2^x(3^x + 2^{x-1}) = (2^x)(3^x) + (2^x)(2^{x-1}) = (2 \cdot 3)^x + 2^{x+x-1} = 6^x + 2^{2x-1}$

If there are two terms in each factor, then there are four terms in the product:

$$(a + b)(c + d) = a(c + d) + b(c + d) = ac + ad + bc + bd.$$

The following special cases of the above product occur frequently. Learning to recognize their forms aids in factoring.

$$(a + b)(a - b) = a^2 - b^2$$
$$(a + b)^2 = a^2 + 2ab + b^2$$
$$(a - b)^2 = a^2 - 2ab + b^2$$

Example 2   Expand the following and simplify by gathering like terms.

(a) $(5x^2 + 2)(x - 4)$

(b) $(2\sqrt{r} + 2)(4\sqrt{r} - 3)$

(c) $(e^x + 1)(2x + e^{-x})$

(d) $\left(3 - \dfrac{1}{2}x\right)^2$

Solution

(a) $(5x^2 + 2)(x - 4) = (5x^2)(x) + (5x^2)(-4) + (2)(x) + (2)(-4) = 5x^3 - 20x^2 + 2x - 8$

(b) $(2\sqrt{r} + 2)(4\sqrt{r} - 3) = (2)(4)(\sqrt{r})^2 + (2)(-3)(\sqrt{r}) + (2)(4)(\sqrt{r}) + (2)(-3) = 8r + 2\sqrt{r} - 6$

(c) $(e^x + 1)(2x + e^{-x}) = (e^x)(2x) + (e^x)(e^{-x}) + (1)(2x) + (1)(e^{-x})$
$$= 2xe^x + e^{x-x} + 2x + e^{-x}$$
$$= 2xe^x + 1 + 2x + e^{-x}$$

(d) $\left(3 - \dfrac{1}{2}x\right)^2 = 3^2 - 2(3)\left(\dfrac{1}{2}x\right) + \left(-\dfrac{1}{2}x\right)^2 = 9 - 3x + \dfrac{1}{4}x^2$

Problems for Section B

Simplify the expressions in Problems 1–2.

1. $-(x - 3) - 2(5 - x)$
2. $(x - 5)6 - 5(1 - (2 - x))$

For Problems 3–20, expand each of the following products.

3. $3(x + 2)$
4. $5(x - 3)$
5. $2(3x - 7)$
6. $-4(y + 6)$
7. $12(x + y)$
8. $-7(5x - 8y)$
9. $x(2x + 5)$
10. $3z(2x - 9z)$
11. $-10r(5r + 6rs)$
12. $x(3x - 8) + 2(3x - 8)$
13. $5z(x - 2) - 3(x - 2)$
14. $(x + 1)(x + 3)$
15. $(x - 2)(x + 6)$
16. $(5x - 1)(2x - 3)$
17. $(x + 2)(3x - 8)$
18. $(y + 1)(z + 3)$
19. $(12y - 5)(8w + 7)$
20. $(5z - 3)(x - 2)$

Multiply and write the expressions in Problems 21–30 without parentheses. Gather like terms.

21. $(3x - 2x^2)(4) + (5 + 4x)(3x - 4)$
22. $(t^2 + 1)(50t) - (25t^2 + 125)(2t)$
23. $P(p - 3q)^2$
24. $(A^2 - B^2)^2$
25. $4(x - 3)^2 + 7$
26. $-(\sqrt{2x} + 1)^2$
27. $u(u^{-1} + 2^u)2^u$
28. $K(R - r)r^2$
29. $(x + 3)\left(\dfrac{24}{x} + 2\right)$
30. $\left(\dfrac{e^x + e^{-x}}{2}\right)^2$

C FACTORING ALGEBRAIC EXPRESSIONS

To write an expanded expression in factored form, we "un-multiply" the expression. Some techniques for factoring are given in this section. We can check factoring by remultiplying.

Removing a Common Factor

It is sometimes useful to factor out the same factor from each of the terms in an expression. This is basically the distributive law in reverse:

$$ab + ac = a(b + c).$$

One special case is removing a factor of -1, which gives

$$\boxed{-a - b = -(a + b)}$$

Another special case is

$$\boxed{(a - b) = -(b - a)}$$

Example 1   Factor the following:

(a) $\dfrac{2}{3}x^2 y + \dfrac{4}{3}xy$

(b) $e^{2x} + xe^x$

(c) $(2p + 1)p^3 - 3p(2p + 1)$

(d) $-\dfrac{s^2 t}{8w} - \dfrac{st^2}{16w}$

Solution

(a) $\dfrac{2}{3}x^2 y + \dfrac{4}{3}xy = \dfrac{2}{3}xy(x + 2)$

(b) $e^{2x} + xe^x = e^x \cdot e^x + xe^x = e^x(e^x + x)$

(c) $(2p + 1)p^3 - 3p(2p + 1) = (p^3 - 3p)(2p + 1) = p(p^2 - 3)(2p + 1)$

(Note that the expression $(2p + 1)$ was one of the factors common to both terms.)

(d) $-\dfrac{s^2 t}{8w} - \dfrac{st^2}{16w} = -\dfrac{st}{8w}\left(s + \dfrac{t}{2}\right).$

Grouping Terms

Even though all the terms may not have a common factor, we can sometimes factor by first grouping the terms and then removing a common factor.

Example 2   Factor $x^2 - hx - x + h$.

Solution $x^2 - hx - x + h = \left(x^2 - hx\right) - (x - h) = x(x - h) - (x - h) = (x - h)(x - 1)$

Factoring Quadratics

One way to factor quadratics is to mentally multiply out the possibilities.

Example 3   Factor $t^2 - 4t - 12$.

Solution   If the quadratic factors, it will be of the form

$$t^2 - 4t - 12 = (t + ?)(t + ?).$$

We are looking for two numbers whose product is -12 and whose sum is -4. By trying combinations, we find

$$t^2 - 4t - 12 = (t - 6)(t + 2).$$

Example 4   Factor $4 - 2M - 6M^2$.

Solution $4 - 2M - 6M^2 = (2 - 3M)(2 + 2M)$

Perfect Squares and the Difference of Squares

Recognition of the special products $(x + y)^2$, $(x - y)^2$ and $(x + y)(x - y)$ in expanded form is useful in factoring. Reversing the results in the last section, we have

$$a^2 + 2ab + b^2 = (a + b)^2,$$
$$a^2 - 2ab + b^2 = (a - b)^2,$$
$$a^2 - b^2 = (a - b)(a + b).$$

When we can see that terms in an expression we want to factor are squares, it often makes sense to look for one of these forms. The difference of squares identity (the third one listed above) is especially useful.

Example 5   Factor: (a) $16y^2 - 24y + 9$ (b) $25S^2R^4 - T^6$ (c) $x^2(x-2) + 16(2-x)$

Solution   (a) $16y^2 - 24y + 9 = (4y - 3)^2$

(b) $25S^2R^4 - T^6 = (5SR^2)^2 - (T^3)^2 = (5SR^2 - T^3)(5SR^2 + T^3)$

(c) $x^2(x-2) + 16(2-x) = x^2(x-2) - 16(x-2) = (x-2)(x^2 - 16) = (x-2)(x-4)(x+4)$

Example 6   Factor $z^{2/3} - z^{1/3} - 6$.

Solution   Notice that $z^{2/3} - z^{1/3} - 6$ is a quadratic. It is helpful to substitute $u = z^{1/3}$. Then

$$z^{2/3} - z^{1/3} - 6 = u^2 - u - 6$$
$$= (u - 3)(u + 2)$$

Now undo the substitution, that is, let $u = z^{1/3}$. Therefore,

$$z^{2/3} - z^{1/3} - 6 = (z^{1/3} - 3)(z^{1/3} + 2).$$

Problems for Section C

For Problems 1–42, factor completely if possible.

1. $2x + 6$
2. $3y + 15$
3. $5z - 30$
4. $4t - 6$
5. $10w - 25$
6. $u^2 - 2u$
7. $3u^4 - 4u^3$
8. $3u^7 + 12u^2$
9. $12x^3y^2 - 18x$
10. $14r^4s^2 - 21rst$
11. $x^2 + 3x + 2$
12. $x^2 + 3x - 2$
13. $x^2 - 3x + 2$
14. $x^2 - 3x - 2$
15. $x^2 + 2x + 3$
16. $x^2 - 2x - 3$
17. $x^2 - 2x + 3$
18. $x^2 + 2x - 3$
19. $2x^2 + 5x + 2$
20. $3x^2 - x - 4$
21. $2x^2 - 10x + 12$
22. $x^2 + 3x - 28$
23. $x^3 - 2x^2 - 3x$
24. $x^3 + 2x^2 - 3x$
25. $x^2 - 1.4x - 3.92$
26. $a^2x^2 - b^2$
27. $\pi r^2 + 2\pi rh$
28. $B^2 - 10B + 24$
29. $c^2 + x^2 - 2cx$
30. $x^2 + y^2$
31. $a^4 - a^2 - 12$
32. $(t + 3)^2 - 16$
33. $hx^2 + 12 - 4hx - 3x$
34. $r(r - s) - 2(s - r)$
35. $y^2 - 3xy + 2x^2$
36. $x^2e^{-3x} + 2xe^{-3x}$
37. $t^2e^{5t} + 3te^{5t} + 2e^{5t}$
38. $(s + 2t)^2 - 4p^2$
39. $P(1 + r)^2 + P(1 + r)^2r$
40. $x \sin x - \sin x$
41. $\cos^2 x - 2\cos x + 1$
42. $e^{2x} + 2e^x + 1$

D   WORKING WITH FRACTIONS

Algebraic fractions are combined in the same manner as numeric fractions–that is, according to the following rules:

$$\frac{a}{b} + \frac{c}{b} = \frac{a(d)}{b(d)} + \frac{(b)c}{(b)d} = \frac{ad + bc}{bd} \qquad \text{find a common denominator}$$

add numerators when denominators are equal, or

$$\frac{ca}{b} \cdot \frac{c}{d} = \frac{a\alpha}{bd} \qquad \text{multiply numerators and denominators for a product}$$

$$\frac{a/b}{c/d} = \frac{a}{b} \cdot \frac{d}{c} = \frac{ad}{bc} \qquad \text{to divide by a fraction, multiply by its reciprocal}$$

(We assume that no denominators are zero.)

To expand the last case, where either the numerator or denominator of a fraction is itself a fraction, remember that

$$\frac{\frac{a}{b}}{c} = \frac{\frac{a}{b}}{\frac{c}{1}} = \frac{a}{b} \cdot \frac{1}{c} = \frac{a}{bc} \quad \text{and} \quad \frac{a}{\frac{b}{c}} = \frac{\frac{a}{1}}{\frac{b}{c}} = \frac{a}{1} \cdot \frac{c}{b} = \frac{ac}{b}.$$

In all cases, we cannot divide by zero; that is, $(a/0)$ is not defined. Also the sign of a fraction is changed by changing the sign of the numerator or the denominator (but not both):

$$-\frac{a}{b} = \frac{-a}{b} = \frac{a}{-b}.$$

Example 1 Perform the indicated operations and express the answers as a single fraction.

(a) $\dfrac{4}{x^2 + 1} - \dfrac{1 - x}{x^2 + 1}$

(b) $\dfrac{M}{M^2 - 2M - 3} + \dfrac{1}{M^2 - 2M - 3}$

(c) $\dfrac{-H^2 P}{17} \cdot \dfrac{\left(PH^{1/3}\right)^2}{K^{-1}}$

(d) $\dfrac{2z/w}{w(w - 3z)}$

Solution

(a) $\dfrac{4}{x^2 + 1} - \dfrac{1 - x}{x^2 + 1} = \dfrac{4 - (1 - x)}{x^2 + 1} = \dfrac{3 + x}{x^2 + 1}$

(b) $\dfrac{M}{M^2 - 2M - 3} + \dfrac{1}{M^2 - 2M - 3} = \dfrac{M + 1}{(M^2 - 2M - 3)} = \dfrac{M + 1}{(M + 1)(M - 3)} = \dfrac{1}{M - 3}$

(c) $\dfrac{-H^2 P}{17} \cdot \dfrac{\left(PH^{1/3}\right)^2}{K^{-1}} = \dfrac{-H^2 P \left(P^2 H^{2/3}\right)}{17 K^{-1}} = -\dfrac{H^{8/3} P^3 K}{17}$

(d) $\dfrac{2z/w}{w(w - 3z)} = \dfrac{2z}{w} \cdot \dfrac{1}{w(w - 3z)} = \dfrac{2z}{w^2(w - 3z)}$

Example 2 Simplify the following expressions:

(a) $2x^{-1/2} + \dfrac{\sqrt{x}}{3}$

(b) $2\sqrt{t + 3} + \dfrac{1 - 2t}{\sqrt{t + 3}}$

Solution

(a) $2x^{-1/2} + \dfrac{\sqrt{x}}{3} = \dfrac{2}{\sqrt{x}} + \dfrac{\sqrt{x}}{3} = \dfrac{2 \cdot 3 + \sqrt{x}\sqrt{x}}{3\sqrt{x}} = \dfrac{6 + x}{3\sqrt{x}} = \dfrac{6 + x}{3x^{1/2}}$

(b) $2\sqrt{t+3} + \dfrac{1-2t}{\sqrt{t+3}} = \dfrac{2\sqrt{t+3}}{1} + \dfrac{1-2t}{\sqrt{t+3}}$

$\qquad\qquad\qquad\quad = \dfrac{2\sqrt{t+3}\sqrt{t+3} + 1 - 2t}{\sqrt{t+3}}$

$\qquad\qquad\qquad\quad = \dfrac{2(t+3) + 1 - 2t}{\sqrt{t+3}}$

$\qquad\qquad\qquad\quad = \dfrac{7}{\sqrt{t+3}} = \dfrac{7}{(t+3)^{1/2}}$

Finding a Common Denominator

We can multiply (or divide) both the numerator and denominator of a fraction by the same non-zero number without changing the fraction's value. This is equivalent to multiplying by a factor of $+1$. We are using this rule when we add or subtract fractions with different denominators. For example, to add $\dfrac{x}{3a} + \dfrac{1}{a}$, we multiply $\dfrac{1}{a} \cdot \dfrac{3}{3} = \dfrac{3}{3a}$. Then

$$\frac{x}{3a} + \frac{1}{a} = \frac{x}{3a} + \frac{3}{3a} = \frac{x+3}{3a}.$$

Example 3   Perform the indicated operations:

(a) $3 - \dfrac{1}{x-1}$
(b) $\dfrac{2}{x^2+x} + \dfrac{x}{x+1}$

Solution   (a) $3 - \dfrac{1}{x-1} = 3\dfrac{(x-1)}{(x-1)} - \dfrac{1}{x-1} = \dfrac{3(x-1)-1}{x-1} = \dfrac{3x-3-1}{x-1} = \dfrac{3x-4}{x-1}$

(b) $\dfrac{2}{x^2+x} + \dfrac{x}{x+1} = \dfrac{2}{x(x+1)} + \dfrac{x}{x+1} = \dfrac{2}{x(x+1)} + \dfrac{x(x)}{(x+1)(x)} = \dfrac{2+x^2}{x(x+1)}$

Note: We can multiply (or divide) the numerator and denominator by the same non-zero number because this is the same as multiplying by a factor of $+1$, and multiplying by a factor of 1 does not change the value of the expression. However, we cannot perform any other operation that would change the value of the expression. For example, we cannot *add* the same number to the numerator and denominator of a fraction *nor* can we square both, take the logarithm of both, etc., without changing the fraction.

Reducing Fractions: Canceling

We can reduce a fraction when we have the same (non-zero) factor in both the numerator and the denominator. For example,

$$\frac{ac}{bc} = \frac{a}{b} \cdot \frac{c}{c} = \frac{a}{b} \cdot 1 = \frac{a}{b}.$$

Example 4   Reduce the following fractions (if possible).

(a) $\dfrac{2x}{4y}$
(b) $\dfrac{2+x}{2+y}$

(c) $\dfrac{5n - 5}{1 - n}$

(d) $\dfrac{x^2(4 - 2x) - (4x - x^2)(2x)}{x^4}$

Solution

(a) $\dfrac{2x}{4y} = \dfrac{2}{2} \cdot \dfrac{x}{2y} = \dfrac{x}{2y}$

(b) $\dfrac{2 + x}{2 + y}$ cannot be reduced further.

(c) $\dfrac{5n - 5}{1 - n} = \dfrac{5(n - 1)}{(-1)(n - 1)} = -5$

(d) $\dfrac{x^2(4 - 2x) - (4x - x^2)(2x)}{x^4} = \dfrac{x^2(4 - 2x) - (4 - x)(2x^2)}{x^4}$

$$= \dfrac{[(4 - 2x) - 2(4 - x)]}{x^2} \left(\dfrac{x^2}{x^2}\right)$$

$$= \dfrac{4 - 2x - 8 + 2x}{x^2} = \dfrac{-4}{x^2}$$

Complex Fractions

A *complex fraction* is a fraction whose numerator or denominator (or both) contains one or more fractions. To simplify a complex fraction, we change the numerator and denominator to single fractions and then divide.

Example 5   Write the following as simple fractions in reduced form.

(a) $\dfrac{\dfrac{1}{x + h} - \dfrac{1}{x}}{h}$

(b) $\dfrac{a + b}{a^{-2} - b^{-2}}$

Solution

(a) $\dfrac{\dfrac{1}{x + h} - \dfrac{1}{x}}{h} = \dfrac{\dfrac{x - (x + h)}{x(x + h)}}{h} = \dfrac{\dfrac{-h}{x(x + h)}}{\dfrac{h}{1}} = \dfrac{-h}{x(x + h)} \cdot \dfrac{1}{h} = \dfrac{-1}{x(x + h)} \dfrac{(h)}{(h)} = \dfrac{-1}{x(x + h)}$

(b) $\dfrac{a + b}{a^{-2} - b^{-2}} = \dfrac{a + b}{\dfrac{1}{a^2} - \dfrac{1}{b^2}} = \dfrac{a + b}{\dfrac{b^2 - a^2}{a^2 b^2}} = \dfrac{a + b}{1} \cdot \dfrac{a^2 b^2}{b^2 - a^2} = \dfrac{(a + b)(a^2 b^2)}{(b + a)(b - a)} = \dfrac{a^2 b^2}{b - a}$

Splitting Expressions

We can reverse the rule for adding fractions to split up an expression into two fractions,

$$\frac{a + b}{c} = \frac{a}{c} + \frac{b}{c}.$$

Example 6   Split $\dfrac{3x^2 + 2}{x^3}$ into two reduced fractions.

Solution $\dfrac{3x^2 + 2}{x^3} = \dfrac{3x^2}{x^3} + \dfrac{2}{x^3} = \dfrac{3}{x} + \dfrac{2}{x^3}$

Sometimes we can alter the form of the fraction even further if we can create a duplicate of the denominator within the numerator. This technique is useful when graphing some rational functions. For example, we may rewrite the fraction $\dfrac{x+3}{x-1}$ by creating a factor of $(x-1)$ within the numerator. To do this, we write

$$\frac{x+3}{x-1} = \frac{x-1+1+3}{x-1}$$

which can be written as

$$\frac{(x-1)+4}{x-1}.$$

Then, splitting this fraction, we have

$$\frac{x+3}{x-1} = \frac{x-1}{x-1} + \frac{4}{x-1} = 1 + \frac{4}{x-1}.$$

Problems for Section D

For Problems 1–23, perform the following operations. Express answers in reduced form.

1. $\dfrac{3}{5} + \dfrac{4}{7}$

2. $\dfrac{7}{10} - \dfrac{2}{15}$

3. $\dfrac{1}{2x} - \dfrac{2}{3}$

4. $\dfrac{6}{7y} + \dfrac{9}{y}$

5. $\dfrac{-2}{yz} + \dfrac{4}{z}$

6. $\dfrac{-2z}{y} + \dfrac{4}{y}$

7. $\dfrac{2}{x^2} - \dfrac{3}{x}$

8. $\dfrac{6}{y} + \dfrac{7}{y^3}$

9. $\dfrac{\frac{3}{4}}{\frac{7}{20}}$

10. $\dfrac{\frac{5}{6}}{15}$

11. $\dfrac{\frac{3}{x}}{\frac{x^2}{6}}$

12. $\dfrac{\frac{3}{x}}{\frac{6}{x^2}}$

13. $\dfrac{13}{x-1} + \dfrac{14}{2x-2}$

14. $\dfrac{14}{x-1} + \dfrac{13}{2x-2}$

15. $\dfrac{4z}{x^2y} - \dfrac{3w}{xy^4}$

16. $\dfrac{10}{y-2} + \dfrac{3}{2-y}$

17. $\dfrac{8y}{y-4} + \dfrac{32}{y-4}$

18. $\dfrac{8y}{y-4} + \dfrac{32}{4-y}$

19. $\dfrac{\frac{1}{x} - \frac{2}{x^2}}{\frac{2x-4}{x^5}}$

20. $\dfrac{9}{x^2+5x+6} + \dfrac{12}{x+3}$

21. $\dfrac{8}{3x^2-x-4} - \dfrac{9}{x+1}$

22. $\dfrac{5}{(x-2)^2(x+1)} - \dfrac{18}{(x-2)}$

23. $\dfrac{15}{(x-3)^2(x+5)} + \dfrac{7}{(x-3)(x+5)^2}$

In Problems 24–35, perform the specified operations. Express answers in reduced form.

24. $\dfrac{3}{x-4} - \dfrac{2}{x+4}$

25. $\dfrac{x^2}{x-1} - \dfrac{1}{1-x}$

26. $\dfrac{1}{2r+3} + \dfrac{3}{4r^2+6r}$

27. $u + a + \dfrac{u}{u+a}$

28. $\dfrac{1}{\sqrt{x}} - \dfrac{1}{(\sqrt{x})^3}$

29. $\dfrac{1}{e^{2x}} + \dfrac{1}{e^x}$

30. $\dfrac{a+b}{2} \cdot \dfrac{8x+2}{b^2-a^2}$

31. $\dfrac{0.07}{M} + \dfrac{3}{4}M^2$

32. $\dfrac{1}{r_1} + \dfrac{1}{r_2} + \dfrac{1}{r_3}$

33. $\dfrac{8y}{y-4} - \dfrac{32}{y-4}$

34. $\dfrac{a}{a^2-9} + \dfrac{1}{a-3}$

35. $\dfrac{x^3}{x-4} \Big/ \dfrac{x^2}{x^2-2x-8}$

In Problems 36–49, simplify, if possible.

36. $\dfrac{\frac{1}{x+y}}{x+y}$

37. $\dfrac{w+2}{\frac{2}{w+2}}$

38. $\dfrac{\frac{1}{(x+h)^2} - \frac{1}{x^2}}{h}$

39. $\dfrac{a^{-2} + b^{-2}}{a^2 + b^2}$

40. $\dfrac{a^2 - b^2}{a^2 + b^2}$

41. $\dfrac{[4 - (x+h)^2] - [4 - x^2]}{h}$

42. $\dfrac{b^{-1}(b - b^{-1})}{b + 1}$

43. $\dfrac{1 - a^{-2}}{1 + a^{-1}}$

44. $\dfrac{x^{-1} + x^{-2}}{1 - x^{-2}}$

45. $p - \dfrac{q}{\dfrac{p}{q} + \dfrac{q}{p}}$

46. $\dfrac{\dfrac{3}{xy} - \dfrac{5}{x^2 y}}{\dfrac{6x^2 - 7x - 5}{x^2 y^2}}$

47. $\dfrac{\frac{1}{x}(3x^2) - (\ln x)(6x)}{(3x^2)^2}$

48. $\dfrac{2x(x^3 + 1)^2 - x^2(2)(x^3 + 1)(3x^2)}{[(x^3 + 1)^2]^2}$

49. $\dfrac{\frac{1}{2}(2x - 1)^{1/2}(2) - (2x - 1)^{1/2}(2x)}{(x^2)^2}$

In Problems 50–55, split into a sum or difference of reduced fractions.

50. $\dfrac{26x + 1}{2x^3}$

51. $\dfrac{\sqrt{x} + 3}{3\sqrt{x}}$

52. $\dfrac{6l^2 + 3l - 4}{3l^4}$

53. $\dfrac{7 + p}{p^2 + 11}$

54. $\dfrac{\frac{1}{3}x - \frac{1}{2}}{2x}$

55. $\dfrac{t^{-1/2} + t^{1/2}}{t^2}$

In Problems 56–61, rewrite in the form $1 + (A/B)$.

56. $\dfrac{x - 2}{x + 5}$

57. $\dfrac{q - 1}{q - 4}$

58. $\dfrac{R + 1}{R}$

59. $\dfrac{3 + 2u}{2u + 1}$

60. $\dfrac{\cos x + \sin x}{\cos x}$

61. $\dfrac{1 + e^x}{e^x}$

Determine whether the statements in Problems 62–67 are true or false.

62. $\dfrac{a + c}{a} = 1 + c$

63. $\dfrac{rs - s}{s} = r - 1$

64. $\dfrac{y}{y + z} = 1 + \dfrac{y}{z}$

65. $\dfrac{2u^2 - w}{u^2 - w} = 2$

66. $\dfrac{x^2 yz}{2x^2 y} = \dfrac{z}{2}$

67. $x^{5/3} - 3x^{2/3} = \dfrac{x^2 - 3x}{x^{1/3}}$

E   CHANGING THE FORM OF EXPRESSIONS

Rearranging Coefficients and Exponents

Changing the form of an expression can often be useful. Manipulations like the following occur frequently:

- $\dfrac{x}{2} = \left(\dfrac{1}{2}\right)x$

- $\dfrac{3}{4(2r + 1)^{10}} = \dfrac{3}{4}(2r + 1)^{-10}$

- $2^{-n} = \left(\dfrac{1}{2}\right)^n$

- $2^{x+3} = 2^x \cdot 2^3 = 8(2^x)$

- $\dfrac{3x + \sqrt{2x}}{\sqrt{x}} = \dfrac{3x}{\sqrt{x}} + \dfrac{\sqrt{2x}}{\sqrt{x}} = \dfrac{3x}{\sqrt{x}} + \dfrac{\sqrt{2}\sqrt{x}}{\sqrt{x}} = 3x^{(1 - 1/2)} + \sqrt{2} = 3x^{1/2} + \sqrt{2}$

Completing the Square

Another example of changing the form of an expression is the conversion of $ax^2 + bx + c$ into the form $a(x - h)^2 + k$. We make this conversion by *completing the square*, a method for producing a perfect square within a quadratic expression. A perfect square is an expression of the form:

$$(x + n)^2 = x^2 + 2nx + n^2$$

for some number n.

In order to complete the square in a given expression, we must find that number n. Observe that when a perfect square is multiplied out, the coefficient of x is 2 times the number n. Therefore, we can find n by dividing the coefficient of the x term by 2. Once we know n, then we know that the constant term in the perfect square must be n^2. In summary:

To complete the square in the expression $x^2 + bx + c$, divide the coefficient of x by 2, giving $b/2$. Then add and subtract $(b/2)^2 = b^2/4$ and factor the perfect square:

$$x^2 + bx + c = \left(x + \frac{b}{2}\right)^2 - \frac{b^2}{4} + c.$$

To complete the square in the expression $ax^2 + bx + c$, factor out a first.

Example 1 Rewrite $x^2 - 10x + 4$ in the form $a(x - h)^2 + k$.

Solution Notice that half of the coefficient of x is $\frac{1}{2}(-10) = -5$. Squaring -5 gives 25. We have

$$\begin{aligned}
x^2 - 10x + 4 &= x^2 - 10x + (25 - 25) + 4 \\
&= (x^2 - 10x + 25) - 25 + 4 \\
&= (x - 5)^2 - 21.
\end{aligned}$$

Thus, $a = +1$, $h = +5$, and $k = -21$.

Example 2 Complete the square in the formula $h(x) = 5x^2 + 30x - 10$.

Solution We first factor out 5:

$$h(x) = 5(x^2 + 6x - 2).$$

Now we complete the square in the expression $x^2 + 6x - 2$.
Step 1: Divide the coefficient of x by 2, giving 3.
Step 2: Square the result: $3^2 = 9$.
Step 3: Add the result after the x term, then subtract it:

$$h(x) = 5(\underbrace{x^2 + 6x + 9}_{\text{Perfect square}} - 9 - 2).$$

Step 4: Factor the perfect square and simplify the rest:

$$h(x) = 5\left((x + 3)^2 - 11\right).$$

Now that we have completed the square, we can multiply by the 5:

$$h(x) = 5(x + 3)^2 - 55.$$

The Quadratic Formula

We derive a general formula for the zeros of $q(x) = ax^2 + bx + c$, with $a \neq 0$, by completing the square. To find the zeros, set $q(x) = 0$:

$$ax^2 + bx + c = 0.$$

Before we complete the square, we factor out the coefficient of x^2:

$$a\left(x^2 + \frac{b}{a}x + \frac{c}{a}\right) = 0.$$

Since $a \neq 0$, we can divide both sides by a:

$$x^2 + \frac{b}{a}x + \frac{c}{a} = 0.$$

To complete the square, we add and then subtract $((b/a)/2)^2 = b^2/(4a^2)$:

$$\underbrace{x^2 + \frac{b}{a}x + \frac{b^2}{4a^2}}_{\text{Perfect square}} - \frac{b^2}{4a^2} + \frac{c}{a} = 0.$$

We factor the perfect square and simplify the constant term, giving:

$$\left(x + \frac{b}{2a}\right)^2 - \left(\frac{b^2 - 4ac}{4a^2}\right) = 0 \qquad \text{since } \frac{-b^2}{4a^2} + \frac{c}{a} = \frac{-b^2}{4a^2} + \frac{4ac}{4a^2} = -\left(\frac{b^2 - 4ac}{4a^2}\right)$$

$$\left(x + \frac{b}{2a}\right)^2 = \frac{b^2 - 4ac}{4a^2} \qquad \text{adding } \frac{b^2 - 4ac}{4a^2} \text{ to both sides}$$

$$x + \frac{b}{2a} = \pm\sqrt{\frac{b^2 - 4ac}{4a^2}} = \frac{\pm\sqrt{b^2 - 4ac}}{2a} \qquad \text{taking the square root}$$

$$x = \frac{-b}{2a} \pm \frac{\sqrt{b^2 - 4ac}}{2a} \qquad \text{subtracting } b/2a$$

$$x = \frac{-b \pm \sqrt{b^2 - 4ac}}{2a}.$$

Problems for Section E

In Problems 1–12, rewrite each expression as a sum of powers of the variable.

1. $3x^2\left(x^{-1}\right) + \dfrac{1}{2x} + x^2 + \dfrac{1}{5}$

2. $10\left(3q^2 - 1\right)(6q)$

3. $\left(y - 3y^{-2}\right)^2$

4. $x(x + x^{-1})^2$

5. $2P^2(P) + (9P)^{1/2}$

6. $\dfrac{(1 + 3\sqrt{t})^2}{2}$

7. $\dfrac{18 + x^2 - 3x}{-6}$

8. $\left(\dfrac{1}{N} - N\right)^2$

9. $\dfrac{-3(4x - x^2)}{7x}$

10. $\dfrac{x^4 + 2x + 1}{2\sqrt{x}}$

11. $\dfrac{ax^2 + bx + c}{x}$

12. $\sqrt{1 + p^2} \cdot (1 + p^2)^{3/2}$

In Problems 13–18, rewrite each expression in the form $a(bx + c)^n$.

13. $\dfrac{12}{\sqrt{3x + 1}}$

14. $\dfrac{250\sqrt[3]{10 - s}}{0.25}$

15. $0.7(x - 1)^3(1 - x)$

16. $\dfrac{1}{2(x^2 + 1)^3}$

17. $4(6R + 2)^3(6)$

18. $\sqrt{\dfrac{28x^2 - 4\pi x}{x}}$

In Problems 19–30, rewrite each expression in the form ab^x or ab^t.

19. $\dfrac{1^x}{2^x}$

20. $\dfrac{1}{2^x}$

21. $10{,}000(1 - 0.24)^t$

22. e^{2x+1}

23. $2 \cdot 3^{-x}$

24. $2^x \cdot 3^{x-1}$

25. $16^{t/2}$

26. $\dfrac{e^3}{e^{-x+4}}$

27. $\dfrac{5^x}{-3^x}$

28. $\dfrac{e \cdot e^x}{0.2}$

29. $\left(10e^t\right)^2$

30. $\dfrac{e^{kt}}{1/A}$

For Problems 31–36, rewrite each expression as a sum of positive powers of the variable.

31. $x^2 + x^{-3}$

32. $\dfrac{5}{x^{-2}} + x + 1$

33. $(2y^2 - 5)3y$

34. $y^3(y + 1)^2$

35. $z^4(1 + z^{-2})^2$

36. $z^5(z^{-3}) - 2z^{-1} + 6$

For Problems 37–42, complete the square for each expression.

37. $x^2 + 8x$

38. $y^2 - 12y$

39. $w^2 + 7w$

40. $2r^2 + 20r$

41. $s^2 + 6s - 8$

42. $3t^2 + 24t - 13$

In Problems 43–46, rewrite each expression in the form $a(x - h)^2 + k$.

43. $x^2 - 2x - 3$

44. $10 - 6x + x^2$

45. $-x^2 + 6x - 2$

46. $3x^2 - 12x + 13$

In Problems 47–52, simplify and rewrite using only positive exponents.

47. $-3\left(x^2 + 7\right)^{-4}(2x)$

48. $-2(1 + 3^x)^{-3}(\ln 2)(2^x)$

49. $-(\sin(\pi t))^{-1}(-\cos(\pi t))\pi$

50. $-(\tan z)^{-2}\left(\dfrac{1}{\cos^2 z}\right)$

51. $\dfrac{-e^x\left(x^2\right) - e^{-x}2x}{\left(x^2\right)^2}$

52. $-x^{-2}(\ln x) + x^{-1}\left(\dfrac{1}{x}\right)$

In Problems 53–60, simplify and rewrite in radical form.

53. $(5x)^{1/2}$

54. $(3x - 2)^{-(1/2)}$

55. $6y(4z - 5)^{1/3}$

56. $(27z)^{5/3}(3w - 1)^{-(1/2)}$

57. $\dfrac{1}{2}(x^2 + 16)^{-1/2}(2x)$

58. $\dfrac{1}{2}(x^2 + 10x + 1)^{-1/2}(2x + 10)$

59. $\dfrac{1}{2}(\sin(2x))^{-1/2}(2)\cos(2x)$

60. $\dfrac{2}{3}\left(x^2 - e^{3x}\right)^{-5/3}\left(3x^2 - e^{3x}(3)\right)$

F   SOLVING EQUATIONS

Solving in Your Head

When we first look at an equation, we see if we can guess the answer by mentally trying numbers. Consider the following equations and mental solutions.

$$\sqrt{x} - 4 = 0 \qquad \textit{"I'm looking for a number whose} \qquad \sqrt{16} - 4 = 0$$
$$\textit{square root is 4."}$$

$$2x - 3 = 0 \qquad \textit{"What value can I use for x that will} \qquad 2\left(\dfrac{3}{2}\right) - 3 = 0$$
$$\textit{give } 2x = 3\textit{?"}$$

$\dfrac{3}{x} + 1 = 0$	*"Three divided by what number gives* -1*?"*	$\dfrac{3}{(-3)} + 1 = 0$
$e^x = 1$	*"What exponent can I use with the base e to get 1?"*	$e^{(0)} = 1$
$x^2(x + 2) = 0$	*"What number makes each factor zero?"*	$0^2 = 0$ and $(-2) + 2 = 0$
$\dfrac{(x + 1)(3 - x)}{(1 - x)^2} = 0$	*"What numbers make the numerator equal to 0?"*	$(-1) + 1 = 0$ and $3 - (3) = 0$
$1 - \sin x = 0$	*"What numbers make the sine value equal 1?"*	$1 - \sin\left(\dfrac{\pi}{2}\right) = 0$

Notice that the last equation, $\sin x = 1$, has many other solutions as well.

Solving Exactly Versus Solving Approximately

Some equations can be solved exactly, often by using algebra. For example, the equation $7x - 1 = 0$ has the exact solution $x = 1/7$. Other equations can be hard or even impossible to solve exactly. However, it is often possible, and sometimes easier, to find an approximate solution to an equation by using a graph or a numerical method on a calculator. The equation $7x - 1 = 0$ has the approximate solution $x \approx 0.14$ (since $1/7 = 0.142857\ldots$). We use the sign $\approx$, meaning approximately equal, when we want to emphasize that we are making an approximation.

Example 1   Give exact and approximate solutions to $x^2 = 3$.

Solution   The exact solutions are $x = \pm\sqrt{3}$; approximate ones are $x \approx \pm1.73$, or $x \approx \pm1.732$, or $x \approx \pm1.73205$. (since $\sqrt{3} = 1.732050808\ldots$). Notice that the equation $x^2 = 3$ has only two exact solutions, but many possible approximate solutions, depending on how much accuracy is required.

Operations on Equations

For more complicated equations, additional steps may be needed in order to find a solution.

Linear Equations

To solve a linear equation, we clear any parentheses and then isolate the variable.

Example 2   Solve $3 - [5.4 + 2(4.3 - x)] = 2 - (0.3x - 0.8)$ for x.

Solution   We begin by clearing the innermost parentheses on each side. This gives

$$3 - [5.4 + 8.6 - 2x] = 2 - 0.3x + 0.8.$$

Then

$$3 - 14 + 2x = 2 - 0.3x + 0.8$$
$$2.3x = 13.8,$$
$$x = 6.$$

Example 3   Solve for q if $p^2q + r(-q - 1) = 4(p + r)$.

Solution

$$p^2q - rq - r = 4p + 4r$$
$$p^2q - rq = 4p + 5r$$
$$q(p^2 - r) = 4p + 5r$$
$$q = \frac{4p + 5r}{p^2 - r}$$

Solving by Factoring

Some equations can be put into factored form such that the product of the factors is zero. Then we solve by using the fact that if $a \cdot b = 0$, then either a or b (or both) is zero.

Example 4   Solve $(x + 1)(x + 3) = 15$ for x.

Solution   Do not make the mistake of setting $x + 1 = 15$ and $x + 3 = 15$. It is not true that $a \cdot b = 15$ means that $a = 15$ or $b = 15$ (or both). (Although it is true that if $a \cdot b = 0$, then $a = 0$ or $b = 0$, or both.) So, we must expand the left-hand side and set the equation equal to zero:

$$x^2 + 4x + 3 = 15,$$

$$x^2 + 4x - 12 = 0.$$

Then, factoring gives

$$(x - 2)(x + 6) = 0.$$

Thus $x = 2$ and $x = -6$ are solutions.

Example 5   Solve $2(x + 3)^2 = 5(x + 3)$.

Solution   You might be tempted to divide both sides by $(x + 3)$. However, if you do this you will overlook one of the solutions. Instead, write

$$2(x + 3)^2 - 5(x + 3) = 0$$
$$(x + 3)(2(x + 3) - 5) = 0$$
$$(x + 3)(2x + 6 - 5) = 0$$
$$(x + 3)(2x + 1) = 0.$$

Thus, $x = -\dfrac{1}{2}$ and $x = -3$ are solutions.

Example 6   Solve $e^x + xe^x = 0$.

Solution   Factoring gives $e^x(1 + x) = 0$. Since e^x is never zero, $x = -1$ is the only solution.

Using the Quadratic Formula

If an equation is in the form $ax^2 + bx + c = 0$, we can use the quadratic formula to find the solutions,

$$x = \frac{-b + \sqrt{b^2 - 4ac}}{2a} \quad \text{or} \quad x = \frac{-b - \sqrt{b^2 - 4ac}}{2a}.$$

provided that $\sqrt{b^2 - 4ac}$ is a real number.

Example 7   Solve $11 + 2x = x^2$.

Solution   The equation is

$$-x^2 + 2x + 11 = 0.$$

The expression on the left does not factor using integers, so we use

$$x = \frac{-2 + \sqrt{4 - 4(-1)(11)}}{2(-1)} = \frac{-2 + \sqrt{48}}{-2} = \frac{-2 + \sqrt{16 \cdot 3}}{-2} = \frac{-2 + 4\sqrt{3}}{-2} = 1 - 2\sqrt{3},$$

$$x = \frac{-2 - \sqrt{4 - 4(-1)(11)}}{2(-1)} = \frac{-2 - \sqrt{48}}{-2} = \frac{-2 - \sqrt{16 \cdot 3}}{-2} = \frac{-2 - 4\sqrt{3}}{-2} = 1 + 2\sqrt{3}.$$

The exact solutions are $x = 1 - 2\sqrt{3}$ and $x = 1 + 2\sqrt{3}$.

The decimal approximations to these numbers $x = 1 - 2\sqrt{3} = -2.46$ and $x = 1 + 2\sqrt{3} = 4.46$ are approximate solutions to this equation. The approximate solutions could be found directly from a graph or calculator.

Fractional Equations

If an equation involves fractions, we can eliminate the fractions by multiplying both sides of the equation by the least common denominator and then solving as before. However, we must check for extraneous solutions at the end.

Example 8   Solve $\dfrac{2x}{x + 1} - 3 = \dfrac{2}{x^2 + x}$ for x.

Solution   To look for a common denominator, factor $x^2 + x$. Then we have

$$\frac{2x}{x + 1} - 3 = \frac{2}{x(x + 1)}.$$

Multiplying both sides by $x(x + 1)$ gives

$$x(x + 1)\left(\frac{2x}{x + 1} - 3\right) = 2$$
$$2x^2 - 3x(x + 1) = 2$$
$$2x^2 - 3x^2 - 3x = 2$$
$$-x^2 - 3x - 2 = 0,$$

or

$$x^2 + 3x + 2 = 0.$$

Factoring, we have

$$(x + 2)(x + 1) = 0,$$

so $x = -2$ and $x = -1$ are potential solutions. However, the original equation is not defined for $x = -1$, so $x = -1$ is extraneous. The only solution is $x = -2$.

Example 9   Solve for P_2 if $\dfrac{1}{P_1} + \dfrac{1}{P_2} = \dfrac{1}{P_3}$.

Solution   Multiplying by $P_1 P_2 P_3$ gives

$$P_2 P_3 + P_1 P_3 = P_1 P_2.$$

We are solving for P_2, so we move all P_2 terms to one side

$$P_2 P_3 - P_1 P_2 = -P_1 P_3.$$

Factoring out P_2 gives

$$P_2(P_3 - P_1) = -P_1 P_3$$
$$P_2 = \frac{-P_1 P_3}{P_3 - P_1} = \frac{P_1 P_3}{P_1 - P_3}.$$

Note that we assume that none of P_1, P_2, or $P_3 = 0$. Also, we assume $P_3 \neq P_1$, or else the denominator of the solution is 0.

Radical Equations

We solve radical equations by raising both sides of the equation to the same power. The principle is that if $a = b$, then $a^r = b^r$. Again, we must check for extraneous solutions.

Example 10   Solve $2\sqrt{x} = x - 3$.

Solution   Squaring both sides gives

$$(2\sqrt{x})^2 = (x - 3)^2$$
$$4x = x^2 - 6x + 9.$$

Then

$$x^2 - 10x + 9 = 0$$
$$(x - 1)(x - 9) = 0,$$

so $x = 1$ and $x = 9$ are potential solutions. Since $x = 1$ is not a solution of the original equation, the only solution is $x = 9$.

Example 11   Solve $4 = x^{-1/2}$.

Solution   Taking both sides to the -2 power:

$$(4)^{-2} = (x^{-1/2})^{-2}$$
$$(4)^{-2} = x,$$
$$x = \frac{1}{16}.$$

Exponential Equations

When the variable we want to solve for is in the exponent, we again "do the same thing" to both sides of the equation. This time we take logarithms using the property that if $a = b$ then $\log a = \log b$, (provided $a, b > 0$). Note that we could also use the natural logarithm. The logarithm rule that $\log(m^x) = x \log m$ enables us to solve the equation.

Example 12   Solve $10^{2x+1} = 3$ for x.

Solution   Taking logs,

$$\log 10^{2x+1} = \log 3$$
$$2x + 1 = \log 3, \qquad \text{Since } \log 10^P = P$$
$$x = \frac{(\log 3) - 1}{2}.$$

The solution $x = ((\log 3) - 1)/2$ is exact; converting the solution to $x \approx -0.2614$ gives an approximate solution.

Example 13   Solve $2e^x = 12$.

Solution   We have

$$e^x = 6 \qquad \text{Dividing both sides by 2}$$
$$\ln e^x = \ln 6 \qquad \text{Taking the natural log of both sides}$$
$$x = \ln 6 \qquad \text{Since } \ln e^P = P.$$

Example 14   Solve $1.07 = 4^{-x}$.

Solution   Taking natural logs of both sides

$$\ln 1.07 = \ln(4^{-x})$$
$$\ln 1.07 = (-x)(\ln 4)$$
$$x = -\frac{\ln 1.07}{\ln 4}$$

When applying the logarithm function to both sides of an equation, we may use log base 10 or log base e (the natural log). In Example 12, log base 10 is most convenient, as is the natural log for Example 13. The answers $x = ((\log 3) - 1)/2$ and $x = \ln 6$ are *exact* solutions. In order to compare answers in different forms or use these solutions in a numerical computation, we use a calculator to find a decimal approximation.

Example 15   Solve for x in Examples 13 and 14 by taking the logarithm base 10 (rather than the natural logarithm) of both sides of the equations. Determine decimal approximations (to the accuracy of your calculator) for the solutions you find and for the solutions given in Examples 13 and 14. Do the answers agree?

Solution   In Example 13, we have

$$2e^x = 12$$
$$e^x = 6$$
$$\log e^x = \log 6$$
$$x \log e = \log 6$$
$$x = \frac{\log 6}{\log e} \approx 1.791759469.$$

The exact answer $x = \ln 6$ given in Example 13 is in a simpler form, but $\ln 6 \approx 1.791759469$, an approximate solution. Yes, the answers agree (to at least nine decimal places)
In Example 14,

$$1.07 = 4^{-x}$$
$$\log 1.07 = \log 4^{-x}$$
$$\log 1.07 = -x \log 4$$
$$x = -\frac{\log 1.07}{\log 4} \approx -0.0488053983.$$

This agrees with the exact solution $x = -\dfrac{\ln 1.07}{\ln 4} \approx -0.0488053983.$
The solutions $-\log 1.07 / \log 4$ and $-\ln 1.07 / \ln 4$ are two different ways of writing the exact solution, while -0.0488053983 is an approximate solution.

Example 16   Solve for t in the equation $P = P_0 e^{kt}$.

Solution   Dividing both sides by P_0, we have

$$\frac{P}{P_0} = e^{kt},$$

so

$$\ln\left(\frac{P}{P_0}\right) = \ln e^{kt},$$

$$\ln\left(\frac{P}{P_0}\right) = kt.$$

Thus, $t = \dfrac{1}{k} \ln\left(\dfrac{P}{P_0}\right).$

Problems for Section F

For Problems 1–23, solve each of the following equations for the variable.

1. $3x = 15$
2. $-2y = 12$
3. $4z = 22$
4. $x + 3 = 10$
5. $y - 5 = 21$
6. $w - 23 = -34$
7. $2x - 5 = 13$
8. $7 - 3y = -14$
9. $13t + 2 = 47$
10. $2x - 5 = 4x - 9$
11. $17 - 28y = 13y + 24$
12. $x^2 + 7x + 6 = 0$
13. $y^2 - 5y - 6 = 0$
14. $2w^2 + w - 10 = 0$
15. $4s^2 + 3s - 15 = 0$
16. $\dfrac{2}{x} + \dfrac{3}{2x} = 8$
17. $\dfrac{3}{x - 1} + 1 = 5$
18. $\sqrt{y - 1} = 13$

19. $\sqrt{5y+3}=7$

20. $\sqrt{2x-1}+3=9$

21. $\dfrac{21}{z-5}-\dfrac{13}{z^2-5z}=3$

22. $-16t^2+96t+12=60$

23. $2(r+5)-3=3(r-8)+21$

For Problems 24–35, solve each of the following equations for the specified variable.

24. $A=l\cdot w$, for l.

25. $C=2\pi r$, for r.

26. $I=Prt$, for P.

27. $C=\frac{5}{9}(F-32)$, for F.

28. $e^{kt}=1.0573$, for k.

29. $0.079=\ln B$, for B.

30. $3xy+1=2y-5x$, for y.

31. $\dfrac{At-B}{C-B(1-2t)}=3$, for t.

32. $\dfrac{a-cx}{b+dx}+a=0$, for x.

33. $Ab^5=C$, for b.

34. $|2x+1|=7$, for x.

35. $P=Qe^{kt}-P$, for t.

Solve the equations in Problems 36–58.

36. $B-4[B-3(1-B)]=42$

37. $1.06s-0.01(248.4-s)=22.67s$

38. $\frac{5}{3}(y+2)=\frac{1}{2}-y$

39. $3t-\dfrac{2(t-1)}{3}=4$

40. $8+2x-3x^2=0$

41. $2p^3+p^2-18p-9=0$

42. $N^2-2N-3=2N(N-3)$

43. $\dfrac{1}{64}t^3=t$

44. $x^2-1=2x$

45. $4x^2-13x-12=0$

46. $60=-16t^2+96t+12$

47. $y^2+4y-2=0$

48. $\dfrac{2}{z-3}+\dfrac{7}{z^2-3z}=0$

49. $\dfrac{x^2+1-2x^2}{(x^2+1)^2}=0$

50. $4-\dfrac{1}{L^2}=0$

51. $2+\dfrac{1}{q+1}-\dfrac{1}{q-1}=0$

52. $\sqrt{r^2+24}=7$

53. $\dfrac{1}{\sqrt[3]{x}}=-2$

54. $3\sqrt{x}=\frac{1}{2}x$

55. $10=\sqrt{\dfrac{v}{7\pi}}$

56. $\dfrac{(3x+4)(x-2)}{(x-5)(x-1)}=0$

57. $5^{2x}-5^x-6=0$

58. $2\cdot16^x-5\cdot4^x=12$

For Problems 59–62, express answers in exact form and give a decimal approximation (to two decimal places).

59. $5000=2500(0.97)^t$

60. $280=40+30e^{2t}$

61. $\frac{1}{2}(2^x)=16$

62. $1+10^{-x}=4.3$

In Problems 63–76, solve for the indicated variable.

63. $\left(\dfrac{1}{2}\right)^{t/1000}=e^{kt}$. Solve for k (to six decimal places).

64. $\frac{1}{2}P_0=P_0(0.8)^x$. Solve for x (to three decimal places).

65. $T=2\pi\sqrt{\dfrac{l}{g}}$. Solve for l.

66. $y'y^2+2xyy'=4y$. Solve for y'.

67. $l=l_0+\dfrac{k}{2}w$. Solve for w.

68. $2x-(xy'+yy')+2yy''=0$. Solve for y'.

69. $by-d=ay+c$. Solve for y.

70. $u(v+2)+w(v-3)=z(v-1)$. Solve for v.

71. $S=\dfrac{rL-a}{r-1}$. Solve for r.

72. $h=v_0t+\dfrac{1}{2}at^2$. Solve for a.

73. $K=\dfrac{MA(y-z)}{N}$. Solve for z.

74. $R=\dfrac{eb+de}{e+f}$. Solve for e.

75. $x+z=\dfrac{y+z}{y}+w$. Solve for z.

76. $\dfrac{3s-t}{2s}=4-\dfrac{v}{w}$. Solve for s.

77. Solve for x by completing the square: $8x^2 - 1 = 2x$.

78. Solve for x: $\dfrac{x^2 - 5mx + 4m^2}{x - m} = 0$.

G   SYSTEMS OF EQUATIONS

To solve for two unknowns, we must have two equations—that is, two relationships between the unknowns. Similarly, three unknowns require three equations, and n unknowns (n an integer) require n equations. The group of equations is known as a *system* of equations. To solve the system, we find the *simultaneous* solutions to all equations in the system.

Example 1   Solve for x and y in the following system of equations.

$$\begin{cases} y + \dfrac{x}{2} = 3 \\ 2(x + y) = 1 - y \end{cases}$$

Solution   Solving the first equation for y, we write $y = 3 - x/2$. Substituting for y in the second equation gives

$$2 \left(x + \left(3 - \frac{x}{2} \right) \right) = 1 - \left(3 - \frac{x}{2} \right).$$

Then

$$2x + 6 - x = -2 + \frac{x}{2}$$
$$x + 6 = -2 + \frac{x}{2}$$
$$2x + 12 = -4 + x$$
$$x = -16.$$

Using $x = -16$ in the first equation to find the corresponding y, we have

$$y - \frac{16}{2} = 3$$
$$y = 3 + 8 = 11.$$

Thus, the solution that simultaneously solves both equations is $x = -16$, $y = 11$.

Example 2   Solve for x and y in the following system.

$$\begin{cases} y = x - 1 \\ x^2 + y^2 = 5 \end{cases}$$

Solution   We substitute the expression $(x - 1)$ for y in the second equation. Then

$$x^2 + (x - 1)^2 = 5$$
$$x^2 + x^2 - 2x + 1 = 5$$
$$2x^2 - 2x - 4 = 0$$
$$x^2 - x - 2 = 0.$$

Factoring gives $(x - 2)(x + 1) = 0$, so $x = 2$ or $x = -1$.

We then find the y-values which correspond to each x. If $x = 2$, then $y = (2) - 1 = 1$. If $x = -1$, then $y = (-1) - 1 = -2$. The solutions to the system are $x = 2$ and $y = 1$ or $x = -1$ and $y = -2$. Notice that $x = 2$ and $y = -2$ is *not* a solution; nor is $x = -1$ and $y = 1$.

Example 3   Solve for Q_0 and a in the system

$$\begin{cases} 90.7 = Q_0 a^{10} \\ 91 = Q_0 a^{13}. \end{cases}$$

Solution   Taking ratios,

$$\frac{Q_0 a^{13}}{Q_0 a^{10}} = \frac{91}{90.7}$$

$$a^3 = \frac{91}{90.7},$$

$$a = \sqrt[3]{\frac{91}{90.7}} \approx 1.0011.$$

To find Q_0,

$$90.7 = Q_0 (1.0011)^{10},$$

$$Q_0 = 89.7083.$$

The simultaneous solution is $a \approx 1.0011$ and $Q_0 \approx 89.7083$.

Graphically, the simultaneous solutions to a system of equations give us the coordinates of the point (or points) of intersection for the graphs of the equations in the system. For example, the solutions to Example 2 give the coordinates of the points where the line $y = x - 1$ intersects the circle centered at the origin with radius $\sqrt{5}$.

Example 4   Find the points of intersection for the graphs in Figure 1.

Solution   We can solve $y = x^2 - 1$ and $y = x + 1$ simultaneously by setting the y-values equal to one another.

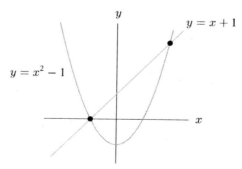

Figure 1

Then

$$x^2 - 1 = x + 1$$

$$x^2 - x - 2 = 0$$

$$(x + 1)(x - 2) = 0,$$

so $x = -1$ and $x = 2$ are solutions. To get the corresponding y-values, we use either equation to find $x = -1$ gives $y = 0$, and $x = 2$ gives $y = 3$. The graphs intersect at the points $(-1, 0)$ and $(2, 3)$.

For some systems of equations, it is impossible to find the simultaneous solution(s) using algebra. In this case, the only choice is to find the solution(s) by approximating the point(s) of intersection graphically.

Example 5   Solve the system:

$$\begin{cases} y = x + 1 \\ y = 3^{x-1} \end{cases}$$

Solution   We are looking for the point or points of intersection of the line $y = x + 1$ and the exponential equation $y = 3^{x-1}$. Setting the expressions for y equal to one another gives

$$x + 1 = 3^{x-1}.$$

We cannot use the algebraic techniques of the previous section to solve this equation. We might try to guess a solution. Note that

$$2 + 1 = 3^{2-1}$$
$$3 = 3,$$

so $x = 2$, $y = 3$ is a solution to the system. If you were not able to guess this solution, you would be able to approximate it from the graph.

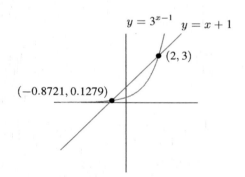

Figure 2 The graphs reveal two intersection points

However, the graphs of the equations in Figure 2 reveal that the system has two solutions. There is also a value of x such that $-1 < x < 0$ where the two graphs intersect. By tracing along the graph, we find

$$x \approx -0.8721, \; y \approx 0.1279.$$

Thus, the solutions to the system are $x = 2$ and $y = 3$ or $x \approx -0.8721$ and $y \approx 0.1279$.

Simultaneous solutions to a system of equations in two variables can always be approximated by graphing, whereas it is only sometimes possible to find exact solutions using algebra.

Problems for Section G

Solve the systems of equations in Problems 1–12 for x and y.

1. $\begin{cases} x + y = 3 \\ x - y = 5 \end{cases}$

2. $\begin{cases} 2x - y = 10 \\ x + 2y = 15 \end{cases}$

3. $\begin{cases} 3x - 2y = 6 \\ y = 2x - 5 \end{cases}$

4. $\begin{cases} x = 7y - 9 \\ 4x - 15y = 26 \end{cases}$

5. $\begin{cases} x^2 + y^2 = 36 \\ y = x - 3 \end{cases}$

6. $\begin{cases} 2x + 3y = 7 \\ y = -\frac{3}{5}x + 6 \end{cases}$

7. $\begin{cases} y = 2x - x^2 \\ y = -3 \end{cases}$

8. $\begin{cases} y = 4 - x^2 \\ y - 2x = 1 \end{cases}$

9. $\begin{cases} y = 1/x \\ y = 4x \end{cases}$

10. $\begin{cases} 2(x + y) = 3 \\ x = y + 3(x - 5) \end{cases}$

11. $\begin{cases} y = x^3 - 1 \\ y = e^x \end{cases}$

12. $\begin{cases} ax + y = 2a \\ x + ay = 1 + a^2 \end{cases}$

13. Let ℓ be the line of slope 3 passing through the origin. Find the points of intersection of the line ℓ and the parabola whose equation is $y = x^2$. Sketch the line and the parabola, and label the points of intersection.

Determine the points of intersection for Problems 14–16.

14.   15.   16.

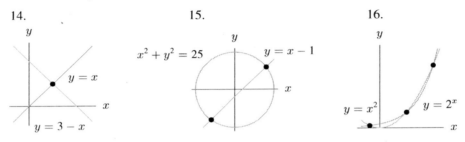

H INEQUALITIES

Just as we can solve some simple equations mentally, we can solve some inequalities mentally. Consider the following examples.

To solve:	We think:	The solution is:
$x - 1 > 0$	*"If x is larger than +1, the left hand side is positive."*	$x > 1$
$x + 4 < 10$	*"As long as x stays smaller than +6, the left hand side will be less than the right hand side."*	$x < 6$
$3 - x < 0$	*"When x gets larger than +3, the left hand side will be negative."*	$x > 3$
$x - 2 \geq 0$	*"If x = 2 then x − 2 is 0. When x is larger than 2, then x − 2 is positive."*	$x \geq 2$
$x^2(x + 5) > 0$	*"The value of x^2 is always positive, so x + 5 needs to be positive."*	$x > -5$

We solve inequalities using some of the techniques used in solving equations. However, there are some important differences in the application of these techniques to inequalities.

For a, b, and c real numbers, if $a < b$, then
$$a + c < b + c$$
$$a \cdot c < b \cdot c \qquad \text{if } c > 0$$
$$a \cdot c > b \cdot c \qquad \text{if } c < 0 \qquad \text{(Inequality reverses direction).}$$
For a and b positive, when $a < b$, then
$$a^2 < b^2, \quad \text{and} \quad \frac{1}{a} > \frac{1}{b} \qquad \text{(Inequality reverses direction).}$$

Linear Inequalities

We solve linear inequalities with the techniques we use to solve linear equations; however, the inequality is reversed when we multiply or divide both sides of the inequality by a negative number.

Example 1   Solve for x:
$$1 - \frac{3}{2}x \leq 16.$$

Solution   We have
$$1 - \frac{3}{2}x - 1 \leq 16 - 1$$
$$-\frac{3}{2}x \leq 15$$
$$\left(-\frac{2}{3}\right)\left(-\frac{3}{2}x\right) \geq \left(-\frac{2}{3}\right)15$$
$$x \geq -10.$$

Example 2   Solve for x:
$$-6 < 4x - 7 < 5.$$

Solution   The solutions to this double inequality is all values of x such that $4x - 7$ is between -6 and 5. We can operate on all three sections of the inequality at once (if we're careful). We start by adding 7 to each part which gives
$$-6 + 7 < 4x - 7 + 7 < 5 + 7.$$
$$1 < 4x < 12$$
$$\frac{1}{4} < x < 3.$$
The solution is all numbers between $1/4$ and 3.

Checking the Sign of an Expression

When an expression is a product or a quotient, we can determine the sign of the expression on an interval by looking at the sign of each factor over the interval.

Example 3   Determine the values of x which make the expression $(4 - x)^2 e^{-x}$ positive, negative, and zero respectively.

Solution   The expression e^{-x} is always positive, and $(4 - x)^2$ is positive for any value of x except $x = 4$, where it equals zero. Therefore, $(4 - x)^2 e^{-x} > 0$ for $x \neq 4$, and $(4 - x)^2 e^{-x} = 0$ if $x = 4$.

Example 4   Determine the values of x which make the expression $(x + 1)(x - 7)$ positive, negative, and zero respectively.

Solution   The expression is zero if $x = -1$ or $x = +7$. The product can change sign at $x = -1$ or $x = +7$. We check the sign of the expression by looking at the sign of each factor over the intervals established by dividing the number line at $x = -1$ and $x = +7$. The expression is positive when both factors have the same sign.

Signs of factors	$(-)(-)$		$(+)(-)$		$(+)(+)$	
Sign of expression	Positive	-1	Negative	7	Positive	x

Thus,

$$(x + 1)(x - 7) = 0 \quad \text{for } x = -1 \text{ or } x = 7,$$
$$(x + 1)(x - 7) < 0 \quad \text{for } -1 < x < 7,$$
$$(x + 1)(x - 7) > 0 \quad \text{for } x < -1 \text{ or } x > 7.$$

Example 5   Determine the values of r for which the expression $\dfrac{2r + 5}{(r - 1)(r - 3)}$ is zero, positive, negative, or undefined.

Solution   A fraction is equal to 0 if the numerator is 0, so this expression equals 0 if $r = -\frac{5}{2}$. The values $r = 1$ and $r = 3$ make the expression undefined because the denominator is zero there. We divide the number line by marking $-\frac{5}{2}$, 1, and 3, and we check the sign of each each factor on each interval. This gives

Signs of factors	$\dfrac{(-)}{(-)(-)}$		$\dfrac{(+)}{(-)(-)}$		$\dfrac{(+)}{(+)(-)}$		$\dfrac{(+)}{(+)(+)}$	
Sign of expression	Negative	$-\frac{5}{2}$	Positive	1	Negative	a	Positive	r

Therefore,

$$\frac{2r + 5}{(r - 1)(r - 3)} \quad \text{is not defined for } r = 1 \text{ or } r = 3.$$
$$\frac{2r + 5}{(r - 1)(r - 3)} = 0 \quad \text{for } r = -\frac{5}{2},$$
$$\frac{2r + 5}{(r - 1)(r - 3)} > 0 \quad \text{for } -\frac{5}{2} < r < 1 \text{ or } r > 3,$$
$$\frac{2r + 5}{(r - 1)(r - 3)} < 0 \quad \text{for } r < -\frac{5}{2} \text{ or } 1 < r < 3,$$

Example 6   Determine y-values which make the expression $\dfrac{\sqrt{y + 2}}{y^3}$ positive, negative, zero, or undefined.

Solution   The expression is zero if $y = -2$. It is not defined if y is less than -2 because we cannot take the square root of a negative number. Furthermore, the quotient is not defined if $y = 0$ because that puts a zero in the denominator. The radical is always positive (where defined), so the numerator is positive. Because the cube of a negative number is negative, we can visualize signs in each interval.

Signs of factors			$\dfrac{(+)}{(-)}$		$\dfrac{(+)}{(+)}$	
Sign of expression	Undefined	-2	Negative	0	Positive	y

So

$$\frac{\sqrt{y+2}}{y^3} \quad \text{is undefined for } y < -2 \text{ or } y = 0,$$

$$\frac{\sqrt{y+2}}{y^3} = 0 \quad \text{for } y = -2,$$

$$\frac{\sqrt{y+2}}{y^3} > 0 \quad \text{for } y > 0.$$

$$\frac{\sqrt{y+2}}{y^3} < 0 \quad \text{for } -2 < y < 0,$$

Solving Nonlinear Inequalities by Factoring and Checking Signs

We can often solve polynomial and rational inequalities by starting out the same way we would with an equation and then using a number line to find the intervals on which the inequality holds.

Example 7 Solve for x if

$$2x^2 + x^3 \leq 3x.$$

Solution We first set the inequality so that zero is on one side. Then

$$x^3 + 2x^2 - 3x \leq 0,$$
$$x(x^2 + 2x - 3) \leq 0,$$
$$x(x + 3)(x - 1) \leq 0.$$

The left hand side equals 0 for $x = 0$, $x = -3$, and $x = 1$. To solve the inequality we want to select the x-values for which the left hand side is negative. We check signs over the four intervals created by marking $x = 0, -3, +1$.

Signs of factors	$(-)(-)(-)$		$(-)(+)(-)$		$(+)(+)(-)$	$(+)(+)(+)$	
Sign of expression	Negative	-3	Positive		0 Negative	1 Positive	x

So $x^3 + 2x^2 - 3x < 0$ for $x < -3$ or $0 < x < 1$ and $x^3 + 2x^2 - 3x = 0$ at $x = 0, x = -3$, and $x = 1$. Therefore, $2x^2 + x^3 \leq 3x$ for $x \leq -3$ or $0 \leq x \leq 1$.

Example 8 Solve for q: $\dfrac{1}{2-q} > q$.

Solution First, put 0 on the right, then combine the fractions on the left.

$$\frac{1}{2-q} - q > 0,$$

$$\frac{1}{2-q} - q\frac{(2-q)}{(2-q)} > 0,$$

$$\frac{1 - q(2-q)}{2-q} > 0,$$

$$\frac{1 - 2q + q^2}{2-q} > 0.$$

We want this quotient to be positive, so the numerator and denominator must have the same sign. Notice that $q \neq 2$. Factoring the numerator, we have $\dfrac{(1-q)^2}{2-q} > 0$. The numerator is never negative, and the denominator is positive if $2 - q > 0$ which gives $q < 2$. However, $(1-q)^2 = 0$ if $q = 1$, so $q = 1$ must be excluded in order to preserve the inequality. Therefore, $\dfrac{1}{2-q} > q$ for $q < 2$ and $q \neq 1$.

Radical inequalities

We can eliminate radicals by raising both sides of an equation to the same power. However, we must check our answers for extraneous roots.

Example 9   Solve for x: $\sqrt{x-6} < 2$.

Solution   The expression $\sqrt{x-6}$ is not defined unless $x \geq 6$, so we can restrict the x-values we consider to $x \geq 6$. Also, $\sqrt{x-6} \geq 0$, so we can square both sides giving

$$(\sqrt{x-6})^2 < 2^2,$$
$$x - 6 < 4,$$
$$x < 10.$$

However, we are only considering x-values which are 6 or larger, so $\sqrt{x-6} < 4$ for $6 \leq x < 10$.

Example 10   Solve for x: $\sqrt{2-x} > 3$.

Solution   Squaring both sides gives

$$(\sqrt{2-x})^2 > 3^2,$$
$$2 - x > 9,$$
$$-x > 7,$$
$$x < -7.$$

In this case, the fact that the radical is only defined for $x \leq 2$ does not affect our solution because any number which is less than -7 is also less than 2.

Inequalities and Interval Notation

Inequalities can be used to describe sets of numbers. For instance $x \leq 5$ represents the set of all real numbers less than or equal to 5. Likewise, $x \geq -2$ represents the set of all real numbers greater than or equal to -2. Graphically, we represent the set of real numbers less than or equal to 5 as

5

The dot at 5 shows that the number 5 is included. Alternatively, this set of real numbers can be represented using interval notation. For example, $x \leq 5$ can be written as $(-\infty, 5]$, where $-\infty$ means that we consider arbitrarily large negative numbers.

Example 11   Represent the intervals (a) $-2 \le y \le 5$ (b) $-2 < y < 5$ graphically and using interval notation.

Solution

(a)

and [−2, 5].

(b)

and (−2, 5).

Notice that the endpoint of an interval is included if the dot on a number line is filled in, or if square brackets, [,], are used in interval notation. If the dot is not filled in or parentheses, (,), are used in the interval notation, the endpoint of the intervals is not included.

Example 12   Use interval notation to represent the following intervals of real numbers:

(a) $-2 \le x < 3$ (b) $r < 0$ (c) $10 < t \le 17.5$

(d) $\dfrac{1}{2} \le w \le \dfrac{9}{2}$ (e) $-12 < r$ (f) $|x| < 9$

Solution

(a) [−2, 3)   (b) (−∞, 0)   (c) (10, 17.5]
(d) [1/2, 9/2]   (e) (−12, ∞)   (f) (−9, 9)

Problems for Section H

Solve the inequalities in Problems 1–15 mentally.

1. $2(x - 7) \ge 0$ 2. $\sqrt{x} > 4$ 3. $x^2 < 25$
4. $x - 3 > 2$ 5. $1 + \sqrt{x + 4} > 0$ 6. $|t| < 5$
7. $x^2 \ge 16$ 8. $1 + x^2 > 0$ 9. $5 - x < 0$
10. $2^{-x} > 0$ 11. $|\theta| - 1 \le 7$ 12. $2x^2 + 1 < 0$
13. $\dfrac{x - 5}{x^2 + 1} > 0$ 14. $e^t(t + 3) < 0$ 15. $\dfrac{2 + z}{5 + z^4} < 0$

Write the statements in Problem 16–21 as inequalities.

16. The x-values which are less than 0.001   17. The y-values between −1 and 1
18. All p-values except 5   19. All the positive values of k
20. All the r-values which are not negative   21. The t-values during or after the year 1995

For Problems 22–35, solve the following inequalities and graph the solutions on a number line.

22. $x - 3 > 1$ 23. $3x - 5 > 1$ 24. $-2x > 8$ 25. $-4x + 7 < 13$

26. $x^2 - 5x + 6 > 0$ 27. $x^2 - 7x < 8$ 28. $\dfrac{1}{x - 3} > 0$ 29. $\dfrac{2}{x - 5} > 3$

30. $|x| > 2$ 31. $|y - 2| > 4$ 32. $|3w - 2| - 4 < 0$ 33. $|2z - 7| < 8$
34. $|r| \ge 0$ 35. $|r| < 0$

In Problems 36–47, determine the real number values of the variable (if any) which will make each expression (a) undefined, (b) zero, (c) positive, (d) negative.

36. $3x^2 + 6x$

37. $(2x)e^x + x^2 e^x$

38. 2^{-x}

39. $6t^2 - 30t + 36$

40. $\frac{1}{3}x^{-2/3}$

41. $\frac{-24}{p^3}$

42. $\frac{1}{2\sqrt{x^2+1}}(2x)$

43. $\frac{\ln x}{x}$

44. $\frac{t-3}{t^2+10}$

45. $\frac{x-1}{x-2}$

46. $\frac{1-3u^2}{(u^2+1)^3}$

47. $-\frac{2x-1}{(x(x-1))^2}$

Solve the inequalities in Problems 48–59.

48. $4 - x^2 > 0$

49. $-1 \le 4x - 3 \le 1$

50. $0 \le \frac{1}{2} - n < 11$

51. $\sqrt{3l} - \frac{1}{4} > 0$

52. $t^2 - 3t - 4 \ge 0$

53. $2(x-1)(x+4) + (x-1)^2 > 0$

54. $\frac{5x}{3} - \frac{3}{2} \le \frac{8x}{5}$

55. $\frac{1}{x} < \frac{1}{2}$

56. $2 + \frac{r}{r-3} > 0$

57. $\frac{1}{x} > \frac{1}{x+1}$

58. $\frac{2x^2 - (2x+1)(2x)}{x^4} < 0$

59. $\frac{3(x+2)^2 - 6x(x+2)}{(x+2)^4} > 0$

I SIGNIFICANT DIGITS

- Scientific Notation
- Significant Digits
- Calculation Accuracy

Many calculations in the real world deal with figures that are only approximate. After a series of calculations with approximate measurements, what can be said about the accuracy of the final answer? It seems reasonable to assume that a final answer cannot be any more accurate than the least accurate figure used in the calculation. This is an important point, since calculators tend to give the impression that greater accuracy is achieved than is warranted. In this section we introduce *scientific notation* and we use this concept in a discussion of *significant digits*. We will then be able to set up conventions for indicating the accuracy of the results of certain calculations involving approximate quantities. We will be guided by these conventions throughout the text when writing a final answer to a problem.

Scientific Notation

Work in science and engineering often involves the use of very large numbers. For example, the distance that light travels in 1 yr is called a **light-year.** This distance is approximately

$$9,440,000,000,000 \text{ km}$$

Very small numbers are also used. For example, the mass of a water molecule is approximately

$$0.000\,000\,000\,000\,000\,000\,000\,03 \text{ g}$$

It is generally troublesome to write and work with numbers of this type in standard decimal form. In fact, these two numbers cannot even be entered into most calculators as they are written. Fortunately, it is possible to represent any decimal form as the product of a number between 1 and 10 and an integer power of 10; that is, in the form

$$a \times 10^n \qquad 1 \le a < 10, n \text{ \textbf{an integer}}, a \text{ \textbf{in decimal form}}$$

A number expressed in this form is said to be in **scientific notation.**

Example 1   Using scientific notation

Each number is written in scientific notation.

$$4 = 4 \times 10^0 \qquad\qquad 0.36 = 3.6 \times 10^{-1}$$
$$63 = 6.3 \times 10 \qquad\qquad 0.0702 = 7.02 \times 10^{-2}$$
$$805 = 8.05 \times 10^2 \qquad\qquad 0.005\ 32 = 5.32 \times 10^{-3}$$
$$3{,}143 = 3.143 \times 10^3 \qquad\qquad 0.000\ 67 = 6.7 \times 10^{-4}$$
$$7{,}320{,}000 = 7.32 \times 10^6 \qquad\qquad 0.000\ 000\ 54 = 5.4 \times 10^{-7}$$

Can you discover a rule that relates the number of decimal places a decimal point is moved to the power of 10 used?

$$7{,}320{,}000 = 7.320\ 000.\ \times 10^6 = 7.32 \times 10^6$$

6 places left

Positive exponent

$$0.000\ 000\ 54 = 0.000\ 000\ 5.4 \times 10^{-7} = 5.4 \times 10^{-7}$$

7 places right

Negative exponent

Matched Problem 1   Write in scientific notation:

(a) 450   (b) 360,000   (c) 0.0372   (d) 0.000 001 43

Most calculators express very large and very small numbers in scientific notation. Read the instruction manual for your calculator to see how numbers in scientific notation are entered into your calculator. Numbers in scientific notation are displayed in most calculators as follows:

Calculator display	Number represented
3.207418 −13	$3.207\ 418 \times 10^{-13}$
5.002193 12	$5.002\ 193 \times 10^{12}$

Significant Digits

Suppose we wish to compute the area of a rectangle with the dimensions shown in Figure 1. As it often happens with approximations, we have one dimension to one decimal place accuracy and the other to two decimal place accuracy.

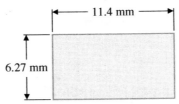

Figure 1:

*Dashed "think boxes" indicate steps that can be performed mentally once a concept or procedure is understood.

Using a calculator and the formula for the area of a rectangle, $A = ab$, we have

$$A = (11.4)(6.27) = 71.478$$

How many decimal places are justified in this calculation? We will answer this question later in this section. First, we must introduce the idea of *significant digits*.

Whenever we write a measurement such as 11.4 mm, we assume that the measurement is accurate to the last digit written. Thus, 11.4 mm indicates that the measurement was made to the nearest tenth of a millimeter—that is, the actual length is between 11.35 mm and 11.45 mm. In general, the digits in a number that indicate the accuracy of the number are called **significant digits.** If (going from left to right) the first digit and the last digit of a number are not 0, then all the digits are significant. Thus, the measurements 11.4 and 6.27 in Figure 1 have three significant digits, the number 100.8 has four significant digits, and the number 10,102 has five significant digits.

If the last digit of a number is 0, then the number of significant digits may not be clear. Suppose we are given a length of 23.0 cm. Then we assume the measurement has been taken to the nearest tenth and say that the number has three significant digits. However, suppose we are told that the distance between two cities is 3,700 mi. Is the stated distance accurate to the nearest hundred, ten, or unit? That is, does the stated distance have two, three, or four significant digits? We cannot really tell. In order to resolve this ambiguity, we give a precise definition of significant digits using scientific notation.

SIGNIFICANT DIGITS

If a number x is written in scientific notation as

$$x = a \times 10^n \qquad 1 \le a < 10, n \text{ an integer}$$

then the number of significant digits in x is the number of digits in a.

Thus,

$$3.7 \times 10^3 \quad \text{has two significant digits}$$
$$3.70 \times 10^3 \quad \text{has three significant digits}$$
$$3.700 \times 10^3 \quad \text{has four significant digits}$$

All three of these measurements have the same decimal representation, 3,700, but each represents a different accuracy.

Example 2   Determining the number of significant digits

Indicate the number of significant digits in each of the following numbers:

(a) 9.1003×10^{-3} (b) 1.080×10 (c) 5.92×10^{22} (d) 7.9000×10^{-13}

Solution   In all cases the number of significant digits is the number of digits in the number to the left of the multiplication sign (as stated in the definition).

(a) Five   (b) Four   (c) Three   (d) Five

Matched Problem 2   Indicate the number of significant digits in each of the following numbers:

(a) 4.39×10^{12} (b) 1.020×10^{-7} (c) 2.3905×10^{-1} (d) 3.00×10

The definition of significant digits tells us how to write a number so that the number of significant digits is clear, but it does not tell us how to interpret the accuracy of a number that is not written in scientific notation. We will use the following convention for numbers that are written as decimal fractions.

SIGNIFICANT DIGITS IN DECIMAL FRACTIONS

The number of significant digits in **a number with no decimal point** is found by counting the digits from left to right, starting with the first digit and ending with the last *nonzero* digit.

The number of significant digits in **a number containing a decimal point** is found by counting the digits from left to right, starting with the first *nonzero* digit and ending with the last digit (which may be 0).

Applying this convention to the number 3,700, we conclude that this number (as written) has two significant digits. If we want to indicate that it has three or four significant digits, we must use scientific notation. The significant digits in the following numbers are underlined.

$$34{,}007 \qquad 920{,}000 \qquad 25.300 \qquad 0.0063 \qquad 0.000\ 430$$

Calculation Accuracy

When performing calculations, we want an answer that is as accurate as the numbers used in the calculation warrant, but no more. In calculations involving multiplication, division, powers, and roots, we adopt the following accuracy convention (which is justified in courses in numerical analysis).

ACCURACY OF CALCULATED VALUES

The number of significant digits in a calculation involving multiplication, division, powers, and/or roots is the same as the number of significant digits in the number in the calculation with the smallest number of significant digits.

Applying this convention to the calculation of the area A of the rectangle in Figure 1, we have

$$A = (11.4)(6.27) \qquad \text{Both numbers have three significant digits.}$$
$$= 71.478 \qquad \text{Calculator computation}$$
$$= 71.5 \qquad \text{The computed area is only accurate to three significant digits.}$$

Example 3   Determining the accuracy of computed values

Perform the indicated operations on the given approximate numbers. Then use the accuracy conventions stated above to round each answer to the appropriate accuracy.

(a) $\dfrac{(204)(34.0)}{120}$

(b) $\dfrac{\left(2.50 \times 10^5\right)\left(3.007 \times 10^7\right)}{2.4 \times 10^6}$

Solution

(a) $\dfrac{(204)(34.0)}{120}$ 120 has the least number of significant digits (two).

$= 57.8$ Calculator computation

$= 58$ Answer must have the same number of significant digits as the number with the least number of significant digits (two).

(b) $\dfrac{(2.50 \times 10^5)(3.007 \times 10^7)}{2.4 \times 10^6}$ 2.4×10^6 has the least number of significant digits (two).

$= 3.132\,291\ldots \times 10^6$ Calculator computation

$= 3.1 \times 10^6$ Answer must have the same number of significant digits as the number with the least number of significant digits (two).

Matched Problem 3

Perform the indicated operations on the given approximate numbers. Then use the rounding conventions stated above to write each answer with the appropriate accuracy.

(a) $\dfrac{2.30}{(0.0341)(2.674)}$ (b) $\dfrac{1.235 \times 10^8}{(3.07 \times 10^{-3})(1.20 \times 10^4)}$

We complete this section with two important observations:

1. Many formulas have constants that represent exact quantities. Such quantities are assumed to have infinitely many significant digits. For example, the formula for the circumference of a circle, $C = 2\pi r$, has two constants that are exact, 2 and π. Consequently, the final answer will have as many significant digits as in the measurement r (radius).
2. How do we round a number if the last nonzero digit is 5? For example, the following product should have only two significant digits. Do we change the 2 to a 3 or leave it alone?

$(1.3)(2.5) = 3.25$ Calculator result: Should be rounded to two significant digits.

We will round to 3.2 following the conventions given in the box.

ROUNDING NUMBERS WHEN LAST NONZERO DIGIT IS 5

(a) If **the digit preceding 5 is odd,** round up 1 to make it even.
(b) If **the digit preceding 5 is even,** do not change it.

We have adopted these conventions in order to prevent the accumulation of round-off errors with numbers having the last nonzero digit 5. The idea is to round up 50% of the time. (There are a number of other ways to accomplish this—flipping a coin, for example.)

Example 4

Rounding numbers when last nonzero digit is 5

Round each number to three significant digits.

(a) 3.1495   (b) 0.004 135   (c) 32,450   (d) $4.314\,764\,09 \times 10^{12}$

Solution   (a) 3.15   (b) 0.00414   (c) 32,400   (d) 4.31×10^{12}

Matched Problem 4

Round each number to three significant digits.

(a) 43.0690   (b) 48.05   (c) 48.15   (d) $8.017\ 632 \times 10^{-3}$

Answers to Matched Problems

1. (a) 4.5×10^2 (b) 3.6×10^5 (c) 3.72×10^{-2} (d) 1.43×10^{-6}
2. (a) Three   (b) Four   (c) Five   (d) Three
3. (a) 25.2   (b) 3.35×10^6
4. (a) 43.1   (b) 48.0   (c) 48.2   (d) 8.02×10^{-3}

Problems for Section I

Write in scientific notation.

1. 640
2. 384
3. 5,460,000,000
4. 38,400,000
5. 0.73
6. 0.00493
7. 0.000 000 32
8. 0.0836
9. 0.000 049 1
10. 435,640
11. 67,000,000,000
12. 0.000 000 043 2

Write as a decimal fraction.

13. 5.6×10^4
14. 3.65×10^6
15. 9.7×10^{-3}
16. 6.39×10^{-6}
17. 4.61×10^{12}
18. 3.280×10^9
19. 1.08×10^{-1}
20. 3.004×10^{-4}

Indicate the number of significant digits in each number.

21. 12.3
22. 123
23. 12.300
24. 0.00123
25. 0.01230
26. 12.30
27. 6.7×10^{-1}
28. 3.56×10^{-4}
29. 6.700×10^{-1}
30. 3.560×10^{-4}
31. 7.090×10^5
32. 6.0050×10^7

Round each to three significant digits.

33. 635,431
34. 4,089,100
35. 86.85
36. 7.075
37. 0.004 652 3
38. 0.000 380 0

Write in scientific notation, rounding to two significant digits.

39. 734
40. 908
41. 0.040
42. 700
43. 0.000 435
44. 635.46813

Indicate how many significant digits should be in the final answer.

45. (32.8)(0.2035)
46. (0.00230)(25.67)
47. $\dfrac{(7.21)(360)}{1,200}$
48. $\dfrac{(0.0350)(621)}{8,543}$
49. $\dfrac{\left(5.03 \times 10^{-3}\right)\left(6 \times 10^4\right)}{8.0}$
50. $\dfrac{3.27\left(1.8 \times 10^7\right)}{2.90 \times 10}$

Using a calculator, compute each of the following, and express each answer with appropriate accuracy.

51. $\dfrac{6.07}{0.5057}$
52. (53,100)(0.2467)
53. $(6.14 \times 10^9)(3.154 \times 10^{-1})$
54. $\dfrac{7.151 \times 10^6}{9.1 \times 10^{-1}}$
55. $\dfrac{6,730}{(2.30)(0.0551)}$
56. $\dfrac{63,100}{(0.0620)(2,920)}$

In the following formulas, the indicated constants are exact. Compute the answer to each problem to an accuracy appropriate for the given approximate values of the variables.

57. Circumference of a Circle $C = 2\pi r$; $r = 25.31$ cm

58. Area of a Circle $A = \pi r^2$; $r = 2.5$ in.

59. Area of a Triangle $A = \frac{1}{2}bh$; $b = 22.4$ ft, $h = 8.6$ ft

60. Area of an Ellipse $A = \pi ab$; $a = 0.45$ cm, $b = 1.35$ cm

61. Surface Area of a Sphere $S = 4\pi r^2$; $r = 1.5$ mm

62. Volume of a Sphere $S = \frac{4}{3}\pi r^3$; $r = 1.85$ in.

In the following formulas, the indicated constants are exact. Compute the value of the indicated variable to an accuracy appropriate for the given approximate values of the other variables in the formula.

63. Volume of a Rectangular Parallelepiped (a Box) $V = lwh$; $V = 24.2$ cm^3, $l = 3.25$ cm, $w = 4.50$ cm, $h = ?$

64. Volume of a Right Circular Cylinder $V = \pi r^2 h$; $V = 1{,}250$ ft^3, $h = 6.4$ ft, $r = ?$

65. Volume of a Right Circular Cone $V = \frac{1}{3}\pi r^2 h$; $V = 1{,}200$ in.^{3}, $h = 6.55$ in., $r = ?$

66. Volume of a Pyramid $V = \frac{1}{3}Ah$; $V = 6{,}000$ m^3, $A = 1{,}100$ m, $h = ?$

J PLANE GEOMETRY

The following four sections include a brief list of plane geometry facts that are of particular use in studying trigonometry. They are grouped together for convenient reference.

J.1 LINES AND ANGLES

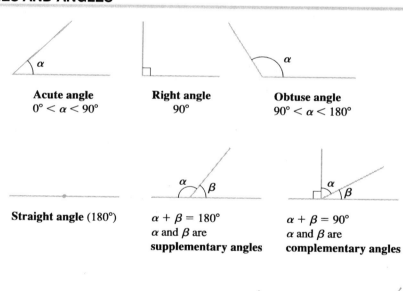

Acute angle
$0° < \alpha < 90°$

Right angle
$90°$

Obtuse angle
$90° < \alpha < 180°$

Straight angle ($180°$)

$\alpha + \beta = 180°$
α and β are
supplementary angles

$\alpha + \beta = 90°$
α and β are
complementary angles

A **straight angle** divided
into equal parts forms
two **right angles**.

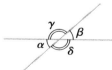

$\alpha = \beta$
$\gamma = \delta$
$\alpha + \delta = \beta + \gamma = 180°$
$\alpha + \delta + \beta + \gamma = 360°$

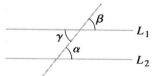

If $L_1 \parallel L_2$, then $\alpha = \beta = \gamma$.
If $\alpha = \beta = \gamma$, then $L_1 \parallel L_2$.

J.2 TRIANGLES

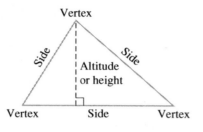

Triangle

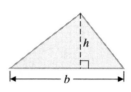

Area: $A = \frac{\pi}{2}bh$

Right triangle
One right angle

(a) **Acute triangle**
All acute angles

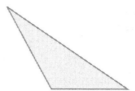

(b) **Obtuse triangle**
One obtuse angle

Oblique triangles
No right angles

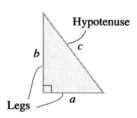

$c^2 = a^2 + b^2$
Pythagorean theorem

$\alpha + \beta = 90°$

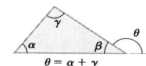

$\theta = \alpha + \gamma$

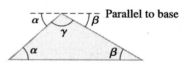

$\alpha + \beta + \gamma = 180°$
The sum of angle measures of
all angles in a triangle is 180°.

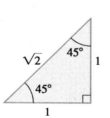

Special triangles

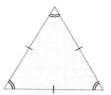

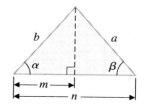

Isosceles triangle
At least two equal sides
At least two equal angles

Equilateral triangle
All sides equal
All angles equal

If $a = b$, then $\alpha = \beta$ and $m = n/2$.
If $\alpha = \beta$, then $a = b$ and $m = n/2$.

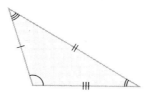

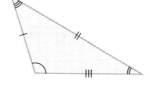

$$\alpha = \alpha', \beta = \beta', \gamma = \gamma'$$

$$\frac{a}{a'} = \frac{b}{b'} = \frac{c}{c'}$$

Similar triangles
Two triangles are similar if two angles of one
triangle are equal to two angles of the other.

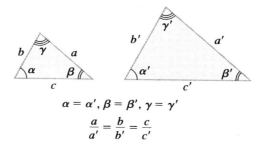

Congruent triangles
Corresponding parts of congruent triangles are equal.

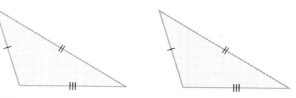

SSS
If three sides of one triangle are equal to the corresponding
sides of another triangle, the two triangles are congruent.

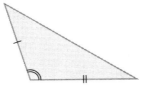
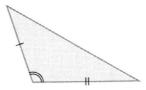

SAS

If two sides and the included angle of one triangle are equal to the corresponding parts of another triangle, the two triangles are congruent.

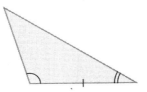
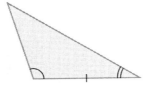

ASA

If two angles and the included side of one triangle are equal to the corresponding parts of another triangle, the two triangles are congruent.

J.3 QUADRILATERALS

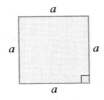
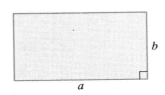

Square
$A = a^2$
$P = 4a$

Rectangle
$A = ab$
$P = 2a + 2b$

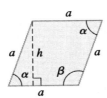
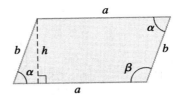

Rhombus
Opposite sides are parallel.
$A = ah$
$P = 4a$
$\alpha + \beta = 180°$

Parallelogram
Opposite sides are parallel.
$A = ah$
$P = 2a + 2b$
$\alpha + \beta = 180°$

J.4 CIRCLES

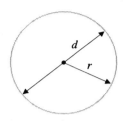
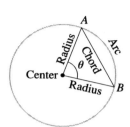

r = Radius
d = Diameter
$d = 2r$
$A = \pi r^2$ (Area)
$C = 2\pi r = \pi d$ (Circumference)
$C/d = \pi$ (For all circles)

$\overset{\frown}{AB}$ = Arc AB
AB = Chord AB
$\angle\,\theta$ subtends AB
$\angle\,\theta$ subtends $\overset{\frown}{AB}$
$\overset{\frown}{AB}$ subtends $\angle\,\theta$
AB subtends $\angle\,\theta$

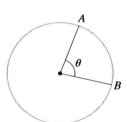
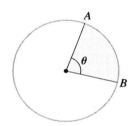

$$\frac{\overset{\frown}{AB}}{C} = \frac{\theta}{360°}$$

(C = Circumference)

Circular sector

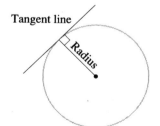
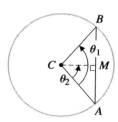
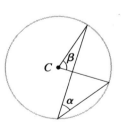

A radius of a circle
is $\perp$ to a tangent line
at the point of tangency.

If $CM \perp AB$, then

$AM = \frac{\pi}{2}AB$

$\theta_2 = \frac{\pi}{2}\theta_1$

$\beta = 2\alpha$

K RIGHT TRIANGLE RATIOS

If you were asked to find your height, you would no doubt take a ruler or tape measure and measure it directly. But if you were asked to find the area of your bedroom floor in square feet, you would not be likely to measure the area directly by laying 1 ft squares over the entire floor and counting them. Instead, you would probably find the area **indirectly** by using the formula $A = ab$ from plane geometry, where A represents the area of the room and a and b are the lengths of its sides, as indicated in the figure in the margin.

$$A = ab \quad b$$

$$a$$

In general, **indirect measurement** is a process of determining unknown measurements from known measurements by a reasoning process. How do we measure quantities such as the volumes of containers, the distance to the center of the earth, the area of the surface of the earth, and the distances to the sun and the stars? All these measurements are accomplished indirectly by the use of special formulas and deductive reasoning.

The Greeks in Alexandria, during the period 300 BC–AD 200, contributed substantially to the art of indirect measurement by developing formulas for finding areas, volumes, and lengths. Using these formulas, they were able to determine the circumference of the earth (with an error of only about 2%) and to estimate the distance to the moon. We will examine these measurements as well as others in the sections that follow.

It was during the early part of this Greek period that trigonometry, the study of triangles, was born. Hipparchus (160–127 BC), one of the greatest astronomers of the ancient world, is credited with making the first systematic study of the indirect measurement of triangles.

K.1 ANGLES, DEGREES, AND ARCS

- Angles
- Degree Measure of Angles
- Angles and Arcs
- Approximation of Earth's Circumference
- Approximation of the Diameters of the Sun and Moon; Total Solar Eclipse

Angles and the degree measure of an angle are the first concepts introduced in this section. Then, a very useful relationship between angles and arcs of circles is developed. This simple relationship between an angle and an arc will enable us to measure indirectly many useful quantities such as the circumference of the earth and the diameter of the sun. (If you are rusty on certain geometric relationships and facts, refer to Appendix C as needed.)

Angles

Central to the study of trigonometry is the concept of angle. An **angle** is formed by rotating a half-line, called a **ray,** around its end point. One ray k, called the **initial side** of the angle, remains fixed; a second ray l, called the **terminal side** of the angle, starts in the initial side position and rotates around the common end point P in a plane until it reaches its terminal position. The common end point P is called the **vertex.** (See Fig. 1.)

We may refer to the angle in Figure 1 in any of the following ways:

Angle θ $\angle \theta$ Angle QPR $\angle QPR$
Angle P $\angle P$

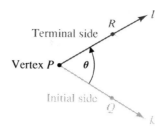

Figure 1: Angle θ: A ray rotated around its end point

The symbol $\angle$ denotes *angle*. The Greek letters theta (θ), alpha (α), beta (β), and gamma (γ) are often used to name angles.

There is no restriction on the amount or direction of rotation in a given plane. When the terminal side is rotated counterclockwise, the angle formed is **positive** (see Figs. 1 and 2a); when it is rotated clockwise, the angle formed is **negative** (see Fig. 2b). Two different angles may have the same initial and terminal sides, as shown in Figure 2c. Such angles are said to be **coterminal.** In this chapter we will concentrate on positive angles; we will consider more general angles in detail in subsequent chapters.

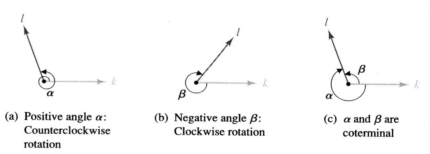

(a) Positive angle α:
Counterclockwise
rotation

(b) Negative angle β:
Clockwise rotation

(c) α and β are
coterminal

Figure 2:

Degree Measure of Angles

To compare angles of different sizes a standard unit of measure is necessary. Just as a line segment can be measured in inches, meters, or miles, an angle is measured in *degrees* or *radians*.

DEGREE MEASURE OF ANGLES

An angle fromed by one complete revolution of the terminal side in a counterclockwise direction has **measure 360 degrees**, written **360°**. An angle of **1 degree measure**, written **1°**, is formed by $\frac{1}{360}$ of one complete revolution in a counterclockwise direction.

360° angle   1° angle

Angles of measure 90° and 180° represent $\frac{90}{360} = \frac{1}{4}$ and $\frac{180}{360} = 12$ of complete revolutions, respectively. A 90° angle is called a **right angle** and a 180° angle is called a **straight angle.** An **acute angle** has angle measure between 0° and 90°. An **obtuse angle** has angle measure between 90° and 180°. (See Fig. 3.)

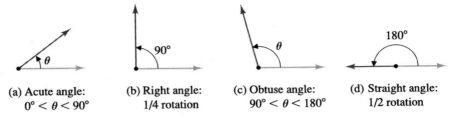

Figure 3: Special angles

Remark

In Figure 3 we used θ in two different ways: to name an angle and to represent the measure of an angle. This usage is common; the context will dictate the interpretation.

Two positive angles are **complementary** if the sum of their measures is 90°; they are **supplementary** if the sum of their measures is 180° (see Fig. 4).

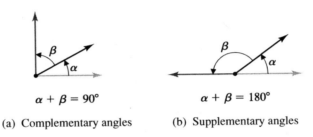

(a) Complementary angles   (b) Supplementary angles

Figure 4

A degree can be divided using decimal notation. For example, 36.25° represents an angle of degree measure 36 plus one-fourth of 1 degree. A degree can also be divided into minutes and seconds just as an hour is divided into minutes and seconds. Each degree is divided into 60 equal parts called minutes ($'$), and each minute is divided into 60 equal parts called seconds ($''$). Thus,

$$5°12'32''$$

is a concise way of writing 5 degrees, 12 minutes, and 32 seconds.

Degree measure in **decimal degree (DD)** form is useful in some instances, and degree measure in **degree-minute-second (DMS)** form is useful in others. You should be able to go from one form to the other as illustrated in Examples 1 and 2. Many calculators can perform the conversion either way automatically, but the process varies significantly among the various types of calculators—consult your user's manual. Examples 1 and 2 first illustrate a nonautomatic approach so that you will understand the process. This is followed by an automatic calculator approach that can be used for efficiency.

Conversion Accuracy

If an angle is measured to the nearest second, the converted decimal form should not go beyond three decimal places, and vice versa.

Example 1   From DMS to DD

Convert $12°6'23''$ to decimal degree form.

Solution   **Method I** *Multistep conversion.* Since

$$6' = \left(\frac{6}{60}\right)^{\circ} \qquad \text{and} \qquad 23'' = \left(\frac{23}{3,600}\right)^{\circ}$$

then

$$12°6'23'' = \left(12 + \frac{6}{60} + \frac{23}{3{,}600}\right)°^*$$

$$= 12.106° \qquad\qquad \text{To three decimal places}$$

Method II *Single-step calculator conversion.* Consult the user's manual for your particular calculator. The conversion shown in Figure 5 is from a graphing calculator.

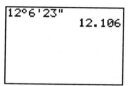

Figure 5: From DMS to DD

Matched Problem 1

Convert $128°42'8''$ to decimal degree form.

EXPLORE/DISCUSS 1

In 1988, Belayneh Densimo of Ethiopia ran the world's fastest recorded time for a marathon: 42.2 km in 2 hr, 6 min, 50 sec. Convert the hour-minute-second form to decimal hours. Explain the similarity of this conversion to the conversion of a degree-minute-second form to a decimal degree form.

Example 2

Convert $35.413°$ to a degree-minute-second form.

Solution

Method I *Multistep conversion.*

$$35.413° = 35°(0.413 \cdot 60')$$

$$= 35°24.78'$$

$$= 35°24'(0.78 \cdot 60)''$$

$$\approx 35°24'47''$$

Method II *Single-step calculator conversion.* Consult the user's manual for your particular calculator. The conversion shown in Figure 6 is from a graphing calculator. Rounded to the nearest second, we get the same result as in method I: $35°24'47''$.

Matched Problem 2

Convert $72.103°$ to degree-minute-second form.

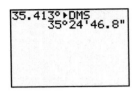

Figure 6: From DD to DMS

Angles and Arcs

Given an arc RQ of a circle with center P, the angle RPQ is said to be the **central angle** that is **subtended** by the arc RQ. We also say that the arc RQ is subtended by the angle RPQ; see Figure 7.

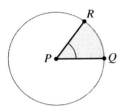

Figure 7: Central angle RPQ subtended by arc RQ

It follows from the definition of degree that a central angle subtended by an arc $\frac{1}{4}$ the circumference of a circle has degree measure 90; $\frac{1}{2}$ the circumference of a circle, degree measure 180, and the whole circumference of a circle, degree measure 360. In general, to determine the degree measure of an angle θ subtended by an arc of s units for a circle with circumference C units, use the following proportion:

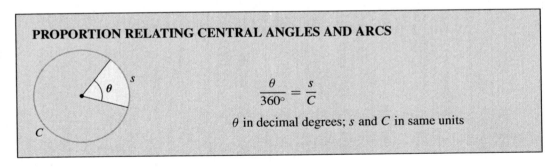

PROPORTION RELATING CENTRAL ANGLES AND ARCS

$$\frac{\theta}{360°} = \frac{s}{C}$$

θ in decimal degrees; s and C in same units

If we know any two of the three quantities, s, C, or θ, we can find the third by using simple algebra. For example, in a circle with circumference 72 in., the degree measure of a central angle θ subtended by an arc of length 12 in. is given by

$$\theta = \frac{12}{72} \cdot 360° = 60°$$

Remark   Note that "an angle of 6°" means "an angle of degree measure 6," and "$\theta = 72°$" means "the degree measure of angle θ is 72."

Approximation of Earth's Circumference

The early Greeks were aware of the proportion relating central angles and arcs, which Eratosthenes (240 BC) used in his famous calculation of the circumference of the earth. He reasoned as follows: It was well-known that at Syene (now Aswan), during the summer solstice, the noon sun was reflected on the water in a deep well (this meant the sun shone straight down the well and must be directly overhead). Eratosthenes reasoned that if the sun rays entering the well were continued down into the earth, they would pass through its center (see Fig. 8). On the same day at the same time, 5,000 stadia (approx. 500 mi) due north, in Alexandria, sun rays crossed a vertical pole at an angle of 7.5° as indicated in Figure 8. Since sun rays are very nearly parallel when they reach the earth, "Eratosthenes concluded that ∠ACS was also 7.5°. (Why?)*

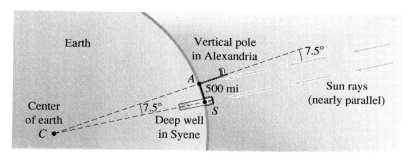

Figure 8: Estimating the earth's circumference

Even though Eratosthenes' reasoning was profound, his final calculation of the circumference of the earth requires only elementary algebra:

$$\frac{s}{C} = \frac{\theta}{360°}$$
$$\frac{500 \text{ mi}}{C} \approx \frac{7.5°}{360°}$$
$$C \approx \frac{360}{7.5}(500 \text{ mi}) = 24,000 \text{ mi}$$

The value calculated today is 24,875 mi.

The diameter of the earth (d) and the radius (r) can be found from this value using the formulas $C = 2\pi r$ and $d = 2r$ from plane geometry. [*Note:* $\pi = C/d$ for all circles.] The constant π has a long and interesting history; a few important dates are listed below:

1650 BC	Rhind Papyrus	$\pi \approx \frac{256}{81} = 3.16049 \cdots$
240 BC	Archimedes	$3\frac{10}{71} < \pi < 3\frac{1}{7}$
		$(3.1408 \ldots < \pi < 3.1428 \ldots)$
AD 264	Liu Hui	$\pi \approx 3.14159$
AD 470	Tsu Ch'ung-chih	$\pi \approx \frac{355}{113} = 3.1415929 \ldots$
AD 1674	Leibniz	$\pi = 4(1 - \frac{1}{3} + \frac{1}{5} - \frac{1}{7} + \frac{1}{9} - \frac{1}{11} + \ldots)$
		$\approx 3.141592653589793238462 6$
		(This and other series can be used to compute π to any decimal accuracy desired.)
AD 1761	Johann Lambert	Showed π to be irrational (π as a decimal is nonrepeating and nonterminating)

---

* If line p crosses parallel lines m and n, then angles α and β have the same measure.

Example 3   Arc length

How large an arc is subtended by a central angle of 6.23° on a circle with radius 10 cm? (Compute the answer to two decimal places.)

Solution   Since

$$\frac{s}{C} = \frac{\theta}{360°} \quad \text{and} \quad C = 2\pi r$$

then

$$\frac{s}{2\pi r} = \frac{\theta}{360°} \qquad \text{Replace C with } 2\pi r.$$

$$\frac{s}{2(\pi)(10 \text{ cm})} = \frac{6.23°}{360°}$$

$$s = \frac{2(\pi)(10 \text{ cm})(6.23)}{360} = 1.09 \text{ cm}$$

Matched Problem 3   How large an arc is subtended by a central angle of 50.73° on a circle with radius 5 m? (Compute the answer to two decimal places.)

Approximation of the Diameters of the Sun and Moon; Total Solar Eclipse

Example 4   Sun's Diameter

If the distance from the earth to the sun is 93,000,000 mi, find the diameter of the sun (to the nearest thousand miles) if it subtends an angle of 0°31′55″ on the surface of the earth.

Solution   For small central angles in circles with very large radii, the **intercepted arc** (arc opposite the central angle) and its **chord** (the straight line joining the end points of the arc) are approximately the same length (see Fig. 9). We thus use the intercepted arc to approximate its chord in many practical problems, particularly when the length of the intercepted arc is easier to compute. We apply these

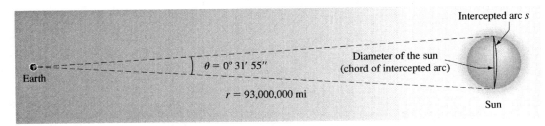

Figure 9

ideas to finding the diameter of the sun as follows:

$$\theta = 0°31′55″ = 0.532°$$

$$\frac{s}{2\pi r} = \frac{\theta}{360°}$$

$$s = \frac{2\pi r \theta}{360} = \frac{2(\pi)(93,000,000 \text{ mi})(0.532)}{360} = 864,000 \text{ mi}$$

Matched Problem 4

If the moon subtends an angle of about $0°31'50''$ on the surface of the earth when it is 239,000 mi from the earth, estimate its diameter to the nearest 10 mi.

Answers to Matched Problem

1. $128.702°$ **2.** $72°6'11''$ **3.** 4.42 m   **4.** $2,160$ mi

---

EXPLORE/DISCUSS 2

A total solar eclipse will occur when the moon passes between the earth and the sun and the angle subtended by the diameter of the moon is at least as large as the angle subtended by the diameter of the sun (see Fig. 10).

(a) Since the distances from the sun and moon to the earth vary with time, explain what happens to the angles subtended by the diameters of the sun and moon as their distances from the earth increase and decrease.

(b) For a total solar eclipse to occur when the moon passes between the sun and the earth, would it be better for the sun to be as far away as possible and the moon to be as close as possible, or vice versa? Explain.

(c) The diameters of the sun and moon are, respectively, 864,000 mi and 2,160 mi. Find the maximum distance that the moon can be from the earth for a total solar eclipse when the sun is at its maximum distance from the earth, 94,500,000 mi.

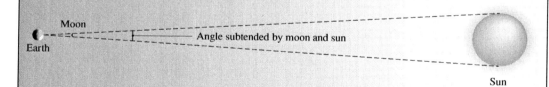

Figure 10: Total solar eclipse

Problems for Section K.1

A In Problems 1 and 2, find the number of degrees in the angle formed by rotating the terminal side counterclockwise through the indicated fraction of a revolution.

1. $\dfrac{1}{2}, \dfrac{1}{6}, \dfrac{3}{8}, \dfrac{7}{12}$

2. $\dfrac{1}{4}, \dfrac{1}{3}, \dfrac{7}{8}, \dfrac{11}{12}$

In Problems 3 and 4, find the fraction of a counterclockwise revolution that will form an angle with the indicated number of degrees.

3. $45°, 150°, 270°$

4. $30°, 225°, 240°$

In Problems 5–12, identify the following angles as acute, right, obtuse, or straight. If the angle is none of these, say so.

5. $50°$ **6.** $150°$ **7.** $90°$

8. $180°$ **9.** $135°$ **10.** $185°$

11. $250°$ **12.** $89°$

*13. Discuss the meaning of an angle of 1 degree.

*14. Discuss the meaning of minutes and seconds in angle measure.

B In Problems 15–20, change to decimal degrees accurate to three decimal places:

15. $25°21'54''$ **16.** $71°43'30''$ **17.** $11°8'5''$

18. $9°3'1''$ **19.** $195°28'10''$ **20.** $267°11'25''$

In Problems 21–26, change to degree-minute-second form:

21. $15.125°$ **22.** $35.425°$ **23.** $79.201°$

24. $52.927°$ **25.** $159.639°$ **26.** $235.253°$

*27. Which of the angle measures, $47°33'41''$ or $47.556°$, is the larger? Explain how you obtained your answer.

*28. Runner A ran a marathon in 3 hr, 43 min, 24 sec, and runner B in 3.732 hr. Which runner is faster? Explain how you obtained your answer.

In Problems 29–34, write $\alpha < \beta, \alpha = \beta$, or $\alpha > \beta$, as appropriate.

29. $\alpha = 47°23'31''$
$\beta = 47.386°$

30. $\alpha = 32°51'54''$
$\beta = 32.865°$

31. $\alpha = 125°27'18''$
$\beta = 125.455°$

32. $\alpha = 80.668°$
$\beta = 80°40'20''$

33. $\alpha = 20.512°$
$\beta = 20°30'50''$

34. $\alpha = 242.311°$
$\beta = 242°18'32''$

In Problems 35–38, perform the indicated operations directly on a calculator. Express the answers in DMS form. For example, a particular graphing calculator performs the following calculation $(67°13'4'' - 45°27'32'')$ as follows:

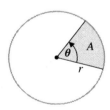

35. $47°37'49'' + 62°40'15''$

36. $105°53'22'' + 26°38'55''$

37. $90° - 67°37'29''$

38. $180° - 121°51'22''$

In Problems 39–46, find C, θ, s, or r as indicated. Refer to the figure:

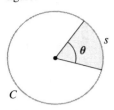

39. $C = 1,000$ cm, $\theta = 36°, s = ?$ (exact)

40. $s = 12$ m, $C = 108$ m, $\theta = ?$ (exact)

41. $s = 25$ km, $\theta = 20°$, $C = ?$ (exact)

42. $C = 740$ mi, $\theta = 72°$, $s = ?$ (exact)

43. $r = 5,400,000$ mi, $\theta = 2.6°$, $s = ?$
(to the nearest 10,000 mi)

C

44. $s = 38,000$ cm, $\theta = 45.3°$, $r = ?$
(to the nearest 1,000 cm)

45. $\theta = 12°31'4''$, $s = 50.2$ cm, $C = ?$
(to the nearest 10 cm)

46. $\theta = 24°16'34''$, $s = 14.23$ m, $C = ?$
(to one decimal place)

In Problems 47–50, find A or θ as indicated. Refer to the figure: The ratio of the area of a sector of a circle (A) to the total area of the circle (πr^2) is the same as the ratio of the central angle of the sector (θ) to $360°$:

$$\frac{A}{\pi r^2} = \frac{\theta}{360°}$$

47. $r = 25.2$ cm, $\theta = 47.3°$, $A = ?$
(to the nearest unit)

48. $r = 7.38$ ft, $\theta = 24.6°$, $A = ?$
(to one decimal place)

49. $r = 12.6$ m, $A = 98.4$ m^2, $\theta = ?$
(to one decimal place)

50. $r = 32.4$ in., $A = 347$ in.^{2}, $\theta = ?$
(to one decimal place)

---

*A problem that requires a written interpretation or comment and not just a numerical answer.

Applications

Biology: Eye In Problems 51–54, find r, θ, or s as indicated. Refer to the following: The eye is roughly spherical with a spherical bulge in front called the cornea. (Based on the article, "The Surgical Correction of Astigmatism" by Sheldon Rothman and Helen Strassberg in The UMAP Journal, *Vol. V, No. 2, 1984.*)

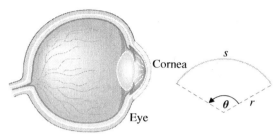

Figure for 51–54

51. $s = 11.5$ mm, $\theta = 118.2°$, $r = ?$
   (to two decimal places)

52. $s = 12.1$ mm, $r = 5.26$ mm, $\theta = ?$
   (to one decimal place)

53. $\theta = 119.7°$, $r = 5.49$ mm, $s = ?$
   (to one decimal place)

54. $\theta = 117.9°$, $s = 11.8$ mm, $r = ?$
   (to two decimal places)

Geography/Navigation In Problems 55–58, find the distance on the surface of the earth between each pair of cities (to the nearest mile), given their respective latitudes. Latitudes are given to the nearest 10′. Note that each chosen pair of cities has approximately the same longitude (ie, lies on the same north–south line). Use $r = 3,960$ mi for the earth's radius. The figure shows the situation for San Francisco and Seattle. [Hint: $C = 2\pi r$]

*55. San Francisco, CA, 37°50′N;
   Seattle, WA, 47°40′N

*56. Phoenix, AZ, 33°30′N;
   Salt Lake City, UT, 40°40′N

*57. Dallas, TX, 32°50′N;   Lincoln, NE, 40°50′N

*58. Buffalo, NY, 42°50′N;   Durham, NC, 36°0′N

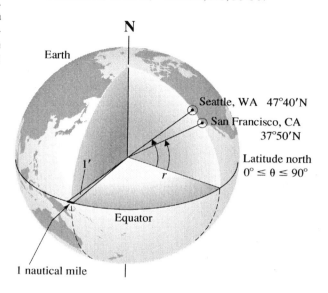

Figure for 55–62

Geography/Navigation

In Problems 59–62, find the distance on the earth's surface, to the nearest nautical mile, between each pair of cities. A **nautical mile** is the length of 1′ of arc on the equator or any other circle on the surface of the earth having the same center as the equator. See the figure. Since there are $60 \times 360 = 21,600′$ in 360°, the length of the equator is 21,600 nautical miles.

59. San Francisco, CA, 37°50′N;   Seattle, WA, 47°40′N

60. Phoenix, AZ, 33°30′N;   Salt Lake City, UT, 40°40′N

61. Dallas, TX, 32°50′N;   Lincoln, NE, 40°50′N

62. Buffalo, NY, 42°50′N;   Durham, NC, 36°0′N

63. Photography

   (a) The angle of view of a 300 mm lens is 8°. Approximate the width of the field of view to the nearest foot when the camera is at a distance of 500 ft.

   (b) Explain the assumptions that are being made in the approximation calculation in part (a).

*The most difficult problems are dobule–starred (**); moderately difficult problem are single-starred (*); easier problems are not marked.

K.2   SIMILAR TRIANGLES

- Euclid's Theorem and Similar Triangles
- Applications

Properties of similar triangles, stated in Euclid's theorem below, are central to this section and form a cornerstone for the development of trigonometry. Euclid (300 BC), a Greek mathematician who taught in Alexandria, was one of the most influential mathematicians of all time. He is most famous for writing the *Elements,* a collection of thirteen books (or chapters) on geometry, geometric algebra, and number theory. In the Western world, next to the Bible, the *Elements* is probably the most studied text of all time.

The ideas on indirect measurement presented here are included to help you understand basic concepts. More efficient methods will be developed in the next section.

Remark   Since calculators routinely compute to eight or ten digits, one could easily believe that a computed result is far more accurate than warranted. **Generally, a final result cannot be any more accurate than the least accurate number used in the calculation. Regarding calculation accuracy, we will be guided by Appendix A.3 on significant digits throughout the text.**

Euclid's Theorem and Similar Triangles

In Section 1.1, problems were included that required knowledge of the distances from the earth to the moon and the sun. How can inaccessible distances of this type be determined? Surprisingly, the ancient Greeks made fairly accurate calculations of these distances as well as many others. The basis for their methods is the following elementary theorem of Euclid:

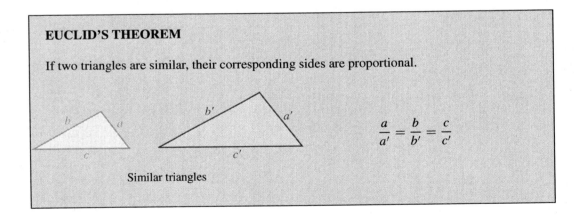

EUCLID'S THEOREM

If two triangles are similar, their corresponding sides are proportional.

$$\frac{a}{a'} = \frac{b}{b'} = \frac{c}{c'}$$

Similar triangles

Remark   Recall from plane geometry that the sum of the measures of the three angles of any triangle is always 180° and that two triangles are similar if two angles of one triangle have the same measure as two angles of the other. If the two triangles happen to be right triangles, then they are similar if an acute angle in one has the same measure as an acute angle in the other. Take a moment to draw a few figures and to think about these statements.

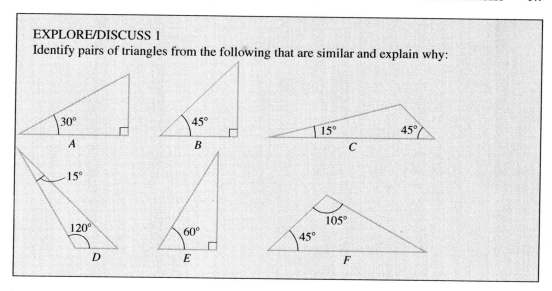

EXPLORE/DISCUSS 1

Identify pairs of triangles from the following that are similar and explain why:

Applications

We now solve some elementary problems using Euclid's theorem.

Example 1   Height of a tree

A tree casts a shadow of 32 ft at the same time a vertical yardstick (3.0 ft) casts a shadow of 2.2 ft (see Fig. 1). How tall is the tree?

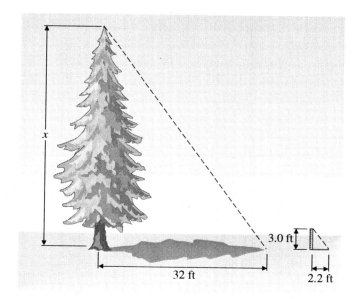

Figure 1

Solution   The parallel sun rays make the same angle with the tree and the yardstick. Since both triangles are right triangles and have an acute angle of the same measure, the triangles are similar. The corresponding sides are proportional, and we can write

$$\frac{x}{3.0 \text{ ft}} = \frac{32 \text{ ft}}{2.2 \text{ ft}}$$

$$x = \frac{3.0}{2.2}(32 \text{ ft})$$

$$= 44 \text{ ft} \qquad \text{To two significants digits}$$

Matched Problem 1   A tree casts a shadow of 31 ft at the same time a 5.0 ft vertical pole casts a shadow of 0.56 ft. How high is the tree?

Example 2   Length of an air vent

Find the length of the proposed air vent indicated in Figure 2.

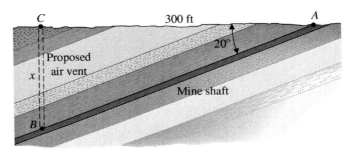

Figure 2

Solution   We make a careful scale drawing of the main shaft relative to the proposed air vent as follows: Pick any convenient length, say 2.0 in., for $A'C'$; copy the 20° angle CAB and the 90° angle ACB using a protractor (see Fig. 3). Now measure $B'C'$ (approx. 0.7 in.), and set up an appropriate proportion:

$$\frac{x}{0.7 \text{ in.}} = \frac{300 \text{ ft}}{2.0 \text{ in.}}$$

$$x = \frac{0.7}{2.0}(300 \text{ ft})$$

$$= 100 \text{ ft} \qquad \text{To one significant digit}$$

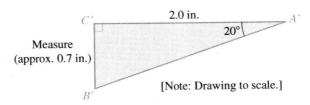

Figure 3

[*Note:* The use of scale drawings for finding indirect measurements is included here only to demonstrate basic ideas. A more efficient method will be developed in Section K.3.]

Matched Problem 2 Suppose in Example 2 that $AC = 500$ ft and $\angle A = 30°$. If in a scale drawing $A'C'$ is chosen to be 3 in. and $B'C'$ is measured as 1.76 in., find BC, the length of the proposed mine shaft.

EXPLORE/DISCUSS 2

We want to measure the depth of a canyon from a point on its rim by using similar triangles and no scale drawings. The process illustrated in Figure 4 was used in medieval times.* A vertical pole of height a is moved back from the canyon rim so that the line of sight from the top of the pole passes the rim at D to a point G at the bottom of the canyon. The setback DC is then measured to be b. The same vertical pole is moved to the canyon rim at D and a horizontal pole is moved out from the rim through D until the line of sight from B to G includes the end of the pole at E. The pole overhang DE is measured to be c. We now have enough information to find y, the depth of the canyon.

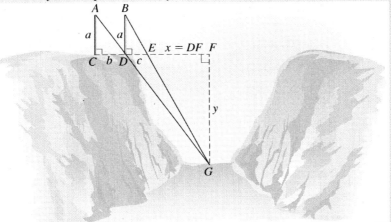

Figure 4: Depth of a canyon

(a) Explain why triangles ACD and GFD are similar.
(b) Explain why triangles BDE and GFE are similar.
(c) Set up appropriate proportions, and with the use of a little algebra, show that

$$x = \frac{bc}{b - c} \qquad y = \frac{ac}{b - c}$$

Answers to Matched Problems

1. 280 ft (to two significant digits)
2. 300 ft (to one significant digit)

---

*This process is mentioned in an excellent article by Victor J. Katz (University of the District of Columbia), titled *The Curious History of Trigonometry*, in *The UMAP Journal*, Winter 1990.

Problems for Section K.2

Round each answer to an appropriate accuracy; use the guidelines from Appendix I.

1. If two angles of one triangle have the same measure as two angles of another triangle, what can you say about the measure of the third angle of each triangle? Why?

2. If an acute angle of one right triangle has the same measure as the acute angle of another right triangle, what can you say about the measure of the second acute angle of each triangle? Why?

Given two similar triangles, as in the figure, find the unknown length indicated.

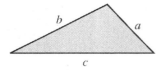 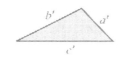

3. $a = 5$, $b = 15$, $a' = 7$, $b' = ?$

4. $b = 3$, $c = 24$, $b' = 1$, $c' = ?$

5. $c = ?$, $a = 12$, $c' = 18$, $a' = 2.4$

6. $a = 51$, $b = ?$, $a' = 17$, $b' = 8.0$

7. $b = 52{,}000$, $c = 18{,}000$, $b' = 8.5$, $c' = ?$

8. $a = 640{,}000$, $b = ?$, $a' = 15$, $b' = 0.75$

9. Can two similar triangles have equal sides? Explain.

10. If two triangles are similar and a side of one triangle is equal to the corresponding side of the other, are the remaining sides of the two triangles equal? Explain.

Given the similar triangles in the figure, find the indicated quantities to two significant digits.

11. $b = 51$ in., $a = ?$, $c = ?$

12. $b = 32$ cm, $a = ?$, $c = ?$

13. $a = 23.4$ m, $b = ?$, $c = ?$

14. $a = 63.19$ cm, $b = ?$, $c = ?$

15. $b = 2.489 \times 10^9$ yd, $a = ?$, $c = ?$

16. $b = 1.037 \times 10^{13}$ m, $a = ?$, $c = ?$

17. $c = 8.39 \times 10^5$ mm, $a = ?$, $b = ?$

18. $c = 2.86 \times 10^8$ cm, $a = ?$, $b = ?$

Find the unknown quantities. (If you have a protractor, make a scale drawing and complete the problem using your own measurements and calculations. If you do not have a protractor, use the quantities given in the problem.)

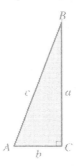

19. Suppose in the figure that $\angle A = 70°$, $\angle C = 90°$, and $a = 101$ ft. If a scale drawing is made of the triangle by choosing a' to be 2.00 in. and c' is then measured to be 2.13 in., estimate c in the original triangle.

20. Repeat Problem 19, choosing $a' = 5.00$ in. and c', a measured quantity, to be 5.28 in.

Applications

21. **Tennis** A ball is served from the center of the baseline into the deuce court. If the ball is hit 9 ft above the ground, travels in a straight line down the middle of the court, and the net is 3 ft high, how far from the base of the net will the ball land if it just clears the top of the net? (See the figure.) Assume all figures are exact and compute the answer to one decimal place.

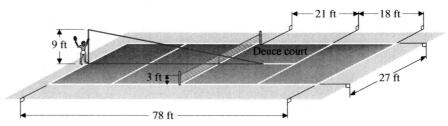

Figures for 21 and 22

22. Tennis If the ball in Problem 21 is hit 8.5 ft above the ground, how far away from the base of the net will the ball land? Assume all figures are exact and compute the answer to two decimal places. (Now you can see why tennis players try to spin the ball on a serve so that it curves downward.)

23. Indirect Measurement Find the height of the tree in the figure given that $AC = 24$ ft, $CD = 2.1$ ft, and $DE = 5.5$ ft.

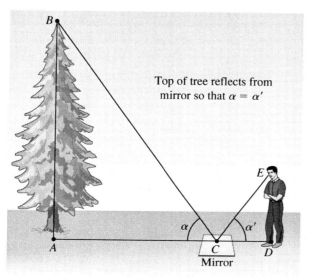

Top of tree reflects from mirror so that $\alpha = \alpha'$

Figures for 23 and 24

24. Indirect Measurement Find the height of the tree in the figure given that $AC = 25$ ft, $CD = 2$ ft 3 in., and $DE = 5$ ft 9 in.

Problems 25 and 26 are optional for those who have protractors and can make scale drawings.

25. Astronomy The following figure illustrates a method that is used to determine depths of moon craters from observatories on earth. If sun rays strike the surface of the moon so that $\angle BAC = 15°$ and AC is measured to be 4.0 km, how high is the rim of the crater above its floor?

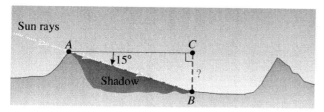

Depth of moon crater
Figure for 25

26. Astronomy The figure illustrates how the height of a mountain on the moon can be determined from earth. If sun rays strike the surface of the moon so that $\angle BAC = 28°$ and AC is measured to be 4.0×10^3 m, how high is the mountain?

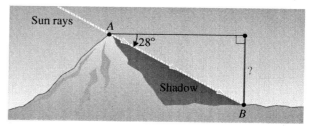

Height of moon mountain
Figure for 26

27. Fundamental Lens Equation Parallel light rays (light rays from infinity) approach a thin convex lens and are focused at a point on the other side of the lens. The distance f from the lens to the **focal point** F is called the **focal length** of the lens [see part (a) of the figure]. A standard lens on many 35 mm cameras has a focal length of 50 mm (about 2 in.), a 28 mm lens is a wide-angle lens, and a 200 mm lens is telephoto. How does a lens focus an image of an object on the film in a camera? Part (b) of the figure shows the geometry involved for a thin convex lens. Point P at the top of the object is selected for illustration (any point on the object would do). Light rays from point P travel in all directions. Those that go through the lens are focused at P'. Since light rays PA and CP' are parallel, AP' and CP pass through focal points F' and F, respectively, which are equidistant from the lens; that is, $FB' = BF' = f$. Also note that $AB = h$, the height of the object, and $BC = h'$, the height of the image.

(a) Explain why triangles PAC and FBC are similar, and why triangles ACP' and ABF' are similar.

(b) From the properties of similar triangles, show that

$$\frac{h + h'}{u} = \frac{h'}{f} \quad \text{and} \quad \frac{h + h'}{v} = \frac{h}{f}$$

(c) Combining the results in part (b), derive the important lens equation

$$\frac{1}{u} + \frac{1}{v} = \frac{1}{f}$$

where u is the distance between the object and the lens, v is the distance between the focused image on the film and the lens, and f is the focal length of the lens.

(d) How far (to three decimal places) must a 50 mm lens be from the film if the lens is focused on an object 3 m away?

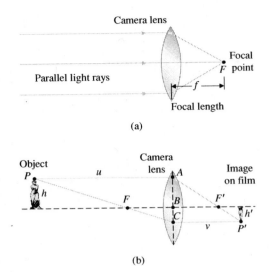

Camera lens

Parallel light rays

Focal point F

f

Focal length

(a)

Object P

h

u

F

Camera lens A

B

C

v

Image on film

F'

h'

P'

(b)

Figures for 27 and 28

28. Fundamental Lens Equation (Refer to Problem 27.) For a 50 mm lens it is said that if the object is more than 20 m from the lens, then the rays coming from the object are very close to being parallel, and v will be very close to f.

(a) Use the lens equation given in part (c) of Problem 27 to complete the following table (to two decimal places) for a 50 mm lens. (Convert meters to millimeters before using the lens equation.)

u(m)	10	20	30	40	50	60
v(m)						

(b) Referring to part (a), how does v compare with f as u increases beyond 20? (Note that 0.1 mm is less than the diameter of a period on this page.)

K.3   TRIGONOMETRIC RATIOS AND RIGHT TRIANGLES

- Trigonometric Ratios
- Complementary Angles and Cofunctions
- Calculator Evaluation
- Solving Right Triangles

In many applications of trigonometry, we are given two sides of a right triangle, or one side and an acute angle, and are asked to find the remaining sides and acute angles. This is called **solving a triangle.** In this section we show how this can be done without using scale drawings. The concepts introduced here will be generalized extensively as we progress through the book.

Trigonometric Ratios

We see in Figure 1 that there are six possible ratios of the sides of a right triangle that can be computed for each angle θ.

$$\frac{b}{c} \quad \frac{c}{b} \quad \frac{a}{c} \quad \frac{c}{a} \quad \frac{b}{a} \quad \frac{a}{b}$$

Figure 1: Six possible ratios of sides

These ratios are referred to as **trigonometric ratios,** and because of their importance, each is given a name: sine (sin), cosine (cos), tangent (tan), cosecant (csc), secant (sec), and cotangent (cot). And each is written in abbreviated form as follows:

TRIGONOMETRIC RATIOS

Right triangle

$$\sin \theta = \frac{b}{c} \qquad \csc \theta = \frac{c}{b}$$

$$\cos \theta = \frac{a}{c} \qquad \sec \theta = \frac{c}{a}$$

$$\tan \theta = \frac{b}{a} \qquad \cot \theta = \frac{a}{b}$$

Side b is often referred to as the **side opposite** angle θ, a as the **side adjacent** to angle θ, and c as the **hypotenuse.** Using these designations, the ratios become:

TRIGONOMETRIC RATIOS

$$\sin \theta = \frac{\text{Opp}}{\text{Hyp}} \qquad \csc \theta = \frac{\text{Hyp}}{\text{Opp}}$$

$$\cos \theta = \frac{\text{Adj}}{\text{Hyp}} \qquad \sec \theta = \frac{\text{Hyp}}{\text{Adj}}$$

$$\tan \theta = \frac{\text{Opp}}{\text{Adj}} \qquad \cot \theta = \frac{\text{Adj}}{\text{Opp}}$$

These trigonometric ratios should be learned, because they will be used extensively in the work that follows. It is also important to note that the right angle in a right triangle can be oriented in any position and that the names of the angles are arbitrary, but the hypotenuse is always opposite the right angle.

EXPLORE/DISCUSS 1

For a given acute angle θ in a right triangle, use Euclid's theorem (from Section 1.2) to explain why the value of any of the six trigonometric ratios for that angle is independent of the size of the triangle.

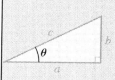 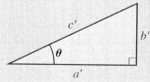

Complementary Angles and Cofunctions

What is the meaning of the prefix *co-* in cosine, cosecant, and cotangent? The *co-* refers to a complementary angle relationship. Recall that two positive angles are complementary if their sum is

90°. The two acute angles in a right triangle are complementary. (Why?)* Referring to the definition of the six trigonometric ratios, we can see the complementary relationships given in the box at the top of the next page.

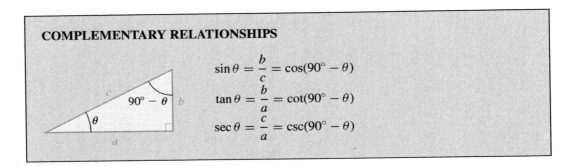

COMPLEMENTARY RELATIONSHIPS

$$\sin \theta = \frac{b}{c} = \cos(90° - \theta)$$

$$\tan \theta = \frac{b}{a} = \cot(90° - \theta)$$

$$\sec \theta = \frac{c}{a} = \csc(90° - \theta)$$

Thus, the sine of θ is the same as the cosine of the complement of θ (which is $90° - \theta$ in the triangle shown), the tangent of θ is the cotangent of the complement of θ, and the secant of θ is the cosecant of the complement of θ. The trigonometric ratios cosine, cotangent, and cosecant are sometimes referred to as the **cofunctions** of sine, tangent, and secant, respectively.

Calculator Evaluation

For the trigonometric ratios to be useful in solving right triangle problems, we must be able to find each for any acute angle. Scientific and graphing calculators can approximate (almost instantly) these ratios to eight or ten significant digits. Scientific and graphing calculators generally use different sequences of steps. Consult the user's manual for your particular calculator.

The use of a scientific calculator is assumed throughout the book, and a graphing utility (graphing calculator or computer with graphing capability) is required for many optional problems. A graphing calculator is a scientific calculator with additional capabilities, including graphing.

Calculators have two trigonometric modes: degree and radian. Our interest now is in *degree mode*. Later we will discuss radian mode in detail.

Caution

Refer to the user's manual accompanying your calculator to determine how it is to be set in degree mode, and set it that way. *This is an important step and should not be overlooked.* Many errors can be traced to calculators being set in the wrong mode.

If you look at the function keys on your calculator, you will find three keys labeled

| sin | | cos | | tan |

These keys are used to find sine, cosine, and tangent ratios, respectively. The calculator also can be used to compute cosecant, secant, and cotangent ratios using the reciprocal‡ relationships, which follow directly from the definition of the six trigonometric ratios.

---

* Since the sum of the measures of all three angles in a triangle is $180°$, and a right triangle has one $90°$ angle, the two remaining acute angles must have measures that sum to $180° - 90° = 90°$. Thus, the two acute angles in a right triangle are always complementary.

‡ Recall that two numbers a and b are **reciprocals** of each other if $ab = 1$; then we may write $a = 1/b$ and $b = 1/a$.

RECIPROCAL RELATIONSHIPS FOR $0° < \theta < 90°$

$$\csc \theta \sin \theta = \frac{c}{b} \cdot \frac{b}{c} = 1 \qquad \text{thus} \qquad \csc \theta = \frac{1}{\sin \theta}$$

$$\sec \theta \cos \theta = \frac{c}{a} \cdot \frac{a}{c} = 1 \qquad \text{thus} \qquad \sec \theta = \frac{1}{\cos \theta}$$

$$\cot \theta \tan \theta = \frac{a}{b} \cdot \frac{b}{a} = 1 \qquad \text{thus} \qquad \cot \theta = \frac{1}{\tan \theta}$$

Caution

When using reciprocal relationships, many students tend to associate cosecant with cosine and secant with sine: just the opposite is correct.

Example 1

Calculator evaluation

Evaluate to four significant digits using a calculator:

(a) $\sin 23.72°$ (b) $\tan 54°37'$

(c) $\sec 49.31°$ (d) $\cot 12.86°$

Solution

First, set the calculator in degree mode.

(a) $\sin 23.72° = 0.4023$

(b) Some calculators require $54°37'$ to be converted to decimal degrees first; others can do the calculation directly—check your user's manual.

$$\tan 54°37' = \tan 54.6166\ldots = 1.408$$

(c) $\sec 49.31° = \dfrac{1}{\cos 49.31°} = 1.534$

(d) $\cot 12.86° = \dfrac{1}{\tan 12.86°} = 4.380$

Matched Problem 1

Evaluate to four significant digits using a calculator:

(a) $\cos 38.27°$ (b) $\sin 37°44'$ (c) $\cot 49.82°$ (d) $\csc 77°53'$

EXPLORE/DISCUSS 2

Experiment with your calculator to determine which of the following two window displays from a graphing calculator is the result of the calculator being set in degree mode and which is the result of the calculator being set in radian mode.

```
sin(1.32)
          .9687
tan(45)
          1.6198
```

```
sin(1.32)
          .0230
tan(45)
          1.0000
```

(a)   (b)

Now we reverse the process illustrated in Example 1. Suppose we are given $\sin \theta = 0.3174$

How do we find θ? That is, how do we find the acute angle θ whose sine is 0.3174? The solution to this problem is written symbolically as either

$$\theta = \arcsin 0.3174 \qquad \text{"arcsin" and "sin}^{-1}\text{" both represent the same thing.}$$

or

$$\theta = \sin^{-1} 0.3174$$

Both of these expressions are read "θ is the angle whose sine is 0.3174."

Caution

It is important to note that $\sin^{-1} 0.3174$ does not mean $1/(\sin 0.3174)$; the -1 "exponent" is a superscript that is part of a *function symbol*. More will be said about this in Chapter 5, where a detailed discussion of these concepts is given.

We can find θ directly using a calculator. The function key $\boxed{\sin^{-1}}$ or its equivalent takes us from a trigonometric sine ratio back to the corresponding acute angle in decimal degrees when the calculator is in degree mode. Thus, if $\sin \theta = 0.3174$, then we can write $\theta = \arcsin 0.3174$ or $\theta = \sin^{-1} 0.3174$. We choose the latter, and proceed as follows:

$$\begin{aligned} \theta &= \sin^{-1} 0.3174 \\ &= 18.506° \qquad && \text{To these decimal places} \\ &\text{or} 18°30'21'' \qquad && \text{To the nearest second} \end{aligned}$$

Check

$$\sin 18.506° = 0.3174$$

Example 2

Finding inverses

Find each acute angle θ to the accuracy indicated:

(a) $\cos \theta = 0.7335$ (to three decimal places)
(b) $\theta = \tan^{-1} 8.207$ (to the nearest minute)
(c) $\theta = \arcsin 0.0367$ (to the nearest 109)

Solution

First, set the calculator in degree mode.

(a) If $\cos \theta = 0.7335$, then

$$\begin{aligned} \theta &= \cos^{-1} 0.7335 \\ &= 42.819° \qquad \text{To three decimal places} \end{aligned}$$

(c) $\theta = \arcsin 0.0367$

$$\begin{aligned} &= 2.103° \\ &= 2°10' \qquad \text{To the nearest 10}' \end{aligned}$$

(b) $\theta = \tan^{-1} 8.207$

$$\begin{aligned} &= 83.053 \\ &= 83°3' \qquad \text{To the nearest minutes} \end{aligned}$$

Matched Problem 2

Find each acute angle θ to the accuracy indicated:

(a) $\tan \theta = 1.739$ (to two decimal places)
(b) $\theta = \sin^{-1} 0.2571$ (to the nearest 100'')
(c) $\theta = \arccos 0.0367$ (to the nearest minute)

We postpone any further discussion of $\cot^{-1}$, $\sec^{-1}$, and $\csc^{-1}$ until Chapter 5. The preceding discussion will handle all our needs at this time.

Solving Right Triangles

To solve a right triangle is to find, given the measures of two sides or the measures of one side and an acute angle, the measures of the remaining sides and angles. Solving right triangles is best illustrated through examples. Note at the outset that accuracy of the computations is governed by Table 1.

Table 1

Angle to nearest	Significant digits for side measure
$1°$	2
$10'$ or $0.1°$	3
$1'$ or $0.01°$	4
$10''$ or $0.001°$	5

Remark   When we use the equal sign ($=$) in the following computations, it should be understood that equality holds only to the number of significant digits justified by Table 1. The approximation symbol ($\approx$) is used only when we want to emphasize the approximation.

Example 3   Solving a right triangle

Solve the right triangle in Figure 2.

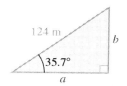

Figure 2

Solution   *Solve for the complementary angle.*

$$90° - \theta = 90° - 35.7° = 54.3 \qquad \text{Remember, } 90° \text{ is exact.}$$

Solve for b. Since $\theta = 35.7°$ and $c = 124$ m, we look for a trigonometric ratio that involves θ and c (the known quantities) and b (an unknown quantity). Referring to the definition of the trigonometric ratios (page 622), we see that both sine and cosecant involve all three quantities. We choose sine, and proceed as follows:

$$\sin\theta = \frac{b}{c}$$
$$b = c\sin\theta$$
$$= (124 \text{ m})(\sin 35.7°)$$
$$= 72.4 \text{ m}$$

Solve for a. Now that we have b, we can use the tangent, cotangent, cosine, or secant to find a. We choose the cosine. Thus,

$$\cos\theta = \frac{a}{c}$$
$$a = c\cos\theta$$
$$= (124 \text{ m})(\cos 35.7°)$$
$$= 101 \text{ m}$$

Matched Problem 3

Solve the triangle in Example 3 with $\theta = 28.3°$ and $c = 62.4$ cm.

Example 4

Solving a right triangle

Solve the right triangle in Figure 3 for θ and $90° - \theta$ to the nearest $10'$ and for a to three significant digits.

Solution

Solve for θ.

$$\sin \theta = \frac{b}{c} = \frac{42.7 \text{ km}}{51.3 \text{ km}}$$
$$\sin \theta = 0.832$$

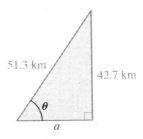

Figure 3

Given the sine of θ, how do we find θ? We can find θ directly using a calculator as discussed in Example 2.

The $\boxed{\text{Sin}^{-1}}$ key or its equivalent takes us from a trigonometric ratio back to the corresponding angle in decimal degrees (if the calculator is in degree mode).

$$\begin{aligned} \theta &= \sin^{-1} 0.832 \\ &= 56.3° \qquad\qquad (0.3)(60) = 18' \approx 20' \\ &= 56°20' \qquad\qquad \text{To the nearest } 10' \end{aligned}$$

Solve for the complementary angle.

$$\begin{aligned} 90° - \theta &= 90° - 56°20' \\ &= 33°40' \end{aligned}$$

Solve for a. Use cosine, secant, cotangent, or tangent. We will use tangent:

$$\begin{aligned} \tan \theta &= \frac{b}{a} \\ a &= \frac{b}{\tan \theta} \\ &= \frac{42.7 \text{ km}}{\tan 56°20'} \\ &= 28.4 \text{ km} \end{aligned}$$

Check   We check by using the Pythagorean theorem.* (See Fig. 4.)

$$28.4^2 + 42.7^2 \overset{?}{=} 51.3^2$$

Compute both sides to three significant digits.

$$2,630 \overset{\checkmark}{=} 2,630$$

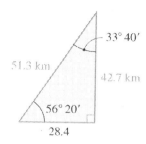

33° 40′

51.3 km

42.7 km

56° 20′

28.4

Figure 4

**Matched
Problem 4**   Repeat Example 4 with $b = 23.2$ km and $c = 30.4$ km.

In this section we have concentrated on technique. In the next section we will consider a large variety of applications involving the techniques discussed in this section.

**Answers to
Matched
Problems**
1. (a) 0.7851   (b) 0.6120   (c) 0.8445   (d) 1.023
2. (a) 60.10°   (b) 14°53′50″   (c) 87°54′
3. $90° - \theta = 61.7°$, $b = 29.6$ cm, $a = 54.9$ cm
4. $\theta = 49°40'$, $90° - \theta = 40°20'$, $a = 19.7$ km

Problems for Section K.3

In Problems 1–6, refer to the figure and identify each of the named trigonometric ratios with one of the following quotients: $a/b, b/a, a/c, c/a, b/c, c/b$. Do not look back in the text.

1. $\cos \theta$ 2. $\sin \theta$ 3. $\tan \theta$

4. $\cot \theta$ 5. $\sec \theta$ 6. $\csc \theta$

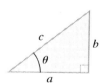

c

b

θ

a

Figure for 1–12

In Problems 7–12, refer to the figure and identify each of the quotients with a named trigonometric ratio from the following list: $\sin \theta$, $\cos \theta$, $\sec \theta$, $\csc \theta$, $\tan \theta$, $\cot \theta$. Do not look back in the text.

7. b/c 8. a/c 9. b/a

10. a/b 11. c/b 12. c/a

* **Pythagorean theorem:** A triangle is a right triangle if and only if the sum of the squares of the two shorter sides is equal to the square of the longest side:

$$a^2 + b^2 = c^2$$

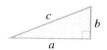

c

b

a

In Problems 13–24, find each trigonometric ratio to three significant digits.

13. $\sin 34.7°$ **14.** $\cos 18.9°$ **15.** $\tan 29°45'$

16. $\cot 15°35'$ **17.** $\sec 42.2°$ **18.** $\csc 22.5°$

19. $\cos 83.4°$ **20.** $\sin 59.3°$ **21.** $\cot 66.7°$

22. $\tan 72.6°$ **23.** $\csc 81°20'$ **24.** $\sec 48°50'$

In Problems 25–32, find each acute angle θ to the accuracy indicated.

25. $\cos \theta = 0.5$ (to the nearest degree)

26. $\tan \theta = 1$ (to the nearest degree)

27. $\sin \theta = 0.8125$ (to two decimal places)

28. $\tan \theta = 2.25$ (to two decimal places)

29. $\theta = \arcsin 0.4517$ (to the nearest 10')

30. $\theta = \arccos 0.2557$ (to the nearest 10')

31. $\theta = \tan^{-1}(2.753)$ (to the nearest minute)

32. $\theta = \cos^{-1}(0.0125)$ (to the nearest minute)

In Problems 33–36, if you are given the indicated measures in a right triangle, explain why you can or cannot solve the triangle.

33. The measures of two adjacent sides a and b

34. The measures of one side and one angle

35. The measures of two acute angles

36. The measure of the hypotenuse c

In Problems 37–46, solve the right triangle (labeled as in the figure at the beginning of the exercise) given the information in each problem.

37. $\theta = 58°40'$, $c = 15.0$ mm

38. $\theta = 62°10'$, $c = 33.0$ cm

39. $\theta = 83.7°$, $b = 3.21$ km

40. $\theta = 32.4°$, $a = 42.3$ m

41. $\theta = 71.5°$, $b = 12.8$ in.

42. $\theta = 44.5°$, $a = 2.30 \times 10^6$ m

43. $b = 63.8$ ft, $c = 134$ ft (angles to the nearest 10')

44. $b = 22.0$ km, $a = 46.2$ km (angles to the nearest 10')

45. $b = 132$ mi, $a = 108$ mi   (angles to the nearest 0.1°)

46. $a = 134$ m, $c = 182$ m   (angles to the nearest 0.1°)

47. The graphing calculator screen below shows the solution of the accompanying triangle for sides a and b. Clearly, something is wrong. Explain what is wrong, and find the correct measures for the two sides.

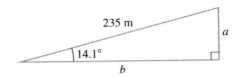

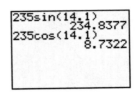

48. In the figure below, side a was found two ways: one using α and sine, and the other using β and cosine. The graphing calculator screen shows the two calculations, but there is an error. Explain the error and correct it.

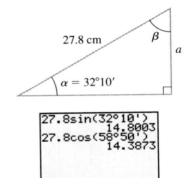

In Problems 49–52, verify each statement for the indicated values.

49. $(\sin \theta)^2 + (\cos \theta)^2 = 1$

   (a) $\theta = 11°$ **(b)** $\theta = 6.09°$ **(c)** $\theta = 43°24'47''$

50. $(\sin \theta)^2 + (\cos \theta)^2 = 1$

   (a) $\theta = 34°$ **(b)** $\theta = 37.281°$ **(c)** $\theta = 87°23'41''$

51. $\sin \theta - \cos(90° - \theta) = 0$

   (a) $\theta = 19°$ **(b)** $\theta = 49.06°$
   (c) $\theta = 72°51'12''$

52. $\tan \theta - \cot(90° - \theta) = 0$

   (a) $\theta = 17°$ **(b)** $\theta = 27.143°$
   (c) $\theta = 14°12'33''$

In Problems 53–58, solve the right triangles (labeled as in the figure at the beginning of the exercise).

53. $a = 23.82$ mi, $\theta = 83°12'$

54. $a = 6.482$ m, $\theta = 35°44'$

55. $b = 42.39$ cm, $a = 56.04$ cm
(angles to the nearest 1′)

56. $a = 123.4$ ft, $c = 163.8$ ft
(angles to the nearest 1′)

57. $b = 35.06$ cm, $c = 50.37$ cm
(angles to the nearest 0.01°)

58. $b = 5.207$ mm, $a = 8.030$ mm
(angles to the nearest 0.01°)

59. Show that $(\sin \theta)^2 + (\cos \theta)^2 = 1$, using the definition of the trigonometric ratios (page 622) and the Pythagorean theorem.

60. Without looking back in the text, show that for each acute angle θ:

(a) $\csc \theta = \dfrac{1}{\sin \theta}$ (b) $\cos(90° - \theta) = \sin \theta$

61. Without looking back in the text, show that for each acute angle θ:

(a) $\cot \theta = \dfrac{1}{\tan \theta}$ (b) $\csc(90° - \theta) = \sec \theta$

62. Without looking back in the text, show that for each acute angle θ:

(a) $\sec \theta = \dfrac{1}{\cos \theta}$ (b) $\cot(90° - \theta) = \tan \theta$

Geometric Interpretation of Trigonometric Ratios Problems 63–68 refer to the figure, where O is the center of a circle of radius 1, θ is the acute angle AOD, D is the intersection point of the terminal side of angle θ with the circle, and EC is tangent to the circle at D.

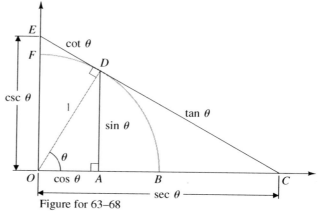

Figure for 63–68

63. Show that:

(a) $\sin \theta = AD$ (b) $\tan \theta = DC$ (c) $\csc \theta = OE$

64. Show that:

(a) $\cos \theta = OA$ (b) $\cot \theta = DE$ (c) $\sec \theta = OC$

65. Explain what happens to each of the following as the acute angle θ approaches 90°:

(a) $\sin \theta$ (b) $\tan \theta$ (c) $\csc \theta$

66. Explain what happens to each of the following as the acute angle θ approaches 90°:

(a) $\cos \theta$ (b) $\cot \theta$ (c) $\sec \theta$

67. Explain what happens to each of the following as the acute angle θ approaches 0°:

(a) $\cos \theta$ (b) $\cot \theta$ (c) $\sec \theta$

68. Explain what happens to each of the following as the acute angle θ approaches 0°:

(a) $\sin \theta$ (b) $\tan \theta$ (c) $\csc \theta$

K.4   RIGHT TRIANGLE APPLICATIONS

Now that you know how to solve right triangles, we can consider a variety of interesting and significant applications.

**Explore/
Discuss 1**

Discuss the minimum number of sides and/or angles that must be given in a right triangle in order for you to be able to solve for the remaining angles and sides.

Example 1   Mine shaft application

Solve the mine shaft problem in Example 2, Section 1.2, without using a scale drawing. See Figure 1.

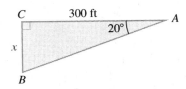

Figure 1

Solution

$$\tan\theta = \frac{\text{Opp}}{\text{Adj}}$$

$$\tan 20° = \frac{x}{300 \text{ ft}}$$

$$x = (300 \text{ ft})(\tan 20°) = 100 \text{ ft} \qquad \text{To one significant digit}$$

Matched Problem 1   Solve the mine shaft problem in Example 1 if $AC = 500$ ft and $\angle A = 30°$.

Before proceeding further, we introduce two new terms: **angle of elevation** and **angle of depression.** An angle measured from the horizontal upward is called an angle of elevation; one measured from the horizontal downward is called an angle of depression (see Fig. 2).

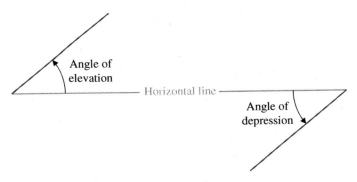

Figure 2

Example 2   Length of air-to-air fueling hose

To save time or because of the lack of landing facilities for large jets in some parts of the world, the military and some civilian companies use air-to-air refueling for some planes (see Fig. 3). If the angle of elevation of the refueling plane's hose is $\theta = 32°$ and b in Figure 3 is 120 ft, how long is the hose?

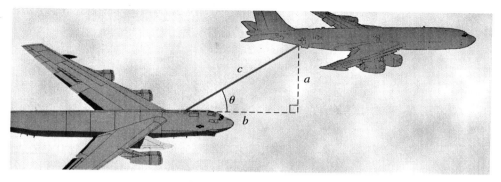

Figure 3: Air-to-air fueling

Solution

$$\sec \theta = \frac{c}{b}$$
$$c = b \sec \theta$$
$$= 120 \ \sec 32^{-1}$$
$$= 120(\cos 32°)^{-1}$$
$$= 140 \text{ ft} \qquad \text{[To two significant digits]}$$

Matched Problem 2   The horizontal shadow of a vertical tree is 23.4 m long when the angle of elevation of the sun is 56.3°. How tall is the tree?

Example 3   Astronomy

If we know that the distance from the earth to the sun is approximately 93,000,000 mi, and we find that the largest angle between the earth–sun line and the earth–Venus line is 46°, how far is Venus from the sun? (Assume that the earth and Venus have circular orbits around the sun—see Fig. 4.)

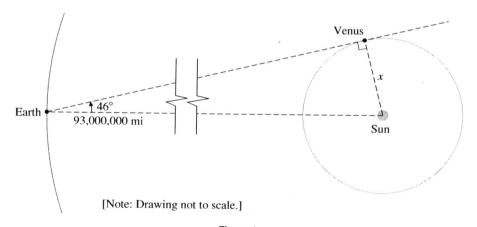

[Note: Drawing not to scale.]

Figure 4

Solution   The earth–Venus line at its largest angle to the earth–sun line must be tangent to Venus's orbit. Thus, from plane geometry, the Venus–sun line must be at right angles to the earth–Venus line at this time. The sine ratio involves two known quantities and the unknown distance from Venus to the sun. To find x we proceed as follows:

$$\sin 46° = \frac{x}{93{,}000{,}000}$$
$$x = 93{,}000{,}000 \sin 46°$$
$$= 67{,}000{,}000 \text{ mi}$$

Matched Problem 3   If the largest angle that the earth–Mercury line makes with the earth–sun line is 28°, how far is Mercury from the sun? (Assume circular orbits.)

Example 4   Coastal Piloting

A boat is cruising along the coast on a straight course. A rocky point is sighted at an angle of 31° from the course. After continuing 4.8 mi, another sighting is taken and the point is found to be 55° from the course (see Fig. 5). How close will the boat come to the point?

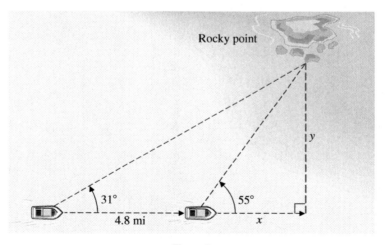

Rocky point

31°   55°

4.8 mi x

y

Figure 5

Solution   Referring to Figure 5, y is the closest distance that the boat will be to the point. To find y we proceed as follows. From the small right triangle we note that

$$\cot 55° = \frac{x}{y}$$
$$x = y \cot 55° \qquad\qquad (1)$$

Now, from the large right triangle, we see that

$$\cot 31° = \frac{4.8 + x}{y}$$
$$y \cot 31° = 4.8 + x \qquad\qquad (2)$$

Substituting equation (1) into (2), we obtain

$$y \cot 31° = 4.8 + y \cot 55°$$
$$y \cot 31° - y \cot 55° = 4.8$$
$$y(\cot 31° - \cot 55°) = 4.8$$
$$y = \frac{4.8}{\cot 31° - \cot 55°}$$
$$y = 5.0 \text{ mi}$$

Matched Problem 4   Repeat Example 4 after replacing 31° with 28°, 55° with 49°, and 4.8 mi with 5.5 mi.

Answers to Matched Problems

1. 300 ft (to one significant digit)
3. 44,000,000 mi

2. 35.1 m
4. 5.4 mi

Problems for Section K.4

Application

1. **Construction**   A ladder 8.0 m long is placed against a building as indicated in the figure. How high will the top of the ladder reach up the building?

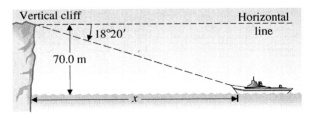

Figure for 3

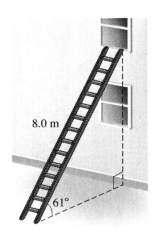

Figure for 1

2. **Construction**   In Problem 1, how far is the foot of the ladder from the wall of the building?

3. **Boat Safety**   Use the information in the figure to find the distance x from the boat to the base of the cliff.

4. **Boat Safety**   In Problem 3, how far is the boat from the top of the cliff?

5. **Geography on the Moon**   Find the depth of the moon crater in Problem 25, Problems for Section K.2.

6. **Geography on the Moon**   Find the height of the mountain on the moon in Problem 26, Problems for Section K.2.

7. **Flight Safety**   A glider is flying at an altitude of 8,240 m. The angle of depression from the glider to the control tower at an airport is 15°40′. What is the horizontal distance (in kilometers) from the glider to a point directly over the tower?

8. Flight Safety The height of a cloud or fog cover over an airport can be measured as indicated in the figure. Find h in meters if $b = 1.00$ km and $a = 23.4°$.

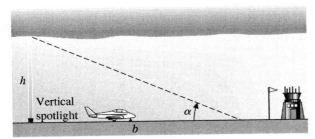

Figure for 8

9. Space Flight The figure shows the reentry flight pattern of a space shuttle. If at the beginning of the final approach the shuttle is at an altitude of 3,300 ft and its ground distance is 8,200 ft from the beginning of the landing strip, what glide angle must be used for the shuttle to touch down at the beginning of the landing strip?

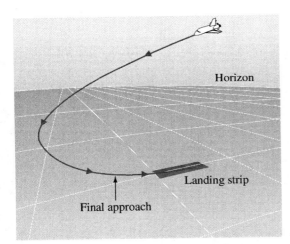

Figure for 9

10. Space Flight If at the beginning of the final approach the shuttle in Problem 9 is at an altitude of 3,600 ft and its ground distance is 9,300 ft from the beginning of the landing strip, what glide angle must be used for the shuttle to touch down at the beginning of the landing strip?

11. Architecture An architect who is designing a two-story house in a city with a 40°N latitude wishes to control sun exposure on a south-facing wall. Consulting an architectural standards reference book, she finds that at this latitude the noon summer solstice sun has a sun angle of 75° and the noon winter solstice sun has a sun angle of 27° (see the figure).

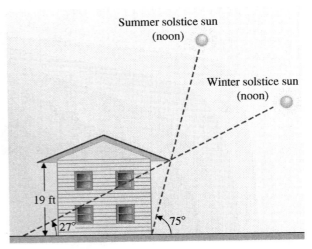

Figure for 11

(a) How much roof overhang should she provide so that at noon on the day of the summer solstice the shadow of the overhang will reach the bottom of the south-facing wall?

(b) How far down the wall will the shadow of the overhang reach at noon on the day of the winter solstice?

12. Architecture Repeat Problem 11 for a house located at 32°N latitude, where the summer solstice sun angle is 82° and the winter solstice sun angle is 35°.

13. Geometry What is the altitude of an equilateral triangle with side 4.0 m? [An equilateral triangle has all sides (and all angles) equal.]

14. Geometry The altitude of an equilateral triangle is 5.0 cm. What is the length of a side?

15. Geometry Find the length of one side of a nine-sided regular polygon inscribed in a circle with radius 8.32 cm (see the figure).

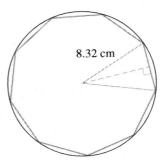

Figure for 15

16. Geometry What is the radius of a circle inscribed in the polygon in Problem 15? (The circle will be tangent to each side of the polygon and the radius will be perpendicular to the tangent line at the point of tangency.)

17. Lightning Protection A grounded lightning rod on the mast of a sailboat produces a cone of safety as indicated in the figure at the top of the next page. If the top of the rod is 67.0 ft above the water, what is the diameter of the circle of safety on the water?

Figure for 17

18. Lightning Protection In Problem 17, how high should the top of the lightning rod be above the water if the diameter of the circle on the water is to be 100 ft?

19. Diagonal Parking To accommodate cars of most sizes, a parking space needs to contain an 18 ft by 8.0 ft rectangle as shown in the figure. If a diagonal parking space makes an angle of 72° with the horizontal, how long are the sides of the parallelogram that contain the rectangle?

Figure for 19

20. Diagonal Parking Repeat Problem 19 using 68° instead of 72°.

21. Earth Radius A person in an orbiting spacecraft (see the figure) h mi above the earth sights the horizon on the earth at an angle of depression of α. (Recall from geometry that a line tangent to a circle is perpendicular to the radius at the point of tangency.) We wish to find an expression for the radius of the earth in terms of h and α.

(a) Express cos a in terms of r and h.
(b) Solve the answer to part (a) for r in terms of h and α.
(c) Find the radius of the earth if $\alpha = 22°47'$ and $h = 335$ mi.

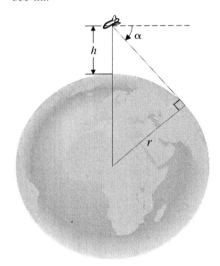

Figure for 21

22. Orbiting Spacecraft Height A person in an orbiting spacecraft sights the horizon line on earth at an angle of depression α. (Refer to the figure in Problem 21.)

(a) Express cos α in terms of r and h.
(b) Solve the answer to part (a) for h in terms of r and α.
(c) Find the height of the spacecraft h if the sighted angle of depression $\alpha = 24°14'$ and the known radius of the earth, $r = 3,960$ mi, is used.

23. Navigation Find the radius of the circle that passes through points P, A, and B in part (a) of the figure at the top of the next page. [*Hint:* The central angle in a circle subtended by an arc is twice any inscribed angle subtended by the same arc—see figure (b).] If A and B are known objects on a maritime navigation chart, then a person on a boat at point P can locate the position of P on a circle on the chart by sighting the angle APB and completing the calculations as suggested. By repeating the procedure with another pair of known points, the position of the boat on the chart will be at an intersection point of the two circles.

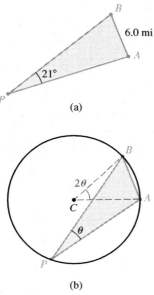

(a)

(b)

Figure for 23

24. **Navigation**   Repeat Problem 23 using 33° instead of 21° and 7.5 km instead of 6.0 mi.

25. **Geography**   Assume the earth is a sphere (it is nearly so) and that the circumference of the earth at the equator is 24,900 mi. A **parallel of latitude** is a circle around the earth at a given latitude that is parallel to the equator (see the figure). Approximate the length of a parallel of latitude passing through San Francisco, which is at a latitude of 38°N. See the figure, where θ is the latitude, R is the radius of the earth, and r is the radius of the parallel of latitude. In general, show that if E is the length of the equator and L is the length of a parallel of latitude at a latitude θ, then $L = E \cos \theta$.

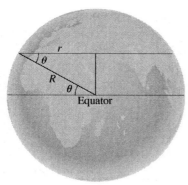

Figure for 25

26. **Geography**   Using the information in Problem 25 and the fact that the circumference of the earth at the equator is 40,100 km, determine the length of the Arctic Circle (66°33′N) in kilometers.

27. **Precalculus: Lifeguard Problem**   A lifeguard sitting in a tower spots a distressed swimmer, as indicated in the figure. To get to the swimmer, the lifeguard must run some distance along the beach at rate p, enter the water, and swim at rate q to the distressed swimmer.

Figure for 27 and 28

(a) To minimize the total time to the swimmer, should the lifeguard enter the water directly or run some distance along the shore and then enter the water? Explain your reasoning.

(b) Express the total time T it takes the lifeguard to reach the swimmer in terms of θ, d, c, p, and q.

(c) Find T (in seconds to two decimal places) if $\theta = 51°, d = 380$ m, $c = 76$ m, $p = 5.1$ m/sec, and $q = 1.7$ m/sec.

(d) The following table from a graphing calculator display shows the various times it takes to reach the swimmer for θ from 55° to 85° (X represents θ and Y1 represents T). Explain the behavior of T relative to θ. For what value of θ in the table is the total time T minimum?

X	Y1
55.000	118.65
60.000	117.53
65.000	116.89
70.000	116.66
75.000	116.80
80.000	117.28
85.000	118.08

X=55

(e) How far (to the nearest meter) should the lifeguard run along the shore before swimming to achieve the minimal total time estimated in part (d)?

28. **Precalculus: Lifeguard Problem**   Refer to Problem 27.

(a) Express the total distance D covered by the lifeguard from the tower to the distressed swimmer in terms of d, c, and θ.

(b) Find D (to the nearest meter) for the values of d, c, and θ in Problem 27c.

(c) Using the values for distances and rates in Problem 27c, what is the time (to two decimal places) it takes the lifeguard to get to the swimmer for the shortest distance from the lifeguard tower to the swimmer? Does going the shortest distance take the least time for the lifeguard to get to the swimmer? Explain. (See the graphing calculator table in Problem 27d.)

29. **Precalculus: Pipeline** An island is 4 mi offshore in a large bay. A water pipeline is to be run from a water tank on the shore to the island, as indicated in the figure. The pipeline costs $40,000 per mile in the ocean and $20,000 per mile on the land.

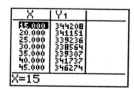

Figure for 29 and 30

(a) Do you think that the total cost is independent of the angle θ chosen, or does it depend on θ? Explain.

(b) Express the total cost C of the pipeline in terms of θ.

(c) Find C for $\theta = 15°$ (to the nearest hundred dollars).

(d) The following table from a graphing calculator display shows the various costs for θ from $15°$ to $45°$ (X represents θ and $Y1$ represents C). Explain the behavior of C relative to θ. For what value of θ in the table is the total cost C minimum? What is the minimum cost (to the nearest hundred dollars)?

X	Y1
15.000	344208
20.000	341151
25.000	339236
30.000	338564
35.000	339307
40.000	341737
45.000	346274

X=15

(e) How many miles of pipe (to two decimal places) should be laid on land and how many miles placed in the water for the total cost to be minimum?

30. **Precalculus: Pipeline**   Refer to Problem 29.

(a) Express the total length of the pipeline L in terms of θ.

(b) Find L (to two decimal places) for $\theta = 35°$.

(c) What is the cost (to the nearest hundred dollars) of the shortest pipeline from the island to the water tank?

Is the shortest pipeline from the island to the water tank the least costly? Explain. (See the graphing calculator table in Problem 29d.)

31. **Surveying** Use the information in the figure to find the height y of the mountain.

$$\tan 42° = \frac{y}{x} \qquad \tan 25° = \frac{y}{1.0 + x}$$

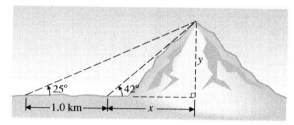

Figure for 31

32. **Surveying**

(a) Using the figure, show that: $h = \dfrac{d}{\cot \alpha - \cot \beta}$

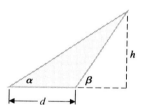

Figure for 32

(b) Use the results in part (a) to find the height of the mountain in Problem 31.

33. **Surveying** From the sunroof of Janet's apartment building, the angle of depression to the base of an office building is $51.4°$ and the angle of elevation to the top of the office building is $43.2°$ (see the figure). If the office building is 847 ft high, how far apart are the two buildings and how high is the apartment building?

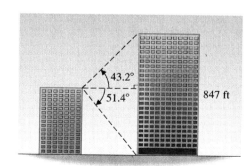

Figure for 33

34. Surveying

(a) Using the figure, show that

$$h = \frac{d}{\cot \alpha + \cot \beta}$$

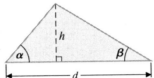

Figure for 34

(b) Use the results in part (a) to find the distance between the two buildings in Problem 33.

35. Precalculus: Physics   In physics one can show that the velocity (v) of a ball rolling down an inclined plane (neglecting air resistance and friction) is given by

$$v = g(\sin \theta)t$$

where g is the gravitational constant and t is time (see the figure).

Galileo's experiment

Figure for 35

Galileo (1564–1642) used this equation in the form

$$g = \frac{v}{(\sin \theta)t}$$

so he could determine g after measuring v experimentally. (There were no timing devices available then that were accurate enough to measure the velocity of a freefalling body. He had to use an inclined plane to slow the motion down, and then he was able to calculate an approximation for g.) Find g if at the end of 2.00 sec a ball is traveling at 11.1 ft/sec down a plane inclined at 10.0°.

36. Precalculus: Physics   In Problem 35 find g if at the end of 1.50 sec a ball is traveling at 12.4 ft/sec down a plane inclined at 15.0°.

37. Geometry   In part (a) of the figure, M and N are midpoints to the sides of a square. Find the exact value of $\sin \theta$. [*Hint:* The solution utilizes the Pythagorean theorem, similar triangles, and the definition of sine. Some useful auxiliary lines are drawn in part (b) of the figure.]

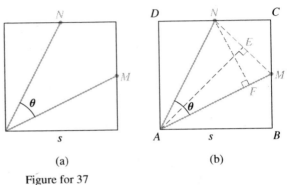

(a)   (b)

Figure for 37

38. Geometry   Find r in the figure. The circle is tangent to all three sides of the isosceles triangle. (An isosceles triangle has two sides equal.) [*Hint:* The radius of a circle and a tangent line are perpendicular at the point of tangency. Also, the altitude of the isosceles triangle will pass through the center of the circle and will divide the original triangle into two congruent triangles.]

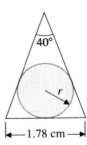

Figure for 38

ANSWERS TO ODD NUMBERED PROBLEMS

Section 1.1

1 $w = f(c)$

3 (a) (I), (III), (IV), (V), (VII), (VIII)
   (b) (i) (V) and (VI) (ii) (VIII)
   (c) (III) and (IV)

5 (a) 4
   (b) 3
   (c) 2
   (d) 2 and 4

7 (a) w
   (b) $(-4, 10)$
   (c) $(6, 1)$

9 Cost ($)

11 D

13 (a) 100.3 m. own phones in 2000
    (b) 20 m. own phones a years after 1990
    (c) b m. own phones in 2010
    (d) n m. own phones t years after 1990

15 (a) $f(3) = 11$
    (b) $f(t) = 3$ for $t = 6$
    (c) $f(5) - f(4) = -2$
    (d) $f(11) - f(10) = 0$

19 (a) Yes
    (b) No
    (c) 8 female senators in 104th Congress
    (d) 13 female senators in 107th Congress

21 distance of bug from light

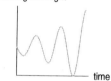

23 $C = 1.06P$

25 (a) 36 seconds
    (b)

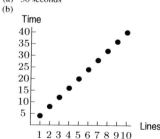

    (c) 36 seconds, 7.5 lines
    (d) $T = 4n$

27 $T(d) = d/5 + (10 - d)/8$

Section 1.2

1 (a) 2.9, -19.5
   (b) 48.5, -26.5

3 (a) (i) $\Delta D = 90$, $\Delta t = 3$
       (ii) $\Delta D = 60$, $\Delta t = 2$
       (iii) $\Delta = 45$, $\Delta t = 1.5$
   (b) 30 miles/hour

5 (a) (i) 2 thousand people/year
              -1 thousand people/year
       (ii) 2 thousand people/year
              -1 thousand people/year
       (iii) 2 thousand people/year
              -1 thousand people/year
   (b) Both change at constant rate

7 (a) 162 calories
   (b) Swimmer
   (c) Increases

9 (a) (i) -2
       (ii) -6
       (iii) -4
   (b) $2 \leq x \leq 4$

11 (a) (i) 5
        (ii) 5
        (iii) 5
    (b) always 5

13 (a) (i) 2
        (ii) $b + a$
        (iii) $2x + h$
    (b) It seems to be the sum of the two
         x-coordinates

15 (a) 5
    (b) 15, 15, 10, 20, 15, 15
    (c) No; $\Delta G / \Delta t$ not constant

Section 1.3

1 No

3 Not linear

5 Could be linear

7 Vert int: $29.99; Slope: $0.05/min

9 Vert int: 54.25 thousand; Slope: $-2/7$
   thousand/yr

11 (b)

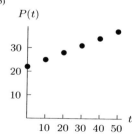

    (c) 22 million
    (d) 0.3 million people/year

13 (b) Cost (dollars)

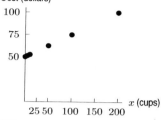

    (c) 0.25
    (d) Start-up cost

15 (a) inches

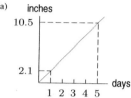

    (b) gallons

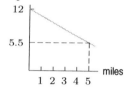

17 (a) Radius and circumference
    (c) 2π

19 (a) Country A is Afghanistan;
         Country B is Sri Lanka.
    (b) 0.24 million/year.
    (c) 16.5 million

21 (a) $F = 2C + 30$
    (b) $-3°$, $-2°$, $1°$, and $.4°$ respectively
    (c) $10°C$

23 NO

25 NO

27 Window: $0 \leq d \leq 20$ and $0 \leq C \leq 41.50$

29 (a)

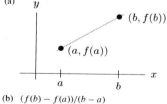

    (b) $(f(b) - f(a))/(b - a)$

Section 1.4

1 $y = 4 - 3/5x$

3 $y = -0.3 + 5x$

5 $y = 2/3 + 5/3x$

7 Not possible

9 $y = 21 - x$

11 $y = 3 - 2x$

13 $y = -5 + 5x/3$

15 $y = 0.03 + 0.1x$

642

17 $q = 2500 - 2000p$

19 $y = 459.7 + 1x$

21 $u = (1/12)n.$

23 $f(x) = 3 - 2x$

25 (b) $p = 12 - s$

(c)

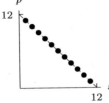

27 (a) $y = -1250 + (9.50)x$
(c) $x = 132$
(d) $x = y/9.50 + 1250/9.50$
(e) 2001

29 (a) $1000, 990.2, 980.4, 970.6, 960.8$
(b) v decreasing at constant rate
(c) Slope: -9.8 meter/sec^2
v-intercept: 1000 meters/sec
t-intercept: 102.04 sec

31 $y = \frac{13}{\sqrt{8}} + \left(\frac{\sqrt{8}-\sqrt{13}}{\sqrt{8}}\right)x$ or
$y = \frac{13\sqrt{2}}{4} + \frac{4-\sqrt{26}}{4}x$

33 $y = f(0) + (f(A) - f(0))/A \cdot x$

35 (a)

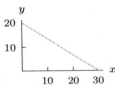

(b) $f(x) = 20 - (2/3)x$
(d)

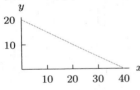

37 (a) $r = 0.005H - 0.03$
(b) $S = 200$

Section 1.5

1 (a) $y = -2 + 3x$
(b) $y = -1 + 2x$

3 (a) $y = (1/4)x$
(b) $y = 1 - 6x$

5 (a) (V)
(b) (IV)
(c) (I)
(d) (VI)
(e) (II)
(f) (III)
(g) (VII)

7 A, h
B, f
C, g
D, j
E, k

9 Parallel

11 Parallel

13 Neither

15 (a) $y = 9 - (2/3)x$
(b) $y = -4 + (3/2)x$
(c)

19 $(4, 3)$

21 $(1, 0)$

23 (a) $P = (a, 0)$
(b) $A = (0, b), B = (-c, 0)$
$C = (a + c, b), D = (a, 0)$

25 (a) Company A: $20 + 0.2x$
Company B: $35 + 0.1x$
Company C: 70
(b)

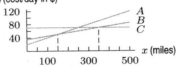

(c) Slope: mileage rate
Vertical intercept: fixed cost/day
(d) A for $x < 150$
B for $150 < x < 350$
C for $x > 350$

27 (a) $y = -5484.1 + 2.84x$
(b) 252.7 million tons

29 (a) $m_1 = m_2$ and $b_1 \neq b_2$
(b) $m_1 = m_2$ and $b_1 = b_2$
(c) $m_1 \neq m_2$
(d) Not possible

Chapter 1 Review

1 Neither

3 Neither

5 Both

7 (a) 9
(b) $\frac{n-k}{m-j}$
(c) $6x + h$

9 No

11 $g(x) = 80 - 0.05x$

13 (a) $y = 5 - 2x$
(b) $y = 7 - 3x$

15 Perpendicular

17 Perpendicular

19 $y = 6 - 3/5x$

21 Parallel line: $y = -4x + 9$
Perpendicular line: $y = 0.25x + 4.75$

23 $\pi(n) = -10,000 + 127n$

25 (a) $r_m(0) - r_h(0) = 185$
(b) $r_m(11) - r_h(11) = -1$
(c) $r_m(t) < r_a(t)$ for $t = 10$ and $t = 11$

27 (a) Yes
(b) No

29

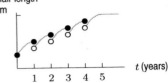

31 $0.945P$

33 (a) 10.71 gallons
(b) 0.25 gallons
(c) 55 mph

35

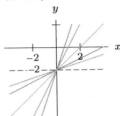

37 (a) $x + y$
(b) $0.15x + 0.18y$
(c) $(15x + 18y)/(x + y)$

39 (a) $R = 0.95x$
$C = 200 + 0.25x$
$P = 200 + 0.70x$

41 (a) \$11,375
(b) \$125
(c) \$5

43 $C(n) = 10.500 + 5n$

45 (a) $i(x) = 2.5x$
(b) $i(0) = 0$

47 (a) $S = -100 + 100p$
(c) Yes, \$1
(d) \$4

49 (a)

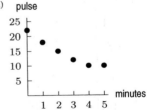

(b) $0 \leq t \leq 4$

53 l_1

Ch. 1 Understanding

1 False

3 True

5 True

7 True

9 True

11 True

13 True

15 True
17 False
19 False
21 False
23 True
25 True
27 False
29 True
31 False
33 False
35 True
37 False
39 False
41 True
43 False
45 True
47 True
49 False
51 True
53 True

Section 2.1

1 $f(-7) = -9/2$
3 $x = 1$
5 $x = \pm 4$
7 (a) 1
  (b) $-1/2$
9 (a) 6
  (b) 2, 3
11 100
13 (a) $t = 6$
   (b) $t = 1, t = 2$
15 (a) (i) $1/(1 - t)$
      (ii) $-1/t$
   (b) $x = 3/2$
17 (a) 24
   (b) 10
   (c) -7
   (d) 0
   (e) 20
19 (a) -1
   (b) $x = \pm 3$
   (c) 0
   (d) -1
   (e) 3, -3
21 (a) Same values; same function
   (b) Same values; not same function
23 (a) 0 ft/sec
   (b) $t = 0, t = 2$ seconds
   (c) Velocity at $t = 3$; ft/sec
25 (a) $4261.50
   (b) $T(x) = 0.8.x$
   (c) $L(x) = 0.0548x - 396.5$
   (d) $4261.50
27 (e) 5050

Section 2.2

1 $f(x) \geq 1$
3 $-4 \leq f(x) \leq 5$
5 Domain: $x \geq 3$

Range: $f(x) \geq 0$
7 Domain: $x, x \neq 0$
  Range: $f(x) > 0$
9 Domain: all real x
  Range: $f(x) \geq -4$
11 Domain: all real x
   Range: all real $f(x)$
13 Domain: all real numbers
   Range: all real numbers
15 Domain: $x \geq 3$ or $x \leq -3$
   Range: $q(x) \geq 0$
17 D and R: All real numbers
19 D: all real numbers; R: all real numbers ≥ 2
21 D: all real numbers; R: all real numbers ≥ 2
23 D: $0 \leq t \leq 12$
   R: $0 \leq f(t) \leq 200$
25 D: $2 \leq x \leq 6$; R: $1 \leq f(x) \leq 3$
27 Domain: integers $0 \leq n \leq 200$
   Range: integers $0 \leq n \leq 800$
29 (a) 162 calories
   (c) (i) Calories = $0.025 \times$ weight

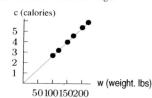

   (ii) (0,0) is the number of calories burned by a weightless runner
   (iii) Domain $0 < w$; range $0 < c$
   (iv) 3.6
31 D: all real numbers $\geq b$;
   R: all real numbers ≥ 6
33 (a) $p(0) = 50$
      $p(10) \approx 131$
      $p(50) \approx 911$
   (c) $50 \leq p(t) < 1000$

Section 2.3

1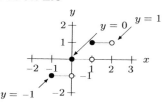

3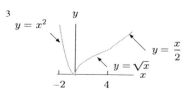

5 $y = \begin{cases} 5 - x & \text{for } x < 3 \\ -1 + (1/2)x & \text{for } x \geq 3 \end{cases}$
7 $y = \begin{cases} 4 - \frac{1}{2}x & \text{for } 1 \leq x \leq 3 \\ -9 + 2x & \text{for } 5 \leq x \leq 8 \end{cases}$
9 (a) Yes

(b) No
(c) $y = 1, 2, 3, 4$
11 (c) Domain: all $x, x \neq 0$
      Range: -1 and 1
   (d) False, $u(0)$ is undefined
13 (a) $n(L) = 2L + 10$
   (b) Domain: $L \geq 5$
      Range: $n(L) = 20, 21, 22, 23 \ldots$

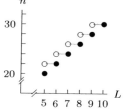

   (c) Domain: All real numbers
      Range: All real numbers
15 (a) cost (dollars)

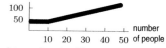

   (b) Integers from 1 to 50
      Even integers from 40 to 120
17 (a) $1.12
      $1.26
   (b) Domain: All positive integers
      Range: All positive multiples of 0.14

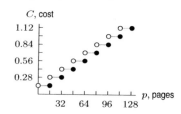

19 (a) First and third
   (b) > 45 mph or < 4 mph
   (c) > 45 mph

Section 2.4

1 Rates of change: 4.35, 4.10, 3.80;
  Concave down
3 Concave down
5 Concave up
7 Concave up
9 Concave up
11 Increasing; concave up
13 Increasing; concave up then down
15 Increasing; concave up then down
17 (a) F, IV
   (b) G, I
   (c) E, II
   (d) H, III
19 (a) From A to F
   (b) From O to A
   (c) From D to E
   (d) From F to I

Section 2.5

1 (a) $-3, 0, 2, 1, -1$
    One unit right
   (b) $-3, 0, 2, 1, -1$
    One unit left
   (c) $0, 3, 5, 4, 2$
    Up three units
   (d) $0, 3, 5, 4, 2$
    One right and three up

3 $(1/2)n^2 + 1$

5 $(1/2)n^2 - 3.7$

7 $(1/2)n^2 + \sqrt{13}$

9 $(1/2)n^2 + 3n + 23/2$

11 $3^w - 3$

13 $3^w + 1.8$

15 $3^{w+2.1} - 1.3$

17 (a) (vi)
   (b) (iii)
   (c) (ii)
   (d) (v)
   (e) (i)
   (f) (iv)

21 Shift down a

23 Shift right a

25 Shift right, $2b$, up ab

27 (a)   (i) 248
      (ii) 142
      (iii) 4
      (iv) 12
      (v) 378
      (vi) -18
      (vii) 248
      (viii) 570
      (ix) 13
   (b)   (i) $x = 2$
      (ii) $x = 8$
      (iii) $x = 7$
   (c) $x = 1, 4$

29 (a) -25
   (b) -4
   (c)

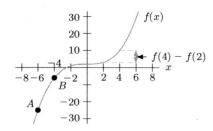

   (d) 7
   (e) $3, 5$
   (f) $2, 2\sqrt[3]{3} \approx 2.884$

31 (a) $T(d) = S(d) + 1$
   (b) $P(d) = S(d) - 1$

33 (a) $h(x) = f(x) - 2$
   (b) $g(x) = f(x + 1)$
   (c) $i(x) = f(x + 1) - 2$

35 Vertical shifts

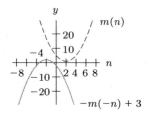

37 (a)
    Temperature, °F

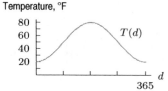

39 (a) $t(x) = 5 + 3x$ for $x > 0$
   (b) $n(x) = t(x) + 1$ (vertical shift)
   (c) $p(x) = 10 + 3(x - 2)$ for $x > 2$, or
    $p(x) = t(x - 2) + 5$ for $x > 2$

Section 2.6

3 Reflected across x-axis;
    $-g(x) = -(1/3)^x$

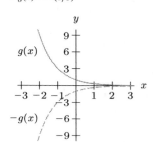

5 $-m(n) = -(n)^2 + 4n - 5$

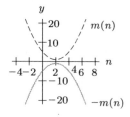

7 $-m(n + 2) = -n^2 - 1$

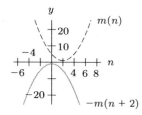

9 $-m(-n) + 3 = n^2 - 4n - 2$

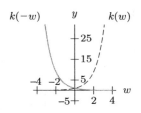

11 $k(-w) = 3^{-w}$

13 $-k(-w) = -3^{-w}$

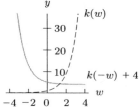

15 $k(-w) + 4 = 3^{-w} + 4$

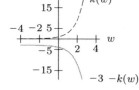

17 $-3 - k(w) = -3 - 3^w$

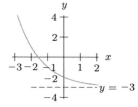

19 Odd

21 Neither

23 (a) $y = 2^{-x} - 3$

(b) $y = 2^{-x} - 3$

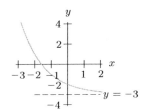

(c) Yes

25 Reflections across x-axis

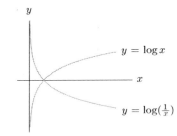

27 (i) c
  (ii) d
  (iii) e
  (iv) f
  (v) a
  (vi) b

29 (a)

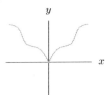

(b)

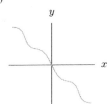

(c)

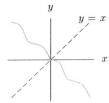

31 $y = x$. $y = -x + b$, where b is an arbitrary constant

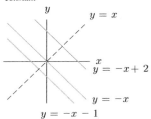

33 If $f(x)$ is odd, then $f(0) = 0$

39 Yes, $f(x) = 0$

Chapter 2 Review

1 54

3 $l = 0$ and $l = 7$

5 (a) $h(1) = b + c + 1$
  (b) $h(b + 1) = 2b^2 + 3b + c + 1$

7 (b)

(c) Domain is $-\infty < x < \infty$
    Range is $-\infty < y < \infty$
(d) Increasing: $-\infty < x < \infty$

9 (b)

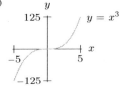

(c) Domain is all real numbers except 0
    Range is $0 < y < \infty$
(d) Increasing: $-\infty < x < 0$
    Decreasing: $0 < x < \infty$

11 (b)

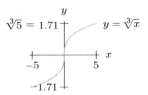

(c) Domain is $-\infty < x < \infty$
    Range is $-\infty < y < \infty$
(d) Increasing: $-\infty < x < \infty$

13 Domain: $x \geq 4$
   Range: $f(x) \geq 0$

15 Domain: all real numbers
   Range: $0 < g(x) \leq 1$

17 (a) $-3(x^2 + x)$
   (b) $2 - x$
   (c) $x^2 + x + \pi$
   (d) $\sqrt{(x^2 + x)}$

(c) $2/(x + 1)$
(f) $(x^2 + x)^2$

19 (a) 4
   (b) 1
   (c) 5
   (d) -2

21 (a) $(6, 5)$
   (b) $(2, 1)$
   (c) $(1/2.5)$
   (d) $(2, 20)$

23 Even

25 Even

27 Neither

29 Neither

31 $y = (x + 1)(x - 3)$

33 $y = -(x - 2)^2$

35 $a/2$

37 $a/(a - a^2 + 1)$

39 $(-3, 0); (3, 0); (9, 0)$

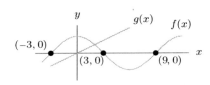

41 g above f to right of 2

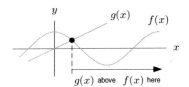

43 (a) 800; 200; -200
   (b)

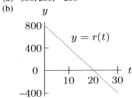

(c) $t = 20$; $t = 0$
(d) Domain: $0 \leq t \leq 30$
    Range: $-400 \leq r(t) \leq 80$

45 (a) $j(h(4)) = 4$
   (b) We don't know $j(4)$
   (c) $h(j(4)) = 4$
   (d) $j(2) = 4$
   (e) We don't know $h^{-1}(-3)$
   (f) $j^{-1}(-3) = 5$
   (g) We don't know $h(g)$
   (h) $h(-3)^{-1} = \frac{1}{5}$
   (i) We don't know $h(2)^{-1}$

47 (a) $(-2, 2)$
   (b) $(-2\sqrt{2}, -2), (2\sqrt{2}, -2)$

(c)

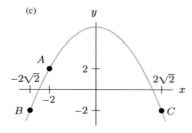

(d) −3

49 (a) $t(400) = 272$
    (d) $t(2x) = t(x)/2$

51 (a) $A = 2\pi r^2 + 710/r$
    (b)

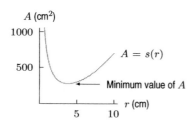

(c) Domain: $r > 0$
     Approximate range: $A > 277.5$ cm^2
(d) ≈ 277.5 cm^2
     $r \approx 3.83$ cm
     $h \approx 7.7$ cm

53 (b) Decreasing

55 (a) VI
    (b) V
    (c) III
    (d) IV
    (e) I
    (f) II

57 $y = -(x + 1)^3 + 1$

59

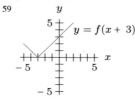

61

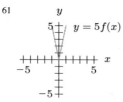

63

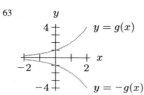

65

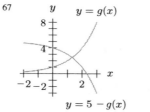

67

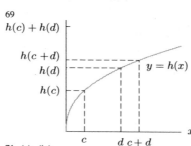

69

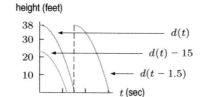

71 (a) (iv)
    (b) (iii)
    (c) (v)
    (d) (i)
    (e) (ii)

73 $y = -h(x - 1)$

75 (a) $f(10) = 6000$; 10 chairs for $6000
    (b) $f(30) = 7450$; 30 chairs for $7450
    (c) $z = 40$; 40 chairs for $8000
    (d) $f(0) = 5000$; tixed cost of
         production

77 (a) $d_1 = 650, d_2 = 550, d_3 = 500$

79 (b) $1.89 f(k)$

81 (b) $T(d) - 32$
    (c) $T(d + 7)$

83 (a) $-16t^2 + 23$ $-16t^2 + 48t + 2$
    (b)

height (feet)

38
30
20
10
    $d(t)$
    $d(t) - 15$
    $d(t - 1.5)$
    t (sec)
1   2   3

(d) 1.541 secs
     1.199 secs
(e) 3.041 secs

Ch. 2 Understanding

1 False
3 False
5 False
7 False
9 True
11 True
13 False
15 False
17 True
19 True
21 True
23 False
.25 True
27 True
29 False
31 False
33 False
35 True
37 False
39 False
41 False
43 False
45 True
47 False
49 True
51 True
53 True
55 False
57 True
59 False
61 False
63 True
65 True
67 False
69 False
71 True
73 True
75 False
77 True

Section 3.0

1 7,794″

2 45°

3 16,000

4 36.33°

5 An angle of degree measure 1 is an angle
   formed by rotating the terminal side of the
   angle $\frac{1}{360}$ of a complete revolution in a
   counterclockwise direction.

6 All three are similar, because all three have
   equal angles.

7 No. Similar triangles have equal angles.

8 The sum of all the angles in a triangle is 180°.
   Two obtuse angles would add up to more than
   180°.

9 720 ft

10 (a) b/c
    (b) c/a
    (c) b/a

(d) c/b
(e) a/c
(f) a/b

11 $90° - \theta = 54.8°$, $a = 16.5$ cm,
     $b = 11.6$ cm

12 $144°$

13 4.19 in.

14 $27.25°$ is larger.

15 (a) $67.709°$
     (b) $129°19'1''$

16 (a) $65°41'52''$
     (b) $327°48'27''$

17 7.1×10^{-6} mm

18 (a) $\cos \theta$
     (b) $\tan \theta$
     (c) $\sin \theta$
     (d) $\sec \theta$
     (e) $\csc \theta$
     (f) $\cot \theta$

19 Two right triangles having an acute angle of
     one equal to an acute angle of the other are
     similar, and corresponding sides of similar
     triangles are proportional.

20 $90° - \theta = 27°40'$, $b = 7.63 \times 10^{-8}$ m,
     $c = 8.61 \times 10^{-8}$ m

21 (a) $68.17°$
     (b) $68°10'$
     (c) $3°12'16''$

22 Window (a) is in radian mode; window (b) is in
     degree mode.

23 $\theta = 40.3°$, $90° - \theta = 49.7°$, $c = 20.6$ mm

24 $\theta = 40°20'$, $90° - \theta = 49°40'$

25 8.7 ft

26 940 ft

27 107 ft^2

28 $\theta = 66°17'$, $a = 93.56$ km,
     $b = 213.0$ km

29 $\theta = 60.28°$, $90° - \theta = 29.72°$,
     $b = 4{,}241$ m

30 1.0853

31 8.8 ft

32 24.5 ft; 24.1 ft

33 $2.3°$; 0.07 or 7%

34 955 mi

35 $46°$

36 830 m

37 1,240 m

38 760 mph

39 (a) $\beta = 90° - \alpha$
     (b) $r = h \tan \alpha$
     (c) $H - h = (R - r) \cot \alpha$

40 (a) In both cases the ladder must get
            longer.
     (b) $L = 5 \csc \theta + 4 \sec \theta$.
     (c)

θ	25°	35°	45°	55°	65°	75°	55°
L	16.24	13.60	12.73	13.08	14.98	20.63	50.91

     (d) L decreases and then increases; L has a
            minimum value of 12.73 when $\theta = 45°$.
     (e) Make up another table for values of θ
            close to 45° and on either side of 45°.

Section 3.1

1 The central angle of a circle has radian
   measure 1 if it intercepts an arc of length equal
   to the radius of the circle.

3 $\pi/6, \pi/3, \pi/2, 2\pi/3, 5\pi/6, \pi, 7\pi/6, 4\pi/3,$
   $3\pi/2, 5\pi/3, 11\pi/6, 2\pi$

5 The angle of radian measure 1 is larger, since 1
   rad corresponds to a degree measure of
   approximately $57.3°$.

7
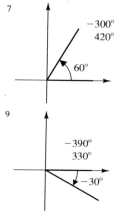

9
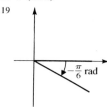

11 $\pi/10$ rad ≈ 0.3142 rad

13 $13\pi/18$ rad ≈ 2.269 rad

15 $(288/\pi)° \approx 91.67°$

17 $3°$ (exact)

19
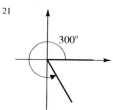

21
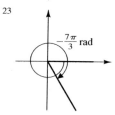

23

25 (a) $28.648°$
     (b) $80.214°$
     (c) $355.234°$
     (d) $-262.988°$

27 (a) 0.436 rad
     (b) 2.862 rad

(c) 11.310 rad
(d) -3.869 rad

29 (a) 0.4 rad; $22.9°$
     (b) 12 rad; $68.8°$
     (c) 2.5P rad; $143.2°$
     (d) 4 rad; $229.2°$

31 (a) 9.45 m
     (b) 5.13 m
     (c) 4.57 m
     (d) 15.27 m

33 Yes. Since $\theta_d = (180/\pi)\theta_r$, if θ_r is doubled,
     then θ_d also must be doubled (multiply both
     sides of the conversion equation by 2).

35 Since $\theta_r = s/r$, if s is held constant while r
     (the denominator) is doubled, then θ_r will be
     cut in half.

37 (a) 144 cm^2
     (b) 31.4 cm^2
     (c) 46.8 cm^2
     (d) 131.9 cm^2

39 Since $s = r\theta$(θ in radian measure),
     $s = 1 \cdot m = m$.

41 II

43 III

45 II

47 III

49 III

51 0.9795 rad

53 $26.5738°$

55 1.530 rad

57 $488.5714°$

59 $7\pi/12$ rad ≈ 1.83 rad

61 12 cm

63 $19°$

65 256 cm

67 1.4×10^6 km

69 175 ft

71 0.2 m; 7.9 in

73 $\pi/26$ rad ≈ 0.12 rad

75 6.800 mi

77 31 ft

79 (a) Since one revolution corresponds to 2π
            radians, n revolutions corresponds to $2\pi n$
            radians.
     (b) No. Radian measure is independent of the
            size of the circle used; hence, it is
            independent of the size of the wheel used.
     (c) 31.42 rad; 22.62 rad

81 6.5 revolutions; 40.8 rad

83 $859°$

Section 3.2

1 $\sin \theta = \frac{4}{5}$, $\csc \theta = \frac{5}{4}$, $\cos \theta = \frac{3}{5}$, $\sec \theta = \frac{5}{3}$, $\tan \theta = \frac{4}{3}$, $\cot \theta = \frac{3}{4}$; same values for $Q(6, 8)$ (Why?)

3 $\sin \theta = -\frac{3}{5}$, $\csc \theta = -\frac{5}{3}$, $\cos \theta = \frac{4}{5}$, $\sec \theta = \frac{5}{4}$, $\tan \theta = -\frac{3}{4}$, $\cot \theta = -\frac{4}{3}$; same values for $Q(12, -9)$ (Why?)

5 $\sin \theta = \frac{4}{5}$, $\tan \theta = \frac{4}{3}$, $\csc \theta = \frac{5}{4}$, $\sec \theta = \frac{5}{3}$, $\cot \theta = \frac{3}{4}$

7 $\sin \theta = -\frac{4}{5}$, $\tan \theta = -\frac{4}{3}$, $\csc \theta = -\frac{5}{4}$, $\sec \theta = \frac{5}{3}$, $\cot \theta = -\frac{3}{4}$

9 $\sin\theta - \frac{4}{5}$, $\cos\theta = -\frac{3}{5}$, $\tan\theta = \frac{4}{3}$, $\sec\theta = -\frac{5}{3}$, $\cot\theta = \frac{3}{4}$

11 No. For all those values of x for which both are defined, $\cos x = 1/\sec x$); hence, either both are positive or both are negative.

13 0.8829

15 -0.2910

17 -1.530

19 -0.8829

21 -0.9004

23 1.100

25 -0.9749

27 1.851

29 -2.475

31 $\sin\theta = \frac{1}{2}$, $\cos\theta = \sqrt{3}/2$, $\tan\theta = 1/\sqrt{3}$, $\csc\theta = 2$, $\sec\theta = 2/\sqrt{3}$, $\cot\theta = \sqrt{3}$

33 $\sin\theta = -\sqrt{3}/2$, $\cos\theta = \frac{1}{2}$, $\tan\theta = -\sqrt{3}$, $\csc\theta = -2/\sqrt{3}$, $\sec\theta = 2$, $\cot\theta = -1/\sqrt{3}$

35 I, IV

37 I, III

39 I, IV

41 III, IV

43 II, IV

45 III, IV

47 $\cos\theta = -\sqrt{5}/3$, $\tan\theta = 2/\sqrt{5}$, $\csc\theta = -\frac{3}{2}$, $\sec\theta = -3/\sqrt{5}$, $\cot\theta = \sqrt{5}/2$

49 $\sin\theta = -\sqrt{2}/3$, $\cos\theta = 1/\sqrt{3}$, $\tan\theta = -\sqrt{2}$, $\csc\theta = -3/\sqrt{2}$, $\cot\theta = -1/\sqrt{2}$

51 Yes, $\cos\alpha = \cos\beta$, since the terminal sides of these angles will coincide and the same point $P(a, b) \neq (0, 0)$ can be chosen on the terminal sides. Thus, $\cos\alpha = a/r = \cos\beta$, where $r = \sqrt{a^2 + b^2} \neq 0$.

53 Use the reciprocal identity $\cot x = 1/(\tan x)$: $\cot x = 1/(-2.18504) = -0.45766$.

55 0.03179

57 2.225

59 -14.82

61 -2.372

63 0.2243

65 -0.08626

67 1.212

69 0.8838

71 -1.587

73 Tangent and secant; since $\tan x = b/a$ and $\sec x = r/a$, neither is defined when the terminal side of the angle lies along the positive or negative vertical axis, because a will be 0 (division by 0 is not defined).

75 (a) $\theta = 1.2$ rad
   (b) $(a, b) = (5\cos 1.2, 5\sin 1.2) = (1.81, 4.66)$

77 (a) $\theta = 2$ rad
   (b) $(a, b) = (1\cos 2, 1\sin 2) = (-0.416, 0.909)$

79 3.22 units

81 $k, 0.94k, 0.77k, 0.50k, 0.17k$

83 Summer solstice: $E = 0.97k$; winter solstice: $E = 0.45k$

85 (a)

n	6	10	100	1,000	10,000
A_n	2.59808	2.93893	3.13953	3.14157	3.14159

   (b) The area of the circle is $A = \pi r^2 = \pi(1)^2 = \pi$, and A_n seems to approach π, the area of the circle, as n increases.
   (c) No. An n-sided polygon is always a polygon, no matter the size of n, but the inscribed polygon can be made as close to the circle as you like by taking n sufficiently large.

89 $I = 24$ amperes

91 (a) 2.01; -0.14
   (b) $y = -0.75x + 3.75$

Section 3.3

1 $\alpha = \theta = 60°$

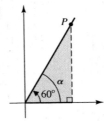

3 $\alpha = |-60°| = 60°$

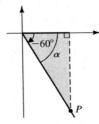

5 $\alpha = |-\pi/3| = \pi/3$

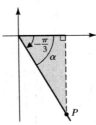

7 $\alpha = \pi - 3\pi/4 = \pi/4$

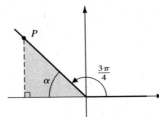

9 $\alpha = 210° - 180° = 30°$

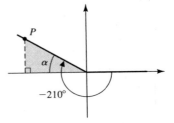

11 $\alpha = 5\pi/4 - \pi = \pi/4$

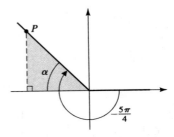

13 0

15 0

17 $\frac{1}{2}$

19 1

21 $2/\sqrt{3}$, or $\frac{2\sqrt{3}}{3}$

23 -1

25 Not defined

27 $-1/\sqrt{2}$ or $-\sqrt{2}/2$

29 $-\sqrt{3}$

31 $-1/\sqrt{2}$ or $-\sqrt{2}/2$

33 $-\sqrt{3}$

35 Not defined

37 $-\sqrt{3}/2$

39 1

41 $-\sqrt{2}$

43 The tangent function is not defined at $\theta = \pi/2$ and $\theta = 3\pi/2$, because than $\theta = b/a$ and $a = 0$ for any point on the vertical axis.

45 The cosecant function is not defined at $\theta = 0$, $\theta = \pi$, and $\theta = 2\pi$, because $\csc\theta = r/b$ and $b = 0$ for any point on the horizontal axis.

47 $\sin(-45°) = -1/\sqrt{2}$, or $-\sqrt{2}/2$

49 $\tan(-\pi/3) = -\sqrt{3}$

51 (a) 30°
   (b) $\pi/6$

53 (a) 120°
   (b) $2\pi/3$

55 (a) 120°
   (b) $2\pi/3$

57 240°, 300°

59 $5\pi/6, 11\pi/6$

61 $3\pi/4$

63 $\pi/6$

65 (a) $x = 14, y = 7\sqrt{3}$

(b) $x = 4/\sqrt{2},\ y = 4/\sqrt{2}$
(c) $x = 10/\sqrt{3},\ y = 5/\sqrt{3}$

67 $3\sqrt{3}\ \text{cm}^2$

69 $150\sqrt{3}\ \text{in.}^2$

Section 3.4

1 Yes

3 Yes

5 No

7 No

9 3

11 4

13

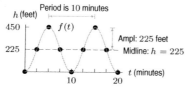

15

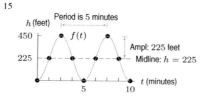

17

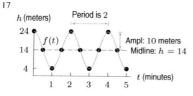

19 3 (or 9) o'clock; descending; 5 minutes; 40 meters; 0 meters: 11.25 minutes

21 3 (or 9) o'clock; rising; 4 minutes; 30 meters; 5 meters; 11 minutes

23 Midline: $y = 10$;
Period: 1;
Amplitude: 4;
Minimum: 6 cm;
Maximum: 14 cm

25 Graph is same except starts at a peak

27 (a)

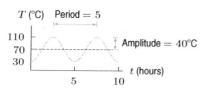

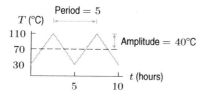

(b) Period: 5 hours;
Amplitude: $40°$;
Midline: $T = 70°$

29 Midline: $h = 2$:
Amplitude: 1;
Period: 1

31 Midline: $y = 5.55$:
Amplitude: 5.15 WBC $\times 10^4/\text{mL}$:
Period: 72 days

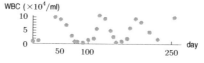

Section 3.5

1 (a) π
   (b) $3\pi/2$

3 (a) $(1, 0)$
   (b) $(0, 1)$
   (c) $(0, 1)$
   (d) $(-1, 0)$
   (e) $(1, 0)$
   (f) $(0, 1)$

5 (a) 0 to 1
   (b) 1 to 0
   (c) 0 to -1
   (d) -1 to 0
   (e) 0 to 1

7 (a) 1 to 0
   (b) 0 to -1
   (c) -1 to 0
   (d) 0 to 1
   (e) 1 to 0

9 $\pi/2, 5\pi/2$

11 $0, \pi, 2\pi, 3\pi, 4\pi$

13 $0, \pi, 2\pi, 3\pi, 4\pi$

15 $3\pi/2, 7\pi/2$

17 $-2\pi, 0, 2\pi$

19 $-3\pi/2, -\pi/2, \pi/2, 3\pi/2$

21 $\pi/2, 3\pi/2, 5\pi/2, 7\pi/2$

23 $0, \pi, 2\pi, 3\pi, 4\pi$

25 0.7

27 -0.7

29 -0.8

31 -2

33 1

35 -2

37 -0.9116

39 0.9134

41 1.008

43 -1.044

45 0.0205

47 0.1566

49 $P(a, b) = P(\cos x, \sin x)$, where $x = -0.898$; x is negative since P is moving clockwise. The quadrant in which P lies is determined by the signs of the coordinates of P: $P(\cos(-0.898), \sin(-0.898)) = (0.6232, -0.7821)$ and P lies in quadrant IV.

51 $P(a, b) = P(\cos x, \sin x)$, where $x = 26.77$; x is positive since P is moving

counterclockwise. The quadrant in which P lies is determined by the signs of the coordinates of P: $P(\cos 26.77, \sin 26.77) = (-0.0664, 0.9978)$ and P lies in quadrant II.

53 $-1/\sqrt{2}$ or $-\sqrt{2/2}$

55 $-\sqrt{2}$

57 Not defined

59 All 0.9525

61 (a) Both 1.6
   (b) Both -1.5
   (c) Both 0.96

63 (a) Both -0.14
   (b) Both 0.23
   (c) Both 0.99

65 (a) 1.0
   (b) 1.0
   (c) 1.0

67 1

69 $\csc x$

71 $\csc x$

73 $\cos x$

75 $s = \cos^{-1} 0.58064516 = 0.951$
   $= \sin^{-1} 0.81415674$

77 (a) Identity (4)
   (b) Identity (9)
   (c) Identity (2)

79 2π

81 $s_1 = 1, s_2 = 1.540302, s_3 = 1.570792,$
   $s_4 = 1.570796, s_5 = 1.570796;$
   $\pi/2 \approx 1.570796$

Section 3.6

1 $2\pi, 2\pi, \pi$

3 (a) 1 unit
   (b) Indefinitely far
   (c) Indefinitely far

5 $-3\pi/2, -\pi/2, \pi/2, 3\pi/2$

7 $-2\pi, -\pi, 0, \pi, 2\pi$

9 No x intercepts

11 (a) None
   (b) $-2\pi, -\pi, 0, \pi, 2\pi$
   (c) $-3\pi/2, -\pi/2, \pi/2, 3\pi/2$

13

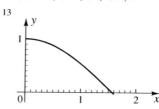

15

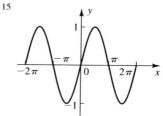

17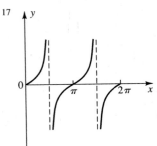

19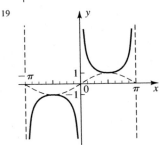

21 (a)
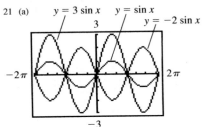
$y = 3 \sin x$ $y = \sin x$ $y = -2 \sin x$

(b) No
(c) 2 units; 1 unit; 3 units
(d) The deviation of the graph from the x axis is changed by changing A. The deviation appears to be $|A|$.

23 (a)
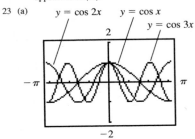
$y = \cos 2x$ $y = \cos x$ $y = \cos 3x$

(b) 1; 2; 3
(c) n

25 (a)
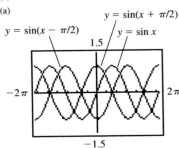
$y = \sin(x + \pi/2)$
$y = \sin(x - \pi/2)$ $y = \sin x$

(b) The graph of $y = \sin x$ is shifted $|C|$ units to the right if $C < 0$ and $|C|$ units to the left if $C > 0$.

27 For each case, the number is not in the domain of the function and an error meassage of some type will appear.

29 (a) The graphs are almost indistinguishable when x is close to the origin.
(b)

x	−0.3	−0.2	−0.1	
tan x	−0.309	−0.203	−0.100	
x	0.0	0.1	0.2	0.3
tan x	0.000	0.100	0.203	0.309

(c) It is not valid to replace tan x with x for small x if x is in degrees, as is clear from the graph.

31 For a given value of T, the y value on the unit circle and the corresponding y value on the sine curve are the same. This is a graphing utility illustration of how the sine function is defined as a circular function. See Figure 3 in this section.

Chapter 3 Review

1 (a) $\pi/3$
(b) $\pi/4$
(c) $\pi/2$

2 (a) $30°$
(b) $90°$
(c) $45°$

3 A central angle of radian measure 2 is an angle subtended by an arc of twice the length of the radius.

4 An angle of radian measure 1.5 is larger, since the corresponding degree measure of the angle would be approximately $85.94°$.

5 (a) $874.3°$
(b) -6.793 rad

6 185 ft/min

7 80 rad/hr

8 $\sin \theta = \frac{3}{5}$; $\tan \theta = -\frac{3}{4}$

9 No, since csc $x = 1/\sin x$, when one is positive so is the other.

10 (a) 0.7355
(b) 1.085

11 (a) 0.9171
(b) 0.9099

12 (a) 0.9394
(b) 5.177

13 (a) $\alpha = 60°$

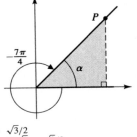
P $120°$ α

(b) $\alpha = \frac{\pi}{4}$

$-\frac{7\pi}{4}$ P α

14 (a) $\sqrt{3}/2$
(b) $1/\sqrt{2}$, or $\sqrt{2}/2$
(c) 0

15 (a) (1,0)
(b) (−1,0)
(c) (0,1)
(d) (0, 1)
(e) (−1, 0)
(f) (0, −1)

16 (a) 0 to 1
(b) 1 to 0
(c) 0 to −1
(d) −1 to 0
(e) 0 to 1
(f) 1 to 0

17 $-11\pi/6$ and $13\pi/6$: When the terminal side of the angle is rotated any multiple of a complete revolution (2π rad) in either direction, the resulting angle will be coterminal with the original. In this case, for the restricted interval, this happens for $\pi/6 \pm 2\pi$.

18 $42°$

19 6 cm

20 $53\pi/45$

21 $15°$

22 (a) -3.72
(b) $264.71°$

23 Yes, since $\theta_d = (180°/\pi \text{ rad})\theta_r$, if θ_r is tripled, then θ_d will also be tripled.

24 No. For example, if $\alpha = \pi/6$ and $\beta = 5\pi/6$, α and β are not coterminal, but $\sin(\pi/6) = \sin(5\pi/6)$.

25 Use the reciprocal identity: csc x $= 1/\sin x = 1/0.8594 = 1.1636$.

26 0; not defined; 0; not defined

27 (a) I
(b) IV

28 -0.992

29 -4.34

30 -1.30

31 0.683

32 0.284

33 -0.864

34 $-\sqrt{3}/2$

35 -1

36 -1

37 0

38 $\sqrt{3}/2$

39 -2

40 -1

41 Not defined

42 $\frac{1}{2}$

43 $\tan(-60°) = -\sqrt{3}$

44 0.40724

45 −0.33884

46 0.64692

47 0.49639

48 $\cos\theta = \frac{3}{5}$; $\tan\theta = -\frac{4}{3}$

49 $7\pi/6$

50 $\cos\theta = \sqrt{21}/5$,
    $\sec\theta = 5/\sqrt{21}$,
    $\csc\theta = -\frac{5}{2}$,
    $\tan\theta = -2\sqrt{21}$,
    $\cot\theta = -\sqrt{21}/2$

51 135°, 315°

52 $5\pi/6, 7\pi/6$

53 (a) 20.3 cm
    (b) 4.71 cm

54 (a) 618 ft²
    (b) 4.71 cm

55 215.6 mi

56 0.422 rad/sec

57 A radial line from the axis of rotation sweeps out an angle at the rate of 12π rad/sec.

58 All 0.754

59 (a) Both −0.871
    (b) Both −1.40
    (c) Both −3.38

60 (d)

61 $\cos x$

62 $\cos x$

63 Since $P(a, b)$ is moving clockwise, $x = -29.37$. By the definition of the circular functions, the point has coordinates $P(\cos(-29.37), \sin(-29.37)) = P(-0.4575, 0.8892)$. P lies in quadrant II, since a is negative and b is positive.

64 The radian measure of a central angle θ subtended by an arc of length s is $\theta = s/r$, where r is the radius of the circle. In this case, $\theta = 1.3/1 = 1.3$ rad.

65 Since $\cot x = 1/(\tan x)$ and $\csc x = 1/(\sin x)$, and $\sin(k\pi) = \tan(k\pi) = 0$ for all integers k, $\cot x$ and $\csc x$ are not defined for these values.

66 $x = 4\pi/3$

67 $s = 0.8905$ unit

68 57 m

69 5.74 units

70 200 rad, $100/\pi \approx 31.8$ revolutions

71 7.5 rev, 15 rev

72 62 rad/sec

73 16,400 mph

74 −17.6 amperes

75 (a) $L = 10\csc\theta + 2\sec\theta$
    (b) As θ decreases to 0 rad, L increases without bound; as θ increases to $\pi/2$, L increases without bound. Between these extremes, there appears to be a value of θ that produces a minimal L.

(c)
θ rad	0.70	0.80	0.90	1.00
L ft	18.14	16.81	15.98	15.59
θ rad	1.10	1.20	1.30	
L ft	15.63	16.25	17.85	

(d) $L = 15.59$ ft for $\theta = 1.00$ rad

76 $\beta = 23.3°$

77 $\alpha = 41.1°$

78 11 mph

Section 4.1

1 $x = \frac{\pi}{4} + 2k\pi$, $x = \frac{3\pi}{4} + k\pi$

3 $x = \frac{\pi}{3} + k\pi$

5 $x = \frac{\pi}{6} + k\pi$

7 $x = (2k + 1)\pi$

9 $x = k\pi$

11 No solution

Section 4.2

1 $y = x^2$, horizontal shift 3 to the right, reflection across the x-axis

3 $y = x^3$, horizontal shift 3 to the left, vertical shift 1 up

5 different, a. has a vertical shift 1 up and b. has a horizontal shift 1 left

7

Vertical Shift	3 up
Horizontal Shift	None
Reflection	None
Midline	$y = 3$
Amplitude	1
Max. value	4
Min. value	2
Period	2π
Begin	$(0, 3)$
Quarter distance	$\frac{\pi}{2}$
1st quarter pt.	$(\frac{\pi}{2}, 4)$
Midpoint	$(\pi, 3)$
3rd quarter pt.	$(\frac{3\pi}{2}, 2)$
End	$(2\pi, 3)$

9

Vertical shift	3 up
Horizontal shift	None
Reflection	Across x
Midline	$y = 3$
Amplitude	1
Max. value	4
Min. value	2
Period	2π
Begin	$(0, 3)$
Quarter distance	$\frac{\pi}{2}$
1st quarter pt.	$(\frac{\pi}{2}, 2)$
Midpoint	$(\pi, 3)$
3rd quarter pt.	$(\frac{3\pi}{2}, 4)$
End	$(2\pi, 3)$

11

Vertical shift	None
Horizontal shift	$\frac{\pi}{4}$ right
Reflection	None
Midline	$y = 0$
Amplitude	1
Max. value	1
Min. value	−1
Period	2π
Begin	$(\frac{\pi}{4}, 1)$
Quarter distance	$\frac{\pi}{2}$
1st quarter pt.	$(\frac{3\pi}{4}, 0)$
Midpoint	$(\frac{5\pi}{4}, -1)$
3rd quarter pt.	$(\frac{7\pi}{4}, 0)$
End	$(\frac{9\pi}{4}, 1)$

13

Vertical shift	None
Horizontal shift	$\frac{\pi}{3}$ left
Reflection	Across x
Midline	$y = 0$
Amplitude	1
Max. value	1
Min. value	−1
Period	2π
Begin	$(-\frac{\pi}{3}, 0)$
Quarter distance	$\frac{\pi}{2}$
1st quarter pt.	$(\frac{\pi}{6}, -1)$
Midpoint	$(\frac{2\pi}{3}, 0)$
3rd quarter pt.	$(\frac{7\pi}{6}, 1)$
End	$(\frac{5\pi}{3}, 0)$

15

Vertical shift	2 up
Horizontal shift	$\frac{\pi}{6}$ left
Reflection	None
Midline	$y = 2$
Amplitude	1
Max. value	3
Min. value	1
Period	2π
Begin	$(-\frac{\pi}{6}, 3)$
Quarter distance	$\frac{\pi}{2}$
1st quarter pt.	$(\frac{\pi}{3}, 2)$
Midpoint	$(\frac{5\pi}{6}, 1)$
3rd quarter pt.	$(\frac{4\pi}{3}, 2)$
End	$(\frac{11\pi}{6}, 3)$

Section 4.3,
Exercises A

1

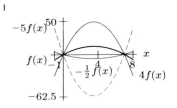

3

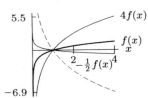

7 (d) All three
9 (i) i
   (ii) c
   (iii) b
   (iv) g
   (v) d

11

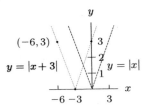

13

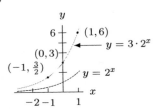

15

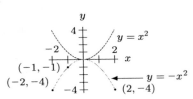

17 (a) (iii)
   (b) (i)
   (c) (ii)

19 I is (b)
   II is (d)
   III is (c)
   IV is (h)

21 (a)

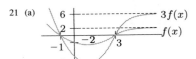

(b)

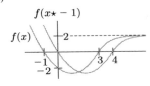

(c)

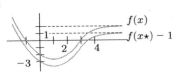

(d)

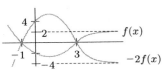

(e)

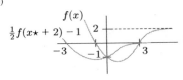

(f)

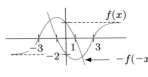

23 (a)

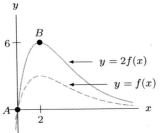

(b)

(c)

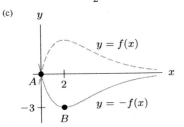

(d)

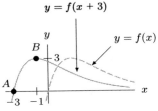

(e)

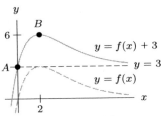

(f)

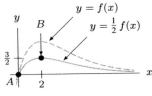

25 (a) $y = f(t) + 2$
       Asymptote: $y = 7$
   (b) $y = f(t + 1)$
       Asymptote: $y = 5$
   (c) $y = f(t - 2) - 3$
       Asymptote: $y = 2$

27 12
35 If $f(x)$ is odd, then $f(0) = 0$
39 Yes, $f(x) = 0$

Section 4.3, Exercises B

1 Same function values for
   $x = -6, -4, -2, 0, 2, 4, 6$

3

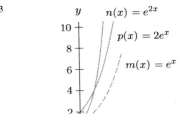

5

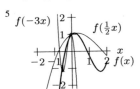

7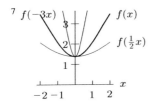

9 (a) (ii)
  (b) (iv)
  (c) (i)
  (d) (iii)

11 (a) $-1 \le x \le 1$, $-1 \le y \le 5$
  (b) $-7.5 \le x \le 7.5$, $-1 \le y \le 5$

13 (a)

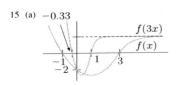

(b)

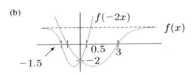

15 (a) -0.33

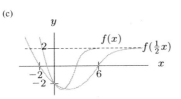

(b)

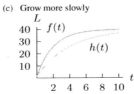

(c)

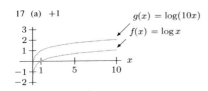

17 (a) $+1$

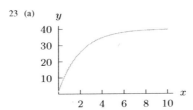

  (b) $\log(10x) = 1 + \log x$
  (c) $k = \log a$

19 (a) III
  (b) II
  (c) I
  (d) IV

21 $r(t)$: half the level
  $s(t)$: half the rate

23 (a)

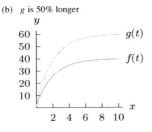

(b) g is 50% longer

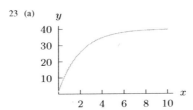

(c) Grow more slowly

Section 4.3, Exercises C

1 a $y = k$
  b A
  c $\frac{2\pi}{B}$
  d h units

3 The 3 causes a horizontal compression of $y = \cos x$

5 Horizontal compression from multiplied 2, horizontal shift 1 left, vertical compression from 1/3 and vertical shift 1 unit down.

7 $y = \sqrt{x}$, horizontal shift 5 left, reflection across the x-axis, vertical compression, and vertical shift 7 units up.

9

Midline	$y = 0$
Amplitude	1
Max. value	1
Min. value	-1
Period	4π
Begin	$(0, 0)$
Quarter distance	π
1st quarter pt.	$(\pi, 1)$
Midpoint	$(2\pi, 0)$
3rd quarter pt.	$(3\pi, -1)$
End	$(4\pi, 0)$

After sketching graph and labeling points check with graphing calculator.

11

Midline	$y = 0$
Amplitude	$\frac{1}{2}$
Max. value	$\frac{1}{2}$
Min. value	$-\frac{1}{2}$
Period	2π
Begin	$(0, -\frac{1}{2})$
Quarter distance	$\frac{\pi}{2}$
1st quarter pt.	$(\frac{\pi}{2}, 0)$
Midpoint	$(\pi, \frac{1}{2})$
3rd quarter pt.	$(\frac{3\pi}{2}, 0)$
End	$(2\pi, -\frac{1}{2})$

After sketching graph and labeling points check with graphing calculator.

13

Midline	$y = 3$
Amplitude	1
Max. value	4
Min. value	2
Period	2π
Begin	$(\frac{\pi}{2}, 4)$
Quarter distance	$\frac{\pi}{2}$
1st quarter pt.	$(\pi, 3)$
Midpoint	$(\frac{3\pi}{2}, 2)$
3rd quarter pt.	$(2\pi, 3)$
End	$(\frac{5\pi}{2}, 4)$

After sketching graph and labeling points check with graphing calculator.

15

Midline	$y = 2$
Amplitude	1
Max. value	3
Min. value	1
Period	$\frac{2\pi}{3}$
Begin	$(0, 2)$
Quarter distance	$\frac{\pi}{6}$
1st quarter pt.	$(\frac{\pi}{6}, 1)$
Midpoint	$(\frac{\pi}{3}, 2)$
3rd quarter pt.	$(\frac{\pi}{2}, 3)$
End	$(\frac{2\pi}{3}, 2)$

After sketching graph and labeling points check with graphing calculator.

17

Midline	$y = -1$
Amplitude	$\frac{1}{2}$
Max. value	$-\frac{1}{2}$
Min. value	$-\frac{3}{2}$
Period	4π
Begin	$(2\pi, -\frac{1}{2})$
Quarter distance	π
1st quarter pt.	$(3\pi, -1)$
Midpoint	$(4\pi, -\frac{3}{2})$
3rd quarter pt.	$(5\pi, -1)$
End	$(6\pi, -\frac{1}{2})$

After sketching graph and labeling points check with graphing calculator.

654

Section 4.4

1 Mid: -8; Amp: 7; Per: $\pi/2$

3 Mid: -1; Amp: π; Per: π

5 Hor: $-4/3$; Phs: -4

7 Both f and g have periods of 1, amplitudes of 1, and midlines $y = 0$

9

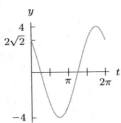

11

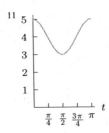

13 $f(t) = 3\cos(\pi t/2)$

15 $h(t) = 4\sin(2\pi t)$

17 $y = 0.8\sin(28\theta)$

19 $g(\theta) = -3\cos(\pi\theta/2) + 3$

21 $f(x) = \sin x, a = \pi/2, b = \pi,$
$c = 3\pi/2, d = 2\pi, e = 1$

23 Amplitude: 20
Period: 3/4 seconds

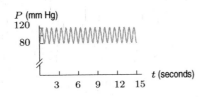

25 $f(t) = 14 + 10\sin(\pi t + \pi/2)$

27 $f(t) = 20 + 15\sin((\pi/2)t + \pi/2)$

29 (a) $12°/\text{min}$
(b) $\theta = (12t - 90)°$
(c) $f(t) = 225 + 225\sin(12t - 90)°$
(d) Amp = Midline = 225 feet
Period = 30 min

31 (a) $P = f(t) =$
$-450\cos(\pi t/6) + 1750$
(c) $t_1 \approx 1.9; t_2 \approx 10.1$

33 $y = 3f(x)$

35 $y = -f(2x)$

37 Amplitude: 41.5;
Period: 12 months

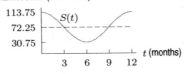

39 (a) and (c)

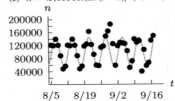

(d) $P = f(t) = 14\sin(\pi t/45) + 93$
(e) $P = f(-10) \approx 84.001$

41 (a) Not exactly regular
(b) Usage repeats each week
(c) $n = 45,000\cos(2\pi(t-2)/7) + 100,000$.

43 $f(t) = -100\cos(\pi t) + 100$ (for $0 \le t \le 1$)
$10\cos(4\pi t) + 190$ (for $1 < t \le 2$)

Section 4.5

1 $x = \frac{7\pi}{12} + k\pi$ or $x = \frac{11\pi}{12} + k\pi$

3 $\theta = \frac{\pi}{9} + \frac{2k\pi}{3}$ or $\theta = \frac{5\pi}{9} + \frac{2k\pi}{3}$

5 $x = (2k+1)\pi$

7 $x = \frac{\pi}{32} + \frac{k\pi}{8}$

9 $t = \frac{9\pi}{2} + 6k\pi$

11 $x = \frac{2k\pi}{5}$

13 No solution

15 $\theta = \frac{k\pi}{3}; \theta = 0, \frac{\pi}{3}, \frac{2\pi}{3}, \pi, \frac{4\pi}{3}, \frac{5\pi}{3}, 2\pi$

17 a $t = \frac{1}{4}$ seconds
b No solution
c $t = \frac{1}{6}$ seconds

Section 4.6

1 Reciprocal identities: $\csc x = 1/(\sin x)$, $\sec x = 1/(\cos x)$, $\cot x = 1/(\tan x)$
Identities for negatives: $\sin(-x) = -\sin x$, $\cos(-x) = \cos x$, $\tan(-x) = -\tan x$

3 (1) is a conditional equation, and (2) is an identity. (1) is true for only one value of x and is false for all other values of x. (2) is true for all values of x for which both sides are defined.

5 $\tan x = 2, \cot x = 1/2, \sec x = \sqrt{5},$
$\csc x = \sqrt{5}/2$

7 $\sin x = -3/\sqrt{10}, \tan x = -3,$
$\cot x = -1/3, \sec x = \sqrt{10}$

9 $\sin x = -1/4, \cos x = -\sqrt{15}/4, \cot x = \sqrt{15}, \csc x = -4$

11 1

13 $\sec x$

15 $\tan x$

17 $\sec\theta$

19 $\cot^2\beta$

21 2

23 Not necessarily. For example, $\sin x = 0$ for infinitely many values ($x = k\pi, k$ any integer), but the equation is not an identity. The left side is not equal to the right side for values other than $x = k\pi, k$ an integer; for example, when $x = \pi/2, \sin x = 1 \ne 0$.

25 $\cos x = -\sqrt{21}/5, \tan x = -2/\sqrt{21},$
$\cot x = -\sqrt{21}/2, \sec x = -5/\sqrt{21},$
$\csc x = 5/2$

27 $\sin x = 1/\sqrt{5}, \cos x = -2/\sqrt{5}, \cot x = -2,$
$\sec x = -\sqrt{5}/2, \csc x = \sqrt{5}$

29 $\sin x = \sqrt{15}/4, \cos x = 1/4, \tan x = \sqrt{15},$
$\cot x = 1/\sqrt{15}, \csc x = 4/\sqrt{15}$

33 (a) -0.4350
(b) $1 - 0.1892 = 0.8108$

35 $-\cot y$

37 $\csc x$

39 0

41 $\csc^2 x$

43 $\cot w$

45 (a) 1
(b) 1

47 I, II

49 II, III

51 All

53 I, IV

55 $a\cos x$

57 $a\sec x$

59 (a) $\frac{x^2}{25} + \frac{y^2}{4} = 1$
(b)

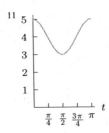

Section 4.7

27 To solve a conditional equation is to find, using equation solving strategies, all replacements of the variable that make the statement true. To verify an identity is to show that one side is equivalent to the other for all replacements of the variable for which both sides are defined. This is done by transforming one side, through a logical sequence of steps, into the other side.

61 (a) No. Use ⟦TRACE⟧ and move from one curve to the other, comparing y values for different values of x. You will see that,

though close, they are not exactly the same.

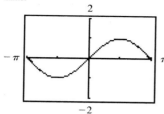

(b) Outside the interval $[-\pi, \pi]$ the graphs differ widely.

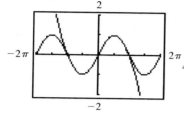

63 An identity

65 Not an identity

67 Not an identity

69 An identity

Section 4.8

1 $\sqrt{3}/2 = \sqrt{3}/2$

3 $-\sqrt{3} = -\sqrt{3}$

5 $\sqrt{2} + \sqrt{3}/2$

7 $2 - \sqrt{3}$

9

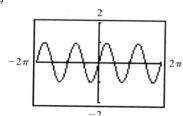

11

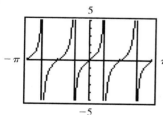

31 $\sin 2x = -\frac{336}{625}$, $\cos 2x = \frac{527}{625}$, $\tan 2x = -\frac{336}{527}$

33 $\sin 2x = -\frac{840}{1.369}$, $\cos 2x = -\frac{1.081}{1.369}$, $\tan 2x = \frac{840}{1.081}$

35 $\sin(x/2) = \sqrt{\frac{3}{8}}$, $\cos(x/2) = \sqrt{\frac{5}{8}}$

37 $\sin(x/2) = \sqrt{\frac{2}{3}}$, $\cos(x/2) = \sqrt{\frac{1}{3}}$

39 $\sin(x/2) = -\sqrt{\frac{2}{5}}$, $\cos(x/2) = \sqrt{\frac{3}{5}}$

41 (a) Since θ is a first-quadrant angle and $\sec 2\theta$ is negative for 2θ in the second quadrant and not for 2θ in the first, 2θ is a second-quadrant angle.

(b) Construct a reference triangle for 2θ in the second quadrant with $a = -4$ and $r = 5$. Use the Pythagorean theorem to find $b = 3$. Thus, $\sin 2\theta = \frac{3}{5}$ and $\cos 2\theta = -\frac{4}{5}$.

(c) The double-angle identities $\cos 2\theta = 1 - 2\sin^2 \theta$ and $\cos 2\theta = 2\cos^2 \theta - 1$

(d) Use the identities in part (c) in the form $\sin \theta = \sqrt{(1 - \cos 2\theta)/2}$ and $\cos \theta = \sqrt{(1 + \cos 2\theta)/2}$. The positive radicals are used because θ is in quadrant I.

(e) $\sin \theta = 3\sqrt{10}/10$; $\cos \theta = \sqrt{10}/10$

43 (a) Approximation improves

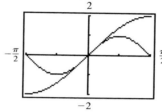

(b) Approximation improves

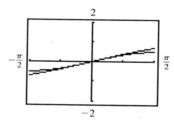

45 $0 \le x \le 2\pi$

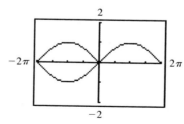

47 $-2\pi \le x \le -\pi$, $\pi \le x \le 2\pi$

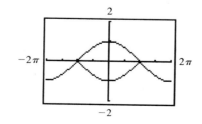

49 $\sin x = \frac{5}{\sqrt{146}}$, $\cos x = \frac{11}{\sqrt{146}}$, $\tan x = \frac{5}{11}$

51 $\sin x = \frac{7}{\sqrt{53}}$, $\cos x = \frac{2}{\sqrt{53}}$, $\tan x = \frac{7}{2}$

53 $\sin x = -\frac{4}{\sqrt{65}}$, $\cos x = \frac{7}{65}$, $\tan x = -\frac{4}{7}$

61 $g(x) = \cot \frac{x}{2}$

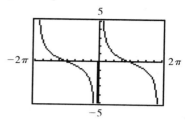

63 $g(x) = \csc 2x$

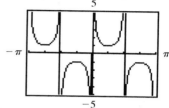

65 $g(x) = 2\cos x - 1$

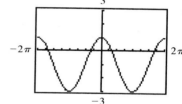

67

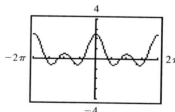

69 (a) $d = \frac{v_0^2 \sin 2\theta}{32}$

(b) d is maximum when $\sin 2\theta$ is maximum, and $\sin 2\theta$ is maximum when $2\theta = 90°$; that is, when $\theta = 45°$.

(c) As θ increases from $0°$ to $90°$, d increases to a maximum of 312.5 ft when $\theta = 45°$, then decreases.

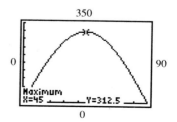

71 (b) $\sin 2\theta$ has a maximum value of 1 when $2\theta = 90°$, or $\theta = 45°$. When $\theta = 45°$, $V = 64$ ft^3.

(c) Max $V = 64.0$ ft^3 occurs when $\theta = 45°$,

Table 4.11

θ (deg)	30	35	40	45	50	55	60
V (ft^3)	55.4	60.1	63.0	64.0	63.0	60.1	55.4

(d) Max $V = 64$ ft^3 when $\theta = 45°$.

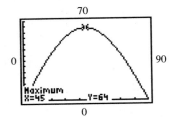

73 $x = 2\sqrt{3} \approx 3.464$ cm; $\theta = 30.000°$

75 $\cos\theta = \frac{4}{5}$

Section 4.9

1 $x = k\pi$ or $x = \frac{2\pi}{3} + 2k\pi$, $x = \frac{4\pi}{3} + 2k\pi$

3 $x = \frac{\pi}{4} + k\pi$

5 $x = \frac{\pi}{2} + k\pi$

7 $x = \frac{\pi}{3} + k\pi$

9 No solution

11 $x = k\pi$ or $x = \frac{5\pi}{6} + 2k\pi$, $x = \frac{7x}{6} + 2k\pi$

Chapter 4 Review

1 Equation (1) is an identity, because it is true for all replacements of x by real numbers for which both sides are defined. Equation (2) is a conditional equation, because it is only true for $x = -2$ and $x = 3$; it is not true, for example, for $x = 0$.

13 $\frac{1}{2} = \frac{1}{2}$

14 $1/\sqrt{2} = 1/\sqrt{2}$

15 $\frac{1}{2}\cos 3t - \frac{1}{2}\cos 13t$

16 $2\sin 3w \cos 2w$

21 The equation is not an identity. The equation is not true for $x = \pi/2$, for example, and both sides are defined for $x = \pi/2$.

22 Graph each side of the equation in the same viewing window and observe that the graphs are not the same, except where the graph of $y_1 = \sin x$ crosses the x axis. (Note that the graph of $y_2 = 0$ is the x axis.)

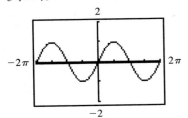

23 (a) 0.9394   (b) 0.1176

24 No. The equation is an identity for all real values of x, except for $x = k\pi$, k an integer

(neither side of the equation is defined for these values).

25 Graph each side of the equation in the same viewing window and observe that the graphs are not the same.

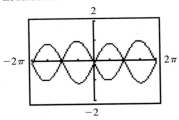

26 Find a value of x for which both sides are defined but are not equal. Try $x = 1$, for example: $\sin(1 - 3) = -0.9093$ and $\sin 1 - \sin 3 = 0.7004$.

42 $\frac{1}{2} - \frac{\sqrt{3}}{4}$

43 $-\sqrt{6}/2$

44 $\sec x = -\frac{3}{2}$, $\sin x = \sqrt{5}/3$, $\csc x = 3/\sqrt{5}$, $\tan x = -\sqrt{5}/2$, $\cot x = -2/\sqrt{5}$

45 $\sin 2x = \frac{24}{25}$, $\cos 2x = -\frac{7}{25}$, $\tan 2x = -\frac{24}{7}$

46 $\sin(x/2) = -3/\sqrt{13}$, $\cos(x/2) = 2/\sqrt{13}$, $\tan(x/2) = -\frac{3}{2}$

47 $\tan(x + \pi/4) = (\tan x + 1)/(1 - \tan x)$

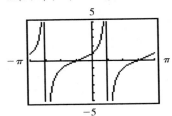

48 $y_2 = \cos(1.8x)$

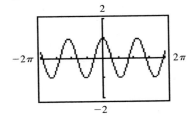

49 Identities for $-2\pi \le x \le 0$

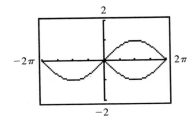

50 (a) Not an identity; for example, both sides are defined for $x = 0$, but are not equal.

(b) An identity

51 $\sin x = -5/\sqrt{26}$, $\cos x = 1/\sqrt{26}$, $\tan x = -5$

58 $g(x) = 4 + 2\cos x$

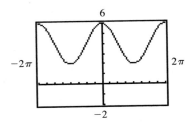

59 $g(x) = \tan 2x$

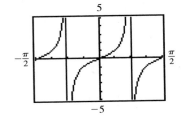

60 $g(x) = 2 - \cos 2x$

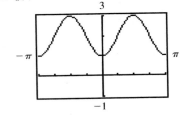

61 $g(x) = -2 + \sec 2x$

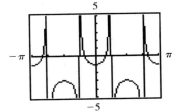

62 $g(x) = 2 + \cot(x/2)$

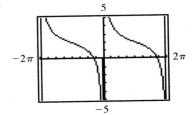

63 $-2\pi \leq x < -\pi, 0 \leq x < \pi$

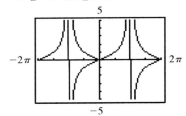

64 $-\pi < x \leq 0, \pi < x \leq 2\pi$

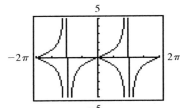

65

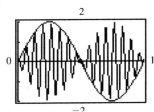

66 $y_1 = \sin 32\pi x - \sin 28\pi x$

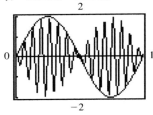

67 $a \tan x$

68 $57.5°$

69 $x = \frac{445}{39} \approx 11.410; \theta \approx 32.005°$

70 $\theta = 0.464$ rad

71 (b) L steadily increases.
    (c)

Table 4.13

θ (deg)	30	35	40	45
L (ft)	250.7	252.6	254.6	256.6
θ (deg)	50	55	60	
L (ft)	258.7	260.8	263.1	

(d) Min $L = 250.7$ ft; Max $L = 263.1$ ft

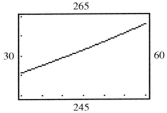

72 $y = 0.6 \sin 130\pi t \sin 10\pi t$; Beat frequency = 10 Hz

73 (a)

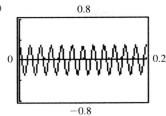

(b)

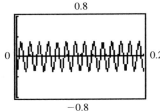

(c)

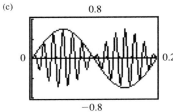

(d)

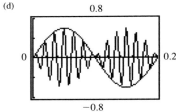

74 $y = 10 \sin(3t + 3.79)$; Amplitude = 10 cm;
    Period = $2\pi/3$ sec; Frequency = $3/2\pi$ Hz;
    Phase shift = -1.26 sec   [*Chap. 4 Group Activity*]

75 t intercepts: $-1.26, -0.21, 0.83, 1.88$;
    Phase shift = -1.26

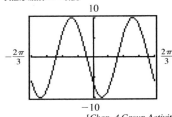

[*Chap. 4 Group Activity*]

Section 5.1

1 $6, -3$

3 $x = -2, x = -\frac{1}{2}$

5 $x = -2/7, x = -2$

7 $x = (23 \pm \sqrt{1821})/(-34) \approx 1.932$ or -0.579

9 $f(x) = a(x - 1)(x - 2)$ for any constant a

11

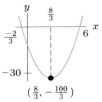

13 4.046 sec

15 For example $y = (x + 2)(x - 3)$

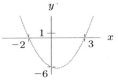

17 -2.4% in 2004

19

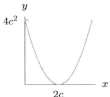

21 (a) 5 km
    (b) 4430 m
    (c) $h \approx -0.000000255d^2 + 5$

23 Conjecture: $x^2 + 1 \geq 2x$

Section 5.2

1 $y = (1/3)x^2 + 2x + 5$

3 $y = -(3/16)(x - 4)^2 + 7$

5 $y = (1/2)(x - 3)^2 + 3$

7 $y = \frac{7}{9}(x - 3)^2 - 5$

9 (a) $a = 1, b = 0, c = 3$
        Axis of symmetry: y-axis
        Vertex: $(0, 3)$
        No zeros
        y-intercept: $y = 3$

(b) $a = -2, b = 4, c = 16$
     Axis of symmetry: $x = 1$
     Vertex: $(1, 18)$
     Zeros: $x = -2, 4$
     y-intercept: $y = 16$

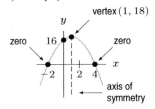

11 Vertex is $(6, -8)$
 Axis of symmetry is $x = 6$

13 Vertex is $(-5, 106)$
 Axis of symmetry is $x = -5$

15 $x = -4 + \sqrt{11} = -0.683$,
 $x = -4 - \sqrt{11} = -7.317$

17 (a) $g(x) = f(x - 3) + 2$
 (b) Yes; $g(x) = x^2 - 6x + 11$
 $a = 1, b = -6, c = 11$
 (c)

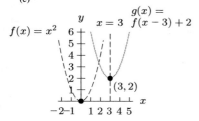

19 Shift $y = x^2$ right by 5 units to get
 $y = (x - 5)^2 = x^2 - 10x + 25$

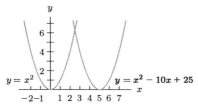

21 Yes. $f(x) = -(x - 1)^2 + 4$

23 $y = -(x - 3)^2$

25 (a)

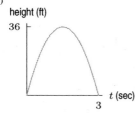

 (b) $t = 0, 3$; being thrown; hitting the ground
 (c) 1.5 seconds
 (d) 36 feet

27 12.5 cm by 12.5 cm; $k/4$ by $k/4$

29 (b) Maximum height: $t = T/2$

Section 5.3

1 $x = \pm 5, x = \pm 1$

3 $w = -4, w = -1$

5 $x = \frac{\pi}{6} + k\pi, x = \frac{5\pi}{6} + k\pi$

7 $x = \frac{\pi}{4} + \frac{k\pi}{2}$

9 $x = \frac{\pi}{2} + 2k\pi$ or $x = \frac{7\pi}{6} + 2k\pi$,
 $x = \frac{11\pi}{6} + 2k\pi$

11 $x = \frac{\pi}{4} + k\pi$ or $x = \frac{7\pi}{12} + k\pi, x = \frac{11\pi}{12} + k\pi$

13 No solution

15 $t = k\pi$ or $t = \frac{3\pi}{4} + k\pi$

17 $x = k\pi$

19 $t = (2k + 1)\pi$ or $t = \frac{\pi}{3} + 2k\pi, t = \frac{5\pi}{3} + 2k\pi$

21 $x = k\pi$ or $x = \frac{\pi}{6} + k\pi, x = \frac{5\pi}{6} + k\pi$

Section 5.4

1 No

3 Yes; $y = 2x^2$

5 Yes; $y = 4x^2$

7 Even

9 Fractional

11 $y = 5x^{1.535}$

13 $y = 2x^{1.194}$

15 $k = 24; y = 24/x; x = 3$

17 $k = 405; c = 405/d^2; c = 16.2$

19 $f(x) = 3x^2$

21 $h(x) = -2x^{-2}$

23 (a) $x^{-10} \to +\infty, -x^{10} \to 0$
 (b) $x^{-10} \to 0, -x^{10} \to -\infty$
 (c) $x^{-10} \to 0, -x^{10} \to -\infty$

27 (a) $f(x) = x^{1/n}$
 $g(x) = x^n$
 (b) $(1, 1)$

29 Formula not unique

31 $y = 1350/n; 14$

33 $d = 0.1x; 32.5$ miles

35 (a) $d = 1.7, 3.4, 20.4, 102$
 $d = 0.34t$
 (b) 9.8 mins
 (c) $A = 9.1, 36.3, 1307, 32685$
 $A = 0.363t^2$
 (d) $P = 11.25t^2$
 (e) 298 see, or approx 5 min

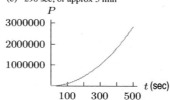

37 (a) $r = 200t$
 (b) $A = 40000\pi t^2$
 (c) 6,157,521.601 m^2

39 (a) $h(x) = -2x^2$
 (b) $j(x) = \frac{1}{4}x^2$

41 (a) $p < 0, x \neq 0$
 (b) $P > 0, y \geq 0$;
 $p < 0, y > 0$;
 $p > 0, y$ is any real;
 $p < 0, y \neq 0$
 (c) p even; y-axis symmetry; p odd: origin symmetry

43 (a) $P = 4.1 \cdot 10^{-10}d^{3/2}$
 (b) 4320 earth days

Section 5.5

1 Yes, 2

3 Yes, 1

5 No

7 $x \approx 0.718, x \approx 1.702$.

9 $y \to \infty$; like x^3

11 $y \to \infty$; like x^9

13 (a)

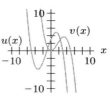

15 $y = \frac{1}{2}x - 1$

17 (a)

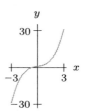

 (b) $f(0.5) = 1.625$;
 $f^{-1}(0.5) \approx -0.424$;

19 (a)

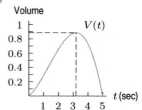

 (b) $V \approx .886$ at $t \approx 3.195$
 (c) $(0, 0)$ and $(5,0)$;
 Lungs empty at beginning and end

21 (a) 500 people
 (b) May of 1908
 (c) 790; February of 1907

23 Yes

25 (a)

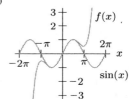

 (b) $-\frac{\pi}{2} \leq x \leq \frac{\pi}{2}$
 (c) Error less than 0.0001%

27 (a) $0 \leq T < 5$
 (b) $0 \leq T < 15$
 (c) $0 \leq T < 30$
 (d) Negative

Section 5.6

1 $x(x + 2)(x - 2)(x - 4)$

3 $h(x) = x(x + 2)^2(x - 3)$

5 $-3, 2, -7$

7 $0, -4, -3$

9

11 C

13 $y = \frac{1}{2}(x + \frac{1}{2})(x - 3)(x - 4)$

15 $y = 2x(x + 2)(x - 2)$

17 $y = 7(x + 2)(x - 3)^2$

19 $y = -\frac{1}{3}(x + 2)^2(x)(x - 2)^2$

21 $g(x) = -\frac{1}{4}(x + 2)^2(x - 2)(x - 3)$

23 $g(x) = -\frac{1}{3}(x + 2)(x - 2)x^2$

25 $j(x) = (x + 3)(x + 2)(x + 1) + 4$

27 $f(x) = 1$

29 $f(x) = x$ (and other answers)

31 $g(x) = -\frac{1}{15}(x - 3)^2(x - 5)(x + 1)$

33 (a) Invertible
   (b) Not invertible

35 None

37 None

39 $x \approx -0.143$

41 $V = 4x^2 + 9x + 3$

43 (b) $x = 0, 1.112, -1.112$
   (d) Same zeros as $a(x)$

45 (a) $f(x) = \frac{2}{15}(x + 2)(x - 3)(x - 5)$
   (b) $f(x) = -\frac{2}{75}(x + 2)(x - 3)(x - 5)^2$
   (c) $f(x) = \frac{1}{15}(x + 2)^2(x - 3)(x - 5)$

Section 5.7

1 Rational; $(x^3 + 2)/(2x)$

3 Not rational

5 Rational; $(x^2 - 5)/(x - 3)$

7 As $x \to \pm\infty$, $f(x) \to 1$, $g(x) \to x$, and $h(x) \to 0$

9 $y = 1$

11 $y = 4$

13 $f^{-1}(x) = (4x + 4)/(5x + 3)$

15 (a) $C(x) = (1 + x)/(2 + x)$
   (b) $C(0.5) = 60\%$;
       $C(-0.5) = 33.333\%$
   (c)

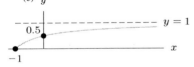

17 (a) $C(n_0)/n_0$
   (b) Slope is average cost for n_0 units

19 (a) $C(x) = 30000 + 3x$
   (b) $a(x) = 3 + 30000/x$
   (c)

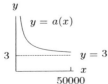

(f) $a^{-1}(y) = 30000/(y - 3)$
(g) 15,000

21 (a) $h(x) = (2x^3 + 2)/(3x^2)$

Section 5.8

1 x-int: $x = 2$
  y-int: $y = 1/2$
  Horiz asy: $y = 1$
  Vert asy: $x = 4$

3 x-int: $x = \pm 2$
  y-int: None
  Horiz asy: $y = 0$
  Vert asy: $x = 0$, $x = -4$

5 Zero: $x = -3$;
  Asymptote: $x = -5$;
  $y \to 1$ as $x \to \pm\infty$

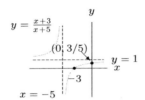

7 Zeros: $x = 4$;
  Asymptote: $x = \pm 3$;
  $y \to 0$ as $x \to \pm\infty$

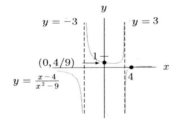

9

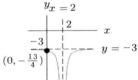

11 (c) Horizontal: $y = 0$
      Vertical: $x = 3$

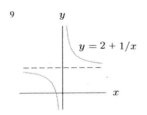

13 (c) Horizontal: $y = 1$
      Vertical: $x = 0$

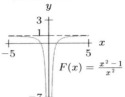

15 (a) $-2, -3$; None
   (b) $-2, -3$; No; $r(x) \to 1$ as $x \to \pm\infty$
   (c) No; Yes at $x = -2$ and $x = 3$;
       $s(x) \to 1$ as $x \to \pm\infty$

17 (a) Small
   (b) Large
   (c) Undefined
   (d) Positive
   (e) Negative

19 (a)

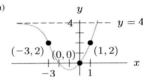

   (b)

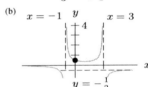

21 $p = 2$, $(0, -13/4)$
   $x = 2$, $y = -3$

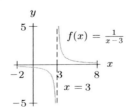

23 (a) $y = (1/x) - 3$
   (b) $y = (-3x + 1)/x$
   (c) $(1/3, 0)$

25 (a) $y = 1/(x - 1) + 2$
   (b) $y = (2x - 1)/(x - 1)$
   (c) $(1/2, 0)$ and $(0, 1)$

27 (a) $y = 1/(x - 2)^2 - 1$
   (b) $y = (-x^2 + 4x - 3)/(x^2 - 4x + 4)$
   (c) $(0, -3/4)$, $(1, 0)$ and $(3, 0)$

29 (a) $1/x^2$
   (b) $y = \frac{1}{(x-3)^2} + 1$

31 (a) $1/x^2$
   (b) $y = \frac{1}{x^2} + 1$

33 7.123 by 4.623 by 1.939 inches

35 $y = -(x + 1)/(x - 2)$

37 $y = x/((x + 2)(x - 3))$

39 $y = -(x - 3)(x + 2)/((x + 1)(x - 2))$

41 $y = (x - 2)/((x + 1)(x - 1))$

43 $g(x) = (x - 5)/((x + 2)(x - 3))$

45 $y = x - 9$; $(2, -7)$

47 $h(x) = (x^4 - 2x^3)/(x - 2)$

Chapter 5 Review

1 Even

3 $f(x) = (3/2) \cdot x^{-2}$

5 3rd degree

7 Degree: 4; Terms: 3;
$x \to \pm\infty : y \to -\infty$

9 6, 2, 3

11 Rational; $(3x + 1)/6$

13 $y = 7/x^{-4}$

15 Graph (i): J;
Graph (ii): L;
Graph (iii): O;
Graph (iv): H

17 $f(x) = -(x + 1)(x - 1)^2$

19 $h(x) = \frac{1}{12}(x + 2)(x + 1)(x - 1)^2(x - 3)$

21 $g(x) = \frac{1}{6}(x + 1)(x - 2)(x - 4) + 4$

23 (a) Even
   (b) Neither
   (c) Odd
   (d) Neither
   (e) Neither
   (f) Even
   (g) Neither
   (h) Even

25 (a) $b = 0$
   (b) $b = d = 0$

27 (a) 1.2 meters/sec
   (b) 21% longer than the existing ship

29 (a) $f(x) = x/(x + 5)$
   (b) $f(7) = 7/12 \approx 58.333\%$
   (c) $x = 0$
   (d) $y = 1$

31 $C < A < 0 < B < D$

33 $A < 0 < C < D < B$

35 $p(x) = \frac{7}{1080}(x + 3)(x - 2)(x - 5)(x - 6)^2$

37 $f(x) = -3(x - 2)(x - 3)/(x - 5)^2$

39 (a) $a \approx 0.2, b \approx 1.36$
   (b) $J = 0$
   (c) Yes

43 $y = 2\cos(\pi x) + 1$

45 $y = 2(x^2 - 4)(x - 1)$

47 $y = \frac{1}{2}(5^x)$

49 (b) Second
   (c) Horizontal: $y = \pi R^2$;
       Vertical: $v = 0$

Ch. 5 Understanding

1 False

3 True

5 True

7 False

9 True

11 True

13 False

15 True

17 False

19 False

21 True

23 False

25 True

27 True

29 True

31 True

33 True

35 False

37 False

39 True

41 True

43 False

45 False

47 False

Section 6.1

1 $r(0) = 4, r(1) = 5, r(2) = 2, r(3) = 0, r(4) = 3, r(5)$ undefined

3 $\pi/2, \pi/3, \pi/4, \pi/6, 0$

5 $(x^2 - 6x + 10)/(x^2 - 6x + 9)$

7 $x + 1$

9 $(x - 3)/(10 - 3x)$

11 $k(m(x)) = 1/(x - 1)^2$

13 $k(n(x)) = 4x^4/(x + 1)^2$

15 $(m(x))^2 = 1/(x^2 - 2x + 1)$

17 Area in terms of time

19 Revenue in terms of fertilizer

21 $f : 2, 2, 0$

   $g : -2, -2, 0$

   $h : 0, -2, -2, 0, -2, -2, 0$

23 (a) 3.7
   (b) 1.2
   (c) 3.6
   (d) 2.2

25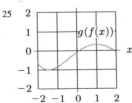

27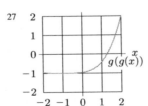

29 (a) 4
   (b) 1
   (c) 4
   (d) 0

31 (a)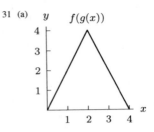

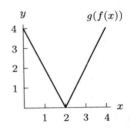

   (b) $0 < x < 2$
   (c) $2 < x < 4$

35 (a) Periodic; Range: $0 \le y \le 1$
   (b) $(\sin x)^2 + (\cos x)^2 = 1$

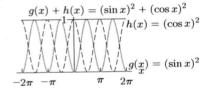

37 $(\sqrt{x + h} - \sqrt{x})/h$

39 $(2^{x+h} - 2^x)/h$

41 $u(x) = \sqrt{x}, v(x) = 3 - 5x$

43 $u(x) = x^2 + x, v(x) = x^2$

45 $u(x) = 2 + x, v(x) = 1/x$

47 $u(x) = 3^x, v(x) = 2x - 1$

49 $h(x) = x^3$

51 $f(x) = 1/x$

53 $j(x) = (x^2 + 3)^2 + 3$

55 $v(x) = x + 1/x$

57 (a) $h(x) = 3x^2$
   (b) $j(x) = 2x + 1$

59 (a) $f(x) = 121.5x$
       $g(x) = 1.02638x$
       $h(x) = 0.00845x$
   (b) $1000 trades for yen,
       then for 1026.675 euros

Section 6.2

1 Not invertible

3 Invertible

9 $h^{-1}(x) = \sqrt[3]{x/12}$

11 $k^{-1}(x) = \frac{1}{2}\ln(x/3)$

13 $n^{-1}(x) = 10^x + 3$

15 $h^{-1}(x) = (x/(1 - x))^2$

17 $f^{-1}(x) = (4x^2 - 4)/(x^2 - 7)$

19 $p^{-1}(x) = 1/e^{(x/2)}$

21 $q^{-1}(x) = (3 + 5e^x)/(e^x - 1)$

23 Quantity manufactured at cost C; number of items

25 $f^{-1}(P) = 50\ln(P/10)$

27 $f^{-1}(N) = I_0 10^{N/10}$

29 $x = (\ln 3/\ln 2) - 5$

31 $x = e^{1.8} - 3$

33 $x = (19 - \sqrt{37})/2$

35 $f^{-1}(3) < f(3) < 0 < f(0)$
     $< f^{-1}(0) < 3$

39 (a) $x = (1/3)\ln(1/2)$
    (b) $x \approx -0.382$
    (c) $x = (1/6)\ln 2$
    (d) $x = (1/4)\ln 2$

41 $1 - t^2$

43 (a) $A = \pi r^2$

    (b)

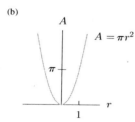

    (c) $r \geq 0$

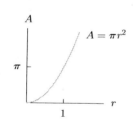

    (d) $f^{-1}(A) = \sqrt{A/\pi}$

    (e)

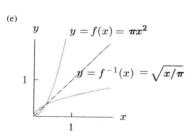

    (f) Yes

45 (a) $P(t) = 150(1.1)^t$
    (b) $P^{-1}(y) =$
         $(\log y - \log 150)/\log 1.1$
    (c) 10.3 years

47 (a) 36 m

(b) 6 seconds
(c) One possibility: $3 \leq t \leq 6$

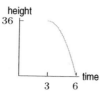

(e)

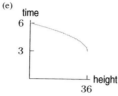

49 (a) A (wrong) guess in 0.99 ml
    (b) $x = C^{-1}(0.98)$
    (c) 50 ml

51 $f^{-1}(L) = -\frac{1}{k}\ln(1 - L/L_\infty)$ $f^{-1}(L) = $ Age of fish of length L Domain: $0 \leq L \leq L_\infty$

Section 6.3

1 $3x^2 + x$

3 $\sqrt{4x^3 + 8x}$

5 $3x/2 - 1/2$

7 (a) $f(x) + g(x) = 3x^2 + x + 1$
   (b) $f(x) - g(x) = -3x^2 + x + 1$
   (c) $f(x)g(x) = 3x^3 + 3x^2$
   (d) $f(x)/g(x) = (x + 1)/(3x^2)$

9 (a) $f(x) + g(x) = 2x$
   (b) $f(x) - g(x) = 10$
   (c) $f(x)g(x) = x^2 - 25$
   (d) $f(x)/g(x) = (x + 5)/(x - 5)$

11 (a) $f(x) + g(x) = x^3 + x^2$
    (b) $f(x) - g(x) = x^3 - x^2$
    (c) $f(x)g(x) = x^5$
    (d) $f(x)/g(x) = x$

13 (a)

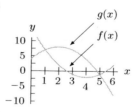

    (c)

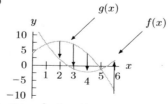

    (f) $f(x) = x^2 - 8x + 14$;
         $g(x) = -x^2 + 4x + 4$;
         $f(x) - g(x) = 2x^2 - 12x + 10$

(g) Yes

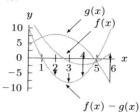

17 (a) $h(x) = x^2 + x, h(3) = 12$
    (b) $j(x) = x^2 - 2x - 3, j(3) = 0$
    (c) $k(x) = x^3 + x^2 - x - 1, k(3) = 32$
    (d) $m(x) = x - 1$ for $x \neq -1, m(3) = 2$
    (e) $n(x) = 2x + 2, n(3) = 8$

(19) (a) $f(x) = 2x + 4, g(x) = \frac{1}{3}x - 1$
      (b)

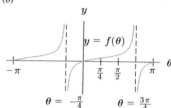

21 \$17.50

23 (a) $f(\theta) = (\tan\theta)/(1 + \tan\theta)$
    (b)

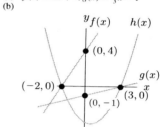

    (c) $f(\theta)$ is periodic

25 (a)

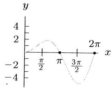

    (b)

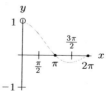

    (c)

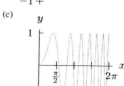

(d)

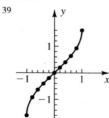

(e)

(f)

29 False

31 (a) $p(t) = f(t) + g(t)$
   (b) $m(t) = g(t) \cdot h(t)$

33 (b) $p(t) = (f_{CA}(t) \cdot g_{CA}(t) + f_{FL}(t) \cdot g_{FL}(t))/(f_{US}(t) \cdot g_{US}(t))$.

Section 6.4

1 0

3 $\pi/6$

5 $\pi/4$

7 $\pi/3$

9 3.127

11 1.329

13 Not defined

15 $x = \sin 37 = 0.601815$

17 $2\pi/3$

19 $-\pi/4$

21 $-\pi/3$

23 $5\pi/6$

25 -0.6

27 $\sqrt{2}/2$

29 $2/\sqrt{5}$

31 $1/\sqrt{5}$

33 -1.328

35 1.001

37 2.456

39

41 $120°$

43 $-45°$

45 $-60°$

47 Not defined

49 $60°$

51 $71.80°$

53 $-54.16°$

55 $-86.69°$

57 0.3; does not illustrate a cosine–inverse cosine identity, because $\cos^{-1}(\cos x) = x$ only if $0 \le x \le \pi$.

59 (a)

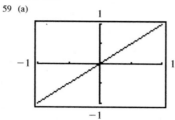

(b) The domain of $\sin^{-1}$ is restricted to $-1 \le x \le 1$; hence no graph will appear for other values of x.

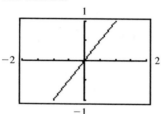

61 $-\frac{1}{2}$

63 $-\frac{24}{25}$

65 $\frac{2\sqrt{2}-2}{3\sqrt{5}}$

67 $\frac{-7}{\sqrt{15}}$

69 $-\sqrt{\frac{5-\sqrt{5}}{10}}$

71 $\sqrt{1-x^2}$

73 $\frac{x}{\sqrt{1-x^2}}$

77 (a) $\cos^{-1} x$ has domain $-1 \le x \le 1$; therefore, $\cos^{-1}(2x - 3)$ has domain $-1 \le 2x - 3 \le 1$, or $1 \le x \le 2$.
   (b) The graph appears only for the domain values $1 \le x \le 2$.

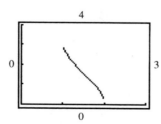

79 (a) $h^{-1}(x) = 1 + \sin^{-1}[(x - 3)/5]$
   (b) $\sin^{-1} x$ has domain $-1 \le x \le 1$; therefore, $1 + \sin^{-1}[(x - 3)/5]$ has domain $-1 \le (x - 3)/5 \le 1$, or $-2 \le x \le 8$.

81 (a)

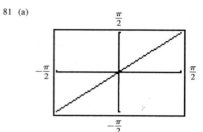

(b) The domain for $\sin x$ is $(-\infty, \infty)$ and the range is $[-1, 1]$, which is the domain for $\sin^{-1} x$. Thus, $y = \sin^{-1}(\sin x)$ has a graph over the interval $(-\infty, \infty)$, but $\sin^{-1}(\sin x) = x$ has a graph only on the restricted domain of $\sin x$, $[-\pi/2, \pi/2]$.

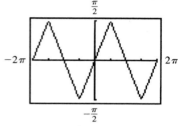

83 (a) $\theta = 2\sin^{-1}(1/M)$, $M > 1$
   (b) $72°$; $52°$

85 (a) It appears that θ increases, and then decreases.
   (c) From the table, Max $\theta = 9.21°$ when $x = 25$ yd.

Table 6.28

x (yd)	10	15	20	25
θ (deg)	6.44	8.19	9.01	9.21
x (yd)	30	35		
θ (deg)	9.04	8.68		

(d) The angle θ increases rapidly until a maximum is reached, and then declines more slowly. Max $\theta = 9.21°$ when $x = 24.68$ yd.

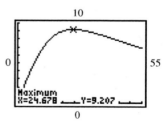

87 (b) 248 ft³
   (c) 2.6 ft

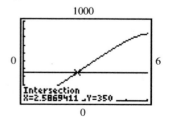

Section 6.5

1 $\pi/6$

3 $\pi/2$

5 $\pi/4$

7 1

9 $\frac{4}{3}$

11 $3\pi/4$

13 $2\pi/3$

15 $-\pi/6$

17 Not defined

19 $\frac{4}{5}$

21 $-\frac{4}{3}$

23 $-\frac{1}{2}$

25 33.4

27 -4

29 1.398

31 1.536

33 Not defined

35 2.875

37 1.637

39 $120°$

41 $135°$

43 $-60°$

45 Not defined

47 $-45°$

49 $165°$

51 $71.80°$

53 $-54.16°$

55 $93.31°$

57 $-\frac{8}{19}$

59 $\frac{24}{7}$

61 $\frac{1}{\sqrt{x^2+1}}$

63 $\frac{|x|}{\sqrt{x^2-1}}$

65 $\frac{2x}{x^2+1}$

69

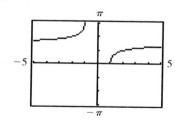

71

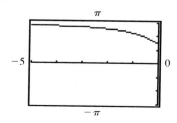

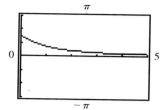

Section 6.6

1 $2\pi/3, 4\pi/3$

3 $2\pi/3 + 2k\pi, 4\pi/3 + 2k\pi$, k any integer

5 $45°, 135°$

7 $45° + k(360°), 135° + k(360°)$, k any integer

9 $104.9314°$

11 $1.1593, 5.1239$

13 $0.6696 + 2k\pi, 2.4720 + 2k\pi$, k any integer

15 $\pi/2, 3\pi/2$

17 $90° + k(180°), 45° + k(180°)$, k any integer

19 $\pi/2$

21 $180°$

23 $90°, 270°$

25 $\pi/6, 5\pi/6, 7\pi/6, 11\pi/6$

27 $104.5°$

29 $0.9987, 5.284$

31 $0.9987 + 2k\pi, -0.9987 + 2k\pi$, k any integer

33 $0.6579 + 2k\pi, 5.625 + 2k\pi$, k any integer

35 $1.946 + 2k\pi, 4.338 + 2k\pi$, k any integer

37 $\cos^{-1}(-0.7334)$ has exactly one value, 2.3941; the equation $\cos x = -0.7334$ has infinitely many solutions, which are found by adding $2\pi k$, k any integer, to each solution in one period of $\cos x$.

39 $0, \pi/2$

41 0

43 $0.002613\, \text{sec}$

45 $33.21°$

47 $64.1°$

49 $(r, \theta) = (1, 30°), (1, 150°)$

51 $\theta = 45°$

Chapter 6 Review Part 1

1 $27x^2 - 2$

3 $3x$

5 $3888x^2 - 1728x + 192$

7 (a) $f(2x) = 4x^2 + 2x$
(b) $g(x^2) = 2x^2 - 3$
(c) $h(1 - x) = (1 - x)/x$
(d) $(f(x))^2 = (x^2 + x)^2$
(e) $g^{-1}(x) = (x + 3)/2$
(f) $(h(x))^{-1} = (1 - x)/x$

(g) $f(x)g(x) = (x^2 + x)(2x - 3)$
(h) $h(f(x)) = (x^2 + x)/(1 - x^2 - x)$

9 $j^{-1}(x) = (x^2 - 1)^2$

11 $k^{-1}(x) = (3 - 2x)^2/(x + 1)^2$

13 $h^{-1}(x) = (5 + 4 \cdot 10^x)/(10^x - 1)$

15 $g^{-1}(x) = \arcsin(\ln x / \ln 2)$

17 $x/(1 + x) + x + 1$

19 $g(x) = \sqrt{x}, h(x) = 1 + \sqrt{x}$

21 $g(x) = \frac{1}{x^2}, h(x) = x + 4$

23 $h(x) = 3x - 6$

25 $h(x) = \dfrac{x + 1}{1 + \sqrt{x - 1}}$

27

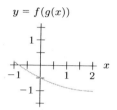

$y = f(g(x))$

29

$y = g(f(x - 2))$

31

$y = 2g(x)$

33

$y = f(x) - g(x)$

35 (a) II
(b) I
(c) None
(d) None
(e) IV
(f) None
(g) None

37 $f^{-1}(r) = I_0 10^r$

39 (a) $x \neq 3$
(b) $x \leq 2$

41 (a) $P(t) = P_0(3)^{t/7}$

(b) 17%

(c) $P^{-1}(x) = (7 \log(x/P_0))/ \log 3$

(d) 4.417 years

Chapter 6 Review Part 2

1 $-\pi/4$

2 $-\pi/3$

3 0

4 $-\pi/6$

5 Not defined

6 $3\pi/4$

7 $-\pi/3$

8 $\pi/2$

9 $2\pi/3$

10 Not defined

11 0.6813

12 2.898

13 1.528

14 2.526

15 Not defined

16 $83.16°$

17 $-5.80°$

18 $\pi/6, 11\pi/6$

19 $0°, 30°, 150°, 180°$

20 $\pi/6, 5\pi/6, 7\pi/6, 11\pi/6$

21 $120°, 180°, 240°$

22 $\pi/16, 3\pi/16$

23 $-120°$

24 $x = 0.906308$

25 0.315

26 -1.5

27 $-\frac{3}{5}$

28 $-2/\sqrt{5}$

29 $\sqrt{10}/3$

30 $2\sqrt{6}/5$

31 -1.192

32 Not defined

33 -0.9975

34 1.095

35 0.9894

36 1.001

37 Figure (a) is in degree mode and illustrates a sine–inverse sine identity, since 2 is in the domain for this identity, $-90° \le \theta \le 90°$. Figure (b) is in radian mode and does not illustrate this identity, since 2 is not in the domain for the identity, $-\pi/2 \le x \le \pi/2$.

38 $90°, 270°$

39 $\pi/12, 5\pi/12$

40 $-\pi$

41 $k(360°), 180° + k(360°), 30° + k(360°), 150° + k(360°), k$ any integer

42 $2k\pi, \pi + 2k\pi, \pi/6 + 2k\pi, -\pi/6 + 2k\pi, k$ any integer

43 $120°, 240°$

44 $7\pi/12, 11\pi/12$

45 $0.7878 + 2k\pi, 2.354 + 2k\pi, k$ any integer

46 $-1.343 + k\pi, k$ any integer

47 $0.6259 + 2k\pi, 2.516 + 2k\pi, k$ any integer

48 $1.178 + k\pi, -0.3927 + k\pi, k$ any integer

49 0.253, 2.889

50 $-0.245, 2.897$

51 ± 1.047

52 ± 0.824

53 0

54 4.227, 5.197

55 0.604, 2.797, 7.246, 8.203

56 0.228, 1.008

57 The domain for y_1 is the domain for $\sin^{-1} x, -1 \le x \le 1$.

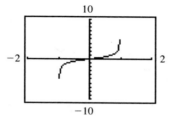

58 (a) $\sin^{-1} x$ has domain $-1 \le x \le 1$; therefore, $\sin^{-1}[(x-2)/2]$ has domain $-1 \le (x-2)/2 \le 1$, or $0 \le x \le 4$.

(b) The graph appears only for the domain values $0 \le x \le 4$.

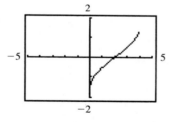

59 No, $\tan^{-1} 23.255$ represents only one number and one solution. The equation has infinitely many solutions, which are given by $x = \tan^{-1} 23.255 + k\pi, k$ any integer.

60 $0, \pi/2$

61 $0, \pi/3, 2\pi/3$

62 0.375, 2.77

63 $-\dfrac{24}{25}$

64 $\dfrac{24}{25}$

65 $\dfrac{x}{\sqrt{1 - x^2}}$

66 $\dfrac{1}{\sqrt{x^2 + 1}}$

67 (a)

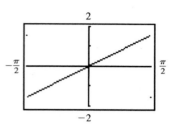

(b) The domain for $\tan x$ is the set of all real numbers, except $x = \pi/2 + k\pi, k$ an integer. The range is R, which is the domain for $\tan^{-1} x$. Thus, $y = \tan^{-1}(\tan x)$ has a graph for all real x, except $x = \pi/2 + k\pi, k$ an integer. But $\tan^{-1}(\tan x) = x$ only on the restricted domain of $\tan x$, $-\pi/2 < x < \pi/2$.

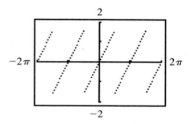

68 0.00024 sec

69 0.001936 sec

70 (a) $\theta = 2 \arctan(500/x)$

(b) $45.2°$

71 (c) From Table 1, Max $\theta = 2.73°$ when $x = 15$ ft.

Table 6.32

x (ft)	0	5	10	15
θ(deg)	0.00	1.58	2.47	2.73
x (ft)	20	25	30	
θ(deg)	2.65	2.46	2.25	

(d) As x increases from 0 ft to 30 ft, θ increases rapidly at first to a maximum of about $2.73°$ at 15 ft, then decreases more slowly.

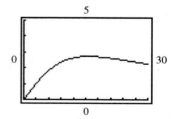

(e) From the graph, Max $\theta = 2.73°$ when $x = 15.73$ ft.

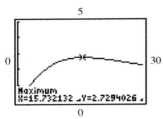

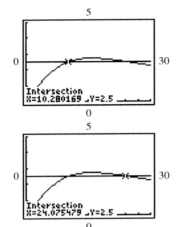

(f) $\theta = 2.5°$ when $x = 10.28$ ft or when $x = 24.08$ ft

72 (b)

Table 6.33

d (ft)	8	10	12	14	16
A (ft^2)	704	701	697	690	682
d (ft)	18	20			
A (ft^2)	670	654			

(c) $d = 17.2$ ft

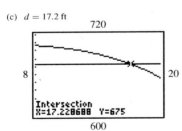

73 2.82 ft

74 (a)

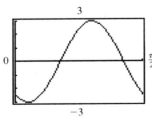

(b) 0.74 sec, 1.16 sec
(c) 0.37 sec, 1.52 sec

Ch. 6 Part 3 Understanding

1 False
3 False
5 True
7 False
9 False
11 False
13 False
15 True
17 True
19 True
21 False
23 False
25 True
27 True
29 False

Section 7.1

1 $P = 70(1.019)^t$

3 $Q = 726(0.94374)^t$

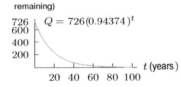

5 1.28 (per decade)

7 0.99 (per day)

9 550

11 1000

13 411.8

15 (a) III
(b) I
(c) II
(d) VI
(e) V
(f) IV

17 (a) $N = 9.8(1.08)^t$
(b) 21.16 million; 4.54 million

19 (a) $C = 100(0.84)^t$
(b) 41.821 mg

21 $f(n) = P_0(0.8)^n$

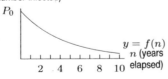

23 (b) Unpaid balance: \$1772.76
Paid off: \$227.24
Interest paid: \$340.84

25 (a) 25 mg
(b) 15%
(c) 4.922 mg
(d) 20 hours

27 $L = 420(0.15)^n$

29 (a) \$573.60 per month
(b) \$440.40 per month
(c) \$645.00 per month
(d) \$12,852
(e) \$55,296

31 (a) Monthly: 13%
(b) Annually: 81.2%
(c) Daily: 0.46%

33 (a) Annually: 4.7%
(b) Monthly: 0.383%
(c) By the decade: 58.295%

Section 7.2

3 (a) $P = 5000 - 100t$
(b) $P = 5000(1 - 0.08)^t = 5000(0.92)^t$

5 B, C, D exponential

7 (a) $g(x)$ is linear
(b) $g(x) = 2x$

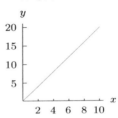

9 (a) $i(x)$ is linear
(b) $i(x) = 18 - 4x$

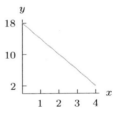

11 $h(x) = 3(5)^x$

13 $g(x) = 2(4)^x$

15 $y = 10^x$

17 $y = 1.2(2)^x$

19 $y = 5(2/3)^x$

21 $f(x) = 16,384(1/4)^x$

23 Exponential; $q(x) = 82.6446 \cdot 1.03228^x$

25 Exponential; $g(t) = 1024 \cdot 0.5^t$

27 $f(x) = 2^{3-x} \cdot d^{0.5(x-1)}$

29 (a) $P(t) = 2.58 + 0.09t$,
increases by 90,000 people per year
(b) $P(t) = 2.68(1.026)^t$,
increases by 2.6% per year

31 (a) $P = 1154.160(1.20112)^t$
(b) \$1154.16
(c) 20.112%

33 (a) $N = 84 + 4.182t$;
increasing by 4.182 million people per year
(b) $N = 84(1.0405)^t$;
increasing by 4.05% per year
(c) Linear: 167.640 million; Exponential: 185.832 million

35 $P = 1046(0.798)^t$; decreasing by 20.2%/yr

37 (a) (v)
  (b) (iii)
  (c) (iv)
  (d) (ii)
  (e) (i)

39 (a) 598,402 people
  (b) 926 bears
  (c) In 2029

Section 7.3

1 D

3 D

5 $x = 7.158$

7 $w = 1.246$

9 Zero

11 (b)

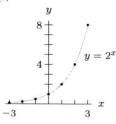

13 $h(x)$ top; $g(x)$ middle; $f(x)$ bottom

15 (a) $P = 651(0.988)^t$
  (b) 576,966
  (c) $t = 13.96$

17 (a) $y = (10{,}000) \cdot (0.9)^t$
  (b) ≈ 5905 cases
  (c) ≈ 21.854 years

19 (a) $V = 8(1.041)^t$; $R = 16 + 0.4t$
  (b) Vulcan: 17.869 million
    Romulus: 24 million
  (c) Approximately 2055
  (d) Approximately 2042

21 Increasing: $b > 1, a > 0$ or $0 < b < 1$,
  $a < 0$;
  Decreasing: $0 < b < 1, a > 0$ or $b > 1$,
  $a < 0$;
  Concave up: $a > 0, 0 < b < 0$ or $b > 1$.

25

27

29 $y = 2$

31 (a) $P = 10(2.02)^t$
  (b) About 6.55 years

33 (a) $S = 92(1.20)^t$; answers may vary

(b)

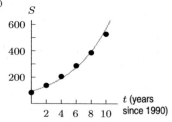

(c) 20%/yr
(d) 3527 million

35 f

37 (a)

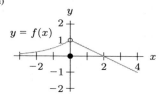

(b) $f(x) < 1$
(c) $(0, 0)$ $(2, 0)$
(d) As $x \to +\infty$, $f(x) \to -\infty$
  As $x \to -\infty$, $f(x) \to 0$
(e) Increasing for $x < 0$, decreasing for $x > 0$

Section 7.4

1

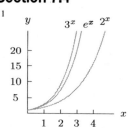

3 (a) $P(t) = 25{,}000e^{0.075t}$
  (b) 7.788%

5 A is continuous, B is annual
  Initial deposit is $500

7 (a) $505
  (b) $505.02
  (c) $505.03
  (d) $505.03

9 (a) $515
  (b) $525.62
  (c) $525.64
  (d) $525.64

11 (a) $A = 50e^{-0.14t}$
  (b) 12.330 mg
  (c) 2016

13 Bottom to top:
  $y = e^x$, $y = 2e^x$, $y = 3e^x$

15 54.931 years

17 46.210 years

19 5.5% compounded annually

21 (a) (i) 6.14%
   (ii) 6.17%
   (iii) 6.18%
   (iv) 6.18%

(b) 1.0618
  The highest possible APR is 6.18%.

23 (a) Nom: 100% Eff: 100%
  (b) Nom: 100% Eff: 144.141%
  (c) Nom: 100% Eff: 171.457%
  (d) Nom: 100% Eff: 171.828%

25 (a) Nom: 6% Eff: 6%
  (b) Nom: 6% Eff: 6.136%
  (c) Nom: 6% Eff: 6.183%
  (d) Nom: 6% Eff: 6.184%

27 (a) $18,655.38
  (b) $18,532.00
  (c) $18,520.84

29 From best to worst: B, C, A

31 5.387%

33 (a) The effective annual yield is 7.763%
  (b) The nominal annual rate is 7.5%

35 $27,399.14

Section 7.5

1 The graph of $g(x)$ is the graph of $f(x)$ shifted 2
  units up.
  The graph of $h(x)$ is the graph of $f(x)$ shifted 2
  to the left.

3 (a) $y = 4^x - 3$
  (b) $(0, -2)$
  (c) $y = -3$
  (d) $(0, -2)$
  (e)

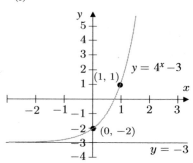

5 The basic function, $y = 3^x$, has been shifted 2
  units to the right and reflected about the
  x-axis.

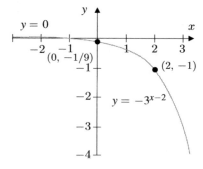

7   $y = 3e^{-x}$

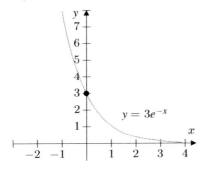

$y = 3e^{-x}$

9   The basic function, $y = e^x$, has been reflected about the y-axis and then about the x-axis.

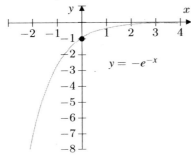

$y = -e^{-x}$

11   (a) $y = 3 \cdot 2^{x-1}$ The graph has been shifted 1 unit to the right and stretched vertically by a factor of 3.

    (b)

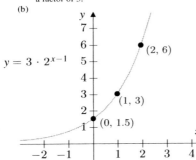

$y = 3 \cdot 2^{x-1}$

(2, 6)

(1, 3)

(0, 1.5)

    (c) $y = \frac{3}{2} \cdot 2^x, a = \frac{3}{2}, \ b = 2$

13   (a) $f(x)$
    (b)   None
    (c) $g(x)$
    (d) $j(x)$
    (e) $j(x)$

15   (a) $y = f(-x) = 2^{-x}$
    (b) $y = -f(-x) = -2^{-x}$
    (c) $y = 2^x + 1.5$
    (d) $y = 5 \cdot 2^x$

17   There are many, many correct answers. Two possible answers are:
    $y = 2^{x-2} - 4$ and $y = -2^{x-2}$

19   (a) $H(t + 15) = 68 + 93(0.91)^{t+15}$
        $H(t) + 15 = 83 + 93(0.91)^t$
    (b) $H(t + 15)$ adds 15 minutes to the time so the temperature is recorded as colder than that of $H(t)$.

$H(t) + 15$ adds 15 degrees to the temperature of $H(t)$ so the temperature is hotter than that of $H(t)$.
    (d) $H(t + 15)$ approaches the same final temperature because the temperature values don't change, only the times at which they occur. The final temperature is $68°$ F, which is room temperature.

Chapter 7 Review

1   (a) $P = 3000 + 200t$
    (b) $P = 3000(1.06)^t$
    (c) $P = 3000e^{0.06t}$
    (d) $P = 3000 - 50t$
    (e) $P = 3000(0.96)^t$
    (f) $P = 3000e^{-0.04t}$

3   (a) $P = 69e^{0.03t}$
    (b)   77.8 million tons
    (c)   Near the end of 2009

5   (a)   (ii)
    (b)   (i)
    (c)   (iv)
    (d)   (ii)
    (e)   (iii)
    (f)   (i)

7   $y = 10(1.260)^x$

9   $y = (1/2)(1/3)^x$

11   $y = 4(0.1)^x$ or $y = 4(10)^{-x}$

13   Linear, $g(x) = 12.8 - 1.3x$

15   (a)   8.300%
    (b)   8.322%
    (c)   8.328%
    (d)   8.329%

17   $f(x) = 2(1/3)^x$

19   $Q = 0.7746 \cdot (0.3873)^t$

21

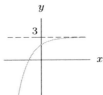

23   Exponential,
    $R(t) = 2.001(1.030)^t$

25   2007

27   (a)   13.4%
    (b)   6.489%

29   $f(x)$: neither
    $g(x) = 3(1/4)^x$
    $h(x) = 4 - (4/3)x$

31   $-0.587 < x < 4.911$

33   (a)   16%
    (b) $1220
    (c)   Accion

35   (a)   Neither
    (b)   Not possible

37   9.712%

39   (a) $a = 12, \ b = 0.841$
    (b) $C = 11.914(0.840)^t$

41   (a) $15.269(1.122)^t$
    (b)   104,066

43   35.97%

45   (i)   (b)

    (ii)   (a)
    (iii)   (c)
    (iv)   (b), (c) and (d)
    (v)   (a) and (e)

47   (a) $f(x) = p_0(2,087,372,982)^x$
    (b)   8.55
    (c)   BAC of 0.051

49   (a)

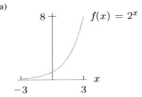

$f(x) = 2^x$

    (b)   0.69
    (c)   1.10
    (d) $e \approx 2.72$

Ch. 7 Understanding

1   True
3   True
5   False
7   True
9   True
11   False
13   False
15   True
17   True
19   False
21   True
23   False
25   True
27   False
29   True
31   False

Section 8.1

1   $26 = e^{3.258}$
3   $19 = 10^{1.279}$
5   $q = e^z$
7   $8 = \log 100,000,000$
9   $v = \log \alpha$
11   $(\log 11)/(\log 2) = 3.459$
13   $(\ln 100)/(0.12) = 38.376$
15   $(\log(48/17))/(\log(2.3)) = 1.246$
17   $2 \log(0.00012)/(-3) = 2.614$
19   3.47712
21   (a)   0
    (b)   0
    (c)   5
    (d)   1/2
    (e)   2
    (f) $-1/2$
23   (a) $2x$
    (b) x^3
    (c) $-3x$
25   (a)   True
    (b)   False
    (c)   False

(d) True
(e) True
(f) False

27 (a) $x + y$
  (b) $3x + \frac{1}{2}y$
  (c) $\log(10^x - 10^y)$
  (d) $\frac{x}{y}$
  (e) $x - y$
  (f) 10^{x+y}

29 (a) $q + 4p$
  (b) $-q$
  (c) p/q
  (d) $3q$

31 (a) 10; 15%
  (b) $t \approx 10.5$
  (c) $t = (\ln 0.2)/(-0.15) = 10.730$

33 $\log(7/4)/\log(1.171/1.088)$

35 $\log(17/3)/\log 2$

37 $(\ln 7 - 5)/(1 - \ln 2)$

39 $-2, 1/3, -1/3$

41 $(\log c - \log a)/\log b$

43 $(\ln Q - \ln P)/k$

45 $\frac{1}{4}(\ln(30/58) - 1)$

47 $(\ln 50 - \ln 44)/(0.15 - \ln 1.2)$

49 (a) 3, 3
  (b) 5, 5
  (c) $-1, -1$
  (d) $-1, -1$
  (e) 2, 2
  (f) 3, 3

51 All three are correct

Section 8.2

1 $t \approx 3.466$

3 About 26 years

5 About 12.3 years

7 6.301 minutes

9 $Q = 2e^{1.099t}$

11 $Q = 973e^{3.763t}$

13 $Q = 0.3 \cdot 2.014^t$

15 $Q = 1(0.980)^t$

17 $y = 100(0.9324)^t$, $-6.76\%/\text{yr}, -7\%/\text{yr}$

19 $y = 5e^{0.1133t}$, 12%/yr, 11.33%/yr

21 (a) 4.729%
  (b) 4.621%

23 18.583 hours

25 $10^{(\log 5)/(4 \log 3)}$

27 No solution

29 2

31 (a) $P = 3(3.218)^t$
  (b) 0.940 hours

33 (a) 13.9% per year
  (b) 7.9 years

35 (a) 2.033 volts
  (b) after 5.365 seconds
  (c) 25.918%

37 (a) $o(t) = 245 \cdot 1.03^t$
  (b) $h(t) = 63 \cdot 2^{t/10} \approx 63 \cdot (1.072)^t$
  (c) 34.162 years

39 5092.013 years ago

41 2.291 hours

43 (a) 7.70%
  (b) 6.18%

45 Yes, after 108.466 years

47 (a) 190°F; 100°F; 77.5°F
  (b) 1.292 hours; 2.292 hours

49 Population q

Section 8.3

1 $A: y = 10^x, B: y = e^x$
  $C: y = \ln x, D: y = \log x$

3 $y = 0, y = 0, x = 0$

5 (a) 0
  (b) $-\infty$

7
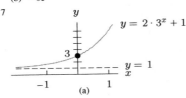
(a)

9
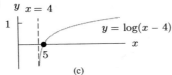
(c)

11 Vertical asymptote at 3, Domain $(3, \infty)$

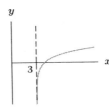

13 10^{-13} moles/l

15 5.012×10^{-9} moles/l

17 1 mole/l

21 $y = b^x, 0 < b < 1$

23 $y = \ln x$

25 $y = -b^x, b > 1$

27 $x > 0$

29 $x > 3$

31 (a) $1.01 \cdot 10^{-5}$ moles/liter
  (b) 4.996

33 37

35 (a) $M_2 - M_1 = \log(W_2/W_1)$
  (b) 20

Section 8.4

1 (i) $y = \log(x) - 3$
  (ii) $(0, \infty)$
  (iii) $x = 0$
  (iv) increasing
  (v) $x = 1000$

3 (i) $y = \log(x - 3) + 3$
  (ii) $(3, \infty)$

  (iii) $x = 3$
  (iv) increasing
  (v) $x = 3.001$

5 (i) $y = -2\ln(x)$
  (ii) $(0, \infty)$
  (iii) $x = 0$
  (iv) decreasing
  (v) $x = 1$

7 (a) $y = \ln(x)$
  (b) reflected across the y-axis and stretched vertically by a factor of 3
  (e) $(-\infty, 0)$

9 (a) iii
  (b) i
  (c) iv
  (d) ii

Section 8.5

1 (a) Neither
  (b) $n(x) = 6 \cdot 8^x$
  (c) $p(x) = 25^x$
  (d) Neither
  (e) $r(x) = 2(\frac{1}{9})^x$
  (f) $s(x) = \frac{4}{5}x^3$

5 $y = 50x^{1.1}$

7 $y = 6x^{35}$

9 3^{-x} approaches zero faster

11 (a) $f(x) = 720x - 702$
  (b) $f(x) = 2(9)^x$
  (c) $f(x) = 18x^4$

13 (a) $f(x) = y = \frac{63}{4}x + \frac{33}{2}$
  (b) $f(x) = 3 \cdot 4^x$
  (c) $f(x) = \frac{3}{4}x^6$

15 (a) $C, f(x)$;
    $A, g(x)$;
    $B, h(x)$
  (b) Yes
  (c) No

17 $m = 2, t = 4, k = \frac{1}{4}$

19 $y \to 0$ as $x \to \pm\infty$

21 $y \to \infty$ as $x \to \infty$
  $y \to -\infty$ as $x \to -\infty$

23 $y \to 0$ as $t \to \infty$
  $y \to 7/9$ as $t \to -\infty$

25 $y \to \infty$ as $x \to \infty$
  $y \to 0$ as $x \to -\infty$

27 $y \to 0$ as $x \to \infty$

29 $y \to \infty$ as $x \to \infty$
  $y \to -\infty$ as $x \to -\infty$

31 $f(x) = 2\sin(\frac{\pi}{2}x) - 4$ (trigonometric);
  $g(x) = \frac{5}{2}x^3$ (power function);
  $h(x) = \frac{1}{3}(\frac{1}{2})^x$ (exponential)

33 ≈ 129 Earth days

35 (b) Neither

37 $f(d) = bd^{p/q}, p < q$;
  $g(d) = ad^{p/q}, p > q$

Chapter 8 Review

1 $Q = 12e^{-0.105t}$

3 $Q = 14e^{-0.208t}$

5 $Q = 7(0.0000454)^t$

7 $(\ln 50)/(\ln 3) = 3.561$

9 $(\ln 0.3)/(-0.2) = 6.020$

11 (a) 3%, 2.96%
(b) 3.05%, 3%
(c) Decay: 6%, 6.19%
(d) Decay: 4.97%, 5.1%
(e) 3.93%, 3.85%
(f) Decay: 2.73%, 2.77%

13 (a) Domain: all x
Range: $y > 0$
Asymptote: $y = 0$
(b) Domain: all $x > 0$
Range: all y
Asymptote: $x = 0$

15 (a) $k = 0.0583$
(b) $b = 1.0747$

17 $(1/0.049) \cdot \ln(25/13) \approx 13.345$

19 $2(x + 1)$

21 $\ln(AB)$

23 ln 1969

25 (a) $M(a) = M_0(0.98)^{(a-30)}$
(b) 64.3 years old

27 (a) $\approx 33.517\%$
(b) $k \approx 4.082\%$, continuous hourly decay rate

29 12,146.082 years old

31 (a) (i) $u - v$
(ii) $-2u$
(iii) $3u + v$
(iv) $\frac{1}{2}(u + v)$
(b) $\frac{1}{2}(u + 2v) = \log\sqrt{50} \approx \log 7$

33 (a) $\frac{1}{1 - \log 3}$
(b) $\ln(\frac{5}{e - e^{-2}})$
(c) 2
(d) 0 or ln 6/ ln 3
(e) $(\ln(e^2 - 3))/4$
(f) $\sqrt{2}$

37 (a) $h(n) = 6(0.9)^n$
(b) 1.695 ft
(c) 41st bounce

39 (a) 176.986 microns
(b) 1769.864 microns
(c) Differs by 1; differs by factor of 10

Chapter 8 Understanding

1 True
3 False
5 True
7 False
9 True
11 True
13 True
15 True
17 True
19 False
21 False
23 False
25 True
27 False
29 False

Section 9.1

1 Maximum: 2;
Minimum: ≈ -0.094

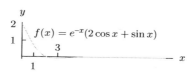

$$f(x) = e^{-x}(2\cos x + \sin x)$$

3 (a) $f(t) = 65 - 25\cos(\pi t/12)$
(b) Period: 24;
Amplitude: 30
(c) $\approx$ 4 am and 1 pm

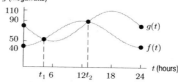

(d) 184.051 mw at 3:21 pm
(e) $h(t) = 145 - \sqrt{1525}\sin(\pi t/12 + 0.6947)$;
max $= 145 + \sqrt{1525} = 184.051$

5 (a) $y = 0$
(b) The function oscillates more and more as $x \to 0$.
(c) No
(d) $z_1 = 1/\pi$
(e) Infinitely many
(f) If $a = 1/(k\pi)$ then $b = 1/((k+1)\pi)$

7 (b) No: no, but possibly for 1979-1989
(c) Multiply by an exponential function:
$s(t) = (e^{0.05t})(-1.4\cos(\frac{2\pi}{6})t + 1.6)$
(d)

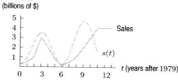

(e) 4.632 billion dollars

9 (a) $h = f(t) = 25 + 15\sin(\pi t/3) + 10\sin(\pi t/2)$
(b) $f(t)$ is periodic with period 12

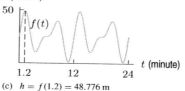

(c) $h = f(1.2) = 48.776$ m

Section 9.2

1 Algebraic
Domain: $(-\infty, -2] \cup [2, \infty)$
Range: $[0, \infty)$
Y intercept: None
X intercept: $x = \pm 2$
Symmetry: about y-axis
Asymptotes: None

3 Algebraic
Domain: $(-\infty, -2) \cup (2, \infty)$
Range: $(0, \infty)$
Y intercept: None
X intercept: None
Symmetry: about y-axis
Asymptotes: $x = \pm 2$, $y = 0$

5 Transcendental
Domain: $(-\infty, -2) \cup (2, \infty)$
Range: $(-0.2172, 1)$
Y intercept: None
X intercept: $x = k\pi$, $k \neq 0$
Symmetry: about y-axis
Asymptotes: $y = 0$

7 Transcendental
Domain: All Reals
Range: All Reals
Y intercept: $y = 0$
X intercept: $x = k\pi$
Symmetry: about y-axis
Asymptotes: None

9 Transcendental
Domain: All Reals
Range: $(-\infty, 0.3678)$
Y intercept: $y = 0$
X intercept: $x = 0$
Symmetry: about the origin
Asymptotes: $y = 0$

11 Transcendental
Domain: All Reals
Range: $[1, \infty)$
Y intercept: $y = 0$
X intercept: $x = 0$
Symmetry: about y-axis
Asymptotes: None

13 (a) $d = \sqrt{(x-4)^2 + y^2}$
(b) $d(x) = \sqrt{(x-4)^2 + x}$; $x \geq 0$
(c) Domain: $[0, \infty)$
Range: $[1.9365, \infty)$
Y intercept: $y = 4$
X intercept: None
Symmetry: None
(d) Use [0, 10, 1] by [0, 10, 1]
(e) Decreasing (0, 3.5) and Increasing (3.5, ∞)
(f) $x = 3.5$, $y = 1.9364917$

Section 9.3

1 (a) w = width
l = length
(b) $2w + l = 600$
$A = w(600 - 2w) = -2w^2 + 600w$
$A(w) = -2w^2 + 600w$
This is a quadratic function.
(c) Practical domain: [0, 300] because $A(w)$ cannot be negative
(d) Table:

w (ft)	A (ft²)
0	0
50	25000
100	40000
150	45000
200	40000
250	25000
300	0

Graph:

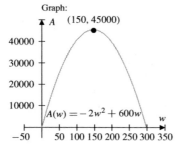

The graph and table support the conclusion that the maximum area is achieved when the width is 150 ft.

(e) The maximum occurs at the vertex:
$w = \frac{-600}{2(-2)} = 150$ feet
The corresponding length will be:
$l = 600 - 2(150) = 300$ feet
The maximum area is obtained if the sides perpendicular to the river are 150 feet and the side parallel to the river is 300 feet. The maximum area will be 45000 square feet.

3 (a) Let l and w be the length and width of the rectangular enclosure.
Let C be the cost of fencing the rectangular enclosure.

decorative fencing: l

w [rectangle   ] w

standard fencing: l

(b)
$$C = 30l + 20w + 20w + 20l$$
$$C = 50l + 40w$$
$$A = lw = 45000 \Rightarrow l = \frac{45000}{w}$$
$$C = 50 * \frac{45000}{w} + 40w$$
$$= \frac{2250000}{w} + 40w$$
$$C = \frac{2250000 + 40w^2}{w}$$
This is a rational function.

(c) Practical domain: $w > 0$ but w can get very large.

(d) Table:

w (ft)	C ($)
50	47000
100	26500
150	21000
200	19250
250	19000
300	19500
350	20429

Graph:

$C = \frac{2250000 + 40w^2}{w}$ (237.2, 18973.67)

Conclusion: The cost of the fencing is a minimum if the width is approximately 237 feet and the length is approximately 190 feet. The cost will be about $18974.

5 (a) Let S be the surface area of the box. The surface area consists of the area of the bottom of the box, the top of the box, and the four sides.
$$S = x^2 + x^2 + 4xy$$
$$S = 2x^2 + 4xy$$
The volume of the box must be 20000 in³, so $x^2y = 20000$. Then $y = \frac{20000}{x^2}$.
Substituting, we get
$$S = 2x^2 + 4x\left(\frac{20000}{x^2}\right)$$
$$S = 2x^2 + \frac{80000}{x}$$
$$S = \frac{80000+2x^3}{x}$$
This is a rational function.

(b) x must be greater than zero but can get very large.

(c) Table:

x (in)	S (in²)
10	8200
20	4800
30	4467
40	5200
50	6600
60	8533
70	10943

Graph:

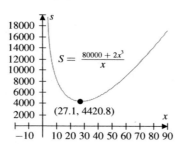

$S = \frac{80000 + 2x^3}{x}$ (27.1, 4420.8)

Conclusion: The surface area of the box will be a minimum if it is roughly a cube. The base should be 27.1 inches by 27.1 inches and the height should be 27.1 inches. This gives a surface area of about 4421 square inches.

7 (a)

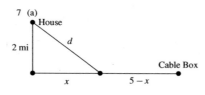

(b) Total distance = $5 - x + d$
$$x^2 + 4 = d^2$$
$$d = \sqrt{x^2 + 4}$$
Total distance = $5 - x + \sqrt{x^2 + 4}$
Total cost = Road cost + Off-road cost
$$C(x) = 10(5 - x) + 14\sqrt{x^2 + 4}$$
(c) Practical domain is [0, 5].

(d) Table:

x (mi)	C ($)
0	78
1	71.31
2	69.60
3	70.48
4	72.61
5	75.39

Graph:

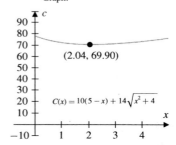

(2.04, 69.90) $C(x) = 10(5 - x) + 14\sqrt{x^2 + 4}$

From the table and graph, the cost will be a minimum if the cable is laid along the road for 2.96 miles (this is $5 - x$) and then turns off the road for 2.86 miles (this is $\sqrt{x^2 + 4}$). The total cost will be about $69.60.

9 (a)

x	$\$2.50x$	p	$R = px$
10	25	525	5250
11	27.50	522.50	5747.50
12	30	520	6240

(b) $p = 550 - 2.50x$
(c) $R = (550 - 2.50x)x$
This is a quadratic function.
The practical domain is $10 \leq x \leq 150$ because there must be at least 10 in the group and the plane has a capacity of 150.

(d) Table:

x	R
90	29250
100	30000
110	30250
120	30000
130	29250

Graph:

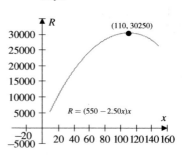

(110, 30250) $R = (550 - 2.50x)x$

The table and graph support the conclusion that the revenue is a maximum if 110 people are in the group. The maximum revenue is $30,250.

(e) Because this is a quadratic function, the maximum occurs at the vertex:
$x = \frac{-550}{2(-2.50)} = 110$
$R(110) = 30{,}250$
Thus, the maximum revenue is $30,250 and 110 people should be in the group.

(f) $P(x) = R(x) - C(x)$
$P(x) = (550x - 2.50x^2) - (9000 + 40x)$
$P(x) = -2.50x^2 + 510x - 9000$
This function is also quadratic so its maximum occurs at the vertex:
$x = \frac{-510}{2(-2.50)} = 102$
$P(102) = 17010$
The company will have a maximum profit of $17,010 if the group has 102 people in it.

11 (a) $x = 0.5t$
(b) $x^2 + y^2 = 18^2 = 324$
(c) $y^2 = 324 - x^2$
$y^2 = 324 - (0.5t)^2$
$y^2 = 324 - 0.25t^2$
$y = \sqrt{324 - 0.25t^2}$
(d) y should not be changing at a constant rate because y is not a linear function of t.

Tables:

t (sec)	y (ft)
0	18
5	17.826
10	17.292
15	16.363
20	14.967

Time Interval	$\frac{\Delta y}{\Delta t}$ (ft/sec)
[0, 5]	−0.0348
[5, 10]	−0.1068
[10, 15]	−0.1858
[15, 20]	−0.2792

Graph:

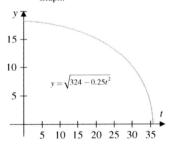

(e) $y = 6 \Rightarrow 6 = \sqrt{324 - 0.25t^2}$
$36 = 324 - 0.25t^2$
$0.25t^2 = 288$
$t^2 = 1152$
$t \approx 33.94$
At about 33.94 seconds, the top of the ladder is 6 feet above the ground.

(f) The practical domain is $0 \le t \le 36$ because in 36 seconds, the ladder hits the ground.

13 (a)

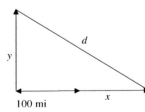

(b) $y = 50t$ and $x = 60t$
(c) $(100 + x)^2 + y^2 = d^2$
$(100 + 60t)^2 + (50t)^2 = d^2$
$6100t^2 + 12000t + 10000 = d^2$
$d = 10\sqrt{61t^2 + 120t + 100}$
(d) d should not be changing at a constant rate because d is not a linear function of t.

Tables:

t (hr)	d (mi)
0	100
1	167.630
2	241.660
3	317.647
4	394.461

Time Interval	$\frac{\Delta d}{\Delta t}$ (mi/hr)
[0, 1]	67.630
[1, 2]	74.03
[2, 3]	75.987
[3, 4]	76.814

Graph:

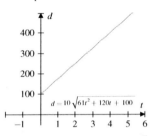

The graph looks linear but as the table shows, the distance is increasing more slowly at first and then a little more quickly as time goes on.

15 (a) $r = 4t$
(b) $V = \frac{4}{3}\pi r^3 = \frac{4}{3}\pi (4t)^3$
$V = \frac{256}{3}\pi t^3$
(c) The volume should not be changing at a constant rate because V is not a linear function of t.

Tables:

t (sec)	V (cm^3)
0	0
1	268.083
2	2144.661
3	7238.229
4	17157.285

Time Interval	$\frac{\Delta V}{\Delta t}$ (cm^3/sec)
[0, 1]	268.083
[1, 2]	1876.578
[2, 3]	5093.568
[3, 4]	9919.056

Graph:

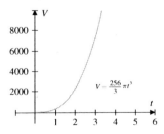

The tables and graph show that the volume is increasing slowly at first and then much more rapidly as time goes on.

Section 9.4

1 $y = 3x - 5$

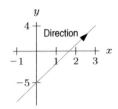

3 $y = 2x^2 + 1$

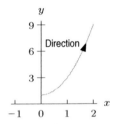

5 $y = (x + 4)^2$

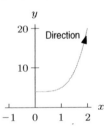

7 $y = x^{3/2}$

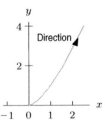

9 $y = (2/3)\ln x,\ x > 0$

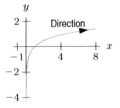

672

11 $(x - 3)^2 + (y - 2)^2 = 1$

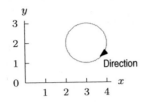

13 Lines from $(0, 1)$ to $(1, 0)$ to $(0, -1)$ to $(-1, 0)$ to $(0, 1)$

15 Lines from $(-1, 1)$ to $(1, 1)$ to $(-1, -1)$ to $(1, -1)$ to $(-1, 1)$

17 (a) $x = t, y = t^2$
$\quad x = t + 1, y = (t + 1)^2$
(b) $x = t, y = (t + 2)^2 + 1$
$\quad x = t + 1, y = (t + 3)^2 + 1$

19 Clockwise for all t

21 Counterclockwise: $t > 0$

23 (a) Right of $(2, 4)$
(b) $(-1, -3)$ to $(2, 4)$
(c) $t < -2/3$

25 (a) Line $y = x$
(b) Circle, with starting point $(1, 0)$ and period 2π
(c) Ellipse, with staring point $(1, 0)$ and period 2π

27 $x = t, y = -4t + 7$

29

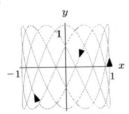

31

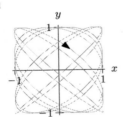

33

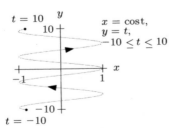

35 (a) $x = t, y = -16t^2 + 48t + 6$

(b)

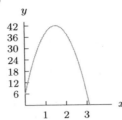

(c) 6 feet
(d) 3 seconds
(e) 42 feet

Section 9.5

1 $(0, 0); 3/2$

3 $(-1, -3); 4$

5 $x = 4\cos t, y = -4\sin t, 0 \le t \le 2\pi$

7 $x = 5\sin t, y = -5\cos t, 0 \le t \le 2\pi$

9 $x = 3 + 5\cos t, y = 4 + 5\sin t, 0 \le t \le 2\pi$

11 $x = -1 - 3\cos t, y = -2 - 3\sin t,$
$\quad 0 \le t \le 2\pi$

13 (a) Center $(2, -4)$, radius $\sqrt{20}$
(b) Center $(-1, 2)$, radius $\sqrt{11}$

15 Parabola:
$y = (x - 2)^2, 1 \le x \le 3$

17 $x = 4(y - 3)^2, 2 \le y \le 4.$

19 Parametric:
$x = e^t, y = c^{2t}$ for all $t,$
Explicit:
$y = x^2$, with $x > 0,$
Implicit:
$x^2 - y = 0$, with $x > 0$

21 Implicit:
$x^2 - 2x + y^2 = 0, y < 0,$
Explicit:
$y = -\sqrt{-x^2 + 2x},$
Parametric:
$x = 1 + \cos t, y = \sin t,$
with $\pi < t \le 2\pi$

23 (a) $a = b = 0, k = 5$ or -5
(b) $a = 0, b = 5, k = 5$ or -5
(c) $a = 10, b = -10, k = \sqrt{200}$ or $-\sqrt{200}$

Section 9.6

1 (a) $(0, 0); 24; 10$
(b) $(x^2/144) + (y^2/25) = 1$

3 (a) $(5, 3); 8; 6$
(b) $((x - 5)^2/16) + ((y - 3)^2/9) = 1$

5 $x = 12\cos t, y = 5\sin t, 0 \le t \le 2\pi$

7 $x = 5 + 4\cos t, y = 3 - 3\sin t, 0 \le t \le 2\pi$

9 Same ellipse, traced at twice speed

11 $((x - 1)^2/4) + (y + 2)^2 = 1; (1, -2); 2; 1$

13 $(x + 2)^2 + (y + 1)^2/4 = 1; (-2, 1); 1; 2$

15 $(x - 1/2)^2 + (y + 1)^2/4 = 1; (1/2, -1); 1; 2$

17 (a) Center $(-1, 3)$, major axis $a = \sqrt{6}$, minar axis $b = 2$

(b) Center $(3/2, -1)$, major axis $a = \sqrt{39}/2,$ minor axis $b = \sqrt{13/2}$

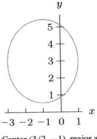

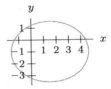

19 $h < k < 0 < a < b$

23 (a) $\left(\frac{2x - r_m + r_c}{r_c + r_m}\right)^2 + \frac{y^2}{b^2} = 1$
(b) $b = \sqrt{r_c r_m}$

Section 9.7

1 (a) $(5, 0); (-5, 0); (0, 0)$
(b) $y = x/5; y = -x/5$
(c) $(x^2/25) - y^2 = 1$

3 (a) $(4, 4); (2, 4); (3, 4)$
(b) $y = 3x - 5; y = -3x + 13$
(c) $(x - 3)^2 - (y - 4)^2/9 = 1$

5 $x = 5/\cos t, y = \tan t;$
Right half: $0 \le t < \pi/2, 3\pi/2 < t < 2\pi$

7 $x = 3 + 1/\cos t, y = 4 + 3\tan t;$
Left half: $\pi/2 < t < 3\pi/2$

9 $((x + 1)^2/4) - (y - 2)^2 = 1$
$(1, 2)$; right left; 2; 1

11 $((x + 1)^2/4) - (y + 3)^2 = 1$
$(-1, -3)$; right-left; 2; 1

13 $(y - 1/2)^2 - ((x - 1)^2/9) = 1$
$(1, 1/2)$; up-down; 3; 1

15 $I; 0 < b < k < h < a.$

17 (a) Center $(-5, 2)$; Vertices $(-5 \pm \sqrt{6}, 2)$;
Asymptotes $y = \pm(2/\sqrt{6})(x - 5) + 2$
(b) Center $(-1, -2)$; Vertices $(-1 \pm \sqrt{14}, -2)$; Asymptotes $y = \pm(x + 1) - 2$

Section 9.8

1 (a) quadratic and linear, two intersections
(b) $(0, -4)$ and $(2, 0)$
(c) $(0, -4)$ and $(2, 0)$

3 (a) Answers may vary
(b) No solution to equation

5 (a) Answers will vary
(b) Answers will vary

7 $(1.44187, 2.07900)$ and $(-1.44187, 2.07900)$

9 $(2, 3)$ and $(-2, -5)$

11 (a) $P(t) = 55.6(1.022)^t$ $P(t)$: millions of people
(b) $P(t) = 55.6e^{0.02176t}$ $P(t)$: millions of people
(c) 124.380 million people
(d) $N(t) = -0.45882t + 115.1$ $N(t)$: millions of people
(e) Answers will vary graph should show intersection
(f) $-0.45882t + 115.1 = 55.6e^{0.02176t}$
(g) (27.99952, 102.25326)
(h) In 1991 there will be around 102 million people in Nigeria and the amount of oil produced will just be enough for those people. After 1991 there will not be enough oil for the population.

Chapter 9 Review

1 Circle; (0, 3); $\sqrt{5}$

3 Hyperbola, (0, 1); 2; 3; left-right

5 Ellipse, (5, 0); 2; 3

7 Hyperbola, (−1/3, 1/2); $\sqrt{3}$; $\sqrt{2}$; up-down

9 $x = 3\cos t, y = -3\sin t, 0 \le t \le 2\pi$

11 $x = -2\cos t, y = 2\sin t,$
   $0 \le t \le 2\pi$

13 $x = 5\cos t, y = 7\sin t,$
   $0 \le t \le 2\pi$

15 $x = -3\cos t, \; y = -7\sin t,$
   $0 \le t \le 2\pi$

17 $x = t, y = 5$

19 $x = 2\cos(t + \pi/2), y = 2\sin(t + \pi/2)$

21 Hyperbola; (1, 1); $a = 1/\sqrt{2}$; $b = 1$; left-right

23 Circle; (2, 1); $\sqrt{5}$

25 Equation of curve is
   $x = 1 - 2y^2, -1 \le y \le 1$

Ch. 9 Understanding

1 True

3 False

5 False

7 True

9 True

11 False

13 False

Section 10.1

1 (a) and (b)

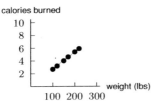
calories burned

weight (lbs)

(c) $r \approx 1$

3 (a) $r = 1$
(b) $r = 0.7$
(c) $r = 0$
(d) $r = -0.98$
(e) $r = -0.25$
(f) $r = -0.5$

5 (a)

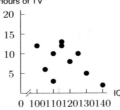
hours of TV

IQ

(b) $r \approx -1/2$
(c) $y = 27.5139 - 0.1674x$
   $r = -0.5389$

7 (a)

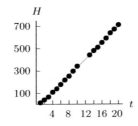
H

(b) Estimates will vary, e.g. $H = 37t - 37$
(c) $H = 37.26t - 39.85, r = 0.9995, r = 1$. The correlation between the data set and the regression line is very good.
(d) Slope gives the average number of home-runs per year, about 37

Section 10.2

1 $f(x) = x^{\ln c / \ln 2}$

3 $h(x) = 2.35(1.44)^x$

5 (a) $f(x) = 201.353x^{2.111}$
(b) $f(20) = 112,313.62$ gm
(c) $x = 18.930$ cm

7 (a) Late in predicting decline
(b) $v = -0.145h^3 + 1.850h^2 - 1.313h + 10.692$; yes

9 (b) $R(p) = -0.0565p^2 + 72.9981p + 4749.85$
(c) $p = \$646, R = \$28,349$

11 (a) $\dot{y} = 3.118t^{1.141}$
(b) $y = 19.633 \cdot 1.058^t$
(c) $y = 0.558t^2 - 23.149t + 229.65$
(d) (a) low (b) best (c) high

13 (a) Quadratic
(b) $y = -0.016x^2 + 1.913x - 10$, answers may vary
(c) $\$38,877$
(d) Age 10, $\$7,530$, not reasonable, answers may vary

15 (a) $h_e = 16.2e^{-t/312.5}; ha = 12.3e^{-t/131.6};$
   $h_b = 14.7e^{-t/149.3}$

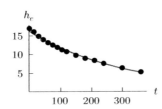
h_c

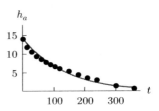
h_a

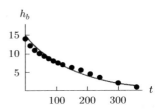
h_b

17 (a)

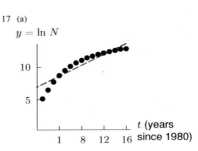
$y = \ln N$

t (years since 1980)

(b) $y = 6.445 + 0.47t$
(c) $N = 630e^{0.47t}$

19 (a)

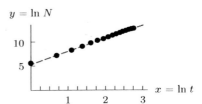
$y = \ln N$

$x = \ln t$

(b) $y = 4.670 + 3.005x$
(c) $N = 107t^{3.005}$

21 (a) $y = 2x$
(b) $y = x^2$
(c) $y = e^{2x}$

23 (a) Negative
(b) $l = 720e^{-0.722}$
(c) $y = b + px$
(e) No

$y = \ln l$

$x = \ln c$

INDEX